...ed or Transferred

Third Edition
Blue Book
of Guitars™

By Steven Cherne

Edited by S. P. Fjestad

Third Edition
Blue Book of Guitars™

Publisher's Note:

This book is the result of nonstop and continual guitar research obtained by attending guitar shows, communicating with guitar dealers and collectors throughout the country each year, and staying on top of trends as they occur. This book represents an analysis of prices for which both recently manufactured and collectible guitars have actually been selling for during that period at an average retail level.

Although every reasonable effort has been made to compile an accurate and reliable guide, guitar prices may vary significantly depending on such factors as the locality of the sale, the number of sales we were able to consider, famous musician endorsement of certain models, regional economic conditions, and other critical factors.

Accordingly, no representation can be made that the guitars listed may be bought or sold at prices indicated, nor shall the editor or publisher be responsible for any error made in compiling and recording such prices.

Copyright ©1996 Blue Book Publications, Inc.
All Rights Reserved.

Blue Book Publications, Inc.
8009 34th Avenue South, Suite 175, Minneapolis, MN 55425
Phone: 800.877.4867 (orders only)
Phone: 612.854.5229
(FAX) 612.853.1486
email: bluebook@bluebookinc.com
http://www.bluebookinc.com

Published and printed in the United States of America
ISBN No. 1-886768-05-6
The Library of Congress Number is pending as this edition went to press.

Distributed in part by
Music Sales Corporation and Omnibus Press
Order # BP 10036
257 Park Avenue South, New York, NY 10010 USA

Cover Layout, Lettering, and Digital Imaging - Walter Horishnyk

Art Director - Walter Horishnyk

Photography - Paul Goodwin

Page Layout and Programming - Tom Lundin

Instruments featured on the front and back covers of the Third Edition of the **Blue Book of Guitars** were photographed at the 19th Annual Greater Southwest Dallas Guitar Show. "No guitars were harmed during production of the Third Edition, and all were returned to the marketplace under the Texas catch-and-release program".

Front Cover

Stromberg, courtesy Dr. Thomas Van Hoose
Van Hoose Vintage Instruments
1412 Main St., Suite 420
Dallas TX 75202-4018
214.760.8627

Gretsch, courtesy Dave Hinson
Hazardware, Inc.
P.O. Box 9172
St. Louis MO 63117
800.646.7795

Paul Reed Smith, courtesy of Jimmy Gravity
J. Gravity Strings
1546 S. Broadway
St. Louis MO 63104
314.241.0190
(FAX) 314.241.8434

Side o' the Book

Dingwall Zebra, courtesy Sheldon Dingwall
Dingwall Designer Guitars
Box 1914 Saskatoon, SK
Canada S7K 7E8
306.242.6201

Back Cover

Mosrite, courtesy Lynn Darling
R. L. Darling Guitars
214.842.3387

1996 Metropolitan, courtesy David Wintz
Metropolitan (Robin Guitars)
3526 East T.C. Jester Blvd.
Houston TX 77018
713.957.0470

7 String Conklin Sidewinder Bass, courtesy of Bill Conklin
Conklin Guitars
P.O. Box 1394
Springfield MO 65801
417.886.3525

Martin, photographed at the 19th Annual Greater Southwest Dallas Guitar Show
The Martin Guitar Company
510 Sycamore Street
Nazareth PA 18064
610.759.2837
(FAX) 610.759.5757
info@mguitar.com

Table of Contents

An Introduction to Guitar Collecting

Until the late 1950s - early 60s, most guitars were bought/sold/traded by musicians. No longer. As we keep tweaking our tone settings for the next millennium, guitars have established themselves as a universal art form - no different than a good Picasso or older Rolls Royce. In every part of the globe, there are guitar enthusiasts including collectors, players, dealers, and maybe even a few investors and speculators.

Getting involved in guitar collecting has, perhaps, never been easier - there are many more ways to buy, sell, or trade an instrument now than even ten years ago. One of the best ways to become familiar in this area of collectibles is to walk through as many music/guitar stores and pawn shops as you can - **you can never predict where a guitar on your shopping list may show up.** More and more major dealers and music stores are also offering their listings on the Internet. Don't forget those classified ads, either. Many professional musicians have bolstered their collections by "making the rounds" at the various locations where they have a gig. You can't wear out too many pairs of tennis shoes if you take this area of collectibility seriously.

I also personally recommend that you attend at least one major guitar show each year. In most major American cities, there are regularly scheduled guitar shows where you can buy, sell or swap your guitars and gain insight into general information, including prices. Also, at the larger national shows, you'll find many prominent and reputable dealers who usually have high-quality merchandise for sale. When you attend, you'll probably see everything including ultra-rare and expensive vintage instruments, state-of-the-art newer guitars, and maybe even some barking guitar biscuits with the two-digit price tags. You can also make price comparisons.

My advice - get to the show at the opening, walk the aisles with orderly precision, avoid back tracking, and when you find a specimen that meets all of your criteria and is on your shopping list - **Buy It**. Too many times I've walked back to a booth ready to buy and a guitar stand is all that remains. **Truly good guitars that are fairly priced sell fast.** One last item: Don't interrupt an exhibitor engaged in selling (even if it's one you want). It's not in the guitar circuit code of ethics. Be patient - don't burn anybody's toast.

Once you have decided what you want to collect, I recommend you talk to everyone who could have any knowledge and provide you with information in your selected area. **You must do the homework!** Recently, I spoke with a dealer friend of mine on what a beginning collector should do to start this fascinating hobby. His comments were: collect what you really like, buy the right books and actually read them, get out and look at what you're interested in (with a magnifying glass if necessary), know your dealers and pick them carefully, listen to them and knowledgeable others, avoid speculation, and don't forget to **get a receipt**. These are always good measures to follow.

My advice would be to pick out an area where knowledge or interest already exists. Once you have found an area that you find interesting and want to collect, formulate a plan on what you would like to purchase. Expand this established base with additional knowledge. Buy the necessary books, magazines, and trade periodicals to make yourself as informed as possible in the niche you've chosen.

In this business, the experience gained by running guitars through your hands has no substitute. I have known people who would quote from memory every special order factory color, fret configuration, options listing, and maybe even the original retail price, yet these same people can't spot a refinished guitar. Knowing the correct factory color, style of wood, finish, production variations, etc., does not come overnight. It takes experience and a well-trained eye. If in doubt about "original finish" someone claims, consult a dealer or collector who does know the difference. It is far better to know the limitations of your expertise than let your ego run interference on your wallet.

The values of guitars are currently determined by condition, rarity, demand, special features, historical significance and/or provenance, and playability (playability is the bottom line on value for most inexpensive guitars). **All values in this text are based on original condition - modifications and/or conversions normally lower an instrument's value.** The value of a collector instrument is always relative to the condition of other examples of the same make, model, and variation. Collectors and investors are usually motivated by acquiring better and/or more examples of what he/she is interested in. Most modern guitars should be purchased within the upper condition factors - 95% - 100%, to help guarantee a good price in the secondary marketplace.

So do your homework, know what you're looking for/at, and spend some C-notes on a regular basis. Don't forget, having a closet full of guitars always beats having a closet full of undersized and out-of-date garments in this book!

S.P. Fjestad, Editor/Publisher
Blue Book of Guitars™

How To Use This Book

The revised Third Edition of the **Blue Book of Guitars**™ differs greatly in its new approach. While there are still hundreds of pages of specific guitar models and pricing, the Third Edition is no longer a "hold-your-hand" pricing guide. In theory, you should be able to read the trademark name off the headstock of the guitar (where applicable), and be able to find out the country of origin, date(s) produced, and other company/model-related facts for that guitar. Where an overview of pricing is not listed for a particular company, there still may be enough information listed for you to effectively make up your mind on the value of the guitar. As in the past, if you own a current edition of the Blue Book of Guitars™ and you still have questions, we will attempt to assist you in identifying/pricing your guitar(s). Please refer to page 12 for this service.

The prices listed in the 3rd Edition of the **Blue Book of Guitars**™ **are based on average national retail prices for both vintage and modern guitars.** This is NOT a wholesale pricing guide; prices reflect the numbers you typically see on a guitar's price tag. **More importantly, do not expect to walk into a music store, guitar or pawn shop and think that the proprietor should pay you the retail price listed within this text for your instrument(s). Dealer offers on most models could be 20%-50% less than values listed, depending upon locality, desirability, and profitability.** In other words, if you want to receive 100% of the price (retail value), then you have to do 100% of the work (become the retailer which also includes assuming 100% of the risk). Business is business, and making a profit is what helps keep the lights on, the front door open, and the after-hour pizzas continued to be delivered at any retail establishment. Currently manufactured guitars are typically listed with 60%-100% condition factors - since condition below 60% is seldomly encountered and obviously, less desirable. Older vintage instruments may only have the 20%-90% condition factors listed since 95%+ condition factors are seldomly encountered and are difficult to price accurately. Please consult our enlarged, 40-page color **Photo Percentage Grading System**™ (pages 33-72) to learn more about the condition of your guitar. This is the first time, to our knowledge, that color plates have been utilized to accurately illustrate each guitar's unique condition factor. Since condition is the overriding factor in price evaluation, study these photos carefully (enlarged in this edition) to learn more about the condition of your specimen(s).

For your convenience, explanations of percentages of condition, conversion to other guitar grading systems, and other grading criteria have been included on page 32 to assist you in learning more about guitar grading systems. This will be especially helpful when evaluating older vintage instruments.

All values within this text assume original condition. From the vintage marketplace or (especially) a collector's point of view, any repairs, alterations, modifications, "enhancements", "improvements", "professionally modified to a more desirable configuration", or any other non-factory changes usually detract from an instrument's value. **Depending on the seriousness of the modification/alteration, you may have to go down 1-3 condition factors when re-computing price for these alterations.** Determining values for damaged and/or previously repaired instruments will usually depend on the parts and labor costs necessary to return them to playable and/or original specifications. The grading lines within the Third Edition have also incorporated other grading nomenclature and are listed under the respective percentages of original condition.

You will note that black-and-white photos have been provided throughout this Third Edition to further assist you with visual identification of certain makes, models, and variations.

The Third Edition **Blue Book of Guitars**™ has identified many company histories, influential luthiers and designers, and other bits of knowledge as a supplement to the straight pricing text. Hopefully, this information will be shared to alleviate those "gray areas" of the unknown, and shed light on the efforts of those luthiers/companies who build the guitars that we play and cherish.

We have designed an easy-to-use text format throughout this publication to aid you in finding specific information within the shortest amount of time.

1. Trademark manufacturer, brand name, or importer is listed in bold face type with a screened line running through the center and will appear alphabetically as follows:

FENDER

MARTIN

PEAVEY

2. Manufacturer information and production dates (if possible) are listed directly beneath the trademark heading:

Instruments built in Nazareth, Pennsylvania since 1838.

3. A company overview, model information, and/or other relative useful pieces of information follow within a smaller block of text:

Cyclone guitars were distributed in the U.S. market by Leban Imports of Baltimore, Maryland.

4. When a proper model-by-model listing is not available, a small paragraph may follow with the company history and related production data. These paragraphs may also include current retail prices. The following example is from Greg Curbow's Curbow Bass company:

The **Petite Basses** have a 34" scale, solid wood bodies, and rockwood processed necks. Rockwood is a composite of birch and phenolic based resins, which produces a neck unaffected by changes in temperature and humidity. Basses are available in 4-string (new list $2,795-$3,795), 5-string ($2,995-$3,995), 6-string ($3,195-$4,195), and 7-string ($3,895-$4,495) configurations.

5. The next major classification under a heading name is a category name that appears in upper-case, is flush left, and inside a shortened and shaded box. A category name refers mostly to a guitar's primary configuration:

ACOUSTIC

ELECTRIC

6. A sub-classification of the category name (upper/lower-case description slightly indented inside a slightly longer, and lighter shaded box) usually indicates a grouping or series within the classification of the category name:

Original Les Paul Series

Solid Bodies

7. Model names appear flush left, are bolded in upper case (typically), and appear in alpha-numerical (normally) sequence which are grouped under the various subheadings:

BROADCASTER, D-28, DUO-JET (Model 6128), FLYING V, VORTEX

8. Variations within a model appear as sub-models, are indented, and appear in both upper and lower case type:

Coronado Wildwood II, ES-175D, Nightbird Deluxe, 330/12

Variant models follow in the text under the description/pricing of the main model(s).

9. Model/sub-model descriptions appear directly under model/sub-model names and appear as follows:

— body configuration and identifying features and materials, neck configuration and construction, wood used on fingerboard/headstock and any discernible inlays/features, type and style of pickups (if any), tuner configuration and style, colors and/or finishes and other definitive descriptive data are further categorized adjacent to the model names in this typeface. This is where most of the information is listed for each specific model.

10. Directly underneath the model description is the pricing line for that model. When a price line such as the example shown below is encountered,

Mfr.'s Sug. Retail $170 $150 $130 $115 $105 $95 $85 $80

it automatically indicates the guitar is currently manufactured and the manufacturer's suggested retail price is shown left of the 100% column.

11. While the current Suggested Manufacturer's price is included in the regular pricing line, the Last Suggested list price (for discontinued models) may appear in smaller typeface flush right:

Last Sug. Mfr.'s list was $1,449.

12. Manufacturer's notes, model information, and available options appear in smaller type and are significant since they contain both important model changes and other up-to-date information:

This guitar had an unusually large headstock, thus giving it the nickname "Hockey Stick". An economy version was produced with an unbound fingerboard with dot inlays.

13. Extra cost features/special orders and other value added/subtracted items (add-ons for currently manufactured guitars reflect an option's retail price), are placed directly under individual price lines, and appear bolder than other descriptive typeface (this example is from the Martin section):

Add 15% for Brazilian rosewood back/sides (available 1966-69 only).

14. Grading lines will appear at the top of each page where applicable or wherever pricing lines change. The most commonly encountered grading line (with corresponding price line) in this text is 100%-60%:

Grading		100%	98% MINT	95% EXC+	90% EXC	80% VG+	70% VG	60% G
Mfr.'s Sug. Retail	$995		$750	$550	$425	$375	$325	$275	$230

On currently manufactured instruments, the price line shown above is typically encountered. These values reflect 100%-60% values (or new to good condition factors). The 100% price on a new instrument is what you can typically expect to pay for that instrument, and may reflect a discount off the Manufacturer's

Suggested List price. Musical instruments, like other consumer goods (for example: automobiles, appliances, or electronics) may be discounted to promote consumer spending - and are generally used as a sales tool within the music industry and include many music/guitar establishments, chain stores, mail-order companies, and other retailers to help sell merchandise. Discounted prices depend on the local market (some markets may not discount at all, but offer quality service and support/advice after your purchase). **The 100% condition factor, when encountered in a currently manufactured guitar, assumes the guitar has not been previously sold at retail and includes a factory warranty.** A currently manufactured new instrument must include EVERYTHING the factory originally provided with the instrument - including the case (if originally included), warranty card, instruction manual (if any), hang tags (if any), etc. The values for the remaining 98%-60% condition factors represent actual selling prices for used instruments. Simply refer to the correct condition column of the instrument in question and refer to the price listed directly underneath. Please consult the **Photo Percentage Grading System**™ located on pages 33-72 to learn more about accurately determining condition or turn to page 32 for a description of grading system terminology. 98% to 95% (exc+ - mint) condition specimens refer to guitars having played a few licks, but are like or virtually new (mint) and/or have been previously sold at retail (they may be without original cases, hang tags, manuals, and etc). In some cases, only the Manufacturer's Suggested List price is given since there is almost no discounting and used instruments simply do not exist. An "N/A" instead of a price means that a firm market price is **N**ot **A**vailable in certain condition factor(s).

15. A price line with 7 values listed (as the example below demonstrates) indicates a

$715 $660 $605 $550 $440 $385 $330

discontinued, out of production model with values shown for 100%-60% conditions. Obviously, "Mfr.'s Sug. Retail" will not appear in the left margin, but a model note may appear below the price line indicating the last Manufacturer's Suggested List price. Also, an N/A may appear in place of values for instruments that are not commonly encountered in lower condition factor(s). **The longer an instrument has been discontinued, the less likely you will find it in 100% condition**. Some instruments that are only 10 years old and have never been taken out-of-the-case (unplayed), may not be 100% (new) as the finish may have slightly cracked, tarnished, faded, or deteriorated. **100% is new — no excuses, period.**.

Some vintage instrument grading lines (used mainly on Pre-WWII instruments) have values listed for 90%-20% condition factors only since condition over 90% is seldom encountered and almost impossible to accurately value:

Grading	90%	80%	70%	60%	50%	40%	20%

To find a particular guitar in this book, first identify the name of the manufacturer, trademark, importer, brand name, or in some cases - headstock logo. Refer to this listing within the correct alphabetical section. Next, locate the correct category name (acoustics, basses, electrics, etc.). Models will be listed first alpha-numerically (example: model 325 SL, then ASX-15), then by model name (example: Bikini, then Blackhawk). Once you find the correct model or sub-model under its respective subheading, determine the guitar's percentage of original condition (see the **Photo Percentage Grading System**™ on pages 33-72), and simply find the corresponding percentage column to ascertain price. Special/limited editions usually appear last under a manufacturer's heading. Some subdivisions also appear in the Index for faster section identification.

Additional sections in this publication that will be of special interest are the Photo Percentage Grading System™, Correspondence Inquiries (involving specific research and appraisals), References, Periodicals, Interest in Contributing, Glossary, Trademark Index, and Serialization Charts. When using the Serialization Charts, make sure your model is listed and find the serial number within the yearly range listings. However, **do not date your instrument on serial number information alone**! Double check parts/finish variations in the text accompanying the model, or reference the coding on your instrument's potentiometers (tone and volume knobs). More research and data regarding serialization is still being compiled, and updates will continue to be published in future editions of the **Blue Book of Guitars**™.

Acknowledgements

When I heard that Jeff Perkins had left the editorship of the **Blue Book of Guitar Values** in 1995, nothing indicated that I would be aaccepting this very responsible position. Then S.P. calls me up in late December and asks, "Want to work our booth at the January Anaheim NAMM Show?" After working four very intense days at the Winter NAMM, the rest, like they say, is history.

Jeff had invited me to the 1995 Greater Southwest Dallas Guitar Show, and took the time to introduce me to numerous players, luthiers, company presidents, and noted vintage guitar dealers. Jeff also introduced me to Guinness Stout, and the quanities needed to relax after ten hours of out-and-out guitar madness (a technique I still use today after vintage shows!) His personal introduction to the world of guitar collecting is still something I respect to this day. I would especially like to thank Steve and Tom Stock for giving me the opportunity, and an open checkbook to complete the revised Third Edition **Blue Book of Guitars**™. To hire "some guitar guy" without a writing and publishing background to helm this book was a big leap of faith, and I hope the results vindicate their jumping skills.

My previous experience with guitar research began with a subscription to *Guitar Player* magazine in the early 1980s. Imagine, a magazine with articles by Teisco Del Rey (Off The Wall), George Gruhn (Rare Bird - and later, Richard Smith), Profiles by Harvey Citron, Dan Hicks, Roger Sadowsky, John Carruthers, Tom Mulhern, Jon Sievert, and other staff writers at the time. All the gear and guitars that I didn't own (and still don't) were discussed on those pages! My personal collection now spans over 25 years of the magazine, and I still re-read the back issues fairly often.

When I sat down to begin outlining the research for this edition, I drew on a number of texts as conerstones for the project. First and foremost was Tom Wheeler's **American Guitars**. Professor Wheeler's text (editions 1, 2 and 3) was my first indication that everything I thought I knew about guitar companies was wrong! The second text was material that I was somewhat familiar with, and is a smaller book than I used at my previous music store job for several years. I hold George Gruhn and Walter Carter's **Gruhn's Guide to Vintage Guitars** as the focal point for identifying and understanding collectible vintage instruments. As a research tool it is invaluable, and to realize that it is a portion of the research and knowledge held by George Gruhn is astounding. In meetings with Mr. Gruhn, he would remind me time and again that he does not get involved with pricing guides (and is not involved with this edition), yet would still point me in the right direction for research information.

Both Michael Wright and Willie G. Moseley are contributing writers in *Vintage Guitar Magazine* with superlative individual books out. Wright's **Guitar Stories Volume One** provided new information on overlooked guitar companies. Speaking with Mr. Wright was like talking to an older, wiser big brother. Even though he had projects and articles to research and write, he took some time to answer my questions and aim me in directions in which I wasn't even aware. Willie Moseley has the rare gift of writing exactly as though he were talking. On the days that I couldn't reach him at home, I would pick up **Stellas & Stratocasters** and get almost the same results. Both books reinforced some research ideas, and have been credited where the authors themselves were unavailable to help directly.

Tony Bacon and Paul Day, together or individually, have written some beautifully researched and helpful books. Bacon's **Ultimate Guitar Book** belongs on the shelf of any self-respecting collector, and Day's **Burns Book** or any collaboration with Bacon is a must-have. Concise, witty, and factual are the best ways to describe any or all of their books. Paul Bechtoldt has also helmed two favorites: **G&L: Leo's Legacy** and the limited "lawsuit" edition of **Guitars from Neptune** (the later with help from Doug Tulloch). Paul Bechtoldt also shared a number of "industry stories" in a confidence that I can't break, although one still amuses me months after I heard it - and I'm sure that Paul knows exactly which one that is! Last, but not least, Mr. Walter Carter has written a number of books both on his own and in conjuntion with Mr. Gruhn that I find irreplaceable (the Gibson, Epiphone, and Ovation histories). Mr. Carter, the current Gibson historian, has always been forthcoming in answers every time I call.

All of these gentlemen should be commended for their contributions to research. Furthermore, for taking the time and sharing personal observations, I would like to thank them for their time and consideration in answering my correspondence, questions, and out-of-the-blue phone calls. Wherever possible, I have pointed out the text where certain ideas or concepts originated, and recommend to readers to buy the original text and get the full story!

The Third Edition of the **Blue Book of Guitars** has employed several Contributing Editors who took their time to help in individual sections of the book. For assistance in research, company information, and model nomenclature, I would like to thank:

Hal Hammer, Jr.: Mr. Hammer profiled a number of luthiers, and amassed a large collection of photographs used throughout this book. Mr. Hammer was also on hand at the 19th Annual Greater Southwest Dallas and 1996 Long Island guitar shows. Officially, Mr. Hammer is the Chief Financial Officer of a marine insurance company in Florida. A tax and small business consultant, Mr. Hammer still finds time to pursue interests as an author and photographer. He has a great love of guitars and the people associated with them, Mr. Hammer has written and provided photos to many publications throughout the years, including *Ink Inc., Cars Magazine, Screenprinting, Speed Sports news,* and *Guitar Player* magazine. Mr. Hammer is a modest collector of guitars, and loves to play the blues. He can be contacted at 29656 U.S. Highway 19 North, Tropicana Industrial Park, Suite #200, Clearwater, Florida 34621 (813.781.5000/FAX 813.781.6900).

Jay and Kay Pilzer: Jay Pilzer, a noted Guild authority, was a key Contributor in the Second Edition's Guild section. Several months ago, Mr. Pilzer approached me with the idea of "doing the Guild section right"! Mr. Pilzer was instrumental in collecting model information, pricing updates, and refining the layout in the entire Guild section. If it looks great, thank Jay for a job well done; if there are any problems, blame me on the transcription of his notes! Jay and Kay Pilzer can be reached at New Hope Guitar Traders: 502 Smith Mill Road, Fayetteville TN 37334 (615.937.7684 — email: jpilzer@vallnet.com — web: http://vallnet.com/nhgtrd)

Robert Hartman: Bob Hartman is a direct descendant from the Larson family, and has become an authority on instruments built by Carl and August Larson. Mr. Hartman recently published **The Larsons' Creations, Guitars and Mandolin** (Centerstream Publishing, P.O. Box 5450, Fullerton, California 92635), a great book that covers the different brands and models built - as well as a CD recording! Rather than second guess information, I went right to the source and had Mr. Hartman supply the proper overviews for this edition. Robert C. and Carol Hartman can be reached either through Centerstream Publishing, or c/o Blue Book Publications, Inc.

Jim Speros: Mr. Speros is currently compiling a book on Stromberg instruments, as well as the company and family history. Mr. Speros provided this edition's Stromberg section, and promises that his forthcoming publication will supply more of the much needed information regarding Charles and Elmer Stromberg. Interested parties can contact Mr. Speros through Stromberg Research, P.O. Box 51, Lincoln, Massachusetts 01773.

William C. Kaman, II: I first met Mr. Bill Kaman at the 19th Annual Greater Southwest Dallas Guitar Show where he was personally manning the Ovation/Hamer/Trace Elliot booth, and displaying a black Travis Bean Wedge guitar. Mr. Kaman was delightful to talk to, and offered his Travis Bean history for this edition. Mr. Kaman is one of the premier Travis Bean guitar collectors, and a wealth of information on the music industry as well. We are pleased to reproduce his article, and hope that this information answers any questions about Travis Bean's innovative designs. Mr. Kaman can be reached via the Kaman Music Corporation, P.O. Box 507, Bloomfield CT 06002-0507 (800.647.2244).

Brian Gidyk: Mr. Gidyk compiled the information on Gittler guitars, as well as shot the photos that accompany the text. Unfortunately, I ran out of space before I ran out of information! The basic text will be greatly expanded next year, and I am grateful for Mr. Gidyk's input in setting the story straight on the innovative designs of luthier/designer Gittler/Bar Rashi.

Dave Rogers, **Eddy Thurston**, and related seasoned employees: Not only is La Crosse, Wisconsin famous for the G. Heileman Brewery complete with the "World's Largest Six Pack", but it is also home to Dave Rogers, one of the larger collectors and dealers (nice guy and advanced ax grinder, to boot). Mr. Rogers has been instrumental in helping gain information and photographs on both new and vintage guitars. La Crosse is also a great stop-over on my drives from the Blue Book Publications, Inc. home office in Minneapolis, Minnesota to my Pointy Dog Productions office in Michigan. See the screws for that bolt-neck or another round at Piggy's, anyone? Contact Mr. Rogers or the rest of the pros at Dave's Guitar Shop, 1227 South 3rd Street, La Crosse, WI 54601 (608.785.7704/email: davesgtr@aol.com).

Scott Freilich: Mr. Freilich spent an informative hour lecturing me at the 1996 Long Island Guitar Show this year, and has always made time for my phone calls since then. Scott apparently enjoys torturing me with guitar brain puzzlers as well, because he has a wealth of knowledge on tap. Scott Freilich can be reached at Top Shelf Music, 1232 Hertel Avenue, Buffalo, NY 14216 (716.876.6544)

Bill Stapelton: I met Bill Stapelton during the **Blue Book of Guitar**'s massive photo shoot at the 19th Annual Greater Southwest Dallas Guitar Show earlier this year (yes, Bill, your guitars are in here). Mr. Stapelton also called to grill me on the condition factors text, suggested a number of changes (some were even implemented!), and offered another view of the vintage versus new marketplace. And what a great sense of humor! Contact Bill Stapelton at American Music, 4450 Fremont Avenue N, Seattle, WA 98103 (206.633.1774).

Craig Brody: Mr. Brody was a great deal of help on both the Second and Third Editions of the **Blue Book**, and runs a great shop in the Sunshine State. A perfect reason to travel south! (Guitar Broker, 2455 East Sunrise Blvd., Ft. Lauderdale, FL 33304; 954.563.5507, http://www.upcyber.com/guitars/)

Brian Goff: While Brian favors dealing in the odder models of guitars, he still maintains a few "regular" models in his booths at shows. Great stuff! (Bizarre Guitars, 415 Ludington Avenue, Madison WI 53704; 608.245.1340)

Bob Ohman: I stayed in Denver for two years without meeting Mr. Ohman, and I end up calling him four months after I left! Bob's research into the lesser known European builders caused me to rethink my original concept of the book, and now look what it turned into! Too much reading and not enough golf at my house (hmmmm...). Bob Ohman can be reached at Fine and Not so Fine European Guitars, 946 South Race Street, Denver CO 80209 (303.722.1243).

Kevin Macy: Mr. Macy is a contemporary of Mr. Ohman's, and in talking to one I got direct access to the other. I met Kevin down at the 19th Annual Greater Southwest Dallas Guitar Show, and was immediately drawn to the cool stuff contained therein. Best of all, I could call after the show and test out some ideas. Guitarbage, 15 Perry Drive, Manhattan KS 66502 (913.539.2401)

Leroy Braxton: Mr. Braxton is one of the up-and-coming staff members at the Guitar Center outside of Detroit (810.354.8075). After witnessing our last meeting at Gordy and Marcia Lupo's Detroit Guitar Show, my fiancee swears the two of us must somehow share the same mind! I still maintain Leroy's the better man - he buys and sells for a living, and I just write. Also, I've heard him play, and he's got me beat there, too.

Rick Powell: It's great to talk to a fellow bass player and have some ideas confirmed. These days, however, Mr. Powell is more than just a fellow bass player - he also runs Virtuoso Guitars (which specializes in collector level instruments, especially Martins), as well as marketing Virtuoso guitar cleaner and polish (refer to page 19 for more information on these). Contact Virtuoso Vintage Guitars at P.O. Box 5267, Katy TX 77491 (800.558.5009/713.395.4332).

Chad Speck: As we began to wrap up production on this edition, Mr. Speck's input helped fill in the blanks on the "other" collectible guitars sometimes overlooked in the vintage market. All that, and a deal on a coral-colored Peavey Milestone! Call Chad at Encore Music, 2407 Lyndale Avenue South, Minneapolis, MN 55405 (612.871.1775).

Edward Abad: Mr. Abad was extremely helpful in a last minute Gretsch debate this year (double cutaways in 1961, eh?), and other "behind the scenes" stories.

This year, a number of independent luthiers took the time to answer questions and provide background biographies for their listings. I'd like to personally thank them for their time and consideration, and for allowing me the opportunity to tell their stories their way. The **Blue Book of Guitars** will continue to expand coverage on luthiers and builders in future editions as well.

Photography for the Third Editions of the **Blue Book of Guitars** came from three primary sources. Photographer **Paul Goodwin** set up a portable studio next to Blue Book Publications, Inc. booth at the 19th Annual Greater Southwest Dallas Guitar Show, and spent the entire weekend shooting wonderful portraits of guitars (including the instruments on the cover). Writer/photographer **Hal Hammer** independently interviewed luthiers and also shot a large collection of photos. Mr. Hammer also attended a number of additional guitar shows in addition to working with a number of private and professional collectors in Florida. The final source of photos was culled from the **Blue Book** archives, which were photographed and maintained at various locations around the planet by **S. P. Fjestad** since 1992. These are the sharp color images used for the Photo Percentage Grading System on pages 33-72. Many of the color photos in the archives were shot "on location" at Dave's Guitar Shop (LaCrosse, Wisconsin), Willie's American Guitars (St. Paul, Minnesota), and LaVonne Wagener Music (Savage, Minnesota).

A number of collectors, dealers, and private individuals allowed the **Blue Book of Guitars** access to their collections, and assisted our efforts in collecting those images. The **Blue Book of Guitars** would like to express its gratitude to:

Scott Chinery: Mr. Chinery graciously allowed the **Blue Book** Staff full access to his **Blue Guitars** collection at the 1996 Long Island Guitar Show. This show was also attended by a large majority of the luthiers involved with the collection, and offered a magnificent opportunity to photograph many examples of their handiwork. Mr. Chinery is also to be commended for his presence as a (the?) premier American guitar collector who provides access to his collection. We anxiously await publication of **his** new book!

Elliot Rubinson: Mr. Rubinson (Thoroughbred Music) granted photographer Hal Hammer access to numerous great guitars. While many photos did wind up in this edition, there are still others waiting in the archives for future editions. We are grateful to Mr. Rubinson's invitation for the photography shoot, and to his dedication in collecting and sales in his fine stores. I can't wait to visit this winter!

Also, we are thankful to collectors such as **Jim Furniss** (those marvelous Martins!), **Steve Burgess** (collects 'em and plays 'em), **John Miller**, **Cassi International**, and **Phil Willhoite** at **Phil's Guitar Works**.

Over the past eight months, a number of people took the time to answer questions, share stories, and stick guitars in my hand to play. I am extremely grateful that they could find the time to properly instruct me in guitar lore:

Jonas Aronson (Amanda's Texas Underground, Annapolis, MD)

David Baas (Roadworthy Guitars and Amps, Bloomington, IN)

Robert and Cindy Benedetto (Making an Archtop Guitar)

Greg Boyd (Stringed Instrument Division, Missoula, MS)

Terry Breese (Huber and Breese, Fraser, MI)

Larry Briggs (Strings West, Tulsa, OK)

John Brinkmann (Waco Vintage Instruments, Mansfield, TX)

Billy Ray and Claudia Bush (Frankfurt, Germany)

Dick Butler (The String Collector, Kalamazoo, MI)

Skip Calvin (Fort Wayne Guitar Exchange, Fort Wayne, IN)

Mario A. Campa (Toys From the Attic, Hartsdale, NY)

Mike Carey (Curator, The Chinery Collection)

Mark Chatfield (Cowtown Guitars, Columbus, OH)

Jim Colclasure (The Guitarcheologist, Kansas City, MO)

Mike Coulson (Fine Vintage Guitars)

John E. DeSilva (Toys From the Attic, Hartsdale, NY)

Ronn David (Vintage World, Cranston, RI)

Gary S. Dick (Gary's Classic Guitars)

Richard Friedman (Sam Ash Music Stores)

Jimmy Gravity (Gravity Strings, St. Louis, MO)

John Carl Hansen (Spectra Promotions, Warren, MI)

Bruce Hastell (Crosstown Management, Milton, WA)

Steve Helgeson (Moonstone Guitars, Eureka, CA)

Larry Henrikson (Ax in Hand, DeKalb, IL)

Dave Hinson (Hazard Ware Inc., St. Louis, MO)

Erin P. Hogan (Rock and Roll Hall of Fame and Museum)

Gregg Hopkins (Vintage Amp Restoration, St. Louis, MO)

Paul Huber (Huber and Breese, Fraser, MI)

Stan Jay (Mandolin Bros., Staten Island NY)

Larry Jenssen (Slow Hand Guitars, Illinois)

Garrie Johnson (Southwest Vintage, Austin, TX)

John and Rhonda Kennimire (JK Lutherie)

Rick King (Guitar Maniacs, Tacoma, WA)

Randy and Julie Knuth (Congratulations! Manistique, MI)

Charles "Duke" and Fritzie Kramer (D & F Products, Cincinnati, OH)

Greg Kurczewski (Rockhaus, Milwaukee, WI)

Dan Lakin (Lakland Basses, Chicago, IL)

Tim Lanham and Doug Will (L & W Corporation, Fort Collins, CO)

Gordy and Marcia Lupo (Gordy's Music, Ferndale, MI)

Chuck McMillen, and Jim Conner (L & W Corporation, Fort Collins, CO)

Fred Matt and Tracy Pace (CD Ltd., Denver, CO)

Tam Milano (Gravity Strings, St. Louis, MO)

Eugene Sharpey (Sharp Recording and Entertainment, Akron, OH)

Gary Shaw (Henri's Music, Appleton, WI)

John Simmons and Randy Blankenship (Mister Music/Mister Pawn, Colorado Springs, CO)

Russ Spaeth (Music Exchange, Colorado Springs, CO)

Buck Sulcer (Guitar Network)

Dana Sutcliffe (St. Louis Music)

Tim Swartz (TubeTone Amplifiers, Haslett, MI)

Jimmy Wallace (Sound Southwest, TX)

Stan Werbin (Elderly Instruments, Lansing, MI)

Nate Westgor (Willie's American Guitars, St. Paul, MN)

Mark Pollock (Charley's Guitar Shop, Dallas, TX)

I'd like to thank my parents (Al and Linda Cherne) and family (Curt and Amy Cherne, Craig and Liz Cherne, Norman Johanning, Dorothy Cherne, and Mona Liska) for the continued support. I especially want to thank my fiancee, Michelle Serafin, for eight years of bands, loud music, lots of guitars, and the past eight months of reading and writing. Next September, let's get married!

Finally, it's only fitting that we pay proper respect to the Creator for giving us trees and other raw materials, luthiers for their skills and desires, and musicians for their talent to constantly remix thirteen notes. Glory be to God.

Last, but not least, I look forward to another successful year of "talking guitars" from coast to coast, and staying in touch with everyone who helped with this year's book. A big "Thank You!" to those who helped in any way, shape, or form — and if it's wrong in the text, it's **MY** fault (and let's get it right next year)!

Play Guitar!

Steven Cherne
Blue Book of Guitars™

Interested In Contributing?

I've always said that once you publish a book, you will find out what you don't know. This publication is no different. However, an annual publication should always get better. Accumulating new research is an ongoing process with the results being published in each new edition.

The **Blue Book of Guitars**™ has been the result of non-stop and continual guitar research obtained by visiting music stores, guitar shops, pawn shops, second-hand stores, and going to guitar/trade shows. Also, a major importance is speaking directly with acknowledged experts (published and unpublished), reading books/catalogues/company "promo" materials, gathering critical and up-to-date manufacturer/luthier information obtained from NAMM Show's and the makers themselves and observing and analyzing market trends by following major vintage dealer and collector pricing and trends.

If you feel that you can contribute in any way to the materials published herein, I would encourage you to submit hard copy regarding your potential additions, revisions, corrections, or any other pertinent information that you feel would enhance the benefits this book provides to the readers. **Unfortunately, I am unable to take your information over the phone (this protects both of us)!** Join the top notch crowd of Contributing Editors, and see that your information can make a difference!

All materials sent in for possible inclusion into the upcoming 4th Edition of the **Blue Book of Guitars**™ should be mailed/FAXed/emailed to us by June 1st, 1997 at the address listed below.

Blue Book Publications, Inc.
Attn: Guitar Contributions
8009 34th Avenue South #175
Minneapolis, MN 55425 USA
FAX: 612-853-1486
email: bluebook@bluebookinc.com
Web: http://www.bluebookinc.com

Once you have sent your contributions in, I will contact you at a later date to discuss their possible inclusion in upcoming editions. I do appreciate your time and consideration in this matter, and will try to respond quickly to any correspondence sent my way.

Steven Cherne, Author
Blue Book of Guitars™

Correspondence Inquiries

As with any ongoing publication, certain models and variations will not be included within the scope of the text. As expanded research uncovers model variations and new companies, the book's body of text will always have some "grey areas". Not believing in ivory towers and one-way traffic, this publisher offers a mechanism for the consumer to get further information about models not listed in these pages. **No book can ever be totally complete in a collectible field as broad as this one.** For that reason, we are offering correspondence and telephone inquiries to help you obtain additional information on items not listed or even questions on the data and prices provided.

With the addition of new personnel, correspondence under normal circumstances takes us between 10-14 working days, one of the fastest turn-around times in the industry. To make sure we can assist you with any correspondence, please include good quality photos of the specimen in question, any information available about that particular specimen, including manufacturer, model, body style, color/finish, unusual or other discernible features (if any) that will assist us with identifying your guitar. **The charge for this comprehensive research program is $20.00 per instrument.** In addition to payment, be sure to include both your address and phone number, giving us an option of how to contact you for best service. To keep up with this constant onslaught of mail/FAXes, we have a large network of both dealers and collectors who can assist us (if necessary) to answer most of your questions within this time frame.

Remember, the charge for this research service is $20.00 per guitar and payment must accompany your correspondence. Your letters/FAXes will be answered in a FIFO system (first in — first out). Thank you for your patience.

Phone calls regarding guitar related questions will be taken between 2-5 pm daily (CST), during most weekdays, unless we are absent.

Time permitting, pink slip calls will be returned, but paid correspondence, FAXes, and email will receive first priority. We are hoping our turnaround time for research will allow us to give prompt service, and the only way to achieve this is to limit phone access time. It's a big job! All correspondence regarding information and appraisals (not potential contributions or buying/selling guitars) should be directed to:

Pointy Dog Productions
Attn: Steven Cherne
207 Terrace Avenue
Manistique, MI 49854
Phone/FAX 800.631.1199
email:guitars@bluebookinc.com
http://www.bluebookinc.com

SORRY - No order or request for research paid by credit card will be processed without a credit card expiration date.

A PUBLISHER'S OVERVIEW OF THE GUITAR MARKETPLACE

The first time I wrote this overview, I was dreading it and nothing's changed. How are words possibly going to explain all the weirdness that goes on in the guitar business? And besides, what I write today could be growing a beard in a few months. It's hard to explain a roller-coaster ride until you've been on one.

This section is an attempt to provide the reader more information on what really goes on and the supply/demand economics that backdrop the guitar marketplace. And since there are many niches and specialized little pockets of interest that generate unique price tags, knowing the total marketplace is truly the big picture, but perhaps impossible to explain in this language. I've talked to older guitar dealers who have simply told me, "Don't try to figure it out, Steve, just have a new box of price tags ready."

First of all, a few basic concepts of 101 Economics have to be considered. There are only two factors that you have to worry about — Supply and Demand. Really, there's nothing else. In a collectible marketplace, demand usually dictates supply. **The guitar marketplace, especially with vintage instruments, can undergo a supply and demand earthquake within a relatively short period of time.** Knowing what's hot and what's not is a never-ending ritual for successful guitar dealers. Crystal-balling supply/demand guitar economics is almost a full-time job.

OK, so let's get into it. Why are mint '54 Tobacco Sunburst finished Fender Stratocasters selling for $10,000+? Is it model rarity? Not. Is it pure Koolness? Maybe, but I hope not. Is it the virtually impossible to obtain condition factor? Now we're getting someplace. Are these prices legit? We'll find out. Is it because the overall desirability factor of this model, year of manufacture, and condition factor has gone up tremendously? Yes.

Since the Second Edition, many vintage instruments have gone through what traders on Wall Street call "a price correction" - read that lower prices. Why? Because, Japanese buyers have not been as bullish during the last two - three years and domestic demand has also gone down somewhat. This does not mean that the vintage guitar marketplace is collapsing or imploding – it simply shows that a price correction has occurred. Not to worry.

Fifteen years ago, I doubt anyone would have bet on a five digit Stratocaster within the next decade. And to clear the rarity argument, remember - there have been more Fender Stratocasters manufactured in the last 40 years than during Martin's entire production over the last 160 years! In this whole process, it seems like rarity is usually mistaken for desirability rather than understanding that a guitar's rarity factor is only one component to determe overall desirability.

To understand any guitar's desirability factor, one has to understand this word's definition fully. To be desirable is to be demanded, but to be rare does not guarantee anything. Desirability insures demand - rarity does not. **In fact, in some cases, the only thing rarer than a particular guitar is the guy who will spend money to own it.** Why is this? Ever gone to a garage sale and seen a home brewed painting under the card table that the owner was pumping up for $20? You would have probably pulled out an "Andy Jackson" rather fast if you would have seen an authentic Picasso signature at the bottom right. Why? Because the demand factor became much larger once the collectible's trademark/status became accurately established.

Let's break down each guitar's desirability into individual elements enabling us to understand both the demand and supply economics one guitar at a time. The following components will always come into play (even though any guitar's unique "mix" of these properties is usually different) when determining a specimen's overall desirability. The key factors when determining a guitar's demand factor (desirability) are as follows:

(1) **Trademark Recognition/Acceptance/Importance.** How popular or collected is the maker's name? Having a Martin, Fender, D'Angelico, Elvis Presley's 1958 Gibson LG-1, Gretsch, Epiphone, etc. is going to be a lot different than having a Magnatone, Maybell, Harmony, vanilla flavored Danelectro, or any one of the hundreds of trademarks nobody is sure of or has heard of. Most of the instruments manufactured by these lesser known trademarks were manufactured to undercut the competition at the time, and while many were (some still are) fair quality, inexpensively made, utilitarian pieces, their value today must be based on the player utility factor only since in most cases, there is little or no collector interest. Many of these companies (or subcontractors) were in business for only a brief time and little history remains on their day-to-day operations. One of the big reasons that Fender, Martin, Gibson, Epiphone, Guild, and others have a large collector following today is because these factories are still in business and company records/documents may authenticate their older instruments. In many cases, however, factory information is non-existent or incomplete when linking

up a serial number with a specific model complete with description and shipping date.

② **Condition.** In most cases a guitar's original condition is what is rare, not the model itself. Original condition for many collectors is the most important factor in determining a guitar's desirability. Many collectors simply will not purchase a guitar below a certain condition factor, regardless of price (unless, of course, it's an early Stratocaster in a rare Dupont color). **Original condition is Polar North for most guitar collectors and investors today.** Once condition decreases on most specimens, the "player utility factor" controls the equation more than the "collector's value" on more recently made models. Major trademark older vintage instruments retain collector interest down to a "no finish left" condition factor since they are collectible regardless of their "playability". Refinished guitars in commonly encountered models in good supply are not as desirable as original condition specimens, and values are generally considered to be 50% less than an original instrument. In other words, a common '70s Guild flat top that has been professionally refinished will never be as desirable as an original specimen, since all things considered, collectors and players would rather concentrate on original condition (if it is available in the marketplace).

③ **Historical Recognition/Notarized Provenance.** In other words, if you can prove by historical documentation that the guitar(s) you own belonged to a Jimi Hendrix, Stevie Ray Vaughn, David Gilmour, Hank Williams, Elvis Presley, President Nixon, etc., the price tag will escalate tremendously. **The sale price will be contingent on how well the personality/organization is known.** Very few people will care (or pay) for a local personality's "main squeeze". A specimen owned by a regionally famous person will command a regional price. If the guitar belonged to John Lennon and you can prove it in front of a judge and jury, then, in most cases, an auction may be the only way of assessing the correct value. In some cases, whoever presented the guitar as a gift may make at least as much difference as whom the guitar was presented to.

④ **Price.** Any guitar becomes a value at the right price. At some subterranean low price, regardless what kind of fretted instrument is being sold, many of us will buy it (justified by becoming more diversified in our collecting). As you would expect, pricing is more predictable as your sampling ratio increases. In other words, the correct price will be much easier to determine on a 1979 Gibson Les Paul than on an inscribed pre-war Stromberg. While there are literally thousands of Les Pauls that are internationally bought/sold annually, only a very few Strombergs will exchange hands during the same time period. If the price seems like it's at the summit, see if it can be budged into the price range you are looking for. If not, give it up and wait until the next opportunity. If the price is close to what you would like to pay, perhaps light "chiseling"may be used with some effectiveness. **Veterans in this business, however, will tell you to pay a little extra to get something that is a little bit better.** The worst feeling at a guitar show is when you walk back to that booth looking for the nice Telecaster Rosewood Re-issue (that you tried to buy a 1/2 hour ago for $75 off a $575 asking price) and all that remains is an empty stand on the table. Does the price make the guitar more desirable or does it detract from it to the point that you can't possibly buy it? These are questions you have to ask yourself on every potential purchase. During the past several years, a new pattern has been established for selling top-shelf trademarks with famous person provenances. Some major auction houses have set new records on many of these historically significant instruments. Recently, an older Martin previously owned by Elvis Presley was gavelled off at over $130,000! This is what can happen to price when you hook up Star notoriety with historical documentation/acceptance, trademark significance, and condition — then let the top dealers, collectors, and investors turbocharge the price tag in the fast and furious atmosphere of an auction house.

My advice on the pricing issue is to do your homework before you get tested under "combat conditions." Map out your area of collecting and buy the necessary pricing guides and reference books that will give you the information that you are going to need. I always chuckle when I hear someone complain about the "high price" of a particular book when it could have saved him/her hundreds of dollars on the non-original guitar he "stole" late Sunday at the last guitar show. In addition, attend a few guitar shows annually (including at least one big show). Get to know a few reputable dealers in your field and make sure you get their inventory listings and pricing information. Last, but certainly not least, BUY SOMETHING! It's good for the economy and your collection.

⑤ **Rarity. Most guitars are not rare. Rather, their condition can make them rare.** Again, while it is true that many instruments may be relatively hard to find, sometimes the potential purchaser for these off-brand trademarks can be rarer than the guitar. Literally, there are hundreds of trademarks/brand names both domestically and internationally that nobody really cares about (or is willing to pay $500 for). In many cases, the configuration of certain makes and models becomes much more important than the headstock markings (i.e., a Danelectro 6-string bass in Coral Green is going to be a lot more desirable than a black standard model). Also remember that because a guitar belonged to a great-uncle or family relative does not make it any rarer (or desirable) in the eyes of the next potential purchaser. Many people think that some popular guitars are rare. As an example, most Fender Stratocasters are not rare — they have made over 500,000 during the past 40 years! A mint 1954 factory white Stratocaster is rare, however, since the color was never very popular and most saw heavy use (and possibly, some abuse). Sometimes, the most commonly encountered features in a particular model end up being the most desirable. Let's pick on early Strats again. Even though it is rarer to find this model without a tremolo bar, values are the same as a specimen that has a factory tremolo unit, since most advanced collectors and even players prefer this factory option. **Be careful when letting the rarity control your pocketbook** — the other factors listed in this article are considerably more important. Exercise caution on those unknown specimens commonly described as, "I don't think I've ever seen another one like it." While a fortunate few have been lucky when adding these rarities to their collections, more have "damaged their estates" by basing value on rarity only.

⑥**Special Order Features/Embellishments/Accessories/ Accouterments**. Many guitars have been special ordered with optional accessories including non-standard hardware, customized electronics, wood and paint finishes, a variety of tuning machines, inlays and ornamentation, personalization, and other custom/special features that have to be taken into consideration to determine the price of any given instrument. **All of these special orders/options act both independently and interdependently to determine the correct value for a particular guitar**. On major trademark specimens it is important that these optional features were done at the factory, not by someone outside the factory at a later date. On modern customized guitars, the resale is hard to predict since a customized guitar was originally created to fit a particular musician's playing style, not someone else's at a later date. Many times on a customized guitar involving resale, "the whole is not the sum of its parts." In other words, the total cost of the guitar and customizing will be more than what it will resell for in the used marketplace. On many rare guitar options/special orders, prices can be very hard to predict accurately, since very few instruments incorporating these special features are bought/sold during the course of each year. Most of the time, a knowledgeable dealer or advanced collector should be consulted on the difference these special orders/options can make on the price of a guitar.

⑦**Supply/Demand Differences**. Some guitars have regional supply and demand economics that affect values. An older Martin flat top with some wear is going to be more desirable in California and New York than it would be in northern Montana. Also, certain currently manufactured models with a low supply factor can have a short-term affect on pricing. A good example of this is the National Reso-Lectric — this model has had very limited manufacture (up to recently, a back-order situation was normal) and because of this, used specimens are selling close to the manufacturer's suggested retail price. As soon as supply can catch demand, this situation could change in a hurry. **Short-term economic situations that present potential downside risk factors are solved by dealers watching their inventory levels very closely during these supply/demand crossovers.**

In closing, I would like you to remember that when purchasing guitars for storing value, consider overall desirability first, condition second, price third, and rarity last. Since the supply of most vintage and some recent out-of-production guitars is decreasing (how many more end up overseas each year?), it is the demand side of the marketplace that determines what is desirable, regardless of rarity. Most collectors like trademarks backed by historical provenance having many models/variations (and existing information) from which to choose and build into an orderly collection. Once a guitar's overall desirability factor has been accurately determined, you will have a much better idea if that next potential guitar purchase deserves input number 1 on your twin Marshall stack.

Steven P. Fjestad
Editor and Publisher
Blue Book of Guitars™

House Brands

"All Cats are Grey in the Dark"
Identifying "House Brands" Musical Instruments

The phenomenon of large production companies producing "house brand" instruments dates back to the late 1800s and early 1900s. A "house brand" is defined as a trademark used by distributors/wholesalers/sellers to represent their respective company instead of the manufacturer. These brands are found (for the most part) on budget instruments, although some models are currently sought after by players and collectors on the basis of playability, tone, or relative degree of "coolness" they project.

In the 1800s, many guitar manufacturers were located in New York and Philadelphia; by the early 1900s large guitar factories were centered in Chicago. The "Big Three" that evolved out of the early 1930s were Harmony, Kay, and Valco. Valco, producer of **National** and **Supro** instruments, produced the **Airline** house brand as well as bodies and resonator parts that were sold to Harmony and Kay. However, the majority of house brand instruments found today probably originated at either Harmony or Kay. On the East Coast, Danelectro was a large builder/supplier to Sears & Roebuck under Sears' **Silvertone** label (sometimes up to 85 percent of Danelectro's output).

Prior to World War II, Harmony and Kay sold straight to wholesalers like catalogue houses and large distributors. In turn, these wholesalers would send their salesmen and "reps" out on the road to generate sales — no territories, no music store chains — just straight sales. Business was fierce, and companies used their own private labels to denote "their" product. House brands were typically used as a marketing tool for distributors, wholesalers, and/or retailers to try to eliminate consumer shopping for the best price on popular makes and models of the time. How could you shop a trademark that didn't exist anywhere else? Tom Wheeler, in his book **American Guitars**, quoted former Harmony president Charles A. Rubovits' recollection that the company built 57 private brands for the wholesalers — and sold over five million guitars.

An informative essay about house brands and their place in the vintage guitar spectrum can be found in **Stellas & Stratocasters** (Vintage Guitar Books) by Willie G. Moseley, feature writer/columnist for *Vintage Guitar Magazine*. Moseley's commentary includes a listing of thirty-eight brands and their retailers/distributors, brief anecdotes about the major American manufacturers of budget instruments (Harmony, Kay, etc.) and photos of twenty-five American made house brand instruments.

Since writing that article, Moseley has advised the **Blue Book of Guitars**: "I've come across a couple of other house brands in my travels; one example was a low-end, Stella-type variant with 'Superior' sloppily screen-printed on its headstock. It was one of those cheap, beginner's instruments that were and still are at the nadir of American-made guitars, but so far I haven't been able to determine anything about its brand name...not that it matters too much!"

"It's my opinion, and I dare say the opinion of most vintage guitar enthusiasts, that a good rule of thumb concerning the collectibility of house brands would be something along the lines of 'If it was a budget instrument **then**, it's **proportionally** a budget instrument **now**.' Regretably, as the interest in vintage guitars continues to grow, some individuals and/or businesses tend to assume that simply because an instrument is 'old' and/or 'discontinued' and/or 'American-made', that automatically makes it 'a collector's item' and/or 'valuable'. That's certainly not the case, **especially** with house brands. It's disheartening to walk into a pawn shop and see a Kay-made Silvertone archtop acoustic from the Sixties labeled as an 'antique' and priced at $499, when the instrument is worth no more than $100 in the vintage guitar market, and such incidents are apparently on the increase. And that's unfortunate for everybody."

The **Blue Book of Guitars** is continuing to collect data and evaluate the collectibility and pricing on these house brand instruments. Condition is a large factor in the pricing, as a thirty-to-forty year old guitar ordered from a catalog may have been used/abused by younger members of a household (to the detriment of the instrument). House brand guitars may be antiques, they may be somewhat collectible, and they may be "classic pieces of Americana" (as one antique shop's sign declared), but they should still be relatively inexpensive when compared to the rest of the vintage guitar market. I believe Mr. Moseley to be correct in his C-note assessment of this aspect of the vintage market (at 80% to 90% condition); other music markets that service players and students may find pricing at a slightly wider range of $75 to $150 depending on other factors (playability, possessing an adjustable truss rod, appearance/"coolness" factor, a solid wood top versus plywood, veneer sides, additional parts, etc.). This is the bottom line: this book should help identify the brand/original company, give a few hints as to the quality and desirability, and a price range. The rest is up to you! We will continue to survey the market for pricing trends and "hot" models — further information will be included in upcoming editions of the **Blue Book of Guitars**.

Steven Cherne, Author
Blue Book of Guitars™

A Unique Concept

The **Blue Book of Guitars**™ is the only book that:

✓ Provides reference text as well as pricing information on almost 1,000 trademarks!

✓ Supplies 80 full color and over 300 b/w photos for easier guitar identification!

✓ Utilizes the Photo Percentage Grading System for condition factors in addition to converting this system to other existing grading systems.

✓ Is updated annually and provides the freshest information available on both the vintage market as well as currently manufactured models!

✓ Is based on actual selling prices. These are real world prices you can actually expect to pay — as opposed to artificial prices that are not based on each guitar's unique condition factor.

✓ Offers you personal consultation by mail on special questions you may have! (No book can cover everything).

✓ Gives detailed serial number information on over 20 major guitar manufacturers!

Individual appraisals and/or additional research can be performed for $20.00 per guitar (see the "Correspondence Inquiries" section on page 12 for more information on this service).

Buying or Selling?

Interested in buying or selling a particular guitar(s)? Or maybe hesitating because you are unsure of what a fair market price should be? Depending on what you are interested in, a referral will be made that will enable you to be sure that you are getting what you paid for (or getting paid a fair price). This referral service is designed to help all those people who are worried or scared about purchasing a potentially "bad guitar" or getting "ripped off" when selling. **There is no charge for this referral service - we are simply connecting you with the best person(s) possible within your field of collecting to ensure that you get a fair deal.** This sort of matchmaking can make a world of difference on potentially buying or selling a guitar. Please phone or write the **Blue Book of Guitars**™ for both availability and dealer referrals that can be relied upon for both buying and selling. All replies are treated strictly confidential. Replies should be directed to:

Blue Book of Guitars™
Attn: Guitar Research
8009 34th Avenue South #175
Minneapolis MN 55425 USA
Phone: 612.854.5229
(FAX) 612.853.1486
email: bluebook@bluebookinc.com
http://www.bluebookinc.com

If You Don't Drive Them And You Don't Sit On Them...

4 oz. V.P. Cleaner $10.00

4 oz. V.P. Polish $10.00

Virtuoso.™

Why Are You Using Car Polish And Furniture Wax On Them?

As a leading dealer in premium vintage guitars, Virtuoso is constantly faced with the problem of cleaning, polishing and protecting the fine instruments it sells. None of the products currently on the market satisfied us. Most were designed for car or furniture finishes. Some products use abrasives and other chemicals harmful to the finish of a guitar.

So, we have created the ultimate guitar cleaner and polish.

Introducing Virtuoso Premium Polish.

It cleans. Instead of abrasives Virtuoso Premium Polish uses a chemical reaction to break down residues allowing them to be easily wiped off without harming the original finish.

It polishes. Virtuoso Premium Polish leaves a high gloss finger print resistant shine that will restore vintage finishes.

It protects. Virtuoso Premium Polish seals the finish preventing further oxidation and forms a layer of 100% UV protection.

Also introducing Virtuoso Premium Cleaner.

We created Virtuoso Premium Cleaner, a more potent product for removing heavy accumulations such as rosins or other stubborn build ups.

You made the decision to invest in a vintage instrument. Isn't it time you protected your investment?

Virtuoso cleaner and polish are available from:

Blue Book Publications, Inc.

Toll Free in USA 800-877-4867
Domestic & International: 612-854-5229
Fax: 612-853-1486
Home Page: http://www.bluebookinc.com
email: bluebook@bluebookinc.com

8009 34th Avenue South #175 • Minneapolis, MN 55425

Please allow 1-3 weeks for delivery.

CALL 1-800 TO ORDER 877-4867

eMedia GUITAR METHOD™
The Easiest Way To Learn Guitar.

$59.95
+$4.00 S/H

CD-ROM EDUCATION

eMedia Guitar Method™ is a complete CD-ROM guitar tutorial package. It offers a fun, practical way to learn acoustic or electric guitar at your own pace. Instructional video and knowledgeable advice from professional guitar instructor and national performer, Kevin Garry, reinforce the 60 detailed lessons and bring a personal touch to the program.

Complemented by over 30 videos and over 3 hours of audio, eMedia Guitar Method offers beginners a better alternative to expensive lessons and hard-to-follow books. The comprehensive lessons guide the student through everything they need to know to begin playing guitar. And with the advantage of interactive CD-ROM, Kevin Garry is able to demonstrate guitar techniques as he would in private lessons. The at-home convenience, extensive reference material and easy-going instruction makes this the ideal approach for beginners.

- ● **60 COMPREHENSIVE LESSONS**
  Basics ranging from, simple chords, strumming styles, playing melodies and fingerpicking. Full motion video and sound complement over 100 exercises and songs such as "Scarborough Fair" and "House of the Rising Sun".

- ● **RECORDER**
  Record and play yourself back! This feature allows you to compare your recordings with the instructor's version, fine tune your skills and accelerate the learning process.

- ● **AUTOMATIC TUNER**
  Tune your guitar quickly and easily. You can play into your computer's microphone and visually determine if you're too high or too low. Also includes full tuning reference notes.

- ● **DIGITAL METRONOME**
  Allows you to set your own tempo and keep a steady beat with audio and/or visual feedback.

- ● **CHORD DICTIONARY**
  Includes fingering charts and recorded sounds for over 250 chords. Easy access helps you learn songs with new chords quickly.

- ● **INTERNET SONG GUIDE**
  The guide includes complete access directions to hundreds of songs appropriate to your specific skill level so you can practice and improve your skills with popular songs such as "Hey Jude", "Hotel California", and "It's The End Of The World As We Know It".

Windows Requirements:
386 PC, Windows 3.1, CD-ROM drive, sound card, VGA+ display, 2 MB Ram, 7 MB hard drive space (MPC 1 with Windows 3.1 or Win 95)

Macintosh Requirements:
68020 or better (or PowerPC), System 7 or greater (with QuickTime), CD-ROM drive, 4MB RAM, 7 MB hard drive space

Customer Satisfaction Guaranteed

Please allow 1-3 weeks for delivery.

The Guitar Method CD-ROM is available from:

$59.95
+$4.00 S/H

 Blue Book Publications, Inc.

8009 34th Avenue South #175 • Minneapolis, MN 55425

Toll Free in USA 800-8774867
Domestic & International 612-854-5229
Fax 612-853-1486
Home Page:
http://www.bluebookinc.com
email:
bluebook@bluebookinc.com

CALL 1-800 TO ORDER

877-4867

22

FENDER- THE SOUND HEARD 'ROUND THE WORLD
by: Richard R. Smith, forward by: T. Wheeler
A marvelously illustrated history that draws from personal letters, patents, business documents, and advertising materials to tell the story of Leo Fender's life and musical revolution. Details as never before the creation of his world famous inventions and the 50-year history of the Fender Musical Instrument Corporation. Full of reminiscences, this work explains how steel guitar design and philosophy extended into the Telecaster and Stratocaster, and how genius, unintended consequences, and shifting tastes all converged to make history. Includes hundreds of illustrations and many rare/previously unpublished B&W and color photos. 316 pages, 8.5" x 11" Hardbound..........$50.00

FENDER CUSTOM SHOP: Guitar Gallery
By: Richard Smith
A stunning photo tour of Fender Custom Shop creations, featuring full page, full color photos of fifty instruments with close-ups, and detailed descriptions from master builders. Included are the Harley Strat, Western Tele, Rocket Caster, Jag Stang, Horse Shoe Thinline, and more. 8 1/2" x 11", 144 Pages, Hardbound...........$39.95

GUITARS FROM NEPTUNE-
A Definitive Journey Into Danelectro Mania
By: Paul Bechtoldt
In 1958 Nate Daniel moved his company, Danelectro, to a new location in Neptune City, New Jersey, thus the name Guitars From Neptune. By that time he had already been building guitar amplifiers for over twenty years, and had been making electric guitars since 1954. You can read how he went on to make the unique guitars and amps you have come to know as Danos, and though this book covers the whole history of the company, it's main emphasis is in the identification section, where you can check out numerous catalog and ad reprints and two guitar and amp charts that were developed for quick reference. Many photos, some in color, softbound........$24.95

CLASSIC GUITARS of the '50s
by: Fifteen of the World's Leading Guitar Writers
The Electric Guitar and the Musical Revolution of the '50s By: Fifteen of the world's leading guitar writers This spectacular book captures the sense of change and opportunity that permeated the magical 1950's, when Rock'n'Roll was born and the electric guitar grew up to find its real purpose at the heart of a musical revolution. Full-color photographs of over seventy five key instruments exemplify the new design ethic that swept popular culture, and a unique team of top guitar writers from around the world contribute special essays that illuminate the decade's significant musical achievements, from Jazz and Blues to Country and Rock'n'Roll, all wrapped up in the people, events and inventions that marked forever a truly outstanding decade. Hardbound........$29.95 Coming Soon!

THE GRETSCH BOOK- Complete History of Gretsch Electric Guitars
by Tony Bacon and Paul Day
Done in the same format as other Bacon & Day books, such as "The Fender Book", with color photos throughout and informative text, this book also adds interesting stories highlighting links with famous guitarists, such as George Harrison, Duane Eddy, and Chet Atkins. A thirty page reference section is included for identifying and dating of models. Hardbound..........$24.95

GUITAR RELATED BOOKS & ITEMS

1997 VINTAGE GUITAR CALENDAR Designed by Bill Rich	$13.95
We also have 1990 thru 1996 calendars in stock	@ $10.00
THE CHINERY COL.- 150 Years of American Guitar / Limited Edition	$75.00
THE CHINERY COLLECTION VIDEO	$29.95
ACOUSTIC GUITARS / George Gruhn & Walter Carter, 288 Pgs. Hbnd	$49.95
THE BASS BOOK / Bacon & Day, $108 pages, Hardbound	$22.95
CLASSIC GUITARS USA / Willie Moseley 159 Pgs. Softbound	$19.95
THE DEVELOPMENT OF THE MODERN GTR / Huber	$12.95
DREAM GUITAR ILLUSTRATED / Dellavalle, 64 Pgs, Sbnd	$14.95
THE ELECTRIC GUITAR- An Illustrated History, / Paul Trynka, Sbnd	$18.95
ELECTRIC GUITARS & BASSES / George Gruhn & Walter Carter	$39.95
GRUHN'S GUIDE / George Gruhn & Walter Carter 350 Pgs. Hardbound	$22.95
EXECUTIVE ROCK / Willie Moseley, 219 Pages, Softbound	$9.95
GUITAR IDENTIFICATION / Duchossoir 48 Pgs. Softbound	$7.95
GUITAR TRADER BULLETIN VOL.I / 185 Pgs. Softbound	$14.95
GUITAR TRADER BULLETIN VOL.II / 284 Pgs. Softbound	$16.95
GUITARS OF THE STARS (RICK NIELSEN) / Rich 182 Pgs.	$40.00
GUITAR STORIES Vol. 1 / Michael Wright, 310 Pages Softbound	$29.95
GUITARS THAT SHOOK THE WORLD / Brad Tolinski, 128 Pages	$24.95
THE GUITAR FROM RENAISSANCE TO THE PRESENT DAY	$15.95
THE GURU'S GTR. GUIDE / Tony Bacon & Paul Day, 91 Pgs Sbnd	$12.95
THE HISTORY. & DEVELOPMENT OF THE AMERICAN. GTR. 200 Pgs.$22.95	
HOW TO BUY A VINTAGE GUITAR (VIDEO) / George Gruhn	$39.95
THE MUSICAL INSTRUMENT. COLLECTOR / Willcutt & Ball 144 Pgs	$5.95
OLD GUITAR MANIA / Blackburn, 88 Pgs. Softbound	$10.95
PICKS! The Colorfull Saga of Vintage Guitar Plectrums	$12.95
STAR GUITARS / N. Marten, 105 Pgs, Softbound	$24.95
STELLAS & STRATOCASTERS / Willie Moseley 278 Pgs.	$19.95
THE STEVE HOWE GUITAR COL / S. Howe & T. Bacon, Hardbound	$27.95
THE ULTIMATE GUITAR BOOK / Tony Bacon, Hardbound	$40.00
VINTAGE GUITARS IN AMERICA VOL.1 & 2 (VIDEO)	@ $29.95

BURNS, DANO, & EPIPHONE

THE BURNS BOOK / DAY 96 Pgs. Softbound	$16.95
GUITARS FROM NEPTUNE, The Danelectro Story / Bechtoldt	$24.95
EPIPHONE- The Complete History / Walter Carter, 146 Pages Softbound	$22.95
Hardbound	$39.95

FENDER

DAVE FUNK'S TUBE AMP WORKBOOK- Vol. 1 FENDER	$35.00
FENDER- The Sound Heard Round the World/ Richard Smith, 316 Pgs, Hardbound	$50.00
FENDER CLASSIC MOMENTS / Alan diPerna, 112 Pages Hardbound	$25.00
FENDER CUSTOM SHOP: Guitar Gallery / Richard Smith, 144 Pgs. Hardbound	$39.95
THE STORY OF THE FENDER STRATOCASTER / Hardbound	$24.95
THE FENDER AMP BOOK / John Morrish, Hardbound	$17.95
FENDER AMPS- THE FIRST 50 YEARS / Teagle & Sprung	$34.95
FENDER- THE INSIDE STORY / Forest White, Softbound	$22.95
GET THAT CLASSIC FENDER SOUND! (VIDEO) Jim Weider	$39.95
GUITAR LEGENDS / George Fullerton 111 Pgs. Softbound	$24.95
THE FENDER BASS / Blasquiz	$9.95
THE FENDER BOOK / Tony Bacon & Paul Day, 96 Pgs. Hardbound	$19.95
THE FENDER CO. / Donald Brosnac 48 Pgs. Softbound	$9.95
THE FENDER GUITAR / Achard 68 Pgs. Softbound	$14.95
THE FENDER STRATOCASTER / A.R. Duchossoir	$14.95
THE FENDER TELECASTER / A.R. Duchossoir 80 Pgs	$14.95

  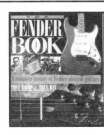 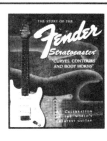  

GIBSON

'BURST - 1958-60 SUNBURST LES PAUL / Jay Scott & Vic Da Pra $24.95
GIBSON ELECTRICS VOLUME I / A.R.Duchossoir 191Pgs. Sbnd $19.95
GIBSON: 100 Years of an American Icon / Walter Carter $40.00
GIBSON ELECTRICS - The Classic Years / A.R. Duchossoir $34.95
GIBSON GUITAR & AMP REPRINT. Catalogs of the 60's, 126 Pgs $12.95
GIBSON SG / Bulli, 48 Pgs. Softbound $9.95
GIBSON SHIPPING TOTALS / J.T.G. Publishing, 66 Pgs. $20.00
GIBSON'S FABULOUS FLAT-TOP GUITARS, 207 Pgs, Softbound $19.95
THE GIBSON LES PAUL BOOK / Tony Bacon & Paul Day, Hardbound $19.95
THE GIBSON GUITAR VOL. I / Bishop, 96 Pgs., Softbound $14.95
THE GIBSON GUITAR VOL. II / Bishop, 100 Pgs., Softbound $14.95
THE GIBSON SUPER 400 / Tom Van Hoose, 224 Pgs., Softbound $24.95

G&L, GRETSCH, GUILD, & HOFNER

G & L: LEO' S LEGACY / Paul Bechtoldt, 52 Pgs, Softbound $11.95
THE GRETSCH BOOK / Bacon & Day, Hardboud $24.95
GUITARS OF THE FRED GRETSCH CO. / Softbound $35.00
          Hardbound $48.00
THE GUILD GUITAR BOOK-The Company & Instruments, 184 Pages $39.95
          Hardbound $49.95
THE HOFNER GUITAR/ A HISTORY / Giltrap & Marten, Hrdbnd $40.00

KAY, & LARSONS

50's COOL KAY GUITARS / SCOTT 64 Pgs. Softbound $14.95
THE LARSONS CREATIONS, Guitars & Mandolin / Robert Hartman $39.95
GTRS. & MAND. IN AMER. / Hartman 187 Pgs. Softbound $14.00

MARTIN, & NATIONAL

THE MARTIN BOOK / Walter Carter, Hardbound $22.95
MARTIN GTRS.; A HISTORY / Longworth, 350 Pgs. Hbnd $29.95
HISTORY OF NATIONAL / Bob Brozman, 289 Pgs Softbound $35.00

RICKENBACKER

THE RICKENBACKER BOOK / Tony Bacon & Paul Day, Hardbound $19.95
HISTORY OF RICKENBACKER / Richard Smith, 244 Pgs. Softbound $29.95

VOX, & WASHBURN

THE VOX STORY / Peterson & Denny 168 Pgs. Sbnd $19.95
WASHBURN: Over 100 Years of Fine Stringed Instr. Sftbnd $29.95
          Hardbound $39.95

AMPLIFIER BOOKS

DAVE FUNK'S TUBE AMP WORKBOOK- Vol. 1 FENDER $35.00
THE ART OF THE AMPLIFIER / Michael Doyle, Softbound $22.95
A DESKTOP REFERENCE OF HIP VINT. GTR AMPS / Gerald Weber $26.95
AMPSI THE OTHER HALF OF R & R / Ritchie Fliegler $24.95
COMPLETE GUIDE TO GTR & AMP MAINTENANCE / Fliegler $14.95
INSIDE TUBE AMPS- Book on Tube Amp Tech / Dan Torres $50.00
THE AMP BOOK / Donald Brosnac, 64 Pgs. Softbound $9.95
THE FENDER AMP BOOK / John Morrish, Hardbound $17.95
FENDER AMPS- The First Fifty Years / Teagle & Sprung, Softbound $34.95
THE TUBE AMP BOOK VOL. 4.1 / Aspen Pittman, 763 Pgs. Sbnd $29.95
HOW TO SER. YOUR TUBE AMP, Book & Video Set $69.95
AUDIO DESIGNERS TUBE REGISTER / Tom Mitchell 144 Pgs $18.00
THE HISTORY OF MARSHALL / Michael Doyle, 250+ Pgs. Softbound ... $32.95
THE HIGH PERFORMANCE MARSHALL HANDBOOK $11.95

FENDER CLASSIC MOMENTS
by: Alan diPerna
Over 100 photos and lively text chronicle great Fender guitar moments and history changing happenings. Includes photos of Elvis singing through a Fender amp at the 1955 Tupelo fair, Dylan's antics at the Newport Folk Festival, Hendrix's fury at Monterey, Clapton at Live Aid, Smashing pumpkins at Lollapalooza, and much more. 112 pages, 11" x 8 1/2" Hardbound..........$25.00

DAVE FUNK'S TUBE AMP WORKBOOK
by: Dave Funk
Learn how tube amplifiers work from the inside out. Identify and date collectable vintage Fender amps. Study electronics and tube technology, all in one volume, loaded with information on components, speakers, transformers, tubes and tube circuits. How to bias an amp, understand tone controls, distortion circuits, reverb, effects and feedback loops and phase inverters. Learn about grounding, safety and noise, with cross-reference material, lookup tables, formulas and the information you'll need to know when your amp is working properly. Comb bound..........$35.00

The History of the OVATION GUITAR
by: WALTER CARTER
The history of the Ovation guitar spans an extraordinary string of innovations. In the thirty short years since the company was founded, it has been responsible for the considerable success of the fiberglass roundback guitar, acoustic electric electric guitar as well as guitars featuring other sometimes radical new designs as well as the use of modern technology and materials. This new 128 page book documents those innovations and the personalities behind them. Appendices detail the chronology of model and serial numbers, over 100 photo's including a color gallery of instruments and players.9" x 12", Softbound $22.95 Hardbound..........$39.95

EPIPHONE- THE COMPLETE HISTORY
by: Walter Carter
This new book, Carter's sixth, reveals the history of this premier company from 1873 into the 1990's. Epiphone's glory years of the 1930's, the Gibson U.S.A. era in the 1960's, and recent Japanese/Korean production are featured in an array of model histories, serial number lists, interviews, and over 150 photos including a sixteen page color section. Large 9" X 12" format, 146 pages. We have stock of both the softbound at.....$22.95, and a limited quantity of the "Collector's Edition" hardbound copies at......$39.95.

GUITAR STORIES Volume One
by: Michael Wright
In this book you can read the interesting stories of: Gibson's experimental 1970's, Gretsch's electrics during the Baldwin era, Ibanez, Japanese guitars in the US, EKO, Dean, Peavey, La Baye, Hondo, Premier, Kapa, Kustom guitars, S.D. Curlee, Renaissance, O'Hagan, Gilbert and Stiles guitars. Also the story of Maestro effects. This book contains over 1100 photos, 100 of which are in full color. 310 pages, 8 1/2" x 11" softbound..........$29.95

Domestic & International 612-854-5229
Fax 612-853-1486
Home Page: http://www.bluebookinc.com
email: bluebook@bluebookinc.com

Blue Book Publications, Inc.

Buy Low!

Rants and Raves from the cheese wizard of the Electric Guitar?

by Teisco Del Rey

ASCAP/Deems Taylor Award winning journalist Teisco Del Rey was the first collector/journalist to make a serious (but not *too* serious) attempt at documenting the unsung "exotic" makes and models of guitars, first with his popular Off The Wall *Guitar Player* column and currently with Teisco's Forbidden Planet in *Guitar Shop*. He has also released two acclaimed rock instrumental CDs, *The Many Moods Of Teisco Del Rey* and *Teisco Del Rey Plays Music For Lovers* (Upstart).

Which brings us to the question, how do you rate a used Fender Relic Series? You know, those pre-aged reproductions, made to look worn-in, or -out, straight from the plant. If you actually play it to the point that it gets even more beat-up, does that increase its value, or have you marred the *just so* distressed, fatigued cachet? (In other words, are your belt buckle wear and fingerboard stains the *right* belt buckle wear and fingerboard stains?) And for that matter, what if you took a genuine pristine '57 Strat and hacked it up a bit? It would decrease its vintage '57 market value, but would that make it worth more or less than a "mint" Relic? And furthermore, what's the point--beyond living out some sorry-excuse lie that *you* were the "Stevie Ray Gallagher" who played the finish off this looks-like-its-paid-its-dues recent relic?

Well, we'll leave these questions (and more before we're outta here) for greater minds to plunder. For those of you wondering who the hell I am and why I'm debating the relative merits of Fender Relic, I'm Teisco Del Rey and I've been collecting exotic (some would say bizarre, others would say el-cheapo) guitars for about 18 years, and writing about them since 1983. If you're thinking there's a Japanese guitar company called Teisco Del Rey, you're right; if you're thinking I'm somehow related to the company, hey, I'm not *that* old. The company, which started in the '50s, was, as near as anyone can remember, named **T**okyo **E**lectric **I**nstrument & **S**ound **CO**mpany. The "Del Rey" was added by a Chicago importer named Jack Westheimer, who's still active (with Cort and other brands). Sounded like a cool name to me, and Mr. Westheimer and the current owners of the recently reactivated Teisco name, Kawai, seemed flattered. (Jack even sent me a Teisco tie clasp from an old NAMM show promotion.)

Greco Bookmatched boomerang pickups, too-cool green sunburst...now try picturing this Japanese 6-string with ten strings, where the two "middle" strings (the G and D) are triple strings, but all others are single strings. Hmm. Wha--? Huh? I know. I know.

*B*y '83 my modest (some would say *extremely* modest) collection numbered maybe two dozen, and that year **Guitar Player** asked me to write a somewhat humorous article and pictorial on these wallflowers, which I titled "Cheap Thrills and Pawnshop Prizes." **Guitar Player** not being known for its wit, reader mail poured in, and then Editor Tom Wheeler asked if I could come up with enough oddball fodder to do a monthly column, which began as Off The Wall later that year. And for one publication or another I've been cranking out a column, shedding light on models best left in the dark, ever since. So, yes, there's *more* than enough strange stuff out there--from Vox's 12-string ping-pong paddle Mando-Guitar to the United States Army government-issue "shovelele" (combination mess kit/ukulele, I kid you not); from the space age all-plastic Maccaferri acoustic to the slanted-fingerboard, stand-up steel Melobar (including a purple metal-flake one custom-painted for Sheb "Purple People Eater" Wooley, now residing at--you guessed it--Chez Del Rey); from the who-needs-guitar-stands Guild Thunderbird (with its built-in kickstand) to the embossed naugehyde Hofner 175 (more aptly renamed the Galaxy). And more.

*A*long the way my collection has expanded and shrunk--up to 110 at its peak, settling at a merely temporarily insane level of 60-some here lately, my most recent purchase being a short-scale Burns of England Nu-Sonic that sounds like Johnny Guitar Watson on "Three Hours Past Midnight." Treble to spare, but I'm looking for a whammy bar for said 6-string icepick.

*W*hen I began documenting the overlooked, the "blue book" on virtually any and all of them would have been in the $150-or-less range. Now some of these ugly sisters of the Res-

Gruggett Stradette Cross a Mosrite (with asymetrical horns) and a Hofner (with a violin-shaped body) and you get - Bullwinkle Moose, as Bakersfield's Bill Gruggett discovered when he left Mosrite and designed the Gruggett Stradette in the late '60s.

o-Glas and Masonite families bring a grand or more--a fact for which some have laid blame and/or credit with *moi*. I'll cop to the fact that some of these electric vampires have decided to come out of the dark; I'll deny any strong connection with their resultant price tags. Factors such as the skyrocketing prices of other models (when Strats get out of reach, ever notice that Teles start showing a resurgence, then Jazzmasters, etc.?), the anti Guitar Hero stance of the punk movement, and bona fide greats with eccentric tastes such as David Lindley and Ry Cooder have had a more direct effect on your and my wallets--whether we're buying *or* selling.

*T*he way I got into guitar collecting, and eventually specializing in the left-field side of luthiery, certainly dispells any notion of influencing the vintage market. I started out on my brother's Kay nylon-string when I was 12, and for my seventeenth birthday my father got me a '61 Les Paul/SG, which I viewed as the ultimate blues-rock machine, even though my dad got it dirt cheap in 1970. Eight years later I was killing time in my hometown of Hayward, California, while my car was getting tuned up. I wandered down the street to Spitzer's Music and hung out all afternoon, playing seemingly every guitar in the place. When I had pulled every Gibson, Fender and Epiphone off every wall, I discovered a corner where an array of off-brand ugly ducklings were literally laying in a pile and extracted a three-pickup, silver metal-flake Italian refugee from the early '60s called a Diamond Ranger. I plugged it in and was surprised at how cool it sounded and took it home for a mere $75.00. Dozens of guitars have passed through my hands since, but I've still got that Diamond Ranger, as well as the '61 Les Paul/SG.

People (even fans who are familiar with my writing) seem amazed that I "actually play" so many of these weirdos onstage and on my two CDs. I'll admit, I've bought more than a few guitars just because they were goofy/rare/there, but when I found that I was glomming onto something that I'd play for a week and lock away in storage, my buying slowed down considerably. My main axe onstage and in the studio is a white '64 Fender Jazzmaster that I got 17 or so years ago for 125 bucks. Not that a crystal ball revealing that Jazzmasters would be fetching two grand these days would have stopped me, but it being my main guitar, I modified it quite a bit to suit my needs. The stock "buzzmaster" bridge was the first to go, replaced by a Tune-a-matic, then a Schaller roller bridge, which was ultimately converted to Michael Christian pickup (so that I can sound amazingly like an acoustic and suddenly wang away a la Duane Eddy). Jazzmasters notoriously have no string angle off the bridge, so I shimmed the neck way back, raised the rear pickup more than it would normally ascend (with the aid of some foam), and jacked the bridge up good and high. I also had the pickups remagnetized, attached one of Aspen Pittman's "Fathead" brass plates to the back of the headstock, had the back of the body autographed by the Ventures and covered it with a clear plastic Fender Body Guard--in addition to a Rat Fink decal, an Elvis stamp, a Chaquita banana sticker, and a Jolt Cola bottlecap for a tone knob. So I've "devalued" the sucker in terms of originality, but it eats any other Jazzmaster I've played for lunch. Besides, its market value is irrelevant; mine is the last collection it will ever reside in.

Hopf Saturn 63 Like other German violin companies, Hopf made some of the most radical electric guitars, beginning in the mid '50s. I'm guessing the Saturn 63 - with metal binding around the body and f-holes (which are both on the body's bass side, by the way) - was built in, oh, around 1963.

So have I modified it or bastardized it? Well, not to place myself in their league, but the notion that you dare not change a screw, much less a pickup or bridge, on a vintage axe has never deterred some of the instrument's greatest stylists--thank God. Probably the most famous Stratocaster of all time, Eric Clapton's beloved Blackie, was mongrelized from four or five Strats of different years, and Stevie Ray Vaughan's beat-to-smithereens "#1" was similarly a hybrid, with neck, body and pickups coming from different guitars. Keith Richards can not only afford vintage Telecasters, not to mention Broadcasters and "No Casters," but can afford to route them out for a PAF in the neck position. (So does the fact that a PAF is a more precious replacement part than a Tele neck pickup make up for the non-original "devaluing" he has wrought, or does the fact that the result was personally played by a Rolling Stone override any such considerations?) Of course, Albert Collins' white-bound Telecaster also had a humbucker in the neck position, and then there's Danny Gatton's completely customized Tele with Joe Barden pickups, Clarence White's chunkier-body Tele with String Bender, not to mention Lonnie Mack's Bigsby-adapted Flying V, Yngwie Malmsteen's scalloped-fret Strats, Ry Cooder's horseshoe-pickup Strat, Junior Brown's Siamese-twin Guit-Steel, and J.J. Cale's backless Harmony flattop which seemed to grow a new knob or pickup every couple of weeks. But the ultimate examples of bastardization are Les Paul's personal Les Pauls, the ones he plays onstage--with "Les Paul" clearly on the headstock. Gooseneck microphones protruding from the top rim, different knob configurations, low-impedance pickups, an onboard delay/loop gadget called a "Les Paulverizer" (Danny Gatton called his variation the "Magic Dingus Box")--ol' Les always plays the guitar bearing his name, but never a stock version that you or I could go into a store and buy.

*O*ne of the oddest illustrations that the player always outweighs the equipment is the case of Dick Dale, the King of Surf Guitar. Dick, one of the most powerful and distinctive guitarists of any genre, is more than a stickler when it comes to equipment, arguing, essentially, that in order to play surf music you have to adopt the same setup as its architect, Dick Dale--pre-CBS Strat, '61 blonde Showman with two 15" JBLs, Fender outboard Reverb, unbendably thick picks, and the proverbial string gauges like telephone cables. But around 1980 Dick sent his famous gold-sparkle "Beast" to the Fender repair shop for refretting, and unbeknownst to him at the time it came back with the original pickups replaced with later-issue Strat pickups. What did this do to Dick Dale's trademark tone? Not a damn thing-- sounds the same as ever.

*T*he mainstay of my collection that seems to generate the most fascination, never failing to prompt a few questions (and scratched heads) at gigs or generate a trickle of mail when I write about it or play it on a CD, is my Guitorgan. Actually I have two: a late '60s M-300 and a mid '70s B-35. Except for a bank of switches and quite a bit of extra weight (and, upon closer inspection, two jacks and a three-prong female input on the lower right rim), the M-300 looks like a Gibson Barney Kessel model, the type Gene Cornish played in the Young Rascals. It's actually a Japanese Venture copy of a Kessel, which is a *big* difference, as I discovered when I began having some neck-warp problems. Its transformation into a keyboard crossdressing as a guitar (or is it the other way around?) was the brainchild of Bob Murrell of Waco, Texas, who first went into production in 1967. His initial models featured fairly large outboard organ guts (in fact, the rig was demonstrated at NAMM shows on a little golf cart) and various models of guitars, until he found organ circuitry small enough (a Baldwin design) and a hollowbody guitar large enough (hence, the Kessel copy) to

Teisco May Queen Hundreds of thousands of Japanese Teiscos made their way to American department stores and pawnshops in the early-mid '60s, but usually the solidbody TG-64 - with or without the "handle" hole through the lower bass bout. The company designed the May Queen (shaped suspiciously close to Vox's Mando-Guitar) just in time to miss the boat.

implant the guts right into the body. So that three-pronged jack? That's where you plug the thing directly into the wall, like a Farfisa organ (or a five-speed blender), which is loads of fun, since the Guitorgan has no ground switch.

Whenever I play the Guitorgan, someone inevitably comments that it "sounds just like an organ." Well, I explain, that's because it *is* an organ; it's just triggered by strings touching frets instead of by fingers pressing keys. As the company's early ads read, "The organ with the built-on guitar." In the pre-guitar synth days, Mr. Murrell decided to segment each fret six times (one "mini fret," as it were, per string) and wire them all to the organ circuit. This means that when you press string to fret, the note sounds--and continues to sound until you lift that finger. It also means that, unless you plug in the jack marked "guitar," you can play one-handed--or two-handed a la Stanley Jordan, since one of Murrell's designed-in features allows you to play two notes on the same string if they're a fifth apart, although when barring a chord the Guitorgan only reads the highest note fretted. Is this amazing or what? If you do plug in the guitar jack, incidentally, you can play guitar in the normal way (if the "organ" input isn't utilized, or if you ease back on a volume pedal), or plug both in and duet with yourself--in stereo if you set up separate amps for each "instrument." Ingenious.

According to interviews I did with the late Mr. Murrell, he showed that his patent pre-dated Vox's "Guitar Organ," although the cease-and-desist letter his company, Musiconics International (or MCI), sent probably coincided with Vox giving up on their temperamental version.

Micro-Frets Guitars' G strings notoriously intonate slightly flat, so Micro-Frets sought to solve the dilemma with the as-complicated-as-it-was-compensated Micro Nut. Of course as soon as you go up the neck one fret, the thing is rendered inconsequential. The early '70s Maryland companyalso gave models names like Spacetone and painted them "Martian Sunburst" (as in green)!

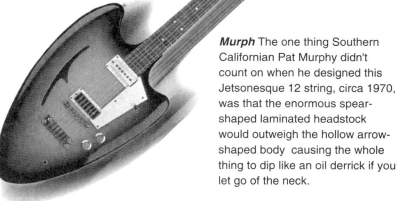

Murph The one thing Southern Californian Pat Murphy didn't count on when he designed this Jetsonesque 12 string, circa 1970, was that the enormous spear-shaped laminated headstock would outweigh the hollow arrow-shaped body causing the whole thing to dip like an oil derrick if you let go of the neck.

If you're wondering how you played open strings on a touch-sensitive instrument, well, you didn't, at least not on the early models. Later versions featured a button that sounded all open strings that weren't being fretted (not *exactly* appropriate in every playing situation), and still later an additional button that sounded only the open low E--as is the case on my B-35. The B-35 features drawbars instead of mini toggles to choose voicings, and this time the circuitry was housed in an oversized volume pedal. Also, since those segmented frets got in the way of string bending, the newer variation had the frets cut at an angle, which facilitates bending a *little* bit better.

Hey, I never said the thing was perfect. But for all its quirks, the Guitorgan delivers what it claims to--the true sound of an organ, instead of my favorite quote from an Andy Summers interview in **Guitar Player**. After attending a concert by a well-know jazz guitarist he declined to name, Andy scoffed, "He spent 45 minutes making his guitar sound like a harmonica. I found it rather odd that with $100,000 worth of equipment, he was making a guitar sound like a five-dollar instrument." A few years ago I got such a ridiculously good deal (or so it seemed) on a used Roland GR-700 (you know, the Pocket Fisherman looking thing with the enormous bank of pedals), I snapped it up--figuring I could graduate from "Red River Rock" and "96 Tears" to, say, "Whiter Shade of Pale" with this thing. I bench tested the two side by side, and while the 700 undeniably whipped the Guitorgan in some categories--it's housed in a better built guitar, you can get countless sounds, you can bend notes--when it came to the meat and potatoes . . . well, "96 Tears" is, after all, a classic. The Guitorgan's one and only sound (save adjusting tone voicings) is the real deal; the limitations as well as advantages of fretting notes are pretty much the same as those of a keyboardist fingering keys.

Unfortunately, Bob Murrell passed away in December of 1994 at the age of 69, thinning out the rare breed of individual guitar innovators a little bit more. It's been a long time since an instrument with as much personality as a Guitorgan, a Melobar (created by the late Walt Smith), or amp-in-case Silvertone (the brainchild of the late Nathan Daniel) came down the pike. I'd say it's time for a new wave of creativity and chance taking.

By the way, I ended up selling the GR-700--for an even more ridiculously lower price.

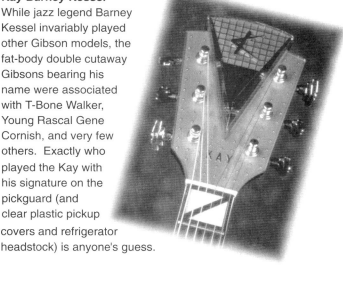

Kay Barney Kessel
While jazz legend Barney Kessel invariably played other Gibson models, the fat-body double cutaway Gibsons bearing his name were associated with T-Bone Walker, Young Rascal Gene Cornish, and very few others. Exactly who played the Kay with his signature on the pickguard (and clear plastic pickup covers and refrigerator headstock) is anyone's guess.

THE BLUE BOOK OF GUITAR VALUES™
PHOTO PERCENTAGE GRADING SYSTEM™

"Beep! Steve, I got a guitar question on line two - do you want to take it?" Sure, no problem.

"I have this old guitar that my uncle used to play with in the Big-Band days - Can you tell me what it's worth?"

"No problem, sir. All you have to do is hold it real close to the microphone so that I can see it better." The next sentence is usually devoted to supporting a rarity factory theory since he/she hasn't been able to find out much information about it in most guitar books (this 3rd Edition should change that also).

Most of us in the biz struggle with this problem on a daily basis - how to determine a guitar's condition accurately. Hopefully, the Photo Percentage Grading System™ will help bring a solution to this problem.

If there is a harder subject to write about than trying to explain a collectible's unique condition factor via the pen-and-ink mode, I'm glad I haven't had a chance to write about it. As with most other collectibles (including guitars), value is usually determined by a variety of factors; the most critical usually being realistically determining the original condition of the specimen in question. Once the condition question has been answered, monetary evaluation will get much easier.

This problem is not unique to the area of collectible guitars — try calling up a coin, car, stamp, baseball card, or antique furniture dealer and ask him/her what he/she will pay you in C-notes for your deceased relative's up-to-this-point previously unknown mother-lode stash of "good stuff". Again, the answer is pretty standard, "I'm going to have to see it before I can make a determination on how much it's worth". In other words, talk is cheap because condition is usually either mis-described or over-described. In the end, the merchandise always speaks for itself better than any verbal description. **If a good photo is worth a thousand words, an axe-in-hand is worth a million.**

The photos on pages 33-72 basically depict three categories of guitars: Solid Body Electrics, Acoustic-Electrics, and Acoustics. Chosen category representative models are as follows: Solid Body Electrics — Fender Stratocasters, Telecasters, Esquires, and the Jazzmaster Bass, in addition to Gibson Les Pauls and related variations, a Paul Reed Smith and two Danelectros; Acoustic-Electrics — miscellaneous Gibsons and a Gretsch; Acoustics — various Martins, Gibsons, Epiphones, and a Guild. Simply compare your guitar(s) against these photos to find the corresponding condition in percentages. If your particular configuration is not pictured, try to interpret areas of wear to the closest category shown.

It is extremely important when examining wear on a guitar to think about how that wear occurred after a period of normal (and possibly abnormal) use. As a player uses a guitar, certain areas will accumulate finish deterioration more rapidly than others. Note the lower bout wear on photos 11 and 37 caused by arm wear created after strumming a couple million chords (i.e., the Grand Canyon effect). Neck wear, however, seems to be somewhat forgivable in lieu of the rest of the instrument's overall condition. This is evident in photos 17 and 18, which depict a Fender Telecaster in 70% overall condition with rather heavy neck wear. In many instances, advanced collectors and dealers can look at a guitar's specific wear areas and tell you if the player specialized in country-western or Led Zeppelin. **Accumulating the knowledge necessary to know the differences in condition and how/why they occured simply takes running a lot of instruments through your hands.**

Almost of equal importance to player wear is how well the instrument was transported, handled, or stored while it was NOT being played. This "off-stage" wear is demonstrated in photos 7, 8, 37, and 38. Note the chips and dings on the body, while the back of the neck appears almost new with virtually no clear lacquer finish removed. Each older guitar thus becomes a unique, one-of-a-kind item that has to be individually examined to determine its unique condition factor(s).

Guitar alterations also have to be integrated into the overall condition formula per instrument. It has been observed that many Gibson instruments have replaced tuners. This is normally not a problem unless the back of the headstock has been redrilled to accept a new tuning machine (observe photo 54). Also, replaced pickups or other changes that do not fall within the original equipment specifications from a particular manufacturing period have to be subtracted from the overall value. In most cases, non-original alterations make an instrument worth less.

Remember, for most guitars in good supply, original condition is Polar North to the serious collector or investor. Not even a professionally refinished guitar (compare photo

32 to photo 31) that could otherwise be readily purchased in mint original condition will approach the price of an original. The key to value in situations like this is the desirability factor **after** the restoration in relation to the value of an original. Most guitar collectors frown on a restored instrument (regardless how good the job). Many dealers consulted during this project simply commented, "Subtract 50% of the value if refinished." There is some debate ongoing that a "refin" in rare or custom colors is worth more than a "refin" in traditional colors or sunbursts.

The bottom line, however, is simple to compute: the original finish was removed in the refinishing process, and **any** color could then be reapplied. In that case, the color of the new finish is immaterial. Knowing how and why these condition factors can override others becomes critical on an accurate price. Pro-rating these condition factors in their proper pecking order is not a job for amateurs and professional advice should be obtained from several sources before the C-notes change hands.

We are lucky that the consistency and uniformity of guitar grading standards have not changed. In the coin business, just when you thought those easy, short-term profits were in your sights, the coin industry changed the grading system making your numismatics fall (not to mention profits) a grade or two. A 90% guitar from 1960 is still a 90% guitar today. Nothing has changed except for the values going up considerably, and the really good stuff has never been harder to find, because guitar collectors usually dispose of their guitars as their last financial alternative. The first thing an investor sells after 4 or 5 years is his/her worst investment. The last thing a guitar collector will sell is his/her main squeeze, unless a cash offer gets tendered that can't be refused.

Always try to buy as much original condition as you can afford. Remember, however, that you can overpay for those last couple of percentage points of a guitar's condition. During the past twelve months, some trademarks/models seem to be linked with some very unpredictable, high price tags. Some dealers have recently indicated that if they priced their better merchandise alongside these high asking prices, not only would they get laughed at on the expensive items, but some potential buyers may think the rest of their merchandise is overpriced as well. Don't forget about those crazed investment (non-collector) diamond buyers who purchased 1-Carat, D-Flawless certified stones (the best quality) for over $80,000 in the early 1980's and flushed them down their portfolio toilets several years later for $12,000. As in any other scope of collecting, it is typically wise to stay away from a model, area, or category that has gone up faster than an F-15 in an alarmingly short time. While it's true that these short-term boomers may continue to rise and take you with them, chances are you may be dropped off at the summit of Mt. Everest with no oxygen for the way down. Inflationary or non-inflationary domestic economics occurring in the next 3-5 years will have the final say on whether today's price tags constitute a value or a long-term tax loss.

If you have any questions regarding either the photos or accompanying captions, please contact me. While no grading system is perfect, hopefully this Photo Percentage Grading System™ will enable you to ascertain the approximate grade of your individual guitars. Only after learning the correct condition of a guitar can you accurately determine its true value.

Sincerely,

Steven P. Fjestad, Editor & Publisher
Blue Book of Guitars™

All photos used on pages 33-72 for the Photo Percentage Grading System™ were taken by S. P. Fjestad

Explaining/Converting The
Photo Percentage Grading System™

As in any other area of collecting, grading standards have a lot to do with the way a collectible is described when buying, selling, or trading. Most fields have at least one or two grading systems which are designed to indicate condition as accurately as possible to those people who are interested. The system that gets used is the system that is most helpful to everyone interested in that area of collecting.

The Photo Percentage Grading System™ has been used successfully in over 530,000 copies of the **Blue Book of Gun Values**™. Since condition has become very important in today's expensive marketplace, we feel the differences between 80% and 100% are so significant, and values must be listed for those extremely important additional condition factors (90%, 95%, 98%, etc.). An alternate guitar grading utilizes terminology such as Exc., Exc.+, VG+ (++), Near Mint, 7 overall, Good condition, and other idioms. At the suggestion of many vintage dealers, we have attempted to combine the percentages with other commonly used terms throughout the text of the Third Edition of the **Blue Book of Guitars**™.

The conversion chart listed below has been provided to help you convert other grading standards into the approximate Photo Percentage Grading System™ factors (i.e. in most cases, percentages ranging from 60%-100%). While no grading system can be perfect, we hope that this percentage type of grading system will provide a more accurate and reliable way to describe each guitar's unique condition once it has become used. All percentage descriptions and/or possible conversions made thereof, are based on original condition — alterations, repairs, refinishing work, and any other non-original changes that has altered the condition of an instrument must be listed additionally and subtracted from the values based on condition throughout this text.

Condition Factors

100% — New with all factory materials including warranty card, owner's manual, case, and other items that were originally included by the manufacturer. On currently manufactured instruments, the 100% price refers to an instrument not previously sold at retail. On out-of-production instruments (including dealer "new, old stock" or NOS), the longer a guitar has been discontinued, the less likely you will find it in 100% condition. Some instruments that are only 20 years old and have never been taken out-of-the-case (unplayed), may not be 100% (new) as the finish may have slightly cracked, tarnished, faded, or deteriorated. Remember, there are no excuses in 100% condition.

98% — Only very slightly used and/or played very little, may have minor "case" wear or light dings on exterior finish only, without finish checking, very close to new condition, also refers to a new instrument that has previously sold at retail with perhaps some slight case wear only, Mint, exceptional, 9+, slight scratch — otherwise as new.

95% — Very light observable wear, perhaps some very light plating deterioration on metal parts, extremely light finish scratching, may have slight neck wear, Near Mint, Exc. +, close to mint, "9.5".

90% — Light exterior finish wear with a few minor dings, no paint chips to wood, normal nicks and scratches, light observable neck wear in most cases, excellent (Exc.), a "9", 9 tacos.

80% — Exterior finish wear that may include minor chips that extend down to the base wood, body wear but nothing real serious, Very Good Plus (VG+), 8, nice shape, honest player wear.

70% — More serious exterior finish wear that could include some major gouges and nicks, or player arm wear, fret deterioration, Very Good (VG), 7 overall, above average condition, "very nice condition for this year", 7 tacos.

60% — Noticeable wear on most areas - normally this consists of some major belt buckle wear and finish deterioration, may include cracking, possible repairs or alterations, 40% of the original finish is gone. When this condition factor is encountered, normally an instrument should have all logos intact, original pickups, minor headstock damage, and perhaps a few non-serious alterations. With or without original case. Good (G), "6".

40% — Major features are still discernible, major parts missing, probably refinished, original logo and case may be missing, structurally sound though usually encountered with non-factory alterations, "4", fair minus (F-) overall, 3 or 4 tacos.

20% — Ending a life sentence (and the Governor's not going to call), not many licks left, must still be playable, 2, poor overall, no condition+, "the parts are worth this much", "have you ever seen another one this bad?", barking guitar biscuit, no tacos and a couple of moldy burritos, etc.

Photos 1 & 2 — 1960 Fender Stratocaster - Ser. #60492, 3-Tone Sunburst finish, 95%-98% (MINT) condition. If you're a Strat player, you'll have a hard time turning this page. Note factory hanging tag and tremolo cover still intact - definite bonuses on any Fender solid body electric. Original paint exhibits almost no fading and back of body shows no belt buckle wear - but a slight ding appears below tremolo cover. Also, close scrutiny reveals slight upper neck wear next to third fret. Rosewood fingerboard. Notice how the 3-Tone Sunburst finish (Red, Black and Orange) differs from photos 7 and 8 - a 2-Tone Sunburst (Black and Orange). It doesn't get much better than this!

 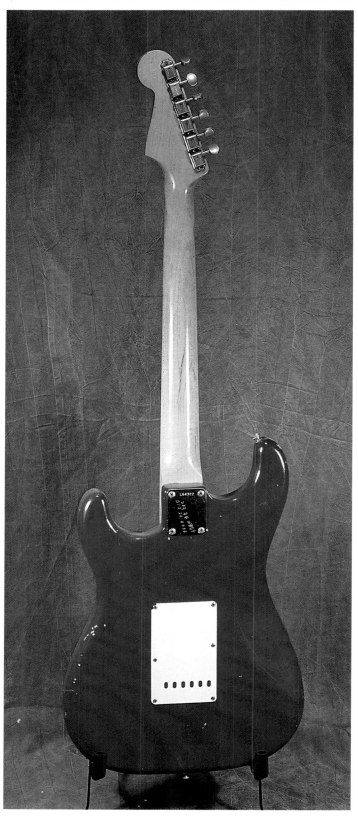

Photos 3 & 4 — 1964 Fender Stratocaster - Ser. #L 64322, Dakota Red finish, 90%-95% (EXC+) overall condition. Again, note original tremolo cover still intact. Careful observation reveals light touching-up on both the front and back of body. Back plate cover has operation ID numbers engraved diagonally by previous owner. Backside of body also exhibits light chipping (note white primer coat showing through). Observe wear on back of upper neck (clear lacquer coat has dulled). Technically, the front of this instrument is 95% (EXC+), while the back is in 80%-90% (VG+) condition.

 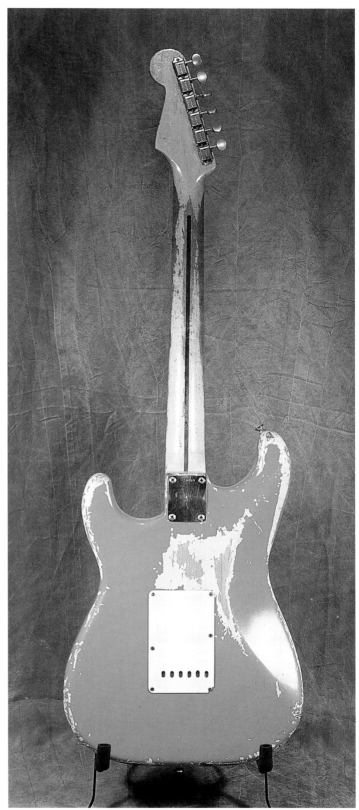

Photos 9 & 10 — 1957 Fender Stratocaster - Ser. #920869, Dupont prototype color, 50%-60% (G) overall condition. Observe how maple fretboard and neck back (with "skunk stripe") have accumulated finish wear down to the raw wood. This much back wear reveals a lot of the original white base coat. You're probably thinking that a guitar with this much finish deterioration is worth $300-$400 - Wrong! Because of the guitar's extreme rarity factor in this special prototype color (one of four known), this instrument's price tag could hit five digits!

 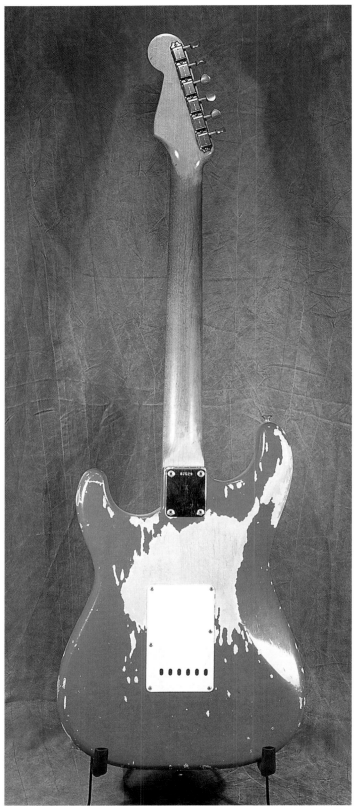

Photos 11 & 12 — 1963 Fender Stratocaster - Ser. #87529, Salmon Pink finish, 50% (G) overall condition. Again, this instrument proves that much player use will remove the color coat where the right arm has rubbed against the body (60% front condition). Back of instrument shows a lot of chipping (40%-45% condition) and back tremolo plate cover condition does not match overall condition. Dark neck further proves this guitar belted out more than a few licks. Originally retailing for approximately $285, this instrument's current value is still over $5,000 - mostly due to the tremendous desirability of the rare color.

 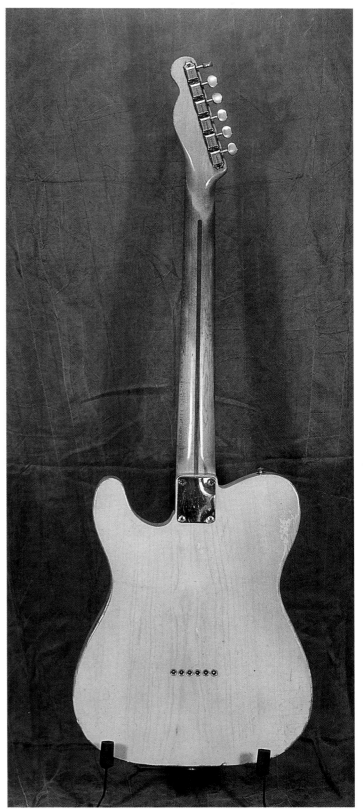

Photos 17 & 18 — 1953 Fender Telecaster - Ser. #3527, Blonde finish, 70% (VG) overall condition. Study the wear on the neck and pickguard, indicative of some serious playing. Back of neck (with "skunk stripe") has gone dark on top. Neck wear is forgivable. Neckplate without serial number is correct through 1953 manufacture - Telecaster serialization appears on the bridgeplate during this period. Telecasters with this amount of original condition are still hot - 95% (EXC+) specimens are extremely hard to find since most of these instruments were exposed to multiple blue collar workouts.

 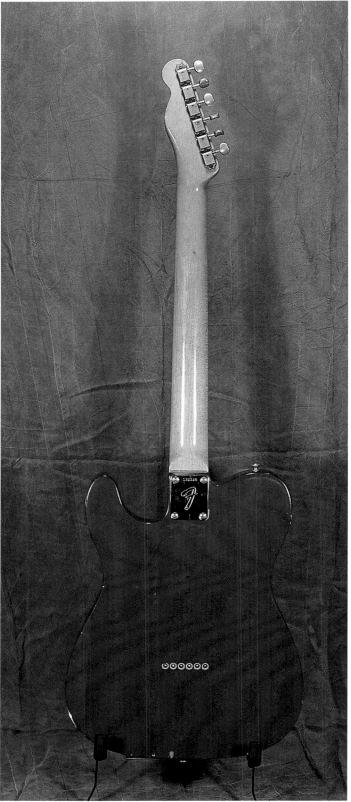

Photos 19 & 20 — 1966 Fender Telecaster - Ser. #132349, Transparent Red prototype finish, 80%-90% (VG+ - EXC) overall condition (note chunk out of lower treble bout). Most people (even a few Fender dealers) would think that this color was a production finish - it was not. Note the transitional logo - sometimes referred to as a "macaroni" logo instead of the "spaghetti" - patent number under name on decal. Single string tree was used until 1972. Rosewood fingerboard is unusual. Also examine recessed ferrules - flush body ferrules became standard after 1967. The top end of this specimen's price is hard to predict due to the extreme rarity factor.

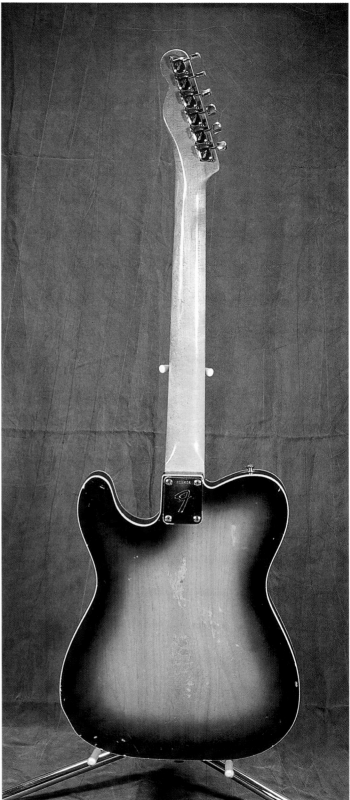

Photos 21 & 22 — 1966 Fender Custom Telecaster - Ser. #215406, 3-Tone Sunburst finish, 70%-80% (VG - VG+) overall condition with belt buckle (?) wear on back of body. This specimen is unusual with original Bigsby vibrato tailpiece (observe Fender logo on bottom). Note the differences in color of the Sunburst finish between the front and back of the instrument. This Telecaster must have been exposed to sunlight for some duration, as the red has mostly faded from the front Sunburst while remaining mostly intact on the backside. Not much player wear, discernible by the clean back of neck.

 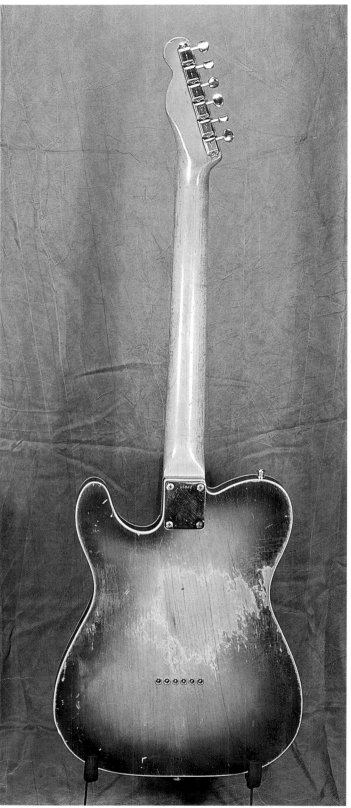

Photos 23 & 24 — 1960 Fender Custom Esquire - Ser. #65882, 3-Tone Sunburst finish, 60% (G) overall condition (due to heavy fading and checking). While appearing to look partially refinished, this Esquire is proof that early Sunburst finishes presented some problems to Fender. Color pigmentation would begin to fade with or without light exposure. Custom Esquires were the first Fenders to have a layered pickguard. Double bound Esquires are rare, especially with custom color finishes. 1960s instruments generally do not have a neck date, and a slab board neck will always add a premium.

 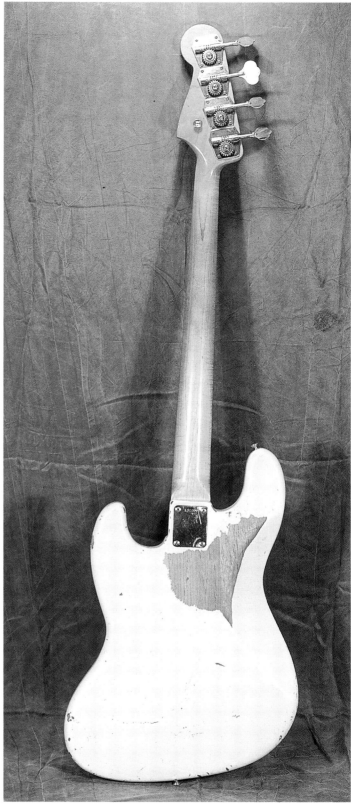

Photos 29 & 30 — 1964 Fender Jazz Bass - Ser. #L 32223, Olympic White finish, 60% (G) overall condition. Lots of bare wood showing, but it's all original. Note the clay dot fingerboard inlays, indicative of pre-CBS features. In late 1964, Fender went to pearl dots, but the real pre-CBS aficionados are looking for these clay dot inlays. Original Olympic White finish with matching color headstock. Notice original strap hook next to tuning machines. Most bass musicians would agree that this continues to be one of Leo's better playing instruments, and in today's vintage marketplace, the prices prove it.

Photo 31 — 1952 Gibson Les Paul - issued without serial number, Gold Top finish, approximately 70%-80% (VG - VG+) overall condition. One of the first LPs produced with a trapeze tailpiece, but without neck binding. Horizontal weather checking striations are normal (see photos 39-41 for more visual evidence). Relatively poor playability on early LPs has affected their value in today's marketplace.

Photo 32 — 1954 Gibson Les Paul - original inked serial number has been restamped, Gold Top finish, 100% refinished condition. Compare the matted color and lack of arch-top dimensionality between this and original finish in photo 31. Also, Gibson dropped the trapeze tailpiece in 1953. Refinishing decreases value 50%, and re-drilled tuner holes for replacement tuners knock off an additional 10%.

Photos 33 & 34 — Gibson Les Paul Custom - Ser. #964991, Black finish, 80%-90% (VG+ - EXC) overall condition. Note split diamond peghead inlays with multi-binding - always indicative of a Les Paul Custom - Gibson's finest. Photographically presenting wear on a black instrument is always difficult, but close scrutiny reveals light chipping on the body back and front. Gold-plated humbucking pickup covers, tunomatic bridge, and stop tailpiece also exhibit quite a lot of wear.

 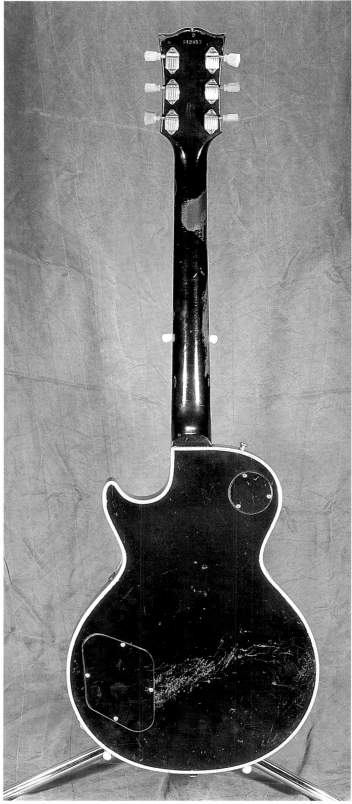

Photos 35 & 36 — 1968 Gibson Les Paul Custom Reissue - Ser. #513053, Black finish, 70%-80% (VG - VG+) original condition. The top and back of this instrument are in approximately the same condition. The hardware is in pretty good condition for the obvious amount of "axe grinding". Detracting areas may be the bent tuner and heavy neck wear, normally not taken into serious consideration when purchasing a used instrument to play - as opposed to collecting. Note unmatched factory pickups and pickguard wear while perusing the next set of photos.

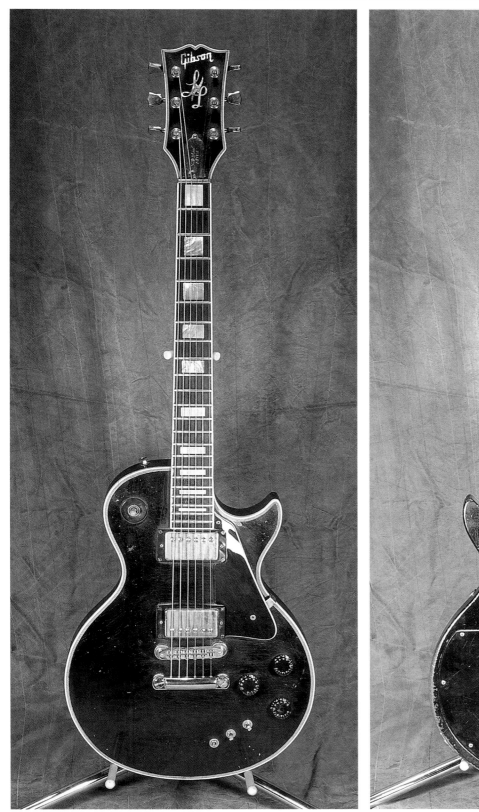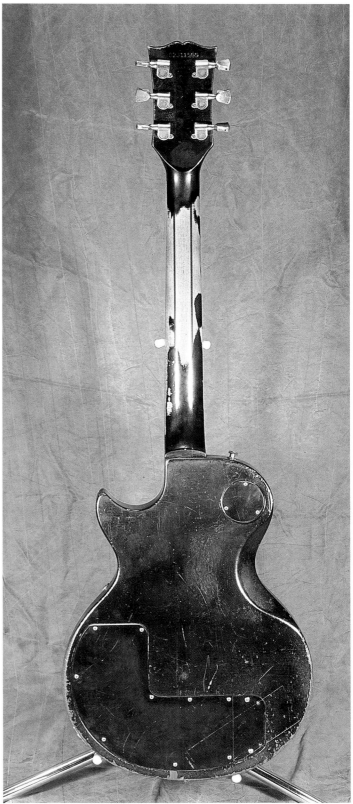

Photos 37 & 38 — 1981 Gibson Les Paul Artist - Ser. #82311565, Black finish, 50%-60% (P - G-) overall condition. A true road warrior; this guitar probably pumped out licks on a nightly basis for years. Note definite model inlays and three control knobs. Bone up on the pickguard wear and cutaway area finish deterioration. White area that appears to be a reflection on top of the pickguard actually indicates "Grand Canyon erosion" after a couple of billion chords wore away the top black layer. Note cutaway area finish is down to the wood and even the pickup ring exhibits wear around the screw. Bottom bout chipping indicates use/abuse accumulated when not playing.

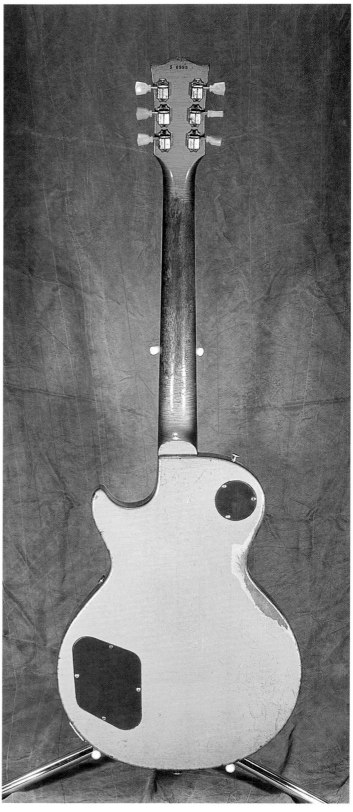

Photos 39 & 40 — 1955 Gibson Les Paul Regular - Ser. #5 6999, Gold Top finish, 60%-70% (G - VG) overall condition. This instrument is an excellent example of an original Gold Top LP featuring P-90 pickups and both natural finish deterioration and player wear. Also note heavy finish checking on both the front and the back created by a variety of temperature/humidity factors - very normal for instruments of this vintage. Again, this instrument exhibits heavy player wear in all the right places. Note no belt buckle wear (C & W players really didn't dig these things in 1955).

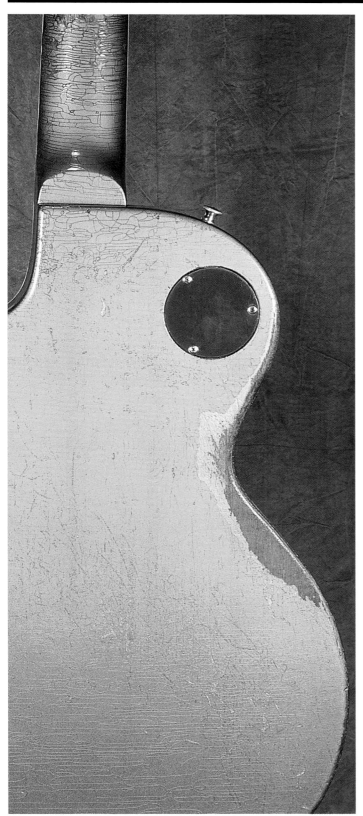

Photo 41 — 1955 Gibson Les Paul Regular - Ser. #5 6999, Gold finish, approx. 50% (G-) original back condition. This is a close-up of the instrument in photos 39-40. The neck is especially interesting since it depicts heavy player wear which has caused a "Sea Algae Green" color that is a natural result of a bronze powder paint additive oxidizing due to the protective finish chipping away.

Photo 42 — 1989 Paul Reed Smith Custom - Ser. #97407, Transparent Burgundy Top finish, close to new condition (100% overall). This is a recently manufactured PRS Custom that has the dove inlays which are normally found on the Artist Series. Extra figured maple tops (curly and quilted) on the top of any desirable guitar will usually command a premium in today's marketplace.

Photo 43 — Masonite Madness! 1956 Danelectro - ser. # not visible, Black finish, 70%-80% (VG - VG+) overall condition. Becoming a cooler instrument every year, many cheesecake aficionados will note this is a first year model complete with aluminum neck and wood sides, and a micro tilt neck adjuster. Large peghead was standard for first couple of years only. Originally $39-$49, now hanging out at $500+.

Photo 44 — 1958 Danelectro - ser. # not visible, rare Green color, "coke-bottle" headstock, 60% (G) overall condition. No real wear spots on this instrument, just lots of little nicks. "Chickenhead" knobs may be non-original. Most Danelectros are black - the rare color makes this one worth 3x normal value.

Photos 45 & 46 — 1962 Gibson ES-175D - Ser. #85879, Tobacco Sunburst finish, 95%+ (EXC+) overall condition. Certainly a mainstay of Gibson acoustic/electrics, this model and close cousins are gathering more of a following every year. Observe F holes, lack of binding on headstock, triple bound body front, and nickel plated trapeze tailpiece which has begun to oxidize. Mother-of-Pearl parallelogram fretboard inlays are also a trademark of this model. During this year, Fender Strats were selling for approximately $285, while this ES-175D model retailed at $340. This type of original condition is always desirable (and saleable).

Photos 47 & 48 — 1955 Gibson ES 175D - Ser. #21525, Sunburst finish, approx. 70% (VG) original condition. Pretty standard stuff for an instrument of this vintage - some flaking on the top due to checking and light player wear on the back. Gibson archtop followers will note the back of the neck has been "sanded" for a more natural player feel. The top half of the neck looks darker due to player wear, but the bottom half seems too light to have the finish worn away from normal playing. This type of alteration on a major trademark instrument normally results in an approx. 40% decrease in value.

Photos 49 & 50 — post-1961 double cutaway Gretsch Chet Atkins Nashville (Model 6120) - Ser. #33926, Western Orange finish, approx. 90% (EXC) overall condition. No electric guitar section would be complete without the inclusion of at least one Gretsch instrument. This specimen is very clean, with only light wear on back of 2-piece neck. Note circular protective pad to prevent premature back of body wear (and disguise trapdoor rear entry cover). Model 6120s have bound f-holes and thumbnail inlays on neck.

Photos 51 & 52 — 1953 Epiphone Zephyr Emperor Regent - Ser. #64658, Sunburst finish, 90% (EXC) original condition. This is an excellent piece of Epiphone archtop history. The huge body of the Emperor (photos 67-68) was married with the cutaway configuration of the Regent and the modern electronics (at the time) of the Zephyr. Dig the sexy push button pickup selector system. Standard volume/tone octagonal controls were original issue on this model. A few more words in the model nomenclature might have eliminated the necessity of a model description! The price tag? Typically determined by collectors, since only a few players are using them.

Photos 53 & 54 — 1964 Gibson J-200 - Ser. #62460, Natural Blonde finish, approx. 80% (VG+) overall condition. Observe wear underneath "mustache" bridge and nicks on back of neck. Observe 3-piece neck, spectacular bookmatched flame maple on back, and extra holes on back of headstock which are usually indicative of replacement tuners. Also, examine neck inlays and definitive pickguard graphics on this model. The J-200 series has many variations.

Photos 55 & 56 — Guild D3JN-T - Ser. #180154, Natural finish, 80% (VG+) overall condition. Notice considerable wear on left side of pickguard below soundhole - the only major area of deterioration on this instrument outside of normal nicks and scratches. This dreadnought features a 2-piece bookmatched spruce top, mahogany back and neck, rosewood fingerboard with dot inlays, and enclosed tuners.

Photos 57 & 58 — Epiphone Texan (FT79N) - Ser. #424923, Natural finish, 70%-80% (VG - VG+) overall condition, Gibson era. No major wear in any one area, just normal scratches, dings, and handling marks. Two-piece mahogany back with normal horizontal finish weather checking. Astute Epiphone acoustic aficionados will recognize the replaced tuners. Note "E" logo on bell and wear on upper neck. Price ranges from $100 to $275, depending on condition. Remember - these sort of prices are determined by players, not collectors.

Photos 59 & 60 — 1957 Martin D-18 - Ser. #168235, Natural finish, approx. 70% (VG) overall condition. An initial observation will conclude that this specimen is in better condition than the D-18 pictured in photos 61 and 62. Close inspection reveals a top surface crack running from the bridge to the bottom of the body. Unprofessional attempts when repairing Martins (and other flattop guitars) will lower values more significantly than an original instrument with natural cracking. Readers without bifocals will still note small operation ID numbers between tuning machines.

Photos 61 & 62 — 1945 Martin D-18 - Ser. #92775, Natural finish, approx. 60% (G) overall condition (back side lowers the average). Examine wear along the sides of the neck above soundhole. It is not uncommon for Martins to have cracked tops because of their 1-piece construction. Note scratching on 2-piece bookmatched mahogany back and relative lack of wear on neck. Good Martin acoustics have always been desirable.

Photos 63 & 64 — 1934 Martin R-18 - Ser. # unknown, Dark Mahogany finish, 70% (VG) overall condition. Small arch top body style with round soundhole and trapeze tailpiece. Note finish deterioration around left side of soundhole and neck, and continuing to top of body. Nice back with minimal scratching. Normal neck wear (although upper back has a few scratches and some finish loss). This Martin is all original - not a bad pre-war Martin. Originality is Polar North for Martin collectors.

Photos 65 & 66 — 1953 Gibson L-7C - Ser. #A-13922, Natural finish, approx. 90% (EXC) overall condition, dings and gouges on lower body bout hurt this guitar's overall condition from 95% to 90%. Professional repairs could bring the price tag back to the 95% value. Examine exceptionally clean bookmatched back and very little wear on back of 2-piece neck. Trapeze tailpiece shows normal dulling due to oxidation. Parallelogram inlays, rosewood bridge, and layered black pickguard are standard features on this model.

Photos 67 & 68 — 1946 Epiphone Emperor - Ser. #55580, Natural finish, 95% (EXC+) overall condition. In wide bodies , Boeing has the 747, and Epiphone had the 18-inch Emperor. Spectacular bookmatched flame maple multi-bound backside with 7-piece laminate neck. Double inlay blocks on fretboard, tortoise shell multi-layered pickguard, and split trapeze tailpiece are all hallmarks of this model.

Photos 69 & 70 — 1942 Gibson Super 400 - Ser. #97668, Regular finish, 80% (VG+) overall condition. Examine finish scratches on upper top of front and sides of back. Gibson's top-of-the-line carved top acoustic, like the Emperor pictured on facing page also had an 18-inch body. Bookmatched flame maple back is an equal to the Epiphone pictured on the facing page. Note front and back headstock inlays, marbled celluloid pickguard, and Super 400 logo on heel.

Photos 71 & 72 — 1935 Gibson L7 - Ser. #90980, Regular finish, approx. 60% (G) condition. While this instrument does not exhibit extreme wear in any one area, multiple scratches and nicks on front, in addition to back of neck wear, reduce this specimen's overall condition to 60%. Observe unusual fretboard inlays, small headstock, and dark finished maple back. All original with no major problems.

Photos 73 & 74 — 1950 Epiphone Zenith - Ser. # unknown, Regular finish, 70% (VG) overall condition. Back side of this instrument is living proof of what a belt buckle can do to the finish over a period of time (and lower the condition factor 10%). Sunburst finish on back of neck reveals 3-piece laminate construction. Trapeze tailpiece (note dulling due to oxidation on this guitar), dot inlays, and adjustable rosewood bridge are all standard features on this model.

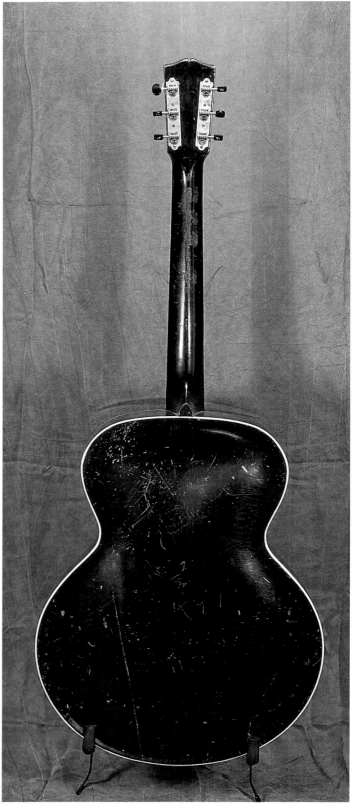

Photos 75 & 76 — 1924 Gibson L-4 - Ser. #92109, Regular finish, approx. 50% (G-) overall condition. Note nasty cracks on right front side of body in addition to more than normal scratches and dings on back side of body caused by excessive jean rivet damage - also note missing pickguard. Observe early Gibson script logo on headstock. Remember - this guitar may have been originally transported by horse and buggy, steam train, or a new Ford Model T truck.

 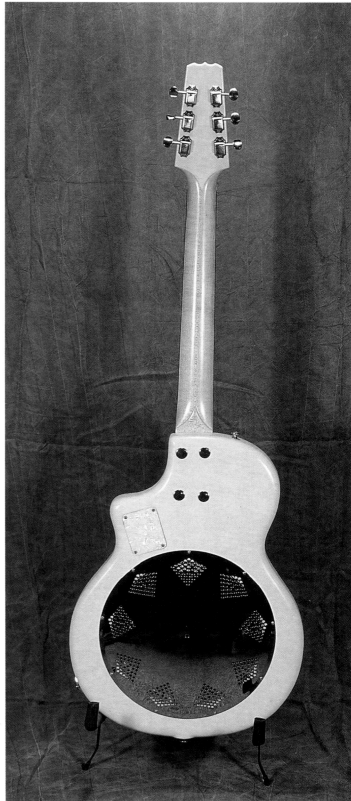

Photos 77 & 78 — 1993 National Reso-Phonic Resolectric - Ser. # not visible, 95% (EXC+) overall condition. An outstanding example of blending an acoustic resonator guitar with a modern Highlander bridge pickup and vintage style single coil pickup. The active electronics allow the player to blend the pickups and control output. This marriage of 1920s resonator design and pickup technology has resulted in a modern-styled guitar.

Photo 79 — Gibson 12 string Les Paul - circa 1993. What happens when the right person calls up the Custom Shop for an LP 12 string? Simple - enter a nicely figured LP body with a slightly elongated headstock with 12 holes and voilá - "We made money on that one!"

Photo 80 — 1961 Gibson Les Paul - Ser. #6227, Cherry finish, 90% (EXC) "on a slow day" finish. Note how nickel finish has dulled due to oxidation on the pickups and tremolo cover.

Glossary

This glossary is divided into 4 sections: General Glossary; Bridges, Pegs, Tailpieces and Tuners; Pickups; and Book Terminology. If you are looking for something and can't find it in one section, please check the others. If you can't find it after you've been through the whole glossary, give us a call. We value your input for future editions.

General Glossary

Abalone — Shellfish material used in instrument ornamentation.

Acoustic — Generic term used for hollow bodied instruments that rely on the body to produce the amplified sound of the instrument, rather than electronic amplification.

Acoustic Electric — A thin hollow bodied instrument that relies on a pickup to further amplify its sound.

Action — Everybody wants a piece of it. It is also the height the strings are off of the fingerboard, stretched between the nut and bridge.

Arch/Arched Top — The top of an instrument that has been carved or pressed to have a "rounded" top.

Avoidire — blonde mahogany.

Binding (bound) — Trim that goes along the outer edge of the body, neck or peghead. It is made out of many different materials, natural and synthetic.

"Black Beauty" — This term is generally used in reference to early (1955-1960) Gibson Les Paul Customs, due to their glossy black finish.

Body — The main bulk of the instrument, usually. It is where the bridge, tailpiece and pickguard are located. On acoustics, the soundhole, or holes, are located on the body top, usually, and the sound is amplified inside it. On electrics it is where the pickups are routed into and the electronics housing is stored. It is what the player cradles.

Bolt On/Bolt On Neck — Construction technique that involves attaching the neck to the body by means of bolts or screws. Bolt-on necks are generally built and finished separately from the guitar body, and parts are assembled together later.

Bound
See BINDING.

Bout/Bouts — The rounded, generally, side/sides on the top and bottom of an instrument's body.

Bridge — Component that touches the top of the instrument and transfers vibrations from string to body. It is usually attached by glue or screws but is also found to be held in place by string tension, the same as a violin.

Carved Top
See ARCH TOP.

Cutaway — An area that has been cut away on the upper bout, or both bouts, to allow access to the higher frets.

Dreadnought — A generic term used to describe steel string guitar configuration consisting of a boxy body and solid headstock.

Ebonized — It means the wood has been stained dark to appear to be ebony.

Ebonol — A synthetic material that is used as replacement for wood.

Electric — A generic term referencing the fact that the instrument relies on pickups to amplify its sound.

F-Hole — Stylized "f" shaped soundhole that is carved into the top of various instruments, most commonly acoustic. It usually comes in pairs.

Fingerboard — An area on top of the neck that the string is pressed against to create the desired note (frequency).

Finish — The outer coat of an instrument. The sealant of the wood. The protector of the instrument. How many ways do you say it? It's all of the above, it's the finish.

Flat Top — Term used to describe an acoustic steel stringed instrument whose top is flat.

Fret — A strip of metal that is embedded at specific intervals into the fingerboard.

Fretboard — Another way of saying fingerboard and specifying that it has frets embedded into it.

Fretless Fingerboard — Commonly found on Bass instruments, this fingerboard is smooth, with no frets.

Graphite — Used in various forms of instrument construction because of its rigidity and weight, this type of carbon is used in the body, neck and nut.

Hardware — Generic term for the bridge, tailpiece, tuners or vibrato system.

Headless — This means the instrument has no peghead.

Headstock
See PEGHEAD.

Heel — On the backside of an instrument, the heel is located at the base of the neck where the neck meets the body.

Inlay — Decoration or identifying marks on an instrument that are inlaid into one of the surface areas. They are made of a number of materials, though abalone, pearl and wood are the most common.

Locking Tuners — These tuners are manufactured with a locking mechanism built right into them, thus preventing string slippage.

Logo — An identifying feature on an instrument: it could be a symbol or a name; and it could appear as a decal, an inlay, or painted on (and it could be missing).

Mother of Pearl — A shellfish (oyster/clam) material used for inlay.

Nato — A lower grade or quality of mahogany, sometimes referred to as lumberyard mahogany.

Neck — The area that the strings of the instrument are stretched along, the peghead sits at the top, the body lies at the bottom.

Octave — In Western Notation, every 12 frets on a stringed instrument is an octave in the musical scale of things.

Pearl — Short for Mother of Pearl, the inside shell from a shellfish. See MOTHER OF PEARL.

Pearloid — A synthetic material made of plastic and pearl dust.

Peghead — The area at the top of an instrument where the tuning machines, or pegs, are located.

Phenolic — A synthetic material that is used as fingerboard wood replacement.

Pickguard — A piece of material used to protect the instrument's top or finish from gouges that are caused by the pick or your fingers.

Pickup — An electronic devise that translates string vibrations into the electronic signal needed for amplification of the sound.
See PICKUP Section.

"Pre-CBS" — Collector's terminology that refers to the CBS purchase of Fender Instruments in 1965. A "Pre-CBS" instrument is one built by Leo Fender's original company.

Purfling — Decorative trim that is found running along the inside of the binding.

Relief — The upward slope of the fingerboard that keeps the strings off the frets.

Resonator — A metal device located in some instruments that is the means of their amplification.

Reverse Headstock (Reverse Peghead) — On this instrument the peghead has been flipped over from the normal configuration and the tuners are all on the highest note side of the instrument (tuners are all located on one side).

Rosette — A decorative design that is placed around the soundhole.

Saddle — The area that a string passes over to create the length needed for an exact note (frequency).

Scale Length — The area between the nut and bridge over which the strings of the instrument are stretched.

Scalloped — This is what the area on the fingerboard between the frets is called when it has been scooped out, creating a dip between the frets.

Scratch Plate — Slang for Pickguard.

See PICKGUARD.

Semi-Acoustic — term used to describe a shallow bodied instrument that is constructed with a solid piece of wood running the length of the center of the body.

Slotted Peghead — A peghead usually associated with classic style instruments. The peghead has slots running lengthwise that allows access to the tuners.

Soundhole — A hole found in the top of acoustic instruments (mostly), that allows the sound to be projected from the body.

Strings — They are the substance that is stretched between the tuners/pegs and the bridge/tailpiece. The weight of the string is what determines the range of frequencies it will cover.

Sunburst (Sunburst Finish) — A finish that is dark at the edge of the instrument's top and gets progressively lighter towards the middle.

Thinline — Original Gibson terminology referring to a hollow bodied instrument that has a shallow depth of body.

Through Body (Thru Body; Neck Through) — Type of construction that consists of the neck wood extending through the entire length of the instrument and the pieces of wood that make up the body being attached to the sides of the neck wood (called "wings").

Tremolo — An regular increase and decrease in the volume of a continuous sound. Many tremolo effects units have controls for Speed (number of volume changes per time period) and Depth (amount of volume change that occurs).

Truss Rod — A rod, or rods, placed in necks made of wood to create stability and a means of adjustment.

Vibrato — The act of physically lengthening or shortening the medium (in this case, it will be strings) to produce a fluctuation in frequency. The pitch altering mechanism on your guitar is a vibrato, not a tremolo!

HARDWARE: *BRIDGES, PEGS, TAILPIECES AND TUNERS*

Acoustic Bridge — The bridge on an acoustic instrument is usually glued to the top and though pins are usually used there are still numerous ways of holding the strings taut.

Banjo Tuners — tuners that are perpendicular to the peghead and pass through it, as opposed to being mounted on the side of the peghead, (like classic style peghead tuners).

Bigsby Vibrato — A vibrato system that involves a roller bar with little pegs that run in a perpendicular line, around which you hook the string balls. One end of the bar has an arm coming off of it, a spring is located under the arm, and the entire apparatus is connected to a trapeze tailpiece. The bridge is separate from the vibrato system. This vibrato was designed by Paul Bigsby.

Bridge — Component that touches the top of the instrument and transfers vibrations from string to body. It is usually attached by glue or screws but is also found to be held in place by string tension, the same as a violin.

Bridge Pin — A peg that passes through the bridge anchoring one end of the string for tuning.

Double Locking Vibrato — A vibrato system that locks the strings into place by tightening down screws on each string, thus stopping the string's ability to slip. There is also a clamp at the top of the fingerboard that holds the strings from the tuners. These more modern designs were formulated separately by Floyd Rose and the Kahler company. As guitarist Billy Gibbons (ZZ Top) is fond of saying, the locking vibratos give you the ability to "turn Steel into Rubber, and have 'er bounce back on a dime".

See VIBRATO SYSTEM.

Fixed Bridge — One piece, usually metal, usually on electric instruments, unit that contains the saddles, bridge and tailpiece all in one and is held onto the body by screws.

Friction Pegs — Wooden dowels that rely on the friction created between itself and the wood of the hole it is put in to keep the tension of the strings constant.

Headless — Term meaning that the instrument's headstock is missing. The top of the neck is capped with a piece of hardware that acts like a regular tailpiece on the instrument body.

Locking Tuners — These tuners are manufactured with a locking mechanism built into them, thus preventing string slippage.

Nut — Device located at the top of the fingerboard (opposite from the bridge) that determines the action and spacing of the strings.

Pegs —See FRICTION PEGS.

Pins — Pegs that are used to anchor the strings in place on the bridge.

Roller Bridge — This is a Gretsch trademark feature. It is an adjustable metal bridge that sits on a wooden base, the saddles of this unit sit on a threaded bar and are easily moved back and forth to allow personal string spacing.

Saddle/Saddles — A part of the bridge that holds the string/strings in place, helps transfer vibrations to the instrument body and helps in setting the action.

Sideways Vibrato — Built off the trapeze tailpiece concept, this unit has a lever that pulls the string attachment bar back along a pair of poles that have springs on them to push the bar back into place. This is all covered by a plate with a design on it.

Single Locking Vibrato — A vibrato system that locks the strings on the unit to keep them from going out of tune during heavy arm use. This style of vibrato does not employ a clamping system at the top of the fingerboard.

Standard Vibrato — Usually associated with the Fender Stratocaster, this unit has the saddles on top and an arm off to one side. The arm allows you to bend the strings, making the frequencies (notes) rise or drop. All of this sits on a metal plate that rocks back and forth. Strings may have an area to attach to on top or they may pass through the body and have holding cups on the back side. A block of metal, usually called the Inertia Block, is generally located under the saddles to allow for increased sustain. The block travels through the instrument's body and has springs attached to it to create the tension necessary to keep the strings in tune.

See VIBRATO SYSTEM.

Steinberger Bridge — A bridge designed by Ned Steinberger, it combines the instrument bridge and tuners all in one unit. It is used with headless instruments.

Steinberger Vibrato — A vibrato system that has the instrument's bridge, vibrato and tuners all in one unit. Like the Steinberger Tailpiece, this was also designed by Ned Steinberger. It is also used with headless instruments.

Stop Tailpiece — This piece of hardware is attached to the top of an instrument by screws and has slots in it to hold the string balls. Generally used with a tunomatic bridge.

Strings Thru Anchoring — A tailpiece that involves the strings passing through an instrument's body and the string balls are held in place by cups.

Stud Tailpiece — See STOP TAILPIECE.

Tailpiece — The device that holds the strings at the body end of the scale. It may be all in one unit that contains the saddle/saddles also, or stands alone.

Tied Bridge — Style of bridge usually associated with "classical" style instruments that have the strings secured by tying them around the bridge.

Trapeze Tailpiece — A type of tailpiece that is hinged, has one end attached to the bottom bout of the instrument and the other end has grooves in it to hold the string balls.

Trem/Tremolo/Tremolo Arm — Terms inaccurately used to mean Vibrato System.
See VIBRATO SYSTEM.

Tuner/Tuners — Mechanical device that is used to stretch the string/strings. These are located on the peghead.

Tunable Stop Tailpiece — A taipiece that rests on a pair of posts and has small fine tuning machines mounted on top of it.

Tunomatic Bridge — A bridge that is attached to the instrument's top by two metal posts and has adjustable saddles on the topside.

Vibrato — Generic term used to describe Vibrato System.

Vibrato System — A device that stretches or slackens the strings by the means of a lever, the arm or bar, and a fulcrum, the pivot pins or blades.

Wang Bar — Slang term used for Vibrato System.

Whammy (Whammy Bar) — Slang terms used for Vibrato System.

Wrapover Bridge — A self contained bridge/tailpiece bar device that is attached to the body, with the strings wrapping over the bar.

Wrapunder Bridge — The same as above except the strings wrap under the bar.

PICKUPS

The Pickup Principle follows this idea: your instrument's pickup is composed of a magnetic core that has wire wrapped about it. This creates a magnetic field that the strings pass through. As the string is plucked it vibrates in this field and creates fluctuations. These fluctuations are then translated into electronic pulses by induction; the magic of having electrons excited into activity by being wrapped next to each other via the wire coils. Once the fluctuations are in electron form they move along the wires in groups called waveforms, which move to an amplifier and get enlarged. The rest is up to you.

Active Electronics — A form of electronic circuitry that involves some power source, usually a 9 volt battery. Most of the time the circuit is an amplification circuit, though it may also be onboard effects circuitry.

Alnico — An alloy commonly used in the construction of pickup magnets. It consists of **Al**uminum, **Ni**ckel and **Co**balt.

Amplify/Amplification — To increase, in this case to increase the volume of the instrument.

Blade — A pickup that uses a blade or rail instead of polepieces.

Bobbin — The structure, usually plastic, that the coil wires are wound around. See COILS.

Ceramic — A substance used in pickup magnets that consists of magnetic particles mixed with a clay-like base.

Coils — Insulated wire wrapped around a nonconductive material.

Coil Split — A switch and a term that means you are splitting the coils in a humbucker and turning it into two single coil pickups.
See SPLIT PICKUP.

Coil Tap — A term and a switch that refers to accessing a coil tap in a pickup.
See TAPPED.

Control/Controls
See POT and POTENTIOMETERS

Crystal
See PIEZO.

Dirty Fingers — Coverless humbucker pickups that have black and white bobbins.

Equalizer — An effect that allows you to boost or cut certain frequencies.

Hex Pickup — A device that has six individual pickups, one for each string, housed in a single unit. This unit is used to provide the signals for synth (synthesizer) instruments.

Humbucker — Consists of two single coil pickups being placed side by side and wired together in such a fashion that the hum is canceled out of the single coils.

J-Style — A single coil pickup, though some are humbucker pickups, designed for electric bass and usually placed near the bridge. It is largely associated with the Fender Jazz Bass.

Lace Sensor — A pickup developed by Don Lace that takes a single bobbin and windings and places it inside a magnetic housing with an open top. This creates an electromagnetic shielding effect and allows only the area directly over the pickup to sense string vibration. As a result, the magnetic force ("string pull") on the string is lessened.

Onboard — Usually referencing effects, it means built into the instrument.

Out Of Phase — When a signal from two pickups are run through a switch that puts their respective signals 180 degrees out of phase with each other.

P-Style — An offset pickup with two magnets per half. They are usually located near the neck and are associated with the Fender Precision Bass.

P.A.F. (Patent Applied For) — Common term used to mean the pickup that Seth Lover designed for Gibson in 1955. The patent was not awarded till 1959, so pickups used in the meantime had the P.A.F. stickers underneath the housing.

Parametric Equalizer — An equalizer that allows you to specifically choose which range of frequencies you wish to affect.

Passive Electronics — Electronic circuitry that has no power supply. Usually it consists of filter circuitry.

Phase Switch — A switch used to accomplish the feat of putting the signal out of phase.
See OUT OF PHASE.

Piezo (piezoelectric) — A crystalline substance that induces an electrical current caused by pressure or vibrations.

Polepiece/Polepieces — Small magnetic rods that are found inside the pickup coils and, usually, situated under the instrument's strings. Some of these polepieces are adjustable.

Pot — Short for "potentiometer".

Potentiometer — A variable resistor that is used to make adjustments.

Preamp — An electronic circuit that amplifies the signal from the pickup/s and preps it for the amplifier.

Rail Pickup
See BLADE.

Shielding — Term used to describe materials (usually copper) used to protect the signal in electronic instruments from outside electrical interference.

Single Coil — See opening paragraph for this section, it applies to this term.

Soap Bar — Term used to describe a specific Gibson single coil pickup, model number: P-90.

Soundhole — An opening in the instrument's top (usually), that allows the amplified sound out of the body cavity.

Split Pickup — A humbucker that has been wired so it has the capability of being split into two single coil pickups.

Stacked Coil — A form of humbucker pickup that is in a stacked configuration so it can be installed as a replacement for a single coil.

Tapped — The process of taking a wire out of the midst of the windings in a pickup and leaving it open for hookup to a switch. This can be done a number of times in one pickup. "Tapping" the pickup allows access to a different amount of winding (a percentage of the full winding) and thus different sounds from the same pickup.

Transducer/Transducer Pickup — A device that converts energy from one form to another, in this instance it is the vibrations caused by the strings, moving along the wood and being converted into electrical energy for amplification.

Book Terms

This glossary section should help you understand the jargon used in the model descriptions of the instruments in this text.

3 Per Side — To the number of tuners on the sides of the peghead.

3/2 Per Side — This is in reference to a 5 string instrument with three tuners on one side of the peghead and two tuners on the other.

335 Style — refers to an instrument that has a body style that is similar to that of the Gibson 335.

4 On One Side — Four tuners on one side of the peghead.

4 Per Side — Four tuners on each side of the peghead an eight string instrument.

4/1 Per Side — On an instrument with five strings this would mean four tuners are on one side of the peghead, and one is on the other.

4/2 Per Side — Four tuners on one side and two on the other side of a peghead.

4/3 Per Side — This instrument has seven strings with four of the tuners located on one side of the peghead and three on the other side.

5 On One Side — All the tuners on one side of the peghead a five string instrument.

6 On One Side — All six tuners on one side of the peghead.

6 Per Side — Talking about a twelve string instrument here and the term means the number of tuners on each side of the peghead.

6/1 Per Side — A seven string instrument with six tuners on one side and one on the other.

7 On One Side — A term referring to a seven string instrument with all the tuners on the peghead are on one side.

12/14 Fret — Term in which the first number describes the fret at which the neck joins the body, and the second number is the total number of frets on the fingerboard.

Dreadnought Style — This term refers to steel string instruments that are fashioned after the traditional build of a Martin instrument, a boxy type instrument with squared top and bottom bouts, approximately 14 inches across the top bouts, 16 inches across the bottom bouts, there is not much of a waist and the depth of instrument is about 4-5 inches.

Explorer style — The instrument's body shape is similar to a Gibson Explorer model.

Jazz Style — A body shape similar to that of a Fender Jazz Bass.

Les Paul Style — Shaped like a Gibson Les Paul.

Point Fingerboard — A fingerboard that has a "V-ed" section on it at the body end of the fingerboard.

Precision Style — The bass guitar's body looks like a Fender Precision Bass.

Strat Style — Shaped like a Fender Stratocaster.

Tele Style — Shaped like a Fender Telecaster.

Thru Body — Type of construction that consists of the neck wood extending through the entire length of the instrument and the pieces of wood that make up the body being attached to the sides of the neck wood.

Tunomatic Stop Tailpiece — This unit is a combination bridge/tailpiece that has adjustable (tunomatic) saddles mounted on a wrap around tailpiece.

V Style — Body style like the Gibson Flying V.

Volume/Tone Control — The instrument has a volume and a tone control. If a two (2) precedes the term then there are two volume and two tone controls.

Common Abbreviations

These abbreviations are used as prefixes and suffixes. They are also just a guide, nothing should be viewed as being the definitive list. A lot of companies will have their own letters or numbers which are that instrument's company code.

A	Ash	L	Left Handed
B	Bass, Brazilian Rosewood, or Blue (finish)	LE	Limited Edition
BK	Black (finish)	LQBA	Leo Quan Bad Ass
C	Cutaway	M	Mahogany or Maple
D	Dreadnought or Double	N	Natural
DC	Double Cutaway	OM	Orchestra Model
E	Electric	R	Reverse (headstock) or Red (finish)
ES	Electric (Electro) Spanish	S	Spanish, Solid Body, Special or Super
F	Fretless or Florentine	SG	Solid Guitar
H	Herringbone	T	Tremolo or Thinline
J	Jumbo	V	V shaped Neck, Venetian, Vibrato or Vintage Series
K	Koa		

Meet The Staff

Blue Book of Guitars
Third Edition
Staff Members

Steven P. Fjestad, Editor and Publisher

Steve Cherne, Author

Michelle Schroeder, Author's Assistant

Lisa M. Winkels, Proofreader

Cathy Cariveau, Proofreader

Carrie Puterbaugh, Proofreader

Tom Lundin, Production Manager

Walter Horishnyk, Art Director

Dorothy Winke, DTP Photo Production

Tom Stock, Chief Financial Officer

Beth Marthaler, Administrative Support

DJ Pallum, Administrative Support

John Allen, Moral Support

Brad Simpson, Moral Support

Lutherie Organizations

Association of Stringed Instrument Artisans (ASIA)
c/o Church of Art
14 South Broad Street
Nazareth PA 18064-2136
610-759-1829

(GUITARMAKER is the quarterly newsletter/publication of ASIA)

Guild of American Luthiers (GAL)
8222 South Park Avenue
Tacoma WA 98408
206.472.7853

(AMERICAN LUTHERIE is the quarterly journal of GAL)

Fretted Instrument Guild of America
c/o Glen Lemmer, Editor
2344 S. Oakley Avenue
Chicago IL 60608

(FIGA, official publication)

Upcoming Shows

1996 - 1997

Throughout the year, there are a number of Music Industry trade shows and Vintage Guitar shows.

October 12th and 13th
1996 Indiana Guitar SHow
Indianapolis, Indiana
Hosted by David Baas
(Roadworthy Guitars)
812.332.2145

October 12th and 13th
Ft. Lauderdale Interantional Guitar Show
Ft. Lauderdale, Florida
Hosted by Paul Cairnes
615.731.1195

October 19th and 20th
Arlington Vintage '96 Fall Nationals
Arlington, Texas
Hosted by the Four Amigos
(Texas Guitar Shows, Inc.)
417.451.1906
(FAX) 817.473.1089

November 2nd and 3rd
Hotlanta Guitar Show
Atlanta, Georgia
Hosted by Johny Milteer
919.209.0011

November 23rd and 24th
2nd Annual St. Louis Master's Show
St. Charles, Missouri
Hosted by Walter Sill
615.824.4646

November 23rd and 24th
The Fall Philly Show
Philadelphia, Pennsylvania
Hosted by Bee-3 Vintage
(Gary and Bonnie Burnette)
704.298.2197
(FAX) 704.298.0020

December 6th, 7th, and 8th
The Kansas City Christmas Show
Independence, Missouri
Hosted by Jim Reynolds
(Phone/FAX) 816.638.4828

December 14th, 15th, and 16th
The Music City Guitar Show
Nashville, Tennessee
Hosted by Jim Reynolds
(Phone/FAX) 816.638.4828

January 11th and 12th
California Vintage '97 Winter Nationals
San Mateo, California
Hosted by the Four Amigos
(Texas Guitar Shows, Inc.)
417.451.1906
(FAX) 817.473.1089

January 18th through January 21st
1997 NAMM Show
Anaheim, California
800.767.6266
619.438.8001
(FAX) 619.438.7327

January 18th and 19th
California VAMM '97 Winter Nationals
Costa Mesa, California
Hosted by the Four Amigos
(Texas Guitar Shows, Inc.)
417.451.1906
(FAX) 817.473.1089

February 22nd and 23rd
The South Carolina Show
Spartanburg, South Carolina
Hosted by Bee-3 Vintage
(Gary and Bonnie Burnette)
704.298.2197
(FAX) 704.298.0020

March 22nd and 23rd
20th Annual Greater Southwest Guitar Show
Dallas, Texas
Hosted by Mark Pollock and Jimmy Wallace
(Charley's Guitar Shop and Sound Southwest)
214.243.4201

April 19th and 20th
Chicago Vintage '97 Spring Nationals
Villa Park, Illinois
Hosted by the Four Amigos
(Texas Guitar Shows, Inc.)
417.451.1906
(FAX) 817.473.1089

April 26th and 27th
Michigan's Annual Guitar Show 1997
Detroit, Michigan
(Michigan State Fair Grounds)
Hosted by Gordy and Marcia Lupo
(Gordy's Music)
810.546.7447
(FAX) 810.546.5249

May 17th and 18th
The Triad City Show
Greensboro, North Carolina
Hosted by Bee-3 Vintage
(Gary and Bonnie Burnette)
704.298.2197
(FAX) 704.298.0020

May 31st and June 1st
Houston Vintage '97
Houston, Texas
Hosted by the Four Amigos
(Texas Guitar Shows, Inc.)
417.451.1906
(FAX) 817.473.1089

July 12th and 13th
Nashville VAMM '97
Nashville, Tennessee
Hosted by the Four Amigos
(Texas Guitar Shows, Inc.)
417.451.1906
(FAX) 817.473.1089

July 26th and 27th
The Great American Show
Valley Forge, Pennsylvania
Hosted by Bee-3 Vintage
(Gary and Bonnie Burnette)
704.298.2197
(FAX) 704.298.0020

October 11th and 12th
1997 Indiana Guitar Show
Indianapolis, Indiana
Hosted by Dave Baas
(Roadworthy Guitars and Amps)
812.332.2145

References

Achard, Ken, *The Fender Guitar*, The Bold Strummer, Ltd., Westport CT, 1990

Achard, Ken, *The History and Development of the American Guitar*, The Bold Strummer, Ltd., Westport CT, 1990

Bacon, Tony, *The Ultimate Guitar Book*, Alfred A. Knopf, Inc., New York NY, 1991

Bacon, Tony and Day, Paul, *The Fender Book*, GPI/Miller Freeman Inc., San Francisco CA, 1992

Bacon, Tony and Day, Paul, *The Gibson Les Paul Book*, GPI/Miller Freeman Inc., San Francisco CA, 1993

Bacon, Tony and Day, Paul, *The Gretsch Book*, GPI/Miller Freeman Inc., San Francisco CA, 1996

Bacon, Tony and Day, Paul, *The Guru's Guitar Guide*, Track Record Publishing, London England, 1990

Bacon, Tony and Day, Paul, *The Rickenbacker Book*, GPI/Miller Freeman Inc., San Francisco CA, 1994

Bacon, Tony and Moorhouse, Barry, *The Bass Book*, GPI/Miller Freeman Inc., San Francisco CA, 1995

Bechtoldt, Paul, *G&L: Leo's Legacy*, Woof Associates, 1994

Bechtoldt, Paul and Tulloch, Doug, *Guitars from Neptune - A Definitive Journey Into Danelectro Mania*, JK Lutherie, Harrison OH, 1996

Bishop, Ian C., *The Gibson Guitar*, The Bold Strummer, Ltd., Westport CT, 1990

Bishop, Ian C., *The Gibson Guitar From 1950 Vol. 2*, The Bold Strummer, Ltd., Westport NY 1990

Blasquiz, Klaus, *The Fender Bass*, Hal Leonard Publishing Corp., Milwaukee WI, 1990

Briggs, Brinkman and Crocker, *Guitars, Guitars, Guitars*, All American Music Publishers, Neosho MO, 1988

Brozeman, Bob, *The History & Artistry of National Resonator Instruments*, Centerstream Publishing, Fullerton CA, 1993

Carter, Walter, *Epiphone, The Complete History*, Hal Leonard Corporation, Milwaukee WI, 1995

Carter, Walter, *Gibson Guitars, 100 Years of an American Icon*, General Publishing, Inc., New York NY, 1994

Carter, Walter, *The History of the Ovation Guitar*, Hal Leonard Corporation, Milwaukee WI, 1996

Carter, Walter, *The Martin Book*, GPI/Miller Freeman Inc., San Francisco CA, 1995

Day, Paul, *The Burns Book*, The Bold Strummer, Ltd., Westport Connecticut, 1990

Denyer, Ralph, *The Guitar Handbook*, Alfred A. Knopf Inc., New York NY, 1982

Duchossoir, A.R., *Gibson Electrics*, Hal Leonard Publishing Corp., Milwaukee WI, 1981

Duchossoir, A.R., *Gibson Electrics - The Classic Years*, Hal Leonard Publishing Corp., Milwaukee WI, 1994

Duchossoir, A.R., *Guitar Identification*, Hal Leonard Publishing Corp., Milwaukee WI, 1983

Duchossoir, A.R., *The Fender Stratocaster*, Hal Leonard Publishing Corp., Milwaukee WI, 1989

Duchossoir, A.R., *The Fender Telecaster*, Hal Leonard Publishing Corp., Milwaukee WI, 1991

Erlewine, Vinolpal and Whitford, *Gibson's Fabulous Flat-Top Guitars*, Miller Freeman Books, San Francisco CA, 1994

Evans, Tom and Mary Anne, *Guitars from the Renaissance to Rock,* Facts on File, New York NY, 1977

Fullerton, George, *Guitar Legends,* Centerstream Publishing, Fullerton CA, 1993

Giel, Kate, et al, *Ferrington Guitars,* HarperCollins, New York NY, 1992

Giltrap, Gordon & Marten, Neville, *The Hofner Guitar - A History,* International Music Publications Limited, Essex England, 1993

Gruhn and Carter, *Acoustic Guitars and Other Fretted Instruments,* Miller Freeman Inc., San Francisco CA, 1993

Gruhn and Carter, *Electric Guitars and Basses,* GPI/Miller Freeman Inc., San Francisco CA, 1994

Gruhn and Carter, *Gruhn's Guide to Vintage Guitars,* GPI/Miller Freeman Inc., San Francisco CA, 1991

Hartman, Robert Carl, *The Larsons' Creations, Guitars and Mandolins,* Centerstream Publishing, Fullerton CA, 1995

Howe, Steve, *The Steve Howe Guitar Collection,* GPI/Miller Freeman, Inc., San Francisco CA, 1993

Juan, Carlos, *Collectables & Vintage,* American Guitar Center, Stuttgart Germany, 1995

Longworth, Mike, *Martin Guitars, a History,* 4 Maples Press Inc., Minisink Hills PA, 1987

Moseley, Willie G., *Classic Guitars U.S.A.,* Centerstream Publishing, Fullerton CA, 1992

Moseley, Willie G., *Stellas & Stratocasters,* Vintage Guitar Books, Bismarck ND, 1994

Moust, Hans, *The Guild Guitar Book, The Company and the Instruments, 1952-1977,* Guitar Archives Publications, The Netherlands, 1995

Rich, Bill and Nielsen, Rick, *Guitars of the Stars, Volume 1: Rick Nielsen,* Gots Publishing Ltd., A Division of Rich Specialties, Inc., Rockford IL, 1993

Rittor Music, *Bizarre Guitars, Vol. 2,* Japan, 1993

Rittor Music, *Guitar Graphic, Vol. 1,* Tokyo Japan, 1994

Schmidt, Paul William, *Acquired of the Angels: The lives and works of master guitar makers John D'Angelico and James L. D'Aquisto,* The Scarecrow Press, Inc., Metuchen, NJ, 1991

Scott, Jay, *'50s Cool: Kay Guitars,* Seventh String Press, Hauppauge NY, 1992

Scott, Jay, *The Guitars of the Fred Gretsch Company,* Centerstream Publishing, Fullerton CA, 1992

Scott, Jay & Da Pra, Vic, *'Burst 1958-'60 Sunburst Les Paul,* Seventh String Press, Hauppauge NY, 1994

Smith, Richard R., *Fender - The Sound Heard 'Round the World,* Garfish Publishing Company, Fullerton CA, 1995

Smith, Richard R., *The History of Rickenbacker Guitars,* Centerstream Publishing, Fullerton CA, 1989

Teagle, John, *Washburn — Over One Hundred Years of Find Stringed Instruments,* Music Sales Corp, New York NY, 1996

Van Hoose, Thomas A., *The Gibson Super 400,* Miller Freeman, Inc., San Francisco, 1991

Wheeler, Tom, *American Guitars,* HarperCollins Publishers, New York NY, 1990

Wheeler, Tom, *The Guitar Book, A Handbook for Electric & Acoustic Guitarists,* Harper & Row, New York NY, 1974

White, Forrest, *Fender — The Inside Story,* GPI/Miller Freeman Books, San Francisco CA, 1994

Wright, Michael, *Guitar Stories, Volume One,* Vintage Guitar Books, Bismarck ND, 1995

Periodicals

You've bought this book so you're obviously interested in stringed instruments. Being knowledgeable about any subject is a good idea and having the up-to-the-minute-news is the best form of knowledge. We recommend the following publications for instrument information, collecting news, updates and show announcements, luthier and artist insights and loads of other information that might interest you.

Acoustic Guitar
The String Letter Press Publishers, Inc., P.O. Box 767, 412 Red Hill Avenue Suite #1, San Anselmo, California 94979.
Phone number: 415.485.6946, (FAX) 415.485.0831.

> Published monthly. 12 month subscription is $29.95 in the USA; however, Acoustic Guitar is offering a **Blue Book of Guitars** special of $23.95 in the USA.

Bass Player
Miller Freeman, Inc., 411 Borel Avenue #100, San Mateo, California 94402.
Phone number: 800.234.1831 (415.358.9500), (FAX) 415.358.9966.
E-mail: bassplayer@mfi.com.

> Published monthly. 12 month subscription is $29.95 in the USA.

Guitar for the Practicing Musician
Cherry Lane Magazines, Inc., 10 Midland Avenue, Port Chester, New York 10573-1490.
Phone number: 914.935.5200.

> Published monthly. 12 month subscription is $22.95 in the USA, and a two year subscription is $37.95 in the USA.

Guitar One
Cherry Lane Magazines, Inc., 10 Midland Avenue, Port Chester, New York 10573-1490.
Phone number: 914.935.5200.

> Published monthly. Available on the newsstands for $4.95 per issue in the USA.

Guitar Player
Miller Freeman, Inc., 411 Borel Avenue #100, San Mateo, California 94402.
Phone number: 800.289.9939 (415.358.9500), (FAX) 415.358.9966.
E-mail: guitplyr@mfi.com.

> Published monthly. 12 month subscription is $29.95 in the USA.

Guitar Shop
Cherry Lane Magazines, Inc., 10 Midland Avenue, Port Chester, New York 10573-1490.
Phone number: 914.935.5200.

> Published bimonthly. 12 month subscription is $17.78 in the USA.

Guitar World
Harris Publications, Inc., 1115 Broadway, New York, New York 10010.
Phone number: 303-678-0439.
E-mail: sounding.board@guitarworld.com.
World Wide Web: http://www.guitarworld.com.

> Published monthly. 12 month subscription is $19.94 in the USA.

Guitar World Acoustic
Harris Publications, Inc., 1115 Broadway, New York, New York 10010.
Phone number: 212.807.7100, (FAX) 212.627.4678.
E-mail: sounding.board@guitarworld.com.
World Wide Web: http://www.guitarworld.com.

> Published monthly. 12 month subscription is $19.94 in the USA.

Musician
33 Commercial Street, Gloucester, Massachusetts 01930.
Phone number: 800.347.6969 (212-536-5208).

> Published monthly. 12 month subscription is $19.97 in the USA.

The National Instrument Exchange
John B. Kinnemeyer, 11115 Sand Run, Harrison, Ohio 45030.
Phone number: 800.827.0682 (513-353-3320), (FAX) 513-353-3320.
Email: guitar@jklutherie.com
World Wide Web: http://www.jklutherie.com/nie

> Published monthly. Guitar Buy and Sell Newsletter. 12 month subscription is $15.00 in the USA.

Vintage Guitar Magazine
Alan J. Greenwood, P.O. Box 7301, Bismarck, North Dakota 58507.
Phone number: 701.255.1197, (FAX) 701-255-0250.

> Published monthly. 12 month subscription is $23.95 in the USA.

20th Century Guitar
Seventh String Press, Inc., 135 Oser Avenue, Hauppauge, New York 11788.
Phone number: 516.273.1674, (FAX) 516.435.1805.

> Published bimonthly. 12 month subscription is $23.95 in the USA.

In addition to the regular publications put out by these publishers, most offer "Special Edition" (i.e., yearly buyers' guides, new product reviews, market overviews, etc.) magazines that are released annually, or bi-annually.

A

See chapter on House Brands.

This trademark has been identified as a "House Brand" of the Alden department store chain. One of the models looks similar to the Harmony-built 'Stratotone' of the 1960s, while a previously identified model dates back to the 1950s.

(Source: Willie G. Moseley, Stellas & Stratocasters)

ABEL AXE

Instruments built in Evanston, Wyoming since 1992. Distributed by Abel Axe of Evanston, Wyoming.

Designer/inventor Jeff Abel spent two years in research and development refining his aluminum body/wood neck concept. Due to the nature of the dense body material, the sustain and harmonics produced are a marked difference over traditional wood technologies. Assisted by his brother, Jim Abel, actual production of the Abel Axe instruments is over one year old. Abel estimates that 250 guitars have been produced to date.

ELECTRIC

Abel Axe Pro
courtesy Abel Axe

Grading	100%	98% MINT	95% EXC+	90% EXC	80% VG+	70% VG	60% G

The Abel Axe body is CNC machined from a solid slab of aircraft grade aluminum and the finished guitar weighs in at only 8 pounds. The colors offered are then anodized to the body, and become part of the aluminum during the process.

Pro Series

Pro Series guitars are offered factory direct from Abel Axe. Abel Axe also offers the aluminum body separately (with strap buttons and back plate) directly from the factory for those players interested in creating their own custom instrument.

ABEL AXE — offset double cutaway aluminum body, bolt-on maple neck, 22 fret rosewood fingerboard with dot inlay, strings thru bridge, 6 on one side Sperzel tuners, black hardware, 2 Kent Armstrong humbucker pickups, volume control, 3 position switch. Available in Red, Black, Blue, Teal, Violet, and Aluminum (Silver) anodized finishes. Mfd. 1994 to current.

Mfr.'s Sug. Retail $1,000 $750 $500

This model has maple fingerboard with dot inlay optionally available.

Tuners can be anodized to match body color.

Abel Axe T — similar to Abel Axe, except has locking vibrato.

Mfr.'s Sug. Retail $1,000 $750 $500

ABEL AXE A-2 — offset double cutaway aluminum body, bolt-on maple neck, 22 fret rosewood fingerboard with dot inlay, string through tailpiece, 6 on one side Sperzel tuners, black hardware, Kent Armstrong humbucker pickup, volume control. Available in Red, Black, Blue, Teal, Violet, and Aluminum (Silver) anodized finishes. Mfd. 1996 to current.

Mfr.'s Sug. Retail $490 $367 $245

The A-2 model is available through music retailers and stores. The body design consists of slots as opposed to the original circle design, and features one Kent Armstrong pickup instead of two.

ELECTRIC BASS

ABEL AXE BASS — offset double cutaway body, bolt-on maple neck, 22 fret rosewood fingerboard with dot inlay, 34" scale, fixed brass bridge, 4 on one side Gotoh tuners, black hardware, Kent Armstrong pickup, volume control. Available in Red, Black, Blue, Teal, Violet, and Aluminum (Silver) anodized finishes. Mfd. 1995 to current.

Mfr.'s Sug. Retail $1,000 $750 $500

This model has maple fingerboard with dot inlay optionally available.

Jim Abel
19th Annual Dallas Show

ACACIA

Instruments built in Pottsdown, Pennsylvania since 1986.

Luthier Matt Friedman has been designing and building high quality custom instruments actively for the past seven years. Friedman began carving bodies back in 1980, and spent a number of years doing repair work for local music stores. In 1989 he began full time production of instruments.

The Acacia 4 and 5 string basses feature a 9-piece multilaminate neck through design while the 6 and 7 string models feature a 13-piece neck. The necks are comprised of Wenge, Mahogany, and other exotics with a select 24 fret hardwood fingerboard. The bodies on all Acacia instruments consist of five pieces, with a customer chosen bookmatched exotic top and back with mahogany tone woods. The 5, 6, and 7 string models have two custom dual expansion truss rods for precise adjustment of neck relief.

All body contours are hand carved. The 24 fret neck is available in 34", 35", and 36" scale lengths and feature ebony or rosewood fingerboards as well as graphite Epoxy neck reinforcement. In addition, luthier Friedman also features the Novax "Fanned Fret" fretboard as a custom option (licensed by Ralph Novak). Basses can be ordered with electronics by Lane Poor, EMG, Shadow, Seymour Duncan Bassline, and Bartolini. Instruments are available in a natural oil finish, or transparent colors over a figured maple top (Blue, Green, Purple, Aqua, Red, Amber, and other custom colors). For availability, wood selection, and pricing information, contact luthier Matt Friedman at Acacia Instruments via the Index of Current Manufacturers located in the back of this book.

ACOUSTIC

Instruments originally produced in Japan during the early 1970s. Distributed by the Acoustic amplifier company of California.

While the Acoustic company was going strong in the amplifier business with models like the 360, they decided to add a guitar and bass model to the product line. The first Black Widows were produced in Japan, and distributed through the Acoustic company. Towards the end of the model, production actually switched to Semie Moseley of Mosrite (models neck dimensions correspond to the Mosrite feel). There has been some indication that Paul Barth's Bartell company may have built some as well.

The most striking feature of the Acoustic Black Widow is the finish. The darkened rosewood fingerboard and deep black maple body, combined with the red pad in the back supposedly resembles the markings of a black widow spider. Instruments had Grover tuners on a 3+3 (2+2 for bass) headstock, 24 frets (20 for bass), and dual humbuckers (single for bass).

AELITA

Instruments were built in Russia during the 1970s.

(Headstock lettering in Cyrillic may appear as a capital A, backwards e, an r, u, m, a. We have anglicized the brandname.)

These solid bodied guitars were produced by the Rostov-on-Don accordian factory, and the design may strike the casual observer as favoring classic Italian designs of the 1960s.

(Source: Tony Bacon, The Ultimate Guitar Book)

AIRCRAFT

Instruments built in Japan.

Guitars carrying the Aircraft logo are actually manufactured by the Morris company, who also build instruments for such brandnames as their own Morris trademark, as well as the Hurricane logo.

AIRLINE

Manufactured by Valco in Chicago, Illinois during the 1960s. See chapter on House Brands.

This trademark has been identified as a "House Brand" of the Montgomery Ward department store chain. Author/researcher Willie G. Moseley indicates that the unique body design is proprietary to the Airline brand. Models can be found constructed of both "Res-O-Glas" (a hollow fiberglass body) and wood. It's hard to believe that these are from the 1960s because that futuristic design just screams the 1950s.

From 1961 to 1964 the Valco company (then-parent company of National, Dobro, and Supro) built fiberglass body electric guitars. The basic Airline wood body guitar came in sunburst finishes; and the deluxe "Res-O-Glas" two piece modeled bodies came with either one or two pickups, a wood bolt-on neck, and 20 frets on the 24 1/2" scale neck. The top of Airline headstocks, just like the Nationals, ran low-to-high from the left to right. Supros, on the other hand, dipped the headstock in the opposite way. Not that it matters with regard to playability and tone, but it's a handy way to win drinks at a bar full of musicians!

(Source: Willie G. Moseley, Stellas & Stratocasters)

AK ADMIRAL

Instruments were produced in Russia in the early 1980s.

These guitars were built in Leningrad as part of a project to mass produce good quality electrics. While the styling and hardware seem more modern in design, the project unfortunately failed. We at the **Blue Book of Guitars** welcome any information on Russian built guitars in our attempt to document trademarks of the world brands.

(Source: Tony Bacon, The Ultimate Guitar Book)

ALAMO

Instruments manufactured in San Antonio, Texas from 1949 to the late 1960s.

In the late 1940s, Charles Eilenberg was recruited by Milton Fink to manufacture electronic gear in San Antonio, Texas. Fink, the owner of Southern Music company, was a publisher and music wholesaler.

By 1950 the company was producing instrument cases, amplifiers, and lap steel guitars. The company continued to expand, and in 1960 introduced its first electric Spanish guitar. Alamo instruments were generally entry level solid body guitars, and designed with the student or beginner player in mind.

(Source: Michael Wright, Guitar Player Magazine, August 1996, pg. 22)

ALEMBIC

Instruments currently built in Santa Rosa, California. Previous production was centered in San Francisco, California. Distribution is handled by Alembic, Inc. of Santa Rosa, California.

Alembic Series I
courtesy Alembic

The Alembic company was founded in San Francisco in 1969, primarily to incorporate new ways to clarify and amplify rock group "The Grateful Dead". The Alembic workshop split into three main areas: a recording studio, P.A. and sound reinforcement, and guitar repair/experimentation. Ron Wickersham, an electronics expert and luthier/designer Rick Turner joined with Bob Matthews (a recording engineer) to officially incorporate Alembic in 1970 as three equal shareholders. The new company turned from customizing existing instruments in 1970 to building new ones in 1971. It is the experiments in customizing basses that led Alembic to the concept of 'active electronics'. Up until this point all electronics were passive systems. Wickersham found that mounting the active circuitry in the instrument itself gave the player a greater degree of control over his tone than ever before.

In 1973, Alembic received a distribution offer from the L D Heater company, a subsidiary of Norlin. Wickersham and Turner then began tooling up for production in earnest. Turner's choices in exotic woods and laminated bodies gained attention for the craftsmanship involved. The right combination of a new distributor, and a new jazz talent named Stanley Clarke actively playing an Alembic bass propelled the company into the spotlight in the early 1970s.

Geoff Gould, an aerospace engineer and bass player, was intrigued by an Alembic-customized bass he saw at a Greatful Dead concert. Assuming that the all-wood construction was a heavy proposition, he fashioned some samples of carbon graphite and presented them to Alembic. An experimental model with a graphite neck was displayed in 1977, and a patent issued in 1978. Gould formed the Modulus Graphite company with other ex-aerospace partners to provide necks for Alembic, and also build necks for Music Man's Cutlass bass model as well as their own Modulus Graphite guitars.

In 1973, Bob Matthews' shares were bought out by Alembic employees. Rick Turner left Alembic in 1978 to form Turner Guitars, and focused more on guitar building than bass production. Turner was succeeded as Alembic's president by Sam Turner, who had been involved with the company for five years. As the company expanded, the workshop continued to move from San Francisco to Cotati to Santa Rosa. In 1989 Alembic settled into a larger facility in Santa Rosa, and currently has a twenty five person staff.

Since 1972 the serial number has been stamped into the back of the headstock, although some 1971 models share this feature. For further dating of Alembic instruments, see the serialization section in the back of this book.

ELECTRIC

Grading	100%	98% MINT	95% EXC+	90% EXC	80% VG+	70% VG	60% G

CALIFORNIA SPECIAL — offset double cutaway maple body, thru body maple neck, brass truss rod cover plate, 24 fret ebony fingerboard with pearl oval inlay, double locking vibrato, brass nut, body matching peghead with bronze logo, 6 on one side tuners, chrome hardware, 2 single coil/1 humbucker Alembic pickups, volume/tone control, 3 mini switches. Available in Metal Ruby Red, Metal Sapphire Blue, Transparent Ruby Red and Transparent Sapphire Blue finishes. Disc. 1993.

	100%	98%	95%	90%	80%	70%	60%
	$2,185	$1,750	$1,375	$1,250	$1,125	$1,030	$935

Last Mfr.'s Sug. Retail was $3,120.

Series I — similar to California Special, except has treble/bass volume/tone control, treble Q/bass Q/pickup switch, 5 pin stereo output jack. Curr. mfr.

	100%	98%	95%	90%	80%	70%	60%
Mfr.'s Sug. Retail	$5,700	$4,560	$3,420	$2,850	$2,280	$2,050	$1,880	$1,710

Series II — similar to California Special, except has master/treble/bass volume control, treble/bass tone control, treble CVQ/bass CVQ/pickup switch, 5 pin stereo output jack. Curr. mfr.

	100%	98%	95%	90%	80%	70%	60%
Mfr.'s Sug. Retail	$7,055	$5,644	$4,233	$3,530	$2,820	$2,540	$2,330	$2,115

ELECTRIC BASS

All models have thru body maple, or maple/mahogany laminate neck construction, dual truss rods, 24 fret ebony fingerboard with pearl oval inlay (unless otherwise listed), adjustable brass saddles/bridge/tailpiece/nut (these items may be chrome or gold plated), active electronics, ebony fingerboard and clear gloss finish. A lot of the earlier instruments were custom ordered so there are a number of options that may be found on these guitars that are not standard items.

The tops of these instruments are bookmatched and the wood types vary widely, though the most common are as follows: bocate, bubinga, burl rosewood, coco bolo, figured maple, figured walnut, flame koa, lacewood, rosewood, tulipwood, vermillion or zebrawood. Also, the body style, peghead style and electronic/hardware configurations and combinations may vary from instrument to instrument due to the custom order nature of the company's early days.

"When I was about 10 years old, I found a 4 string guitar and 4 string banjo in our closet at home. They had belonged to a distant relative and somehow they found their way here. I was primarily attracted to the guitar."
—*Jim Fisch on Howard Alden*
TCG, Feb. 1996

Grading	100%	98% MINT	95% EXC+	90% EXC	80% VG+	70% VG	60% G

ELAN — offset double cutaway asymmetrical body, Honduras mahogany back, brass truss rod plate, body matching peghead with bronze logo, gold Alembic-Gotoh tuners, 2 P-style Alembic pickups, volume/tone/balance control, active electronics switch. Curr. mfr.

4 String — 4 on one side tuners.
| Mfr.'s Sug. Retail | $2,770 | $2,216 | $1,662 | $1,385 | $1,110 | $1,000 | $915 | $830 |

5 String — 4/1 per side tuners.
| Mfr.'s Sug. Retail | $3,090 | $2,472 | $1,854 | $1,545 | $1,230 | $1,110 | $1,020 | $930 |

6 String — 3 per side tuners.
| Mfr.'s Sug. Retail | $3,415 | $2,732 | $2,049 | $1,710 | $1,430 | $1,230 | $1,125 | $1,025 |

7 String — 4/3 per side tuners.
| Mfr.'s Sug. Retail | $5,220 | $4,176 | $3,132 | $2,610 | $2,040 | $1,880 | $1,720 | $1,565 |

8 String — 4 per side tuners.
| Mfr.'s Sug. Retail | $3,570 | $2,856 | $2,142 | $1,785 | $1,430 | $1,285 | $1,175 | $1,070 |

10 String — 5 per side tuners.
| Mfr.'s Sug. Retail | $4,325 | $3,460 | $2,595 | $2,265 | $1,820 | $1,685 | $1,545 | $1,400 |

EPIC — offset double cutaway mahogany body, standard woods top, brass truss rod plate, 3 piece maple set neck, body matching peghead with brass logo, chrome Alembic-Gotoh tuners, 2 Alembic MXY pickups, volume/pan/treble/bass controls, active electronics. Mfd. 1994 to date.

4 String — 2 per side tuners.
| Mfr.'s Sug. Retail | $1,580 | $1,264 | $948 | $820 | $660 | $505 | $460 | $420 |

5 String — 3/2 per side tuners.
| Mfr.'s Sug. Retail | $1,860 | $1,395 | $930 | $910 | $645 | $575 | $530 | $480 |

6 String — 5 piece maple set neck, 3 per side tuners. New 1995.
| Mfr.'s Sug. Retail | $2,280 | $1,710 | $1,140 | $1,010 | $855 | $775 | $630 | $580 |

ESSENCE — offset double cutaway body, flame maple top, rock maple back, brass truss rod plate, body matching peghead with bronze logo, chrome Alembic-Gotoh tuners, 2 Alembic MXY pickups, volume/tone/balance control. Curr. mfr.

4 String — 2 per side tuners.
| Mfr.'s Sug. Retail | $1,950 | $1,560 | $1,170 | $975 | $780 | $700 | $640 | $585 |

5 String — 3/2 per side tuners.
| Mfr.'s Sug. Retail | $2,175 | $1,740 | $1,305 | $1,090 | $870 | $785 | $720 | $655 |

6 String — 3 per side tuners.
| Mfr.'s Sug. Retail | $2,550 | $2,040 | $1,530 | $1,275 | $1,020 | $920 | $840 | $765 |

EUROPA — offset double cutaway asymmetrical Honduras mahogany body, brass truss rod plate, body matching peghead with bronze logo, gold Alembic-Gotoh tuners, 2 Alembic MXY pickups, volume/tone/balance control, bass/treble/Q switches. Curr. mfr.

4 String — 4 on one side tuners.
| Mfr.'s Sug. Retail | $3,215 | $2,572 | $1,929 | $1,610 | $1,290 | $1,160 | $1,060 | $965 |

5 String — 4/1 per side tuners.
| Mfr.'s Sug. Retail | $3,420 | $2,736 | $2,052 | $1,710 | $1,370 | $1,230 | $1,130 | $1,025 |

6 String — 3 per side tuners.
| Mfr.'s Sug. Retail | $3,730 | $2,984 | $2,238 | $1,865 | $1,490 | $1,345 | $1,230 | $1,120 |

7 String — 4/3 per side tuners.
| Mfr.'s Sug. Retail | $5,325 | $4,260 | $3,195 | $2,665 | $2,130 | $1,915 | $1,755 | $1,600 |

8 String — 4 per side tuners.
| Mfr.'s Sug. Retail | $3,855 | $3,084 | $2,313 | $1,930 | $1,540 | $1,390 | $1,270 | $1,155 |

10 String — 5 per side tuners.
| Mfr.'s Sug. Retail | $4,590 | $3,672 | $2,754 | $2,295 | $1,835 | $1,650 | $1,510 | $1,375 |

SERIES I — offset double cutaway mahogany core body with bottom bout point, figured wood top/back, brass truss rod plate, body matching peghead with sterling silver logo, chrome Schaller tuners, chrome plated hardware, single coil/dummy humbucker/single coil pickups, treble/bass volume/tone control, treble Q/bass Q/pickup switch, 5 pin stereo output jack. Curr. mfr.

4 String — 2 per side tuners.
| Mfr.'s Sug. Retail | $5,700 | $4,560 | $3,420 | $2,850 | $2,280 | $2,050 | $1,880 | $1,710 |

5 String — 3/2 per side tuners.
| Mfr.'s Sug. Retail | $6,120 | $4,896 | $3,672 | $3,060 | $2,450 | $2,205 | $2,020 | $1,835 |

Grading	100%	98% MINT	95% EXC+	90% EXC	80% VG+	70% VG	60% G
6 String — 3 per side tuners.							
Mfr.'s Sug. Retail	$6,425	$5,140	$3,855	$3,215	$2,570	$2,315	$2,120	$1,930
7 String — 4/3 per side tuners.							
Mfr.'s Sug. Retail	$8,245	$6,596	$4,947	$4,125	$3,300	$2,970	$2,720	$2,475
8 String — 4 per side tuners.							
Mfr.'s Sug. Retail	$6,640	$5,312	$3,984	$3,320	$2,655	$2,390	$2,190	$1,990
10 String — 5 per side tuners.							
Mfr.'s Sug. Retail	$7,225	$5,780	$4,335	$3,615	$2,890	$2,600	$2,385	$2,170

SERIES II — offset double cutaway mahogany core body, figured wood top/back, brass truss rod plate, body matching peghead with gold plated sterling silver logo, gold Schaller tuners, gold plated hardware, single coil/dummy humbucker/single coil pickups, master/treble/bass volume control, treble/bass tone control, treble CVQ/bass CVQ/pickup switch, 5 pin stereo output jack. Curr. mfr.

4 String — 2 per side tuners.							
Mfr.'s Sug. Retail	$7,055	$5,644	$4,233	$3,530	$2,820	$2,540	$2,330	$2,115
5 String — 3/2 per side tuners.							
Mfr.'s Sug. Retail	$7,565	$6,052	$4,539	$3,785	$3,330	$2,725	$2,495	$2,270
6 String — 3 per side tuners.							
Mfr.'s Sug. Retail	$7,865	$6,292	$4,719	$3,935	$3,145	$2,830	$2,595	$2,360
7 String — 4/3 per side tuners.							
Mfr.'s Sug. Retail	$9,675	$7,740	$5,805	$4,840	$3,870	$3,485	$3,195	$2,900
8 String — 4 per side tuners.							
Mfr.'s Sug. Retail	$8,085	$6,468	$4,851	$4,095	$3,235	$2,910	$2,665	$2,425
10 String — 5 per side tuners.							
Mfr.'s Sug. Retail	$9,085	$7,268	$5,451	$4,545	$3,635	$3,270	$2,995	$2,725

SIGNATURE SERIES — brass truss rod plate, body matching peghead with gold plated sterling silver logo, brass hardware, 2 humbucker pickups, volume/2 tone/balance controls, 2 Q switches, 5 pin stereo output jack.

In 1994, these instruments came in 2 designations, descriptions given below. Both are available in the style/configurations listed hereafter.

Mark King 1994 — offset double cutaway body with bottom bout point, long scale length, Mark King signature on peghead with gold plated sterling silver logo, 2 per side gold Alembic-Gotoh tuners.

Stanley Clarke 1994 — offset double cutaway body with rounded bottom bout, short scale length, Stanley Clarke signature on peghead with gold plated sterling silver logo, 2 per side gold Alembic-Gotoh tuners.

Signature Deluxe 4 — 5 piece body with mahogany core/exotic woods top, 2 per side tuners. New 1994.							
Mfr.'s Sug. Retail	$3,810	$2,857	$1,905	$1,900	$1,520	$1,365	$1,255	$1,140
Signature Deluxe 5 — 5 piece body with mahogany core/exotic woods top, 2/3 per side tuners. New 1994.							
Mfr.'s Sug. Retail	$4,060	$3,045	$2,030	$2,025	$1,620	$1,460	$1,335	$1,215
Signature Standard 4 — 3 piece mahogany body, 2 per side tuners. New 1994.							
Mfr.'s Sug. Retail	$2,815	$2,252	$1,689	$1,410	$1,125	$1,015	$930	$895
Signature Standard 5 — 3 piece mahogany body, 2/3 per side tuners. New 1994.							
Mfr.'s Sug. Retail	$3,065	$2,298	$1,532	$1,532	$1,226	$1,105	$1,010	$920

Mark King — offset double cutaway mahogany core body with bottom bout point, long scale length, Mark King signature on peghead with gold plated sterling silver logo, 2 per side gold Alembic-Gotoh tuners. Disc. 1993.

		$1,970	$1,690	$1,410	$1,125	$1,015	$930	$895

Last Mfr.'s Sug. Retail was $2,815.

Stanley Clarke — offset double cutaway mahogany core body with rounded bottom bout, short scale length, Stanley Clarke signature on peghead with gold plated sterling silver logo, 2 per side gold Alembic-Gotoh tuners. Disc. 1993.

		$1,970	$1,690	$1,410	$1,125	$1,015	$930	$895

Last Mfr.'s Sug. Retail was $2,815.

SPOILER — offset double cutaway Honduras mahogany body, brass truss rod plate, body matching peghead with bronze logo, chrome Alembic-Gotoh tuners, 2 humbucker pickups, volume/tone control, pickup/Q switch. Curr. mfr.

4 String — 2 per side tuners.							
Mfr.'s Sug. Retail	$2,635	$2,108	$1,581	$1,320	$1,055	$950	$870	$790
5 String — 3/2 per side tuners.							
Mfr.'s Sug. Retail	$2,815	$2,252	$1,689	$1,410	$1,125	$1,015	$930	$895

ALHAMBRA

Instruments built in Spain. Distributed by Quality First Products of Forest City, North Carolina.

Alhambra classical guitars are medium to very high quality Spanish instruments. Prices range from $425 up to $8,000 depending on design, inlays, and woods used in construction.

ALLEN

Instruments built in Colfax, California since 1982.

Luthier Randy Allen began repairing guitars and other stringed instruments in 1980. In 1982, Allen built his first guitar. Since then, Allen has been handcrafting quality guitars and mandolins (and some Dobros).

Standard features on the guitar models include East Indian Rosewood or Honduran Mahogany back and sides, a Sitka spruce top; bound Ebony fingerboards, bridge, and peghead overlay; and a bound headstock and Mother of Pearl position dots. Basic models include the Dreadnaught ($2,595), Small Jumbo ($2,795), The OM ($2,795) and a Dobro Squareneck ($2,595).

All models have options ranging from a cutaway body design, abalone edging, different fingerboard inlays, and wood bindings. For further information, contact luthier Allen through the Index of Current Manufacturers located in the rear of this book.

ALLIGATOR

Guitars built in England in 1983.

In celebration of Alligator Amplifications's first anniversary, Reeve Guitars (UK) built a number of instruments designed by Pete Tulett.

(Source: Tony Bacon and Paul Day, The Guru's Guitar Guide)

ALMCRANTZ

Instruments built in America in the late 1800s.

An Almcrantz acoustic guitar bearing a label reading "July 1895" was featured in the first edition of Tom Wheeler's outstanding reference book "American Guitars" (HarperCollins Publishers, New York). Research is continuing on the company history, and further information will be updated in future editions of the **Blue Book of Guitars**.

ALOHA

Instruments built in San Antonio, Texas and Chicago, Illinois. Distributed by the Aloha Publishing and Musical Instrument Company of Chicago, Illinois.

The Aloha company was founded in 1935 by J. M. Raleigh. True to the nature of a "House Brand" distributor, Raleigh's company distributed both Aloha instruments and amplifiers and Raleigh brand instruments through his Chicago office. Acoustic guitars were supplied by Harmony, and initial amplifiers and guitars were supplied by the Alamo company of San Antonio, Texas. By the mid 1950s, Aloha was producing their own amps, but continued using Alamo products.

(Source: Michael Wright, Vintage Guitar Magazine, August 1996, pg. 22)

ALRAY

Instruments built in Neodesha, Kansas during the late 1960s. Distributed by Holman-Woodell, Inc. of Neodesha, Kansas.

The Holman-Woodell company built guitars during the late 1960s in Neodesha, Kansas (around 60 miles due south from Topeka). While they were producing guitars for Wurlitzer, they also built their own Holman brand as well as instruments trademarked Alray and 21st Century. The Holman-Woodell company is also famous for building the **La Baye 2 x 4** guitars for Wisconsin-based inventor Dan Helland.

(Source: Michael Wright, Guitar Stories Volume One, pg. 163)

ALVAREZ

Alvarez instruments are manufactured in either Japan or Korea. Distributed by St. Louis Music of St. Louis, Missouri.

While the St. Louis Music Supply Company was originally started in 1922, the Alvarez trademark was established in 1967. Initially, Alvarez guitars were built in Japan during the late 1960s, and distributed through St. Louis Music (as were the Electra and Westone brands). St. Louis Music currently manufactures Crate and Ampeg amplifiers in the U.S., while Alvarez instruments are designed in St. Louis and produced overseas.

ACOUSTIC

All Alvarez acoustic steel string guitars (except the 5212, 5214 and 5216) have a stylized double A abalone inlay on their pegheads.

"...a brief discussion pertaining to supply and demand as related to vintage instruments is in order. Ladies and gents, we only have a finite number of these gems available to us. As supplies decrease, demand rises along with their prices. This theory of supply and demand is a constant concept, especially when it pertains to collectibles."
—Joe LoSchiavo
TCG, Feb. 1996

Grading	100%	98% MINT	95% EXC+	90% EXC	80% VG+	70% VG	60% G

Artist Series

5002 MAHOGANY CLASSIC — classical style, laminated spruce top, round soundhole, bound body, wooden inlay rosette, mahogany back/sides, nato neck, 12/19 fret rosewood fingerboard, rosewood bridge, rosewood veneer on peghead, 3 per side gold tuners. Available in Natural finish. Current mfr.

Mfr.'s Sug. Retail	$410	$307	$205	$180	$130	$115	$105	$95

5004 ROSEWOOD CLASSIC — similar to 5002, except has rosewood back/sides.

Mfr.'s Sug. Retail	$485	$363	$242	$185	$150	$135	$120	$110

5014 MOUNTAIN FOLK — folk style, laminated spruce top, round soundhole, multi bound body, 3 ring rosette, tortoise pickguard, mahogany back/sides/neck, 14/20 fret rosewood fingerboard with pearl dot inlay, stylized bird wings inlay at 12th fret, rosewood bridge with white black dot pins, blackface peghead with pearl logo inlay, 3 per side chrome die cast tuners. Available in Sunburst finish. New 1995.

Mfr.'s Sug. Retail	$450	$337	$225

5019 MIDNIGHT SPECIAL — dreadnought style, laminated spruce top, round soundhole, 5 stripe bound body, abalone inlay rosette, black pickguard, mahogany back/sides, nato neck, 14/20 fret rosewood fingerboard with pearl dot inlay, stylized bird wings inlay at 12th fret, rosewood bridge with white pearl dot pins, 3 per side chrome tuners. Available in Black finish. Current mfr.

Mfr.'s Sug. Retail	$560	$420	$280	$230	$185	$165	$150	$140

5019AV — similar to 5019, except has pickup system, 3 band EQ. Mfd. 1994 only.

	$560	$495	$415	$330	$300	$275	$250

Last Mfr.'s Sug. Retail was $825.

5020 MOUNTAIN — dreadnought style, laminated spruce top, round soundhole, bound body, 5 stripe rosette, black pickguard, mahogany back/sides, 14/20 fret rosewood fingerboard with pearl dot inlay, stylized bird wings inlay at 12th fret, rosewood bridge with black pearl dot pins, rosewood veneer on peghead, 3 per side chrome tuners. Available in Natural and Sunburst finishes. Mfd. 1991 to 1995.

Mfr.'s Sug. Retail	$285	$228	$171	$145	$115	$105	$95	$85

5020M — similar to 5020 Mountain, except has laminated mahogany top. Disc. 1995.

	$280	$255	$215	$170	$155	$140	$130

Last Mfr.'s Sug. Retail was $400.

5021 — similar to 5020, except has 12 strings, 6 per side tuners. Disc. 1993.

	$280	$255	$215	$170	$155	$140	$130

Last Mfr.'s Sug. Retail was $425.

5040 KOA — dreadnought style, laminated koa top, round soundhole, 3 stripe bound body and rosette, brown pickguard, koa back/sides, nato neck, 14/20 fret rosewood fingerboard with pearl dot inlay, stylized bird wings inlay at 12th fret, rosewood bridge with black pearl dot pins, koa veneer on peghead, 3 per side chrome tuners. Available in Natural finish. Current mfr.

Mfr.'s Sug. Retail	$500	$375	$250	$200	$160	$145	$130	$120

5043 BURGUNDY ARTIST — dreadnought style, laminated oak top, round soundhole, multi bound body, abalone rosette, oak back/sides, mahogany neck, 20 fret rosewood fingerboard with pearl cross inlay, rosewood bridge with black white dot pins, oak peghead veneer with pearl logo inlay, 3 per side diecast tuners. Available in Burgundy Stain finish. Mfd. 1994 to date.

Mfr.'s Sug. Retail	$575	$460	$345	$290	$200	$180	$165	$150

5055 BLUESMAN — jumbo style, laminated spruce top, f holes, raised black pickguard, multi bound body, mahogany back/sides/neck, 14/22 fret bound rosewood fingerboard with pearl dot inlay, stylized bird wings inlay at 12th fret, rosewood bridge with white black dot pins, blackface peghead with pearl logo inlay, 3 per side chrome die cast tuners. Available in Sunburst finish. New 1995.

Mfr.'s Sug. Retail	$540	$405	$270

5072 JUMBO — jumbo style, laminated spruce top, round soundhole, tortoise pickguard, abalone bound body/rosette, mahogany back/sides, 14/20 fret rosewood fingerboard with pearl dot inlay, stylized bird wings inlay at 12th fret, rosewood bridge with white black dot pins, rosewood peghead veneer with pearl logo inlay, 3 per side diecast tuners. Available in Natural finish. Mfd. 1994 to date.

Mfr.'s Sug. Retail	$525	$393	$262	$225	$180	$160	$150	$135

5220C — single cutaway dreadnought style, spruce top, round soundhole, 3 stripe bound body and rosette, black pickguard, mahogany back/sides, nato neck, 20 fret rosewood fingerboard with pearl dot inlay, rosewood bridge with black pearl dot pins, 3 per side chrome tuners. Available in Natural finish. Disc. 1995.

	$235	$195	$150	$120	$110	$100	$90

Last Mfr.'s Sug. Retail was $350.

5220CEQ — similar to 5220C, except has pickup system, 3 band EQ. Current production.

Mfr.'s Sug. Retail	$640	$480	$320	$295	$220	$200	$180	$165

Add $10 for a Cherry (5220CEQCH) or Burst (5220CEQVS) finish.

Grading	100%	98% MINT	95% EXC+	90% EXC	80% VG+	70% VG	60% G

5237 CURLY MAPLE — dreadnought style, laminated spruce top, round soundhole, 5 stripe bound body/rosette, curly maple back/sides, nato neck, 14/20 fret rosewood fingerboard with pearl dot inlay, stylized bird wings inlay at 12th fret, rosewood bridge with white pearl dot pins, 3 per side chrome tuners. Available in Sunburst finish. Disc. 1995.

	$320	$270	$220	$160	$145	$130	$120

Last Mfr.'s Sug. Retail was $475.

Professional Series

5009 ROSEWOOD — classical style, solid spruce top, round soundhole, bound body, wooden inlay rosette, rosewood back/sides, nato neck, 19 fret rosewood fingerboard, rosewood bridge, rosewood veneer on peghead, 3 per side gold tuners. Available in Natural finish. Current. mfr.

Mfr.'s Sug. Retail	$600	$450	$300	$290	$185	$165	$150	$140

5022 GLENBROOKE — dreadnought style, solid spruce top, round soundhole, tortoise pickguard, herringbone bound body/rosette, rosewood back/sides, mahogany neck, 14/20 fret rosewood fingerboard with pearl dot inlay, stylized bird wings inlay at 12th fret, rosewood bridge with white pearl dot pins, rosewood peghead veneer with pearl logo inlay, 3 per side chrome tuners. Available in Natural finish. Current mfr.

Mfr.'s Sug. Retail	$550	$412	$275	$260	$210	$190	$170	$160

5032 TIMBER RIDGE — similar to 5022, except has wooden bound body, wooden inlay rosette, mahogany back/sides. Mfd. 1994 to date.

Mfr.'s Sug. Retail	$640	$480	$320	$275	$220	$200	$180	$165

5045 MOUNTAIN — similar to 5022, except has no pickguard, peghead logo decal. Disc. 1995.

	$350	$300	$250	$200	$180	$165	$150

Last Mfr.'s Sug. Retail was $500.

5045 G MOUNTAIN — similar to 5045, except has graphite bridge. New 1996.

Mfr.'s Sug. Retail	$600	$450	$300	$250	$200	$180	$165	$150

5054 — dreadnought style, solid spruce top, round soundhole, herringbone bound body and rosette, tortoise pickguard, rosewood back/sides, nato neck, 14/20 fret rosewood fingerboard with pearl dot inlay, 12th fret has stylized bird wings inlay, rosewood bridge with white pearl dot pins, rosewood veneer on peghead, 6 per side chrome tuners. Available in Natural finish. Disc. 1994.

	$420	$360	$300	$240	$215	$195	$180

Last Mfr.'s Sug. Retail was $600.

5202 MAHOGANY — similar to 5009, except has African mahogany back/sides.

Mfr.'s Sug. Retail	$525	$393	$262	$230	$170	$150	$135	$125

5224 — dreadnought style, solid spruce top, round soundhole, 3 stripe bound body and rosette, black pickguard, mahogany back/sides, nato neck, 14/20 fret rosewood fingerboard with pearl dot inlay, rosewood bridge with black dot pins, rosewood veneer on peghead, 3 per side chrome tuners. Available in Natural finish. Disc. 1995.

	$300	$250	$205	$150	$135	$120	$110

Last Mfr.'s Sug. Retail was $450.

5225 — similar to 5224, except has tiger rosewood back/sides, bound fingerboard, peghead. Disc. 1994.

	$320	$275	$230	$185	$165	$150	$140

Last Mfr.'s Sug. Retail was $460.

6010 ELEGANCE SIGNATURE — dreadnought style, solid spruce top, round soundhole, multi bound body, abalone rosette, mahogany back/sides/neck, 14/20 fret bound rosewood fingerboard with pearl double A inlay at 12th fret, rosewood bridge with white pearl dot pins, bound peghead with rosewood veneer/pearl logo inlay, 3 per side gold die cast tuners. Available in Natural finish. New 1995.

Mfr.'s Sug. Retail	$775	$581	$387

6015 ELEGANCE ROSE — dreadnought style, solid spruce top, round soundhole, multi bound body, abalone rosette, tortoise pickguard, mahogany back/sides/neck, 14/20 fret rosewood fingerboard with pearl rose inlay at 12th fret, rosewood bridge with black pearl dot pins, rosewood peghead veneer with pearl logo inlay, 3 per side gold die cast tuners. Available in Natural finish. New 1995.

Mfr.'s Sug. Retail	$950	$712	$475

Regent Series

5201 CLASSIC — classical style, laminated spruce top, round soundhole, bound body, wooden inlay rosette, mahogany back/sides/neck, 12/19 fret rosewood fingerboard, rosewood wraparound bridge, 3 per side tuners with plastic buttons. Available in Natural finish. Mfd. 1994 to 1995.

	$210	$180	$150	$120	$110	$100	$90

Last Mfr.'s Sug. Retail was $300.

5208N — dreadnought style, laminated spruce top, round soundhole, bound body, 3 stripe rosette, black pickguard, mahogany back/sides/neck, 14/20 fret rosewood fingerboard with pearl dot inlay, rosewood bridge with black pins, 3 per side chrome tuners. Available in Natural finish. New 1995.

Mfr.'s Sug. Retail	$250	$187	$125

Grading	100%	98% MINT	95% EXC+	90% EXC	80% VG+	70% VG	60% G

5208M — similar to 5208N, except has laminated mahogany top. New 1995.
  Mfr.'s Sug. Retail $225 $168 $112

5210 SATIN — dreadnought style, laminated spruce top, round soundhole, bound body, 3 stripe rosette, tortoise pickguard, mahogany back/sides/neck, 14/20 fret rosewood fingerboard with pearl dot inlay, rosewood bridge with white pins, 3 per side chrome tuners. Available in Natural finish. Mfd. 1994 to date.
  Mfr.'s Sug. Retail $335 $251 $167 $140 $110 $100 $90 $80

5212 SPECIAL — dreadnought style, laminated spruce top, round soundhole, bound body, 3 stripe rosette, tortoise pickguard, mahogany back/sides/neck, 14/20 fret rosewood fingerboard with pearl dot inlay, rosewood bridge with white pins, 3 per side chrome tuners. Available in Natural and Sunburst finishes. Current mfr.
  Mfr.'s Sug. Retail $355 $266 $177 $150 $110 $90 $80 $70
      Add $25 for black pickguard, Black finish (5212BK).

5214 DELUXE — similar to 5212, except has black pickguard, black with white dot bridge pins.
  Mfr.'s Sug. Retail $375 $281 $187 $155 $100 $90 $80 $75

  521412 12 String — similar to 5212, except has 12 string, black pickguard, black with white dot bridge pins, 6 per side tuners.
  Mfr.'s Sug. Retail $550 $412 $275

5216 FOLK — similar to 5212, except has parlor style body.
  Mfr.'s Sug. Retail $265 $212 $159 $140 $110 $100 $90 $80

Silver Anniversary Series

2551 ROSEWOOD — dreadnought style, solid spruce top, round soundhole, 5 stripe bound body, abalone rosette, rosewood back/sides, mahogany neck, 14/20 fret rosewood fingerboard with pearl diamond inlay, rosewood bridge with white black dot pins, rosewood veneer on bound peghead with Silver Anniversary inlay, 3 per side chrome tuners. Available in Natural finish. Current Mfg.
  Mfr.'s Sug. Retail $650 $487 $325 $320 $240 $215 $195 $180

  2551/12 — similar to 2551, except has 12 strings. Disc. 1995.
                              $540 $450 $370 $280 $250 $230 $210
                                                          Last Mfr.'s Sug. Retail was $800.

2552 — dreadnought style, spruce top, round soundhole, 5 stripe bound body, abalone rosette, mahogany back/sides/neck, 14/20 fret rosewood fingerboard with pearl dot inlay, rosewood bridge with black white dot pins, rosewood veneer on peghead, 3 per side chrome tuners. Available in Natural finish. Disc. 1993.
                              $280 $240 $200 $160 $145 $130 $120
                                                          Last Mfr.'s Sug. Retail was $400.

2555 — single sharp cutaway jumbo style, laminated spruce top, round soundhole, 5 stripe bound body, abalone flake rosette, mahogany back/sides/neck, 21 fret rosewood fingerboard with abalone offset bar inlay, rosewood bridge with black white pins, rosewood veneer on bound peghead with Silver Anniversary inlay, 3 per side chrome tuners, bi-phonic pickup system and controls. Available in Natural and Sunburst finishes. Disc. 1995.
                              $685 $565 $455 $355 $290 $265 $240
                                                          Last Mfr.'s Sug. Retail was $1,050.

      In 1995, Natural finish was discontinued.

  2555BK — similar to 2555, except has single sharp cutaway folk style body, abalone bound body/rosette. Available in Black finish. Mfd. 1994 only.
                              $630 $540 $450 $360 $325 $300 $275
                                                          Last Mfr.'s Sug. Retail was $900.

Wildwood Series

5037 12 STRING — dreadnought style, solid cedar top, round soundhole, 5 stripe bound body/rosette, mahogany back/sides, nato neck, 14/20 fret rosewood fingerboard with pearl dot inlay, 12th fret has stylized bird wings inlay, rosewood bridge with white black dot pins, rosewood veneer on peghead, 6 per side gold tuners with amber buttons. Available in Natural finish. Curr. mfr.
  Mfr.'s Sug. Retail $550 $440 $330 $300 $240 $215 $195 $180
      In 1995, solid spruce top replaces original item.

5062 NATURAL — dreadnought style, solid spruce top, round soundhole, 5 stripe bound body/rosette, mahogany back/sides, nato neck, 14/20 fret rosewood fingerboard with pearl dot inlay, 12th fret has stylized bird wings inlay, rosewood bridge with white black dot pins, 3 per side chrome tuners. Available in Natural finish. Curr. mfr.
  Mfr.'s Sug. Retail $525 $393 $262 $215 $175 $155 $140 $130

5063 — similar to 5062, except has gold tuners with amber buttons. Available in Natural finish. Disc. 1993.
                              $300 $260 $215 $175 $155 $140 $130
                                                          Last Mfr.'s Sug. Retail was $430.

"My first guitar was a $15.00 local music store special, plywood, with action as high as the Brooklyn Bridge. I thought it was great!"
—Jim Fisch on Mitch Seidman
TCG, April 1995

Grading	100%	98% MINT	95% EXC+	90% EXC	80% VG+	70% VG	60% G

5086 — similar to 5062, except has single cutaway, gold tuners with amber buttons, and bi-phonic pickup system and controls. Disc. 1995.

	$625	$515	$420	$330	$270	$245	$225

Last Mfr.'s Sug. Retail was $950.

Willow Ridge Series

2531 — single round cutaway classical style, spruce top, round soundhole, wooden inlay rosette, bound body, mahogany back/sides/neck, 19 fret rosewood fingerboard, rosewood wraparound bridge, 3 per side chrome tuners with plastic buttons, piezo bridge pickups, 3 band EQ. Available in Natural finish. Mfd. 1994 only.

	$735	$630	$525	$420	$380	$345	$315

Last Mfr.'s Sug. Retail was $1,050.

2532 — single round cutaway dreadnought style, spruce top, black pickguard, 3 stripe bound body/rosette, maple back/sides, mahogany neck, 22 fret rosewood fingerboard with pearl dot inlay, rosewood bridge with white black dot pins, 3 per side diecast tuners, piezo bridge pickups, 3 band EQ. Available in Natural finish. Disc. 1995.

	$735	$630	$525	$420	$380	$345	$315

Last Mfr.'s Sug. Retail was $1,050.

This model also available with mahogany back/sides (2533).

ACOUSTIC ELECTRIC

Fusion Series

5008C CLASSIC — single round cutaway classical style, laminated spruce top, round soundhole, bound body, wooden inlay rosette, mahogany back/sides/neck, 19 fret rosewood fingerboard, rosewood wraparound bridge, rosewood peghead veneer with pearl logo inlay, 3 per side gold tuners with plastic buttons, piezo bridge pickups, 3 band EQ. Available in Natural finish. Mfd. 1994 only.

Mfr.'s Sug. Retail	$900	$720	$540	$450	$360	$325	$300	$275

5072CBK — single round cutaway jumbo style, laminated spruce top, round soundhole, multi bound body, abalone rosette, black pickguard, mahogany back/sides/neck, 20 fret rosewood fingerboard with pearl dot inlay, stylized bird wings inlay at 12th fret, rosewood bridge with white pearl dot pins, bound blackface peghead with abalone logo, 3 per side chrome die cast tuners, piezo bridge pickups, 3 band EQ. Available in Black finish. New 1995.

Mfr.'s Sug. Retail	$875	$656	$437

5080N NATURAL — round cutaway dreadnought style, laminated spruce top, round soundhole, 3 stripe bound body, abalone rosette, mahogany back/sides/neck, 20 fret rosewood fingerboard with pearl dot inlay, stylized bird wings inlay at 12th fret, rosewood bridge with black pearl dot pins, abalone logo peghead inlay, 3 per side chrome tuners, piezo bridge pickups, volume/tone control. Available in Natural finish. Current mfr.

Mfr.'s Sug. Retail	$725	$543	$362	$345	$260	$235	$215	$195

5081N/5083N —similar to 5080N, except has laminated curly maple top, curly maple back/sides. Available in Transparent Blue, Transparent Violin and Transparent Red finishes, respectively. Current mfr.

Mfr.'s Sug. Retail	$800	$600	$400	$355	$280	$235	$215	$195

In 1995, Transparent Violin finish was discontinued (5082N).

5084N — similar to 5080N, except has Black finish. Mfd. 1994 to date.

Mfr.'s Sug. Retail	$750	$600	$450	$390	$315	$280	$260	$235

5088C — single round cutaway dreadnought style, laminated spruce top, round soundhole, tortoise pickguard, 3 stripe bound body/rosette, mahogany back/sides/neck, 20 fret rosewood fingerboard with pearl dot inlay, pearl curlicue inlay at 12th fret, rosewood bridge with black white dot pins, pearl logo peghead inlay, 3 per side diecast tuners, piezo bridge pickups, 3 band EQ. Available in Natural finish. Mfd. 1994 to date.

Mfr.'s Sug. Retail	$825	$660	$495	$415	$330	$300	$275	$250

5088CBK — similar to 5088C, except has black pickguard, abalone flake rosette, white black dot bridge pins. Available in Black finish. Mfd. 1994 to date.

Mfr.'s Sug. Retail	$875	$700	$525	$450	$360	$325	$300	$275

This model also available with no pickguard, White finish (5088CWH).

5088/12 — similar to 5088C, except has 12 strings, 6 per side tuners. Mfd. 1994 only.

Mfr.'s Sug. Retail	$850	$680	$510	$425	$340	$305	$280	$255

ACOUSTIC ELECTRIC BASS

4070 — single round jumbo style, laminated spruce top, round soundhole, 3 stripe bound body/rosette, mahogany back/sides/neck, 23 fret rosewood fingerboard, rosewood bridge with white black dot pins, bound rosewood peghead with pearl logo inlay, 2 per side diecast tuners, piezo bridge pickups, 3 band EQ. Mfd. 1994 to date.

Mfr.'s Sug. Retail	$1,000	$800	$600	$500	$400	$360	$330	$300

Add $50 for Black finish (4070BK).

Grading	100%	98% MINT	95% EXC+	90% EXC	80% VG+	70% VG	60% G

ELECTRIC

Dana Scoop Series

The Scoop guitar model was designed by luthier Dana Sutcliffe in 1988, and won the Music and Sound Retailer magazine's "Most Innovative Guitar of the Year Award" in 1992. Produced between 1992 and 1995, the scoop-shaped slot in the guitar body's design reinforces and channels neck vibrations into a single point where the neck and body meet.

AE600 — offset double cutaway maple body with a "scoop" cutaway, bolt-on maple neck, 22 fret rosewood fingerboard with pearl block inlay, double locking vibrato, 6 on one side tuners, black hardware, single coil/humbucker pickups, volume/tone control, 3 position switch. Available in Dark Metallic Blue and Fire Red finishes. Disc. 1995.

	$565	$510	$425	$340	$305	$280	$255

Custom Alvarez Scoop
courtesy Dana Sutcliffe

In 1994, active electronics, Blue Pearl and Red Glow finishes were added.

Last Mfr.'s Sug. Retail was $850.

AE600MA — similar to AE600, except has figured maple top, maple fingerboard. Available in Honey Burst finish. Mfd. 1994 only.

	$715	$655	$545	$435	$395	$360	$330

Last Mfr.'s Sug. Retail was $1,090.

AE6001 — similar to AE600, except has Modulus Graphite neck/fingerboard. Available in Black finish. Disc. 1993.

	$600	$540	$450	$360	$325	$300	$275

Last Mfr.'s Sug. Retail was $900.

AE650 — offset double cutaway maple body with a "scoop" cutaway, bolt-on maple neck, 22 fret rosewood fingerboard with pearl dot inlay, double locking vibrato, 6 on one side tuners, black hardware, single coil/triple Dana pickups, volume/tone control, 5 position switch. Available in Black and Transparent White finishes. Mfd. 1994 only.

	$530	$480	$400	$320	$290	$265	$240

Last Mfr.'s Sug. Retail was $800.

Also available with maple fingerboard with black dot inlay.

AE655 — similar to AE650, except has maple fingerboard with black dot inlay, gold hardware.

	$610	$540	$450	$360	$325	$300	$275

Last Mfr.'s Sug. Retail was $900.

AE3000 — offset double cutaway alder body with a "scoop" cutaway, bolt-on maple neck, 22 fret rosewood fingerboard with pearl dot inlay, double locking vibrato, 3 per side tuners, smoked chrome hardware, 2 single coil/1 humbucker Dana pickups, volume/tone control, 5 position switch, active electronics. Available in Ivory finish. Mfd. 1994 only.

	$520	$480	$400	$320	$290	$265	$240

Last Mfr.'s Sug. Retail was $800.

AE5000 — similar to AE3000, except has fixed bridge.

	$450	$410	$350	$280	$250	$230	$210

Last Mfr.'s Sug. Retail was $700.

Dana Signature Series

Luthier Dana Sutcliffe has over twenty years experience in the music industry. Combining his experiences as a practicing musician, Sutcliffe has been designing quality forward-thinking guitars and amplifiers.

In 1990, Sutcliffe co-designed the Alvarez Electric Guitar line for St. Louis Music. Innovative designs include the "Tri-Force" pickups, The Dana "Scoop" slotted body design, and the Dana "Off Set" bass design. Sutcliffe regularly holds clinics to demonstrate Alvarez, Crate, and other St. Louis Music products.

AED100 — offset double cutaway alder body, bolt-on maple neck, 22 fret rosewood fingerboard with pearl block inlay, tunomatic bridge/stop tailpiece, 6 on one side tuners, chrome hardware, 2 DSR humbucker pickups, volume/2 tone controls, 3 position and coil tap switches. Available in Black finish. Disc. 1995.

	$340	$300	$250	$200	$180	$165	$150

Last Mfr.'s Sug. Retail was $500.

AED200 — offset double cutaway hardwood body, bolt-on maple neck, 22 fret maple fingerboard with black dot inlay, standard vibrato, 6 on one side tuners, chrome hardware, 2 single coil/1 humbucker Alvarez pickups, volume/tone control, 5 position switch. Available in Black and White finishes. Mfd. 1994 only.

	$250	$220	$185	$150	$135	$120	$110

Last Mfr.'s Sug. Retail was $375.

AED250 — offset double cutaway hardwood body, bolt-on maple neck, 22 fret rosewood fingerboard with pearl dot inlay, fixed bridge, 3 per side tuners, chrome hardware, single coil/triple Dana pickup, volume/tone control, 5 position switch. Available in Red finish. Mfd. 1994 only.

	$265	$235	$195	$155	$140	$125	$115

Last Mfr.'s Sug. Retail was $390.

AED260 — similar to AED250, except has alder body, figured maple top, transparent pickguard, maple fingerboard with black dot inlay, gold hardware. Available in Transparent Red finish. Mfd. 1994 to date.

Mfr.'s Sug. Retail	$550	$440	$330	$275	$220	$200	$180	$165

Grading	100%	98% MINT	95% EXC+	90% EXC	80% VG+	70% VG	60% G

AED275 — offset double cutaway alder body, transparent pickguard, bolt-on maple neck, 22 fret rosewood fingerboard with pearl dot inlay, double locking vibrato, 3 per side tuners, chrome hardware, single coil/triple Dana pickup, 1 volume/2 tone controls, 5 position switch. Available in Red and White finishes. New 1994.

Mfr.'s Sug. Retail	$575	$431	$287	$285	$230	$205	$190	$175

Add $50 for Blue Pearl/Transparent Red finish (AED275VR).

AED280 — similar to AED275, except has humbucker/single coil/humbucker pickups. Available in Blue Pearl finish.

Mfr.'s Sug. Retail	$635	$508	$381	$320	$255	$230	$210	$190

AED300 — offset double cutaway alder body, bolt-on maple neck, 22 fret rosewood fingerboard with pearl dot inlay, double locking vibrato, 6 on one side tuners, black hardware, 2 single coil/1 humbucker DSR pickups, volume/2 tone controls, 5 position switch. Available in Fire Red and White finishes. Disc. 1995.

			$330	$300	$250	$200	$180	$165	$150

Last Mfr.'s Sug. Retail was $500.

In 1994, White finish became available.

Regulator Series

AE10 CLASSIC 1 — single round cutaway alder body, pearloid pickguard, bolt-on maple neck, 21 fret maple fingerboard with black dot inlay, fixed bridge, 3 per side tuners, chrome hardware, 2 single coil pickups, volume/tone control on metal plate, 3 position switch. Available in Black finish. Mfd. 1994 to date.

Mfr.'s Sug. Retail	$350	$280	$210	$175	$140	$125	$115	$105

AE20 CLASSIC 2 — offset double cutaway alder body, pearloid pickguard, bolt-on maple neck, 21 fret maple fingerboard with black dot inlay, standard vibrato, 3 per side tuners, chrome hardware, 2 single coil/1 humbucker pickups, 1 volume/2 tone controls, 5 position switch. Available in Black and Burst finishes. Mfd. 1994 to date.

Mfr.'s Sug. Retail	$350	$280	$210	$175	$140	$125	$115	$105

In 1995, Black finish was introduced.

AE40 CLASSIC 4 — offset double cutaway alder body, black lam pickguard, bolt-on maple neck, 22 fret rosewood fingerboard with pearl dot inlay, strings thru bridge, 3 per side tuners, chrome hardware, 2 single coil/1 humbucker pickups, volume/tone control, 5 position switch. Available in Tobacco Sunburst and Walnut finishes. Mfd. 1994 to date.

Mfr.'s Sug. Retail	$550	$440	$330	$275	$220	$200	$180	$165

AE50 CLASSIC 5 — similar to AE40, except has standard vibrato, roller nut, gold hardware. Available in Ivory and Vintage Sunburst finishes. Mfd. 1994 to date.

Mfr.'s Sug. Retail	$575	$431	$287	$285	$230	$205	$190	$175

In 1995, Ivory finish was introduced.

AE100 — offset double cutaway alder body, black pickguard, bolt-on maple neck, 22 fret maple fingerboard with black dot inlay, standard vibrato, 6 on one side tuners, chrome hardware, 2 single coil/1 humbucker EMG pickups, volume/2 tone controls, 5 position switch. Available in Transparent Blue and Transparent Red finishes. Disc. 1993.

			$315	$270	$225	$180	$160	$150	$135

Last Mfr.'s Sug. Retail was $450.

AE200 — similar to AE100, except has maple body, rosewood fingerboard with pearl dot inlay, gold hardware and humbucker/single coil/humbucker EMG pickups. Available in Cherry Sunburst finish. Disc. 1995.

			$455	$390	$325	$260	$235	$215	$195

Last Mfr.'s Sug. Retail was $650.

AE300 — similar to AE100, except has maple body, Modulus Graphite neck/fingerboard, gold hardware and humbucker/single coil/humbucker EMG pickups. Available in Black finish. Disc. 1993.

			$330	$280	$240	$200	$180	$165	$150

Last Mfr.'s Sug. Retail was $500.

AE400 — offset double cutaway alder body, black pickguard, bolt-on maple neck, 22 fret maple fingerboard with black dot inlay, double locking vibrato, 3 per side tuners, chrome hardware, 1 single coil/1 triple Alvarez pickups, volume/tone control, 5 position switch. Available in Black finish. Mfd. 1994 only.

			$400	$360	$300	$240	$215	$195	$180

Last Mfr.'s Sug. Retail was $600.

Also available with black hardware, single coil/humbucker Dan Armstrong pickups (AE500).

Trevor Rabin Signature Series

This series was designed in conjunction with Trevor Rabin.

AER100 — offset double cutaway alder body, arched maple top, maple neck, 24 fret ebony fingerboard with slanted abalone inlay, double locking Kahler vibrato, 6 on one side tuners, black hardware, 2 humbucker Alnico pickups, volume/2 tone controls, 3 position switch. Available in Black and White finishes. Disc. 1995.

			$605	$555	$465	$370	$335	$305	$280

Last Mfr.'s Sug. Retail was $925.

In 1993, Black finish was discontinued.

Grading	100%	98% MINT	95% EXC+	90% EXC	80% VG+	70% VG	60% G

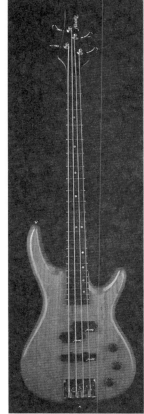

Alvarez Bass
courtesy Dana Sutcliffe

AER200 — similar to AER100, except has fixed bridge, gold hardware and 1 tone control. Available in White finish. Disc. 1993.

	$840	$780	$650	$520	$470	$430	$390

Last Mfr.'s Sug. Retail was $1,300.

AER300 — similar to AER100, except has bolt-on maple neck, rosewood fingerboard with pearl dot inlay, standard vibrato, chrome hardware, 2 single coil/1 humbucker pickups and 5 position switch. Available in Red finish. Disc. 1993.

	$650	$580	$500	$400	$360	$330	$300

Last Mfr.'s Sug. Retail was $1,000.

Villain Series

AEV410 — offset double cutaway alder body, bolt-on maple neck, 22 fret rosewood fingerboard with pearl dot inlay, double locking Kahler vibrato, 6 on one side tuners, chrome hardware, 2 single coil/1 humbucker Dan Armstrong pickups, volume/tone controls, 5 position switch. Available in Black, Red and White finishes. Disc. 1993.

	$425	$380	$325	$260	$235	$215	$195

Last Mfr.'s Sug. Retail was $650.

AEV425 — similar to AEV410, except has Modulus Graphite neck/fingerboard and black hardware. Available in Dark Grey Metallic and Red Pearl finishes. Disc. 1993.

	$520	$460	$380	$320	$290	$265	$240

Last Mfr.'s Sug. Retail was $800.

AEV520 — similar to AEV410, except has maple body, black hardware and humbucker/single coil/humbucker Dan Armstrong pickups. Available in Cherry Sunburst finish. Disc. 1993.

	$600	$510	$420	$330	$300	$275	$235

Last Mfr.'s Sug. Retail was $900.

ELECTRIC BASS

Dana Signature Series

This series was designed by Dana Sutcliffe.

The Alvarez Dana Off Set Bass design was nominated for the 1992 "Most Innovative Bass of the Year" award during its first year of production.

AE700 — offset double cutaway asymmetrical alder body, bolt-on maple neck, 24 fret rosewood fingerboard with pearl block inlay, fixed bridge, 4 on one side tuners, black hardware, P-style/J-style pickups, volume/2 tone controls, 3 position switch. Available in Black and Dark Blue Metallic finishes. Disc. 1993.

	$450	$410	$330	$260	$240	$210	$180

Last Mfr.'s Sug. Retail was $700.

Pantera Series

AEBP1 — offset double cutaway alder body, bolt-on maple neck, 24 fret ebony fingerboard with abalone slant inlay, fixed bridge, 2 on one side tuners, gold hardware, 2 bass pickups, volume/2 tone controls, 3 position switch. Available in Black and White finishes. Disc. 1995.

	$490	$440	$375	$300	$270	$245	$225

Last Mfr.'s Sug. Retail was $750.

In 1993, Black finish was discontinued.

AEBP2 — similar to AEBP1, except has rosewood fingerboard with pearl dot inlay and chrome hardware. Available in Black finish. Disc. 1993.

	$590	$510	$450	$360	$325	$300	$275

Last Mfr.'s Sug. Retail was $900.

Villain Series

AE800 — offset double cutaway alder body, bolt-on maple neck, 24 fret rosewood fingerboard with pearl dot inlay, fixed bridge, 2 per side tuners, black hardware, P-style/J-style EMG pickups, 2 volume/1 tone controls. Available in Black, Red Pearl, Transparent Black and Transparent Red finishes. Disc. 1995.

	$425	$380	$320	$240	$215	$195	$180

Last Mfr.'s Sug. Retail was $685.

AE800CS — similar to AE800, except has maple body. Disc. 1993.

	$525	$450	$375	$300	$270	$245	$225

Last Mfr.'s Sug. Retail was $750.

AE800WA — similar to AE800, except has Natural finish. Mfd. 1994 only.

	$475	$415	$360	$290	$260	$240	$220

Last Mfr.'s Sug. Retail was $725.

AE900 — similar to AE800, except has 5 strings, 3/2 per side tuners. Disc. 1993.

	$455	$390	$325	$260	$235	$215	$195

Last Mfr.'s Sug. Retail was $650.

Grading	100%	98% MINT	95% EXC+	90% EXC	80% VG+	70% VG	60% G

AE7000 — offset double cutaway asymmetrical alder body, bolt-on maple neck, 24 fret rosewood fingerboard with pearl dot inlay, brass fixed bridge, 2 per side tuners, chrome hardware, J-style/P-style/J-style Dana pickups, volume/treble/mid/bass controls, 3 position switch. Available in Transparent Black and Transparent Red finishes. Mfd. 1994 only.

| | $525 | $450 | $375 | $300 | $270 | $245 | $225 |

Last Mfr.'s Sug. Retail was $750.

AE7050 — similar to AE7000, except has fretless ceramic fingerboard. Available in Transparent White finish. Mfd. 1994 only.

| | $540 | $460 | $385 | $310 | $280 | $255 | $230 |

Last Mfr.'s Sug. Retail was $775.

AEB200 — offset double cutaway alder body, bolt-on maple neck, 22 fret rosewood fingerboard with pearl dot inlay, fixed bridge, 2 per side tuners, chrome hardware, P-style/J-style pickups, 2 volume/1 tone controls. Available in Transparent Black and Transparent Red finishes. Mfd. 1994 to date.

| Mfr.'s Sug. Retail | $475 | $356 | $237 | $235 | $190 | $170 | $155 | $140 |

AEB250 — similar to AEB200, except has 5 strings, 3/2 per side tuners, active electronics. Available in Natural and Transparent Red finishes. New 1995.

| Mfr.'s Sug. Retail | $575 | $431 | $287 |

AEB260 — similar to AEB200, except has 6 strings, 3 per side tuners, active electronics. Available in Natural finish. New 1995.

| Mfr.'s Sug. Retail | $950 | $712 | $475 |

ALVAREZ YAIRI

Alvarez Yairi instruments are built in Japan. Distributed by St. Louis Music located in St. Louis, Missouri.

Alvarez Yairi acoustics were imported starting in 1966 exclusively by St. Louis Music. Alvarez Yairi instruments are now a division of Alvarez and St. Louis Music. These quality acoustic guitars are designed by both the respected luthier Yairi in Japan and St. Louis Music.

ACOUSTIC

All Alvarez Yairi acoustic steel string guitars have abalone or pearl peghead logo inlay.

All Alvarez Yairi models may be purchased with Alvarez Natural Response pickups.
Add $110 for installed pickup without volume/tone control.
Add $135 for installed pickup with volume/tone control.

AY20 SIGNATURE — concert style, solid cedar top, round soundhole, wood bound body, abalone rosette, walnut back/sides, mahogany neck, 14/20 fret rosewood fingerboard, 12th fret abalone diamond/slash inlay, rosewood bridge with black abalone dot pins, walnut peghead veneer with abalone logo inlay, 3 per side gold tuners. Available in Natural finish. Mfd. 1994 to date.

| Mfr.'s Sug. Retail | $1,250 | $1,000 | $750 | $625 | $500 | $450 | $415 | $375 |

DC1 VIRTUOSO — round shoulder dreadnought style, solid spruce top, round soundhole, tortoise pickguard, ivoroid bound body, herringbone purfling/rosette, rosewood back/sides, mahogany neck, 12/19 fret rosewood fingerboard with pearl cross/elispe inlay, ebony bridge with white pearl dot pins, ebony veneered peghead with pearl logo inlay, 6 per side chrome die cast tuners. Available in Natural finish. New 1995.

| Mfr.'s Sug. Retail | $1,600 | $1,200 | $800 |

GY2 VIRTUOSO DELUXE — single round cutaway jumbo style, solid spruce top, round soundhole, tortoise pickguard, ivoroid bound body, abalone purfling/rosette, lacewood back/sides, mahogany neck, 20 fret bound ebony fingerboard with pearl dot inlay, 12th fret pearl curlicue inlay, abalone bound ebony bridge, rosewood veneered peghead with pearl logo inlay, 3 per side gold die cast tuners. Available in Natural finish. New 1995.

| Mfr.'s Sug. Retail | $2,000 | $1,500 | $1,000 |

This instrument was co-designed with Jerry Garcia.

JY10 NASHVILLE JUMBO — jumbo style, solid spruce top, round soundhole, tortoise pickguard, ivoroid bound body, abalone purfling/rosette, maple back/sides, mahogany neck, 14/20 fret rosewood fingerboard with pearl dot inlay, 12th fret pearl curlicue inlay, ebony bridge with white black dot pins, ebony veneered bound peghead, 3 per side gold tuners. Available in Sunburst finish. Mfd. 1994 to date.

| Mfr.'s Sug. Retail | $1,400 | $1,120 | $840 | $700 | $560 | $505 | $460 | $420 |

YM1 YAIRI MASTER INSTRUMENT — dreadnought style, solid cedar top, multi bound top, abalone/mahogany rosette, mahogany back/sides/neck, 14/20 fret rosewood fingerboard, 12th fret abalone stripe/pearl cross inlay, rosewood bridge with black pearl dot pins, ebony veneered peghead with pearl logo inlay, 3 per side gold die cast tuners. Available in Natural finish. New 1995.

| Mfr.'s Sug. Retail | $1,500 | $1,125 | $750 |

Classic Series

All classical guitars have rosewood veneer on their pegheads.

Grading	100%	98% MINT	95% EXC+	90% EXC	80% VG+	70% VG	60% G

CY116 — classical style, solid cedar top, round soundhole, 3 stripe bound body, wooden inlay rosette, mahogany back/sides/neck, 12/19 fret ebony fingerboard, ebony bridge, 3 per side gold tuners with pearloid buttons. Available in Natural finish. Mfd. 1991 to date.

Mfr.'s Sug. Retail	$1,075	$806	$537	$475	$370	$305	$280	$255

In 1994, burled mahogany back/sides replaced original items.

CY118 — similar to CY116, except has jacaranda back/sides.

Mfr.'s Sug. Retail	$1,175	$881	$587	$510	$400	$325	$300	$275

CY127CE — similar to CY116, except has thin line body style, venetian cutaway, rosewood back/sides, Alvarez Natural Response pickup system and volume/tone control.

Mfr.'s Sug. Retail	$1,375	$1,031	$687	$530	$420	$355	$325	$295

CY140 — classical style, cedar top, round soundhole, wooden inlay bound body and rosette, jacaranda back/sides, mahogany neck, 12/19 fret ebony fingerboard, rosewood bridge, 3 per side gold tuners with pearl buttons. Available in Natural finish. Mfd. 1991 to date.

Mfr.'s Sug. Retail	$1,400	$1,050	$700	$645	$510	$430	$395	$360

Dreadnought Series

DY38 WOODRIDGE — dreadnought style, solid spruce top, round soundhole, 3 stripe bound body, 5 stripe rosette, black pickguard, mahogany back/sides/neck, 14/20 fret rosewood fingerboard with pearl dot inlay, 12th fret has pearl snowflake inlay, rosewood bridge with black white dot pins, 3 per side chrome tuners. Available in Natural finish. Mfd. 1991 to date.

Mfr.'s Sug. Retail	$875	$656	$437	$390	$280	$250	$230	$210

DY45 WOODRIDGE VINTAGE — dreadnought style, solid spruce top, round soundhole, 3 stripe bound body, 5 stripe rosette, black pickguard, mahogany back/sides/neck, 14/20 fret rosewood fingerboard with pearl dot inlay, 12th fret has pearl snowflake inlay at 12th fret, ebony bridge with black white dot pins, 3 per side chrome tuners. Available in Dark Satin Antique finish. Mfd. 1991 to date.

Mfr.'s Sug. Retail	$875	$656	$437	$390	$280	$250	$230	$210

In 1995, maple back/sides replace original item.

DY45AV — similar to DY45, except has piezo bridge pickup, 3 band EQ. Mfd. 1994 only.

	$750	$645	$535	$430	$390	$355	$325

Last Mfr.'s Sug. Retail was $1,075.

DY50N — dreadnought style, cedar top, round soundhole, 3 stripe bound body, abalone rosette, tortoise pickguard, jacaranda back/sides, mahogany neck, 14/20 fret bound rosewood fingerboard with abalone diamond inlay, rosewood bridge with white pearl dot pins, rosewood veneer on bound peghead, 3 per side gold tuners. Available in Natural finish. Mfd. 1991 to 1995.

	$840	$690	$560	$400	$360	$330	$300

Last Mfr.'s Sug. Retail was $1,275.

DY50NEQ — similar to DY50N, except has piezo bridge pickup, 3 band EQ. Mfd. 1994 only.

	$1,100	$945	$785	$630	$565	$515	$470

Last Mfr.'s Sug. Retail was $1,575.

DY52 CANYON CREEK — dreadnought style, solid spruce top, round soundhole, 3 stripe bound body, abalone rosette, tortoise pickguard, rosewood back/sides, mahogany neck, 14/20 fret rosewood fingerboard with pearl dot inlay, 12th fret has pearl snowflake inlay, rosewood patented Direct Coupled bridge with black pearl dot pins, rosewood veneer on peghead, 3 per side chrome tuners. Available in Natural finish. Mfd. 1991 to date.

Mfr.'s Sug. Retail	$975	$731	$487	$440	$320	$290	$265	$240

In 1994, coral rosewood back/sides replaced original item.

DY53N — jumbo style, spruce top, round soundhole, 5 stripe bound body and rosette, tortoise pickguard, rosewood back/sides, mahogany neck, 14/20 fret bound rosewood fingerboard with pearl block inlay, rosewood bridge with white pearl dot pins, rosewood veneer on bound peghead, 3 per side chrome tuners. Available in Natural finish. Mfd. 1991 to 1995.

	$730	$605	$490	$360	$325	$300	$275

Last Mfr.'s Sug. Retail was $1,100.

In 1994, coral rosewood back/sides replaced original item.

DY70 GRAPHITE MAPLE — dreadnought style, solid spruce top, round soundhole, 5 stripe bound body/rosette, flamed maple back/sides, mahogany neck, 14/20 fret rosewood fingerboard with pearl dot inlay, 12th fret pearl curlicue inlay, graphite bridge with black abalone dot pins, graphite peghead veneer with pearl logo inlay, 3 per side chrome tuners. Available in Natural finish. Mfd. 1994 to date.

Mfr.'s Sug. Retail	$975	$731	$487	$485	$390	$355	$325	$295

DY71 GRAPHITE KOA — similar to DY70, except has tortoise pickguard, koa back/sides.

Mfr.'s Sug. Retail	$1,000	$800	$600	$500	$400	$360	$330	$300

Grading	100%	98% MINT	95% EXC+	90% EXC	80% VG+	70% VG	60% G

DY74 WELLINGTON — dreadnought style, solid spruce top, round soundhole, 5 stripe bound body and rosette, tortoise pickguard, rosewood back/sides, mahogany neck, 14/20 fret rosewood fingerboard with varying pearl inlay, rosewood bridge with white pearl dot pins, rosewood veneer on peghead, 3 per side chrome tuners. Available in Natural finish. Mfd. 1991 to date.

Mfr.'s Sug. Retail	$1,100	$825	$550	$490	$360	$325	$300	$275

Add $100 for single round cutaway (DY74C).

DY74C — similar to DY74, except has single round cutaway.

Mfr.'s Sug. Retail	$1,300	$975	$650

DY74CEQ1 — similar to DY74, except has single round cutaway, piezo bridge pickups, 3 band EQ. New 1995.

Mfr.'s Sug. Retail	$1,500	$1,125	$750

DY75 — dreadnought style, spruce top, round soundhole, wooden inlay bound body/rosette, tortoise pickguard, rosewood back/sides, mahogany neck, 14/20 fret rosewood fingerboard with pearl dot inlay, rosewood Direct Coupled bridge, rosewood veneer on bound peghead, 3 per side chrome tuners. Available in Natural finish. Mfd. 1991 to 1995.

		$860	$715	$580	$420	$380	$345	$315

Last Mfr.'s Sug. Retail was $1,300.

DY77N — dreadnought style, solid spruce top, round soundhole, herringbone bound body/rosette, tortoise pickguard, rosewood back/sides, mahogany neck, 14/20 fret ebony fingerboard with abalone diamond inlay, rosewood Direct Coupled bridge, rosewood veneer on bound peghead, 3 per side chrome tuners. Available in Natural finish. Mfd. 1991 to 1995.

		$800	$665	$545	$400	$360	$330	$300

Last Mfr.'s Sug. Retail was $1,200.

DY77NEQ — similar to DY77, except has piezo bridge pickup, 3 band EQ. Mfd. 1994 only.

		$1,050	$900	$750	$600	$540	$495	$450

Last Mfr.'s Sug. Retail was $1,500.

DY80 CANYON CREEK 12 — dreadnought style, spruce top, round soundhole, 3 stripe bound body, abalone rosette, tortoise pickguard, rosewood back/sides, mahogany neck, 14/20 fret rosewood fingerboard with pearl dot inlay, 12th fret has pearl snowflake inlay, rosewood patented Direct Coupled bridge with black pearl dot pins, rosewood veneer on peghead, 6 per side chrome tuners. Available in Natural finish. Mfd. 1991 to date.

Mfr.'s Sug. Retail	$1,150	$862	$575	$515	$370	$335	$305	$280

DY90 — dreadnought style, solid spruce top, round soundhole, abalone bound body and rosette, black pickguard with Alvarez Yairi logo, rosewood back/sides, mahogany neck, 14/20 fret bound ebony fingerboard with abalone diamond inlay, abalone bound ebony bridge with black pearl dot pins, rosewood peghead veneer with abalone logo inlay, 3 per side gold tuners. Available in Natural finish. Mfd. 1991 to 1995.

		$980	$810	$660	$480	$430	$395	$360

Last Mfr.'s Sug. Retail was $1,475.

DY91 DELUXE KOA — similar to DY90, except has koa back/sides, koa peghead veneer. Mfd. 1994 to date.

Mfr.'s Sug. Retail	$1,500	$1,200	$900	$750	$600	$540	$495	$450

DY92 — dreadnought style, spruce top, round soundhole, herringbone bound body and rosette, mahogany/rosewood/maple lute style back, 14/20 fret bound ebony fingerboard with pearl dot inlay, ebony bridge with black pearl dot pins, 3 per side gold tuners. Available in Natural finish. Disc. 1993.

		$1,945	$1,665	$1,390	$1,110	$1,000	$915	$830

Last Mfr.'s Sug. Retail was $2,775.

Signature Series

All Signature models have Kazuo Yairi's signature on them.

DY61 — dreadnought style, solid cedar top, round soundhole, 5 stripe wooden bound body, abalone rosette, mahogany back/sides/neck, 14/20 fret rosewood fingerboard, 12th fret has pearl diamond/abalone slash inlay, rosewood bridge with black abalone dot pins, burl mahogany veneer on peghead with abalone/wooden strip inlays, abalone logo peghead inlay, 3 per side gold tuners with amber buttons. Available in Natural finish. Mfd. 1991 to date.

Mfr.'s Sug. Retail	$1,175	$881	$587	$525	$380	$345	$315	$285

In 1994, burled mahogany back/sides replaced original item.

DY62 — similar to DY61, except has round cutaway, Alvarez Bi-phonic system, 2 volume/tone controls and selector switch.

Mfr.'s Sug. Retail	$1,600	$1,200	$800	$700	$490	$440	$405	$370

DY69 — similar to DY61, except has spruce top, tortoise pickguard, wooden inlay rosette, burled mahogany back/sides, upper belly bridge with white abalone dot pins. Mfd. 1994 only.

		$1,080	$810	$675	$540	$485	$445	$405

Last Mfr.'s Sug. Retail was $1,350.

Grading	100%	98% MINT	95% EXC+	90% EXC	80% VG+	70% VG	60% G

DY72 — similar to DY61, except has 12 strings and rosewood veneer on peghead.

Mfr.'s Sug. Retail	$1,275	$956	$637	$565	$400	$360	$330	$300

Virtuoso Series

GY 1 — round cutaway dreadnought style, solid spruce top, round soundhole, 5 stripe bound body and rosette, tortoise pickguard, rosewood back/sides, mahogany neck, 20 fret bound ebony fingerboard with varied abalone inlay, rosewood bridge with white abalone dot pins, rosewood veneer on bound peghead with pearl tulip inlay, 3 per side gold tuners, bridge pickup, 3 band EQ. Available in Natural finish. Mfd. 1991 to date.

Mfr.'s Sug. Retail	$1,700	$1,275	$850	$725	$565	$450	$415	$375

This model was designed for Jerry Garcia.

WY 1 VIRTUOSO — round cutaway jumbo style, solid cedar top, round soundhole, herringbone bound body, abalone rosette, rosewood back/sides, mahogany neck, 20 fret rosewood fingerboard, 12th fret has pearl diamond/abalone slash inlay, rosewood Direct Coupled bridge with black abalone dot pins, rosewood veneer on peghead with abalone and wooden strip inlays, 3 per side gold tuners, bridge pickups, 3 band EQ. Available in Natural finish. Mfd. 1991 to date.

Mfr.'s Sug. Retail	$1,700	$1,275	$850	$725	$565	$450	$415	$375

This model was designed for Bob Weir.

In 1994, folk style body replaced original item.

WY 1BK Virtuoso — similar to WY1 Virtuoso, except has folk style body, laminated cedar top, mahogany back/sides. Available in Black finish. New 1995.

Mfr.'s Sug. Retail	$1,650	$1,237	$825

ACOUSTIC ELECTRIC

Express Series

DY87 — round cutaway dreadnought style, curly maple top, round soundhole, 5 stripe bound body and rosette, maple back/sides, mahogany neck, 21 fret ebony fingerboard with pearl dot inlay, 12th fret has pearl snowflake inlay, ebony bridge with white abalone dot pins, 3 per side chrome tuners, bridge pickup, 3 band EQ. Available in Transparent Black finish. Mfd. 1991 to 1995.

			$945	$775	$630	$490	$395	$365	$330

Last Mfr.'s Sug. Retail was $1,450.

DY87/12 — similar to DY87, except has 12 strings, 6 per side tuners. Available in Violin Sunburst finish. Mfd. 1991 to 1995.

			$1,030	$840	$680	$530	$430	$395	$360

Last Mfr.'s Sug. Retail was $1,575.

DY88 EXPRESS PRO — similar to DY87, except has no soundhole, abalone bound body, 23 fret fingerboard with pearl dot pyramid inlay, gold hardware. Available in Black finish. Mfd. 1991 to date.

Mfr.'s Sug. Retail	$1,575	$1,181	$787	$680	$530	$430	$395	$360

DY88/12 Express Pro — similar to DY87, except has 12 strings, no soundhole, abalone purfling, 23 fret fingerboard with pearl dot pyramid inlay, 6 per side gold tuners. Available in Black finish. Mfd. 1991 to date.

Mfr.'s Sug. Retail	$1,700	$1,360	$1,020	$850	$680	$610	$560	$510

AMADA

Instruments produced in the Czech Republic. Distributed by Geneva International Corporation of Wheeling, Illinois.

These handcrafted guitars are available in numerous sizes for the younger entry level student. Billed as "extremely affordable", the Amada guitars are available from a 17" scale up to a 25.5" scale. Models start with the 1/4 size, 1/2 size, 3/4 size, 7/8 size up to full size in classical stylings, and have a rosewood fingerboard. For further information, contact the Geneva International Corporation through the Index of Current Manufacturers located in the back of this book.

AMERICAN SHOWSTER

Instruments built in Bayville, New Jersey since 1995.

The American Showster company first debuted the tailfin-bodied AS-57 solid body guitar at the NAMM show in the late 1980s, but production problems slowed down actual delivery of individual guitars. American Showster re-debuted in 1995, and both Jack Dombrowski and David S. Litarowich have added two new models in addition to the original model.

While prices have not yet been finalized, two prototypes were built and displayed at the 1996 Summer NAMM show in Nashville, Tennessee. The **Biker** model features a body design reminiscent of a motorcycle gas tank. Echoing a more classic design, the **Seal** is an offset double cutaway solid body, and the stop tailpiece features the same chevron-styled "v" as their logo. Both models have bolt-on necks, six on a side Schaller tuners, three Floyd Rose "ER" single coil pickups, chrome hardware, and either a fixed Schaller bridge or an original Floyd Rose tremolo.

American Showster AS-57
courtesy American Showster

Ampeg Banner
courtesy Ryland Fitchett

ELECTRIC

The tailfin brakelight on the AS-57 model is fully functional. The brakelight is activated by either the push-pull tone pot on the fixed-bridge model or by depressing the vibrola on the Floyd Rose-equipped model.

AS-57 — Alder body shaped like the tailfin of a '57 Chevy, operational chromed tailfin brake-light assembly, six bolt maple neck, 22 fret rosewood or maple fingerboard with dot inlay, six on a side Schaller tuners, Schaller Tune-a-matic bridge and custom through body bolt chevron stop tailpiece, chrome hardware, 25 1/2" scale, three Floyd Rose "ER" single coil pickups, master volume knob, master treble-cut tone control, five way pickup selector switch. Available in original '57 colors: Tropical Turquoise, Matador Red, and Black Onyx. Current production.

Mfr.'s Sug. Retail $2,399 $1,799 $1,199
    Add $199.99 for Floyd Rose Original tremolo.

AMIGO

Instruments manufactured in Asia. Distributed by Midco International of Effingham, Illinois.

Amigo acoustic guitars are designed and priced with students and entry level players in mind. The Amigo line features three 1/2 scale guitars (AM 11, AM15, and AM16), three 3/4 scale guitars (AM21, AM30, and AM31) and two full scale guitars (AM40, AM41). New retail prices range from $79.95 for the AM15 up to $165 for the AM41. For further information, consult the Index of Current Manufacturers located in the back of this book.

AMKA

Instruments built in Holland.

Amka instrument were produced by the Veneman family. Later, Kope Veneman moved to the U.S. and opened a music store in Maryland. In the 1960s, Kope Veneman introduced the Kapa instrument line, and his crown shield logo was similar to his father's Amka logo. The **Blue Book of Guitars** will continue updating further information on Amka guitars, and Dutch readers/players are invited to write with any relevant information for future editions.

(Source: Michael Wright, Guitar Stories Volume One, pg. 25)

AMPEG

DAN ARMSTRONG AMPEG

See also ARMSTRONG, DAN.

Instruments built in the U.S. from the early 1960s through the early 1970s. Some Ampeg models were also built in Japan, and distributed in part by Selmer.

The Ampeg company was founded in late 1940s by Everett Hull and Jess Oliver. While this company is perhaps better known for its B-15 "flip top" Portaflex or SVT bass amplifiers, the company did build various guitar and bass designs during the 1960s. As both Hull and Oliver came from jazz music traditions (and were musicians), the first Ampeg bass offered was an electric upright-styled "Baby Bass". Constructed of fiberglass bodies and wood necks, the Baby Bass was produced first by the Dopyera Brothers (See DOBRO and VALCO) as an electric pickup-equipped upright "mini-bass" under the **Zorko** trademark. In 1962, Everett Hull from Ampeg acquired the rights to the design. Hull and company improved the design, and Jess Oliver devised a new 'diaphragm-style' pickup.

With the relative success of the Ampeg electric upright and their tube bass amps among jazz and studio musicians, Ampeg launched the first production fretless solid body electric in 1966. Named the AUB-1 (Ampeg Unfretted Bass), this fretless was designed by Dennis Kager. The Fender Instrument company did not release a fretless model until 1970, and even then the first model was a fretless "Precision" (ironic considering the name, and Leo Fender's design intention back in 1951). Ampeg also offered the AEB-1 (Ampeg Electric Bass) in late 1966. Both instruments featured the Ampeg "scroll" headstock, and a pair of f-holes that were designed through the body. A third model, designed by Mike Roman, features exaggerated horns (nicknamed "devil horns" by collectors).

In 1969, luthier/designer Dan Armstrong proposed a guitar that had a wood neck and a plastic body. The use of the plastic was to increase sustain, and was not intended as a gimmick. Neverless, the guitars and basses gained the nickname "see-through", and were produced from 1969 to 1971. The instruments featured formica pickguards that read "Dan Armstrong Ampeg" and clear acrylic bodies (although a small number were cast in black as well).

In the late 1970s, Ampeg teamed up with the Swedish Hagstrom company to design an early guitar synthesizer. Dubbed the "Patch 2000", the system consisted of a guitar and a footpedal-controlled box which generated the synthesizer sounds. While advertising included both guitar and bass models, it is unlikely that any of the bass systems ever got beyond the prototype stage.

(Source: Tony Bacon and Barry Moorhouse, The Bass Book)

ANDERBILT

Instruments (possibly) built in Corpus Christi or Brownsville, Texas during the mid to late 1960s.

Ampeg AEB-1
courtesy Chris Smart

With the help of repairman Gene Warner of Meteor Music (San Antonio), Teisco Del Rey attempted to track down the origins of the Anderbilt (also possibly ANDERTONE) guitars. The builder was rumored to be a Baptist minster, and the guess made that his last name was Anderson.

The most striking feature of Anderbilt guitars is the vibrato: rather than located on the bridge or tailpiece, the **neck** is the mechanism! Built in the style of a pump shotgun, the entire neck has to be pushed in toward the body and pulled away to raise or lower the pitch. Features on the guitar include a six on a side headstock, 2 pickups, a "coat-of-arms" body design, and separate volume and tone knobs for each pickup. Anyone with further information to share on the Anderbilt guitars is invited to write to the **Blue Book of Guitars**.

(Source: Teisco Del Rey, Guitar Player magazine, October 1988)

ANDERSEN STRINGED INSTRUMENTS

Instruments built in Seattle, Washington since 1978. In addition to the luthier, instruments are also available through Pioneer Music in Portland, Oregon; and Elderly Instruments located in Lansing, Michigan.

Luthier Steven Andersen built his first guitar in 1973, and has earned his living solely as a guitar maker since 1978. Andersen specializes in custom building to meet the player's needs. Working alone, Andersen builds two or three instruments at a time, generally completing sixteen to eighteen a year. Andersen guitars have been sold across the U.S., as well as in a dozen countries around the world.

Andersen currently features six different archtop guitar models, and one flattop acoustic model. In addition, he also builds mandolins, mandolas, and mandocellos. Although Steven Andersen doesn't actively pursue the endorsements of famous musicians, he has been fortunate in having a number of well known players purchase his instruments (Steve Miller, Bill Frisell, and mandolinist Sam Bush). While work backlog is around twenty months, a delivery date will be confirmed when an order is placed. For those who prefer to purchase a guitar without the wait, Andersen occasionally has completed guitars available for sale.

ACOUSTIC

Andersen archtop guitars all share certain specifications. The body depth is three inches, and the scale lengths available are either 24.9" or 25.4". The soundboard is either Engelman or Sitka spruce, although Adirondack spruce is available as an option (add $500). The back, sides and neck are highly figured maple; and the pickguard, bridge, fretboard and peghead face are ebony. The instrument's tailpiece is a graphite composite with an ebony face, and the base price also includes a standard hardshell case. The archtops are finished in Amber blonde or clear blonde (sunburst finish is $300 extra). Steven Andersen does offer several options on various models, as well as suggestions for floating pickups.

The **Emerald City** ($7,500) and **Metropolitan** ($7,500) are the most ornate members of the Andersen family of archtop guitars. The designs are reminiscent of the Art Deco style popular in the 1930s and 1940s. Construction details include hand engraved mother-of-pearl inlays, ivoroid binding around the body, f-holes, neck and and peghead; and the most highly figured maple for the back, sides, and neck. The Emerald City is available in either a 17" or 18" body width, and the Metropolitan is only available in a 17" body width. The Metropolitan was designed in collaboration with vintage guitar enthusiasts John G. Stewart and K. C. Wait.

The **Emerald City Reserve** ($10,000) is a limited edition model built with rare woods reserved especially for this model. Wood combinations include a European spruce top and European maple back, or an Adirondack spruce top with a 90-year-old one piece American maple back. Further information will be supplied by the luthier.

The **Model 17** ($5,500) and the **Model 18** ($5,800) are elegant in their simplicity. By using a minimal amount of inlay and decoration, Andersen is able to build a guitar whose design and materials are first class, yet at a price somewhat less than more ornate instruments. Body, f-holes, neck and peghead are bound in ivoroid.

The **Oval Hole Archtop** model ($5,000) is Andersen's newest model. Designed as an archtop with a warmer sound than a traditional, the oval soundhole allows the guitar to sustain more than an f-hole top. The overall design of this model is intended to make the guitar as lightweight and resonant as possible.

Andersen also produces a **Concert** model flattop guitar ($3,200) with numerous top, sides, and back tone wood options. Contact luthier Andersen for further information through the Index of Current Manufacturers located in the back of this book.

TOM ANDERSON GUITARWORKS

Instruments produced in Newbury Park, California since 1984.

Luthier/designer Tom Anderson founded Tom Anderson Guitarworks in 1984, following a stint at Schecter as vice president from 1977 to 1984. Anderson's interest and exploration of tonewoods and the overall interaction of the guitar's parts have led to a refined and defined tone in his instruments.

All specs and orders are maintained on the company database. For anyone interested in recreating his or her favorite Anderson instrument, each guitar has a file in the database. Furthermore, there's a good chance the original builder is still on staff - and that someone will probably remember the first instrument! According to Roy Fought, less than 6,000 instruments have been produced in the company's seven year history. Fought stresses that the company is structured towards building guitars that are built towards the individual player's style, and that the tonewood and pickup combinations are combined to enhance what the player wants to get out of his instrument.

ELECTRIC

All models in this series are available in these finishes: 6120 Orange, Baby Blue, Black, Blonde, Bora Bora Blue, Candy Apple Red, Cherry Burst, Electric Blue, Honey Burst, Metallic Purple, Natural, Seafoam Green, Three-Color Burst, Tobacco Burst, Transparent Amber/Blonde/Blue/Green/Magenta/ Purple/Red/White/Yellow, White and White Pearl.

Grading	100%	98% MINT	95% EXC+	90% EXC	80% VG+	70% VG	60% G

Drop Top T model courtesy Tom Anderson Guitarworks

COBRA — single cutaway basswood or mahogany body, bound figured maple top, bolt-on mahogany or maple neck, 22 fret rosewood fingerboard with pearl dot inlay, fixed bridge, 6 on one side locking tuners, gold hardware, 2 humbucker pickups, volume/tone control, 5 position switch. Current production.

Mfr.'s Sug. Retail $2,400 $1,800 $1,200 $1,150 $920

Hollow Cobra — similar to Cobra, except has two hollow sound chambers. Mfd. 1994 to date.

Mfr.'s Sug. Retail $2,460 $1,845 $1,230 $1,200 $960

DROP TOP — offset double cutaway basswood body, bound figured maple top, bolt-on maple neck, 22 fret maple fingerboard with black dot inlay, standard vibrato, 6 on one side locking tuners, gold hardware, 2 single coil/1 humbucker pickups, volume/tone control, 4 mini switches. Current production.

Mfr.'s Sug. Retail $2,400 $1,800 $1,200 $1,150 $920

This model is also available with the following options: alder body, figured koa top, pau ferro, palisander or rosewood fingerboard, fixed bridge, double locking vibrato, chrome hardware, various pickup configurations and left handed. This model is also offered with hollowed internal tone chambers as the **Hollow Drop Top** ($2,460).

Drop Top Classic — similar to Drop Top, except has pearloid or black satin pickguard.

Mfr.'s Sug. Retail $2,400 $1,800 $1,200 $1,150 $920

This model is also offered with hollowed internal tone chambers as the **Hollow Drop Top Classic** ($2,460).

Drop Top T — similar to Drop Top, except has single cutaway body. Current production.

Mfr.'s Sug. Retail $2,400 $1,800 $1,200 $1,150 $920

GRAND AM — offset double cutaway lacewood body, bolt-on maple neck, 22 fret maple fingerboard with black dot inlay, double locking vibrato, 6 on one side tuners, gold hardware, 2 single coil/1 humbucker pickups, volume/tone control, 4 mini switches. Disc. 1994.

                $1,660 $1,410 $1,150 $920 $N/A $N/A $N/A

Last Mfr.'s Sug. Retail was $2,400.

This model is also available with the following options: alder body, figured koa top, palisander, pau ferro or rosewood fingerboard with pearl dot inlay, fixed bridge, double locking vibrato, chrome hardware, various pickup configurations and left handed.

HOLLOW T — single cutaway swamp ash body with two hollow sound chambers, bolt-on maple neck, 22 fret maple fingerboard with black dot inlay, fixed bridge, 6 on one side locking tuners, chrome hardware, humbucker/single coil/humbucker pickups, volume/tone control, 4 mini switches. Curr. mfr.

Mfr.'s Sug. Retail $2,210 $1,657 $1,105 $1,090 $870

This model is available with these options: pau ferro, palisander or rosewood fingerboard with pearl dot inlay, standard or double locking vibrato, gold hardware, various pickup and electronic configurations and left handed.

Hollow T Classic — similar to Hollow T, except has pearloid pickguard, 2 single coil pickups, 5 position switch.

Mfr.'s Sug. Retail $2,210 $1,657 $1,105 $1,090 $870

No options are available on this model.

Hollow T Classic Contoured — similar to Hollow T, except has contoured top/back, redesigned sound chambers, pearloid pickguard, 2 single coil pickups, 5 position switch. New 1995.

Mfr.'s Sug. Retail $2,270 $1,816 $1,362 $1,170 $935

Hollow T Contoured — similar to Hollow T, except has contoured top/back, redesigned sound chambers. New 1995.

Mfr.'s Sug. Retail $2,270 $1,816 $1,362 $1,170 $935

PRO AM — offset double cutaway swamp ash body, bolt-on maple neck, 22 fret pau ferro fingerboard with pearl dot inlay, double locking vibrato, 6 on one side tuners, chrome hardware, volume/tone control, 4 mini switches. Curr. mfr.

Mfr.'s Sug. Retail $2,000 $1,500 $1,000 $950 $760

This model is also available with the following options: alder or basswood body, maple, palisander or rosewood fingerboard, fixed bridge, standard vibrato, locking tuners, gold hardware, various pickup and electronic configurations and left handed.

THE CLASSIC — offset double cutaway swamp ash body, pearloid pickguard, bolt-on maple neck, 22 fret maple fingerboard with black dot inlay, standard vibrato, 6 on one side locking tuners, chrome hardware, 3 single coil pickups, volume/tone control, 4 mini switches. Curr. mfr.

Mfr.'s Sug. Retail $2,000 $1,500 $1,000 $950 $760

This model is also available with the following options: alder or basswood body, black satin pickguard, palisander, pau ferro or rosewood fingerboard with pearl dot inlay, fixed bridge, double locking vibrato, gold hardware, various pickup and electronic configurations and left handed. This model is also offered with hollowed internal tone chambers as the **Hollow Classic** ($2,270).

ANGELICA

Instruments were built in Japan from 1967 to 1975.

The Angelica trademark is a brandname used by UK importers Boosey & Hawkes on these entry level guitars based on classic American designs. Some of the original designs produced are actually better in quality.

(Source: Tony Bacon and Paul Day, The Guru's Guitar Guide)

ANGUS

Instruments built in Laguna Beach, California since the mid 1970s.

Luthier Mark Angus built his first guitar over two decades ago, and combines his many years as a player and craftsman to deliver an exceptionally versatile instrument. Angus currently works full time as head of the repair department at the Guitar Shoppe in Laguna Beach, California, and builds between six to eight guitars a year. The Guitar Shoppe, which is owned by Kirk Sand (see SAND GUITARS) and Jim Matthews, produces some of the finest custom instruments built today as well as being one of the premier repair facilities on the West Coast.

Angus guitars are handcrafted instruments consisting of Honduran mahogany necks, Engleman, Sitka or European spruce bodies, Indian Rosewood back and sides, and an ebony fretboard. These custom guitars come in many shapes and sizes, including one model with a seven piece back of maple and rosewood. Prices run between $2,000 and $3,000 per instrument on the average. For further information, contact luthier Angus via the Index of Current Manufacturers listed in the back of this book.

ANTARES

Instruments manufactured in Korea. Distributed in the U.S. market by Vega Musical Instruments (VMI) Industries of Brea, California.

Antares guitars are designed for entry level musicians and guitar students. Designs range from a six string classical model, to six string steel string models of various finishes and even a twelve string model. Advertised prices start at $100 and up. VMI also supplies student level 10 and 20 watt guitar amplifiers under the "Animal" trademark.

ANTONIO LORCA

Instruments currently built in Spain. Distributed in the U.S. market by David Perry Guitar Imports.

Antonio Lorca Guitars feature solid cedar tops on flamenco style acoustics. Student models begin at $369, recital models begin at $529, and concert level guitars begin at $599 (all prices 1996 retail).

ANTORIA

See GUYATONE.

Instruments originally built in Japan in the 1950s, later switching to Korean-built models.

The ANTORIA trademark was a brandname used by a UK importer for guitars produced by Guyatone. Guyatone began building guitars in 1933, and started producing solid body electrics in the late 1950s. While the original Antorias were cheap entry level models, the quality level rose when production switched to the same factory that was producing Ibanez guitars. Currently, the trademark has been applied to solid and semi-hollowbody guitars built in Korea.

(Source: Tony Bacon and Paul Day, The Guru's Guitar Guide)

APOLLO

Instruments produced in Japan during the 1960s.

Apollo instruments were generally entry to medium quality guitars that featured original designs which incorporated American ideas.

(Source: Rittor Music, 60s Bizarre Guitars)

APP

Instruments built in the early 1960s.

Guitar instructor/inventor O.W. Appleton was another forerunner to the electric solid body guitar concept. Rickenbacker in Los Angeles, California had marketed the solid body lap steel since the 1930s; Lloyd Loar's Vivi-Tone had attempted to market an electric Spanish guitar. In 1941, guitar marvel Les Paul had begun work on "The Log", a solid 4" x 4" neck-through design with pickups that he had attached body wings (built after hours at the original Epiphone facilities). Appleton initially built his solid body in the early 1940s but received no interest from the major manufacturers. Guitars bearing the **APP** trademark appeared in the early 1960s. One such model appeared in Teisco Del Rey's column in Guitar Player (June 1985), and featured an offset double cutaway body that was shaped like an inverted "V". Further research will appear in updated future editions of the **Blue Book of Guitars**.

(Source: Tom Wheeler, American Guitars)

APPLAUSE

Instruments are manufactured in Korea since 1980. Originally produced in New Hartford, Connecticut from 1975 to 1979. Distributed by the Kaman Music Corporation of Bloomfield, Connecticut.

The Applause instruments were originally designed to be the entry level version of the Ovation guitars. In 1975, the new line of guitars was first offered to Ovation dealers as the "Ovation Medallion". A year later, the Applause trademark was offered to Kaman distributors. The Medallion name ran into some trademark claim problems, and was changed to Matrix. Matrix "Applauses" carried a list price of $249. In 1983, The Ovation Celebrity (also Korean, with U.S. produced synthetic backs) was introduced, again serving as an entry point to Ovation guitars.

Applause instruments feature the same guitar design and synthetic "bowl back" that the American built Ovations possess. While engineered and manufactured with the same attention to quality, production of these models overseas is Kaman's key to offering good quality guitars for players on a budget.

Applause guitars are offered in acoustic and acoustic/electric models. The acoustic/electrics offer similar under-the-saddle piezoelectric systems with volume and tone controls as the Ovation guitars. Models encoded with an "AA" are Applause Acoustics, while an "AE" denotes an Applause Electric. The "AN" code indicates an Applause Nylon string model. All Applause instruments feature a solid Walnut bridge, Sitka spruce top (some models may be laminated tops), Ping tuning machines, a steel reinforced truss rod, and solid mahogany neck, mother-of-pearl inlay dots. All models are available in a Natural finish; some models may also be Black, White, Brownburst, "Barnboard" (enhanced grain), and Purpleburst.

ACOUSTIC

Grading	100%	98% MINT	95% EXC+	90% EXC	80% VG+	70% VG	60% G

AA 12 — 1/2 size single round cutaway, 3 stripe bound body/rosette, mini bowl, 20 fret bound fingerboard with pearl dot inlay, 3 per side tuners. Available in Natural finish. Current production.

Mfr.'s Sug. Retail	$260	$208	$156	$140	$115	$90	$80	$75

AA 13 — similar to AA 12, except has 3/4 size body.

Mfr.'s Sug. Retail	$280	$224	$168	$150	$125	$100	$90	$80

AA 31 — dreadnought style, black pickguard, 5 stripe bound body/rosette, deep bowl, 14/20 fret fingerboard with pearl dot inlay, body matching peghead, 3 per side tuners. Available in Barnboard, Brownburst and Natural finishes. Current production.

Mfr.'s Sug. Retail	$310	$248	$186	$175	$145	$115	$100	$90

AA 33 — classic style, bound body, decal rosette, deep bowl, 12/19 fret fingerboard, wraparound walnut bridge, 3 per side gold tuners. Available in Natural finish. Current production.

Mfr.'s Sug. Retail	$310	$248	$186	$175	$145	$115	$100	$90

AA 35 — dreadnought style, black pickguard, 5 stripe bound body/rosette, deep bowl, 14/20 fret fingerboard with pearl dot inlay, 6 per side tuners. Available in Black and Natural finishes. Current production.

Mfr.'s Sug. Retail	$390	$312	$234	$215	$175	$140	$125	$115

ACOUSTIC ELECTRIC

AE 32 — dreadnought style, black pickguard, 5 stripe bound body/rosette, deep bowl, 14/20 fret bound fingerboard with pearl diamond inlay, 3 per side tuners. Available in Natural finish. Current production.

Mfr.'s Sug. Retail	$390	$312	$234	$215	$175	$140	$125	$115

AE 34 — single round cutaway classic style, bound body, decal rosette, shallow bowl, 12/19 fret fingerboard, wraparound walnut bridge, 3 per side gold tuners. Available in Natural finish. Current production.

Mfr.'s Sug. Retail	$430	$344	$258	$245	$195	$155	$140	$130

AE 35 — dreadnought style, black pickguard, 5 stripe bound body/rosette, deep bowl, 14/20 fret fingerboard with pearl dot inlay, 6 per side tuners. Available in Black and Natural finishes. Current production.

Mfr.'s Sug. Retail	$470	$376	$282	$255	$190	$170	$155	$140

AE 36 — dreadnought style, black pickguard, 5 stripe bound body/rosette, deep bowl, 14/20 fret bound fingerboard with pearl diamond inlay, 3 per side tuners. Available in Barnboard, Brownburst, Natural and White finishes. Current production.

Mfr.'s Sug. Retail	$410	$328	$246	$205	$165	$145	$135	$125

AE 38 — dreadnought style, black pickguard, 5 stripe bound body/rosette, shallow bowl, 14/20 fret bound fingerboard with pearl diamond inlay, 3 per side tuners. Available in Barnboard, Black, Brownburst, Natural, Purpleburst and White finishes. Current production.

Mfr.'s Sug. Retail	$450	$360	$270	$245	$195	$165	$145	$130

ACOUSTIC ELECTRIC BASS

AE 40 — single round cutaway dreadnought style, Sitka spruce top, round soundhole, 5 stripe bound body/rosette, deep bowl, mahogany neck, 19 fret walnut fingerboard with pearl dot inlay, strings thru walnut bridge, logo decal on peghead, 2 per side chrome tuners. Available in Black and Natural finishes. Current production.

Mfr.'s Sug. Retail	$490	$392	$294	$275	$205	$175	$160	$150

AE 40F — similar to AE 40, except features a fretless neck.

Mfr.'s Sug. Retail	$515	$412	$309	$275	$205	$175	$160	$150

ARBITER

Instruments built in Japan during the mid 1960s to late 1970s.

The ARBITER trademark is the brand of a UK importer. Original models are of entry level quality, later models are good quality copy designs and some original designs.

(Source: Tony Bacon and Paul Day, The Guru's Guitar Guide)

ARBOR

Instruments manufactured in Asia. Distributed in the U.S. market by MIDCO International of Effingham, Illinois.

Arbor guitars are aimed at the entry level student to the intermediate player. The Midco International company has been importing and distributing both acoustic and solid body guitars to the U.S. market for a good number of years, and now offers a five-year warranty on their acoustic guitar line. Model coding carries an "A for acoustic, double digits (such as A30) for straight acoustic, and triple digits (A700) for acoustic/electric models.

> Acoustic models feature a dreadnought body size; mahogany neck, sides and back; rosewood fingerboard and bridge, and chromed tuning pegs.

> The A600 acoustic/electric features a separate volume and tone control, while the A700 and A800 models feature a volume slider and four band EQ. All acoustic/electric models also have a single rounded cutaway, chromed tuning machines, rosewood fingerboards and bridges (the A600 has hardwood fingerboard and bridge) and piezo pickups.

> Electric Arbor solid body guitars feature a range of designs based on classic American designs. Again, hardware and pickup options are geared towards the entry level and student players. Most models feature bolt-on neck designs, laminate bodies and solid finishes, and adjustable truss rods.

ARDSLEYS

Instruments built in Japan during the mid 1960s.

These entry level instruments can also be found with "Elite" or "Canora" on the headstock, depending on the U.S. importer. A fine example of a matching set can be found on the cover of The Shaggs "Philosophy of the World" LP (reissued by Rounder Records), which was spotlighted in Teisco Del Rey's record album column in the October 1984 issue of **Guitar Player** magazine.

ARIA

Company founded in Japan during the early 1960s. Current models now built in the U.S., Japan, Korea, China, Indonesia, and Spain.

ARIA is the trademark of the Arai Company of Japan, which began producing guitars in the early 1960s. Original designs gave way to a greater emphasis on copies of American designs in the late 1970s. Ironically, the recognition of well-produced replicas led to success in later original designs. The Aria trademark has always reflected high quality in production, and currently there has been more emphasis on original designs (especially in bass designs such as the AVB-SB).

ACOUSTIC

Grading	100%	98% MINT	95% EXC+	90% EXC	80% VG+	70% VG	60% G

AK-70 — classic style, mahogany top, round soundhole, bound body, wooden inlay rosette, mahogany back/sides/neck, 12/19 fret rosewood fingerboard/bridge, 3 per side nickel tuners. Available in Natural finish. Mfd. 1991 to 1993.

	100%	98%	95%	90%	80%	70%	60%
	$140	$120	$100	$80	$70	$65	$60

Last Mfr.'s Sug. Retail was $200.

AK-75 — classic style, spruce top, round soundhole, bound body, wooden inlay rosette, mahogany back/sides/neck, 12/19 fret rosewood fingerboard/bridge, 3 per side nickel tuners. Available in Natural finish. Mfd. 1991 to date.

	100%	98%	95%	90%	80%	70%	60%
Mfr.'s Sug. Retail	$319	$239	$159	$115	$90	$80	$70	$65

AK-100 — similar to AK-75, except has different rosette and rosewood veneer on peghead. Disc. 1993.

	100%	98%	95%	90%	80%	70%	60%
	$170	$145	$120	$95	$85	$80	$75

Last Mfr.'s Sug. Retail was $240.

AK-200 3/4 — similar to AK-75, except is three-quarter body size. Disc. 1993.

	100%	98%	95%	90%	80%	70%	60%
	$170	$145	$120	$95	$85	$80	$75

Last Mfr.'s Sug. Retail was $240.

AK-200 — similar to AK-75, except has different rosette and rosewood veneer on peghead. Disc. 1993.

	100%	98%	95%	90%	80%	70%	60%
	$170	$145	$120	$95	$85	$80	$75

Last Mfr.'s Sug. Retail was $240.

AK-210 — classic style, cedar top, round soundhole, bound body, wooden inlay rosette, mahogany back/sides/neck, 12/19 fret rosewood fingerboard/bridge, 3 per side chrome tuners. Available in Natural finish. Mfd. 1994 to date.

	100%	98%	95%	90%	80%	70%	60%
Mfr.'s Sug. Retail	$329	$246	$164	$135	$110	$100	$90	$80

Grading	100%	98% MINT	95% EXC+	90% EXC	80% VG+	70% VG	60% G

"To an extent, the guitar has never done quite what I wanted so it [has] also been natural to delve into it or saw something off. It's not sacred as far as I'm concerned. It has not been blessed and nobody has soaked it, it's a tool. And if a tool does not work, you saw a bit off or add something to it. I've enjoyed that area of the guitar."

—L. Acunto on Adrian Legg
TCG, April 1995

AK-310 — similar to AK-210, except has gold tuners. New 1994.

Mfr.'s Sug. Retail	$439	$329	$219	$175	$140	$125	$115 $105

AK-600 — classic style, solid spruce top, round soundhole, 5 stripe bound body, wooden inlay rosette, rosewood back/sides, mahogany neck, 12/19 fret rosewood fingerboard/bridge, rosewood veneer on peghead, 3 per side gold tuners. Available in Natural finish. Mfd. 1991 to date.

Mfr.'s Sug. Retail	$400	$300	$200	$190	$150	$135	$120 $110

AK-900 — similar to AK-600, except has solid cedar top. Mfd. 1991 to date.

Mfr.'s Sug. Retail	$559	$419	$279	$225	$185	$165	$150 $140

AK-1000 — classic style, spruce top, round soundhole, bound body, wooden inlay rosette, mahogany back/sides/neck, 12/19 fret rosewood fingerboard/bridge, rosewood peghead veneer, 3 per side nickel tuners. Available in Natural finish. Mfd. 1991 to 1993.

	$490	$420	$350	$280	$250	$230	$210

Last Mfr.'s Sug. Retail was $700.

AW-70 — dreadnought style, mahogany top, round soundhole, black pickguard, bound body, 5 stripe rosette, mahogany back/sides/neck, 14/20 fret rosewood fingerboard with pearl dot inlay, rosewood bridge with black pins, 3 per side nickel tuners. Available in Walnut finish. Mfd. 1991 to 1993.

	$140	$120	$100	$80	$70	$65	$60

Last Mfr.'s Sug. Retail was $200.

AW-75 — similar to AW-70, except has spruce top. Available in Brown Sunburst and Natural finishes. Curr. Mfr.

Mfr.'s Sug. Retail	$240	$180	$120	$100	$80	$70	$65 $60

Add $10 for Black, Blue Shade and Red Shade finishes.

In 1994, Brown Sunburst finish was discontinued.

This model also available in grand concert style body (AF-75D), available in Natural finish.

AW-100 — dreadnought style, spruce top, round soundhole, black pickguard, bound body, 3 stripe rosette, black pickguard, mahogany back/sides/neck, 14/20 fret rosewood fingerboard with pearl dot inlay, rosewood bridge with black white dot pins, 3 per side chrome tuners. Available in Natural finish. Disc. 1991.

	$195	$165	$140	$110	$100	$90	$80

Last Mfr.'s Sug. Retail was $275.

AW-100C — similar to AW-100, except has single round cutaway. Disc. 1991.

	$210	$180	$150	$120	$110	$100	$90

Last Mfr.'s Sug. Retail was $300.

AW-110N — dreadnought style, cedar top, round soundhole, black pickguard, bound body, 3 stripe rosette, black pickguard, mahogany back/sides/neck, 14/20 fret rosewood fingerboard with pearl dot inlay, rosewood bridge with black white dot pins, 3 per side chrome tuners. Available in Natural finish. Mfd. 1991 to date.

Mfr.'s Sug. Retail	$329	$246	$164	$125	$100	$90	$80 $75

Also available in lefthanded model as **AW-100LN** ($359).

AW-110C — similar to AW-110, except has single round cutaway. Mfd. 1991 to date.

Mfr.'s Sug. Retail	$349	$261	$174	$140	$110	$100	$90 $80

AW-110CT — similar to AW-110C, except has 12 strings. Disc 1991.

	$245	$210	$175	$140	$125	$115	$105

Last Mfr.'s Sug. Retail was $350.

AW-110T — similar to AW-110, except has 12 strings. Disc 1991.

	$210	$180	$150	$120	$110	$100	$90

Last Mfr.'s Sug. Retail was $300.

AW-200 — dreadnought style, spruce top, round soundhole, black pickguard, bound body, 3 stripe rosette, black pickguard, mahogany back/sides/neck, 14/20 fret rosewood fingerboard with pearl dot inlay, rosewood bridge with white black dot pins, 3 per side chrome diecast tuners. Available in Antique Violin, Brown Sunburst, Black, and Natural finishes. Mfd. 1991 to date.

Mfr.'s Sug. Retail	$399	$299	$199	$150	$120	$110	$100 $90

In 1993, Brown Sunburst finish was discontinued.

This model also available in a folk style body (AW-200F). Disc 1993.

AW-200C — similar to AW-200, except has single round cutaway. Mfd. 1991 to date.

Mfr.'s Sug. Retail	$429	$321	$214	$175	$140	$125	$115 $105

AW-200E — similar to AW-200, except has piezo pickup and 3 band EQ. Available in Black and Natural finishes. Mfd. 1991 to date.

Mfr.'s Sug. Retail	$529	$396	$264	$205	$165	$145	$135 $125

AW-200CE — similar to AW-200E, except has single round cutaway. Mfd. 1991 to date.

Mfr.'s Sug. Retail	$549	$411	$274	$210	$170	$150	$135 $125

AW-200T — similar to AW-200, except has 12 strings, 6 per side tuners. Mfd. 1991 to date.

Mfr.'s Sug. Retail	$449	$336	$224	$155	$120	$110	$100 $90

Grading	100%	98% MINT	95% EXC+	90% EXC	80% VG+	70% VG	60% G

AW-200CTE — similar to AW-200, except has 12 strings, single round cutaway, 6 per side tuners, piezo pickup, 3 band EQ. Curr. mfr.

Mfr.'s Sug. Retail	$589	$441	$294	$250	$200	$180	$165	$150

AW-250 — dreadnought style, figured maple top, round soundhole, black pickguard, 3 stripe bound body/rosette, flamed maple back/sides, mahogany neck, 14/20 fret rosewood fingerboard with pearl dot inlay, rosewood bridge with white black dot pins, 3 per side chrome diecast tuners. Available in Black Sunburst and Vintage Sunburst finishes. Mfd. 1994 to date.

Mfr.'s Sug. Retail	$450	$360	$270	$225	$180	$160	$150	$135

AW-310 — dreadnought style, cedar top, round soundhole, herringbone bound body/rosette, ovankol back/sides, mahogany neck, 14/20 fret rosewood fingerboard with pearl dot inlay, rosewood bridge with white black dot pins, 3 per side chrome diecast tuners. Available in Natural finish. Mfd. 1991 to 1992.

	$235	$200	$170	$135	$125	$115	$105

Last Mfr.'s Sug. Retail was $335.

AW-310C — similar to AW-310, except has single round cutaway. Mfd. 1991 to 1992.

	$280	$240	$200	$160	$145	$130	$120

Last Mfr.'s Sug. Retail was $400.

AW-310CE — similar to AW-310, except has single round cutaway, piezo pickup, 3 band EQ. Mfd. 1991 to 1992.

	$330	$280	$235	$190	$170	$155	$140

Last Mfr.'s Sug. Retail was $470.

AW-310T — similar to AW-310, except has 12 strings. Mfd. 1991 to date.

Mfr.'s Sug. Retail	$400	$300	$200	$185	$140	$125	$115	$105

AW-320T — similar to AW-310, except has 12 strings, gold hardware. Mfd. 1991 to date.

Mfr.'s Sug. Retail	$450	$360	$270	$225	$180	$160	$150	$135

AW-410 — jumbo style, cedar top, round soundhole, herringbone bound body/rosette, black pickguard, ovankol back/sides, mahogany neck, 14/20 fret rosewood fingerboard with pearl dot inlay, rosewood bridge with white black dot pins, 3 per side chrome diecast tuners. Available in Natural finish. Mfd. 1991 to 1992.

	$250	$215	$180	$145	$130	$120	$110

Last Mfr.'s Sug. Retail was $360.

AW-600 — dreadnought style, spruce top, round soundhole, black pickguard, 3 stripe bound body/rosette, rosewood back/sides, mahogany neck, 14/20 fret bound rosewood fingerboard with pearl dot inlay, rosewood bridge with white black dot pins, rosewood veneer on bound peghead, 3 per side chrome diecast tuners. Available in Natural finish. Curr. Mfr.

Mfr.'s Sug. Retail	$479	$359	$239	$205	$150	$135	$120	$110

This model also available with mahogany back/sides.

In 1994, gold tuners replaced original item.

AW-650 — similar to AW-600, except has solid spruce top, mahogany back/sides, gold tuners. New 1994.

Mfr.'s Sug. Retail	$450	$360	$270	$225	$180	$160	$150	$135

AW-700 — dreadnought style, solid spruce top, round soundhole, black pickguard, 3 stripe bound body/rosette, rosewood back/sides, mahogany neck, 14/20 fret rosewood fingerboard with pearl diamond inlay, rosewood bridge with white black dot pins, rosewood veneer peghead, 3 per side gold diecast tuners. Available in Natural finish. Mfd. 1991 only.

	$275	$235	$195	$155	$140	$125	$115

Last Mfr.'s Sug. Retail was $390.

AW-800 — dreadnought style, solid spruce top, round soundhole, tortoise shell pickguard, herringbone bound body/rosette, rosewood back/sides, mahogany neck, 14/20 fret rosewood fingerboard with pearl diamond inlay, rosewood bridge with white black dot pins, rosewood veneer on peghead, 3 per side gold diecast tuners. Available in Natural finish. Curr. Mfr.

Mfr.'s Sug. Retail	$559	$419	$279	$240	$190	$170	$155	$140

AW-800T — similar to AW-800, except has 12 strings, 6 per side tuners.

Mfr.'s Sug. Retail	$599	$449	$299	$275	$220	$200	$180	$165

LJ-8 — jumbo style, cedar top, round soundhole, 3 stripe bound body/rosette, black pickguard, bubinga back/sides, mahogany neck, 14/20 fret rosewood fingerboard with pearl dot inlay, ebonized maple bridge with white black dot pins, 3 per side chrome diecast tuners. Available in Natural finish. Mfd. 1994 to date.

Mfr.'s Sug. Retail	$530	$424	$318	$265	$210	$190	$175	$160

LW-8 — similar to LJ-8, except has dreadnought style, spruce top, ovankol back/sides. Available in Natural finish. Mfd. 1994 to date.

Mfr.'s Sug. Retail	$530	$424	$318	$265	$210	$190	$175	$160

LW-10 — dreadnought style, spruce top, round soundhole, 3 stripe bound body/rosette, black pickguard, mahogany back/sides/neck, 14/20 fret rosewood fingerboard with pearl dot inlay, ebonized maple bridge with white black dot pins, 3 per side chrome diecast tuners. Available in Black, Natural, Tobacco Brown and Wine Red finishes. Mfd. 1991 to 1992.

	$390	$335	$280	$225	$205	$190	$165

Add $15 for 12 string version (LW-10T).

Last Mfr.'s Sug. Retail was $560.

LW-12 — dreadnought style, cedar top, round soundhole, herringbone bound body/rosette, tortoise pickguard, walnut back/sides, mahogany neck, 14/20 fret rosewood fingerboard with pearl dot inlay, ebonized maple bridge with white black dot pins, rosewood veneer on peghead, 3 per side chrome diecast tuners. Available in Black and Natural finishes. Disc. 1992.

	$380	$325	$270	$215	$195	$180	$165

Add $35 for 12 string version of this model (LW-12T).

Last Mfr.'s Sug. Retail was $540.

LW-14 — dreadnought style, sycamore top, round soundhole, herringbone bound body/rosette, black pickguard, walnut back/sides, mahogany neck, 14/20 fret rosewood fingerboard with pearl dot inlay, ebonized maple bridge with white black dot pins, sycamore veneer on peghead, 3 per side chrome diecast tuners. Available in Tobacco Sunburst finish. Disc. 1993.

	$405	$345	$285	$230	$205	$190	$175

Last Mfr.'s Sug. Retail was $575.

LW-18 — dreadnought style, spruce top, round soundhole, 5 stripe bound body/rosette, rosewood back/sides, mahogany neck, 14/20 fret rosewood fingerboard with pearl dot inlay, ebonized maple bridge with white black dot pins, rosewood veneer on peghead, 3 per side chrome diecast tuners. Available in Natural finish. Disc. 1993.

	$420	$360	$300	$240	$215	$195	$180

Last Mfr.'s Sug. Retail was $600.

LW-18T — similar to LW-18, except has 12 strings, 6 per side tuners. Disc. 1993.

	$450	$385	$320	$255	$230	$210	$195

Last Mfr.'s Sug. Retail was $640.

SW-8 — dreadnought style, solid cedar top, round soundhole, tortoise shell bound body/rosette/pickguard, mahogany back/sides/neck, 14/20 fret rosewood fingerboard with pearl dot inlay, ebonized maple bridge with white black dot pins, rosewood veneer on peghead, 3 per side chrome diecast tuners. Available in Natural finish. Disc. 1993.

	$450	$385	$320	$255	$230	$210	$195

Last Mfr.'s Sug. Retail was $640.

SW-8C — similar to SW-8, except has single round cutaway. Disc. 1993.

	$500	$430	$360	$290	$260	$240	$220

Last Mfr.'s Sug. Retail was $715.

SW-8CT — similar to SW-8, except has single round cutaway, 12 strings, 6 per side tuners. Disc. 1993.

	$525	$450	$375	$300	$270	$245	$225

Last Mfr.'s Sug. Retail was $750.

SW-8T — similar to SW-8, except has 12 strings, 6 per side tuners. Disc. 1993.

	$470	$400	$335	$265	$240	$220	$200

Last Mfr.'s Sug. Retail was $670.

Concert Classic Series

Made in Spain. All instruments in this series have classical style body, round soundhole, wood inlay rosette, mahogany neck, 12/19 fret fingerboard, tied rosewood bridge, rosewood veneered slotted peghead, 3 per side tuners with pearloid buttons. Available in Natural finish. New 1995.

AC25 — solid cedar top, African sapelli back/sides, rosewood fingerboard, nickel hardware. Current production.

Mfr.'s Sug. Retail	$375	$281	$187	$175	$140	$125	$115	$105

AC35 — solid cedar top, African sapelli back/sides, rosewood fingerboard, gold hardware. Current production.

Mfr.'s Sug. Retail	$450	$337	$225	$210	$170	$150	$135	$125

AC35A — similar to AC35, except has **alto (530mm scale)** style, solid spruce top, single flat cutaway.

Mfr.'s Sug. Retail	$455	$341	$227	$225	$180	$160	$150	$135

AC50 — solid cedar top, rosewood back/sides/fingerboard, gold hardware. Current production.

Mfr.'s Sug. Retail	$675	$540	$405	$340	$270	$245	$225	$205

AC50A — similar to AC50, except has **alto (530mm scale)** style, single flat cutaway.

Mfr.'s Sug. Retail	$575	$431	$287	$285	$225	$205	$185	$170

This model has solid spruce top optionally available.

AC75CB — **contra bass (750mm scale)** style, solid cedar top, African sapelli back/sides, rosewood fingerboard, gold hardware.

Mfr.'s Sug. Retail	$1,095	$821	$547	$545	$435	$395	$360	$330

AC75B — similar to AC75CB, except has **bass (700mm scale)** style.

Mfr.'s Sug. Retail	$1,095	$821	$547	$545	$435	$395	$360	$330

AC80 — solid spruce top, rosewood back/sides, ebony fingerboard, gold hardware. Current production.

Mfr.'s Sug. Retail	$975	$731	$487	$475	$380	$345	$315	$285

AC85A — single flat cutaway **alto (530mm scale)** style, solid spruce top, rosewood back/sides, ebony fingerboard, gold hardware.

Mfr.'s Sug. Retail	$1,075	$806	$537	$535	$430	$390	$355	$325

Grading	100%	98% MINT	95% EXC+	90% EXC	80% VG+	70% VG	60% G

AC90CB — contra bass (750mm scale) style, solid spruce top, rosewood back/sides, ebony fingerboard, gold hardware.
 Mfr.'s Sug. Retail $1,255 $1,004 $753 $630 $500 $450 $415 $375

AC90B — similar to AC90CB, except has bass (700mm scale) style.
 Mfr.'s Sug. Retail $1,255 $1,004 $753 $630 $500 $450 $415 $375

Pepe Series

The Pepe Series models are made in Spain. All instruments in this series have classical style body, solid cedar top, round soundhole, wood inlay rosette, African sapelli back/sides, mahogany neck, 12/19 fret rosewood fingerboard, tied rosewood bridge, rosewood veneered slotted peghead, 3 per side gold tuners with pearloid buttons. Available in Natural finish. New 1995.

PS48 — 480mm scale.
 Mfr.'s Sug. Retail $375 $281 $187 $185 $150 $135 $120 $110

PS53 — 530mm scale.
 Mfr.'s Sug. Retail $375 $281 $187 $185 $150 $135 $120 $110

PS58 — 580mm scale.
 Mfr.'s Sug. Retail $375 $281 $187 $185 $150 $135 $120 $110

ACOUSTIC ELECTRIC

CES-50 — single round cutaway classic style, spruce top, bound body, wooden inlay rosette, mahogany body/neck, 22 fret extended rosewood fingerboard, rosewood bridge, 3 per side gold tuners, piezo pickups, volume/tone control. Available in Black, Natural and White finishes. Mfd. 1992 to 1994.
 $420 $360 $300 $240 $215 $195 $180
 Last Mfr.'s Sug. Retail was $600.

This model is a solid body with a routed out soundhole and installed plastic dish for resonance.

CE-60 — single round cutaway classic style, spruce top, round soundhole, bound body, wooden inlay rosette, mahogany back/sides/neck, 19 fret rosewood fingerboard/bridge, rosewood veneer on peghead, 3 per side gold tuners, piezo pickups with 3 band EQ. Available in Natural finish. Mfd. 1991 to 1994.
 $490 $420 $350 $280 $250 $230 $210
 Last Mfr.'s Sug. Retail was $700.

CE-60S — similar to CE-60, except has 22 fret extended fingerboard with pearl dot inlay, steel strings with white black dot bridge pins. Disc. 1994.
 $490 $420 $350 $280 $250 $230 $210
 Last Mfr.'s Sug. Retail was $700.

CE-60/14 — similar to CE-60, except has 22 fret extended fingerboard. Disc. 1994.
 $490 $420 $350 $280 $250 $230 $210
 Last Mfr.'s Sug. Retail was $700.

FEA-10 — single round cutaway dreadnought style, cedar top, round soundhole, bound body, wooden inlay rosette, mahogany back/sides/neck, 22 fret rosewood fingerboard with pearl dot inlay, rosewood bridge with black pearl dot pins, 3 per side diecast tuners, piezo pickup, 3 band EQ. Available in Natural and Walnut finishes. Mfd. 1992 to 1995.
 $615 $525 $440 $330 $300 $275 $250
 Last Mfr.'s Sug. Retail was $900.

FEA-15 — similar to FEA-10, except has spruce top. Available in Brown Sunburst, Natural and Transparent Black finishes. Disc. 1993.
 $665 $570 $475 $380 $345 $315 $285
 Last Mfr.'s Sug. Retail was $950.

FEA-16N — single round cutaway dreadnought style, figured sycamore top, round soundhole, bound body, wooden inlay rosette, mahogany back/sides/neck, 22 fret rosewood fingerboard with pearl dot inlay, rosewood bridge with black pearl dot pins, 3 per side diecast tuners, piezo pickup, 3 band EQ. Available in Natural finish. Mfd. 1994 only.
 $735 $630 $525 $420 $380 $345 $315
 Last Mfr.'s Sug. Retail was $1,050.

FEA-20 — single round cutaway dreadnought style, sycamore top, round soundhole, bound body, abalone designed rosette, sycamore back/sides, mahogany neck, 22 fret bound rosewood fingerboard with pearl dot inlay, rosewood bridge with black pearl dot pins, 3 per side gold diecast tuners, piezo pickup, 3 band EQ. Available in Transparent Black and Transparent Blue finishes. Mfd. 1991 to date.
 Mfr.'s Sug. Retail $1,300 $975 $650 $605 $480 $415 $380 $345

FET-85 — single sharp cutaway jumbo style, arched spruce top, oval soundhole, 5 stripe bound body/rosette, chestnut back/sides, mahogany neck, 21 fret bound rosewood fingerboard with pearl diamond inlay, rosewood bridge with black pearl dot pins and pearl diamond inlay, bound peghead with chestnut veneer, 3 per side gold diecast tuners, piezo pickup, 3 band EQ. Available in Amber Natural and Antique Sunburst finishes. Mfd. 1991 to 1992.
 $980 $840 $700 $560 $505 $460 $420
 Last Mfr.'s Sug. Retail was $1,400.

This model had rosewood back/sides optionally available.

A

Grading	100%	98% MINT	95% EXC+	90% EXC	80% VG+	70% VG	60% G

FET-100 — cutaway jumbo style, arched chestnut/spruce laminated top, oval soundhole, 3 stripe bound body and rosette, chestnut arched back/sides, maple neck, 21 fret bound ebony fingerboard with abalone/pearl split block inlay, rosewood bridge with white pearl dot pins and pearl diamond inlay, bound peghead, 3 per side gold diecast tuners, piezo pickup, 3 band EQ. Available in Amber Natural, Blue Shade and Red Shade finishes. Mfd. 1991 to 1992.

	100%	98%	95%	90%	80%	70%	60%
	$1,050	$900	$750	$600	$540	$495	$450

Last Mfr.'s Sug. Retail was $1,500.

FET-500 (formerly the FET-SPL) — round cutaway jumbo style, spruce top, oval soundhole, 5 stripe bound body and rosette, mahogany arched back/sides/neck, 21 fret rosewood bound fingerboard with pearl dot inlay, rosewood bridge with white pearl dot pins, bound peghead, 3 per side diecast tuners, piezo pickup, volume/tone control. Available in Antique Sunburst, Black Sunburst and Transparent Red finishes. Mfd. 1991 to 1992.

	$405	$345	$285	$230	$205	$190	$175

Last Mfr.'s Sug. Retail was $575.

FET-600 (formerly the FET-DLX) — cutaway jumbo style, arched sycamore top, oval soundhole, 5 stripe bound body and rosette, sycamore arched back/sides, mahogany neck, 21 fret bound rosewood fingerboard with pearl diamond inlay, rosewood bridge with white pearl dot pins, bound peghead, 3 per side diecast tuners, piezo pickup, 3 band EQ. Available in Amber Natural and Antique Sunburst finishes. Mfd. 1991 to 1992.

	$535	$460	$380	$305	$275	$250	$230

Last Mfr.'s Sug. Retail was $765.

This model also available in 12 string version (FET-600/12).

ACOUSTIC ELECTRIC BASS

FEB-DLX — single round cutaway dreadnought style, arched flame maple top, f holes, multi bound body, figured maple back/sides/neck, 21 fret rosewood fingerboard with pearl cross inlay, string thru rosewood bridge, flame maple peghead veneer with pearl flower/logo inlay, 2 per side gold tuners, piezo bridge pickup, 4 band EQ. Available in Brown Sunburst, Natural and Violin Sunburst finishes. New 1994.

Mfr.'s Sug. Retail	$1,000	$800	$600	$500	$400	$360	$330	$300

FEB-STD — similar to FEB-DLX, except has spruce top, mahogany back/sides, chrome tuners.

Mfr.'s Sug. Retail	$850	$680	$510	$425	$340	$305	$280	$255

ELECTRIC

615 Series

This series has 5 bolt bolt-on maple necks, pearloid pickguard with 3 Tone Sunburst and Red finishes, red pickguard with White finish.

615 CST — single sharp cutaway alder body, pickguard, metal control plate, 22 fret rosewood fingerboard with pearl dot inlay, strings thru Wilkinson bridge, screened peghead logo, 6 on one side tuners with pearloid buttons, chrome hardware, 3 single coil Seymour Duncan pickups, volume/tone controls, one 5 position/1 mini-rhythm switches. Available in 3 Tone Sunburst, Red and White finishes. New 1995.

Mfr.'s Sug. Retail	$999	$799	$599	$500	$400	$360	$330	$300

This instrument is Made in U.S.A.

615 DLX — similar to 615 CST, except has Don Lace pickups. New 1995.

Mfr.'s Sug. Retail	$850	$680	$510	$425	$340	$305	$280	$255

This instrument is Made in U.S.A.

615 SPL — similar to 615 CST, except has 2 single coil Aria pickups. New 1995.

Mfr.'s Sug. Retail	$399	$351	$307	$300	$240	$215	$195	$180

615 STD — similar to 615 CST, except has Aria pickups. New 1995.

Mfr.'s Sug. Retail	$599	$479	$359	$350	$280	$250	$230	$210

Aquanote Series

CR-60 — offset double cutaway alder body, bolt-on maple neck, 24 fret rosewood fingerboard with pearl dot inlay, standard vibrato, 6 on one side locking tuners, chrome hardware, 2 single coil/1 humbucker pickups, volume/tone control, 5 position switch, coil split on tone control. Available in Black, Midnight Cherry, Navy Blue and Pearl White finishes. Disc. 1993.

	$595	$510	$425	$340	$305	$280	$255

Last Mfr.'s Sug. Retail was $850.

CR-65 — similar to CR-60, except has sen body, black hardware, single coil/humbucker pickups, 3 position and separate coil split switches. Available in Amber Natural, Dark Red Shade and Purple Shade finishes. Disc. 1993.

	$665	$570	$475	$380	$345	$315	$285

Last Mfr.'s Sug. Retail was $950.

CR-65/12 — similar to CR-60, except has 12 strings, fixed bridge. Disc. 1993.

	$595	$510	$425	$340	$305	$280	$255

Last Mfr.'s Sug. Retail was $850.

Grading	100%	98% MINT	95% EXC+	90% EXC	80% VG+	70% VG	60% G

CR-100 — offset double cutaway ash body, set in maple neck, 24 fret rosewood fingerboard with pearl oval inlay, standard vibrato, 6 on one side locking tuners, silver black hardware, Seymour Duncan single coil/humbucker pickups, volume/tone control, 3 position switch, coil split in tone control. Available in Blue Shade, Dark Red Shade, Purple Shade and Vintage Sunburst. Disc. 1993.

	$1,050	$900	$750	$600	$540	$495	$450

Last Mfr.'s Sug. Retail was $1,500.

Excel Series

XL-STD-3 — offset double cutaway hardwood body, bolt-on maple neck, 22 fret bound rosewood fingerboard with pearl wedge inlay, standard vibrato, 6 on one side tuners, black hardware, 2 single coil/1 humbucker pickups, volume/tone control, 5 position switch, coil split in tone control. Available in Black, Candy Apple, Midnight Blue and White finishes. Disc. 1995.

	$280	$240	$200	$160	$145	$130	$120

Last Mfr.'s Sug. Retail was $400.

XL-SPT-3 — similar to XL-STD-3, except has KKT-2 double locking vibrato. Disc. 1991.

	$350	$300	$250	$200	$180	$165	$150

Last Mfr.'s Sug. Retail was $500.

XL-DLX-3 — similar to XL-STD-3, except has ART-10 double locking vibrato. Disc. 1995.

	$360	$275	$260	$220	$200	$180	$165

Last Mfr.'s Sug. Retail was $500.

XL-CST-3 — similar to XL-STD-3, except has curly maple top/back, ART-10 double locking vibrato, gold hardware. Available in Transparent Black, Transparent Blue and Transparent Red finishes. Disc. 1994.

	$420	$360	$300	$240	$215	$195	$180

Last Mfr.'s Sug. Retail was $600.

Full Acoustic Series

FA-70 VS — single round cutaway hollow style, arched maple top/back/sides, bound body/f holes, raised black pickguard, maple neck, 20 fret bound rosewood fingerboard with pearl split block inlay, rosewood bridge, trapeze tailpiece, bound peghead with pearl Aria Pro II logo and dove inlay, 3 per side tuners, gold hardware, 2 humbucker pickups, 2 volume/tone controls, 3 position switch. Available in Brown Sunburst and Vintage Sunburst finishes. Mfd. 1991 to date.

Mfr.'s Sug. Retail	$849	$636	$424	$395	$290	$260	$240	$220

In 1993, Brown Sunburst finish was discontinued.

FA-70TR — similar to FA-70, except has rosewood/metal bridge, vibrato tailpiece. Disc. 1993.

	$560	$480	$400	$320	$290	$265	$240

Last Mfr.'s Sug. Retail was $800.

Fullerton Series

FL05 — offset double cutaway alder body, white pickguard, bolt-on maple neck, 22 fret maple fingerboard with black dot inlay, strings thru bridge, screened peghead logo, 6 on one side tuners, chrome hardware, 3 single coil pickups, 1 volume/2 tone controls, 5 position switch. Available in 3 Tone Sunburst, Black, Blue and Red finishes. New 1995.

Mfr.'s Sug. Retail	$269	$201	$134	$125	$100	$90	$80	$75

FL10 — similar to FL05, except has standard vibrato. New 1995.

Mfr.'s Sug. Retail	$279	$209	$139	$130	$100	$90	$80	$75

FL10H — similar to FL05, except has standard vibrato, 2 single coil/1 humbucker pickups. New 1995.

Mfr.'s Sug. Retail	$289	$216	$144	$135	$110	$100	$90	$80

FL20 — offset double cutaway alder body, white pickguard, bolt-on maple neck, 22 fret rosewood fingerboard with pearl dot inlay, standard vibrato, screened peghead logo, 6 on one side tuners, chrome hardware, 3 single coil pickups, 1 volume/2 tone controls, 5 position switch. Available in Seethru Black, Seethru Blue and Seethru Red finishes. New 1995.

Mfr.'s Sug. Retail	$359	$269	$179	$175	$140	$125	$115	$105

FL20H — similar to FL20, except has 2 single coil/1 humbucker pickups, coil tap in push/pull tone switch. Available in 3 Tone Sunburst, Seethru Black and Seethru Red finishes. New 1995.

Mfr.'s Sug. Retail	$369	$276	$184	$180	$145	$130	$120	$110

FL30 — similar to FL20, except has ash body, pearloid pickguard, Gotoh tuners, black hardware, 2 single coil/1 humbucker pickups, coil tap in push/pull tone switch. Available in Seethru Black, Seethru Blue and Seethru Red finishes. New 1995.

Mfr.'s Sug. Retail	$479	$359	$239	$230	$185	$165	$150	$140

FL40 — similar to FL20, except has ash body, no pickguard, Wilkinson standard vibrato, Gotoh locking tuners, humbucker/single coil/humbucker pickups, volume/tone controls, coil tap in push/pull volume/tone switches. Available in Natural and Seethru Red finishes. New 1995.

Mfr.'s Sug. Retail	$699	$524	$349	$330	$265	$240	$220	$200

Grading	100%	98% MINT	95% EXC+	90% EXC	80% VG+	70% VG	60% G

FL50 — offset double cutaway alder body, pearloid pickguard, bolt-on maple neck, 22 fret rosewood fingerboard with pearl dot inlay, Wilkinson vibrato, screened peghead logo, 6 on one side Sperzel locking tuners, chrome hardware, 3 single coil Don Lace pickups, volume/tone controls. Available in 2 Tone Sunburst, Blue, Candy Apple Red and White finishes. New 1995.

Mfr.'s Sug. Retail	$999	$799	$599	$500	$400	$360	$330	$300

This instrument has 5 bolt neck joint and is Made in U.S.A.

FL60 — similar to FL50, except has 2 single coil/1 mini humbucker Seymour Duncan pickups. Available in Red and White finishes. New 1995.

Mfr.'s Sug. Retail	$1,299	$1,039	$779	$650	$520	$470	$430	$390

This instrument has white pearloid pickguard with Red finish, red pearloid pickguard with White finish, 5 bolt neck joint and is Made in U.S.A.

Magna Series

Instruments in this series have carved tops.

MA-09 — offset double cutaway hardwood body, bolt-on maple neck, 24 fret maple fingerboard with black dot inlay, standard vibrato, 6 on one side tuners, chrome hardware, 2 single coil/1 humbucker pickups, volume/tone controls, 5 position switch. Available in Black, Blue and Red finishes. Mfd. 1994 only.

			$260	$220	$185	$150	$135	$120	$110

Last Mfr.'s Sug. Retail was $370.

MA-10 — offset double cutaway alder body, bolt-on maple neck, 22 fret rosewood fingerboard with pearl dot inlay, standard vibrato, roller nut, 6 on one side tuners, black hardware, 2 single coil/1 humbucker pickups, volume/tone control, 5 position switch, coil split in tone control. Available in Black, Fiero Red, Metallic Red Shade, Metallic Blue Shade and White finishes. Curr. mfr.

Mfr.'s Sug. Retail	$400	$320	$240	$200	$160	$145	$130	$120

In 1993, Fiero Red finish was discontinued.

MA-15 — similar to MA-10, except has sen body. Available in Transparent Black, Transparent Blue and Transparent Red finishes. Mfd. 1994 to date.

Mfr.'s Sug. Retail	$500	$400	$300	$250	$200	$180	$165	$150

MA-15ST — similar to MA-10, except has sen body, fixed strings thru bridge. Available in Transparent Blue and Transparent Red finishes. Mfd. 1994 to date.

Mfr.'s Sug. Retail	$430	$344	$258	$215	$175	$155	$140	$130

MA-22 (formerly MA-20) — similar to MA-10, except has double locking vibrato, chrome hardware. Available in Metallic Red Shade, Purple Pearl Burst and Silver Metallic finishes. Curr. mfr.

Mfr.'s Sug. Retail	$550	$412	$275	$250	$200	$180	$165	$150

MA-28 — similar to MA-10, except has figured maple top, double locking vibrato. Available in Transparent finishes. Curr. mfr.

Mfr.'s Sug. Retail	$600	$450	$300	$275	$220	$200	$180	$165

MA-30 — similar to MA-10, except has 24 fret fingerboard, double locking vibrato. Available in Black, Navy Blue, Purple Cherry and Pearl White finishes. Curr. mfr.

Mfr.'s Sug. Retail	$900	$675	$450	$405	$300	$270	$245	$225

MA-35 — offset double cutaway alder body, bolt-on maple neck, 24 fret rosewood fingerboard with pearl dot inlay, double locking vibrato, roller nut, 6 on one side tuners, black hardware, single coil/humbucker pickups, volume/tone control, 3 position switch, coil split in tone control. Available in Metallic Blue, Metallic Burgundy and Metallic Violet finishes. Mfd. 1991 only.

		$630	$540	$450	$360	$325	$300	$275

Last Mfr.'s Sug. Retail was $900.

MA-40 — offset double cutaway alder body, bolt-on maple neck, 24 fret rosewood fingerboard with pearl dot inlay, double locking vibrato, roller nut, 6 on one side tuners, black hardware, 2 single coil/1 humbucker pickups, volume/2 EQ controls, 3 position and 2 EQ switches, active electronics. Available in Black, Metallic Blue, Metallic Burgundy, Metallic Violet, Navy Blue, Pearl White and Purple Cherry finishes. Mfd. 1991 only.

		$670	$575	$480	$385	$350	$320	$290

Last Mfr.'s Sug. Retail was $960.

MA-45 — similar to MA-40, except has bound fingerboard with pearl oval inlay, tunomatic bridge/stop tailpiece, gold hardware. Disc. 1991.

		$720	$615	$510	$410	$370	$340	$310

Last Mfr.'s Sug. Retail was $1,025.

MA-50 — offset double cutaway alder body, bolt-on maple neck, 24 fret rosewood fingerboard with pearl dot inlay, standard vibrato, roller nut, 6 on one side tuners, gold hardware, 2 single coil/1 humbucker pickups, volume/tone control, three 3 position switches, coil split in tone control. Available in Black, Metallic Blue, Metallic Burgundy, Metallic Violet, Navy Blue, Pearl White and Purple Cherry finishes. Disc. 1993.

		$700	$600	$500	$400	$360	$330	$300

Last Mfr.'s Sug. Retail was $1,000.

Grading	100%	98% MINT	95% EXC+	90% EXC	80% VG+	70% VG	60% G

MA-55 — offset double cutaway sen body, bolt-on maple neck, 24 fret rosewood fingerboard with pearl dot inlay, standard vibrato, roller nut, 6 on one side locking tuners, 2 single coil/1 humbucker pickups, volume/tone control, 5 position and coil split switches. Available in Amber Natural, Blue Shade and Dark Red Shade finishes. Mfd. 1992 only.

	$735	$630	$525	$420	$380	$345	$315

Last Mfr.'s Sug. Retail was $1,050.

MA-60 — offset double cutaway alder body, maple neck, 24 fret bound rosewood fingerboard with pearl oval inlay, double locking vibrato, roller nut, 6 on one side tuners, gold hardware, 2 single coil/1 humbucker pickups, volume/2 EQ controls, 3 position and 2 EQ switches, active electronics. Available in Black, Metallic Blue, Metallic Burgundy, Metallic Violet, Navy Blue, Pearl White and Purple Cherry finishes. Mfd. 1991 only.

	$770	$660	$550	$440	$395	$365	$330

Last Mfr.'s Sug. Retail was $1,100.

MA-75 — offset double cutaway sen body, bolt-on maple neck, 22 fret rosewood fingerboard with pearl oval inlay, double locking vibrato, 6 on one side tuners, gold hardware, humbucker/single coil/humbucker pickups, volume/tone control, 5 position and coil split switches. Available in Amber Natural, Cherry Sunburst, Purple Shade and Vintage Sunburst finishes. Mfd. 1992 only.

	$805	$690	$575	$460	$415	$380	$345

Last Mfr.'s Sug. Retail was $1,150.

MA-90 — offset double cutaway alder body, bolt-on maple neck, 24 fret bound rosewood neck with pearl oval inlay, double locking vibrato, 6 on one side tuners, silver black hardware, 2 single coil/1 Seymour Duncan humbucker pickups, volume/tone control, 5 position switch, coil split in tone control. Available in Emerald Green Sunburst, Gunmetal Grey, Navy Blue Sunburst and Rose Red Sunburst finishes. Mfd. 1991 to 1992.

	$905	$775	$645	$515	$465	$425	$385

Last Mfr.'s Sug. Retail was $1,295.

MA-100 — similar to MA-90, except has set neck. Available in Gunmetal Grey finish. Mfd. 1991 only.

	$980	$840	$700	$560	$505	$460	$420

Last Mfr.'s Sug. Retail was $1,400.

Pro Electric Series

PE-JR600 — single sharp cutaway maple body, bolt-on maple neck, 22 fret rosewood fingerboard with pearl dot inlay, tunomatic bridge/stop tailpiece, 3 per side tuners, chrome hardware, 2 single coil pickups, 2 volume/tone controls, 3 position switch. Available in Black, Metallic Blue Shade and Metallic Violet Shade finishes. Disc. 1991.

	$540	$460	$385	$310	$280	$255	$230

Last Mfr.'s Sug. Retail was $775.

PE-JR750 — similar to PE-JR600, except has bound body, vibrato tailpiece, gold hardware, volume/tone control. Available in Cherry Sunburst, Pearl White and Vintage Sunburst finishes. Disc. 1991.

	$700	$600	$500	$400	$360	$330	$300

Last Mfr.'s Sug. Retail was $1,000.

PE-1000TR — single sharp cutaway mahogany body, bound maple top, set in maple neck, 22 fret bound rosewood fingerboard with abalone/pearl split block inlay, standard vibrato, 3 per side locking tuners, gold hardware, 2 humbucker pickups, volume/tone control. Available in Blondy Natural, Transparent Scarlet and Twilight Black finishes. Mfd. 1991 to 1992.

	$910	$780	$650	$520	$470	$430	$390

Last Mfr.'s Sug. Retail was $1,300.

PE SPL — single sharp cutaway mahogany body, bound maple top, set in maple neck, 22 fret bound ebony fingerboard with abalone/pearl snowflake inlay, tunomatic bridge/stop tailpiece, 3 per side locking tuners, gold hardware, 2 humbucker pickups, 2 volume/2 tone controls, 2 mini switches. Available in Antique Violin finish. Mfd. 1994 to date.

Mfr.'s Sug. Retail	$749	$561	$374	$350	$280	$250	$230	$210

STG Series

STG 012S — offset double cutaway hardwood body, white pickguard, bolt-on maple neck, 22 fret maple fingerboard with black dot inlay, fixed bridge, 6 on one side tuners, chrome hardware, 2 single coil pickups, volume/tone control, 3 position switch. Available in Black, Blue and Sunburst finishes. Mfd. 1994 to date.

Mfr.'s Sug. Retail	$279	$209	$139	$120	$95	$85	$80	$75

STG 013S — offset double cutaway hardwood body, white pickguard, bolt-on maple neck, 22 fret maple fingerboard with black dot inlay, strings thru bridge, 6 on one side tuners, chrome hardware, 3 single coil pickups, volume/tone controls, 5 position switch. Available in Black, Blue and Brown Sunburst finishes. Mfd. 1994 to date.

Mfr.'s Sug. Retail	$349	$261	$174	$150	$120	$110	$100	$90

STG 013X — similar to STG 013S, except has standard vibrato, 2 single coil/1 humbucker pickups. Mfd 1994 to date.

Mfr.'s Sug. Retail	$360	$288	$216	$180	$145	$130	$120	$110

Grading	100%	98% MINT	95% EXC+	90% EXC	80% VG+	70% VG	60% G

STG 023C — offset double cutaway figured maple body, black pickguard, bolt-on maple neck, 22 fret rosewood fingerboard with pearl dot inlay, double locking vibrato, 6 on one side tuners, chrome hardware, 2 single coil/1 humbucker pickups, volume/tone control, 5 position switch. Available in Dark Blue Shade, Dark Red Shade and Tobacco Sunburst finishes. Mfd. 1994 to date.

	100%	98%	95%	90%	80%	70%	60%
Mfr.'s Sug. Retail	$440	$352	$264	$220	$175	$160	$145	$135

STG 023X — similar to STG023C, except has gold hardware.

	100%	98%	95%	90%	80%	70%	60%
Mfr.'s Sug. Retail	$550	$440	$330	$275	$220	$200	$180	$165

Thin Acoustic Series

TA-40 — double rounded cutaway semi hollow style, mahogany arched top/back/sides, bound body and f holes, raised black pickguard, mahogany neck, 22 fret bound rosewood fingerboard with pearl dot inlay, tunomatic bridge/stop tailpiece, 3 per side tuners, chrome hardware, 2 humbucker pickups, 2 volume/tone controls, 3 position switch. Available in Walnut and Wine Red finishes. Curr. mfr.

	100%	98%	95%	90%	80%	70%	60%
Mfr.'s Sug. Retail	$499	$374	$249	$225	$180	$160	$150	$135

TA-60 — double rounded cutaway semi hollow style, mahogany arched top/back/sides, bound body and f holes, raised white pickguard, mahogany neck, 22 fret bound rosewood fingerboard with pearl block inlay, tunomatic bridge/stop tailpiece, 3 per side tuners, gold hardware, 2 humbucker pickups, 2 volume/tone controls, 3 position switch. Available in Pearl Black, Walnut and Wine Red finishes. Curr. mfr.

	100%	98%	95%	90%	80%	70%	60%
Mfr.'s Sug. Retail	$559	$419	$279	$260	$210	$190	$170	$160

In 1993, Walnut finish was discontinued.

TA-61 — similar to TA-60, except has maple top/back/sides, transparent pickguard, bound peghead, tone selector switch. Available in Amber Natural, Cherry and Vintage Sunburst finish.

	100%	98%	95%	90%	80%	70%	60%
Mfr.'s Sug. Retail	$659	$494	$329	$300	$240	$215	$195	$180

In 1993, Cherry finish was discontinued.

TA-65TR — similar to TA-60, except has vibrato tailpiece. Available in Amber Natural, Cherry, Vintage Sunburst, Walnut and Wine Red finishes. Disc. 1991.

	95%	90%	80%	70%	60%		
	$490	$420	$350	$280	$250	$230	$210

Last Mfr.'s Sug. Retail was $700.

TA-900 (formerly the TA-STD) — double cutaway semi hollow body, maple arched top/back/sides, f holes, bound body, raised black pickguard, mahogany neck, 22 fret bound rosewood fingerboard with pearl dot inlay, bridge/stop tailpiece, 3 per side tuners, unbound peghead, chrome hardware, 2 humbucker pickups, 2 volume/tone controls, 3 position switch. Available in Black, Brown Sunburst and Transparent Red finishes. Mfd. 1991 to 1992.

	95%	90%	80%	70%	60%		
	$875	$750	$625	$500	$450	$415	$375

Last Mfr.'s Sug. Retail was $1,250.

TA-1300 (formerly the TA-DLX) — double rounded cutaway semi hollow style, sycamore top/back/sides, bound body and f holes, raised bound tortoise pickguard, mahogany neck, 22 fret bound ebony fingerboard with abalone/pearl split block inlay, tunomatic bridge/stop tailpiece, bound peghead with pearl Aria Pro II logo and dove inlay, 3 per side tuners, gold hardware, 2 humbucker pickups, 2 volume/tone controls, 3 position switch. Available in Brown Sunburst and Vintage Sunburst finishes. Mfd. 1991 to 1992.

	95%	90%	80%	70%	60%		
	$1,225	$1,050	$875	$700	$630	$575	$525

Last Mfr.'s Sug. Retail was $1,750.

Viper Series

VP-30 — offset double cutaway maple body, bolt-on maple neck, 22 fret rosewood fingerboard with pearl dot inlay, standard vibrato, roller nut, 6 on one side tuners, chrome hardware, 2 single coil/1 humbucker pickups, volume/tone control, 5 position switch. Available in Black, Fiero Red and White finishes. Mfd. 1991 only.

	95%	90%	80%	70%	60%		
	$275	$235	$195	$155	$140	$125	$115

Last Mfr.'s Sug. Retail was $390.

VP-40 — offset double cutaway alder body, pearloid pickguard, bolt-on maple neck, 22 fret rosewood fingerboard with pearl wedge inlay, locking vibrato, 6 on one side tuners, black hardware, 2 single coil/1 humbucker pickups, volume/tone control, 5 position switch. Available in Black, Fiero Red, Navy Blue, Pearl White and White finishes. Mfd. 1991 only.

	95%	90%	80%	70%	60%		
	$350	$300	$250	$200	$180	$165	$150

Last Mfr.'s Sug. Retail was $500.

VP-50 — similar to VP-40, except has coil split switch. Available in Black, Candy Apple, Navy Blue, Midnight Cherry and Pearl White finishes. Disc. 1995.

	95%	90%	80%	70%	60%		
	$650	$540	$420	$300	$270	$245	$225

Last Mfr.'s Sug. Retail was $1,000.

VP-65 — similar to VP-40, except has pearloid pickguard, humbucker/single coil/humbucker pickups, coil split switch. Available in Black, Metallic Lavender Shade and Pearl Blue finishes. Disc 1993.

	95%	90%	80%	70%	60%		
	$695	$595	$500	$400	$360	$330	$300

Last Mfr.'s Sug. Retail was $995.

Grading	100%	98% MINT	95% EXC+	90% EXC	80% VG+	70% VG	60% G

VP-90 — semi-solid offset double cutaway maple body, figured maple top, wedge soundhole, bound body and soundhole, maple neck, 22 fret bound rosewood fingerboard with pearl dot inlay, standard vibrato, 6 on one side locking tuners, chrome hardware, volume/tone control, 3 position and coil split switch. Available in Cherry Sunburst and Natural finishes. Disc. 1993.

		$170	$145	$120	$95	$85	$80	$75

Last Mfr.'s Sug. Retail was $240.

ELECTRIC BASS

Avante Bass Series

AVB-40 — offset double cutaway alder body, bolt-on maple neck, 24 fret rosewood fingerboard with dot inlay, fixed bridge, 4 on one side tuners, chrome hardware, P-style/J-style pickups, 2 volume/1 tone controls. Available in Natural, Transparent Blue and Transparent Red finishes. Mfd. 1994 to date.

Mfr.'s Sug. Retail	$499	$399	$299	$250	$200	$180	$165	$150

AVB-45 — offset double cutaway alder body, bolt-on maple neck, 24 fret rosewood fingerboard with pearl oval inlay, fixed bridge, 4 on one side tuners, black hardware, P-style/J-style pickups, volume/treble/bass/balance controls, active controls. Available in Natural, Transparent Blue and Transparent Red finishes. New 1994.

Mfr.'s Sug. Retail	$699	$524	$349	$325	$260	$235	$215	$195

AVB-45/5 — similar to AVB-45, except has 5 strings, 4/1 per side tuners, 2 J/style pickups.

Mfr.'s Sug. Retail	$749	$561	$374	$350	$280	$250	$230	$210

AVB-50 — offset double cutaway alder body, bolt-on maple neck, 24 fret rosewood fingerboard with pearl dot inlay, fixed bridge, 4 on one side tuners, chrome hardware, P-style/J-style pickups, 2 volume/1 tone controls. Available in Black, Fiero Red and White finishes. Mfd. 1991 only.

		$345	$295	$245	$195	$175	$160	$150

Last Mfr.'s Sug. Retail was $490.

AVB-55 — similar to AVB-50, except has carved top and black hardware. Available in Alsace Red, Black, Navy Blue and Pearl White finishes. Disc. 1993.

		$595	$510	$425	$340	$305	$280	$255

Last Mfr.'s Sug. Retail was $850.

AVB-80 — similar to AVB-50, except has carved top, gold hardware and active electronics. Available in Black, Navy Blue Sunburst, Pearl White and Rose Red Sunburst. Disc. 1993.

		$770	$660	$550	$440	$395	$365	$330

Last Mfr.'s Sug. Retail was $1,100.

AVB-95 — offset double cutaway sen body, carved top/back, bolt-on maple neck, 24 fret rosewood fingerboard with pearl dot inlay, fixed bridge, 4 on one side tuners, silver black hardware, P-style/J-style Seymour Duncan pickups, volume/bass/treble and mixed controls, bypass switch. Available in Blue Shade, Dark Red Shade, Natural and Purple Shade finishes. Curr. mfr.

Mfr.'s Sug. Retail	$1,600	$1,200	$800	$750	$560	$505	$460	$420

AVBSB-4 — offset double cutaway ash body, multilam tortoise pickguard, bolt-on maple neck, 24 fret ebony fingerboard with pearl dot inlay, fixed bridge, 4 on one side tuners, pearl nickel hardware, 2 J-style pickups, volume/concentric treble/bass controls. Available in Tobacco Sunburst finish. Mfd. 1994 to date.

Mfr.'s Sug. Retail	$939	$704	$469	$450	$360	$325	$300	$275

This model has fretless fingerboard (AVBSB-4FL) optionally available.

This model was designed in collaboration with Steve Bailey and Trev Wilkinson.

AVBSB-5 — similar to AVBSB-4, except has 5 strings, 4/1 per side tuners, pearl black hardware. Mfd. 1994 to date.

Mfr.'s Sug. Retail	$1,059	$794	$529	$500	$400	$360	$330	$300

This model has fretless fingerboard (AVBSB-5FL) optionally available.

AVBSB-6 — similar to AVBSB-4, except has 6 strings, 4/2 per side tuners, black hardware, 2 humbucker pickups. Mfd. 1994 to date.

Mfr.'s Sug. Retail	$1,259	$944	$629	$600	$480	$430	$395	$360

This model has fretless fingerboard (AVBSB-6FL) optionally available.

AVBTN4 — offset double cutaway alder body, thru body maple neck, 24 fret rosewood fingerboard with pearl oval inlay, fixed bridge, 4 on one side tuners, black hardware, 2 J-style pickups, 2 volume/1 tone controls, active electronics. Available in Natural and Walnut finishes. Mfd. 1994 to date.

Mfr.'s Sug. Retail	$949	$711	$474	$450	$360	$325	$300	$275

AVBTN5 — similar to AVBTN4, except has 5 strings, 4/1 per side tuners. Mfd. 1994 to date.

Mfr.'s Sug. Retail	$999	$749	$499	$465	$370	$335	$305	$280

"The archtop has a rich heritage and an important place in American history over the last seventy years. I think we are in the middle of the instrument's renaissance..."

—L. Acunto on Scott Chinery

TCG, Nov. 1995

Grading		100%	98% MINT	95% EXC+	90% EXC	80% VG+	70% VG	60% G

AVBTN6 — similar to AVBTN4, except has 6 strings, 4/2 per side tuners. Mfd. 1994 to date.

Mfr.'s Sug. Retail	$1,099	$824	$549	$500	$400	$360	$330	$300

Integra Bass Series

IGB-SPT — jazz style maple body, bolt-on maple neck, 24 fret rosewood fingerboard with pearl dot inlay, fixed bridge, 2 per side tuners, black hardware, P-style/J-style pickups, 2 volume/1 tone controls. Available in Alsace Red, Black, Navy Blue and White finishes. Disc 1991.

	$440	$380	$315	$250	$225	$205	$190

Last Mfr.'s Sug. Retail was $630.

IGB-STD — similar to IGB-SPT, except has chrome hardware. Curr. mfr.

Mfr.'s Sug. Retail	$900	$675	$450	$410	$320	$290	$265	$240

IGB-DLX — similar to IGB-SPT, except has black hardware, volume/bass/treble/mix controls.

Mfr.'s Sug. Retail	$1,000	$750	$500	$470	$360	$325	$300	$275

IGB-DLX/5 — similar to IGB-SPT, except has 5 strings, 4/1 per side tuners, black hardware, volume/bass/treble/mix controls.

Mfr.'s Sug. Retail	$1,100	$825	$550	$520	$400	$360	$330	$300

IGB-CST — similar to IGB-SPT, except has sen body, gold hardware and volume/bass/treble/mix controls. Available in Blue Shade, Dark Red Shade, Transparent Black and Transparent White finishes. Disc 1993.

	$700	$600	$500	$400	$360	$330	$300

Last Mfr.'s Sug. Retail was $1,000.

Magna Bass Series

MAB-09 — offset double cutaway hardwood body, bolt-on maple neck, 22 fret maple fingerboard with black dot inlay, fixed bridge, 4 on one side tuners, chrome hardware, P-style/J-style pickups, 1 volume/2 tone controls. Available in Black, Blue and Red finishes. Mfd. 1994 to date.

Mfr.'s Sug. Retail	$400	$320	$240	$200	$160	$145	$130	$120

MAB-20 — offset double cutaway alder body, bolt-on maple neck, 22 fret rosewood fingerboard with pearl dot inlay, fixed bridge, 4 on one side tuners, black hardware, P-style/J-style pickups, 2 volume/1 tone controls. Available in Apple Red, Black, Midnight Blue and White finishes. Curr. mfr.

Mfr.'s Sug. Retail	$500	$400	$300	$250	$200	$180	$165	$150

MAB-20/5 — similar to MAB-20, except has 5 strings, 24 frets and 2 J-style pickups. Available in Apple Red, Black and White finishes. Curr. mfr.

Mfr.'s Sug. Retail	$530	$397	$265	$250	$200	$180	$165	$150

MAB-40 — similar to MAB-20, except has active EQ in tone control, 3 position and bypass switch. Available in Black, Midnight Cherry, Navy Blue, Pearl Black, Pearl White and White finishes. Curr. mfr.

Mfr.'s Sug. Retail	$700	$525	$350	$320	$240	$215	$195	$180

MAB-50 — similar to MAB-20, except has 24 frets, gold hardware, volume/bass/treble/mix controls, active electronics. Available in Midnight Cherry, Pearl Black and Pearl White finishes. Disc. 1991.

	$695	$595	$500	$400	$360	$330	$300

Last Mfr.'s Sug. Retail was $995.

MAB-60 — offset double cutaway sen body, bolt-on maple neck, 24 fret rosewood fingerboard with pearl dot inlay, fixed bridge, 4 on one side tuners, gold hardware, 2 J-style pickups, volume/bass/treble/mix controls. Available in Blue Shade, Dark Red Shade, Purple Shade and Vintage Sunburst finishes. Disc. 1991.

	$835	$715	$600	$480	$430	$395	$360

Last Mfr.'s Sug. Retail was $1,195.

MAB-60/5 — similar to MAB-60, except has 5 strings, ebony fingerboard, black hardware and 2 double coil pickups. Available in Midnight Cherry, Navy Blue, Pearl Black and Pearl White finishes. Disc. 1991.

	$835	$715	$600	$480	$430	$395	$360

Last Mfr.'s Sug. Retail was $1,195.

Super Bass Series

SB-JR600 — jazz style alder body, bolt-on maple neck, 24 fret rosewood fingerboard with pearl dot inlay, fixed bridge, 2 per side tuners, black hardware, P-style/J-style pickup, 2 volume/1 tone controls. Available in Midnight Cherry, Navy Blue, Pearl Black and Pearl White finishes. Disc. 1991.

	$595	$510	$425	$340	$305	$280	$255

Last Mfr.'s Sug. Retail was $850.

SB-JR750 — similar to SB-JR600, except has maple/walnut/sen body, gold hardware and volume/bass/treble and mixed controls. Available in Amber Natural, Deep Blue and Dark Cherry Shade finishes.

	$770	$660	$550	$440	$395	$365	$330

Last Mfr.'s Sug. Retail was $1,100.

Grading	100%	98% MINT	95% EXC+	90% EXC	80% VG+	70% VG	60% G

SB-1000 — jazz style sen body, maple/walnut thru body neck, 24 fret rosewood fingerboard with pearl dot inlay, fixed bridge, 2 per side tuners, gold hardware, 2 humbucker pickups, 2 volume/1 tone controls, active electronics in tone control. Available in Black, Light Oak, Transparent Black and Transparent Red finishes. Disc. 1993.

		$980	$840	$700	$560	$505	$460	$420

Last Mfr.'s Sug. Retail was $1,400.

SB-LTD — similar to SB-1000, except has ebony fingerboard with pearl oval inlay and Alembic pickups. Available in Transparent Black and Transparent Red finishes. Disc. 1994.

	$1,260	$1,080	$900	$720	$650	$595	$540

Last Mfr.'s Sug. Retail was $1,800.

STB Series

STBPB-01 — offset double cutaway hardwood body, bolt-on maple neck, 20 fret rosewood fingerboard with pearl dot inlay, fixed bridge, 4 on one side tuners, chrome hardware, P-style/J-style pickups, volume/tone controls, 3 position switch. Available in Black, Blue and Vintage Sunburst finishes. Mfd. 1994 to date.

Mfr.'s Sug. Retail	$370	$296	$222	$185	$150	$135	$120	$110

STBPB-01 — offset double cutaway hardwood body, figured maple top, black pickguard, bolt-on maple neck, 20 fret rosewood fingerboard with pearl dot inlay, fixed bridge, 4 on one side tuners, gold hardware, P-style/J-style pickups, volume/tone controls, 3 position switch. Available in Dark Blue Sunburst and Dark Red Sunburst finishes. Mfd. 1994 to date.

Mfr.'s Sug. Retail	$379	$303	$227	$225	$180	$160	$150	$135

ARIRANG

Instruments built in Korea during the early 1980s.

This trademark consists of entry level copies of American designs, and some original designs.

(*Source: Tony Bacon and Paul Day, The Guru's Guitar Guide*)

ARISTONE

See FRAMUS.

See also BESSON.

Instruments made in West Germany during the late 1950s through the early 1960s.

While ARISTONE was the brandname for a UK importer, these guitars were made by and identical to certain FRAMUS models. Research also indicates that the trademark BESSON was utilized as well.

(*Source: Tony Bacon and Paul Day, The Guru's Guitar Guide*)

ARITA

Instruments manufactured in Japan.

Arita instruments were distributed in the U.S. market by the Newark Musical Merchandise Company of Newark, New Jersey.

(*Source: Michael Wright, Guitar Stories Volume One, pg. 76*)

DAN ARMSTRONG

See AMPEG.

Instruments produced in England between 1973 and 1975.

Luthier/designer Dan Armstrong has been involved in the music industry for over thirty years. Dan Amrstrong originally was a musician involved with studio recording in New York, and used to rent equipment from a music shop called Carol's. In 1965, he first began his luthier and repair skills in a shop on 48th Street across from Manny's Music, and one of his first customers was John Sebastian (Loving Spoonful). Armstrong's shop used to retail new instruments as well. Armstrong used to stabilize Danelectros by changing the factory tuners for after-market Klusons, and by replacing the factory bridges. Nat Daniels (Danelectro) once visited his shop, and upon discovering Armstrong's "stabilizing" techniques, got mad and left.

A year after MCA folded the Danelectro company in 1968, Armstrong met William C. Herring at a swap meet in New Jersey. Herring had bought the company from MCA in late 1968/early 1969, and Armstrong acquired some interest in the trademark. The facilities produced some 650 to 700 single cutaway models that had one humbucker, no peghead logo, and Dan Armstrong Modified Danelectro on the pickguard. Armstrong still retains the rights to the trademark.

During the same time period, Armstrong was contracted by Ampeg to produce solid body guitars and basses. Prototypes of the lucite bodied-instruments were produced in 1969, and production ran from 1970 to 1971. Lucite was chosen for its sustaining properties but the novelty of a transparent body lead

Dan Armstrong/
Ampeg Lucite Guitar
courtesy Elliot Rubinson

Dan Armstrong/
Ampeg Lucite Bass
courtesy Elliot Rubinson

to the nickname "See Throughs" (which Ampeg later had copywritten). The clear bodied guitars featured interchangeable pickups designed by Bill Lawrence; however, the plastic was prone to expanding when the body warmed up. While most of the production was clear lucite, a number of instruments were also cast in black lucite.

In 1973, Armstrong moved to England and produced wood body guitars based on the lucite designs. These guitars had the same sliding pickup design, and an anodized aluminum pickguard. The English wood body instruments were produced between 1973 and 1975.

Armstrong produced a number of non-guitar designs as well. Armstrong assisted in some designs for Ampeg's SVT bass amp and the V-4 guitar amplifiers. Musictronics produced the Dan Armstrong Boxes in the mid 1970s, while Armstrong was still living in England. These six small boxes of circuitry plugged into the guitar directly, and then a cable was attached to the amplifier. Modules included the Red Ranger (EQ), Blue Clipper (distortion), Purple Peaker (EQ), Green Ringer (ring modulator), Yellow Humper (EQ) and the acclaimed Orange Squeezer (compression). Armstrong also had a hand in devising the Mutron Octave divider, Volume Wah, and "Gizmo".

Dan Armstrong stayed busy in the early to mid 1980s inventing circuit designs and building prototypes of amplifiers in a consulting fashion. Armstrong was featured in numerous **Guitar Player** magazine articles on aftermarket rewiring schematics that expanded the potential voicings of Fender and Gibson production models. Armstrong built some guitar prototypes for the Westone product line in the late 1980s, and his most recent project was the "Hot Cabs" instrument speaker line for Cerwin Vega. Dan Armstrong currently resides in Sylmar, California, and can be reached through the Index of Current Manufacturers located in the rear of this book.

(Biographical information courtesy Dan Armstrong)

May/June 1996.

ROB ARMSTRONG

Instruments built in England during the late 1970s, possibly also the early to mid 1980s as well.

Luthier Rob Armstrong is known for his custom guitar building. One of his more famous jobs appears to be a Kellogg's Corn Flakes box-turned-guitar for Simon Nicol (Fairport Convention).

(Source: Tony Bacon, The Ulitmate Guitar Book)

ARMY & NAVY SPECIAL

See chapter on House Brands.

This trademark has been identified as a Gibson built budget line available only at military post exchanges (PXs) towards the end of World War I (1918). They will have a label different from the standard Gibson label of the time, yet still be credited to the "Gibson Mandolin - Guitar Co." of 'Kalamazoo, Mich., USA'. As a budget line Gibson these guitars will possess no adjustable truss rod in the neck.

(Source: Walter Carter, Gibson: 100 Years of an American Icon)

ARTISAN

Instruments produced in Japan.

Artisan instruments were distributed in the U.S. market by the Barth-Feinberg company of New York.

(Source: Michael Wright, Guitar Stories Volume One, pg. 76)

ARTISTA

Instruments built in Spain. Distributed by Musicorp, a division of MBT of Charleston, South Carolina.

These reasonably priced handmade guitars are designed for the beginning classical guitar student. The Artista line features three models: the **Granada** ($275) has an Oregon Pine top, Sapelle (mahogany) body, and a jacaranda fingerboard; the **Morena** ($350) has the same Oregon Pine top combined with a Mongoy (Brazilian jacaranda) body, and mahogany neck; and the **Segovia** ($525) features a solid cedar top, rosewood back and sides, and a rosewood fingerboard.

ASAMA

Instruments built in Japan during the early 1980s.

Guitars with this trademark are generally medium to good quality copies of American design as well as some original designs.

(Source: Tony Bacon and Paul Day, The Guru's Guitar Guide)

ASHLAND

These instruments are manufactured in Asia; and distributed by V M I Industries of Brea, California.

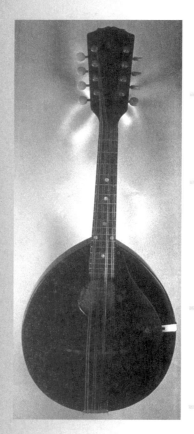

Army & Navy Mandolin
courtesy Darrell Spatafore

Ashland instruments are manufactured for the entry level or beginning guitarist. Ashland offers three dreadnought style guitars with a spruce top and mahogany back and sides. Prices start at $249 (AD 26), to $269 (AD 36), up to $299 (AD 39). A fourth model, the AE 16 ($279) is an acoustic/electric that features a fingerboard-mounted pickup with adjustable polepieces.

ASI

Instruments built in Korea. Distributed in the U.S. market by Audio Sound International, Inc. of Indianapolis, Indiana.

ASI, the company that also supplies Quantum amplifiers and Rackmaster gear, developed a number of solid body guitars to market the 'Sustainiac' pickup system. The Sustainiac system (developed by Maniac Music) features on-board magnetic circuitry to create real string sustain. Similar to the system that Kaman/Hamer put in the Chaparral Elite, ASI used both the GA2 and GA4 in a number of Taiwan-, Korean-, and Japanese-built guitars in an effort to bring the system to a more affordable price in the guitar market. The **AE 7S** was an earlier model from 1990, and was followed by the **AS-121** in 1991. Two more maple-bodied models followed (the **AS 100** and **AS 85**). Used prices must be weighed from the pickup system against the quality of the guitar it is installed in.

ASTURIAS

Instruments built on the island of Kyushu, Japan. Distribution in the U.S. market by J.T.G. of Nashville, located in Nashville, Tennessee.

The Asturias Workshops in southern Japan employ seventeen people who have worked at Asturias most of their lives or have a family connection. Guided by chief luthier Wataru Tsuji, these luthiers take great care with their production methods to ensure a quality guitar.

ATHELETE

Instruments currently built in New York, New York.

Luthier Fumi Nozawa has been creating these high quality 4, 5, or 6 string acoustic basses, as well as acoustic guitars for several years.

ATLANSIA

Instruments built in Japan.

The best way to describe instruments designed and built by luthier N. Hayashi is **sleek**. Every curve on any model seems aerodynamic, and the instruments have a nice balance to them. Atlansia high quality guitars and basses are readily identifiable by the Atlansia logo on the headstock; some models will possess either covered rectangular magnets or a series of round pickups (1 per string) the size of dimes. During the early 1980s, models like the Concorde, Stealth, and Galaxie were offered in the U.S. market (the U.S. distributor was based in Texas). One model, The Solitaire, featured a body shaped like a pool cue with a single string, bridge unit, and pickup. Other models were not that extreme, however, and any of the 4, 5, or 6 string models should be well-balanced and playable.

(Source: Rittor Music, Inc., Guitar Graphics, Volume One)

ATLAS

See chapter on House Brands.

This trademark has been identified as a "House Brand" of the RCA Victor Records Stores.

(Source: Willie G. Moseley, Stellas & Stratocasters)

AUDIO OPTICS

Instruments are manufactured in Japan by Tune Guitar Technology Co., Ltd.; the Lightwave pickups (based on optical technology) are built in Santa Barbara, California. Distributed by Audio Optics, Inc. of Santa Babara, California.

The Audio Optics systems use a new technology of optical scanning in their innovative pickup designs in place of the magnetic field system. The design team at Audio Optics spent ten years devising and perfecting the system, which is composed of an optical/piezo sensing elements. The company plans to release their own equipped bass models, as a retrofit kit, or as an OEM system for other manufacturers.

According to the company, here's how it works: a string of any composition is illuminated by an infrared light source so that the string casts a shadow on a pair of high speed photodetectors. When the string is vibrated, the size and shape of the shadow changes in direct proportion to the frequency. This modulates a current passing through the photo sensors - and the current is then amplified.

A

ELECTRIC BASS

Augustino LoPrinzi

QED 4 — offset double cutaway asymmetrical mahogany body with pointed bottom bout, carved padauk top, black thumbrest, mahogany neck, 36 fret ebony fingerboard with offset white dot inlay, fixed bridge, 2 per side tuners, black hardware, optical transducer pickup, volume/tone/5 position rotary controls, 3 position switch, mono/stereo output, active electronics, power cable. Available in Natural finish. Current production.

Mfr.'s Sug. Retail	$3,295	$2,471	$1,647	$1,595	$1,275

Various hardwoods are used for the carved top.

This instrument was designed by Hatsukazu Fujitani. It uses infrared sensors (the optical transducer) to detect string vibrations. The rotary control works in conjunction with the 3 position switch, which is used to select presets adjusted by an inboard 14 band EQ.

QED 5 — similar to QED 4, except has 5 strings, 2/3 per side tuners. Current production.

Mfr.'s Sug. Retail	$3,495	$2,796	$2,097	$1,750	$1,400

AUDITION

See chapter on House Brands.

This trademark has been identified by researcher Willie G. Moseley as a "House Brand" of the F. W. Woolworth (Woolco) department stores.

Further information from authors Tony Bacon and Paul Day indicate that guitars with this trademark originated in Japan (later Korea) during the 1960s and 1970s.

(Source: Tony Bacon and Paul Day, The Guru's Guitar Guide)

AUERSWALD

Instruments built in Konstanz, Germany during the early 1990s.

Luthier Jerry Auerswald builds high quality original design solid body guitars and basses that are visually exciting as well. Models feature maple bodies, cherry/wenge necks, EMG pickups, Sperzel hardware, and Auerswald custom tremolo and EQ systems. The **Cleo** bass and the **Anastasia** guitar both feature a "sustain bow", a body arm that attaches to the headstock and provides extra stiffening support to the upper end of the neck. Both the **Naomi Sign** and **Gloria** models are of similar designs; however, the Gloria features tuned air chambers in the body for fuller resonance.

Auerswald electrics are identifiable by the unique body/neck design, the additional body arm on some models, and the logo on the truss rod cover and on the bridge hardware.

AUGUSTINO

Augustino LoPrinzi
in his workshop

Instruments currently built in Florida.

Luthier Augustino LoPrinzi originally was trained by his father to be a barber. A self-taught guitar builder, LoPrinzi's original Flemmington, New Jersey barbershop also had a guitar workshop in the back. After ten years dividing his interests, LoPrinzi (and his brother Thomas) founded LoPrinzi guitars in New Jersey in 1972. The business grew from a two- and three-man operation into a staff of 18 employees. Modern production techniques enabled the LoPrinzi brothers to pare the number of employees back to 7 while still producing 60 to 80 guitars a month in 1975. LoPrinzi, tired of overseeing production, sold the business to Maark Corporation (a subsidiary of AMF). Refusing to sign a "Non-compete" clause, LoPrinzi opened "Augustino Guitars" two weeks later - and literally right next door to his original plant! He continued to produce guitars there until 1978, and then moved to Florida. The AMF-owned LoPrinzi company continued producing guitars for a number of years, and finally closed the doors in 1980. Years later, Augustino called AMF to request his old trademark back. Working with vice president Dick Hargraves, Augustino officially had the trademark transferred back, and has combined it to form the current **Augustino LoPrinzi** line of classical guitars. LoPrinzi still builds classical guitars full time (about 8 guitars a month), and is assisted by his daughter, Donna Chavis, and woodworker Bill Kreutzer.

(Source: Hal Hammer)

Through the years, Augustino LoPrinzi has consulted or designed instruments for many companies including Guild, Martin, Kramer, Fender, and others. His high quality limited production classical guitars feature quality tonewoods, and range in price from $2,300 to $3,100. LoPrinzi also builds several flamenco models, and a smaller number of steel string acoustics. For further information regarding models, availability, and pricing, please contact luthier LoPrinzi via the Index of Current Manufacturers located in the rear of this book.

AUROC

Instruments built in England from 1988 to current.

Luthier Pat Luckett builds guitars with a 'strat'-styled synthetic marble body coupled with a graphite neck. A promising design that may eliminate the "tweakage" phenomenon of wood necks. The **Blue Book of Guitars** encourages anyone with further information to contact us for future edition updates.

AVANTI

Instruments produced in Europe during the 1960s.

Research continues into this trademark. Most models that are encountered seem to have a resounding feel of 1960s entry level Italian production. Further information will be updated in future editions of the **Blue Book of Guitars**.

(Source: Rittor Books, 60s Bizarre Guitars)

AVON

Instruments built in Japan during the early to late 1970s.

The AVON trademark is the brandname of a UK importer. Avons are generally low to medium quality copies of American designs.

(Source: Tony Bacon and Paul Day, The Guru's Guitar Guide)

AXE

Instruments built in Korea from 1988 to 1989.

Entry level two pickup guitar that came in a "starter pack". Although we're not familiar with the guitar, the idea of a package containing all sorts of guitar paraphenalia (how-to booklet, strings, tuner of some sort, strap, etc) actually sounds like a novel idea if coupled with lessons.

(Source: Tony Bacon and Paul Day, The Guru's Guitar Guide)

AXELSON

Instruments currently built in Duluth, Minnesota.

Luthier Randy Axelson has been providing top-notch guitar repair, restoration, and custom guitar building on a regular basis. For information, pricing, and availability contact luthier Axelson through the Index of Current Manufacturers located in the back of this book.

AXEMAN

Instruments built in Japan during the late 1970s.

The AXEMAN trademark is the brandname of a UK importer. The guitars are generally medium quality copies of American designs.

(Source: Tony Bacon and Paul Day, The Guru's Guitar Guide)

AXIS

Instruments built in Korea circa 1989.

The AXIS trademark is the brandname of a UK importer. Axis guitars are entry level to medium quality solidbody copies of American design.

(Source: Tony Bacon and Paul Day, The Guru's Guitar Guide)

AXTECH

See listing under SAEHAN.

Instruments built in Korea.

Axtech instruments are generally entry level to medium quality solid body and acoustic guitars based on Classic American designs.

AXTRA

Instruments built in Kenosha, Wisconsin. Distributed by Axtra Guitars, Inc. of Kenosha, Wisconsin.

Luthier Bill Michaelis has been designing and custom building guitars for over twenty years. About nine years ago, Michaelis went public and opened a medium sized shop that he describes as "not the basement, but it's not Gibson sized either". Other family members are part of the Axtra team, which produces high quality custom solid body guitars. Michaelis offers a number of body designs, as well as the flexibilty of a custom concept. Hardware, pickups, and other options are at the customer's choice. For further information, contact luthier Michaelis through the Index of Current Manufacturers located in the back of this book.

AZOLA

Instruments currently built in San Marcos, California.

Austin Hatchet
courtesy World Wide Guitars

A

The Azola Music Products company is currently distributing a modified new version of an old favorite: Ampeg's Baby Bass! Azola is also offering replacement parts and accessories for the original 1960s Baby Basses, like a complete magnetic diaphragm pickup retrofit kits, padded cases, or a hard cases.

ELECTRIC BASS

The **Azola Baby Bass** ($2,695) features a fibreglass body with a Birch inner structure, 2 piece maple neck with graphite reinforcing, a Pau Ferro fingerboard, 41.5" scale, and a piezo bridge pickup. Available in Red, White, and Black. Azola's **MiniBass** ($1,695) shares many of the specifications of the Baby Bass, except the sleek contoured body is contructed of solid Alder. The newest model, the **BugBass** ($1,195) has an ultra compact, violin-shaped Alder body, and a tripod stand. All three models had prices quoted in the Basic model. For upgrade to the Latin configuration with Magnetic Diaphram pickup system and passive volume/tone controls, add $300. To further upgrade to a combination of piezo and Magnetic systems with an active EQ, add $500.

Azola offers an upright, violin-shaped Mahogany body **StradiBass** ($4,995) with a Clevinger-designed floating Spruce Top. The instrument also features a Figured Maple laminated neck, Ebony fingerboard, 41.5" scale, Maple bridge, gold hardware, and a multi-piezo bridge pickup system with 3-band active EQ.

AZUMI

See LEW CHASE.

Instruments built in Japan during the early 1980s.

Azumi guitars were generally medium quality solidbodys of original design. Further updates in future editions of the **Blue Book of Guitars** will explore these body designs. Readers with information are encouraged to write in!

(Source: Tony Bacon and Paul Day, The Guru's Guitar Guide)

B & G

See chapter on House Brands.

B & G instruments were built by Danelectro in Neptune City, New Jersey in the late 1950s/early 1960s.

(Source: Willie G. Moseley, Stellas & Stratocasters)

B & J

See chapter on House Brands.

This trademark has been identified as a "House Brand" of the B & J company.

(Source: Willie G. Moseley, Stellas & Stratocasters)

BACON & DAY

See VEGA.

JAMES R. BAKER

Instruments currently built in Huntington Station, New York.

Luthier James R. Baker has been building conventional design archtop guitars and experimental archtops designed to enhance the electric guitar capabilities. While his **Classic** features traditionally placed f-holes, Baker's innovative **Legend** and **Special** models have teardrop-shaped soundholes in the lower body bout area. All handmade instruments feature exotic wood contruction, custom finishes, Shaller or Grover tuning machines, Bartolini or EMG pickups, and a retail list price of $5,000. For further information, contact luthier Baker via the Index of Current Manufacturers located in the rear of this book.

Baker Classic
courtesy James R. Baker

BAKES

Instruments built in Elgin, Illinois since 1983. Distributed by Bakes Guitars of Elgin, Illinois.

Luthier Robert Bakes has been handcrafting fine guitars since 1983. Over the past twelve years, Bakes has been performing repairs and custom building instruments out of the Bakes Guitars shop in Elgin, Illinois. Ably assisted by his wife Beverly, the Bakes also produce two vintage instrument shows: Guitar Madness (September) is now in its ninth year, and the spring Chicago Vintage Guitar Expo (February). For further information, contact Robert and Beverly Bakes via the Index of Current Manufacturers located in the rear of this book.

BALDWIN

Instruments produced in Booneville, Arkansas from 1965 to 1979. Distribution of instruments handled by the Baldwin Piano Company of Chicago, Illinois.

In 1962, as Leo Fender's health was faltering, he discussed the idea of selling Fender Electric Instruments company to Don Randall (head of Fender Sales). While Randall toyed with the idea even as late as the summer of 1963, they eventually concluded to sell to a third party who had money. Negotiations began with the Baldwin Piano Company in April of 1964, who offered $5 million (minus Fender's liabilities). When talks bogged down over acoustic guitar and electric piano operations, Randall met with representatives of the Columbia Broadcasting System (CBS). An agreement with CBS was signed in October, 1964, for $13 million that took effect in January of 1965.

Baldwin, outbid by CBS but still looking to diversify, then bought the Burns manufacturing facilities from Jim Burns (regarded as "the British Leo Fender") in September, 1965. The Baldwin company then began assembling the imported Burns parts in Booneville, Arkansas. Baldwin also acquired the Gretsch trademark when Fred Gretsch, Jr. sold the company in 1967. As part of a business consolidation, The New York Gretsch operation was moved to the Arkansas facility in 1970 (for further Baldwin/Gretsch history, see GRETSCH).

BALEANI

Instruments were built in Italy during the mid 1960s.

These solid body guitars are generally entry level quality, but the sparkle/pearloid plastic finish says "Las Vegas" everytime!

(Source: Tony Bacon and Paul Day, The Guru's Guitar Guide)

BAMBU

Instruments were built in Japan in the late 1970s.

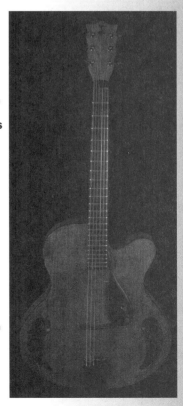

Baker Legend
courtesy James R. Baker

Sal Salvador model
courtesy Carl Barney

The model CB625 was a solid body built by the Maya company, and featured a laminated bamboo neck, two humbuckers and active circuitry.

(Source: Tony Baco and Paul Day, The Guru's Guitar Guide)

BARBERO

Instruments were built in Spain.

This brandname belonged to Marcelo Barbero (1904-1955), considered one of the great flamenco guitar makers.

(Source: Tony Bacon, The Ultimate Guitar Book)

BARCLAY

See chapter on House Brands.

While this trademark has been identified as a "House Brand", the Distributor is still unknown. Further research is underway.

(Source: Willie G. Moseley, Stellas & Stratocasters)

CARL BARNEY

Instruments built in Southbury, Connecticut since 1968.

Luthier Carl Barney has been creating fine handcrafted archtop guitars since the late 1960s. Barney offers three versions of his Jazzmaster Series (I-$3,300, II-$3,800, Deluxe-$4,200) that offer his design in different packages (exotic woods, inlays). Furthermore, Barney also offers the OV Jazz model ($2,600), which is based on the 1960s Howard Robert Epiphone model; and flatop top steel strings ($1,400), Classicals ($1,800), and even solid body designs ($1,000). Prices quoted are for base models; for further information please contact luthier Barney through the Index of Current Manufacturers located in the rear of this book.

BARON

See chapter on House Brands.

This trademark has been identified as a "House Brand" of the RCA Victor Records Store; furthermore, KAY exported guitars bearing this trademark to the Thibouville-Lamy company of France.

(Source: Willie G. Moseley, Stellas & Stratocasters)

BARRINGTON

Instruments produced by Terada of Japan in the late 1980s. Distribution in the U.S. market was handled by Barrington Guitars of Barrington, Illinois; the company now specializes in brass instruments as the L.A. Sax Company of Barrington, Illinois.

Barrington Guitars offered both solid body electric guitars and basses during the late 1980s, as well as acoustic and acoustic/electric Barrington Gruhn signature series models as well. The acoustics were similar in a design produced in collaboration between George Gruhn and Collings guitars in 1988, and carried a new retail list price between $1,225 and $1,325 (a Fishman transducer pickup was optional equipment on the four models). The AT-1 and AT-2 f-hole archtops listed new at $1,650.

BARTELL

See BARTH.

Instruments built in Riverside, California between 1964 and 1969.

The Bartell company was formed by Paul Barth (engineer) and Ted Peckles (owner and company president) in the mid 1960s after Barth returned from Magnatone's facilities on the East Coast. One of Barth's co-workers at Rickenbacker was Roger Rossmeisl, who introduced the "German Carve" (a beveled ridge around the top of a guitar) to Rickenbacker, and later Fender designs. The same "German Carve" can be found on both Bartell and Mosrite guitars. Bartells were produced from 1964 to 1969, and former owner Peckles estimates that around 2,000 instruments were produced. The Bartell company also built instruments for rebranding for Hohner, St. George, and later edition Acoustic 'Black Widow' models.

Bartell guitars feature a strat-style offset double cutaway body, a Mosrite-inspired headstock, "German Carve" ridge, and two single coil pickups. Electronics include a volume and tone knob, two on/off pickup selector switches, and a third switch for in/out of phase between the two pickups. There is also mention of a semi-hollowbody that features a design that is a cross between the above model and an ES-335.

(Source: Teisco Del Rey, Guitar Player magazine, July 1990)

BARTH

Instruments built in Southern California during the mid to late 1950s.

Luthier/designer Paul Barth, nephew to National's John Dopyera, was one of the three men responsible for Rickenbacker's "Frying Pan" solid body electric steel guitar (along with George Beauchamp and

Jazzmaker II
courtesy Carl Barney

Adolph Rickenbacker). Barth left Rickenbacker in 1956, and formed his own company briefly to build and market guitars with the Barth trademark. One of Paul Barth's employees at Rickenbacker was Semie Moseley in the early 1950s; and when Moseley later formed his own company, Barth briefly used Moseley's finishing skills to complete an order of guitars. Barth later went to work for Magnatone in the early 1960s, designing models at Magnatone's Torrance, California facilities.

For further biographical information, see BARTELL.

(Source: Teisco Del Rey, Guitar Player magazine, July 1990)

BARTOLINI

Instruments were built in Italy during the 1960s.

Author Tony Bacon in his book, "The Ultimate Guitar Book", notes that Italy, like many other European countries, experienced the 1960's pop music popularity that led to a larger demand for electric guitars. However, many electric guitar builders were also manufacturers of accordians. As a result, many guitars ended up with accordian-style finishes. Wacky or not, Leo Fender was using this same sort of heat-molded acetate finish on some of his lap steel models in the early 1950s. What Leo wasn't using was the accordion-style pushbuttons, however.

BILL BARTOLINI

Instruments built in 1960s. Bartolini now produces a line of high quality guitar pickups in Livermore, California.

Luthier Bill Bartolini used to build classical guitars in California during the 1960s. Research on resonances produced during this time formed the basis for his pickup designs, and his clear, high quality pickups are standard features on numerous luthiers' creations.

BASS COLLECTION

Instruments manufactured in Japan from 1985 to 1992. Originally distributed by Meisel Music, Inc. for a number of years, their on-hand stock was purchased by the Sam Ash music store chain of New York in 1994 and sold through the Sam Ash stores.

While Bass Collection and Guitar Collection instruments were available in the U.S. market for a number of years, a recent survey failed to turn up the current distributor. This section is maintained for model information and used pricing, but the trademark will be considered discontinued for the Third Edition. The **Blue Book of Guitars** will update further information as it becomes readily available.

ELECTRIC BASS

Grading	100%	98% MINT	95% EXC+	90% EXC	80% VG+	70% VG	60% G

300 Series

SB301 — offset double cutaway alder body, bolt-on maple neck, 24 fret rosewood fingerboard, fixed bridge, 2 per side Gotoh tuners, black hardware, P-style/J-style pickups, 2 volume/2 tone controls. Available in Black, Magenta, Metallic Grey and Sunburst finishes. Disc. 1994.

$480	$410	$330	$265	$240	$220	$200

Last Mfr.'s Sug. Retail was $700.

This model has ash body with Transparent Red finish optionally available.

SB302 — similar to SB301, except has fretless fingerboard. Available in Black, Magenta and Metallic Grey finishes.

$480	$410	$330	$265	$240	$220	$200

Last Mfr.'s Sug. Retail was $700.

This model has ash body with Transparent Red finish optionally available.

SB305 — similar to SB301, except has 5 strings, 2 J-style pickups.

$485	$425	$360	$305	$275	$250	$230

Last Mfr.'s Sug. Retail was $670.

This model has ash body with Transparent Red finish optionally available.

SB305FL — similar to SB301, except has 5 strings, fretless fingerboard, 2 J-style pickups.

$560	$480	$400	$320	$290	$265	$240

Last Mfr.'s Sug. Retail was $800.

This model has ash body with Transparent Red finish optionally available.

"The interesting characteristic of wood is the way that it expands and contracts with the changing humidity. As wood dries, it contracts across the grain and expands along the grain. This is related to the cellular structure of the wood."
—B. Jurevich & B. Handy
TCG, Nov. 1995

Grading	100%	98% MINT	95% EXC+	90% EXC	80% VG+	70% VG	60% G

400 Series

SB401 — offset double cutaway basswood body, bolt-on maple neck, 24 fret rosewood fingerboard, fixed bridge, 2 per side Gotoh tuners, black hardware, P-style/J-style pickups, 2 volume/2 tone controls, active electronics, 2 band EQ. Available in Black, Metallic Red and Pearl White finishes. Disc. 1994.

		$695	$595	$500	$400	$360	$330	$300

Last Mfr.'s Sug. Retail was $995.

SB402 — similar to SB401, except has fretless fingerboard.

		$695	$595	$500	$400	$360	$330	$300

Last Mfr.'s Sug. Retail was $995.

SB405 — similar to SB401, except has 5 strings and 2 J-style pickups.

		$835	$715	$600	$480	$430	$395	$360

Last Mfr.'s Sug. Retail was $1,195.

500 Series

SB501 — offset double cutaway alder body, bolt-on 3 piece maple neck, 24 fret ebony fingerboard, fixed bridge, 2 per side tuners, black hardware, P-style/J-style pickups, 2 volume/2 tone controls, active electronics with 2 band EQ. Available in Black, Natural and Pearl White finishes. Disc. 1994

		$835	$715	$600	$480	$430	$395	$360

Last Mfr.'s Sug. Retail was $1,195.

Add $100 for left handed version.

SB502 — similar to SB501, except has fretless fingerboard.

		$795	$665	$540	$400	$360	$330	$300

Last Mfr.'s Sug. Retail was $1,195.

Add $200 for left handed version.

SB505 — similar to SB501, except has 5 strings.

		$975	$835	$700	$560	$505	$460	$420

Last Mfr.'s Sug. Retail was $1,395.

This model has ash body with Transparent Red finish optionally available.

600 Series

SB611 — offset double cutaway asymmetrical maple body with padauk or walnut top, bolt-on maple neck, 24 fret ebony fingerboard, fixed bridge, 2 per side Gotoh tuners, gold hardware, P-style/J-style pickups, 2 volume/2 tone controls, active electronics with 2 band EQ. Available in Oil finishes. Disc. 1994

		$1,045	$895	$750	$600	$540	$495	$450

Last Mfr.'s Sug. Retail was $1,495.

This model has fretless fingerboard optionally available (SB612).

SB615 — similar to SB611, except has 5 strings.

		$1,155	$990	$825	$660	$595	$545	$495

Last Mfr.'s Sug. Retail was $1,650.

DB Series

DB41R — asymmetrical double cutaway ash body, bolt-on maple neck, 24 fret rosewood fingerboard with abalone dot inlay, fixed bridge, 2 per side tuners, chrome hardware, 2 J-style pickups, 2 volume/2 tone controls. Available in Transparent Black and Transparent Red finishes. Disc. 1994.

		$840	$720	$600	$480	$430	$395	$360

Last Mfr.'s Sug. Retail was $1,150.

DB43E — similar to DB41R, except has padauk/maple/mahogany laminated or walnut/maple/mahogany laminated body, ebony fingerboard, gold hardware, 2 humbucker pickups. Available in Oil finishes. Disc. 1994.

		$1,140	$980	$815	$650	$585	$535	$490

Last Mfr.'s Sug. Retail was $1,630.

DB51R — similar to DB41R, except has 5 strings.

		$1,090	$935	$780	$625	$560	$515	$470

Last Mfr.'s Sug. Retail was $1,560.

DB53E — similar to DB41R, except has 5 strings, padauk/maple/mahogany laminated or walnut/maple/mahogany laminated body, ebony fingerboard, gold hardware, 2 humbucker pickups. Available in Oil finishes. Mfd. 1991 to 1992.

		$1,400	$1,200	$1,000	$800	$720	$660	$600

Last Mfr.'s Sug. Retail was $2,000.

BASS O LIN

Instruments built in New York, New York since 1994.

Designer Danny Agostino is currently offering "the world's most versatile electric bass". Inspired in the early 1970s by Jimmy Page's explorations of a Les Paul and a violin bow, Agostino developed a bass design in the early 1980s that could be played by tapping, plucking, or bowing. The bass's unique design allows 5 different playing positions: 3 different strap configurations standing, or on either leg in a sitting position. The bridge is constructed similar to an upright bass's bridge, with different planes for bowing capabilities. Agostino also offers an optional stand that will provide two more playing positions (grand total of 7 different playing positions).

While compact, the instrument has a 34" scale. Models are offered with 3 piece curly maple necks, African Mahogany or Quilted Maple bodies, fretted or unfretted Rosewood or Ebony fingerboards, and custom designed Agostino radiused pickups. Future models will be offered with an RMC 8 crystal piezo "Power bridge". For further information, contact designer Agostino via the Index of Current Manufacturers located in the back of this book.

BAUER

See S.S. STEWART.

George Bauer, a noted guitar builder in Philadelphia during the late 1800s, entered into a partnership with banjo producer S.S. Stewart. The two produced guitars under the Stewart & Bauer trademark. After Stewart passed away, Bauer continued to release instruments under the Stewart & Bauer label, and also under the Monogram trademark.

(Source: Tom Wheeler, American Guitars)

BAY STATE

Instruments manufactured in Boston, Massachusetts from 1865 to the early 1900s.

The Oliver Ditson Company, Inc. was formed in 1835 by music publisher Oliver Ditson (1811-1888). Ditson was a primary force in music merchandising, distribution, and retail sales on the East Coast. He also helped establish two musical instrument manufacturers: The John Church Company of Cincinnati, Ohio, and Lyon & Healy (Washburn) in Chicago, Illinois.

In 1865 Ditson established a manufacturing branch of his company under the supervision of John Haynes, called the John C. Haynes Company. This branch built guitars for a number of trademarks, such as Bay State, Tilton, and Haynes Excelsior.

(Source: Tom Wheeler, American Guitars)

Bass O Lin
courtesy Danny Agostino

B.C. RICH

Instruments currently built in Hesperia, California (American Handmade series) and Asia (Platinum and NJ series). Distributed by B.C. Rich Guitars International, Inc. of San Bernadino, California and B.C. Rich Guitars USA.

Luthier Bernardo Chavez Rico used to built classical and flamenco guitars at Bernardo's Valencian Guitar Shop, the family's business in Los Angeles. During the mid 1960s folk music boom (and boom in guitar sales), a distributor suggested a name change - and B.C. Rich guitars were born. The company began producing custom guitars based on Fender and Gibson designs, but Rico wanted to produce designs that represented his tastes and ideals. The Seagull solid body (first produced in 1971) was sleek, curvy, and "made for rock & roll". Possessing a fast neck, hot-rodded circuitry and pickups, and a unique body profile was (and still is) an eye-catching design.

In 1974, Neal Mosher joined the company. Mosher also had a hand in some of the guitars designed, and further explored other designs with models like the Mockingbird, Eagle, Ironbird, and the provocatively-named Bich. In the mid 1980s, B.C. Rich moved from Los Angeles to El Monte, California. The company began to import a Japanese-built line of B.C. Rich designs under the 'NJ' series, and production of this series later moved to Korea. In late 1989 or early 1990, Rico sold his design licenses to Class Axe. Class Axe moved production of the U.S.-built guitars to a facility in Warren, New Jersey, and stepped up importation of the NJ series, lower priced Platinum series, and an entry level series called the Rave series.

Unfortunately, the lower priced series soon began to show a marked drop in quality. In 1994, Rico came back out of semi-retirement, retook control over his trademark, and began to rebuild the company. Rico became partners with Bill Shapiro, and the two divided up areas of responsibility. Rico once more began building acoustic and high end electrics at his Hesperia facilities; and Shapiro is maintaining quality control over the imported NJ and Platinum series in San Bernadino.

Grading	100%	98% MINT	95% EXC+	90% EXC	80% VG+	70% VG	60% G

American Made Series

ACOUSTIC

B30-D — dreadnought sized flat top body, spruce top, round soundhole, rosewood bound body, abalone rosette, quilted maple back/sides, mahogany neck, 21 fret rosewood fingerboard with abalone diamond inlay, rosweeood bridge, white pearl dot bridge pins, figured maple veneered peghead with pearl logo inlay, 3 per side Grover Imperial chrome tuners. Available in Natural, Transparent Red, Transparent Blue, Transparent Pagan Gold, and Transparent Emerald Green finishes. Current production.

Mfr.'s Sug. Retail	$1,499	$1,199	$899	$845	$675	$605	$555	$505

B30-C — similar to B30-D, except has a single cutaway dreadnought style body. Current production.

Mfr.'s Sug. Retail	$1,499	$1,394	$1,349	$1,250	$1,000	$900	$825	$750

B35-D — dreadnought style, spruce top, round soundhole, maple bound body, herringbone purfling/rosette, 3 piece rosewood/figured maple back, rosewood sides, mahogany neck, 14/21 fret maple bound ebony fingerboard with abalone cloud inlay, ebony bridge with pearl cloud inlay, white pearl dot bridge pins, maple bound rosewood veneered peghead with abalone logo inlay, 3 per side Grover Imperial chrome tuners. Available in Natural finish. New 1995.

Mfr.'s Sug. Retail	$1,699	$1,359	$1,019	$995	$795	$720	$660	$600

B35-C — similar to B30-D, except has a single cutaway style body. Current production.

Mfr.'s Sug. Retail	$1,699	$1,495	$1,308	$1,250	$1,000	$900	$825	$750

B41-C — single round cutaway flat top body, spruce top, diamond soundhole, bound body, abalone purfling/rosette, rosewood back/sides, mahogany neck, 21 fret bound ebony fingerboard with abalone cloud inlay, ebony bridge with pearl cloud inlay, white pearl dot bridge pins, bound rosewood veneered peghead with abalone logo inlay, 3 per side Grover Imperial gold tuners. Available in Natural finish. New 1995.

Mfr.'s Sug. Retail	$2,699	$2,159	$1,619	$1,450	$1,160	$1,040	$955	$870

B41-D — similar to B41-C, except has noncutaway dreadnought style body, 14/21 fret rosewood fingerboard. Available in Natural finish. New 1995.

Mfr.'s Sug. Retail	$2,495	$1,996	$1,497	$1,250	$1,000	$900	$825	$750

ELECTRIC

B.C. Rich models all have different body profiles. However, the main body design may be offered in one of five different series, and those different series have different price levels. Any American-built neck-through guitar or bass with **B.C. Rich** or **Rico** logos have new retail prices between $1,399 to $2,100. There are a few American-built models with bolt-on construction, and these are priced a bit lower between $999 to $1,399.

The imports are also very straight forward. All imports feature a bolt-on neck, mostly solid colors, and entry level hardware and pickups. The new **U.S.** series is priced where the old (discontinued) **Rave** series was: between $299 and $399. The **Platinum** series is more moderate, being priced between $479 and $549. Finally, the **NJ** series ranges between $669 and $699. With each step up in pricing, there is an equivalent step up in quality.

ASSASSIN — offset double cutaway alder body, bolt-on maple neck, 24 fret ebony fingerboard, double locking Floyd Rose vibrato, blackface peghead with screened logo, 6 on one side Sperzel tuners, black hardware, single coil/humbucker pickups, 2 volume/1 tone controls, 3 position switch. Available in Black, Candy Blue, Candy Red, Deep Metallic Purple, Pearl Emerald, Red and Transparent Colors finishes. Curr. mfr.

Mfr.'s Sug. Retail	$1,199	$959	$719	$600	$480	$430	$395	$360

This model has standard Wilkinson vibrato optionally available.

In 1995, pearl blade fingerboard inlay, Blue, Purple, Turquoise and White finishes were introduced, Candy Color finishes became optionally available, Deep Metallic Purple, Pear Emerald and Transparent Color finishes were discontinued.

Assassin MMT — similar to Assassin, except has figured maple top, chrome or black hardware, 3 different pickup/electronic configurations (see model notes), all variations use 2 volume/1 tone controls. Available in Translucent Black, Translucent Blue, Translucent Emerald Green, Translucent Golden Yellow, Translucent Magenta, Translucent Red and Translucent Tangerine. Curr. mfr.

Mfr.'s Sug. Retail	$1,399	$1,119	$839	$750	$600	$540	$495	$450

This model available in one of the following; 3 single coil pickups with 3 mini switches, single coil/humbucker pickups with mini switches, 2 humbucker pickups with 3 position switch.

In 1995, Translucent Pagon Gold finish was introduced, Translucent Black, Translucent Golden Yellow, Translucent Magenta and Translucent Tangerine finishes were discontinued.

Assassin Neckthru — similar to Assassin, except has thru body maple neck, chrome or black hardware, 3 different pickup/electronic configurations (see model notes), all variations use 2 volume/1 tone controls. Available in Black, Blue, Emerald Green, Golden Yellow, Magenta, Red and Tangerine. All finishes are Translucent. New 1995.

Mfr.'s Sug. Retail	$1,399	$1,119	$839	$750	$600	$540	$495	$450

This model available in one of the following; 3 single coil pickups with 3 mini switches, single coil/humbucker pickups with mini switches, 2 humbucker pickups with 3 position switch.

Grading		100%	98% MINT	95% EXC+	90% EXC	80% VG+	70% VG	60% G

Assassin MMT Neckthru — offset double cutaway mahogany body, figured maple top, thru body maple neck, 24 fret ebony fingerboard, double locking Floyd Rose vibrato, blackface peghead with screened logo, 6 on one side Sperzel tuners, black hardware, 2 humbucker DiMarzio pickups, 2 volume/1 tone controls, 3 position switch. Available in Emerald Green, Red Tangerine, Transparent Blue, Transparent Gold and Transparent Purple finishes. Disc. 1995.

		$1,190	$1,020	$850	$680	$610	$560	$510

Last Mfr.'s Sug. Retail was $1,499.

This model had B.C. Rich stop bridge/tailpiece or standard Wilkinson vibrato optionally available.

In 1995, pearl blade fingerboard inlay, Translucent Blue, Translucent Cherry Red, Translucent Emerald Green and Translucent Pagon Gold finishes were introduced. Emerald Green, Red Tangerine, Transparent Blue, Transparent Gold and Transparent Purple finishes were discontinued.

Assassin Hollow — offset double cutaway semi hollow mahogany body, figured maple top, f holes, set maple neck, 24 fret ebony fingerboard, B.C. Rich stop bridge/tailpiece, blackface peghead with screened logo, 6 on one side tuners, black hardware, 2 humbucker DiMarzio pickups, 2 volume/1 tone controls, 3 position switch. Available in Emerald Green, Translucent Blue, Translucent Pagon Gold and Translucent Cherry Red finishes. Disc. 1995.

		$1,050	$900	$750	$600	$540	$495	$450

Last Mfr.'s Sug. Retail was $1,499.

BICH — offset double cutaway alder body with bottom bout cutaways, thru body mahogany neck, 24 fret rosewood fingerboard with pearl diamond inlay, stop bridge/tailpiece, blackface peghead with screened logo, 3 per side tuners, chrome hardware, 2 humbucker DiMarzio pickups, 2 volume/1 tone controls, 3 position switch. Available in Black, Blue, Red, White and Yellow finishes. New 1995.

Mfr.'s Sug. Retail		$1,399	$1,119	$839	$700	$560	$505	$460	$420

This model has double locking Floyd Rose vibrato, black chrome hardware, Candy Color finishes optionally available.

This model also available in a bolt-neck format as the **Bich Bolt-On** ($1,099).

Bich Special — offset double cutaway figured maple body with bottom bout cutaways, thru body maple neck, 24 fret ebony fingerboard with pearl diamond inlay, stop bridge/tailpiece, blackface peghead with pearl logo inlay, 3 per side tuners, 2 humbucker pickups, 2 volume/1 tone controls, 3 position switch. Available in Translucent Blue, Translucent Emerald Green, Natural, Translucent Purple, Translucent Tangerine and Translucent Red finishes. Curr. mfr.

Mfr.'s Sug. Retail		$1,599	$1,279	$959	$800	$640	$575	$530	$480

This model has standard Wilkinson vibrato, double locking Floyd Rose vibrato, 6 on one side tuners, black or gold hardware optionally available.

In 1995, Translucent Cherry Red, Translucent Emerald and Translucent Orange finishes were introduced, koa body became optionally available, Translucent Emerald Green, Translucent Tangerine and Translucent Red finishes were discontinued.

Bich Supreme — similar to Bich Standard, except has bound fingerboard with pearl cloud inlay, bound peghead, active electronics.

Mfr.'s Sug. Retail		$1,899	$1,519	$1,139	$950	$760	$685	$625	$570

This model has koa body with Natural finish, abalone fingerboard inlay optionally available.

EAGLE SPECIAL — offset double cutaway figured maple body, thru body maple neck with ebony stringers, 24 fret ebony fingerboard with pearl diamond inlay, B.C. Rich bridge/stop tailpiece, blackface peghead with pearl logo inlay, 3 per side tuners, 2 humbucker pickups, 2 volume/1 tone controls, 3 position switch. Available in Translucent Blue, Translucent Emerald Green, Natural, Translucent Purple, Translucent Tangerine and Translucent Red finishes. Curr. mfr.

Mfr.'s Sug. Retail		$1,600	$1,280	$960	$800	$640	$575	$530	$480

This model has standard Wilkinson vibrato, double locking Floyd Rose vibrato, 6 on one side tuners, black or gold hardware optionally available.

In 1995, Translucent Cherry Red, Translucent Emerald and Translucent Orange finishes were introduced, koa body became optionally available, Translucent Emerald Green, Translucent Tangerine and Translucent Red finishes were discontinued.

Eagle Supreme — similar to Eagle Standard , except has bound fingerboard with pearl cloud inlay, bound peghead, active electronics.

Mfr.'s Sug. Retail		$1,899	$1,519	$1,139	$950	$760	$685	$625	$570

This model has koa body with Natural finish, abalone fingerboard inlay optionally available.

Eagle Arch Top Supreme — similar to Eagle, except has mahogany body, carved bound figured maple top, thru body mahogany neck, bound fingerboard with abalone cloud inlay, bound peghead, active electronics. Available in Gold Top, Transparent Blue, Transparent Emerald Green, Transparent Purple, Transparent Tangerine and Transparent Red finishes. Current production.

		$1,899	$1,200	$1,000	$800	$720	$660	$600

Last Mfr.'s Sug. Retail was $2,000.

GUNSLINGER — offset double cutaway alder body, bolt-on maple neck, 22 fret maple fingerboard with black dot inlay, standard Wilkinson vibrato, reverse blackface peghead with screened logo, 6 on one side tuners, black hardware, humbucker pickup, volume control, dual sound switch. Available in Black, Cobalt Blue, Emerald Green, Purple, Red, White and Yellow finishes. Curr. mfr.

Mfr.'s Sug. Retail		$999	$799	$599	$500	$400	$360	$330	$300

In 1995, Power Blue finish was introduced, double locking Floyd Rose vibrato replaced original item, Candy Color finishes became optionally available, Cobalt Blue and Emerald Green finishes were discontinued.

Gunslinger 2 — similar to Gunslinger, except has 2 humbucker pickups, 2 volume/1 tone controls, 3 position switch. Curr. mfr.

Mfr.'s Sug. Retail		$1,099	$879	$659	$550	$440	$395	$365	$330

In 1995, Power Blue finish was introduced, double locking Floyd Rose vibrato replaces original item, Candy Color finishes became optionally available, Cobalt Blue and Emerald Green finishes were discontinued.

"Hendrix says to me, 'I'm going to be the greatest.' The thing that was going through my mind was, 'Oh, great. Another bloody American who wants something for nothing.'"

—*L. Acunto on James Marshall*

TCG, May/June 1994

Grading	100%	98% MINT	95% EXC+	90% EXC	80% VG+	70% VG	60% G

IRONBIRD — angular offset double cutaway alder body, thru body mahogany neck, 24 fret rosewood fingerboard with pearl diamond inlay, stop bridge/tailpiece, blackface peghead with screened logo, 3 per side tuners, chrome hardware, 2 humbucker DiMarzio pickups, 2 volume/1 tone controls, 3 position switch. Available in Black, Blue, Red, White and Yellow finishes. New 1995.

Mfr.'s Sug. Retail	$1,399	$1,119	$839	$700	$560	$505	$460	$420

This model has double locking Floyd Rose vibrato, black chrome hardware, Candy Color finishes optionally available.

Ironbird Bolt-On — angular offset double cutaway alder body, bolt-on maple neck, 22 fret maple fingerboard with black dot inlay, double locking Floyd Rose vibrato, 6 on one side tuners, black hardware, 2 humbucker pickups, 2 volume/1 tone controls, 3 position switch. Available in Black, Blue, Emerald Green, Red, White and Yellow finishes. Curr. mfr.

Mfr.'s Sug. Retail	$1,099	$879	$659	$550	$440	$395	$365	$330

In 1995, Candy Color finishes became optionally available, Emerald Green finish was discontinued.

MOCKINGBIRD — offset double cutaway asymmetrical alder body, thru body mahogany neck, 22 fret rosewood fingerboard with pearl dot inlay, double locking Floyd Rose vibrato, blackface peghead with screened logo, 3 per side tuners, chrome hardware, 2 humbucker DiMarzio pickups, 2 volume/1 tone controls, 3 position switch. Available in Black, Blue, Red, White and Yellow finishes. New 1995.

Mfr.'s Sug. Retail	$1,399	$1,119	$839	$700	$560	$505	$460	$420

This model has double locking Floyd Rose vibrato, black chrome hardware, Candy Color finishes optionally available.

Mockingbird Bolt-On — offset double cutaway asymmetrical alder body, bolt-on maple neck, 22 fret rosewood fingerboard with pearl dot inlay, double locking Floyd Rose vibrato, 6 on one side tuners, black hardware, 2 humbucker pickups, 2 volume/1 tone controls, 3 position switch. Available in Black, Blue, Candy Blue, Candy Red, Emerald Green, Red, White and Yellow finishes. Curr. mfr.

Mfr.'s Sug. Retail	$1,099	$879	$659	$550	$440	$395	$365	$330

Mockingbird Archtop — offset double cutaway asymmetrical semi hollow mahogany body, figured maple top, f holes, maple set neck, 22 fret rosewood fingerboard with pearl dot inlay, B.C. Rich bridge/stop tailpiece, 3 per side Grover Imperial tuners, chrome hardware, 2 humbucker DiMarzio pickups, 2 volume/1 tone controls, 3 position switch. Available in Translucent Blue, Translucent Cherry Red, Translucent Emerald Green and Translucent Pagon Gold finishes. New 1995.

Mfr.'s Sug. Retail	$1,899	$1,519	$1,139	$950	$860	$735	$660	$520

Mockingbird Special — offset double cutaway asymmetrical figured maple body, thru body maple neck with ebony stringers, 24 fret ebony fingerboard with pearl diamond inlay, B.C. Rich bridge/stop tailpiece, blackface peghead with pearl logo inlay, 3 per side tuners, 2 humbucker pickups, 2 volume/1 tone controls, 3 position switch. Available in Translucent Blue, Translucent Emerald Green, Natural, Translucent Purple, Translucent Tangerine and Translucent Red finishes. Curr. mfr.

Mfr.'s Sug. Retail	$1,599	$1,279	$959	$850	$680	$610	$560	$510

This model was designed for "Slash" (Guns 'n Roses).

This model has standard Wilkinson vibrato, double locking Floyd Rose vibrato, 6 on one side tuners, black or gold hardware optionally available.

In 1995, Translucent Cherry Red, Translucent Emerald and Translucent Orange finishes were introduced, koa body became optionally available, Translucent Emerald Green, Translucent Tangerine and Translucent Red finishes were discontinued.

This model is also available with a locking Floyd Rose Tremolo and other upgrades as the **Mockingbird SL** (Slash Limited Edition) for $1,699.

Mockingbird Supreme — similar to Mockingbird Standard, except has bound fingerboard with pearl cloud inlay, bound peghead, active electronics.

Mfr.'s Sug. Retail	$1,899	$1,519	$1,139	$950	$760	$685	$625	$570

This model has koa body with Natural finish, abalone fingerboard inlay optionally available.

SEAGULL WOODIE JR — sculpted single cutaway mahogany body, maple set neck, 22 fret rosewood fingerboard with pearl dot inlay, B.C. Rich bridge/stop tailpiece, blackface peghead with pearl logo inlay, 3 per side Grover Imperial tuners, chrome hardware, 2 humbucker DiMarzio pickups, 2 volume/1 tone controls, 3 position switch. Available in Black, Blue, DiMarzio Creme, Porsche Red, Translucent Blue and White finishes. New 1995.

Mfr.'s Sug. Retail	$1,000	$800	$600	$500	$400	$360	$330	$300

ST 2001 — offset double cutaway mahogany body, figured maple top, bolt-on maple neck, 22 fret maple fingerboard with black dot inlay, B.C. Rich bridge/stop tailpiece, 6 on one side tuners, chrome hardware, 2 humbucker pickups, 2 volume/1 tone controls, 3 position switch. Available in Translucent Black, Translucent Blue, Translucent Emerald Green, Translucent Golden Yellow, Translucent Magenta, Translucent Red and Translucent Tangerine finishes. Curr. mfr.

Mfr.'s Sug. Retail	$1,299	$1,039	$779	$750	$620	$570	$430	$390

This model has double locking Floyd Rose vibrato optionally available.

In 1995, Translucent Pagon Gold finish was introduced, Translucent Black, Translucent Golden Yellow, Translucent Magenta and Translucent Tangerine finishes were discontinued.

ST MSS — Similar to ST 2001, except has neck thru construction. New 1995.

Mfr.'s Sug. Retail	$1,599	$1,279	$959	$850	$720	$670	$530	$490

Grading	100%	98% MINT	95% EXC+	90% EXC	80% VG+	70% VG	60% G

WARLOCK — angular offset double cutaway alder body with large V bottom bout cutaway, thru body mahogany neck, 24 fret rosewood fingerboard with pearl diamond inlay, stop bridge/tailpiece, blackface peghead with screened logo, 3 per side tuners, chrome hardware, 2 humbucker DiMarzio pickups, 2 volume/1 tone controls, 3 position switch. Available in Black, Blue, Red, White and Yellow finishes. New 1995.

Mfr.'s Sug. Retail	$1,399	$1,119	$839	$700	$560	$505	$460	$420

This model has double locking Floyd Rose vibrato, black chrome hardware, Candy Color finishes optionally available.

Warlock Bolt-On — angular offset double cutaway alder body with large V bottom bout cutaway, bolt-on maple neck, 22 fret maple fingerboard with black dot inlay, double locking Floyd Rose vibrato, 6 on one side tuners, black hardware, 2 humbucker pickups, 2 volume/1 tone controls, 3 position switch. Available in Black, Blue, Emerald Green, Red, White and Yellow finishes. Curr. mfr.

Mfr.'s Sug. Retail	$1,099	$879	$659	$550	$440	$395	$365	$330

In 1995, Candy Color finishes became optionally available, Emerald Green finish was discontinued.

ELECTRIC BASS

BICH — offset double cutaway maple body with asymmetrical bottom bout cutaways, thru body maple neck, 24 fret rosewood fingerboard with pearl diamond inlay, fixed Wilkinson bridge, blackface peghead with pearl logo inlay, 2 per side tuners, black hardware, P-style/J-style DiMarzio pickups, 2 volume/1 tone controls, 3 position switch. Available in Black, Red, White and Wine Purple finishes. New 1995.

Mfr.'s Sug. Retail	$1,499	$1,124	$749	$600	$480	$430	$395	$360

This model has Candy Color finishes optionally available.

Bich Supreme — offset double cutaway figured maple body with asymmetrical bottom bout cutaways, thru body maple neck with koa stringers, 24 fret ebony fingerboard with pearl cloud inlay, fixed Wilkinson bridge, blackface peghead with pearl logo inlay, 2 per side tuners, black hardware, P-style/J-style DiMarzio pickups, 2 volume/1 tone controls. Available in Natural finish. Curr. mfr.

Mfr.'s Sug. Retail	$1,899	$1,519	$1,139	$950	$760	$685	$625	$570

This model has koa body/neck optionally available.

In 1995, active electronics, Translucent Blue, Translucent Emerald Green, Translucent Pagon Gold and Translucent Red finishes were introduced, bound fingerboard/peghead replace original items.

EAGLE SUPREME — offset double cutaway figured maple body, thru body maple neck with koa stringers, 24 fret ebony fingerboard with pearl cloud inlay, fixed Wilkinson bridge, blackface peghead with pearl logo inlay, 2 per side tuners, black hardware, P-style/J-style pickups, 2 volume/1 tone controls. Available in Natural finish. Curr. mfr.

Mfr.'s Sug. Retail	$1,900	$1,520	$1,140	$950	$760	$685	$625	$570

This model has koa body/neck optionally available.

In 1995, active electronics, Translucent Blue, Translucent Emerald Green, Translucent Pagan Gold and Translucent Red finishes were introduced, bound fingerboard/peghead replace original items.

GUNSLINGER — offset double cutaway ash body, bolt-on rock maple neck, 22 fret rosewood fingerboard with pearl dot inlay, fixed bridge, blackface peghead with screened logo, 4 on one side tuners, chrome hardware, humbucker DiMarzio pickups, volume/tone controls. Available in Black, Creme, Porsche Red, and White finishes. Current production.

Mfr.'s Sug. Retail	$1,199	$899	$599	$500	$400	$360	$330	$300

INNOVATOR 4 — offset double cutaway koa body, thru body koa neck with maple stringers, 24 fret maple fingerboard with abalone cloud inlay, fixed bridge, maple peghead veneer with screened logo, 4 on one side tuners, black hardware, P-style/J-style Bartolini pickups, 2 volume/2 tone/pan controls. Available in Natural finish. Current production.

Mfr.'s Sug. Retail	$1,499	$1,199	$899	$750	$650	$600	$500	$450

This model has ebony fingerboard, chrome or black hardware optionally available.

Innovator 5 — similar to Innovator 4, except has 5 strings, thru body maple neck with rosewood stringers, ebony fingerboard with pearl cloud inlay, 4/1 per side tuners, 2 humbucker Bartolini pickups.

Mfr.'s Sug. Retail	$1,599	$1,279	$959	$800	$700	$660	$530	$500

Innovator 6 — similar to Innovator 4, except has 6 strings, thru body maple neck with rosewood stringers, ebony fingerboard with pearl cloud inlay, 3 per side tuners, 2 humbucker Bartolini pickups.

	$1,400	$1,200	$1,000	$800	$720	$660	$600	

Last Mfr.'s Sug. Retail was $2,000.

IRONBIRD — angular offset double cutaway maple body, thru body rock maple neck, 22 fret rosewood fingerboard with pearl diamond inlay, fixed bridge, blackface peghead with screened logo, 4 on one side tuners, black hardware, P-style/J-style DiMarzio pickups, 2 volume/1 tone controls, 3 position switch. Available in Black, Red and White finishes. New 1995.

Mfr.'s Sug. Retail	$1,499	$1,124	$749	$650	$520	$470	$430	$390

This model has Candy Color finishes optionally available.

MOCKINGBIRD — offset double cutaway asymmetrical maple body, thru body maple neck, 24 fret rosewood fingerboard with pearl diamond inlay, fixed Wilkinson bridge, blackface peghead with pearl logo inlay, 2 per side tuners, black hardware, P-style/J-style DiMarzio pickups, 2 volume/1 tone controls, 3 position switch. Available in Black, Red, White and Wine Purple finishes. New 1995.

Mfr.'s Sug. Retail	$1,499	$1,124	$749	$600	$480	$430	$395	$360

This model has Candy Color finishes optionally available.

Grading	100%	98% MINT	95% EXC+	90% EXC	80% VG+	70% VG	60% G

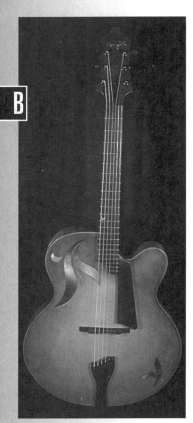

La Cremora Azzurria
courtesy Scott Chinery

Mockingbird Supreme — offset double cutaway asymmetrical maple body, thru body maple neck with koa stringers, 24 fret ebony fingerboard with pearl cloud inlay, fixed Wilkinson bridge, blackface peghead with pearl logo inlay, 2 per side tuners, black hardware, P-style/J-style pickups, 2 volume/1 tone controls. Available in Natural finish. Curr. mfr.

Mfr.'s Sug. Retail	$1,899	$1,519	$1,139	$950	$760	$685	$625	$570

This model has koa body/neck optionally available.

In 1995, active electronics, Translucent Blue, Translucent Emerald Green, Translucent Pagon Gold and Translucent Red finishes were introduced, bound fingerboard/peghead replace original items.

WAVE — offset double cutaway ash body with bottom bout cutaway, thru body rock maple neck, 22 fret rosewood fingerboard with pearl diamond inlay, fixed bridge, blackface peghead with pearl logo inlay, 2 per side tuners, black hardware, 2 P-style/J-style DiMarzio pickups, 2 volume/1 tone controls, 3 position switch. Available in Black, Sunburst, Turquoise and White finishes. Disc. 1995.

		$910	$780	$650	$520	$470	$430	$390

Last Mfr.'s Sug. Retail was $1,299.

This model had Candy Color finishes optionally available.

Wave Supreme — similar to Wave, except has figured maple body, 24 fret bound ebony fingerboard with pearl cloud inlay, 2 volume/2 tone controls, preamp. Available in Translucent Blue, Translucent Emerald Green, Natural, Translucent Pagan gold and Translucent Red finishes. Disc. 1995.

		$1,120	$960	$800	$640	$575	$530	$480

Last Mfr.'s Sug. Retail was $1,600.

WARLOCK — offset double cutaway maple body with asymmetrical bottom bout cutaways, thru body maple neck, 24 fret rosewood fingerboard with pearl diamond inlay, fixed Wilkinson bridge, blackface peghead with pearl logo inlay, 2 per side tuners, black hardware, P-style/J-style DiMarzio pickups, 2 volume/1 tone controls, 3 position switch. Available in Black, Red, White and Wine Purple finishes. New 1995.

Mfr.'s Sug. Retail	$1,499	$1,124	$749	$600	$480	$430	$395	$360

This model has Candy Color finishes optionally available.

BELLA

Instruments currently built in Chalmette, Louisiana.

Company offers the **Bella Beluxe** ($2,400), which offers a mahogany body, Curly Maple or Quilted Maple (or other exotic tops), Rosewood fingerboard, Schaller tuners, Seymour Duncan or DiMarzio pickups, and a 25 1/2" scale. Contact Bella Guitars for further information via the Index of Current Manufacturers located in the rear of this book.

BELLTONE

Instruments manufactured in Japan, or shared Japanese-built parts during the late 1960s.

Belltone was the brandname of the Peter Sorkin Music Company. The Sorkin company distributed Premier guitars, which were built at the Multivox company of New York. Other guitars built or distributed (possibly as rebrands) were ROYCE, STRAD-O-LIN, BELLTONE, and MARVEL. Parts varied, as pickups were Japanese, while the roller bridges may be Italian or Japanese.

(Source: Michael Wright, Guitar Stories Volume One, pg. 16)

BELTONE

See chapter on House Brands.

This trademark has been identified as a "House Brand" of the Monroe Catalog House.

(Source: Willie G. Moseley, Stellas & Stratocasters)

BENEDETTO

Instruments currently built in East Stroudsburg, Pennsylvania.

Master Luthier Robert Benedetto, widely acknowledged as the world's foremost maker of archtop guitars, has been building instruments since 1968. Benedetto, author of "Making an Archtop Guitar" (Centerstream Publishing, 1994) was born in New York in 1946. Both his father and grandfather were master cabinetmakers, and Benedetto's uncles were musicians. While growing up in New Jersey, Benedetto began playing the guitar professionally at age thirteen. Being near the New York/New Jersey jazz music scene, Benedetto had numerous opportunities to perform repair and restoration work on other classic archtops. Benedetto built his first archtop in 1968, and has maintained production ever since.

Benedetto moved to Homosassa, Florida in 1976. Three years later, he relocated to Clearwater, Florida. In 1982, Benedetto began concentrating on the acoustic properties of the guitar designs, and started a movement to strip away unnecessary adornment (inlays, bindings). While continuing his regular work on archtop building, Benedetto also built violins between 1983-1987. Benedetto even built a small number of electric solid body guitars and basses (which debuted at the 1987 NAMM show) in addition to his regular archtop production schedule.

Benedetto moved to his current location in East Stroudsberg, Pennsylvania in 1990, and continues to produce instruments from that location. His endorsers span three generations of jazz guitarists. Not since John D'Angelico has anyone made as many archtop guitars nor had as many well known players endorsing and recording with his guitars. Closer scrutiny reveals nuances found only from a maker of his stature. His minimalist delicate inlay motif has become a trademark as have his novel use of black, rather than gold, tuning machines, black bridge height adjustment wheels, and an ebony nut (versus bone), all of which harmonize with the ebony fittings throughout the guitar. He is the originator of the solid ebony tailpiece, uniquely fastened to the guitar with cello tail adjustor. Likewise, he was the first to use exotic and natural wood veneers on the headstock and pioneered the use of violin-pigments to shade his guitars. His "honey blonde" finish is now widely used within the guitar industry. Benedetto is also well known for refining the 7-string archtop and is that unique model's most prolific maker.

Benedetto is a regular columnist for the "Just Jazz Guitar" magazine, and this fall will be releasing a ten hour video entitled "Archtop Guitar Design & Construction" that details construction techniques for archtop guitars. He also markets a "floating" pickup for his (and other) archtop acoustic guitars.

(Biographical information courtesy Cindy Benedetto)

As of August 1996, luthier Bob Benedetto has built over 650 instruments. While the majority are archtop guitars, he has also produced 157 electric solid body guitars, 52 electric basses, 45 violins, 5 violas, and 2 mandolins. Benedetto currently schedules his production to 30 archtop guitars a year.

ACOUSTIC ARCHTOP

All Benedetto guitars share some similar design and construction features. All tops and backs are hand graduated and tuned, and all models feature a single cutaway (except the Americana model). They have a 25" scale, and the necks feature 21 frets. Bodies may be 16", 17", or 18" across the lower bout, and have a depth of 3". The fingerboard, bridge, pickguard, and harp-style tailpiece are all solid Ebony, and the guitars are finished in nitro cellulose lacquer.

The **Manhattan** ($10,000) and **Fratello** ($11,000) models share corresponding aged Spruce tops, Flamed Maple back and sides, and 3 piece Flamed Maple neck. However, the Fratello has a more traditional styled bound pickguard, large mother-of-pearl fingerboard inlays, and gold Schaller M6 tuners with gold buttons. The Manhattan has a Neo-classical fingerboard, and a narrow "Chuck Wayne" style finger rest, and gold Schaller tuners with solid Ebony buttons. The **7-String** ($11,500) shares similar appointments to the Manhattan, except features a seven string configuration instead of six.

The **La Venezia** ($15,000) was inspired by a unique guitar built for Chuck Wayne in 1982, and features an intermingling of design ideas from violin and archtop building. Back and sides are created from Flamed European Maple, while the top consists of a tight-grained European Spruce.

Both the **Americana** ($18,000) and **Limelite** ($25,000) models offer a tribute to the early days of archtop building and big bands. While similar in construction materials to the Manhattan, the Americana has a large flared headstock, no cutaway, and an 18" body. The Limelite features intricate inlay work on the pickguard and tailpiece, split fingerboard inlays, a traditionally-shaped bound pickguard, and again a large flared headstock.

The **Cremona** was Benedetto's first standard model, and current instruments feature the finest and rarest woods. Both the top and back are hand carved and tuned from European cello woods, with matching sides. The burl-veneered headstock features an elegant mother-of-pearl/abalone inlay. List price in 1996 was $40,000.

BENEDICT GUITARS

Instruments are built in Cedar, Minnesota since 1981. Distribution is handled by the Benedict Guitar Company of Cedar, Minnesota (about 40 miles north of Minneapolis).

Luthier Roger Benedict began building guitars back in 1974 out east in Elizabethtown, New York. Benedict moved to Minneapolis, Minnesota in 1981, and continued to build custom guitars. In 1988, he unveiled the Groovemaster model (as named by Jackson Browne, who owns two), a Strat-styled semi-hollowbody design. Unfortunately, Benedict passed away in 1994. He was remembered all over Minneapolis by musicians as a generous man who was easy going and a great luthier. In late 1995, Bill Hager bought the rights to the trademark and designs from the estate, and continues to produce Benedict guitars. Hager, a printer and luthier, was apprenticed to Roger Benedict for five years. Hager continues to offer the Groovemaster, as well as a baritone guitar, an acoustic/electric, and custom models. Contact Benedict Guitars through the Index of Current Manufacturers located in the back of this book.

La Cremona Azzurria, closeup courtesy Scott Chinery

"If somebody, a good player, asked us to make a red guitar, we would have made it. We were in business not only to make money, but to make friends."
—L. Acunto on Ted McCarty
Ex-Gibson President ('48-'66)
TCG, May/June 1994

Grading	100%	98% MINT	95% EXC+	90% EXC	80% VG+	70% VG	60% G

ELECTRIC

BENELECTRO — single round cutaway mahogany body, black pickguard, bolt on maple neck, 21 fret maple fingerboard with black dot inlay, string thru bridge, 6 on one side Kluson style tuners, chrome hardware, 2 humbucker Seymour Duncan pickups, 2 volume/1 tone control. Available in Natural finish. Mfd. 1993 to date.

Mfr.'s Sug. Retail $695 $556 $417 $350

> This model has walnut body, rosewood fingerboard with pearl dot inlay, Chandler lipstick tube pickups optionally available.

Groovemaster Series

CUSTOM — semi hollow offset double cutaway spruce body, f hole by lower bout, white pickguard, bolt-on maple neck, 21 fret rosewood fingerboard with pearl dot inlay, string thru bridge, 6 on one side Kluson style vintage tuners, chrome hardware, 3 single coil Seymour Duncan pickups, volume/2 tone controls, 5 position switch. Available in Black, Ivory, Seafoam Green and Sunburst finishes. Current production.

Mfr.'s Sug. Retail $1,895 $1,516 $1,137 $950

Deluxe — similar to Custom, except is available with alder body and maple fingerboard.

Mfr.'s Sug. Retail $1,395 $1,116 $837 $700

Standard — similar to Custom, except has alder body. Available in Black, Ivory, Seafoam Green or Surf Green finishes.

Mfr.'s Sug. Retail $1,195 $956 $717 $600

> This model has maple fingerboard with black dot inlay optionally available.

ELECTRIC BASS

Groovemaster Series

CUSTOM — semi hollow offset double cutaway alder body, f-hole by lower bout, tortoise pickguard, thru body maple neck, 20 fret rosewood fingerboard with pearl dot inlay, fixed Schaller bridge, 4 on one side mini tuners, P-style/J-style Bartolini pickups, volume/tone control, 3 position switch. Available in Black, Ivory, Seafoam Green or Sunburst finishes. Current production.

Mfr.'s Sug. Retail $2,295 $1,836 $1,377 $1,150

> This model has a curly maple top and an ebony fingerboard (with or without frets) optionally available.

Deluxe — similar to Custom, except has bolt-on maple neck, maple fingerboard, vintage Schaller tuners, Seymour Duncan pickups.

Mfr.'s Sug. Retail $1,495 $1,196 $897 $750

> This model has rosewood fingerboard with pearl dot inlay optionally available.

5 String Bass — similar to Custom, except has 5 strings.

Mfr.'s Sug. Retail $2,495 $1,996 $1,497 $1,250 $1,000

BENTLY

Instruments are manufactured in Asia. Distributed by the St. Louis Music company of St. Louis, Missouri.

Bently instruments are entry level to medium quality solid body guitars and basses that feature designs based on Classic American favorites.

BERT WEEDON

Instruments were built in West Germany in the mid 1960s.

While the BERT WEEDON trademark was a brandname used by a UK importer, Bert Weedon was a famous British guitarist best know for his daily guitar lessons on British radio. Weedon was normally associated with Hofner guitars throughout his career. The Zero One model was a semi-hollowbody with a single cutaway and two pickups.

(Source: Tony Bacon and Paul Day, The Guru's Guitar Guide)

BESSON

See FRAMUS.

See also ARISTONE.

Instruments made in West Germany during the late 1950s through the early 1960s.

While BESSON was the brandname for a UK importer, these guitars were made by and identical to certain FRAMUS models. Research also indicates that the trademark ARISTONE was utilized as well.

(Source: Tony Bacon and Paul Day, The Guru's Guitar Guide)

BEVERLY

See chapter on House Brands.

This trademark has been identified as a "House Brand" of SELMER UK in England.

(Source: Willie G. Moseley, Stellas & Stratocasters)

BIAXE

Instruments built in Stamford, Connecticut from 1978 to 1985.

The newly reformed Biaxe company has few characteristics of the original Biaxe Guitars (founded in 1978). Instead of manufacturing instruments, the new version of the company manufacturers retrofit devices that enhance existing guitars and basses, giving them the sounds of other instruments in addition to their own sounds.

The Fretless Wizard is a reftrofit that yields the sound of a "fretless bass" on a fretted neck bass guitar. The retrofit kit is available in 4, 5, and 6 string kits, and includes an instructional cassette. For further information, contact Biaxe through the Index of Current Manufacturers located towards the back of this book.

PAUL BIGSBY

Instruments built in Downey, California during the late 1940s and 1950s.

Paul A. Bigsby was a pattern-maker who was fond of motorcycle repair and racing. During the 1940s, Bigsby was contacted by country music star Merle Travis to repair a worn-out Vibrola on his Gibson L-10. Rather than just repair it, Bigsby produced a better vibrato tailpiece. The Bigsby vibrato was marketed for a number of years after he finished the first prototype. In 1965, Ted McCarty bought Bigsby's vibrato company, and models are still available today.

Paul Bigsby also had success with his electric pedal steel guitar beginning in the late 1940s and after. In 1947-1948 Travis and Bigsby collaborated on a solid body electric which featured a six on a side headstock, single cutaway, neck-through body construction, and a string-through body bridge and tailpiece. Bigsby produced guitars like this in small numbers (the amount is estimated to be 12) on a custom order basis.

There has been some controversy over Bigsby's design influencing Leo Fender's later development of the first commercially successful electric solid body guitar. However, Fender's first prototype featured a bolt-on neck and a 3+3 headstock. One account of the story worth reading is Forrest White's book, "Fender: The Inside Story" (GPI Books, 1994).

(Source: Tom Wheeler, American Guitars)

BILL LAWRENCE

Instruments produced in Japan by the Morris Guitar company.

These medium quality solid body guitars feature designs based on classic Amercian favorites. The MB-120 features an offset cut body, 3+3 headstock, 2 humbucking pickups, and a stop tailpiece. The BLIR-150 features more of a Strat-style design, and has two humbuckers, a volume knob, and a pickup selector switch.

(Source: Rittor Music, Guitar Graphic Vol. 1)

BISCAYNE

See PALMER.

BLACK HILLS

See chapter on House Brands.

This trademark has been identified as a "House Brand" of the Wall Drug stores.

(Source: Willie G. Moseley, Stellas & Stratocasters)

BLACKHURST

Instruments currently built in Roseville, California.

Luthier Dave Blackhurst presently is building high quality custom designed guitars and basses that feature numerous options. The **Tigershark** series has a sleek double cutaway body design, and prices range from $1,295 up to $2,250. New this year is a playable guitar or bass shaped like a fish called **The Big One** ($2,000). Other models include the more traditional STX and TLX that feature deeper body cutaways. For further information, contact Blackhurst through the Index of Current Manufacturers located in the rear of this book.

BLACKJACK

Instruments produced in Japan.

Although the Blackjack trademark is a brandname on these instruments, the U.S. distributor has not yet been identified. Updates will appear in future editions of the **Blue Book of Guitars**.

(Source: Michael Wright, Guitar Stories Volume One, pg 50)

BLADE

Instruments produced in Switzerland since 1987.

Designer Gary Levinson combined traditional-designed guitars with modern updates and parts. The resulting instruments had more tonal options than previous vintage models, but still maintained the "feel" that players are familiar with. Currently, the **Blue Book of Guitars** has not been able to discover any distributor for the U.S. market, and recent attempts to personally contact Gary Levinson or the Blade company have failed. This section is maintained for model information and last listed retail price information, but the trademark will be considered discontinued for the Third Edition. The **Blue Book of Guitars** will update further information as it becomes readily available.

ELECTRIC

Levinson's Blade guitars featured designs based on popular American classic bolt-neck models, except they possess upgraded hardware and pickups. The **R3** model had an offset double cutaway maple body, one piece maple neck or maple neck with ebony fingerboard, 3 Levinson single coil pickups, Variable Spectrum Control electronics, and Sperzel tuners. The R3 had opaque (solid) colors, and the last suggested retail price was between $1,675 and $1,799. The R3 was available in Black, Ice Blue, Iridescent White and Purple Rain finishes. The **R4** had similar specifications, but had an Ash body and translucent colors such as Ocean Blue and Transparent Red (last suggested retail prices ranged from $1,799 and $1,999).

The Blade **T2** was a single cutaway ash body, and featured a bolt-on maple neck, 22 fret maple fingerboard with black dot inlay, fixed bridge, graphite nut, 6 on one side tuners, gold hardware, 2 single coil pickups, volume/tone control, 3 position switch, Variable Spectrum Control electronics and VSC switch. The T2's last retail price was between $1,289 and $1,329, and was available in Harvest Gold, Misty Violet, Ocean Blue and Transparent Red finishes.

In 1993, the R3's opaque colors were discontinued, and model packages were designated. An ash body and maple neck was named the **Abilene**, while the R4 became the **Classic**. A similar model with a humbucker in the bridge position was named the **Austin**, and the T2 was designated the **Delta**, or with rosewood fingerboard, the **Legend**.

ELECTRIC BASS

The Blade **B3** bass featured an offset double cutaway asymmetrical maple body, bolt-on maple neck, 20 fret ebony fingerboard with pearl dot inlay, fixed bridge, 4 on one side Gotoh tuners, 2 J-style pickups, volume/tone and mixed controls, Variable Spectrum Control electronics and VSC switch, and was available in Black, Ice Blue, Purple Rain and Snow White finishes. The last suggested retail price from 1991 was $1,740. Blade also offered a **B4** ($1,970) model, which was similar to the B3 except it had gold hardware and was available in Ocean Blue, Transparent Red, Honey, and Misty Violet.

In 1993, the B3's opaque colors were discontinued, and model packages were designated. An ash body and maple neck with rosewood fingerboard was named the **Tetra 4**, while a 5-string model became the **Penta 5**.

BLAIR

Instruments currently built in Ellington, Connecticut.

Blair Guitars Ltd. custom builds the **Mutant Twin** ($1,999), a double neck guitar with an acoustic half and a solid body half. Designer Douglas Blair has over twenty years experience in the music field, and has been building his own guitars since his teens. Blair has also recorded and toured with international acts, and spent numerous years switching between his electric guitar and an Ovation acoustic on a stand for live performances. In 1990, Blair conceived of the "Mutant" as a way to solve the problem, and prototypes were developed with the aid of Ovation head R & D Don Johnson. These guitars are available on a custom order only. For further information, contact Douglas Blair through the Index of Current Manufacturers located in the rear of this book.

BLUE SAGE

See MELODY.

The Italian-built Blue Sage series debuted in 1982, and was part of the overall Melody guitar line. The Blue Sage series of original designs was of higher quality than the traditional offerings of the company.

(Source: Tony Bacon, Ultimate Guitar Book)

BLUE STAR MUSIC

Instruments built in Lovingston, Virginia since 1995.

Luthiers Joe Madison and Jack Roy hand-sculpt designs right into the face of the guitar body. Originally the bodies were displayed at art galleries and sparked a lot of interest. These sculptures were then crafted into guitars, and feature a hand-carved headstock to echo the body design.

Each guitar has a unique figure carved into the wood, be it a dragon, a face, a snake, or almost any design. Custom guitars can be standard shape or radical designs with many wood choices and unlimited electronic configurations. Prices range from $1,000 to $4,500, depending on the intricacy of the sculpting and design. All are outfitted with top quality

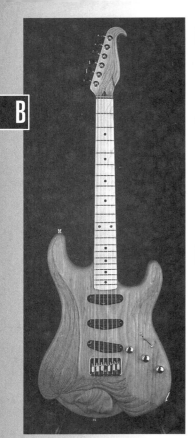

Carved Face Custom
courtesy Jack Roy

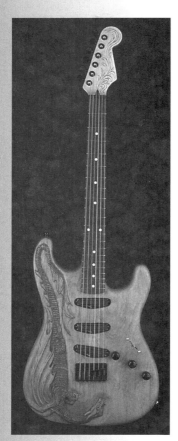

Carved Dragon Custom
courtesy Jack Roy

hardware. For further information, contact Blue Star Music through the Index of Current Manufacturers in the back of this book.

BLUESOUTH

Instruments currently built in Muscle Shoals, Alabama.

Ronnie Knight began Bluesouth Guitars in 1991 with the idea of building stringed musical instruments which celebrate the musical heritage of the American South. Blues, jazz, coutry, rock, and spiritual music were all created in the southern American states. This small area from Texas to the Carolinas, from Kentucky to Florida, has been the hotbed of the world's musical culture in the twentieth century. Several small towns within the southeast have had a huge impact on today's popular music: Muscle Shoals, Alabama, Macon, Georgia, and Clarksdale, Mississippi. The results of this project have been unique, light-bodied guitars with large, comfortable necks. Bluesouth contends that "fierce individualism" is the key ingredient in their guitar making operation. Starting in a small shop over a record store in early 1992, Bluesouth moved to a much larger industrial facility in the spring of 1995. To date, the company offers 7 models, including 2 electric basses. Bluesouth also builds its own cases and pickups in house.

(Company history courtesy Ronnie Knight, April 17, 1996)

All Bluesouth instruments feature mahogany or swamp ash bodies in sleek ergonomic designs, a mahogany set-neck with rosewood fingerboard, 24 3/4" scale (basses are 34" scale), Sperzel locking tuners, Wilkinson or Gotoh hardware, and Bluesouth's own pickups. Models run from the Clarksdale ($995), Muscle Shoals ($1,095), Gris Gris ($1,295), Macon ($1,495), up to the J.Johnson Original Swamper and Muscle Shoals Deluxe ($1,695). The Clarksdale 4 string bass retails at $1,295 (5 string is $400 extra). For further information, y'all call the boys from Bluesouth through the Index of Current Manufacturers located in the back of this book.

BLUNDELL

Instruments built in England during the early 1980s.

These British-built solid body guitars were patterned after the Explorer and Flying V designs.

(Source: Tony Bacon and Paul Day, The Guru's Guitar Guide)

B M

Instruments were built in both Japan and Britain during the early 1960s through the mid 1980s.

The B M trademark was utilized by the UK importer Barnes & Mullins. While the company did import some entry level to medium quality guitars in from Japan, they also distributed some British-built SHERGOLD originals under their trademark.

(Source: Tony Bacon and Paul Day, The Guru's Guitar Guide)

BOGART

Instruments built in Taunusstein, Germany. Distributed in the U.S. by Salwender International of Trabuco Canyon, California. Distribution in Germany by S K C Graphite of Aschaffenburg, Germany.

Bogart has been producing high quality basses since 1991. Models feature a patented "Blackstone" material for the bodies and bolt-on graphite necks. "Blackstone" is a wood core surrounded by epoxy foam - yet the neck, pickups, and hardware bolt to the wood core. Bogart features Bartolini pickups and Schaller tuners. Four string models begin at $2,617, and range up to the custom six string at $4,088. Contact Bogart Basses through the Index of Current Manufacturers located in the back of this book.

BOND

Instruments built in England between 1984 and 1986.

Advanced design BOND guitars were designed by Scotland's Andrew Bond. The Electraglide model featured such innovations as a graphite body, "stepped" ridges instead of frets, and a digital LED readout. Despite interest in the innovations and feel of the guitar, production lagged and the retail cost climbed. The company eventually closed in 1986, despite considerable financial investment and endorsements by The Edge (U2's guitarist).

The Electraglide featured a dual cutaway graphite body, synthetic 'stepped ridges' fingerboard (not a conventional fretted neck), 3 single coil pickups, 5 pushbuttons, 3 rocker switches, a digital LED that lets the player know what preset was called up, and an optional vibrato.

BOOGALOO

Instruments built in Britain from 1986 on.

The BOOGALOO trademark is used by luthier Frank Lemaux on his original designed high quality solidbody guitars.

(Source: Tony Bacon and Paul Day, The Guru's Guitar Guide)

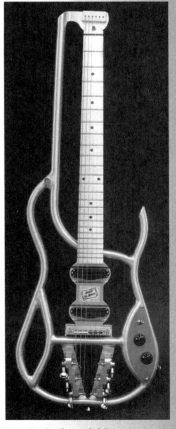

Born To Rock model F4c
courtesy Robert Kunstadt

BOOGIE BODY

Instruments currently built in Gig Harbor, Washington.

Twenty years ago, Lynn Ellsworth and Wayne Charvel started Boogie Body guitars. The company produced electric guitar bodies of exotic woods during the 1970s, and had an impressive client roster of Eddie Van Halen (the red and white striped guitars), The Who, and Steppenwolf. Ellsworth closed Boogie Body in 1982, but reopened the company later in Gig Harbor, Washington.

The current "Mayan Gold" series features an offset body with lengthened bass bout design made from cocobolo. Designed by Bishop Cochran, the instruments feature a six bolt neck, EMG or Seymour Duncan pickups, and a 2TEK bridge. Prices range from $1,495 to $1,995. For further information, contact Boogie Body through the Index of Current Manufacturers located in the rear of this book.

> *(Source: Hal Hammer, Jr.)*

> Lynn Ellsworth recently developed the 2TEK bridge, an innovative through-body bridge system that improves the overall sound of guitars and basses. Boogie Body/VVT Technologies is also building **Speedster** hand-crafted amplifers.

BOOM

Instruments currently built in Chico, California.

Boom is currently building high quality custom basses.

BORN TO ROCK

Instruments currently built in New York, New York.

Designer Robert Kunstadt came up with a new way to answer the age-old problem of neck warpage: by redesigning the nature of the neck/body/headstock interface, and by building the resulting innovative design out of aluminum tubing. The hollow aluminum tubing adds a new dimension to the instrument's sustain, and the neck joint assures that the neck will always line up straight with the strings.

> Both the six string guitar (F4c) and four string bass (F4b) carry a new retail price of $3,380 each.

BORYS

Instruments built in Burlington, Vermont from the mid 1970s to the 1980s.

Luthier Roger Borys began guitar repair work in the early 1970s, and completed building his first guitar in 1976. Borys has concentrated on building versatile, high quality instruments designed for the jazz guitarist. In 1980, Borys united with James D'Aquist and musician Barry Galbraith to design the BG 100 Jazz electric. This instrument, later labeled the B 120, was co-built between Borys and Chip Wilson. Other instruments have included the B 222 Jazz Solid, which has a solid jazz "voice", but can be used in playing other forms of music.

BOSS AXE

Instruments produced in Japan.

Although the U.S. distributor is unknown, Boss Axe instruments are built in Japan by the Shimokura company.

BOSSA

Instruments currently built in Japan. Exclusively distributed by Soniq Trading, Inc. of North Hollywood, California.

Bossa builds dependable high quality basses.

ELECTRIC BASS

All instruments have the following: offset double cutaway asymmetrical body, 3 piece maple neck, 24 fret ebony fingerboards with pearl dot inlay, fixed bridge, logo peghead decal, chrome hardware, 2 humbucker pickups, 2 volume controls, treble/mid/bass controls. Available in Antique White, Natural, Transparent Red, Turquoise Sunburst and Violet finishes. Current production.

Add $100 for fretless fingerboard.

These models have maple fingerboards, C.A.T. vibratos, black or gold hardware optionally available. The OB-4 has 2 per side tuners, the OB-5 features a 3/2 per side tuners, and the OB-6 has 3 per side tuners.

Grading	100%	98% MINT	95% EXC+	90% EXC	80% VG+	70% VG	60% G

OB-4

Light ash body.

Mfr.'s Sug. Retail	$1,750	$1,400	$1,050	$875	$700	$630	$575	$525

Walnut body.

Mfr.'s Sug. Retail	$1,950	$1,560	$1,170	$975	$780	$700	$645	$580

Walnut body and quilted maple top.

Mfr.'s Sug. Retail	$2,250	$1,800	$1,350	$1,125	$900	$810	$740	$675

OB-5

Light ash body.

Mfr.'s Sug. Retail	$1,950	$1,560	$1,170	$975	$780	$700	$645	$580

Walnut body.

Mfr.'s Sug. Retail	$2,150	$1,720	$1,290	$1,075	$860	$775	$710	$645

Walnut body and quilted maple top.

Mfr.'s Sug. Retail	$2,450	$1,960	$1,470	$1,225	$980	$875	$805	$735

OB-6

Light ash body.

Mfr.'s Sug. Retail	$2,150	$1,720	$1,290	$1,075	$860	$775	$710	$645

Walnut body.

Mfr.'s Sug. Retail	$2,350	$1,880	$1,410	$1,175	$940	$845	$775	$705

Walnut body and quilted maple top.

Mfr.'s Sug. Retail	$2,650	$2,120	$1,590	$1,325	$1,060	$955	$875	$795

BOUCHET

Instruments built in Paris, France from 1946 to possibly the late 1970s.

Luthier and painter Robert Bouchet (1898-1986) began building guitars in Paris in the mid 1940s. A keen guitarist, he produced very high quality guitars in small numbers.

(Source: Tony Bacon, The Ultimate Guitar Book)

Bozo Chicagoan
courtesy Scott Chinery

DANA BOURGEOIS GUITARS

Instruments currently produced in Lewiston, Maine.

Luthier Dana Bourgeois has spent twenty years honing his craft as a custom builder and restorer of vintage guitars. Before starting his own company, Bourgeois was a co-founder of Schoenberg guitars. Bourgeois designed the acclaimed Schoenberg Soloist, and personally voiced each Schoenberg guitar during its construction by the C.F. Martin company. He later served as design consultant to Gibson during the start up of their acoustic guitar plant in Montana. While working as a product designer for Paul Reed Smith, he learned CAD drawing from Bob Taylor (Taylor Guitars). Bourgeois currently builds guitars with his own company, and applies his knowledge of traditional and modern techniques to current designs.

(Company history courtesy Dana Bourgeois Guitars)

All Bourgeois models carry certain similar specifications. All guitars have a single piece mahogany neck, Ivoroid fretboard and headstock binding, a 25 1/2" scale, and a gloss lacquer finish. In the **Standard** package, the top is constructed of Sitka Spruce, and the body and sides are mahogany. Both the fretboard and bridge are Indian rosewood. The **Rosewood** package offers Indian rosewood back and sides, an ebony fingerboard and bridge, abalone inlays, and certain models have a curly maple body binding. Finally, the **Deluxe** package adds abalone top border and rosette, 3-layer back and side purfling, the signature series label, and Schaller gold tuners with ebony buttons. All models are offered with a wide variety of custom options.

Bourgeois offers seven different model acoustics, and one archtop guitar. The **Orchestra Model** ($2,180) is also available in **Jumbo** ($2,040) and **12 Fret** (where neck joins the body - $2,840). The **Dreadnought**'s standard package begins at $2,420, and is offered in three other variants. The **17" Archtop** begins at $5,000. While this list is a pale reflection of the materials and quality built in to each instruments, it is meant to be used as a guide. Please contact luthier Bourgeois for further information and model specifications through the Index of Current Manufacturers located in the back of this book.

BŌZO

Instruments currently built in Englewood, Florida. Some designs were constructed in Japan during the late 1970s.

Luthier Bozidar Podunavac has been creating guitars for forty years. Bozo (pronounced Bo-Zho) was originally apprenticed to luthier Milutin Mladenuvic in his native Yugoslavia. In 1959, Bozo and his wife Mirjana emigrated to the U.S., and located in Chicago, Illinois. Bozo initially did repair work for various music stores, and later opened his own shop in 1965. His original guitars were designed after the dreadnought body style, but changed to his own original 'Bell Western' design in 1968.

Breedlove C-2
courtesy Breedlove Guitar Company

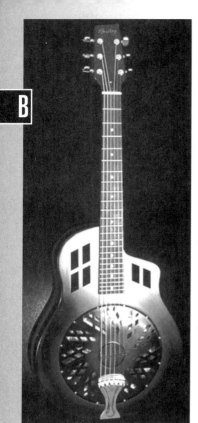

Cutaway Steel Body model
courtesy Clint Briley

The Podunavacs moved to Escondido (near San Diego), California in 1972, and to San Diego three years later. In 1978, Bozo opened a school of lutherie, which he ran for a number of years. The family later relocated to Florida, where current production is based today.

Bozo builds guitars of all sizes, both flattop and arch top designs. His instruments usually feature very ornate detailing and inlay work, as well as a large headstock. For information regarding pricing and availability, contact Bozo through Gulf Coast Guitars (941.474.1214) or at his workshop via the Index of Current Manufacturers located in the back of this book.

BRADFORD

See chapter on House Brands.

This trademark has been identified as a "House Brand" of W. T. Grant company.

(Source: Willie G. Moseley, Stellas & Stratocasters)

BRADLEY

Instruments produced in Japan.

The American distributor for this trademark was Veneman Music of Bethseda, Maryland.

(Source: Michael Wright, Guitar Stories Vol. 1)

BREEDLOVE

Instruments built in Tumalo, Oregon since 1990. Distributed by the Breedlove Guitar Company of Tumalo, Oregon.

Larry Breedlove and Steve Henderson spent time refining their lutherie skills with Bob Taylor (Taylor Guitars). The two partners then moved up into the Pacific Northwest and founded the Breedlove Guitar Company in the early 1990s. Henderson and Breedlove experimented with other tonewoods, and offer instruments built with Walnut, Myrtlewood, and Red Cedar as well as the traditional Maple, Spruce, Rosewood, and Mahogany.

Using high quality woods and original designs, they offer 8 different models of flat top steel string instruments, ranging in price from the standard C1 ($2,145) to the ornate C5/Northwest ($3,295). Various options are also available at an additional cost.

Breedlove also offers the "S" series of guitars, which may not be as ornate as the regular line but are built with the same materials and same attention to detail. Prices on the four models range from $1,695 to $1,845, and do have several additional cost custom options offered. For further information, contact Breedlove Guitar Company through the Index of Current Manufacturers located in the rear of this book.

BRIAN MOORE CUSTOM GUITARS

Instruments produced in Brewster, New York since 1994. Distributed by Brian Moore Custom Guitars of Brewster, New York.

Pat Cummings and Brian Moore teamed up with Kevin Kalagher in 1992 to begin prototype designs on the MC/1. Both Cummings and Moore had prior experience in producing guitars for another company, but elected to stay in New York when their division was moved south by headquarters. Moore designed the composite body shapes and incorporated the tonewood tops while Cummings arranged the electronics and pickup configurations. After testing seven prototypes, the MC (Moore/Cummings) 1 debuted in 1993.

The company's instrument features an offset double cutaway body and neck of one solid piece of composite material, and a variety of figured wood tops with natural binding. Various pickup and electronic configurations are offered along with choice of hardware. All pegheads have screened logos with 2/4 per side tuners. List prices on the MC/1 start at $2,995. In 1996, the company offered variants in the same design, but with solid wood bodies and no synthetic backs. The C-series also offered different pickup configurations and tonewood tops. Prices range from the C-50 ($1,695), to the C-70 ($1,995), up to the C-90 ($2,495). All models are available with the Fishman Powerbridge for an additional $150.

CLINT BRILEY

Instruments currently built in Florida.

This company was founded by Clint Briley in 1989, motivated by his experience of making new parts for his vintage National Duolian Resonator guitar. Briley, a machinist, has a background in die making. With assistance from local luthier/repairman (and friend) Charlie Jirousek, Briley hand built necks and steel bodies as he established his new company.

(Source: Hal Hammer)

Briley currently offers two models that feature his own spun resonator cones and parts. The **Cutaway Steel Body** ($1,500) has a mahogany neck and rosewood fingerboard, and meets the metal body at the twelfth fret. The **Econo-Steel** ($800) has no cutaway on its steel body.

BROADWAY

Instruments were built in Britain, Japan, and West Germany in the early to late 1960s.

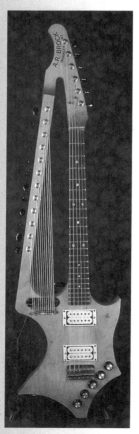

A.R.Brock Harp Guitar
19th Annual Dallas Show

The BROADWAY trademark is the brandname of a UK importer. The solid and semi-hollowbody guitars were of original design, but entry level quality.

(Source: Tony Bacon and Paul Day, The Guru's Guitar Guide)

A. R. BROCK

Instruments built in Brooklyn, New York.

Sometimes you have to throw out some bait to catch anything. Staff members of the **Blue Book** were approached by Robert Knott this year at the 19th Annual Dallas Vintage Guitar show. Knott was the current owner of a yet-unidentified guitar, an A.R. Brock "Harp Guitar". The only clue appeared on the headstock, which read "Brooklyn, New York". Any readers with further information on A.R. Brock guitars are invited to write to the **Blue Book of Guitars**, and any further updates will occur in future editions.

BRONSON

See chapter on House Brands.

While this trademark has been identified as a "House Brand", the distributor is still unknown. More research is underway.

(Source: Willie G. Moseley, Stellas & Stratocasters)

BRUBAKER

Instruments built in Reisterstown, Maryland since 1993.

Luthier/designer Kevin Brubaker builds basses that feature carved sculpted tops of exotic woods. Brubaker has been building custom instruments in the Maryland region since 1986, and only recently "went public" in the last three years to bring his design to the marketplace. In 1986, Brubaker began working on the prototype with designer Michael Scuito, the sculpted top has evolved in time to its current lines. Brubaker also designed a bolt-on neck that sits three quarters of the way into the body for his bass. While the technology is bolt-on, the neck response is somehow more like a set-neck (or perhaps a new combination of the two) due to the interaction of the extended neck pocket. The heel is sculpted in a taper as the body flows into the neck. Brubaker also continues to work evenings in a three piece band, and continues to apply practical knowledge to his designs.

Brubaker Lexa bass
courtesy Kevin Brubaker

ELECTRIC BASS

The **Lexa** model is available in 4, 5, or 6 string configurations, and in either 34" or 35" scale lengths. The bolt-on one piece Hard Maple neck has a 24 fret Wenge fingerboard, and the soft maple body is topped with Purpleheart or Padauk and Curly Maple. Either passive or active Seymour Duncan pickups, Gotoh tuners, and a 2TEK bridge round out the package. Available in Natural, Cherry Red, Scarlett Red, Rose Red, Juniper Green, Forest Green, Sapphire Blue, and Indigo waterborne lacquers. Retail list prices begin at $2,750 (four string), to $3,100 (five string), and finally up at $3,600 (six string model).

In the summer of 1996, Brubaker introduced the **Bo Axe**, a slim bodied upright bass with 35" scale. The Bo Axe mounts to a support stand, and can be played both in an upright stance, or sideways by re-adjusting the stand. Retail price still pending.

C. BRUNO & SON

See chapter on House Brands.

C. Bruno & Son was originally formed in Macon, Georgia in 1834. The company has been in the music distribution business since then. C. Bruno & Son guitars were built by another manufacturer, and distributed by the company. C. Bruno & Son distributors is currently part of Kaman Music Corporation.

In 1838, Charles Bruno and C.F. Martin entered into a partnership to produce and distribute acoustic guitars. These guitars will be labeled with both names, and were produced in New York. In 1839, Martin moved the company to Nazareth, Pennsylvania and dissolved the partnership. C.F. Martin did not provide the guitars that bear the "Bruno" or "C. Bruno & Sons" logos on the peghead.

(Source: Mike Longworth, Martin Guitars)

BSX

Instruments built in Aliquippa, Pennsyvania since 1989.

BSX has been producing a sleek electric upright bass for over seven years. The instrument features a 41½ scale on a 55 inch long instrument. The trim body is constructed of poplar, and features a hard rock maple neck, rosewood or ebony fingerboard, Bartolini pickups, and Hipshot tuners. The newest model introduced is the BSX Traveler, which features a detachable neck and a Piezo bridge. In the seven years of operation, the company estimated that maybe a total of 500 instruments have been produced.

DAVID BUNKER

Instruments built in Seattle and Tacoma, Washington during the mid-1960s through the mid-1980s.

See also P B C.

Luthier/designer David Bunker built numerous radically designed guitars during the mid 1960s and 1970s. Rather than be different for different's sake, Bunker's creations were designed to solve certain inherent

BSX Upright model
courtesy BSX Bass

solid body design flaws. Later designs began to follow more traditional forms, but still included some advanced design concepts. Bunker is currently involved with PBC Guitar Technology, Inc., which is having success with the "Tension-Free" neck design and the Wishbone hollowbody series.

Bunker guitars such as the detachable body **Galaxy** or the **Sunspot** generally range between $800 and $1,200.

Burns Reissue Baritone
courtesy Mark Sampson

BURNS

Instruments were built in Britain from the late 1950s to current; the exception being Baldwin-built Burns from 1965 to 1972, which were U.S. produced by assembling imported parts in Booneville, Arkansas.

Currently, Burns London Ltd. of Surrey, England is being distributed in the U.S. by Matchless LLC (of Matchless Amplifier fame) located in Santa Fe Springs, California. James O. Burns is acting as a consultant for Burns London Ltd.

Jim Burns has been hailed as "the British Leo Fender" due to his continual and on-going electric guitar designs and innovations. Widely accepted in England and Europe, Burns guitars never really caught on in the U.S. market.

James Ormsted Burns was born in 1925, and built his first lap steel while still serving in the Royal Air Force in 1944. By 1952 he completed his first solid body electric; along with partner Alan Wooten, Burns built his first twenty guitars under the Supersound name in 1958. Burns' first production guitars were built with Henry Weill in 1959 under the Burns-Weill trademark, then later under the Burns logo. The 'Burns, London' (1960 to 1965) was the watermark of Jim Burns' career, as the company stayed very successful producing guitars, basses, amplifiers, and accessories. Even while many popular British artists used Burns instruments, Jim Burns then turned to exporting his instruments to the U.S. under both the Ampeg and Burns trademarks.

In 1965, the Baldwin company lost to CBS in its bid to acquire Fender. Searching for another proven winner, Baldwin bought Burns and began importing the instruments under the Baldwin or Baldwin/Burns trademarks. Jim Burns stayed on as managing director and "idea man" through 1966, then left to pursue other projects. Baldwin eventually began assembling imported parts in Booneville, Arkansas. By 1970, Baldwin decided to concentrate on production of Gretsch guitars and drums (acquired in 1967, the Gretsch operation was also moved down to Arkansas).

In 1969 Jim Burns returned to the musical instrument world as a design consultant to Dallas-Arbiter's Hayman trademark. Along with ex-Vox employee Bob Pearson, Burns was reunited with Jack Golder (ex-Burns mainstay) but only continued his affiliation until 1971. A new Burns organization arose in 1973 as "Burns, U.K.", but this company met with less success than intended and folded in 1977. A later stab at affairs continued as the "Jim Burns Company" from 1979 to 1983.

Currently, Jim Burns is serving as an acting consultant at **Burns, London Ltd.** This Surrey, England-based company is making classic Burns guitars once again available worldwide.

(Source: Paul Day, The Burns Book)

The most collectable Burns instruments would be from the company's heyday between 1960 and 1965. The Burns-Weill models are relatively scarce, and the "Ampeg by Burns of London" models were only distributed from 1963 to 1964. Baldwin models, while not plentiful, do surface in the U.S. vintage market - and some example pop up in Elvis Presley's 1960s movies! One model is currently on display in Graceland. Later Burns' companies probably contributed smaller guitar productions, although the Burns U.K. Flite model has a pretty cool body design.

BURNSIDE

See GUILD.

Instruments were built in Korea during the late 1980s.

In the late 1980s, Guild introduced a line of imported entry level instruments to augment their sales line. The headstock trademark reads "Burnside by Guild" and consisted of 4 guitar models and 2 bass models.

(Source: Michael Wright, Vintage Guitar Magazine, December 1995)

BUSCARINO

Instruments currently built in Largo, Florida. Distributed by the Buscarino Guitar Company of Largo, Florida.

Luthier John Buscarino apprenticed with Master acoustic guitar builder Augustino LoPrinzi for over a year in 1978, and with Bob Benedetto of archtop lutherie fame from 1979 to 1981. Later that year, Buscarino formed Nova U.S.A., which built high quality solid body electrics, and acoustic/electric instruments. In 1990, Buscarino changed the company name to **Buscarino Guitars**, to reflect the change to building acoustic instruments. Buscarino continues to produce limited production custom guitars, and is currently focusing on archtop guitar building.

Other Buscarino designs include the **Starlight** Electric/Acoustic model which was offered in a 6- and 12-string configuration, Nylon, and acoustic bass. Buscarino also built a number of solid body designs such as the **Classic**, **Telstar**, **Nashville St.**, and **Pro Bass** models. However, Buscarino is concentrating currently on both archtop (the **Monarch** model) and carved-back flattop (the **Artisan**) models. For information regarding current models, pricing, and availability, please contact luthier John Buscarino through the Index of Current Manufacturers located in the back of this book.

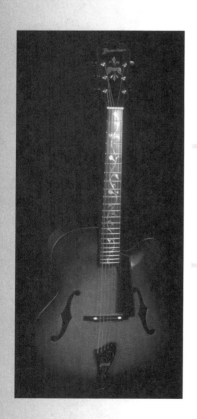

Buscarino Virtuoso
courtesy Scott Chinery

C

CADENZA

Instruments currently produced in Korea. Distributed by the Kimex Company of Seoul, Korea.

Cadenza features a wide range of steel-string, classical, and bass acoustic guitars.

CAIRNES

See also COLT.

Instruments were built in Britain during the 1980s.

Company featured high quality and original designs on models named Solo, Stud, Starguard, and Colt Peacemaker. These solid body guitars also came equipped with luthier Jim Cairnes' own pickups and hardware.

(Source: Tony Bacon and Paul Day, The Guru's Guitar Guide)

CALVIN CRAMER

Instruments built in Markneukirchen, Germany since 1996. Distributed in the U.S. by Musima North America of Tampa, Florida.

Calvin Cramer concert guitars debuted in the United States, Canada, and South American markets in 1996. The guitars are built by Musima, Germany's largest acoustic guitar manufacturer. The company headquarters in Markneukirchen, Germany are near the Czech border.

In 1991, Musima was purchased by industry veteran Helmet Stumpf following the German re-unification. The Musima facilities currently employ 130 workers, and continue to produce Musima stringed instruments as well as the Calvin Cramer concert guitars.

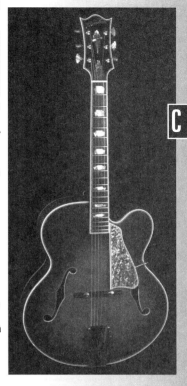

Campellone Special
courtesy Scott Chinery

CAMPELLONE

Instruments currently built in Providence, Rhode Island.

Luthier Mark Campellone originally began building solid body guitars in the late 1970s, and turned his attention to archtops around 1987. Campellone currently builds three different models of solid wood carved acoustics, and each model is available in a 16", 17", or 18" Venetian cutaway body.

The **Standard** series ($3,000) features a carved Spruce top, Figured Maple back and sides, Maple neck, bound Rosewood fingerboard, multi-bound top, Rosewood bridge, gold hardware, shell inlays. The **Deluxe** ($4,500) steps up with a Selected Spruce top, multi-bound Ebony fingerboard with three-piece 'keystone' position markers, bound f-holes, an Ebony bridge, peghead inlay, and Deluxe series tailpiece. The top package, the **Special** series ($6,000), has matching back and sides of choice Figured Maple, multi-bound top and f-holes, mutli-bound Ebony fingerboard with five-piece 'keystone' position markers of mother-of-pearl and abalone, a Special Series peghead inlay, rear peghead inlay, pearl truss rod cover, and Special series tailpiece.

CAPITAL

See chapter on House Brands.

This Gibson built budget line of guitars has been identified as a "House Brand" of the J. W. Jenkins Company of Kansas City. While built to the same standards as other Gibson guitars, they lack the one 'true' Gibson touch: an adjustable truss rod. "House Brand" Gibsons were available to musical instrument distributors in the late 1930s and early 1940s.

(Source: Walter Carter, Gibson Guitars: 100 Years of an American Icon)

CARELLI

Instruments built in the U.S., possibly during the 1930s.

Staff members from the **Blue Book** were approached by Gary Sullivan this year at the 19th Annual Dallas Vintage Guitar show. Sullivan had possession of a yet-unidentified guitar, a Carelli "Artist E". Estimates at dating this archtop guitar centered around the 1930s, but there was no firm consensus. Any readers with further information on Carelli guitars are invited to write to the **Blue Book of Guitars**. Further updates will occur in future editions.

CARL THOMPSON

Instruments built in Brooklyn, New York since 1974.

Luthier Carl Thompson moved to New York in 1967, and began working as a repairman in Dan Armstrong's guitar shop as a means to round out his income as a musician. In 1971 he formed a new

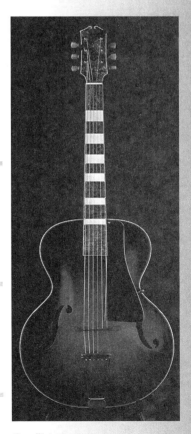

Carelli Artist E
courtesy Gary Sullivan

shop with fellow guitarist Joel Frutkin, and by 1974 was working on his own bass guitar designs. Thompson has built basses for such luminaries as Anthony Jackson, Stanley Clarke, and Les Claypool.

Luthier Thompson generally produces five or six basses a year. Thompson maintains a small shop in Stahlstown, Pennsylvania to rough out body blanks or cut neck blanks, while his final shaping, finishing, and electronics are performed in his Brooklyn workshop.

(Source: Tom Wheeler, American Guitars)

CARMINE STREET GUITARS

Instruments built in New York City, New York.

Carmine Street Guitars offers custom built instruments. The **Kellycaster** model is offered in a solid body or soundchambered version, with carved tops and one piece necks. The suggested retail price is $1,500 and features different pickup and bridge options.

Kelly Kustoms begin at a retail price of $1,000 for custom-shaped one-of-a-kind designs that are customer specified, or one of the over 20 ideas from the shop. For further information, contact Carmine Street Guitars via the Index of Current Manufacturers located in the back of this book.

CARSON ROBISON

See chapter on House Brands.

Carson J. Robison was a popular country singer and songwriter in the 1930s who endorsed a RECORDING KING flattop model. RECORDING KING was the "House Brand" for Montgomery Ward, and GIBSON built the high end models for the line (cheaper models were built by someone else). Early models had only a white paint stencil of "Carson J. Robison" on the peghead (hence this listing) but later models had the Recording King Logo as well.

(Source: Walter Carter, Gibson Guitars: 100 Years of an American Icon)

CARVIN

Instruments produced in Escondido, California since 1969. Previous production was located in Covina, California from 1950 to 1969. Carvin instruments are sold through direct catalog sales, as well as through their three factory stores in California: San Diego, Santa Ana, and Hollywood.

Established in 1946 by Lowell Kiesel in Los Angeles, Carvin originally manufactured lap steel guitars, small tube amps and pickups. The Carvin trademark is derived from Kiesel's two oldest sons, Carson and Gavin. Carvin has always been a mail-order only company. Guitars were originally offered in kit form, or by parts since the 1950s; Carvin began building complete guitars in 1964. By 1978, the glued set-neck design replaced the bolt-on necks. Carvin offers the players a wide range of options on the individual models; and even though they can't be tried out before they're bought, Carvin offers a 10 day money back guarantee.

ACOUSTIC ELECTRIC

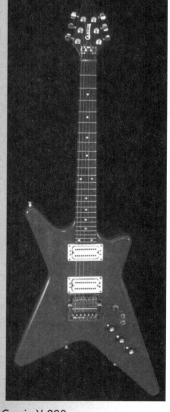

Carvin V-220
courtesy Steve Burgess

Grading	100%	98% MINT	95% EXC+	90% EXC	80% VG+	70% VG	60% G

AC175 — single cutaway routed out mahogany body, spruce top, round soundhole, thru body mahogany neck, 24 fret ebony fingerboard with pearl dot inlay, ebony bridge with black pins, blackface peghead with screened logo, 3 per side gold tuners, transducer bridge Fishman pickup, volume/treble/bass controls, active electronics. Available in Classic White, Ferrari Red, Jet Black, Natural, Pearl Blue, Pearl Red and Pearl White finishes. New 1994.

Mfr.'s Sug. Retail	$1,650	$1,320	$990	$825	$660	$595	$545	$495

ELECTRIC

Unless otherwise listed, all models in this series are available in the following standard colors: Classic White, Electric Green, Ferrari Red, Jet Black, Pearl Blue, Pearl Red and Pearl White.

In 1992, Carvin made a production change from double locking Carvin/Floyd Rose vibratos to locking Carvin/Floyd Rose vibratos with locking Sperzel tuners. In 1993, Carvin changed to a standard Carvin/Wilkinson vibrato and locking Sperzel tuners combination. In 1994, both versions were offered.

AE150 — offset double cutaway poplar body, thru body maple neck, 24 fret ebony fingerboard with pearl dot inlay, fixed bridge, blackface peghead with screened logo, 6 on one side locking Sperzel tuners, 2 humbucker/1 acoustic bridge Carvin pickups, 1 volume/2 tone/1 mix controls, 3 position switch. New 1994.

Mfr.'s Sug. Retail	$1,600	$1,280	$960	$800	$640	$575	$530	$480

AE160 — single cutaway poplar body, thru body maple neck, 24 fret ebony fingerboard with pearl dot inlay, fixed bridge, blackface peghead with screened logo, 6 on one side locking Sperzel tuners, 2 humbucker/1 acoustic bridge Carvin pickups, 1 volume/2 tone/1 mix controls, 3 position switch. New 1994.

Mfr.'s Sug. Retail	$1,600	$1,280	$960	$800	$640	$575	$530	$480

Grading	100%	98% MINT	95% EXC+	90% EXC	80% VG+	70% VG	60% G

DC120 — offset double cutaway poplar body, thru body maple neck, 24 fret ebony fingerboard with pearl block inlay, fixed bridge, graphite nut, 6 per side locking Sperzel tuners, chrome hardware, 2 humbucker Carvin pickups, volume/treble/bass and mix controls, bright boost, phase/coil split switches, active electronics. Curr. mfr.

Mfr.'s Sug. Retail	$1,630	$1,304	$978	$815	$650	$585	$535	$490

DC125 — offset double cutaway poplar body, thru body maple neck, 24 fret ebony fingerboard with pearl dot inlay, fixed bridge, graphite nut, 6 on one side locking Sperzel tuners, chrome hardware, 1 humbucker Carvin pickup, volume control, one coil split switch. Mfd. 1991 to date.

Mfr.'s Sug. Retail	$1,050	$840	$630	$525	$420	$380	$345	$315

Add $150 for standard vibrato (DC125T).

DC127 — offset double cutaway poplar body, thru body maple neck, 24 fret ebony fingerboard with pearl dot inlay, fixed bridge, graphite nut, 6 on one side locking Sperzel tuners, chrome hardware, 2 humbucker Carvin pickup, volume/tone control, 3 position/2 coil split switches. Mfd. 1991 to date.

Mfr.'s Sug. Retail	$1,150	$920	$690	$600	$480	$430	$395	$360

DC127C — similar to DC127, except has double locking Floyd Rose vibrato. Mfd. 1993 to date.

Mfr.'s Sug. Retail	$1,370	$1,096	$822	$685	$550	$495	$450	$410

DC127T — similar to DC127, except has standard Carvin/Wilkinson vibrato.

Mfr.'s Sug. Retail	$1,300	$1,040	$780	$650	$520	$470	$430	$390

DC135 — offset double cutaway poplar body, thru body maple neck, 24 fret ebony fingerboard with pearl dot inlay, fixed bridge, graphite nut, 6 on one side locking Sperzel tuners, chrome hardware, 2 single coil/1 humbucker Carvin pickups, volume/tone control, 3 pickup mini switches. Mfd. 1991 to date.

Mfr.'s Sug. Retail	$1,200	$960	$720	$620	$495	$445	$410	$370

DC135C — similar to DC135, except has double locking Floyd Rose vibrato.

Mfr.'s Sug. Retail	$1,430	$1,144	$858	$715	$570	$510	$465	$425

DC135T — similar to DC135, except has standard Carvin/Wilkinson vibrato.

Mfr.'s Sug. Retail	$1,350	$1,080	$810	$700	$560	$505	$460	$420

DC145 — offset double cutaway poplar body, thru body maple neck, 24 fret ebony fingerboard with pearl dot inlay, fixed bridge, graphite nut, reverse peghead, 6 on one side locking Sperzel tuners, chrome hardware, humbucker/single coil/humbucker Carvin pickups, volume/tone controls, 5 position/coil split switches. Mfd. 1991 to 1993.

		$840	$720	$600	$480	$430	$395	$360

Last Mfr.'s Sug. Retail was $1,200.

DC145T — similar to DC145, except has standard Carvin/Wilkinson vibrato.

		$960	$820	$685	$550	$495	$450	$410

Last Mfr.'s Sug. Retail was $1,370.

DC150 — double cutaway maple body, thru body maple neck, 24 fret ebony fingerboard with pearl dot inlay, tunomatic bridge/stop tailpiece, 3 per side tuners, chrome hardware, 2 humbucker Carvin pickups, volume/tone control, 3 position switch. Available in Classic White, Clear Maple, Ferrari Red, Jet Black, Pearl Blue, Pearl Red and Pearl White finishes. Mfd. 1991 only.

		$700	$600	$500	$400	$360	$330	$300

Last Mfr.'s Sug. Retail was $1,000.

DC150C — similar to DC150, except has double locking Floyd Rose vibrato.

		$840	$720	$600	$480	$430	$395	$360

Last Mfr.'s Sug. Retail was $1,200.

DC200 — offset double cutaway poplar body, thru body maple neck, 24 fret ebony fingerboard with pearl block inlay, fixed bridge, graphite nut, 6 on one side locking Sperzel tuners, chrome hardware, 2 humbucker Carvin pickups, volume/treble/bass and mix controls, bright boost, phase and coil split switches, active electronics, built-in headphone amp. Curr. mfr.

Mfr.'s Sug. Retail	$1,450	$1,160	$870	$725	$580	$520	$475	$435

DC200C — similar to DC200, except has double locking Floyd Rose vibrato. New 1994.

Mfr.'s Sug. Retail	$1,680	$1,344	$1,008	$840	$675	$605	$555	$505

DC200T — similar to DC200, except has standard Carvin/Wilkinson vibrato.

Mfr.'s Sug. Retail	$1,600	$1,280	$960	$800	$640	$575	$530	$480

DC400 — offset double cutaway koa body, figured maple top, koa thru body neck, 24 fret ebony fingerboard with abalone block inlay, fixed bridge, body matching headstock, graphite nut, 6 on one side locking Sperzel tuners, chrome hardware, 2 humbucker Carvin pickups, volume/treble/bass and mix controls, bright boost, phase and coil split switches, built-in headphone amp. Available in Cherry Sunburst, Emerald Green, Sapphire Blue, Tobacco Sunburst and Vintage Yellow finishes. Curr. mfr.

Mfr.'s Sug. Retail	$2,050	$1,640	$1,230	$1,025	$820	$745	$675	$615

This model has gold or black hardware optionally available.

In 1993, poplar body, thru body maple neck replaced original items.

DC400C — similar to DC400, except has double locking Floyd Rose vibrato. New 1994.

Mfr.'s Sug. Retail	$2,280	$1,824	$1,368	$1,140	$910	$820	$750	$685

"To me, vintage guitars are only as good as they sound and play. I'm in a band and I play, buy, sell and trade guitars, but to have them for the sake of looking at them…well, who cares after awhile."
—Bob Young on Perry Margaloff
TCG, May/June 1994

Grading	100%	98% MINT	95% EXC+	90% EXC	80% VG+	70% VG	60% G

DC400T — similar to DC400, except has standard Carvin/Wilkinson vibrato.

Mfr.'s Sug. Retail	$2,200	$1,760	$1,320	$1,100	$880	$790	$725	$660

DN612 — offset sharp double cutaway poplar body, 2 maple thru-body necks in a 12/6 configuration, 24 fret ebony fingerboards with pearl dot inlays, fixed bridges, graphite nut, 6 per side on 12 string neck, 3 per side on 6 string neck, locking Sperzel tuners, chrome hardware, 2 humbucker Carvin pickups, volume/tone control, two 3 position/1 neck selector switches, 2 output jacks. Curr. mfr.

Mfr.'s Sug. Retail	$3,200	$2,560	$1,920	$1,600	$1,280	$1,150	$1,055	$960

This model is also available with bass neck, instead of 12 string neck, (DN640) or two bass necks (DN440).

LS175 — offset double cutaway poplar body, thru body maple neck, 22 fret ebony fingerboard with pearl dot inlay, tunomatic bridge/stop tailpiece, 6 on one side tuners, chrome hardware, 3 stacked humbucker Carvin pickups, volume/tone controls, 5 position switch. Available in Classic White, Ferrari Red, Jet Blue, Natural, Pearl Blue, Pearl Red and Pearl White finishes. Disc. 1991.

		$800	$685	$570	$460	$410	$375	$340

Last Mfr.'s Sug. Retail was $1,140.

LS175C — similar to LS175, except has double locking Floyd Rose vibrato. Disc. 1991.

		$940	$805	$670	$535	$480	$440	$400

Last Mfr.'s Sug. Retail was $1,340.

TL60 — single cutaway poplar body, thru body maple neck, 24 fret ebony fingerboard with pearl dot inlay, fixed bridge, graphite nut, 6 per side locking Sperzel tuners, chrome hardware, 2 stacked coil pickups, volume/tone control, 3 position switch. Mfd. 1993 to date.

Mfr.'s Sug. Retail	$1,150	$920	$690	$600	$495	$445	$410	$370

TL60T — similar to TL60, except has standard Carvin/Wilkinson vibrato.

Mfr.'s Sug. Retail	$1,300	$1,040	$780	$675	$550	$495	$455	$415

ULTRA V — V shape poplar body, maple thru body neck, 24 fret ebony fingerboard with pearl dot inlay, fixed bridge, graphite nut, 6 on one side locking Sperzel tuners, chrome hardware, 2 humbucker pickups, volume/tone control, 3-way switch. Mfd. 1991 to 1994.

		$740	$635	$530	$425	$385	$350	$320

Last Mfr.'s Sug. Retail was $1,060.

Ultra VT — similar to Ultra V, except has standard Carvin/Wilkinson vibrato.

		$855	$730	$610	$485	$435	$400	$365

Last Mfr.'s Sug. Retail was $1,220.

X220 — offset double cutaway V shape poplar body, maple thru body neck, 24 fret ebony fingerboard with pearl dot inlay, fixed bridge, graphite nut, 6 on one side locking Sperzel tuners, chrome hardware, 2 humbucker pickups, volume/tone control, 3-way/2 coil split switches. Mfd. 1991 to 1992 .

		$800	$685	$570	$460	$410	$375	$340

Last Mfr.'s Sug. Retail was $1,140.

X220C — similar to X220, except has standard Carvin/Wilkinson vibrato.

		$940	$805	$670	$535	$480	$440	$400

Last Mfr.'s Sug. Retail was $1,340.

ELECTRIC BASS

All models in this series are also available fretless and come with these standard colors: Classic White, Electric Green, Ferrari Red, Jet Black, Pearl Blue, Pearl Red and Pearl White.

BB70 — offset double cutaway poplar body, thru body maple neck, 24 fret ebony fingerboard with offset pearl dot inlay, fixed bridge, graphite nut, 2 per side tuners, chrome hardware, 2 J-style pickups, volume/treble/bass/mix controls, active electronics. New 1994.

Mfr.'s Sug. Retail	$1,650	$1,320	$990	$825	$660	$595	$545	$495

BB75 LIMITED — offset double cutaway poplar body, thru body maple neck, 24 fret ebony fingerboard with offset pearl dot inlay, fixed bridge, graphite nut, 3/2 per side tuners, chrome hardware, 2 J-style pickups, volume/treble/bass and mix controls, active electronics. Curr. mfr.

Mfr.'s Sug. Retail	$1,800	$1,350	$900	$870	$680	$610	$560	$510

This model has fretless fingerboard (BB75F Limited) optionally available.

LB20 — offset double cutaway poplar body, maple thru body neck, 24 fret ebony fingerboard with pearl dot inlay, fixed bridge, graphite nut, 4 on one side locking Sperzel tuners, chrome hardware, 2 J-style pickups, 2 volume/1 tone controls. Mfd. 1991 to date.

Mfr.'s Sug. Retail	$1,200	$960	$720	$600	$480	$430	$395	$360

This model has fretless fingerboard (LB20F) optionally available.

LB70 — offset double cutaway poplar body, maple thru body neck, 24 fret ebony fingerboard with pearl dot inlay, fixed bridge, graphite nut, 4 on one side locking Sperzel tuners, chrome hardware, 2 J-style pickups, volume/bass/treble/mix controls, active electronics. Mfd. 1991 to date.

Mfr.'s Sug. Retail	$1,300	$1,040	$780	$650	$520	$470	$430	$390

This model has fretless fingerboard (LB70F) optionally available.

Grading	100%	98% MINT	95% EXC+	90% EXC	80% VG+	70% VG	60% G

LB75 — similar to LB70, except has 5 strings, 5 on one side tuners, built-in headphone amp.

Mfr.'s Sug. Retail	$1,500	$1,200	$900	$750	$600	$540	$495	$450

This model has fretless fingerboard (LB75F) optionally available.

In 1992, 3/2 per side tuners replaced original item.

LB76 — similar to LB70, except has 6 strings, built-in headphone amp. Mfd. 1992 to date.

Mfr.'s Sug. Retail	$1,800	$1,440	$1,080	$900	$720	$650	$595	$540

This model has fretless fingerboard (LB76F) optionally available.

Castelfidardo Excelsior
courtesy David J. Pavlick

CASIO

Instruments produced in Japan by Fuji Gen Gakki from 1987 to 1988.

The Casio company of Tokyo, Japan began producing keyboards in 1980. By the late 1980s, they unveiled the angular model MG-500 and vaguely Fenderish MG-510 electric guitars that could also be used as controllers by sending MIDI information. In 1988, Casio introduced the PG-380, a strat-styled guitar with an on-board synthesizer as well as a MIDI port. The PG-380 also has a companion module that takes up two rack spaces, and offers extra processing facilities.

Casio also produced a number of guitar shaped "Digital Guitars" in 1987. The DG10 is more self contained, while the DG20 can send processing information to an external synthesizer. Both models have plastic bodies, plastic "strings" and a number of buttons and built in features. These may appeal more to keyboard players, or entry level guitar synthesist enthusiasts.

CASTELFIDARDO

Circa unknown.

David Pavlick is the current owner of this "mystery guitar". The 3+3 headstock features a decal which reads "Castelfidardo - Excelsior - New York", and features a 15 5/16" archtop body, two pickups, bound 22 fret neck, 2 volume/2 tone controls, 3-way pickup selector on the upper bass bout, and trapeze tailpiece. Inside both f-holes there is "1 52" stamped into the back wood. Any readers with further information are invited to write to the **Blue Book of Guitars**.

(Source: David J. Pavlick, Woodbury, Connecticut)

CATALINA

See chapter on House Brands.

This trademark has been identified as a "House Brand" of the Abercrombie & Fitch company.

(Source: Willie G. Moseley, Stellas & Stratocasters)

C B ALYN

Instruments currently built in Pacific Palisades, California.

The **Rosebud** models are high quality, solid top (no soundholes) acoustic guitars with a piezo pickup system. Retail list ranges from $1,499 (basic) to $1,599 (RB70 Artist).

CELEBRITY

Instruments are built in Korea, and distributed by the Kaman Music Corporation of Bloomfield, Connecticut since the late 1980s.

The Celebrity line of bowl back guitars was introduced in 1983 as a Korean-built entry level "introduction" to the American-built Ovation line. Celebrity models offer similar design features, and a variety of options as their overseas production saves money on their retail price.

CHANDLER

Instruments are built in Burlingame, California since 1982 to current.

Chandler has been located in Burlingame, California since 1980. The company originally focused on providing high quality replacement guitar parts, and then expanded to include guitar production beginning in 1985. Chandler's high quality models feature some original design innovations, and in 1996 began offering a line of lap steels.

The company continues to offer a line of guitar accessories such as pickups and pickguards, as well as other related components.

Grading	100%	98% MINT	95% EXC+	90% EXC	80% VG+	70% VG	60% G

ELECTRIC

"555" — double sharp cutaway alder body, maple neck, white pickguard, 22 fret rosewood fingerboard with pearl dot inlay, fixed bridge, classical peghead, 3 per side tuners, chrome hardware, 3 mini humbucker Chandler pickups, volume/tone control, 5 position switch. Available in Black, Crimson Red, Vintage Blonde and Transparent Wine Red finishes. Mfd. 1992 to date.

Mfr.'s Sug. Retail	$1,200	$960	$720	$600	$480	$430	$395	$360

In 1994, Crimson Red finish was added, Transparent Wine Red finish was discontinued.

AUSTIN SPECIAL — single sharp cutaway asymmetrical bound alder body, bolt-on maple neck, 22 fret rosewood fingerboard with pearl dot inlay, fixed bridge, 6 on one side tuners, chrome hardware, 3 single coil lipstick pickups, volume/tone control, 3 position switch. Available in Black and White finishes. Mfd. 1992 to date.

Mfr.'s Sug. Retail	$1,200	$960	$720	$600	$480	$430	$395	$360

In 1994, White finish became available.

Austin Special 5 — similar to Austin Special, except has 5 strings. Mfd. 1993 to date.

Mfr.'s Sug. Retail	$1,700	$1,360	$1,020	$850	$680	$610	$560	$510

METRO (Baritone Guitar) — single sharp cutaway asymmetrical bound alder body, bolt-on maple neck, 24 fret rosewood fingerboard with pearl dot inlay, tremolo bridge, 6 on one side tuners, chrome hardware, 2 single coil lipstick pickups, volume/tone control, 3 position switch. Available in Black, Surf Green, and White finishes. Mfd. 1995 to date.

Mfr.'s Sug. Retail	$1,499	$1,124	$749

Add $100 for Super Sparkle finish.

TELEPATHIC — single round cutaway alder body, lam pearloid pickguard, bolt on maple neck, 22 fret maple fingerboard with ebony dot inlay, fixed bridge, 6 on one side Gotoh tuners, chrome hardware, single coil pickup, volume/tone control. Available in 2 Tone Sunburst, Gloss Black, Olympic White, Surf Green and Vintage Blonde finishes. New 1994.

Mfr.'s Sug. Retail	$650	$520	$390	$325	$260	$235	$215	$195

Telepathic Deluxe — similar to Telepathic, except has bound body. Available in 3 Tone Sunburst, Cherry Sunburst and Gloss Black finishes.

Mfr.'s Sug. Retail	$725	$543	$362	$360	$290	$260	$240	$220

CHARVEL

Trademark established in 1978 by Charvel/Jackson Guitar Company. Manufacturer's headquarters located in Fort Worth, Texas, since 1980. Charvel San Dimas and Charvel USA guitars are built in California. Other production models are built in Japan; with the exception of the CHS electrics and the Acoustic models which are built in Korea.

Releasing its first instruments in 1978, Charvel rapidly acquired a reputation for making custom high quality instruments. Beginning with a two-man shop in California, Charvel continued to expand, and then added the higher end Jackson line of instruments.

As a general rule of thumb, you can identify the country of origin on earlier instruments that have the guitar shaped Charvel logo by the color of the logo. The guitars with gold logos were manufactured in the U.S.A., the ones with white or black logos were manufactured overseas.

Another way to determine the origin of manufacture is manufacturer's retail price point. In most cases, the lower the retail price (last retail price on discontinued models) the more likely the instrument was manufactured overseas. As the years went by and the Charvel line expanded, its upper end models were phased out and moved into the Jackson line (which had been the Charvel/Jackson Company's line of custom made instruments) and were gaining more popularity. For example, the Charvel Avenger, mfd. 1991 to 1992, became the Jackson Rhoads EX Pro, mfd. 1992 to date. See the Jackson Guitars section in this book for further details.

ACOUSTIC

125S — dreadnought style, solid spruce top, round soundhole, 7 stripe bound body/rosette, mahogany back/sides/neck, 14/20 fret bound rosewood fingerboard with abalone dot inlay, rosewood bridge with white black pins, rosewood veneered peghead with pearl logo inlay, 3 per side chrome tuners. Available in Natural and Tobacco Sunburst finishes. New 1994.

Mfr.'s Sug. Retail	$595	$476	$357	$300	$240	$215	$195	$180

125SE — similar to 125S, except has transducer bridge pickup, 3 band EQ. Available in Natural and Tobacco Sunburst finishes. New 1994.

Mfr.'s Sug. Retail	$695	$556	$417	$350	$280	$250	$230	$210

150SC — single round cutaway dreadnought style, solid spruce top, round soundhole, 7 stripe bound body/rosette, rosewood back/sides, mahogany neck, 14/20 fret bound rosewood fingerboard with abalone dot inlay, rosewood bridge with white black pins, rosewood veneered peghead with pearl logo inlay, 3 per side chrome tuners. Available in Natural and Tobacco Sunburst finishes. New 1994.

Mfr.'s Sug. Retail	$595	$476	$357	$300	$240	$215	$195	$180

Grading	100%	98% MINT	95% EXC+	90% EXC	80% VG+	70% VG	60% G

150SEC — similar to 150SC, except has transducer bridge pickup, 3 band EQ. Available in Natural and Tobacco Sunburst finishes. New 1994.

Mfr.'s Sug. Retail	$695	$556	$417	$350	$280	$250	$230	$210

525 — single round cutaway dreadnought style, spruce top, round soundhole, 5 stripe bound body and rosette, mahogany arched back/sides/neck, 22 fret bound rosewood fingerboard with pearl dot inlay, rosewood bridge with white black dot pins, bound peghead with abalone Charvel logo inlay, 3 per side chrome tuners. Available in Cherry Sunburst, Metallic Black, Natural and Tobacco Sunburst. Disc. 1994.

			$280	$240	$200	$160	$145	$130	$120

Last Mfr.'s Sug. Retail was $400.

525D — similar to 525, except has transducer bridge pickup with 3 band EQ. Available in Metallic Black, Natural and Tobacco Sunburst finishes. Disc. 1994.

			$350	$300	$250	$200	$180	$165	$150

Last Mfr.'s Sug. Retail was $500.

550 — dreadnought style, spruce top, round soundhole, black pickguard, 3 stripe bound body/rosette, mahogany back/sides/neck, 14/20 fret rosewood fingerboard with pearl dot inlay, rosewood bridge with black white dot pins, rosewood veneered peghead with pearl logo inlay, 3 per side chrome tuners. Available in Mahogany and Natural finishes. New 1994.

Mfr.'s Sug. Retail	$225	$180	$135	$115	$90	$80	$70	$65

Add $40 for single round cutaway (550C).

550E — similar to 550, except has transducer bridge pickup, 3 band EQ. Available in Natural finish. New 1994.

Mfr.'s Sug. Retail	$325	$243	$162	$160	$130	$115	$105	$95

Add $40 for single round cutaway (550CE).

625 — single round cutaway jumbo style, spruce top, round soundhole, 5 stripe bound body and rosette, nato back/sides, mahogany neck, 20 fret rosewood fingerboard with abalone dot inlay, rosewood bridge with white black dot pins, rosewood veneer on peghead with abalone Charvel logo inlay, 3 per side gold tuners. Available in Black, Cherry Sunburst, Metallic Sunburst, Natural and Tobacco Sunburst finishes. Mfd. 1992 to date.

Mfr.'s Sug. Retail	$365	$273	$182	$165	$130	$120	$110	$100

In 1994, Metallic Sunburst and Natural finishes were introduced, Black finish was discontinued.

625C — similar to 625, except has abalone bound body/rosette, rosewood back/sides, 24 fret bound extended fingerboard, abalone dot pins, bound peghead, transducer bridge pickup, 3 band EQ, active electronics. Mfd. 1992 to date.

Mfr.'s Sug. Retail	$550	$412	$275	$245	$180	$160	$150	$135

625C-12 — similar to 625, except has 12 strings, abalone bound body/rosette, rosewood back/sides, 24 fret bound extended fingerboard, abalone dot pins, bound peghead, 6 per side tuners, transducer bridge pickup, 3 band EQ, active electronics. Available in Metallic Black, Natural and Tobacco Sunburst finishes. New 1994.

Mfr.'s Sug. Retail	$695	$556	$417	$350	$280	$250	$230	$210

625D — similar to 625, except has transducer bridge pickup, 3 band EQ, active electronics.

Mfr.'s Sug. Retail	$475	$356	$237	$215	$160	$145	$130	$120

625F — similar to 625, except has figured maple top. Available in Tobacco Sunburst, Transparent Black and Transparent Red. New 1994.

Mfr.'s Sug. Retail	$650	$520	$390	$325	$260	$235	$215	$195

725 — jumbo style, solid spruce top, round soundhole, 7 stripe bound body/rosette, mahogany back/sides/neck, 14/20 fret rosewood fingerboard with pearl offset dot inlay, rosewood bridge with white black pins, rosewood veneered peghead with pearl logo inlay, 3 per side chrome tuners. Available in Natural finish. New 1994.

Mfr.'s Sug. Retail	$495	$371	$247	$245	$195	$175	$160	$150

725E — similar to 725, except has transducer bridge pickup, 3 band EQ. Available in Natural finish. New 1994.

Mfr.'s Sug. Retail	$595	$476	$357	$300	$240	$215	$195	$180

750E — jumbo style, solid spruce top, round soundhole, 7 stripe bound body/rosette, figured maple back/sides, mahogany neck, 14/20 fret rosewood fingerboard with pearl offset dot inlay, rosewood bridge with white black pins, figured maple veneered peghead with pearl logo inlay, 3 per side gold tuners. Available in Natural finish. New 1994.

Mfr.'s Sug. Retail	$695	$556	$417	$350	$280	$250	$230	$210

CM-100 — dreadnought style, cedar top, round soundhole, multibound body, 3 stripe rosette, figured mahogany back/sides, mahogany neck, 14/20 fret bound rosewood fingerboard with pearl dot inlay, ebony bridge with white black dot pins, bound rosewood veneered peghead with pearl logo inlay, 3 per side chrome tuners. Available in Natural finish. New 1994.

Mfr.'s Sug. Retail	$895	$671	$447	$445	$360	$325	$300	$275

CM-400 — jumbo style, solid spruce top, round soundhole, maple bound/abalone purfling body, abalone rosette, jacaranda back/sides, mahogany neck, 14/20 fret ebony fingerboard with pearl cloud inlay, ebony bridge with black abalone dot pins, abalone bound rosewood veneered peghead with abalone logo inlay, 3 per side gold tuners. Available in Natural finish. New 1994.

Mfr.'s Sug. Retail	$3,995	$2,996	$1,997	$1,995	$1,595	$1,435	$1,315	$1,195

This is a Limited Edition instrument.

"Who's got the money to buy these things? I've sold lots of my guitars over the years to do things like put my kids through school."

—L. Acunto on Rick Nielsen

TCG, May/June 1994

Grading		100%	98% MINT	95% EXC+	90% EXC	80% VG+	70% VG	60% G

ACOUSTIC ELECTRIC

325SL — double offset cutaway asymmetrical style, spruce top, offset wedge soundhole, bound body and soundhole, nato back/sides/neck, 22 fret rosewood fingerboard with offset abalone dot inlay, rosewood bridge with white pearl dot pins, rosewood veneer with abalone Charvel logo, 3 per side chrome tuners, transducer bridge pickup, 3 band EQ, active electronics. Available in Black, Bright Red and Turquoise finishes. Mfd. 1992 to 1994.

		$350	$300	$250	$200	$180	$165	$150

Last Mfr.'s Sug. Retail was $500.

325SLX — similar to 325SL, except has figured maple top, rosewood back/sides, bound fingerboard with shark fin inlay, bound peghead, active electronics with built-in chorus. Available in Cherry Sunburst, Tobacco Sunburst and Transparent Red finishes.

		$420	$360	$300	$240	$215	$195	$180

Last Mfr.'s Sug. Retail was $600.

ATX — single cutaway hollow mahogany body, bound maple top, maple neck, 24 fret rosewood fingerboard with offset pearl dot inlay, thru strings rosewood bridge, six on one chrome tuners, Fishman transducer bridge pickup, volume/3 band EQ controls. Available in Black, Deep Metallic Blue, Dark Metallic Red and Deep Metallic Violet finishes. Mfd. 1993 to date.

Mfr.'s Sug. Retail	$895	$671	$447	$445	$360	$325	$300	$275

In 1994, Dark Metallic Red finish was introduced, Deep Metallic Violet finish was discontinued.

ATX (Trans) — similar to ATX, except has figured maple top. Available in Tobacco Sunburst, Transparent Black and Transparent Violet finishes.

Mfr.'s Sug. Retail	$995	$796	$597	$500	$400	$360	$330	$300

CHS Series

CHS 1 — offset double cutaway alder body, white pickguard, bolt-on maple neck, 22 fret rosewood fingerboard with pearl dot inlay, standard vibrato, screened peghead logo, 6 on one side tuners, black chrome hardware, 3 single coil exposed pickups, volume/tone controls, 5 position switch. Available in Black, Bright Red, Metallic Blue and Snow White finishes. New 1995.

Mfr.'s Sug. Retail	$345	$276	$207	$175	$140	$125	$115·	$105

CHS 2 — similar to CHS 1, except has 2 single coil/1 humbucker exposed humbucker pickups. Available in Black, Bright Red, Metallic Blue and Snow White finishes. New 1995.

Mfr.'s Sug. Retail	$345	$276	$207	$175	$140	$125	$115	$105

CHS 3 — similar to CHS 1, except has no pickguard, 24 fret fingerboard, 2 humbucker exposed pickups. Available in Black, Bright Red, Metallic Blue and Snow White finishes. New 1995.

Mfr.'s Sug. Retail	$395	$296	$197	$195	$155	$140	$125	$115

San Dimas Series

This series is entirely hand made at the Jackson Custom Shop located in Ontario, California.

SAN DIMAS I — offset double cutaway lacewood body, bolt-on birdseye maple neck, 24 fret rosewood fingerboard with pearl dot inlay, double locking Floyd Rose vibrato, screened peghead logo, 6 on one side Gotoh tuners, gold hardware, 2 exposed humbucker DiMarzio pickups, volume control, 3 position switch. Available in Natural Oil finish. New 1995.

Mfr.'s Sug. Retail	$1,395	$1,116	$837	$700	$560	$505	$460	$420

Add $100 for koa body.

This model has mahogany body optionally available.

SAN DIMAS II — similar to San Dimas I, except has standard Wilkinson vibrato, locking Sperzel tuners, black hardware. Available in Natural Oil finish. New 1995.

Mfr.'s Sug. Retail	$1,295	$971	$647	$645	$515	$465	$425	$385

Add $100 for koa body.

This model has mahogany body optionally available.

SAN DIMAS III — offset double cutaway mahogany body, quilted maple top, bolt-on birdseye maple neck, 24 fret pau ferro fingerboard with pearl dot inlay, double locking Floyd Rose vibrato, screened peghead logo, 6 on one side Gotoh tuners, black hardware, 2 single coil rail/1 exposed DiMarzio pickups, volume/tone controls, 5 position/coil tap switches. Available in Transparent Green, Transparent Purple, Transparent Red and Vintage Sunburst finishes. New 1995.

Mfr.'s Sug. Retail	$1,495	$1,196	$897	$750	$600	$540	$495	$450

SAN DIMAS IV — similar to San Dimas III, except has koa body, bound quilted maple top, body matching peghead with screened logo, gold hardware, no coil tap. Available in Transparent Green, Transparent Purple, Transparent Red and Vintage Sunburst finishes. New 1995.

Mfr.'s Sug. Retail	$1,695	$1,271	$847	$845	$675	$605	$555	$505

SAN DIMAS STANDARD — offset double cutaway alder body, bolt-on maple neck, 24 fret rosewood fingerboard with pearl dot inlay, standard vibrato, screened peghead logo, 6 on one side locking Sperzel tuners, chrome hardware, 2 single coil/1 humbucker exposed DiMarzio pickups, volume/tone controls, 5 position switch. Available in Black, Forest Green, Garnet Red, Sapphire Blue and Snow White finishes. New 1995.

Mfr.'s Sug. Retail	$995	$796	$597	$500	$400	$360	$330	$300

Grading	100%	98% MINT	95% EXC+	90% EXC	80% VG+	70% VG	60% G

SAN DIMAS TRADITIONAL — offset double cutaway alder body, pearloid pickguard, bolt-on maple neck, 22 fret rosewood fingerboard with pearl dot inlay, standard Wilkinson vibrato, string tree, screened peghead logo, 6 on one side locking Sperzel tuners, black hardware, 3 single coil exposed DiMarzio pickups, volume/tone controls, 5 position switch. Available in Black, Forest Green, Garnet Red, Sapphire Blue and Snow White finishes. New 1995.

Mfr.'s Sug. Retail $995 $796 $597 $500 $400 $360 $330 $300

Surfcaster Series

SURFCASTER — offset double rounded cutaway asymmetrical semi hollow basswood body, offset wedge sound-hole, bound body and soundhole, pearloid pickguard, bolt-on maple neck, 24 fret bound rosewood fingerboard with pearl shark fin inlay, standard vibrato, bound peghead, roller nut, 3 per side tuners, chrome hardware, 2 single coil lipstick pickups, volume/tone control, 3 position switch, phase reversal in tone control. Available in Black, Magenta and Turquoise finishes. Mfd. 1992 to 1994.

$695 $595 $500 $400 $360 $330 $300
Last Mfr.'s Sug. Retail was $995.

Surfcaster (Trans) — similar to Surfcaster, except has figured maple top/mahogany body. Available in Star Glo, Transparent Orange and Transparent Red finishes.

$765 $655 $545 $435 $395 $360 $330
Last Mfr.'s Sug. Retail was $1,095.

SURFCASTER HT — offset double round cutaway asymmetrical semi hollow basswood body, bound wedge soundhole, bound body, pearloid pickguard, bolt-on maple neck, 24 fret bound rosewood fingerboard with pearl shark fin inlay, tunomatic bridge/trapeze tailpiece with stylized C, bound peghead with screened logo, roller nut, 3 per side tuners, chrome hardware, 2 single coil lipstick pickups, volume/tone control, 3 position switch, phase reversal in tone control. Available in Black, Metallic Violet and Turquoise finishes. Mfd. 1992 to 1994.

$645 $565 $480 $400 $360 $330 $300
Last Mfr.'s Sug. Retail was $895.

In early 1994, single coil/humbucker pickups configuration replaced original item.

Surfcaster HT (Trans) — similar to Surfcaster HT, except has figured maple top/mahogany body. Available in Natural Green Burst, Natural Red Burst, Star Glo, Tobacco Sunburst, Transparent Orange and Transparent Red finishes. Mfd. 1992 to 1994.

$715 $625 $530 $435 $395 $360 $330
Last Mfr.'s Sug. Retail was $995.

In early 1994, Natural Green Burst, Natural Red Burst and Tobacco Sunburst finishes were introduced, single coil/humbuckers pickup configuration replaced original item, Star Glo, Transparent Orange and Transparent Red finishes were discontinued.

SURFCASTER 12 — offset double round cutaway asymmetrical semi hollow basswood body, bound wedge soundhole, bound body, pearloid pickguard, bolt-on maple neck, 24 fret bound ebony fingerboard with pearl shark fin inlay, fixed bridge, bound peghead with screened logo, roller nut, 6 per side tuners, chrome hardware, 2 single coil lipstick pickups, volume/tone control, 3 position switch, phase reversal in tone control. Available in Black, Magenta and Turquoise finishes. Mfd. 1992 to 1994.

$760 $665 $570 $480 $430 $395 $360
Last Mfr.'s Sug. Retail was $1,050.

In early 1994, bound rosewood fingerboard replaced original item.

Surfcaster 12 (Trans) — similar to Surfcaster 12, except has figured maple top/mahogany body. Available in Star Glo, Transparent Orange and Transparent Red finishes.

$830 $725 $615 $515 $465 $425 $385
Last Mfr.'s Sug. Retail was $1,150

ACOUSTIC ELECTRIC BASS

425 SL — offset double rounded cutaway asymmetrical style, spruce top, offset wedge soundhole, bound body and soundhole, nato back/sides/neck, 22 fret rosewood fingerboard with offset abalone inlay, rosewood bridge with abalone dot inlay, abalone Charvel logo peghead inlay, 2 per side chrome tuners, transducer bridge pickup, 3 band EQ, active electronics. Available in Bright Red, Metallic Black and Turquoise finishes. Mfd. 1992 to 1994.

$385 $330 $275 $220 $200 $180 $165
Last Mfr.'s Sug. Retail was $550.

425SLX — similar to 425SL, except has figured maple top, rosewood back/sides, bound fingerboard/peghead, active electronics with built-in chorus. Available in Cherry Sunburst, Tobacco Sunburst and Transparent Red finishes. Mfd. 1992 to 1994.

$455 $390 $325 $260 $235 $215 $195
Last Mfr.'s Sug. Retail was $650.

ATX BASS — single cutaway hollow mahogany body, bound maple top, maple neck, 22 fret rosewood fingerboard with offset pearl dot inlay, thru strings rosewood bridge, 4 on one side chrome tuners, volume/3 band EQ controls. Available in Black, Deep Metallic Blue and Deep Metallic Violet finishes. Mfd. 1993 to date.

Mfr.'s Sug. Retail $995 $796 $597 $500 $400 $360 $330 $300

ATX Bass (Trans) — similar to ATX Bass, except has figured maple top. Available in Tobacco Sunburst, Transparent Black and Transparent Violet finishes.

Mfr.'s Sug. Retail $1,095 $821 $547 $545 $435 $395 $360 $330

Grading	100%	98% MINT	95% EXC+	90% EXC	80% VG+	70% VG	60% G

C

SURFCASTER BASS — offset double rounded cutaway asymmetrical, basswood body, pearloid pickguard, bolt-on maple neck, 21 fret bound rosewood fingerboard with offset pearl inlay, fixed bridge, bound peghead, 2 per side tuners, chrome hardware, 2 single coil lipstick pickups, volume/tone control, 3 position switch, phase reversal in tone control. Available in Black, Magenta and Turquoise finishes. Mfd. 1992 to 1994.

	100%	98%	95%	90%	80%	70%	60%
	$695	$595	$500	$400	$360	$330	$300

Last Mfr.'s Sug. Retail was $995.

Surfcaster Bass (Trans) — similar to Surfcaster Bass, except has figured maple top/mahogany body. Available in Star Glo, Transparent Orange and Transparent Red finishes.

	100%	98%	95%	90%	80%	70%	60%
	$765	$655	$545	$435	$395	$360	$330

Last Mfr.'s Sug. Retail was $1,095.

ELECTRIC

STANDARD 1 — offset double cutaway hardwood body, white pickguard, bolt-on maple neck, 22 fret maple fingerboard with black dot inlay, standard vibrato, 6 on one side tuners, chrome hardware, 1 humbucker DiMarzio pickup, volume control. Available in Black, Blue, Red and White finish. Mfd. 1983 to 1985.

	100%	98%	95%	90%	80%	70%	60%
	$670	$575	$480	$385	$350	$320	$290

Last Mfr.'s Sug. Retail was $960.

STANDARD 2 — similar to Standard 1, except has 2 humbucker Dimarzio pickups, 3 position switch. Mfd. 1985 only.

	100%	98%	95%	90%	80%	70%	60%
	$720	$615	$510	$410	$370	$340	$310

Last Mfr.'s Sug. Retail was $1,030.

STANDARD 3 — similar to Standard 1, except has 3 single coil DiMarzio pickups, 3 mini switches. Mfd. 1983 to 1985.

	100%	98%	95%	90%	80%	70%	60%
	$730	$625	$520	$415	$375	$340	$310

Last Mfr.'s Sug. Retail was $1,040.

Classic Series

STX CUSTOM — offset double cutaway basswood body, pearloid pickguard, bolt-on maple neck, 22 fret rosewood fingerboard with pearl dot inlay, double locking vibrato, 6 on one side tuners, chrome hardware, 2 single coil/1 humbucker Jackson pickups, volume/tone control, 5 position switch. Available in Black and Deep Metallic Blue. Mfd. 1991 to 1994.

	100%	98%	95%	90%	80%	70%	60%
	$625	$535	$445	$360	$325	$300	$275

Last Mfr.'s Sug. Retail was $895.

STX Custom (Trans) — similar to STX Custom, except has ash body. Available in Tobacco Sunburst, Transparent Blue and Transparent Red. Mfd. 1991 to 1994.

	100%	98%	95%	90%	80%	70%	60%
	$695	$595	$500	$400	$360	$330	$300

Last Mfr.'s Sug. Retail was $995.

STX DELUXE — similar to STX Custom, except has standard vibrato. Available in Black, Deep Metallic Blue, Dark Metallic Red, Pearl White and Turquoise finishes. Mfd. 1991 to 1994.

	100%	98%	95%	90%	80%	70%	60%
	$485	$415	$350	$280	$250	$230	$210

Last Mfr.'s Sug. Retail was $695.

TX CUSTOM (formerly TE Custom) — single cutaway basswood body, pearloid pickguard, bolt-on maple neck, 22 fret maple fingerboard with black dot inlay, fixed bridge, 6 on one side tuners, chrome hardware, volume/tone control, 5 position switch. Available in Black, Dark Metallic Red, Tobacco Sunburst and Turquoise finishes. Mfd. 1992 to date.

Mfr.'s Sug. Retail	100%	98%	95%	90%	80%	70%	60%
$795	$596	$397	$350	$280	$250	$230	$210

The fingerboard is also available in rosewood with pearl dot inlay.

In 1994, Tobacco Sunburst finish was introduced, Dark Metallic Red finish was discontinued.

TX Custom (Trans) — similar to TX Custom, except has ash body. Available in Tobacco Sunburst finish.

	100%	98%	95%	90%	80%	70%	60%
	$555	$475	$395	$315	$280	$260	$235

Last Mfr.'s Sug. Retail was $795.

The fingerboard was also available in rosewood with pearl dot inlay.

TTX — single cutaway basswood body, pearloid pickguard, bolt-on maple neck, 24 fret maple fingerboard with black dot inlay, standard vibrato, 6 on one side locking tuners, chrome hardware, single coil/humbucker Jackson pickup, 3 position/mini switches. Available in Black, Deep Metallic Blue, Deep Metallic Red and Metallic Purple finishes. Mfd. 1993 only.

	100%	98%	95%	90%	80%	70%	60%
	$415	$360	$300	$240	$215	$195	$180

Last Mfr.'s Sug. Retail was $595.

Grading	100%	98% MINT	95% EXC+	90% EXC	80% VG+	70% VG	60% G

TTX (Trans) — similar to TTX, except has ash body. Available in Transparent Black, Transparent Blue and Transparent Red finishes. Mfd. 1993 only.

	$450	$385	$320	$260	$235	$215	$195

Last Mfr.'s Sug. Retail was $645.

Contemporary Series

275 DELUXE CLASSIC — offset double cutaway hardwood body, white pickguard, bolt-on maple neck, 22 fret maple fingerboard with black dot inlay, double locking vibrato, 6 on one side tuners, chrome hardware, single coil/humbucker pickups, volume control, 5 position switch. Available in Candy Blue, Ferrari Red, Midnite Black and Snow White finishes. Mfd. 1991 to 1992.

	$420	$360	$300	$240	$215	$195	$180

Last Mfr.'s Sug. Retail was $600.

275 Deluxe Contemporary — similar to 275 Deluxe Classic, except has rosewood fingerboard with pearl dot inlay, black hardware, 3 stacked coil pickups (2 side by side at the bridge). Mfd. 1988 to 1991.

	$485	$415	$350	$280	$250	$230	$210

Last Mfr.'s Sug. Retail was $695.

375 DELUXE CLASSIC — offset double cutaway hardwood body, white pickguard, bolt-on maple neck, 22 fret maple fingerboard with black dot inlay, double locking vibrato, 6 on one side tuners, chrome hardware, 2 single coil/1 humbucker pickups, volume/tone controls, 5 position switch. Available in Candy Red, Desert Crackle, Magenta, Metallic Black, Pearl Blue, Pearl White and Platinum finishes. Mfd. 1988 to 1991.

	$490	$420	$350	$280	$250	$230	$210

Last Mfr.'s Sug. Retail was $700.

Add 10% for figured wood body with Natural finish.

375 Deluxe Contemporary — similar to 375 Deluxe Classic, except has rosewood fingerboard with pearl dot inlay. Available in Candy Red, Magenta, Metallic Black, Pearl Blue and Pearl White finishes. Mfd. 1991 to 1992.

	$555	$475	$395	$315	$280	$260	$235

Add 10% for figured wood body with Natural finish.
This model has maple fingerboard with black dot inlay optionally available.

Last Mfr.'s Sug. Retail was $795.

475 SPECIAL CLASSIC — offset double cutaway hardwood body, white pickguard, bolt-on maple neck, 22 fret maple fingerboard with black dot inlay, double locking vibrato, 6 on one side tuners, chrome hardware, 2 stacked coil/1 Jackson humbucker pickups, volume/2 tone controls, 5 position switch. Available in Candy Red, Desert Crackle, Magenta, Metallic Black, Pearl Blue and Pearl White finishes. Mfd. 1988 to 1991.

	$490	$420	$350	$280	$250	$230	$210

Add 10% for figured wood body with Natural finish.

Last Mfr.'s Sug. Retail was $700.

475 Special Contemporary — similar to 475 Special Classic, except has bound rosewood fingerboard with pearl sharkfin inlay, bound peghead, black hardware, active electronics. Available in Candy Red, Magenta, Metallic Black, Pearl Blue and Pearl White finishes. Mfd. 1991 to 1992.

	$695	$595	$500	$400	$360	$330	$300

Add 10% for figured wood body with Natural finish.

Last Mfr.'s Sug. Retail was $995.

550 XL PROFESSIONAL — offset double cutaway hardwood body, thru body maple neck, 22 fret bound rosewood fingerboard with pearl sharkfin inlay, double locking vibrato, 6 on one side tuners, black hardware, Jackson humbucker pickup, volume control. Available in Candy Red, Metallic Black, Pearl White, Platinum and Snow White finishes. Mfd. 1988 to 1991.

	$680	$580	$485	$390	$355	$325	$295

Last Mfr.'s Sug. Retail was $970.

650 XL CONTEMPORARY — offset double cutaway hardwood body, thru body maple neck, 22 fret bound rosewood fingerboard with pearl sharkfin inlay, double locking vibrato, 6 on one side tuners, gold hardware, 2 stacked coil/1 Jackson humbucker pickups, volume/2 tone controls, 5 position switch, active electronics. Available in Candy Red, Metallic Black, Pearl White and Snow White finishes. Mfd. 1991 to 1992.

	$905	$775	$645	$515	$465	$425	$385

Last Mfr.'s Sug. Retail was $1,295.

650 XL Professional — similar to 650 XL Contemporary, except has 2 single coil/1 humbucker pickups. Available in Candy Red, Desert Crackle, Metallic Black, Pearl White, Platinum and Snow White finishes. Mfd. 1988 to 1991.

	$770	$660	$550	$440	$395	$365	$330

Last Mfr.'s Sug. Retail was $1,100.

750 XL PROFESSIONAL — offset double cutaway hardwood body, bolt-on maple neck, 22 fret bound rosewood fingerboard with pearl sharkfin inlay, double locking vibrato, 6 on one side tuners, gold hardware, 2 Jackson humbucker pickups, volume/tone controls, 5 position switch, active electronics. Available in Candy Red, Desert Crackle, Metallic Black, Pearl White, Platinum and Snow White finishes. Mfd. 1988 to 1991.

	$820	$700	$585	$470	$425	$390	$355

Add 10% for figured maple top with Natural finish.

Last Mfr.'s Sug. Retail was $1,170.

Grading	100%	98%	95%	90%	80%	70%	60%
		MINT	EXC+	EXC	VG+	VG	G

AVENGER — sharkfin style hardwood body, bolt-on maple neck, 22 fret rosewood fingerboard with white dot inlay, double locking vibrato, 6 on one side Gotoh tuners, black hardware, 3 stacked coil Charvel pickups (2 side by side at the bridge), volume control, 5 position switch. Available in Candy Blue, Ferrari Red, Midnite Black and Snow White finishes. Mfd. 1991 to 1992.

	$485	$415	$350	$280	$250	$230	$210

Last Mfr.'s Sug. Retail was $695.

PREDATOR — offset double cutaway hardwood body, bolt-on maple neck, 22 fret rosewood fingerboard with white dot inlay, double locking vibrato, reverse headstock, 6 on one side tuners, black hardware, blade stacked coil/humbucker Jackson pickups, volume control, 5 position switch. Available in Candy Blue, Candy Red, Magenta, Midnite Black and Pearl White finishes. Mfd. 1991 only.

	$555	$475	$395	$315	$280	$260	$235

Last Mfr.'s Sug. Retail was $795.

SPECTRUM — similar to Predator, except has white pickguard, chrome hardware, 3 stacked coil Jackson pickups, active electronics with switch. Available in Candy Red, Midnite Black, Sea Green and Tobacco Sunburst finishes. Mfd. 1991 only.

	$625	$535	$445	$360	$325	$300	$275

Last Mfr.'s Sug. Retail was $895.

This model was also available with maple fingerboard with black dot inlay.

CX Series

This series was manufactured in KOREA.

CX290 — strat style, basswood body, white pickguard, bolt-on maple neck, 22 fret rosewood fingerboard with pearl dot inlay, standard vibrato, 6 per side tuners, chrome hardware, 3 single coil Jackson pickups, volume/tone control, 5 position switch. Available in Black, Bright Red, Deep Metallic Blue and Snow White finishes. Mfd. 1992 to date.

Mfr.'s Sug. Retail	$395	$296	$197	$195	$155	$140	$125	$115

This model also available with 2 single coil/1 humbucker pickup configuration (CX291).

CX390 — strat style, basswood body, black pickguard, bolt-on maple neck, 22 fret rosewood fingerboard with pearl dot inlay, double locking vibrato, 6 on one side tuners, chrome hardware, 2 single coil/1 Jackson humbucker pickups, volume/tone control, 5 position switch. Available in Black, Bright Red, Deep Metallic Blue and Snow White finishes. Mfd. 1992 to date.

Mfr.'s Sug. Retail	$495	$371	$247	$245	$195	$175	$160	$150

This model also available with humbucker/single coil/humbucker pickup configuration (CX391).

Fusion Series

FUSION CUSTOM — offset double cutaway poplar body, bolt-on maple neck, 24 fret rosewood fingerboard with white dot inlay, double locking vibrato, 6 on one side tuners, black hardware, 2 rail stacked coil/1 Jackson humbucker pickups, volume/tone control, 5 position switch. Available in Candy Blue, Candy Red, Metallic Black and Snow White finishes. Mfd. 1991 only.

	$625	$535	$445	$360	$325	$300	$275

Last Mfr.'s Sug. Retail was $895.

FUSION DELUXE — similar to Fusion Custom, except has chrome hardware, rail stacked coil/humbucker Jackson pickups, volume control. Mfd. 1991 only.

	$555	$475	$395	$315	$280	$260	$235

Last Mfr.'s Sug. Retail was $795.

This model was also available with maple fingerboard with black dot inlay.

FUSION PLUS — offset double cutaway ash body, bolt-on maple neck, 24 fret rosewood fingerboard with offset white dot inlay, double locking vibrato, 6 on one side tuners, black hardware, 2 humbucker Jackson pickups, volume/tone control, 5 position switch with coil split. Available in Tobacco Sunburst, Transparent Amber, Transparent Red, Transparent Violet and Transparent White finishes. Disc. 1992

	$625	$535	$445	$360	$325	$300	$275

Last Mfr.'s Sug. Retail was $895.

FUSION SPECIAL — offset double cutaway poplar body, thru body maple neck, 24 fret rosewood fingerboard with white dot inlay, double locking vibrato, 6 on one side tuners, black hardware, 3 stacked coil Charvel pickups (2 side by side at the bridge), volume control, 5 position switch. Available in Candy Blue, Ferrari Red, Midnite Black and Snow White finishes. Mfd. 1991 only.

	$485	$415	$350	$280	$250	$230	$210

Last Mfr.'s Sug. Retail was $695.

LS Series

LS-1 — offset double cutaway asymmetrical bound carved mahogany body, mahogany neck, 22 fret bound rosewood fingerboard with pearl dot inlay, tunomatic bridge, string thru body tailpiece, bound blackface peghead with screened logo, 3 per side tuners, chrome hardware, 2 humbucker Jackson pickups, volume/tone control, 3 position switch. Available in Black, Deep Metallic Blue and Gold finishes. Mfd. 1993 to date.

Mfr.'s Sug. Retail	$995	$796	$597	$500	$400	$360	$330	$300

Grading	100%	98% MINT	95% EXC+	90% EXC	80% VG+	70% VG	60% G

LSX-I — offset double cutaway asymmetrical ash body, figured maple top, mahogany neck, 22 fret rosewood fingerboard with pearl dot inlay, Wilkinson vibrato, roller nut, blackface peghead with screened logo, 3 per side tuners, black hardware, 2 humbucker Jackson pickups, volume/tone control, 3 position switch. Available in Natural Green Sunburst, Natural Purple Sunburst and Natural Red Sunburst finishes. New 1994.

Mfr.'s Sug. Retail	$895	$671	$447	$445	$360	$325	$300	$275

LSX-II — offset double cutaway asymmetrical mahogany body, mahogany neck, 22 fret rosewood fingerboard with pearl dot inlay, double locking vibrato, blackface peghead with screened logo, 3 per side tuners, black hardware, 2 humbucker Jackson pickups, volume/tone control, 3 position switch. Available in Black and Transparent Red finishes. New 1994.

Mfr.'s Sug. Retail	$795	$596	$397	$395	$315	$280	$260	$235

LSX-III — offset double cutaway asymmetrical ash body, mahogany neck, 22 fret rosewood fingerboard with pearl dot inlay, string thru body bridge, blackface peghead with screened logo, 3 per side tuners, black hardware, 2 humbucker Jackson pickups, volume/tone control, 3 position switch. Available in Tobacco Sunburst, Transparent Blue and Transparent Red finishes. New 1994.

Mfr.'s Sug. Retail	$695	$556	$417	$350	$280	$250	$230	$210

Model Series

MODEL 1 — offset double cutaway hardwood body, white pickguard, bolt-on maple neck, 22 fret maple fingerboard with black dot inlay, fixed bridge, 6 on one side tuners, chrome hardware, humbucker pickup, volume/tone controls, 5 position switch. Available in Ferrari Red, Midnite Black, Royal Blue and Snow White finishes. Mfd. 1986 to 1989.

$280	$240	$200	$160	$145	$130	$120

Last Mfr.'s Sug. Retail was $400.

Model 1A — similar to Model 1, except has 3 single coil pickups, 5 position switch.

$315	$270	$225	$180	$160	$150	$135

Last Mfr.'s Sug. Retail was $450.

MODEL 2 — similar to Model 1, except has standard vibrato. Mfd. 1986 to 1989.

$385	$330	$275	$220	$200	$180	$165

Last Mfr.'s Sug. Retail was $550.

MODEL 3 — similar Model 1, except has 2 single coil/1 humbucker pickups, 5 position switch. Mfd. 1986 to 1989.

$455	$390	$325	$260	$235	$215	$195

Last Mfr.'s Sug. Retail was $650.

Model 3A — similar to Model 1, except has 2 humbucker pickups, standard vibrato. Mfd. 1986 to 1988.

$420	$360	$300	$240	$215	$195	$180

Last Mfr.'s Sug. Retail was $600.

MODEL 4 — similar Model 1, except has standard vibrato, 2 humbucker pickups, 5 position switch, active electronics. Mfd. 1986 to 1989.

$595	$510	$425	$340	$305	$280	$255

Last Mfr.'s Sug. Retail was $850.

MODEL 5 — similar Model 1, except has thru body neck, standard vibrato, 2 humbucker pickups, 5 position switch. Mfd. 1986 to 1989.

$665	$570	$475	$380	$345	$315	$285

Last Mfr.'s Sug. Retail was $950.

MODEL 6 — similar Model 1, except has standard vibrato, 2 single coil/1 humbucker pickups, 5 position switch, active electronics. Mfd. 1986 to 1989.

$735	$630	$525	$420	$380	$345	$315

Last Mfr.'s Sug. Retail was $1,050.

ELECTRIC BASS

575 DELUXE CLASSIC — offset double cutaway hardwood body, bolt-on maple neck, 21 fret rosewood fingerboard with white dot inlay, fixed bridge, 4 on one side tuners, chrome hardware, P-style/J-style pickups, 2 volume/2 tone controls. Available in Candy Blue, Ferrari Red, Midnite Black, Platinum and Snow White finishes. Mfd. 1988 to 1991.

$420	$360	$300	$240	$215	$195	$180

Last Mfr.'s Sug. Retail was $600.

575 Deluxe Contemporary — similar to 575 Deluxe Classic, except has rosewood fingerboard with pearl dot inlay, volume/tone control, 3 position switch. Available in Candy Blue, Candy Red, Metallic Black and Snow White finishes. Mfd. 1991 to 1992.

$485	$415	$350	$280	$250	$230	$210

Last Mfr.'s Sug. Retail was $695.

850 XL PROFESSIONAL — offset double cutaway hardwood body, bolt-on maple neck, 21 fret rosewood fingerboard with white dot inlay, fixed bridge, 4 on one side tuners, chrome hardware, P-style/J-style pickups, volume/treble/bass/mix controls. Available in Candy Blue, Ferrari Red, Midnite Black, Platinum and Snow White finishes. Mfd. 1988 to 1991.

$700	$600	$500	$400	$360	$330	$300

Last Mfr.'s Sug. Retail was $1,000.

This instrument was manufactured in KOREA.

"I knew they had value because the quality was great. I was never thinking that this was going to be a big business. I just liked them."

—L. Acunto on Rick Nielsen

TCG, May/June 1994

Grading	100%	98% MINT	95% EXC+	90% EXC	80% VG+	70% VG	60% G

CX490 — offset double cutaway poplar body, bolt-on maple neck, 22 fret rosewood fingerboard with pearl dot inlay, fixed bridge, 4 on one side tuners, chrome hardware, P-style/J-style Jackson pickups, volume/tone and mix controls. Available in Black, Bright Red, Deep Metallic Blue and Snow White finishes. Mfd. 1992 to date.

| Mfr.'s Sug. Retail | $495 | $371 | $247 | $245 | $195 | $175 | $160 | $150 |

This instrument is manufactured in KOREA.

ELIMINATOR — offset double cutaway hardwood body, bolt-on maple neck, 24 fret rosewood fingerboard with white dot inlay, fixed bridge, 4 on one side tuners, black hardware, P-style/J-style Charvel pickups, volume/treble/bass and mix controls, active electronics. Available in Candy Blue, Ferrari Red, Midnite Black and Snow White finishes. Mfd. 1991 only.

| | $485 | $415 | $350 | $280 | $250 | $230 | $210 |

Last Mfr.'s Sug. Retail was $695.

FUSION IV — offset double cutaway hardwood body, bolt-on maple neck, 24 fret rosewood fingerboard with offset pearl dot inlay, pearl Charvel block inlay at 12th fret, fixed bridge, 4 on one side tuners, black hardware, P-style/J-style Charvel pickups, volume/treble/bass and mix controls, active electronics. Available in Candy Blue, Ferrari Red, Magenta, Metallic Black and Pearl White finishes. Mfd. 1991 only.

| | $555 | $475 | $395 | $315 | $280 | $260 | $235 |

Last Mfr.'s Sug. Retail was $795.

Fusion V — similar to Fusion IV, except has 5 strings.

| | $695 | $595 | $500 | $400 | $360 | $330 | $300 |

Last Mfr.'s Sug. Retail was $995.

JX BASS — offset double cutaway asymmetrical poplar body, bolt-on maple neck, 22 fret rosewood fingerboard with pearl dot inlay, fixed bridge, 4 on one side tuners, chrome hardware, P-style/J-style Jackson pickups, volume/tone/mix controls. Available in Black, Deep Metallic Blue, Dark Metallic Red, Snow White and Turquoise finishes. Mfd. 1992 to 1994.

| | $485 | $415 | $350 | $280 | $250 | $230 | $210 |

Last Mfr.'s Sug. Retail was $695.

This instrument was manufactured in KOREA.

LS-1 — offset double cutaway asymmetrical bound mahogany body, mahogany neck, 21 fret bound rosewood fingerboard with pearl dot inlay, tunomatic bridge, thru body ring and ball holder tailpiece, 2 humbucker Jackson pickups, volume/treble/bass/mix control. Available in Black, Deep Metallic Blue and Gold finishes. Mfd. 1993 to date.

| Mfr.'s Sug. Retail | $1,195 | $956 | $717 | $600 | $480 | $430 | $395 | $360 |

MODEL 1B — offset double cutaway hardwood body, bolt-on maple neck, 21 fret rosewood fingerboard with pearl dot inlay, fixed bridge, 4 on one side tuners, chrome hardware, P-style Charvel pickup, volume/tone controls. Available in Black, Red and White finishes. Mfd. 1986 to 1989.

| | $315 | $270 | $225 | $180 | $160 | $150 | $135 |

Last Mfr.'s Sug. Retail was $450.

MODEL 2B — similar Model 1B, except has P-style/J-style pickups, 2 volume/2 tone controls. Mfd. 1986 to 1989.

| | $420 | $360 | $300 | $240 | $215 | $195 | $180 |

Last Mfr.'s Sug. Retail was $600.

MODEL 3B — similar to Model 1B, except has thru body neck, 2 J-style pickups, 2 volume/2 tone controls. Mfd 1986 to 1989.

| | $595 | $510 | $425 | $340 | $305 | $280 | $255 |

Last Mfr.'s Sug. Retail was $850.

STANDARD 1 — offset double cutaway hardwood body, white pickguard, bolt-on maple neck, 21 fret maple fingerboard with black dot inlay, fixed bridge, 4 on one side tuners, chrome hardware, P-style Charvel pickups, volume/tone controls. Available in Black, Red and White finishes. Mfd. 1985 only.

| | $670 | $575 | $480 | $385 | $350 | $320 | $290 |

Last Mfr.'s Sug. Retail was $960.

STANDARD 2 — offset double cutaway asymmetrical hardwood body, bolt-on maple neck, 21 fret maple fingerboard with black dot inlay, fixed bridge, 4 on one side tuners, chrome hardware, 2 J-style Charvel pickups, 2 volume/1 tone controls. Available in Black, Red and White finishes. Mfd. 1983 to 1985.

| | $720 | $615 | $510 | $410 | $370 | $340 | $310 |

Last Mfr.'s Sug. Retail was $1,030.

CHARVETTE

Instruments produced in Korea from 1989 to 1994. Charvette, an entry level line to Charvel, was distributed by the International Music Corporation of Ft. Worth, Texas.

The Charvette trademark was distributed by the Charvel/Jackson company as a good quality entry level guitar based on their original Jackson USA "superstrat" designs. Where the Charvel and Jackson models may sport 'Jackson' pickups, Charvettes invariably had 'Charvel' pickups to support a company/product unity.

All models in this series were available in Ferrari Red, Midnite Black, Royal Blue, Snow White and Splatter finishes, unless otherwise listed.

Grading	100%	98% MINT	95% EXC+	90% EXC	80% VG+	70% VG	60% G

C

ACOUSTIC ELECTRIC

500 — single round cutaway flat top style, maple top, plectrum shape soundhole, one stripe bound body/rosette, bolt-on maple neck, 22 fret rosewood fingerboard with pearl dot inlay, rosewood bridge with black pins, 6 on one side tuners, black hardware, 6 piezo bridge pickups, volume/treble/bass controls, active electronics. Available in Ferrari Red, Midnite Black and Snow White finish. Mfd. 1991 to 1992.

	$345	$295	$245	$195	$175	$160	$150

Last Mfr.'s Sug. Retail was $495.

ELECTRIC

100 — offset double cutaway hardwood body, bolt-on maple neck, 22 fret rosewood fingerboard with white dot inlay, standard vibrato, reverse peghead, 6 on one side tuners, black hardware, stacked coil/humbucker Charvel pickup, volume/tone control, 3 position switch. Mfd. 1989 to 1992.

	$260	$220	$180	$145	$130	$120	$110

Last Mfr.'s Sug. Retail was $365.

150 — similar to 100, except has locking vibrato, standard peghead. Mfd. 1989 to 1992.

	$275	$235	$195	$155	$140	$125	$115

Last Mfr.'s Sug. Retail was $395.

170 — similar to 100, except has double locking vibrato, standard peghead, no tone control. Mfd. 1991 to 1992.

	$345	$295	$245	$195	$175	$160	$150

Last Mfr.'s Sug. Retail was $495.

175 — similar to 100, except has 24 fret fingerboard, standard peghead, no tone control. Mfd. 1989 to 1991.

	$295	$250	$210	$170	$150	$135	$125

Last Mfr.'s Sug. Retail was $420.

200 — similar to 100, except has 2 single coil/1 humbucker Charvel pickups. Mfd. 1989 to 1992.

	$260	$220	$185	$150	$135	$120	$110

Last Mfr.'s Sug. Retail was $375.

250 — similar to 100, except has locking vibrato, standard peghead, stacked coil/single coil/humbucker Charvel pickups. Mfd. 1989 to 1992.

	$295	$250	$210	$170	$150	$135	$125

Last Mfr.'s Sug. Retail was $425.

270 — similar to 100, except has double locking vibrato, standard peghead, stacked coil/single coil/humbucker Charvel pickups, no tone control. Mfd. 1991 to 1992.

	$370	$315	$260	$210	$190	$170	$160

Last Mfr.'s Sug. Retail was $525.

275 — similar to 100, except has 24 fret fingerboard, standard peghead, locking vibrato, stacked coil/single coil/humbucker pickups, no tone control. Mfd. 1989 to 1991.

	$300	$260	$215	$175	$155	$140	$130

Last Mfr.'s Sug. Retail was $430.

300 — similar to 100, except has 3 single coil Charvel pickups. Mfd. 1989 to 1992.

	$345	$295	$245	$195	$175	$160	$150

Last Mfr.'s Sug. Retail was $495.

ELECTRIC BASS

400 — offset double cutaway hardwood body, bolt-on maple neck, 21 fret rosewood fingerboard with pearl dot inlay, fixed bridge, 4 on one side tuners, chrome hardware, P-style Charvel pickup, volume/tone control. Mfd. 1989 to 1992.

	$295	$250	$210	$170	$150	$135	$125

Last Mfr.'s Sug. Retail was $425.

450 — similar to 400, except has J-style/P-style pickups, 2 volume/2 tone controls. Mfd. 1991 to 1992.

	$345	$295	$245	$195	$175	$160	$150

Last Mfr.'s Sug. Retail was $495.

CHRIS

See chapter on House Brands.

This trademark has been identified as a separate budget line of guitars from the Jackson-Guldan company of Columbus, Ohio.

(Source: Willie G. Moseley, Stellas & Stratocasters)

CHRIS LARKIN

Instruments built in Ireland from 1979 to current.

Citron handcrafted instrument courtesy Harvey Citron

If there's a shamrock on the headstock, then you've got a CHRIS LARKIN. These high quality guitars feature original designs, and have model names like the Reacter, Razer, and Mutha-T-Razer.

(Source: Tony Bacon and Paul Day, The Guru's Guitar Guide)

CIMAR

Instruments were built in Japan during the 1970s and 1980s.

Cimar produced good-to-medium quality guitars that featured similar versions of classic American designs, as well as some original and thinline hollowbody designs.

(Source: Tony Bacon and Paul Day, The Guru's Guitar Guide)

CIPHER

Instruments produced in Japan.

Cipher guitars were distributed in the U.S. market by Inter-Mark.

(Source: Michael Wright, Guitar Stories Volume One, pg. 76)

CITATION

Instruments produced in Japan.

The U.S. distributor of Citation guitars was the Grossman company of Cleveland, Ohio.

(Source: Michael Wright, Guitar Stories Volume One, pg. 76)

CITRON

Instruments built in Woodstock, New York since 1983.

Luthier Harvey Citron has been building high quality, innovative, solid body guitars since the early 1970s. Citron, a noted guitarist and singer, co-founded the Veillette-Citron company in 1975, and during that partnership's eight years built some of the finest handcrafted electric guitars, basses, and baritone guitars. Citron also designed the X-92 for Guild and is a regular contributing writer for numerous guitar magazines. For further information, please contact luthier Citron via the Index of Current Manufacturers located in the rear of this book.

CLEARSOUND

Instuments were built in Japan during the 1970s.

Shades of Dan Armstrong! The Clearsound "Strat" model of the late 1970s was built of see-through plastic with a wood neck and three single coil pickups. In conjunction with the original Dan Armstrong Ampeg lucite "see-throughs", Renaissance original designs, as well as Univox and Ibanez Dan Armstrong copies, this bring the total count of companies who attempted to produce these type of plastic guitars to five!

(Source for Clearsound: Tony Bacon, The Ultimate Guitar Book)

CLEVINGER

Instruments currently built in Oakland, California.

Partners Robert Lee and Martin Clevinger have been building their solid body electric double bass for a number of years.

The slim body is constructed of poplar, while the neck is Rock Maple and features an Ebony fingerboard. The 56" instrument has a scale length of 41 1/2", and has a telescoping endpin. Pickups technology is designed by Clevinger, and the tuners are by Hipshot. Prices range from the Bassic Upright with 4 strings ($2,250) up to the customized 6 string ($3,150). Prices are derived from the 1995 retail price list. Please contact the Clevinger Bass company for further information and pricing via the Index of Current Manufacturers located in the rear of this book.

CLEVINGER, AZOLA, AND LEE

See CLEVINGER or AZOLA.

Instruments built in either Oakland or San Marcos, California.

The C.A.L. upright bass is a joint venture between the Clevinger and Azola companies.

CLIFTON

Instruments built in Blackheath, England since 1986.

Luthier Mo Clifton builds a series of high quality solid body instruments. Clifton became involved in instrument design as a result of shoulder problems incurred from playing a bass guitar with a heavy headstock. As a result, Clifton basses have a balanced body design and no headstock (guitar and upright models do feature headstocks). For further information, please contact luthier Clifton via the Index of Current Manufacturers located in the back of this book.

CLOVER

Instruments currently built in Recklinghausen, Germany. Information and distribution are available through Dan Lenard at the Luthiers Access Group of Chicago, Illinois.

Clover produces several high quality bass guitars.

C M I

Cleartone Musical Instruments

See NED CALLAN.

Instruments originally produced in England, later imports were built in Japan during the 1970s and 1980s.

The C M I trademark was used by UK importer/distributor Cleartone Musical Instruments. Early instruments were built by NED CALLAN in England, but were later joined by Japanese-built copies.

(Source: Tony Bacon and Paul Day, The Guru's Guitar Guide)

COBRA

See JOHN BIRCH.

Instruments built in England during the early 1980s.

Luthier John Birch, known for his custom guitar building, teamed up with Barry Kirby to create models under this trademark.

(Source: Tony Bacon and Paul Day, The Guru's Guitar Guide)

CODE

Instruments manufactured in New Jersey during the 1950s.

Luthier John D'Angelico supplied finished necks to the Code (pronounced ko-day) company for a series of plywood body guitars that bear the D'Angelico trademark. The D'Angelico/Code guitars were similar in appearance to Gibson's ES-175.

(Source: Paul William Schmidt, Acquired of the Angels)

COLLINGS

Instruments built in Austin, Texas since 1986. Distributed by Collings Guitars, Inc. of Austin, Texas.

Luthier Bill Collings moved to Texas from Ohio back in 1975, and began building his first guitars. In 1986 he founded Collings Guitars. Collings produces three types of archtop guitars in addition to the flattop models. These handcrafted archtop models range in prices from $8,500 to $10,000.

ACOUSTIC

All models are available with the following options:
Add $150 for abalone rosette.
Add $425 for 12 string version.
Add $400 for rounded single cutaway.

Collings 18" Special
courtesy Scott Chinery

Grading	100%	98% MINT	95% EXC+	90% EXC	80% VG+	70% VG	60% G

C Series

C-10 — folk style, spruce top, round soundhole, pearloid pickguard, ivoroid bound body/rosette, mahogany back/sides/neck, 14/20 fret bound ebony fingerboard, ebony bridge with white black dot pins, pearloid veneer on bound peghead with inscribed logo, 3 per side gold Kluson tuners. Available in Black, Blue, Natural and Red finishes. Curr. mfr.

Mfr.'s Sug. Retail	$2,150	$1,612	$1,075	$1,045	$820	$745	$675	$615

C-10 Deluxe — similar to C-10, except has tortoise pickguard, Indian rosewood back/sides, pearl dot fingerboard inlay, ebony peghead veneer with pearl logo inlay, gold Schaller mini tuners. Available in Natural finish.

Mfr.'s Sug. Retail	$2,650	$1,987	$1,325	$1,280	$1,000	$900	$825	$750

C-100 — similar to C-10, except has dreadnought style body.

Mfr.'s Sug. Retail	$2,225	$1,668	$1,112	$1,080	$840	$755	$690	$630

Grading	100%	98% MINT	95% EXC+	90% EXC	80% VG+	70% VG	60% G

C-100 Deluxe — similar to C-10, except has small jumbo style body.

Mfr.'s Sug. Retail	$2,725	$2,043	$1,362	$1,315	$1,040	$915	$840	$765

D Series

D-1 — dreadnought style, spruce top, round soundhole, tortoise pickguard, 3 stripe bound body/rosette, mahogany back/sides/neck, 14/20 fret bound ebony fingerboard, ebony bridge with white black dot pins, ebony or rosewood veneer on bound peghead with pearl logo inlay, 3 per side chrome Gotoh tuners. Available in Natural finish. Curr. mfr.

Mfr.'s Sug. Retail	$2,100	$1,575	$1,050	$1,015	$790	$715	$655	$590

D-2 — similar to D-1, except has Indian rosewood back/sides, pearl diamond/square peghead inlay.

Mfr.'s Sug. Retail	$2,300	$1,725	$1,150	$1,125	$900	$810	$740	$675

Add $50 for herringbone bound body (D2H).

D-3 — similar to D-1, except has abalone purfling/rosette, Indian rosewood back/sides.

Mfr.'s Sug. Retail	$2,775	$2,081	$1,387	$1,335	$1,030	$925	$850	$775

OM Series

OM-1 — grand concert style, spruce top, round soundhole, tortoise pickguard, 3 stripe bound body/rosette, mahogany back/sides/neck, 14/20 fret bound ebony fingerboard, ebony bridge with white black dot pins, ebony or rosewood veneer on bound peghead with pearl logo inlay, 3 per side chrome Gotoh tuners. Available in Natural finish. Curr. mfr.

Mfr.'s Sug. Retail	$2,100	$1,575	$1,050	$1,015	$790	$715	$655	$590

OM-2 — similar to OM-1, except has Indian rosewood back/sides, pearl diamond/square peghead inlay.

Mfr.'s Sug. Retail	$2,300	$1,725	$1,150	$1,125	$900	$810	$740	$675

Add $50 for herringbone bound body (OM2H).

OM-3 — similar to OM-1, except has abalone purfling/rosette, Indian rosewood back/sides.

Mfr.'s Sug. Retail	$2,775	$2,081	$1,387	$1,335	$1,030	$925	$850	$775

OOO-2H 12-FRET — orchestra style, spruce top, round soundhole, tortoise pickguard, 3 stripe bound body/rosette, mahogany back/sides/neck, 12/20 fret bound ebony fingerboard, ebony bridge with white black dot pins, ebony or rosewood veneer on bound peghead with pearl logo inlay, 3 per side chrome Gotoh tuners. Available in Natural finish. Curr. mfr.

Mfr.'s Sug. Retail	$2,850	$2,137	$1,425	$1,370	$1,090	$955	$875	$795

SJ Series

SJ — small jumbo style, spruce top, round soundhole, tortoise pickguard, 3 stripe bound body/rosette, maple back/sides/neck, 14/20 fret bound ebony fingerboard with pearl diamond inlay, ebony bridge with white black dot pins, ebony veneer on bound peghead with pearl diamond and logo inlay, 3 per side gold Schaller mini tuners. Available in Natural finish. Curr. mfr.

Mfr.'s Sug. Retail	$2,850	$2,137	$1,425	$1,370	$1,090	$955	$875	$795

COLT

See also CAIRNES.

Instruments were built in England in the late 1970s.

These solidbody guitars from the Guitarzan company were shaped like guns, and featured 2 pickups.

(Source: Tony Bacon and Paul Day, The Guru's Guitar Guide)

COLUMBUS

Instruments originally built in Japan, then manufacturing switched to Korea during the late 1960s.

The COLUMBUS trademark was the brandname of a UK importer. Although the first models were cheap entry level guitars, subsequent Japanese-built guitars raised up to medium quality copies of American designs. Manufacturer then switched to Korean production.

(Source: Tony Bacon and Paul Day, The Guru's Guitar Guide)

BILL COMINS

Instruments built in Willow Grove, Pennsylvania since 1991.

Luthier Bill Comins has been building quality arch top guitars for a number of years.

Comins Chester Avenue
courtesy Scott Chinery

COMMODORE

Instruments built in Japan during the late 1960s through the 1970s.

The COMMODORE trademark was the brandname of a UK importer. In an unusual switch, the Japanese-built guitars started out as cheap entry level instruments of original design and then progressed into copying American designs. To further this twist, one of the models copied was the Dan Armstrong "see through" lucite design!

(Source: Tony Bacon and Paul Day, The Guru's Guitar Guide)

CONCERTONE

See chapter on House Brands.

This trademark has been identified as a "House Brand" of Montgomery Wards. Instruments were built by either KAY or HARMONY.

(Source: Michael Wright, Guitar Stories Volume One)

CONKLIN

Instruments built in Springfield, Missouri since 1984. Distributed by Conklin Guitars of Springfield, Missouri.

Bill Conklin began producing one-of-a-kind custom instruments in 1984 after designing the "Quick Co-Necked" Doubleneck; a guitar and bass component system in which the individual components can be played separately or in any doubleneck configuration.

Early Conklin models incorporate traditional body styles but were carefully evaluated for perfect balance, comfort, and playability. More recent Conklin standards are steeped in tradition while pushing the envelope of innovation.

In 1991, Conklin created an entirely new guitar construction technique called "Melted Tops". These 2-, 3-, and 5-piece tops differ from the standard bookmatched variety in that they consist of several species of wood arranged in various patterns. Each "Melted Top" is unique in its species selection, orientation, and grain patterns, ensuring virtually limitless combinations of rare and exotic tops.

The "Sidewinder" 7-string bass (now in its 5th year of production) offers such features as full stereo panning, pickup splitting, an onboard parametric EQ, and the full range and versatility of up to a three octave fingerboard. Tuned from the low B to high F, the "Sidewinder" 7-string is perfect for chording, soloing, slap and funk styles.

In 1995, Conklin introduced the "M.E.U." or Mobile Electric Upright bass. This totally unique upright bass is strapped on like an electric bass but hangs on the body in an upright position. The "M.E.U." can be plucked or bowed, and is fully mobile and easily transported. It's even small enough to fit the overhead compartment of most airplanes.

Conklin's "New Century Series" guitars and basses feature all the quality and attention to detail of their custom line, but with limited option availability resulting in a lower list price, making it easier for players and dealers to acquire the Conklin name. All instruments carry a limited lifetime warranty.

(Company information courtesy Bill Conklin)

Conklin hand-crafted instruments are available with numerous custom options. Retail list prices on the **New Century** series ranges from $1,800 to $2,900; and Custom instruments start at $2,800 on up. The **M.E.U.** is offered in either a 4-string (#3,200) or 5-string ($3,500) configuration. For further information regarding specifications, pricing, and availability, please contact Conklin Guitars via the Index of Current Manufacturers located in the back of this book.

CONN

Instruments built in Japan.

The U.S. distributor for Conn brandname instruments was Conn/Continental Music Company of Chicago, Illinois. The Conn trademark is perhaps more recognizable for their brass band instruments. Conn is based in Elkhart, Indiana.

(Source: Michael Wright, Guitar Stories Volume One, pg. 76)

CONRAD

Instruments produced in Japan.

The Conrad trademark was a brandname used by U.S. importers David Wexler and Company of Chicago, Illinois.

(Source: Michael Wright, Guitar Stories Volume One, pg. 76)

CONTESSA

Instruments built in Italy between 1966 and 1969.

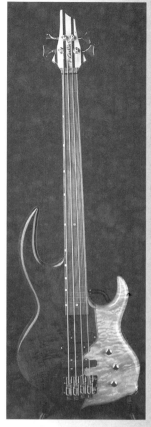

Conklin 4 String Bass
courtesy Bill Conklin

Conklin Sidewinder
courtesy Bill Conklin

These medium quality guitars were based on original designs, and the company produced the 'HG' series of both solid and semi-hollowboy models.

(Source: Tony Bacon and Paul Day, The Guru's Guitar Guide)

CONTINENTAL

See also CONN.

Instruments produced in Japan.

As well as distributing the Conn guitars, the Continental Music Company of Chicago, Illinois also distributed their own brandname guitars under the Continental logo in the U.S.

(Source: Michael Wright, Guitar Stories Volume One, pg. 76)

CORAL

Instruments and amplifiers were produced in Neptune City, New Jersey from 1967 to 1968 by the Danelectro Corporation. Distributed by MCA, after buying the Danelectro company and trademark.

In 1967, after MCA purchased the Danelectro Corporation, the Coral trademark was introduced. The Coral line was MCA's marketing strategy for direct wholesale selling to individual dealers, instead of Sears, Roebuck. Once the company went that route, however, they came up against competition from the larger guitar manufacturers at the dealer level. The Coral line of guitars and amplifiers was only produced for about one year.

CORT

Instruments currently produced in Korea. Distributed in the U.S. by Cort Musical Instruments of Northbrook, Illinois.

Since 1960, Cort has been providing entry level, beginner's, and medium quality acoustic and solid body guitars.

The **Sterling Series** features an original design and models have a new list price between $400-$450; the **Performer Series** features models based on classic American boltneck designs ($495-$650); the **Viva Series** features sleek, modern designs with rounded neck/body joints ($699-$749). Entry level models begin at $299 on up and solid top acoustics begin at $399.

Cort Sterling S-2000
courtesy Cort Musical Instruments

COTE'

Instruments currently built in Largo, Florida. Previously based in St. Petersburg, Florida.

Charles Cote' Basses is a family owned business that was founded in Atlanta, Georgia in 1992. Cote' worked as a guitar builder from 1989 to 1991 at John Buscarino's Nova Guitar Company. A professional bassist for a number of years, Cote' brings his "player's experience" to his designs, and hand-crafts each instrument. The initial body design was inspired by a drawing by graphic artist Cris Rosario. Retail prices range from $1,899 (**R 4** 4-string) up to $2,499 (6-string model). For further information, availability, and custom options, please contact the Cote Company through the Index of Current Manufacturers located in the rear of this book.

CRAFTER

Instruments are built in Korea. Currently distributed in the U.S. by HSS (a Division of Hohner, Inc.), located in Richmond, Virginia.

The Crafter guitar line consists of acoustic guitars with wood or fiberglass backs, and are equipped with Shadow pickup systems with built in four band EQs.

CRAFTERS OF TENNESSEE, LLC

Instruments currently built in Old Hickory, Tennessee.

President Mark Taylor currently offers the "Rich & Taylor" high quality acoustic guitars.

The **Tut Taylor** resophonic models have a retail list between $1,495-$2,095. The company also offers high quality, ornate banjos.

CRAFTSMAN

Instruments produced in Japan during the late 1970s through the mid 1980s.

Craftsman built entry level to medium quality copies of American designs.

(Source: Tony Bacon and Paul Day, The Guru's Guitar Guide)

CRESTLINE

Instruments built in Japan during the mid 1970s.

Charles Cote'

These entry level to intermediate solid body guitars featured designs based on classic American favorites. One model based on Gibson's Les Paul design had Grover tuners, 2 Japanese covered humbuckers, and decent wood; consider the time period. Possibly built by one of the bigger Japanese guitar producers and 'rebranded' for the U.S. market.

STEVE CRIPE

Instruments were built in Trilby, Florida from 1990 to 1996.

Although he is best known for building the "Lightning Bolt" and "Top Hat" guitars for Jerry Garcia, Cripe built many different shapes and styles. A self-taught luthier, Cripe's previous background was hand-building ornate wood interiors for sailboats. Cripe's guitar designs were based on photos and video footage of Jerry Garcia's performances, not actual guitar templates. However, the guitars produced were very acceptable to Garcia, who continued using them up to his unfortunate death. Cripe also built a number of instruments for other players across the country and completed a workshop for guitar production. Unfortunately, Stephen R. Cripe died in a devastating explosion in his workshop on June 18, 1996.

(Source: Hal Hammer)

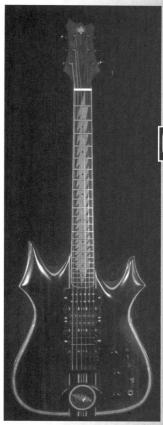

SRC Lightning Bolt
courtesy S.R. Cripe estate

CROMWELL

See chapter on House Brands.

While the distribution of this trademark was handled by midwestern mail order companies, Gibson built this line of budget guitars sometimes in the mid 1930s to the early 1940s. While the guitars were built to roughly similar Gibson standards, they lack the adjustable truss rod in the neck that differentiates them from a true Gibson of the same period.

(Source: Walter Carter, Gibson Guitars: 100 Years of an American Icon)

CROW

Instruments currently built in Longmont, Colorado.

Luthier Arthur Crow hand-builds quality archtop guitars. For further information on availability and pricing, contact luthier Crow via the Index of Current Manufacturers located in the rear of this book.

CROWN

Instruments were produced in Japan during the mid 1970s.

Author/researcher Michael Wright reports that the U.S. distributor for this trademark is still currently unknown. These solid body guitars are generally cheap entry level instruments. If not playable, they'll still keep the house warm - but I prefer to buy my firewood by the truckload, not individually with strings.

(Source: Tony Bacon and Paul Day, The Guru's Guitar Guide)

CRUCIANELLI

See ELITE.

Instruments produced in Italy during the 1960s.

Author Tony Bacon in his book, "The Ultimate Guitar Book", notes that Italy, like many other European countries, experienced the 1960's pop music popularity that led to a larger demand for electric guitars. However, many electric guitar builders were also manufacturers of accordians. As a result, many guitars ended up with accordian-style finishes. Wacky or not, Leo Fender was using this same sort of heat-molded acetate finish on some of his lap steel models in the early 1950s. Players, to your sunglasses! On your mark, get set...Strum!

CSL

Instruments built in Japan during the 1970s through the late 1980s.

The C S L trademark was used by UK importer C. Summerfield Ltd. The 1970s copies of American designs were built at the same source as IBANEZ (and Ibanez copies were good enough for a lawsuit from NORLIN!); later solid body designs in the 1980s look vaguely Fender-ish. C S L owners who want to testify about the quality of their instruments are invited to write to the **Blue Book of Guitars**. Any photos used in future editions will probably be backlit and silhouetted, and placed in witness protection programs!

(Source: Tony Bacon and Paul Day, The Guru's Guitar Guide)

CURBOW

Instruments currently built in Morgantown, Georgia.

Luthier Greg Curbow offers a line of high quality basses.

The **Petite Basses** have a 34" scale, solid wood bodies, and rockwood processed necks. Rockwood is a composite of birch and phenolic based resins, which produces a neck unaffected by changes in temperature and humidity. Basses

SRC Saturn
courtesy S.R. Cripe estate

are available in 4-string (new list $2,795-$3,795), 5-string ($2,995-$3,995), 6-string ($3,195-$4,195), and 7-string ($3,895-$4,495) configurations.

CUSTOM GUITAR WORKS

Instruments currently built in Tulsa, Oklahoma.

The Custom Guitar Works builds guitars under the G.H. Reno trademark, and both models feature custom-ported mahogany bodies, maple necks, rosewood or ebony fingerboards, and gold or black hardware. The **Honky Tonk** ($795) has a single humbucking pickup, while the **Hideaway** ($895) has two single coils and a five way switch.

Company also crafts quality custom basses. The G.H. Reno model ($795) has a Honduran mahogany body, bolt-on maple neck, choice of rosewood or ebony fingerboard, 3+1 headstock, and choice of gold or black hardware. For more information contact the company through the Index of Current Manufacturers located in the rear of this book.

CUSTOM GUITAR COMPANY

Instruments currently built in Santa Clara, California.

These quality custom instruments are built in Southern California. For more information contact the company through the Index of Current Manufacturers located in the rear of this book.

CUSTOM KRAFT

See chapter on House Brands.

This trademark has been identified as a "House Brand" of St. Louis Music. The St. Louis Music Supply Company was founded in 1922 in St. Louis, Missouri. The earlier KAY and VALCO built guitars date from the 1960s, while later models were probably built in Japan.

(Source: Willie G. Moseley, Stellas & Stratocasters)

CYCLONE

Instruments produced in Japan.

Cyclone guitars were distributed in the U.S. market by Leban Imports of Baltimore, Maryland.

(Source: Michael Wright, Guitar Stories Volume One, pg. 76)

D

DAIMARU

Instruments produced in Japan.

Daimaru guitars were distributed in the U.S. by the Daimaru New York Corporation of New York, New York.

(Source: Michael Wright, Guitar Stories Volume One, pg. 76)

DAION

Instruments were built in Japan in the late 1970s through the 1980s.

Some guitars may also carry the trademark of JOODEE or YAMAKI.

These high quality guitars copied popular designs in the 1970s, but turned to original designs like the 'Power Series' solid bodies or 'Headhunter Series' semi-hollowbodies in the 1980s.

(Source: Tony Bacon and Paul Day, The Guru's Guitar Guide)

DALLAS

Instruments were made in England, West Germany, and Japan during the early to mid 1960s.

Some guitars may also carry the trademark of TUXEDO.

The DALLAS and TUXEDO trademarks are the brandnames used by a UK importer/distributor. Early solid body guitars were supplied by either FENTON-WEILL or VOX in Britain, with entry level German and Japanese original design guitars imported in.

(Source: Tony Bacon and Paul Day, The Guru's Guitar Guide)

Danelectro 6/4 Doubleneck
courtesy Elliot Rubinson

DANELECTRO

Instruments originally manufactured in Red Bank, New Jersey from 1956 to 1959. Production was then moved to Neptune, New Jersey from 1960 through company's demise in 1968.

While distribution was handled by the Danelectro Corporation of Neptune, New Jersey, the majority of instruments were sold/distributed by Sears & Roebuck from roughly 1956 to 1967. Finally, distribution was handled by the MCA Corporation in the last year (1967-1968) after purchasing Danelectro.

Nathan I. Daniels (1912-1994) was a New York electronics buff who began assembling amplifiers at home in 1934. In the mid 1930s, he was contracted by Epiphone (NYC) to build Electar amps, and successfully created a reputation and finances to start the Danelectro Corporation in 1948. Daniels' new company had offices and a factory in Red Bank, New Jersey.

By 1953, the first guitar was designed, and introduced in 1954. It has been indicated that Daniels had consulted his long time friend John D'Angelico for assistance in the fret spacing and bridge placement. While most people believe the body frame under the masonite is pine, Paul Bechtoldt confirmed that the body is poplar (and his source was Vinnie Bell!). In 1959 or 1960 the company moved to 207 West Sylvania Avenue in Neptune City, New Jersey, where it remained until its demise in 1968.

All models were assembled in the Neptune City factory, and the majority were sold to Sears, Roebuck under their **Silvertone** trademark. Many of the popular designs should be considered "semi-hollow-bodies", for they have a masonite top and back mounted on a pine frame. The renowned "Lipstick Tube" pickups are exactly that: Danelectro bought the lipstick casings from a manufacturer who serviced the cosmetics industry, and then sent them to another contractor for plating before the pickup was installed inside.

The company grew during the 1960s guitar boom from under 100 employees to a peak of 503. George Wooster, Danelectro's production manager, estimated that the company produced 150 to 200 guitars a day during peak periods.

In late 1967 MCA (the entertainment conglomerate) bought Danelectro. In the same year, they introduced the Coral line. While 85% of Danelectro's output (guitars and amps) was for Sears, the Coral line was Danelectro's catalog line. The bodies for the Coral series were built in Japan, but the parts and assembly were done in the New Jersey plant. After MCA purchased the company, they began to do business with individual music shops instead of the big distributors - which brought them into competition with Fender and Gibson. Rather than point out the problem with that corporate thinking, let History do the talking: MCA folded Danelectro in 1968.

William C. Herring bought Danelectro's factory from MCA for $20,000 in late 1968 or 1969. Herring met Dan Armstrong (ex-Ampeg) and the pair visited the empty facilities and found numerous partially completed guitars and machinery. Armstrong contracted to build Danelectros for Ampeg, but by then

Danelectro Convertible
courtesy Steve Burgess

'60 D'Angelico New Yorker
courtesy Dr. Tom Van Hoose

the amplifier company was in financial straits and couldn't pay for them. These models have the single cutaway bodies, and Dan Armstrong Modified Danelectro on the pickguard. In a recent conversation this year, Dan Armstrong confirmed that he still holds the rights to the Danelectro trademark.

(Source: Paul Bechtoldt and Doug Tulloch, Guitars From Neptune)

The vintage market is stronger now on Danelectros and Silvertones than in the past. With the arrival of a solid reference book to help differentiate between the models produced (Bechtoldt and Tulloch's **Guitars from Neptune**), and a time frame indicated for model production, dealers are more confident in displaying model nomenclature. Danelectros have a different tone, feel, and vibe from Fenders, Gibsons, and Rickenbackers - and perhaps the players and dealers are beginning to respond. A Danelectro guitar was a modern production-built instrument, and the company made quite a few of them. But as in any marketplace, when the demand/supply ratio changes, prices can go up.

Danelectros have been trading stronger in the past twelve months than in previous years. The usual single pickup models range from $199 to $350, the amp-in-case model (guitar plus case) are $599, and the more unusual designs and colors/desirable models range between $725 and $1,100.

D'AGOSTINO

Instruments produced in Italy by the EKO company between 1978 and 1982. Instruments contracted by the EKO custom shop in Milwaukee, Wisconsin, and distributed by D'Agostino Corporation of New Jersey. After 1982, instruments were produced in Japan.

Pat D'Agostino (ex-Gibson/Maestro effects) began his own instrument importing company in 1975. The Italian-built **Benchmark Series** of guitars featured laminated neck thru designs.

D'ANGELICO

Instruments built in New York City, New York between 1932 and 1964.

Master Luthier John D'Angelico (1905-1964) was born and raised in New York City, New York. In 1914, he apprenticed to his Granduncle, and learned the luthier trade of building stringed instruments and repair. After 18 years of working on stringed instruments, he opened his own shop on Kenmare street (D'Angelico was 27). D'Angelico guitars were entirely handcrafted by D'Angelico with assistance from shop employees such as Vincent DiSerio (assistant/apprentice from 1932 to 1959). In the early 1950s, D'Angelico's workshop had a bench and counter for guitar work, and a showcase with new United or Favilla guitars, used "trade-ins" and a few amplifiers from Nat Daniel's Danelectro or Everett Hull's Ampeg company. A very young James D'Aquisto became the second assistant to the shop in 1953.

In 1959, the building where D'Angelico worked and lived was condemned by the city due to an unsafe foundation. While scouting out new locations, D'Angelico and DiSerio had a serious argument over finances. DiSerio left and accepted work at the Favilla guitar plant. After a number of months went by, D'Angelico and D'Aquisto finally reopened the guitar shop at its new location. Unfortunately, D'Angelico's health began to take a turn for the worst. John D'Angelico passed away in his sleep in September of 1964.

(Source: Paul William Schmidt, Acquired of the Angels)

Luthier John D'Angelico built archtop guitars with either 16", 17", or 18" across the lower bout. All his guitars share similarities in the basic structure; but there are numerous variations in the craftsmanship of the bracing, depth, neck shaping, and cosmetic features. D'Angelico built models as cutaway or non-cutaway (customer's preference) and some with a round or oval sound hole. Both models Excel and New Yorker were in demand as they were being built, and are still in demand today from guitar players and collectors. John D'Angelico created 1,164 numbered guitars, as well as unnumbered violins, mandolins, and novelty instruments.

Because each guitar was normally custom built per individual specifications, there is very little standardized pricing structure within the variations. The price range of a D'Angelico guitar can get as low as $10,000-$15,000, while the high can be in excess of $100,000 - depending on the condition, rarity, and even previous owner premium in some cases. It is highly recommended that several professional appraisals be secured before buying/selling/trading any D'Angelico guitar.

D'ANGELICO II

Instruments built in America. Distributed by Archtop Enterprises, Inc. of Merrick, New York.

The D'Angelico II company is currently producing high quality reproductions of John D'Angelico's New Yorker and Excel models. Models share similar construction features such as Spruce tops, figured Maple back and sides, Ebony fingerboard with mother-of-pearl inlays, and gold-plated Grover tuners and tailpiece. All guitars are individually handcrafted and hand engraved.

The 18" New Yorker is offered in cutaway ($12,000) and non-cutaway ($11,750) versions, and in a sunburst or antique natural finish. The Excel cutaway model ($11,500), Style B non-cutaway ($9,500), and Jazz Classic ($7,250) share a 17" body (measured across the lower bout). A smaller single pickup electric model called the Jazz Artist ($4,650) has a 16" body. Finally, a semi-hollowbody electric archtop called the Fusion ($3,750) is offered in an antique natural, New Yorker sunburst, or flaming red nitro cellulose lacquer finish.

D'ANGELICO REPLICA

Instruments built in Arcadia, California since 1995. Distributed by the Working Musician of Arcadia, California.

Frank W. Green is currently offering a replica of a D'Angelico Excel (Deluxe LB-175). Green, author of the book "D'Angelico, What's in a Name" is making available a 17" instrument with a handcarved

D'Angelico 17" Special
courtesy John Miller

Engelmann Spruce top, Western Curly Maple back and sides, a curly Maple neck, bound Ebony fingerboard with 'split block' inlays, Grover tuners, and gold plated 'stairstep' tailpiece. Green's price is listed as $ TBA. Contact the Working Musician via the Index of Current Manufacturers located in the rear of this book.

D'AQUISTO

Instruments built in Huntington, New York, as well as Greenport, New York, between 1965 to 1995.

Master Luthier James L. D'Aquisto (1935-1995) met John D'Angelico around 1953. At the early age of 17 D'Aquisto became D'Angelico's apprentice, and by 1959 was handling the decorative procedures and other lutherie jobs. When D'Angelico had a falling out with another member of the shop during the move of the business, D'Aquisto began doing actual building and shaping work. D'Aquisto worked with D'Angelico until the time of John's death in 1964. The loss of D'Aquisto in 1964 not only affected D'Aquisto personally, but professionally. Although he took over the business and shop with the encouragement of D'Angelico's brother, business under his own trademark started slowly. D'Aquisto continued to work in D'Angelico's shop repairing instruments at the last address - 37 Kenmare Street, New York City, New York. Finally, one year after D'Angelico's death, D'Aquisto summoned the nerve to build a guitar with the "D'Aquisto" inlay on the headpiece.

In 1965, D'Aquisto moved his shop to Huntington, New York, and sold his first instrument, styled after a D'Angelico New Yorker. Most of D'Aquisto's instruments are styled after John D'Angelico's Excel and New Yorker, with D'Aquisto adding refinements and improvements. D'Aquisto set up a deal with the Swedish-based Hagstrom company to produce guitars based on his designs in 1968, and the Ampeg company was one of the U.S. distributors. In 1973, D'Aquisto relocated his business once again, this time setting up shop in Farmingdale, New York. He produced his first flat top guitar in 1975, and his first solid body electric one year later. The Fender Musical Instrument corporation produced a number of D'Aquisto-designed guitars beginning in the 1980s, and two models in the Designer series (D'Aquisto Ultra and Deluxe) are still in production today at the Fender USA Custom shop.

*D'Aquisto Centura
courtesy Scott Chinery*

In the late 1980s, D'Aquisto moved his shop to Greenport, New York, and continued to produce instruments from that location. In 1987, D'Aquisto broke away from archtop design tradition when he debuted the "Avant Garde". The Excel and New Yorker models were discontinued in 1991, as D'Aquisto concentrated on creating more forward-looking and advanced archtops. In 1994, models such as the Solo (with its four soundholes), and Centura models were introduced. James L. D'Aquisto passed away in 1995.

(Source: Paul William Schmidt, Acquired of the Angels)

James D'Aquisto built several hundred instruments, from archtops to flat tops to solid body electrics. Used and vintage Prices may start at $10,000, with the model configuration and special order embellishments adding considerably to the base price. Like D'Angelico, most of D'Aquisto's instruments were made to order and varied in dimensions and details. When buying/selling/appraising a D'Aquisto, it is the recommendation of the **Blue Book of Guitars** that two or three professional appraisals be obtained.

DAVE ANDREWS GUITAR RESEARCH

Instruments built in California during the early to mid 1980s.

The explorer-style solid body guitar with triangular cut-outs was designed by California luthier David Andrews. In 1984, the Guild company introduced this design as the "X-100 Bladerunner", and produced the model for about one year. Another year after production of this model ceased, the body design became the basis for Schecter's Genesis Series.

DAVE MAIZE

Instruments currently built in Talent, Oregon.

Luthier Dave Maize hand-builds acoustic bass guitars with environmentally-friendly woods (either from a sustained yield source, a non-endangered species or reclaimed material). These instruments typically have Redwood or Cedar soundboards and bodies of figured Black Walnut, Maple, Black Locust or other select woods. Standard features include solid wood construction throughout, 34" scale 24 fret neck, Sperzel tuners, adjustable truss rod and a beautiful peghead inlay.

Maize offers several custom options (prices vary). The 4-string acoustic bass model has a retail price of $2,100 and the 5-string model lists at $2,350.

DAVE KING

Instruments currently built in Portland, Oregon.

Luthier Dave King hand-builds quality bass guitars on a custom basis. King currently offers 5 different models. List prices begin at $1,400-$2,400 and up. For further information, contact luthier King through the Index of Current Manufacturers located in the back of this book.

DAVOLI

Instruments built in Italy from the early 1960s through the early 1970s.

See WANDRE.

See also GHERSON.

*Dave Maize acoustic bass
courtesy Dave Maize*

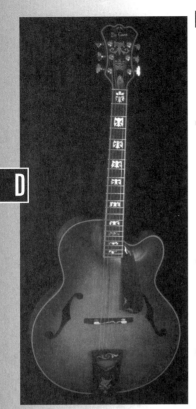

De Cava Classic
courtesy James R. De Cava

See also **KRUNDAAL**.

The Davoli company built Wandre and Krundaal guitars in the 1960s, and progressed towards the Gherson trademark in the 1970s.

(Source: Tony Bacon and Paul Day, The Guru's Guitar Book)

DE CAVA

Instruments currently built in Stratford, Connecticut.

Luthier Jim De Cava offers 2 different archtop guitar models based on his fond memories of 1960s archtops.

De Cava archtop guitars share similar features such as a 16" or 17" body, figured maple back, sides and neck, ebony fingerboard, tailpiece, bridge and pickguard, multiple bindings, bound f-holes, a sunburst finish and gold hardware. The **Stylist** model ($3,900) features pearl block inlays and a pearl logo and scroll design on peghead. The **Classic** model ($4,200) has 10 delicately cut position markers in fingerboard, a pearl nut, an engraved pearl truss rod cover, and hand-engraved inlay pieces.

DE LACUGO

Instruments currently built in Atascadero, California.

De Lacugo Guitars offers 2 models that feature mahogany bodies, and 22 fret bolt-on maple necks. The **D.C. Guitar** ($1,695) has 2 DiMarzio or Seymour Duncan humbucking pickups and a fixed bridge, while the **Excelsior** ($1,795) features a Floyd Rose or Wilkinson tremolo system.

DE WHALLEY

Instruments built in England during the mid 1980s.

This original design solid body was available in Standard, Deluxe, and Custom. Anyone with further information on the CV model is invited to write to the **Blue Book of Guitars**. We will update future editions as the information becomes available.

(Source: Tony Bacon and Paul Day, The Guru's Guitar Guide)

DEAN

Instruments currently produced in Plant City, Florida (American Custom, the U.S. series) and Korea (The D series). Distributed by Armadillo Enterprises, which is based in Clearwater, Florida.

Previously, Dean guitars with the set-neck design were built in Evanston, Illinois from 1977 to 1986. By the early 1980s, Dean began production of some models in Japan. Later Dean bolt-neck models were built in Korea during the late 1980s.

The original Evanston, Illinois-based company was founded by Dean Zelinsky in 1977, after graduating high school in 1976. Zelinsky began manufacturing high quality electric solid body instruments of popular existing designs and eventually started developing his own designs. Originally, there were three models: The **V** (similar to the Flying V), The **Z** (Explorer body shape), and the **ML** (sort of a cross between the V and an Explorer; and named after the initials of Matt Lynn, Zelinsky's best friend growing up). Zelinsky originally got into the guitar building business to fill a void he felt the larger companies had: a high quality, set neck, eye-catching stage guitar. Though new designs continued to be developed, manufacturing of these instruments was shifted more and more to overseas builders. In 1986, Dean closed the USA Shop, leaving all construction to be completed overseas. The U.S. market had shifted towards the then-popular bolt neck "super-strat" design, and Zelinsky's personal taste leaned in the opposite direction. He sold Dean Guitars in 1990 to Oscar Medros, founder and owner of Tropical Music which is based in Miami, Florida. The Dean Guitars facility is currently run by Tracy Hoeft and Jon Hill, and new guitars are distributed to markets in the U.S., Japan, Korea, and Europe.

ELECTRIC

Listed below are standard configurations of instruments. Being a highly handcrafted product though, instruments can be found with numerous options. Several finishes were used throughout this trademark's early life, including Cheetah, Tiger and Zebra Graphic finishes, and models are not necessarily limited to finishes listed. In 1983, all USA made instruments were manufactured with small fork (nicknamed the "shrimp fork") peghead. Zelinsky estimates that between 6,000 and 7,000 (possibly 8,000) guitars were built in the U.S. between 1977 and 1986. Production of American built Dean guitars has resumed at the facilities in Plant City, Florida.

Dean ML
19th Annual Dallas Show

Grading	100%	98% MINT	95% EXC+	90% EXC	80% VG+	70% VG	60% G

D

BEL AIRE — offset double cutaway maple body, bolt-on maple neck, 22 fret rosewood fingerboard with pearl dot inlay, standard vibrato, 3 per side tuners, chrome hardware, 2 single coil/1 humbucker pickups, 2 volume/tone controls, 5 position switch. Available in Black, Blueburst, Pearl, Pinkburst and White finishes. Mfd. 1983 to 1989.

	$500	$430	$360	$285	$260	$235	$215

Last Mfr.'s Sug. Retail was $1,050.

This model had maple fingerboard optionally available.

In 1984, double locking Kahler vibrato became optionally available.

In 1985, 6 on one side tuners replaced original item.

The bodies for these instruments were produced and instruments assembled in the USA by Dean (the serial numbers were stamped under the neck plate area), with the remaining parts being made in Japan by ESP. By 1985, total production had moved to Japan.

MACH V — this model was designed in 1985 and had a very limited run. Produced in KOREA, there are very few of these instruments in circulation.

Too few of these exist for accurate statistical representation.

Mach VII — this model was designed in 1985 and had a very limited run. Produced in the USA, there are very few of these instruments in circulation.

Too few of these exist for accurate statistical representation.

ML FLAME — single horn cutaway V shape mahogany body, V shape strings plate, mahogany neck, 22 fret bound rosewood fingerboard with pearl dot inlay, tunomatic bridge/strings thru body tailpiece, V shape peghead with screened logo, 3 per side Kluson tuners, chrome hardware, 2 humbucker DiMarzio pickups, 2 volume/1 tone controls, 3 position switch. Available in Black, Brasiliaburst, Cherry, Cherryburst, Metallic and White finishes. Mfd. 1978 to 1985.

	$750	$640	$535	$430	$390	$355	$325

Last Mfr.'s Sug. Retail was $1,100.

In 1981, Blueburst, Pearl and Pinkburst finishes were introduced.

ML Standard — similar to ML Flame, except has bound maple top, ebony fingerboard, Grover tuners. Available in Black, Brasiliaburst, Cherry, Cherryburst, Metallic and White finishes. Mfd. 1977 to 1986.

	$850	$730	$610	$485	$435	$400	$365

Last Mfr.'s Sug. Retail was $1,190.

This model had black, cream, multiply and white body binding optionally available.

In 1981, Blueburst, Pearl and Pinkburst finishes were introduced.

'80 lefthanded Dean V
courtesy Thoroughbred Music

V FLAME — V shape mahogany body, V shape strings plate, mahogany neck, 22 fret bound rosewood fingerboard with pearl dot inlay, tunomatic bridge/strings thru body tailpiece, V shape peghead with screened logo, 3 per side Kluson tuners, chrome hardware, 2 humbucker DiMarzio pickups, 2 volume/1 tone controls, 3 position switch. Available in Black, Brasiliaburst, Cherry, Cherryburst, Metallic and White finishes. Mfd. 1978 to 1985.

	$650	$555	$465	$370	$335	$305	$280

Last Mfr.'s Sug. Retail was $1,100.

In 1981, Blueburst, Pearl and Pinkburst finishes were introduced.

V Standard — similar to V Flame, except has bound maple top, ebony fingerboard, Grover tuners. Available in Black, Brasiliaburst, Cherry, Cherryburst, Metallic and White finishes. Mfd. 1977 to 1986.

	$700	$600	$500	$400	$360	$330	$300

Last Mfr.'s Sug. Retail was $1,190.

This model had black, cream and white body binding optionally available.

In 1981, Blueburst, Pearl and Pinkburst finishes were introduced.

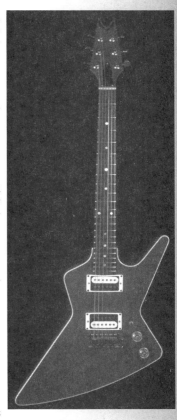

Z FLAME — single horn cutaway asymmetrical hourglass mahogany body, mahogany neck, 22 fret bound rosewood fingerboard with pearl dot inlay, tunomatic bridge/stop tailpiece, V shape peghead with screened logo, 3 per side Kluson tuners, chrome hardware, 2 humbucker DiMarzio pickups, 2 volume/1 tone controls, 3 position switch. Available in Black, Brasiliaburst, Cherry, Cherryburst, Metallic and White finishes. Mfd. 1978 to 1985.

	$650	$555	$465	$370	$335	$305	$280

Last Mfr.'s Sug. Retail was $1,100.

In 1981, Blueburst, Pearl and Pinkburst finishes were introduced.

Z Standard — similar to Z Flame, except has bound maple top, ebony fingerboard, Grover tuners. Available in Black, Brasiliaburst, Cherry, Cherryburst, Metallic and White finishes. Mfd. 1977 to 1986.

	$700	$600	$500	$400	$360	$330	$300

Last Mfr.'s Sug. Retail was $1,190.

This model had black, cream and white body binding optionally available.

In 1981, Blueburst, Pearl and Pinkburst finishes were introduced.

1990s Series

This series is manufactured overseas. All instruments in this series are available in Black, Blueburst, Grayburst, Red and White finishes, unless otherwise listed.

DS90E — offset double cutaway hardwood body, bolt-on maple neck, 24 fret rosewood fingerboard with pearl wings inlay, standard vibrato, blackface peghead with screened logo, 6 on one side tuners, black hardware, 2 single coil/1 humbucker pickups, 1 volume/2 tone controls, 5 position switch. Curr. mfr.

Mfr.'s Sug. Retail	$340	$272	$204	$170	$135	$125	$115	$105

'82 Dean Baby Z
courtesy Thoroughbred Music

Grading	100%	98% MINT	95% EXC+	90% EXC	80% VG+	70% VG	60% G

DS91E — similar to DS90E, except has bound carved top, double locking Floyd Rose vibrato, humbucker/single coil/humbucker pickups. Curr. mfr.

| Mfr.'s Sug. Retail | $520 | $416 | $312 | $260 | $210 | $190 | $170 | $160 |

DS92E — similar to DS90E, except has carved maple top, double locking Floyd Rose vibrato, gold hardware. Available in Sunburst finish. Curr. mfr.

| Mfr.'s Sug. Retail | $540 | $432 | $324 | $270 | $215 | $195 | $180 | $165 |

DS96E — similar to DS90E, except has ash body, double locking Floyd Rose vibrato, gold hardware, humbucker/single coil/humbucker pickups. Available in Natural finish. Curr. mfr.

| Mfr.'s Sug. Retail | $560 | $448 | $336 | $280 | $225 | $205 | $190 | $170 |

Baby Series

This series began production with the large V shape peghead, but shortly after switched to the small fork style peghead that is the most common found. The large V shape peghead was optionally offered.

ML — single horn cutaway V shape poplar body, poplar neck, 22 fret rosewood fingerboard with pearl dot inlay, tunable wrapover tailpiece, body matching peghead with screened logo, 3 per side tuners, chrome hardware, exposed humbucker DiMarzio pickup, volume/tone controls. Available in Black, Blueburst, Pearl Blue, Pearl Pink, Pearl Red, Pearl White, Red and White finishes. Mfd. 1982 to 1986.

| | $400 | $340 | $285 | $230 | $205 | $190 | $170 |

Last Mfr.'s Sug. Retail was $660.

This model had 24 fret fingerboard optionally available.

V — V shape poplar body, poplar neck, 22 fret rosewood fingerboard with pearl dot inlay, tunable wrapover tailpiece, body matching peghead with screened logo, 3 per side tuners, chrome hardware, exposed humbucker DiMarzio pickup, volume/tone controls. Available in Black, Blueburst, Pearl Blue, Pearl Pink, Pearl Red, Pearl White, Red and White finishes. Mfd. 1982 to 1986.

| | $400 | $340 | $285 | $230 | $205 | $190 | $170 |

Last Mfr.'s Sug. Retail was $660.

This model had 24 fret fingerboard optionally available.

Z — single horn cutaway asymmetrical hourglass poplar body, poplar neck, 22 fret rosewood fingerboard with pearl dot inlay, tunable wrapover tailpiece, 3 per side tuners, chrome hardware, exposed humbucker DiMarzio pickup, volume/tone controls. Available in Black, Blueburst, Pearl Blue, Pearl Pink, Pearl Red, Pearl White, Red and White finishes. Mfd. 1982 to 1986.

| | $400 | $340 | $285 | $230 | $205 | $190 | $170 |

Last Mfr.'s Sug. Retail was $660.

This model had 24 fret fingerboard optionally available.

E'lite Series

E'LITE — single horn cutaway round bottom mahogany body, mahogany neck, 22 fret bound rosewood fingerboard with pearl dot inlay, tunomatic bridge/stop tailpiece, blackface peghead with logo, 3 per side tuners, chrome hardware, 2 exposed humbucker DiMarzio pickups, 2 volume/2 tone controls, 3 position switch. Available in Brasiliaburst, Caine White, Cherry, Cherryburst, Opaque Black and Walnut finishes. Mfd. 1978 to 1985.

| | $600 | $515 | $430 | $345 | $310 | $285 | $260 |

Last Mfr.'s Sug. Retail was $1,030.

E'lite Deluxe — similar to E'lite, except has bound body, bound ebony fingerboard. Available in Bursts and Natural finishes. Mfd. 1981 to 1985.

| | $625 | $535 | $445 | $360 | $325 | $300 | $275 |

Last Mfr.'s Sug. Retail was $1,230.

Cadillac — similar to E'lite, except has bound body, bound ebony fingerboard with pearl block inlay, bound peghead, gold hardware, 3 humbucker pickups, active preamp. Available in wide variety of finishes. Mfd. 1979 to 1985.

| | $700 | $600 | $500 | $400 | $360 | $330 | $300 |

Last Mfr.'s Sug. Retail was $1,600.

This model had 2 humbucker pickups optionally available.

Golden E'lite — similar to E'lite, except has bound body, bound ebony fingerboard with abalone dot inlay, gold hardware, covered pickups. Available in Walnut finish. Mfd. 1979 to 1981.

| | $650 | $555 | $465 | $370 | $335 | $305 | $280 |

Last Mfr.'s Sug. Retail was $1,200.

E'lite Special Edition — similar to E'lite, except has bound curly maple top, bound ebony fingerboard with abalone dot inlay, gold hardware, covered pickups. Available in Natural finish. Mfd. 1982 to 1984.

| | $725 | $620 | $520 | $415 | $375 | $340 | $310 |

Last Mfr.'s Sug. Retail was $1,200.

Hollywood Series

This series was manufactured in KOREA. They were available in Black, Blueburst, Bolt, Flames, Pearl Blue, Pearl Pink, Pearl Red, Pearl White, Red, Wedge, White and Zebra Graphic finishes.

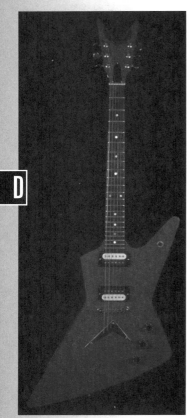

'82 Dean Z
courtesy Russell Farrow

Grading	100%	98% MINT	95% EXC+	90% EXC	80% VG+	70% VG	60% G

HOLLYWOOD BEL AIRE — offset double cutaway hardwood body, bolt-on maple neck, 24 fret rosewood fingerboard with pearl dot inlay, tunomatic bridge/stop tailpiece, body matching small fork peghead with screened logo, 3 per side tuners, chrome hardware, 2 humbucker pickups, volume/tone control, 3 position switch. Mfd. 1985 to 1987.

	$200	$170	$145	$115	$105	$95	$85

Last Mfr.'s Sug. Retail was $350.

Hollywood Bel Aire V — similar to Hollywood Bel Aire, except has double locking vibrato.

	$225	$195	$160	$130	$115	$105	$95

Last Mfr.'s Sug. Retail was $450.

HOLLYWOOD V — V shape hardwood body, bolt-on maple neck, 24 fret rosewood fingerboard with pearl dot inlay, tunomatic bridge/stop tailpiece, body matching small fork peghead with screened logo, 3 per side tuners, chrome hardware, 2 humbucker pickups, volume/tone controls, 3 position switch. Mfd. 1985 to 1987.

	$200	$170	$145	$115	$105	$95	$85

Last Mfr.'s Sug. Retail was $500.

Hollywood V V — similar to Hollywood V, except has double locking vibrato.

	$225	$195	$160	$130	$115	$105	$95

Last Mfr.'s Sug. Retail was $600.

HOLLYWOOD Z — single horn cutaway asymmetrical hourglass hardwood body, bolt-on maple neck, 24 fret rosewood fingerboard with pearl dot inlay, tunomatic bridge/stop tailpiece, body matching small fork peghead with screened logo, 3 per side tuners, chrome hardware, 2 humbucker pickups, volume/tone controls, 3 position switch. Mfd. 1985 to 1987.

	$200	$170	$145	$115	$105	$95	$85

Last Mfr.'s Sug. Retail was $350.

Hollywood Z V — similar to Hollywood Z, except has double locking vibrato.

	$225	$195	$160	$130	$115	$105	$95

Last Mfr.'s Sug. Retail was $450.

Playmate Series

This series is manufactured overseas.

DLS89 — offset double cutaway hardwood body, bolt-on maple neck, 22 fret rosewood fingerboard with pearl dot inlay, double locking vibrato, 6 on one side diecast tuners, chrome hardware, 2 single coil/1 humbucker pickups, 1 volume/2 tone controls, 5 position switch. Available in Black, Red and White finishes. Curr. mfr.

Mfr.'s Sug. Retail	$400	$320	$240	$200	$160	$145	$130	$120

DLS89GRA — similar to DLS89, except has Bloody Hand/Eye, Dragon, Multi Skulls, Planet, Thoughtful Skull and Viper Graphic finishes. Curr. mfr.

Mfr.'s Sug. Retail	$520	$416	$312	$260	$210	$190	$170	$160

DS89 — offset double cutaway hardwood body, bolt-on maple neck, 22 fret rosewood fingerboard with pearl dot inlay, standard vibrato, 6 on one side diecast tuners, chrome hardware, 2 single coil/1 humbucker pickups, 1 volume/2 tone controls, 5 position switch. Available in Black, Red and White finishes. Curr. mfr.

Mfr.'s Sug. Retail	$260	$208	$156	$130	$100	$90	$80	$75

DS89GRA — similar to DS89, except has Bloody Hand/Eye, Dragon, Multi Skulls, Planet, Thoughtful Skull and Viper Graphic finishes. Curr. mfr.

Mfr.'s Sug. Retail	$400	$320	$240	$200	$160	$145	$130	$120

Reissue Series

This series is manufactured overseas.

CADILLAC — single horn cutaway hardwood body, bound figured maple top, thru body mahogany neck, 24 fret bound rosewood fingerboard with pearl block inlay, tunomatic bridge/stop tailpiece, bound rosewood veneered peghead with screened logo, 3 per side tuners, gold hardware, 2 covered humbucker pickups, 2 volume/2 tone controls, 3 position switch. Available in Cherry Sunburst, Natural, Transparent Blue and Transparent Red finishes. Curr. mfr.

Mfr.'s Sug. Retail	$790	$632	$474	$395	$315	$280	$260	$235

ELITE K — single horn cutaway hardwood body, thru body mahogany neck, 22 fret rosewood fingerboard with pearl dot inlay, double locking vibrato, body matching peghead with screened logo, 3 per side tuners, chrome hardware, 2 humbucker pickups, 2 volume/2 tone controls, 3 position switch. Available in Black, Blueburst, Grayburst, Red and White finishes. Curr. mfr.

Mfr.'s Sug. Retail	$790	$632	$474	$395	$315	$280	$260	$235

ML — single horn cutaway V shape hardwood body, thru body mahogany neck, 22 bound rosewood fingerboard with pearl dot inlay, double locking vibrato, V shape peghead with screened logo, 3 per side tuners, chrome hardware, 2 exposed humbucker pickups, 2 volume/1 tone controls, 3 position switch. Available in Black finish. Curr. mfr.

Mfr.'s Sug. Retail	$800	$640	$480	$400	$320	$290	$265	$240

Add $60 for Lightning Graphic finish.

Signature Series

This series is manufactured in the USA.

'94 Cadillac Ultima
courtesy Dean Guitar Company

Grading	100%	98% MINT	95% EXC+	90% EXC	80% VG+	70% VG	60% G

DEMON DIME — single horn cutaway V shape mahogany body, thru body mahogany neck, 22 bound Brazilian rosewood fingerboard with abalone dot inlay, Floyd Rose double locking vibrato, V shape peghead with screened logo, 3 per side tuners, chrome hardware, 2 exposed humbucker pickups, 2 volume/1 dummy controls, 3 position switch. Available in Lightning Graphic finish. Curr. mfr.

Mfr.'s Sug. Retail	$1,700	$1,360	$1,020	$850	$680	$610	$560	$510

ML — similar to Demon Dime, except has Black finish. Curr. mfr.

Mfr.'s Sug. Retail	$1,575	$1,181	$787	$785	$630	$565	$515	$470

U.S.A. Series

This series is manufactured in the USA.

ML-92 — single horn cutaway V shape mahogany body, carved figured maple top, V shape strings plate, thru body mahogany neck, 22 bound ebony fingerboard with pearl dot inlay, Schaller tunomatic bridge/strings thru body tailpiece, V shape peghead with screened logo, 3 per side tuners, chrome hardware, 2 exposed humbucker pickups, 2 volume/1 tone controls, 3 position switch. Available in Cherry Sunburst, Natural, Transparent Blue and Transparent Red finishes. Curr. mfr.

Mfr.'s Sug. Retail	$1,600	$1,280	$960	$800	$640	$575	$530	$480

ELITE-92 — single horn cutaway mahogany body, bound carved figured maple top, thru body mahogany neck, 22 bound ebony fingerboard with pearl dot inlay, Schaller tunomatic bridge/stop tailpiece, bound V shape peghead with screened logo, 3 per side tuners, chrome hardware, 2 exposed humbucker pickups, 2 volume/2 tone controls, 3 position switch. Available in Cherry Sunburst, Natural, Transparent Blue and Transparent Red finishes. Curr. mfr.

Mfr.'s Sug. Retail	$1,600	$1,280	$960	$800	$640	$575	$530	$480

ELECTRIC BASS

MACH V — This model was designed in 1985 and had a very limited run. Produced in KOREA, there are very few of these instruments in circulation.

Mach VII — This model was designed in 1985 and had a very limited run. Produced in the USA, there are very few of these instruments in circulation.

ML I — single horn cutaway V shape mahogany body, V shape strings plate, maple neck, 22 fret bound rosewood fingerboard with pearl dot inlay, fixed bridge, V shape peghead with screened logo, 2 per side Kluson tuners, chrome hardware, humbucker coil pickup, volume/tone controls, active electronics. Available in Black, Blueburst, Pearl Blue, Pearl Pink, Pearl Red, Pearl White, Red and White finishes. Mfd. 1980 to 1985.

		$500	$430	$360	$285	$260	$235	$215

Last Mfr.'s Sug. Retail was $1,050.

ML II — similar to ML I, except has bound figured maple top, 2 humbucker pickups, 2 volume/1 tone controls.

		$550	$470	$395	$315	$285	$260	$235

Last Mfr.'s Sug. Retail was $1,200.

Z I — single horn cutaway asymmetrical hourglass mahogany body, maple neck, 22 fret bound rosewood fingerboard with pearl dot inlay, fixed bridge, V shape peghead with screened logo, 2 per side Kluson tuners, chrome hardware, humbucker pickup, volume/tone control, active electronics. Available in Black, Blueburst, Pearl Blue, Pearl Pink, Pearl Red, Pearl White, Red and White finishes. Mfd. 1982 to 1985.

		$500	$430	$360	$285	$260	$235	$215

Last Mfr.'s Sug. Retail was $1,050.

Z II — similar to Z I, except has bound figured maple top, 2 humbucker pickups, 2 volume/1 tone controls.

		$550	$470	$395	$315	$285	$260	$235

Last Mfr.'s Sug. Retail was $1,200.

1990s Series

This series is manufactured overseas. All instruments in this series are available in Black, Blueburst, Grayburst, Red and White finishes, unless otherwise listed. Curr. mfr.

DB91 — offset double cutaway hardwood body, bolt-on maple neck, 24 fret rosewood with pearl wings inlay, fixed bridge, 2 per side tuners, black hardware, P-style/J-style pickups, 2 volume/1 tone controls, 3 position switch.

Mfr.'s Sug. Retail	$380	$304	$228	$190	$150	$135	$120	$110

DB94 — similar to DB91, except has gold hardware, volume/treble/bass/mix controls, no 3 position switch, active electronics.

Mfr.'s Sug. Retail	$580	$464	$348	$290	$230	$205	$190	$175

DB95 — similar to DB91, except has 5 strings, 3/2 per side tuners, gold hardware, volume/treble/bass/mix controls, no 3 position switch, active electronics.

Mfr.'s Sug. Retail	$600	$480	$360	$300	$240	$215	$195	$180

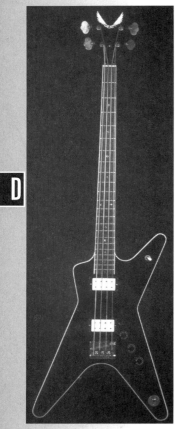

'81 Dean ML Bass
courtesy Thoroughbred Music

Grading		100%	98% MINT	95% EXC+	90% EXC	80% VG+	70% VG	60% G

DB96 — similar to DB91, except has 6 strings, 3 per side tuners, gold hardware, volume/treble/bass/mix controls, no 3 position switch, active electronics.

Mfr.'s Sug. Retail	$580	$464	$348	$290	$230	$205	$190	$175

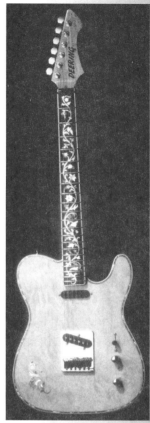

Baby Series

ML — single horn cutaway V shape poplar body, poplar neck, 22 fret rosewood fingerboard with pearl dot inlay, fixed bridge, body matching peghead with screened logo, 2 per side tuners, chrome hardware, single coil pickup, volume/tone controls. Available in Black, Blueburst, Pearl Blue, Pearl Pink, Pearl Red, Pearl White, Red and White finishes. Mfd. 1983 to 1985.

			$300	$260	$215	$175	$155	$140	$130

Last Mfr.'s Sug. Retail was $800.

Z — single horn cutaway asymmetrical hourglass poplar body, poplar neck, 22 fret bound rosewood fingerboard with pearl dot inlay, fixed bridge, 2 per side tuners, chrome hardware, single coil pickup, volume/tone controls. Available in Black, Blueburst, Pearl Blue, Pearl Pink, Pearl Red, Pearl White, Red and White finishes. Mfd. 1983 to 1985.

			$300	$260	$215	$175	$155	$140	$130

Last Mfr.'s Sug. Retail was $800.

DECCA

Instruments produced in Japan.

The Decca trademark is a brandname used by U.S. importers Decca Records.

(Source: Michael Wright, Guitar Stories Volume One, pg. 76)

Deering GD-800T
courtesy Janet Deering

DEERING

Guitars were built in Lemon Grove, California from 1990-1991. Deering continues to produce high quality banjos in Lemon Grove.

In 1975, Greg and Janet Deering began producing quality banjos. While continuing to offer innovative banjo designs, the Deerings also offer several models from entry level to professional play. In the late 1980s, Deering offered 4 different solid body guitar models in 2 variations that carried a retail price between $1,498-$2,850. The guitar models were also offered with some custom options, but were only produced for little over one year.

DEFIL

Instruments are built in Poland.

The long-established Defil company is the only mass producer of guitars in Poland. Defil has a wide range of solid body and semi-hollow body designs.

(Source: Tony Bacon, The Ultimate Guitar Book)

DEMARINO

Instruments built in Copiague, New York since 1973.

Deeply rooted in music, Ronald J. DeMarino's career spans four decades. DeMarino was playing New York clubs in 1956, when he had his first meeting with John D'Angelico (DeMarino was having his 1948 Gibson L-5 repaired!). D'Angelico took a liking to him, and after spending a great deal of time in his shop, DeMarino was fascinated with the idea of guitar building. DeMarino experimented for years, and finally launched his own shop.

DeMarino Guitars was established in 1967, and has been in continuous operation since the inception of the business. For 27 years DeMarino has specialized in the restoration of fine instruments, as well as custom building special order guitars and basses. DeMarino is a second generation family owned business. In addition to the quality standard model configurations, DeMarino also offers custom options such as Flame Maple or Big Leaf Quilt Maple tops, Ebony fingerboards, abalone or mother-of-pearl inlays, and other exotic woods (Spalted or Burled Maple, Burled Walnut, or Lacewood).

(Source: Hal Hammer)

DeMarino "Mary K"
courtesy Ronald J. DeMarino

ELECTRIC

Contour Series

The **Contour Standard** offers a cutaway Alder or Ash body, a Maple set-in neck, Rosewood fingerboard, Sperzel tuners, EMG pickups, and either a DeMarino custom bridge or Wilkinson tremolo system. The **Contour Custom** upgrades the body woods to a Honduran Mahogany body and set-in neck, as well as a figured Maple top and an Ebony fingerboard. A DeMarino fixed bridge and a hand rubbed Nitro-cellulose finish complete the package. On a slightly different note, the **Contour Pro** consists of an Alder body, a Maple bolt-on neck with rosewood fingerboard, and a Wilkinson tremolo combined with locking Sperzel tuners. A Floyd Rose locking tremolo system is optionally available.

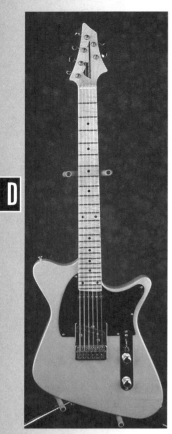

Demarino "Black Guard"
courtesy Ronald J. DeMarino

Thin-Line Series

Four models comprise the Thin-Line Series. The primary models **Pro-1** and **Pro-2** both feature an Alder body, custom color lacquer finishes, and a flat-mount Wilkinson bridge. The Pro-1 has 2 single coil pickups, and the Pro-2 has 2 EMG humbuckers. The **Thin-Line Standard** offers a Swamp Ash body topped with a figured Maple top, Rosewood fingerboard, EMG-T pickups, and a Wilkinson "Tele-bridge". The top of the line **Custom** has a Honduran Mahogany body under the Maple top, an Ebony fingerboard, and two EMG humbuckers.

Vintage Series

The Vintage models offer a sleek single cutaway body design with finishes and parts that seem right at home in the vintage guitar market. The **TV Contour** is offered with either one single coil pickup ("Single") or two ("Double"). Both models have a Honduran Mahogany body and neck, a 'Vintage' limed mahogany finish, Rosewood fingerboard, and a 'wrap-around' stud tailpiece. The **"Mary K."** combines a Swamp Ash body with a Maple bolt-on neck, gold hardware, a 'see-through' blonde finish, and three EMG-SV single coils. Change the finish to a "butter-scotch" lacquer, substitute a pair of EMG-T pickups and a black vintage-styled pickguard, and the results would be the **"Black Guard"** model.

For further information, availability, and pricing contact the DeMarino Guitar company through the Index of Current Manufacturers located in the back of this book.

D'HAITRE

Instruments were built in Maple Falls, Washington during the early 1990s.

Luthier Andy Beech offered several quality solid body guitar and bass models that featured a neck-through body design. Beech, with 18 years experience playing and building guitars, offered handcrafted work and select hardwoods in his constructions. The **Blue of Guitars** will continue to research luthier Beech and D'Haitre for future updates.

DIAMOND

See ARIA.

Instruments were built in Korea during the 1980s.

These entry level instruments were originally distributed by the Pennino Musical Corporation, and later by Aria USA. Designs mostly fell in the 'strat' or 'superstrat' guitar configuration, and a pointy headstock/sleek curves 'P-Bass' bass guitar. The trademark on the headstock generally read "DIAMOND by Aria".

DIAMOND-S

Instruments built in Independence, Virginia during the 1970s.

When Micro-Frets closed operations in Maryland in either 1974 or 1975, the company assets were purchased by David Sturgill. Sturgill, who served as the company president of Grammer Guitars for three years, let his sons John and Danny gain access to leftover Micro-Frets parts. In addition to those parts, they had also purchased the remains of New Jersey's Harptone guitar company. The two assembled a number of solid body guitars which were then sold under the 'Diamond-S' trademark. Unfortunately, that business venture did not catch on, and dissipated sometime in 1976.

DILLON

Instruments currently built in Bloomsburg, Pennsylvania.

Dillon Guitars offers quality custom built instruments. For further information, contact Dillon Guitars via the Index of Current Manufacturers located in the back of this book.

DINGWALL

Instruments currently built in Saskatoon, Canada.

Luthier Sheldon Dingwall founded Dingwall Designer Guitars in the mid 1980s, after years of actively playing music and doing guitar repair work.

While Dingwall is concentrating on bass guitars, he used to offer several high quality electric guitars models. All models featured bolt-on necks, 3+3 headstock with Sperzel or Gotoh tuners, and passive pickups. The **Roadster** fetured a single cutaway body, stop tailpiece, mini-humbucker (neck postion) and single coil (bridge). The **ATV** had an offset double cutaway body, tremolo bridge, and three single coils wired to a custom switching harness that delivered 10 distinct tones! The **LVQ** (Low Volume Resonance) model offered similar stylings to the ATV, except the design featured tone chambers (semi-hollowbody) and a stop tailpiece. Contact Dingwall Designer Guitars for availability.

ELECTRIC BASS

All VooDoo series custom basses feature the Novax fanned fret system on the fingerboards. This system is licensed from famed inventor/luthier Ralph Novak, and contributes a more accurate intonation and harmonic system to the staggered bridge design developed by Dingwall.

Dingwall basses all have an innovative bridge design that allows each string the proper scale length to achieve optimum tone. Thus, the scale length is staggered from the low B string (37") up to the G string (34") on a five string bass.

VooDoo Series

PRIMA 4 STRING — offset double cutaway Black American Walnut body, bookmatched top and back of Quilted Maple, Flame Maple, or Madrone burl, nine piece rock maple bolt-on neck that is reinforced with carbon fibre, Pau Ferro fretboard, 2+2 headstock design featuring Sperzel tuning machines, 2 Bartolini custom "Soapbar" pickups, black hardware, Kahler/Dingwall custom bridge, master volume knob, pickup blend knob, treble/bass concentric knob. Available in Oil finish. Current production.

  Mfr.'s Sug. Retail $2,595
    Add $100 for Hipshot Detuner.
    Add $250 for Translucent finish instead of Oil.

PRIMA 5 STRING — similar to the Prima 4 string, except has five strings and a 2+3 headstock. Current production.
  Mfr.'s Sug. Retail $2,695
    Add $250 for Translucent finish instead of Oil.

ZEBRA 4 STRING — shares similar specifications to the Prima, except body is constructed out of solid Northern Ash and finished in bright transparent colors that highlight the grain pattern (thus the Zebra name). Current production.

  Mfr.'s Sug. Retail $2,595
    Add $100 for Hipshot Detuner.

ZEBRA 5 STRING — similar to the Zebra 4 string, except has five strings and a 2+3 headstock. Current production.
  Mfr.'s Sug. Retail $2,695

DITSON

Instruments manufactured in Boston, Massachusetts from 1865 to the early 1900s.

The Oliver Ditson Company, Inc. was formed in 1835 by music publisher Oliver Ditson (1811-1888). Ditson was a primary force in music merchandising, distribution, and retail sales on the East Coast. He also helped establish two musical instrument manufacturers: The John Church Company of Cincinnati, Ohio, and Lyon & Healy (Washburn) in Chicago, Illinois.

In 1865 Ditson established a manufacturing branch of his company under the supervision of John Haynes, called the John C. Haynes Company. This branch built guitars for a number of trademarks, such as Bay State, Tilton, and Haynes Excelsior.

(Source: Tom Wheeler, American Guitars)

D'Leco Charlie Christian Solo Flite
courtesy Maurice Johnson

D'LECO

Instruments built in Oklahoma City, Oklahoma since 1992. Distributed by the D'Leco company of Oklahoma City, Oklahoma.

James Dale, Jr., like his father, had a backround in cabinet making that the two shared since 1953. Recently, Dale decided to begin building guitars full time. It was the love of jazz guitars that sparked the desire to build archtops. In the summer of 1992, Dale maet a young jazz guitarist and entrepreneur named Maurice Johnson. After seeing one of Dale's archtops, Maurice was impressed and proposed a coolaboration to build and market D'Leco guitars. In 1994, D'Leco acquired the rights to produce the "Charlie Christian" tribute model. IN 1995, Samick/Valley Arts began backing the proposed tribute model, and signed an exclusive agreement to build three unique production models based on the original guitars that was designed by D'Leco.

(Source: Hal Hammer)

  D'Leco offers the **Charlie Christian** Tribute model. The **Solo Flight S-15** ($5,000) electric hollowbody has a hand carved top, 15" bout, 16th fret neck joint, 5 layer binding, gold plated humbuckers, ebony or cocobolo fretboard, bridge and pickguard. The **Solo Flight S-16** had a hand carved spruce top, curly maple back and sides, 16" bout, 15th fret neck joint, bound fretboard, Charlie Christian Straight Bar 'floating' pickup, and hand rubbed lacquer. Portions of the sales proceeds go to the Christian family.

  D'Leco also offers electric solid body bass guitars custom built by a young Oklahoma City luthier David Stys. Stys was discovered by James Dale while he already building basses, and accepted the opportunity to join the D'Leco company and further his skills and development. D'Leco/Stys basses feature exotic wood tops, a through-body neck and state of the art electronics.

DOBRO

Instruments currently manufactured by Original Musical Instruments Company, located in Huntington Beach, California. Distributed by the Gibson Guitar Corporation, located in Nashville, Tennessee.

The original Dobro company was formed in 1928 in Los Angeles.

The Dopyera family emigrated from the Austro-Hungary area to Southern Califonia in 1908. In the early 1920s, John and Rudy Dopyera began producing banjos in Southern California. They were approached by guitarist George Beauchamp to help solve his 'volume' (or lack thereof) problem with other instruments in the vaudeville orchestra. In the course of their conversation, the idea of placing aluminum resonators in a guitar body for amplification purposes was developed. John Dopyera and his four brothers (plus some associates, like George Beauchamp) formed National in 1925. The initial partnership between Dopyera and Beauchamp lasted for about two years, and then John Dopyera left National to

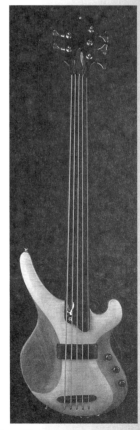

D'Leco/Stys 4 String Bass
courtesy David Stys

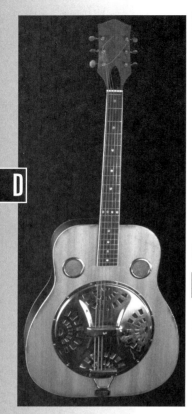

Resonator acoustic
1996 Tampa Vintage Show

form the Dobro company. The Dobro name was chosen as a contraction of the Dopyera Brothers (and it also means "good" in Slavic languages).

The Dobro and National companies were later remerged by Louis Dopyera in 1931 or 1932. The company moved to Chicago, Illinois in 1936; and a year later granted Regal the rights to manufacture Dobros. The "revised" company changed its name to VALCO in 1943, and worked on war materials during World War II. In 1959, VALCO transferred the Dobro name and tools to Emil Dopyera. Between 1966 and 1967, the Dobro trademark was sold to Semie Moseley (Mosrite). Moseley constructed the first Dobros out of parts from Emil's California plant, and later built his own necks and bodies. Moseley also built "Mobros", a Mosrite-inspired Dobro design. After Mosrite collapsed, the name was still held by Moseley; so in the late 1960s, Emil's company produced resonator guitars under the tradename of **Hound Dog** and **Dopera** (note the missing 'y') **Originals**. When the Dobro name finally became available again, Emil and new associates founded the Original Musical Instruments Company, Inc. (OMI) in 1970. OMI has been producing Dobros ever since. In 1993, OMI was sold to the Gibson Guitar Corporation, although production is still centered in California.

(Early company history courtesy Bob Brozman, The History and Artistry of National Resonator Instruments)

ACOUSTIC

Grading	100%	98% MINT	95% EXC+	90% EXC	80% VG+	70% VG	60% G

BOTTLENECK 90 — hollow style, chrome plate bell brass body, f holes, single cone resonator, maple neck, 14/19 fret rosewood fingerboard with white dot inlay, biscuit bridge/trapeze tailpiece, chrome hardware, 3 per side tuners. Available in Hawaiian scene finish. Curr. mfr.

Mfr.'s Sug. Retail	$1,450	$1,160	$870	$725	$580	$520	$475	$435

This model has oval or square neck optionally available.

DOBRO — hollow style, chrome plate bell brass body, f holes, single cone resonator, maple neck, 14/19 fret rosewood fingerboard with white dot inlay, spider bridge/trapeze tailpiece, chrome hardware, 3 per side tuners. Curr. mfr.

Mfr.'s Sug. Retail	$1,400	$1,120	$840	$700	$560	$505	$460	$420

Dobro Special — similar to Dobro, except has biscuit bridge, engraved Dobro shield finish. Curr. mfr.

Mfr.'s Sug. Retail	$3,000	$2,400	$1,800	$1,500	$1,200	$1,080	$990	$900

This model has spider bridge optionally available.

HAWAIIAN/SAILBOAT — hollow style, chrome plate bell brass body, f holes, single cone resonator, maple neck, 14/19 fret rosewood fingerboard, spider bridge/trapeze tailpiece, chrome hardware, 3 per side tuners. Available in etched Hawaiian and etched Sailboat scene finishes. Curr. mfr.

Mfr.'s Sug. Retail	$1,400	$1,120	$840	$700	$560	$505	$460	$420

HULA BLUES — hollow style, maple top, f holes, single cone resonator, maple back/sides/neck, 12/19 fret rosewood fingerboard with pearl dot inlay, spider bridge/trapeze tailpiece, chrome hardware, slotted peghead, 3 per side tuners. Available in Green and Red with screened Hawaiian scene finish. Curr. mfr.

Mfr.'s Sug. Retail	$700	$560	$420	$350	$280	$250	$230	$210

LILY — hollow style, chrome plate bell brass body, f holes, single cone resonator, maple neck, 14/19 fret ebony fingerboard with pearl diamond inlay, spider bridge/trapeze tailpiece, pearl logo peghead inlay, chrome hardware, 3 per side tuners. Available in engraved Lily of the Valley finish. Curr. mfr.

Mfr.'s Sug. Retail	$2,150	$1,720	$1,290	$1,075	$860	$775	$710	$645

ROSE — hollow style, chrome plate bell brass body, f holes, single cone resonator, maple neck, 14/19 fret rosewood fingerboard, biscuit bridge/trapeze tailpiece, chrome hardware, 3 per side tuners. Available in etched Rose finish. Curr. mfr.

Mfr.'s Sug. Retail	$1,850	$1,480	$1,110	$925	$740	$670	$610	$555

WOOD BODY 90 — hollow style, maple top, f holes, single cone resonator, maple back/sides/neck, 12/19 fret rosewood fingerboard with pearl dot inlay, biscuit bridge/trapeze tailpiece, chrome hardware, slotted peghead, 3 per side tuners. Available in Sunburst finish. Curr. mfr.

Mfr.'s Sug. Retail	$850	$680	$510	$425	$340	$305	$280	$255

Wood Body 90 Soft Cutaway — similar to Wood Body 90, except has single round cutaway, multiple soundholes. Available in Natural finish. Curr. mfr.

Mfr.'s Sug. Retail	$900	$720	$540	$450	$360	$325	$300	$275

Classic Series

F HOLE CLASSIC — hollow style, maple top, f holes, single cone resonator, maple back/sides/neck, 14/19 fret rosewood fingerboard with pearl dot inlay, spider bridge/trapeze tailpiece, slotted peghead with logo decal, chrome hardware, 3 per side tuners with plastic buttons. Available in Dark Sunburst finish. Curr. mfr.

Mfr.'s Sug. Retail	$650	$520	$390	$325	$260	$235	$215	$195

BRIGHTBURST CLASSIC — similar to F Hole Classic, except has 2 screened/3 clear soundholes, bound body. Available in 3 Tone Sunburst finish. Curr. mfr.

Mfr.'s Sug. Retail	$1,000	$800	$600	$500	$400	$360	$330	$300

Grading	100%	98% MINT	95% EXC+	90% EXC	80% VG+	70% VG	60% G

DARKBURST CLASSIC — similar to F Hole Classic, except has 2 screened/3 clear soundholes, bound body. Available in Darkburst finish. Curr. mfr.

Mfr.'s Sug. Retail	$1,000	$800	$600	$500	$400	$360	$330	$300

MAHOGANY CLASSIC — similar to F Hole Classic, except has mahogany body, 2 screened/3 clear soundholes, bound body/fingerboard/peghead, pearl diamond/dot fingerboard inlay. Available in Natural finish. Curr. mfr.

Mfr.'s Sug. Retail	$1,100	$880	$660	$550	$440	$395	$365	$330

NATURAL CLASSIC — similar to F Hole Classic, except has 2 screened/3 clear soundholes, bound body. Available in Natural finish. Curr. mfr.

Mfr.'s Sug. Retail	$1,050	$840	$630	$525	$420	$380	$345	$315

WALNUT CLASSIC — hollow style, walnut top, 2 screened/3 clear soundholes, single cone resonator, walnut back/sides, maple neck, 14/19 fret bound ebony fingerboard with pearl vine inlay, spider bridge/trapeze tailpiece, chrome hardware, slotted peghead with logo decal, 3 per side tuners with plastic buttons. Available in Natural finish. Curr. mfr.

Mfr.'s Sug. Retail	$1,200	$960	$720	$600	$480	$430	$395	$360

ZEPHYR SUNBURST — single sharp cutaway hollow style, maple top, multiple soundholes, single cone resonator, bound body, maple back/sides/neck, 19 fret ebony fingerboard with abalone seagull inlay, spider bridge/trapeze tailpiece, chrome hardware, slotted peghead, 3 per side tuners with plastic buttons. Available in Sunburst finish. Curr. mfr.

Mfr.'s Sug. Retail	$1,400	$1,120	$840	$700	$560	$505	$460	$420

Dodge guitar
courtesy Rick and Janice Dodge

DODGE

Instruments built in Tallahassee, Florida since 1996. Distributed by the Dodge Guitar Company of Tallahassee, Florida.

Rick Dodge apprenticed to master stringed instrument maker Paris Bancetti in the mid 1970s, and has been a luthier for over 20 years, making both acoustic and electric guitars for personal use and for friends and family. Each guitar was carefully crafted from fine woods, and guitars made by Dodge achieved high quality aesthetics and sound. After building many electric guitars and experimenting with different electronic configurations, Dodge was struck with the idea of making a modular guitar that could completely exchange the electronics without sacrificing the high quality sound or beauty of a fine instrument. Dodge then developed the idea of a rear-mounted modular system: the pickups and electronics would be mounted on a section that could be inserted into the body area.

Dodge formed the Dodge Guitar Company in the spring of 1996. Production of modular guitars will begin in September, 1996.

(Company information courtesy Janice Dodge, July 25, 1996)

A standard package of one electric guitar with three differently configured electronics-containing modules will retail for about $2,150, but prices will vary considerably depending on what features are included and which brands and designs of electronics are installed. A modular bass guitar model will be offered in the winter of 1977. Contact luthier Dodge for prices and customizing options via the Index of Current Manufacturers located in the rear of this book.

DOLCE

See chapter on House Brands.

This trademark has been identified as the "House Brand" used by such stores as Marshall Fields, Macy's, and Gimbles.

(Source: Willie G. Moseley, Stellas & Stratocasters)

DOMINO

Instruments manufactured in Japan during the 1960s.

These Japanese-produced guitars and basses were imported to the U.S. market by the Maurice Lipsky company of New York, New York. By 1967, the design focus spotlighted copies of Fender's Jazzmaster/Jaguar and Mustang models renamed the "Spartan" and the "Olympic".

(Source: Michael Wright, Guitar Stories Volume One)

DON GROSH

Instruments currently built in Canyon Country, California.

Luthier/designer Don Grosh offers several quality guitar models. For further information on specifications, pricing, and custom options please contact luthier Grosh via the Index of Current Manufacturers located in the rear of this book.

Duesenberg Starplayer II
courtesy Salwender International

Dyer Symphony Harp Guitar Style
#7
courtesy Robert Carl Hartman

DUESENBERG

Instruments are built in Germany, and distributed by Salwender International of Trabuco Canyon, California.

Duesenburg guitars were designed by Dieter Golsdorf, and these semi-hollowbody guitars feature a single f-hole and 'retro' styling.

The **Starplayer I** ($2,229) has a mahogany body and laminated maple/spruce top, a hard rock maple neck, 22 fret rosewood neck, fixed bridge, and two Alnico pickups. The **Starplayer II** ($2,299) features similar construction and a Bigsby tailpiece.

GUITARES MAURICE DUPONT

Instruments currently built in France. Distributed by Paul Hostetter of Santa Cruz, California.

After spending a number of years repairing and restoring Selmer/Maccaferri guitars, luthier Maurice Dupont began building Selmer replicas that differ in the fact the Dupont features a one-piece neck with adjustable trussrod inside (Selmers had a three piece neck), and better construction materials. Dupont also hand builds his own classical, flamenco, steel-string, and archtop guitars. Both the **Excellence** and **Privilege** archtops are offered in 16" or 17" bodies, and with a Florentine or Venetian cutaway. For further information on either the Selmer-type guitars, or his other Dupont models, please contact Paul Hostetter in Santa Cruz, California.

(Dupont history courtesy Paul Hostetter)

DWIGHT

See chapter on House Brands.

This trademark has been identified as a "House Brand" of the Dwight company, an American music retailer. One guitar model researched appears to be a 'rebranded' Epiphone Coronet model, with "Dwight" on the headstock and a "D" in the center of the pickguard. If so, this would be a Gibson built Epiphone from the 1960s - and American Epiphone production didn't stop until 1970.

Dwight also marketed some Valco-built guitars. Additional information on the Dwight company would be welcomed for future editions of the **Blue Book of Guitars**.

W.J. DYER & BRO.

See LARSON BROTHERS (1900-1944).

From the 1880s to the 1930s, the Dyer store in St. Paul was "the" place for musical merchandise for the midwest in the areas northwest of Chicago. They sold about anything music related on the market at that time. The Larson brothers of Maurer & Co., Chicago were commissioned to build a line of "Symphony" harp-guitars and "Symphony" harp-mandolin orchestra pieces along with the J.F. Stetson brand of guitars. They started building these great instruments circa 1910.

The original design of these harp-style instruments came from that of Chris Knutsen who had been building that style since 1898. The early Larsons showed a resemblance to the Knutsen ideas but evolved to a final design by 1912. The harp-guitars are labeled Style #4 through #8 whereas the higher the number, the better the grade of material and intricacy of the trim. The Style #4 is very plan with dot inlays in the fingerboard and no binding on the back. The Style #8 has a pearl trimmed top, fancy peghead inlay and the beautiful tree-of-life fingerboard. This tree-of-life pattern is also used on the fanciest Maurers and Prairie States having the 12 fret-to-the-body necks.

The harp-mandolin series includes a harp-mandola and harp-mando-cello also in different degrees of ornamentation. Some of the Stetson guitars are Larson-made, but others were possibly made by Harmony, Lyon & Healy, or others. If the Stetson trademark is burned into the inside back strip, it is probably a Larson.

For more information regarding other Larson-made brands, see MAURER, PRAIRIE STATE, EUPHONON, WM. C. STAHL and THE LARSON BROTHERS.

For more detailed information regarding all Larson brands, see The Larsons' Creations, Guitars and Mandolins, *by Robert Carl Hartman, Centerstream Publishing, P.O. Box 5450, Fullerton, CA 92635, phone/fax (714) 779-9390.*

DYNELECTRON

Instruments built in Italy between 1974 and 1976.

This company specialized in reproducing the DANELECTRO 'Guitarlin' model. Like Jerry Jones, they took an existing model - and built it better! However, vintage Danelectro models are still more valuable to collectors. If an enterprising reader wishes to contrast the three different companies' versions of the 'Guitarlin' for future editions, please send the results to the **Blue Book of Guitars**.

(Source: Tony Bacon and Paul Day, The Guru's Guitar Guide)

E

EAGLE

Instruments currently built in Murr, Germany.

Eagle Country Instruments produces the smallest full-size electric bass guitar (34" scale, 36" overall length). This innovative design features a paduk/maple/mahogany construction, reverse stringing/no headstock. Retail prices run from $1,480 (4-string) to $1,620 (5-string).

EASTWOOD

Custom Instruments built in England.

The EASTWOOD trademark indicates custom work by luthier Brian Eastwood. One of his better known commissioned custom guitars is featured in Tony Bacon's book, **The Ultimate Guitar Book**.

ECCLESHALL

Instruments built in England since the early 1970s.

Luthier Christopher J. Eccleshall is known for the high quality guitars that he produces. Some of the original designs carry the model designation of Excalibur, EQ, and Craftsman. Luthier Eccleshall was also the first UK maker to have Japanese-built solid body guitars.

(Source: Tony Bacon and Paul Day, The Guru's Guitar Guide)

EGMOND

See ROSETTI.

See also LION.

Instruments built in Holland between 1960 and 1972.

In response to the pop music boom of the 1960s, guitar companies kept turning out instruments to try to meet the generated demand. These entry level guitars were aimed at the novice guitar player, and featured a line of Dutch-built solid and semi-hollow body designs.

(Source: Tony Bacon and Paul Day, The Guru's Guitar Guide)

EGYPT

Instruments produced in England between 1985 and 1987.

The EGYPT trademark was utilized by Scottish builders Maurice Bellando and James Cannell in the mid to late 1980s. These high quality, strikingly original solid body designs also featured Egyptian names. The luthiers also produced a range of Fender/Gibson-style models as well.

(Source: Tony Bacon and Paul Day, The Guru's Guitar Guide)

EHLERS

Instruments built in Oregon from 1985 to current.

Luthier Rob Ehlers has been building high quality acoustic steel string guitars in his workshop over the last ten years. For information regarding availability, pricing, and model nomenclature, please contact luthier Ehlers through the Index of Current Manufacturers located in the rear of this book.

EHLERS & BURNS

See EHLERS.

Instruments custom built in Oregon from 1974 to 1984.

The E & B (EHLERS & BURNS) trademark was used by luthiers Rob Ehlers and Bruce Burns during a ten year period. Most instuments produced then were custom ordered. After 1984, Bruce Burns was no longer involved in the contruction of the instruments.

EKO

Instruments were built in Italy from the early 1960s through the mid 1980s. Distribution in the U.S. market by the LoDuca Bros. of Milwaukee, Wisconsin.

The LoDuca Bros. musical distribution company was formed in 1941 by brothers Tom and Guy LoDuca. Capitalizing on money made through their accordian-based vaudevillian act, lessons, and accordian repair, the LoDucas began importing and selling Italian accordians. Throughout the 1940s and 1950s,

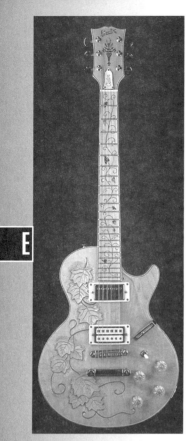

Electra Carved Top
courtesy John Boyer

the LoDucas built up a musical distributorship with accordians and sheet music. By the late 1950s, they were handling Magnatone amplifiers and guitars.

In 1961, the LoDucas teamed up with Italy-based Oliviero Pigini & Company to import guitars. Pigini, one of the LoDuca's accordian manufacturers, had formed the EKO company in anticipation of the boom in the guitar market. The LoDucas acted as technical designers and gave input on EKO designs (as well as being the exclusive U.S. dealers), and EKO built guitars for their dealers. Some of the sparkle finishes were no doubt inspired by the accordians produced in the past. In fact, the various on/off switches and tone settings are down right reminiscent of accordian voice settings! The plastic covered-guitars lasted through to the mid 1960s, when more conventional finishes were offered. EKO also built a number of guitars for Vox, Goya, and Thomas companies.

By 1967 EKO had established dealers in 57 countries around the world. EKO produced a number of different models, like the semi-hollowbody 335-ish **Barracuda** series; or electric/acoustic cutaway models like the Escort, Commander, and Mascot. EKO offered violin-shaped guitars and basses; and solid body guitars like the double offset cutaway **Lancer** series, or the rocket ship-shaped **Roke** guitars and basses. More traditional were the **Kadett** and **Cobra** lines. A number of designs were based on Fender's Jazzmaster model; however, that model was their current top of the line. During the late 1960s and early 1970s the guitar market began to get soft, and many guitar builders began to go out of business. EKO continued on, but cut back the number of models offered. In the late 1970s, EKO introduced a "custom shop" branch that built neck-through designed guitars for other trademarks. Once such company was D'Agostino, and EKO produced the Bench Mark models from 1978 to 1982.

The EKO company kept producing models until 1985. By the mid-1980s, the LoDuca Bros. company had begun concentrating on guitar case production, and stopped importing the final "Alembic-styled" set-neck guitars that were being produced. As of this edition, the EKO trademark was again revived in Italy, and appears on entry level solid body guitars built in Asia.

(Source: Michael Wright, Guitar Stories Volume One, pgs. 165–185)

Prices on EKO models run between $250 on up to $650, according to condition, appeal, and relative coolness of the piece. This call is a matter of personal taste.

EL DEGAS

Instruments produced in Japan.

The El Degas trademark was a brandname used by U.S. importers Buegeleisen & Jacobson of New York, New York.

(Source: Michael Wright, Guitar Stories Volume One, pg. 76)

ELECTRA

Instruments built in Japan.

Electra guitars, like Alvarez, were a brandname used by the St. Louis Music Supply company of St. Louis, Missouri. The Electra brand was introduced in the late 1970s, and in 1984 St. Louis Music announced that it would be merged with the Japanese-built Westone brand. Through the mid 1980s, models were sold under the Electra/Westone imprint, then Westone only as the Electra aspect was discontinued.

ELGER

Instruments originally produced in Ardmore, Pennsylvania from 1959 to 1965. Elger began importing instruments produced in Japan during the early 1960s.

The Elger company became partners with Hoshino Gakki Gen (a principal producer to Elger), and introduced the Ibanez trademark to the U.S. market.

Elger instruments were distributed in the U.S. by the Elger Company of Ardmore, Pennsylvania. The roots of the Elger company were founded in 1954 by Harry Rosenbloom when he opened Medley Music in Bryn Mawr, Pennsylvania. In 1959, Rosenbloom decided to produce his own acoustic guitars as the Elger Company (named after his children, Ellen and Gerson). Rosenbloom soon turned from U.S. production to Japanese, but maintained the Pennsylvania facilities to check incoming shipments and correct any flaws. For further company history, see IBANEZ.

(Source: Michael Wright, Guitar Stories Volume One,)

ELITE

See CRUCIANELLI.

Instruments were built in Italy during the mid 1960s.

Entry level solid body guitars that featured similar accordian-style finishes. Many Italian instrument producers were building accordians before the worldwide explosion of guitar popularity in the 1960s, and those eye catching finishes are the direct result. ELITE semi-hollowbody guitars were more normal in appearance.

(Source: Tony Bacon and Paul Day, The Guru's Guitar Guide)

Electra MPC
courtesy Elliot Rubinson

ELK

Instruments produced in Japan during the 1960s.

Elk instruments were mid-quality solid body guitars that featured some designs based on classic American favorites. Elk also produced a line of amplifiers with circuitry and cosmetics similar to Fender amps.

(Source: Rittor Books, 60s Bizarre Guitars)

EL MAYA

See MAYA.

Instruments built in Japan from the mid 1970s to the mid 1980s.

The El Maya instruments were generally good quality solid body guitars featuring original designs and some based on Fender styles. The El Maya trademark was part of range offered by the Maya guitar producer.

(Source: Tony Bacon and Paul Day, The Guru's Guitar Guide)

ELRICK

Instruments currently built in Chicago, Illinois.

Luthier Robert Elrick handcrafts bass guitars from the finest exotic hardwoods. All instruments are constructed with bodies of koa or swamp ash, and feature bookmatched exotic wood tops and backs. For further information, contact lutheir Robert Elrick through the Index of Current Manufacturers located in the rear of this book.

EMERY

Instruments built in Britt, Minnesota. Distributed by Resound Vintage Guitars of Britt, Minnesota.

Luthier Jean-Paul Emery has been customizing and building guitars as well as performing restoration work on vintage instruments for several years. For further information, contact luthier Emery through the Index of Current Manufacturers located in the rear of this book.

EMPERADOR

Instruments built in Japan.

The Emperador trademark was a brandname used in the U.S. market by a yet unidentified importer. For further information, please check future updates of the **Blue Book of Guitars**.

(Source: Michael Wright, Guitar Stories Volume One, pg. 76)

ENCORE

Instruments are currently produced in Asia. Represented in the U.S. Market by the Chandler company of Burlingame, California. U.K. Distribution by John Hornby Skewes & Co., Ltd. of Garforth (Leeds), England.

The ENCORE trademark is the brand name of UK importer John Hornby Skewes & Co., Ltd. The company was founded in 1965 by the namesake, Mr. John Hornby Skewes. The Encore line consists of solidly built guitars and basses that feature designs based on popular American favorites. Encore instruments are of medium to good quality, and their model E83 bass was named Most Popular U.K. Bass Guitar in 1992, 1993, and 1994.

In addition to the Encore line, the John Hornby Skewes company is the exclusive U.K. representative for Ovation, Charvel/Jackson, Manual Rodriguez, SKB, Hughes & Kettner, and other major brands.

ACOUSTIC

The current Encore line of acoustic guitars is well represented by over 17 models. The **CE** (cutaway electric) series features a Nato body and a spruce laminate top, as well as an on-board piezo pickup system. The **E400** Dreadnought is offered in six or twelve string configurations, as well a piezo equipped model. Construction is similar to the CE series. There are currently 6 classical models (three full size, two 3/4 scale, and one 1/2 scale), and construction ranges from a Beech laminate top to solid Spruce, with either a Maple laminate or Beech laminate back and sides.

ELECTRIC

Encore offers a wide range of models from which to choose. The **MOD** series offers four varieties of the 'superstrat' model; the **RK** series is based on popular Rickenbacher stylings; and Les Pauls are the basis for the **P** series. Both the **Vintage Custom Deluxe** and **Vintage Standard** series offer a step up in quality with Wilkinson tremolos, Don Lace/AGI pickups, and Grover machineheads. The ash body design is reminiscent of a Strat, and features a maple neck with a 21 fret rosewood fingerboard. There are a number of entry-level/student solid body guitars as well.

ELECTRIC BASS

The three bass models fit solidly into the "P-Bass" mold. The **E83** if offered with options such as a fretless neck or left-handed configuration. The **E84** is a variant of the E83 offered with P/J pickups. The shorter scaled **PK12** is aimed at the entry-level bassist.

ENSENADA

Instruments produced in Japan.

The Ensenada trademark was a brandname of U.S. importers Strum & Drum of Chicago, Illinois. Strum and Drum were later owners of the National trademark, acquired when Valco's holdings were auctioned off.

(Source: Michael Wright, Guitar Stories Volume One, pg. 76)

EPIPHONE

Currently, most models are built in Korea. There are a number of USA designated models built in Nashville, Tennessee and the Gibson Montana facility. EPIPHONE is a division of the Gibson Guitar Corporation of Nashville, Tennessee.

In 1917, Epaminondas "Epi" Stathopoulos began using the **House of Stathopoulo** brand on the family's luthiery business. By 1923 the business was incorporated, and a year later the new trademark was unveiled on a line of banjos. Stathopoulos combined his nickname Epi with the Greek word for sound, phone. When the company was recapitalized in 1928, it became the Epiphone Banjo Company.

Guitars were introduced in 1930, and were built in New York City, New York through 1953. Company manufacturing was moved to Philadelphia due to union harrassment in New York, and Epiphone continued on through 1957. When Epiphone moved to Philadelphia, a number of craftsmen elected to stay in New York and remain in their local communities. Many of these craftsmen were soon hired by Al Dronge's new Guild Guitar Company.

In 1959, Gibson bought Epiphone after a series of financial problems. Gibson/CMI intended to purchase the bass guitar branch, and instead wound up with the complete company. Parts and materials were shipped to the new home in Kalamazoo, Michigan. Ex-Epiphone workers in New Berlin, New York "celebrated" by hosting a bonfire behind the plant with available lumber (finished and unfinished!). After Epiphone was moved to Kalamazoo, instruments were built in the U.S through 1969. In 1970, production was moved overseas. Instruments were originally built in Japan (1970-1983), but during the early 1980s, Japanese production costs became pricey due to the changing ratio of the dollar/yen. In 1984, production was moved to Korea.

(Source: Walter Carter, Epiphone: The Complete History)

ACOUSTIC

Grading	100%	98% MINT	95% EXC+	90% EXC	80% VG+	70% VG	60% G

BEVERLY — folk style, spruce top, f holes, raised black pickguard, mahogany back/sides/neck, 14/20 fret rosewood fingerboard with pearl dot inlay, adjustable rosewood bridge/trapeze tailpiece, blackface peghead, 3 per side tuners. Available in Brown finish. Mfd. 1931 to 1937.

	100%	98%	95%	90%	80%	70%	60%
	$425	$295	$250	$210	$170	$150	$135

This instrument originally sold for $35.

BLACKSTONE — dreadnought style, arched spruce top, f holes, raised black pickguard, bound body, maple back/sides, 14/20 fret bound rosewood fingerboard with pearl dot inlay, adjustable rosewood bridge/trapeze tailpiece, bound blackface peghead with pearl logo inlay, 3 per side plate mounted tuners. Available in Sunburst finish. Mfd. 1931 to 1950.

	100%	98%	95%	90%	80%	70%	60%
	$1,200	$840	$720	$600	$480	$430	$395

In 1933, pearl Masterbilt banner peghead inlay was added.

In 1934, enlarged body, mahogany back/sides, redesigned unbound peghead with redesigned inlay replaced original items.

In 1937, parallelogram fingerboard inlay replaced original item, auditorium style body, maple back/sides, diamond/script logo peghead inlay replaced respective items.

In 1939, cloud style peghead replaced respective item.

In 1941, Blonde finish became optionally available.

In 1945, abalone oval/logo peghead inlay replaced respective items.

Epiphone Ritz
courtesy Clay Leighton

Grading	100%	98% MINT	95% EXC+	90% EXC	80% VG+	70% VG	60% G

BROADWAY — grand auditorium style, carved spruce top, f holes, raised black pickguard, multibound body, walnut back/sides, mahogany neck, 14/20 fret bound ebony fingerboard with pearl diamond inlay, adjustable ebony bridge/trapeze tailpiece, blackface peghead with pearl Masterbilt banner/logo inlay, 3 per side nickel tuners. Available in Sunburst finish. Mfd. 1931 to 1958.

	$1,600	$1,120	$960	$800	$640	$575	$530

This instrument originally sold for $175.

In 1934, bound pickguard, block fingerboard inlay, vine/block logo peghead inlay, gold hardware replaced original items.

In 1937, redesigned body/pickguard/tailpiece/logo replaced respective items, bound peghead replaced original item.

In 1939, maple back/sides, Frequensator tailpiece, redesigned peghead replaced respective items.

In 1941, Blonde finish optionally available.

In 1944, pearl flower peghead inlay replaced respective item.

CABALLERO — dreadnought style, mahogany top, round soundhole, tortoise pickguard with logo, bound body, 1 stripe rosette, mahogany back/sides/neck, 14/20 fret rosewood fingerboard with pearl dot inlay, reverse rosewood bridge with white pins, 3 per side tuners with plastic buttons. Available in Natural finish. Mfd. 1958 to 1970.

	$290	$205	$175	$145	$115	$105	$95

In 1961, non logo pickguard replaced original item.

In 1963, adjustable saddle replaced original item.

CORTEZ — dreadnought style, spruce top, round soundhole, tortoise pickguard with stylized E, bound body, mahogany back/sides/neck, 20 fret rosewood fingerboard with pearl dot inlay, rosewood bridge with white pins, metal logo plate mounted on peghead, 3 per side tuners. Available in Natural and Sunburst finishes. Mfd. 1958 to 1970.

	$375	$260	$220	$185	$150	$135	$120

In 1962, Natural finish with adjustable bridge became optionally available.

C70-CE — rounded cutaway classic style, spruce top, round soundhole, bound body, wooden inlay rosette, rosewood back/sides, mahogany neck, 19 fret rosewood fingerboard, rosewood tied bridge, rosewood peghead veneer with circles/star design, 3 per side chrome tuners with pearl buttons, piezo pickup, volume/3 band EQ. Available in Natural finish. Curr. mfr.

Mfr.'s Sug. Retail	$500	$400	$300	$250	$200	$180	$165	$150

DE LUXE — auditorium style, carved spruce top, f holes, multibound body, black/white diagonal purfling on top, figured maple back/sides, 5 piece figured maple neck, 14/20 fret bound rosewood fingerboard with pearl slotted diamond inlay, adjustable rosewood bridge/trapeze tailpiece, bound blackface peghead with pearl Masterbilt banner inlay, 3 per side gold die cast tuners. Available in Sunburst finish. Mfd. 1931 to 1955 in New York. In 1957, 70 instruments were produced in Gibson's Kalamazoo plant.

	$2,750	$1,925	$1,650	$1,375	$1,100	$990	$905

In 1934, floral fingerboard inlay, vine/logo peghead inlay replaced original items, raised white pickguard added.

In 1937, grand auditorium style body, redesigned black pickguard, bound f holes, resigned tailpiece replaced original items, cloud fingerboard inlay, script peghead logo replaced respective items.

In 1939, Frequensator tailpiece replaced respective item, Natural finish optionally available.

In 1949, cutaway version introduced.

FT De Luxe — similar to De Luxe, except has a flat top, round soundhole, tortoise pickguard, 3 stripe body/rosette. Available in Natural and Sunburst finishes. Mfd. 1939 to 1942.

	$1,750	$1,225	$1,050	$875	$700	$630	$575

EJ-200 — jumbo style, spruce top, round soundhole, tortoise pickguard with engraved flowers/pearl dot inlay, 3 stripe bound body/rosette, maple back/sides/neck, 14/20 fret bound pointed fingerboard with pearl crown inlay, rosewood mustache bridge with pearl block inlay, white black dot bridge pins, bound blackface peghead with pearl crown/logo inlay, 3 per side gold tuners. Available in Ebony, Natural and Vintage Sunburst finishes. Curr mfr.

Mfr.'s Sug. Retail	$700	$560	$420	$350	$280	$250	$230	$210

EMPEROR — grand auditorium style, carved spruce top, multibound f holes, raised bound tortoise pickguard, multibound body, maple back/sides/neck, 14/20 fret bound ebony fingerboard with pearl split block inlay, adjustable ebony bridge/logo engraved trapeze tailpiece, bound peghead with pearl vine/logo inlay, 3 per side gold tuners. Available in Cremona Brown Sunburst finish. Mfd. 1936 to 1955.

	$4,500	$3,150	$2,700	$2,250	$1,800	$1,620	$1,485

This model originally sold for $400.

In 1939, Frequensator tailpiece, pearl block/abalone triangle fingerboard, redesigned peghead replaced original items, Natural finish optionally available.

In 1950, rosewood fingerboard replaced original item.

Emperor Cutaway — similar to Emperor, except has single round cutaway. Mfd. 1950 to 1955 in New York. In 1957, 70 instruments were produced in Gibson's Kalamazoo plant.

	$4,500	$3,150	$2,700	$2,250	$1,800	$1,620	$1,485

EO-1 — rounded cutaway folk style, spruce top, round soundhole, 3 stripe bound body/rosette, mahogany back/sides/neck, 21 fret bound rosewood fingerboard with pearl dot inlay, rosewood bridge with white black dot pins, rosewood veneer on bound peghead with star/crescent inlay, 3 per side chrome tuners. Available in Natural finish. Mfd. 1992 to date.

Mfr.'s Sug. Retail	$630	$504	$378	$315	$250	$225	$205	$190

Grading	100%	98% MINT	95% EXC+	90% EXC	80% VG+	70% VG	60% G

1942 Epiphone Zenith
courtesy Robert Aponte

EO-2 — similar to EO-1, except has arched walnut top, oval soundhole, walnut back/sides, piezo pickup, volume/tone control.

Mfr.'s Sug. Retail	$700	$560	$420	$350	$280	$250	$230	$210

This model has a wooden butterfly inlay between the soundhole and bridge.

SPARTAN — grand auditorium style, carved spruce top, round soundhole, raised black pickguard, one stripe rosette, bound body, maple back/sides, mahogany neck, 14/20 fret bound rosewood fingerboard with pearl dot inlay, adjustable rosewood bridge/nickel trapeze tailpiece, bound peghead with pearl wedge/logo inlay, 3 per side nickel tuners. Available in Sunburst finish. Mfd. 1934 to 1950.

	$1,025	$720	$615	$510	$410	$370	$340

This model originally sold for $100.

In 1937, f holes, walnut back/sides, block fingerboard inlay, column/logo peghead inlay replaced original items.

In 1939, redesigned peghead replaced original item.

In 1941, white mahogany back/sides replaced respective item, Blonde finish optionally available.

TRIUMPH — grand auditorium style, carved spruce top, f holes, raised black pickguard, bound body, walnut back/sides, mahogany neck, 14/20 fret bound rosewood fingerboard with pearl diamond inlay, adjustable rosewood bridge/trapeze tailpiece, bound peghead with pearl Masterbilt banner/logo inlay, 3 per side nickel tuners. Available in Sunburst finish. Mfd. 1931 to 1948.

	$2,260	$1,580	$1,350	$1,130	$900	$810	$740

This instrument originally sold for $125.

In 1934, maple back/sides, unbound peghead with pearl fleur-de-lis/logo inlay replaced original items.

In 1935, redesigned peghead logo replaced respective item.

In 1937, redesigned body, bound pickguard, redesigned tailpiece replaced original items, bound peghead replaced respective item.

In 1939, Frequensator tailpiece replaced respective item.

In 1941, redesigned peghead replaced respective item, Blonde finish optionally available.

In 1949, redesigned pickguard with stylized E, column peghead inlay replaced respective items.

Triumph Regent — similar to Triumph, except has single round cutaway. Mfd. 1949 to 1958.

	$2,000	$1,400	$1,200	$1,000	$800	$720	$660

ZENITH — folk style, carved spruce top, f holes, raised black pickguard, bound body, maple back/sides, mahogany neck, 14/20 fret rosewood fingerboard with pearl dot inlay, adjustable rosewood bridge/trapeze tailpiece, blackface peghead, 3 per side single unit nickel tuners with plastic buttons. Available in Sunburst finish. Mfd. 1931 to 1958.

	$850	$595	$510	$425	$340	$305	$280

This instrument originally sold for $50.

In 1934, grand concert style body, walnut back/sides replaced original items, pearl wedge/logo peghead inlay added.

In 1937, grand concert style body, diamond/script logo peghead inlay replaced respective items.

In 1942, redesigned peghead replaced original item.

In 1954, pearl oval peghead inlay replaced respective item, Blonde finish optionally available.

PR Series

PR-5E — single sharp cutaway folk style, figured maple top, round soundhole, multi-bound body/rosette, mahogany back/sides/neck, 20 fret bound rosewood fingerboard with pearl diamond slot inlay, rosewood bridge with white black dot pins, blackface peghead with pearl crown/logo inlay, 3 per side gold tuners, piezo bridge pickup, 4 band EQ. Available in Natural and Vintage Sunburst finishes. Mfd. 1992 to date.

Mfr.'s Sug. Retail	$730	$584	$438	$365	$290	$260	$240	$220

PR-200 — dreadnought style, spruce top, round soundhole, tortoise pickguard, 2 stripe rosette, bound body, mahogany back/sides/neck, 14/20 fret rosewood fingerboard with pearl dot inlay, rosewood bridge with white pins, 3 per side chrome tuners. Available in Natural finish. Mfd. 1992 only.

	$170	$145	$120	$95	$85	$80	$75

PR-350 — dreadnought style, spruce top, round soundhole, tortoise pickguard with stylized "E", 3 stripe bound body/rosette, mahogany back/sides/neck, 14/20 fret rosewood fingerboard with pearl snowflake inlay, pearl crown/logo inlay, 3 per side chrome tuners. Available in Natural finish. Mfd. 1992 to date.

Mfr.'s Sug. Retail	$350	$280	$210	$175	$140	$125	$115	$105

In 1993, mahogany top replaced original item (PR-350M).

PR-350M-E — similar to PR-350, except has mahogany top, piezo bridge pickup. New 1993.

Mfr.'s Sug. Retail	$480	$384	$288	$240	$190	$170	$155	$145

PR-350S — similar to PR-350, except has spruce top. Mfd. 1992 only.

	$375	$260	$220	$185	$150	$135	$120

Add $10 for lefthanded version (PR-350SL).

Grading	100%	98% MINT	95% EXC+	90% EXC	80% VG+	70% VG	60% G

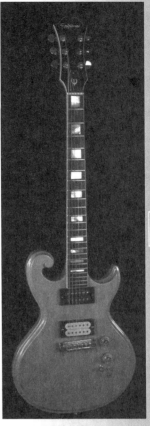

Epiphone solidbody electric
courtesy Michelle Oleck

PR-720S — dreadnought style, solid spruce top, round soundhole, tortoise shell pickguard, 3 stripe rosette, bound body, African ovankol back/sides, mahogany neck, 14/20 fret rosewood fingerboard with pearl diamond inlay, rosewood bridge with white pins, 3 per side chrome tuners. Available in Natural finish. Mfd. 1992 only.

	$310	$265	$220	$175	$160	$145	$135

PR-775S — dreadnought style, solid spruce top, round soundhole, tortoise shell pickguard, abalone bound body/rosette, rosewood back/sides, mahogany neck, 14/20 fret bound rosewood fingerboard with abalone pearl block/triangle inlay, rosewood bridge with white black dot pins, rosewood veneer on bound peghead with crescent/star/logo inlay, 3 per side chrome tuners. Available in Natural finish. Curr. mfr.

Mfr.'s Sug. Retail	$500	$400	$300	$250	$200	$180	$165	$150

This model also available in 12 string version (PR-775-12).

ELECTRIC

BROADWAY — single round cutaway hollow style, spruce top, f holes, raised bound black pickguard, bound body, maple back/sides/neck, 20 fret bound rosewood fingerboard with pearl block inlay, adjustable rosewood bridge/Frequensator tailpiece, bound blackface peghead with pearl column/logo inlay, 3 per side nickel tuners with plastic buttons, 2 single coil pickups, volume/tone control, 3 position switch. Available in Blonde, Cherry and Sunburst finishes. Mfd. 1968 to 1970.

	$1,600	$1,120	$960	$800	$640	$575	$530

In 1961, mini humbucker pickups replaced original items.

In 1963, tunomatic bridge replaced original item.

In 1967, Cherry finish became optionally available.

EM-1 — offset sweeping double cutaway basswood body, bolt-on maple neck, 24 fret rosewood fingerboard with pearl trapezoid inlay, standard vibrato, reverse peghead, 6 on one side tuners, gold hardware, humbucker/single coil/humbucker covered pickups, volume/tone control, 5 position/mini switches. Available in Black, Red and White finishes. Curr. mfr.

Mfr.'s Sug. Retail	$450	$360	$270	$225	$180	$160	$150	$135

EM-2 — similar to EM-1, except has double locking Floyd Rose vibrato.

Mfr.'s Sug. Retail	$550	$440	$330	$275	$220	$200	$180	$165

EMPEROR — single round cutaway hollow style, arched bound maple top, f holes, bound tortoise pickguard with stylized E logo and Joe Pass' signature, maple back/sides/neck, 20 fret bound rosewood fingerboard with pearl block inlay, adjustable rosewood bridge/stylized trapeze tailpiece, bound peghead with pearl vine/logo inlay, 3 per side tuners, gold hardware, 2 humbucker covered pickups with exposed screws, 2 volume/tone controls, 3 position switch. Available in Sunburst finish. Curr. mfr.

Mfr.'s Sug. Retail	$730	$584	$438	$365	$290	$260	$240	$220

This model has laminated body and neck wood.

EMPEROR REGENT — single round cutaway hollow style, arched bound spruce top, bound f holes, raised bound black pickguard with stylized E logo, maple back/sides/neck, 20 fret bound rosewood fingerboard with pearl block/abalone triangle inlay, adjustable rosewood bridge/Frequensator tailpiece, bound peghead with pearl vine/logo inlay, 3 per side tuners, gold hardware, humbucker covered pickup with exposed screws, pickguard mounted volume/tone controls. Available in Antique Sunburst, Natural and Vintage Cherry Sunburst finishes. New 1994.

Mfr.'s Sug. Retail	$1,000	$800	$600	$500	$400	$360	$330	$300

G-310 — double sharp cutaway mahogany body, black pickguard, mahogany neck, 22 fret rosewood fingerboard with pearl dot inlay, tunomatic bridge/stop tailpiece, black face peghead with pearl logo inlay, 3 per side tuners, chrome hardware, 2 humbucker covered pickups, 2 volume/tone controls, 3 position switch. Available in Black, Red and White finishes. Curr. mfr.

Mfr.'s Sug. Retail	$340	$272	$204	$170	$135	$125	$115	$105

G-400 — similar to G-310, except has smaller pickguard, exposed pickups.

Mfr.'s Sug. Retail	$450	$360	$270	$225	$180	$160	$150	$135

HOWARD ROBERTS STANDARD — single sharp cutaway hollow style, arched spruce top, bound oval soundhole/body, mahogany back/sides/neck, 20 fret bound rosewood fingerboard with pearl slotted block inlay, adjustable rosewood bridge/trapeze tailpiece, blackface peghead with pearl cloud/logo inlay, 3 per side tuners, nickel tuners, mini humbucker pickup, volume/tone control. Available in Cherry finish. Mfd. 1964 to 1970.

	$1,800	$1,260	$1,080	$900	$720	$650	$595

This instrument was co-designed by Howard Roberts.

In 1965, 3 stripe purfling was introduced, Natural and Sunburst finishes became optionally available.

In 1967, tunomatic/rosewood base bridge replaced original item.

In 1968, Natural and Sunburst finishes became standard, Cherry finish was discontinued.

LES PAUL CUSTOM — Les Paul style mahogany body, arched bound maple top, raised black pickguard, mahogany neck, 22 fret bound rosewood fingerboard with pearl block inlay, tunomatic bridge/stop tailpiece, bound peghead with pearl split diamond/logo inlay, 3 per side tuners, gold hardware, 2 humbucker pickups, 2 volume/tone controls, 3 position switch. Available in Black and White finishes. Mfd. 1991 to date.

Mfr.'s Sug. Retail	$730	$584	$438	$365	$290	$260	$240	$220

This is a Gibson authorized version of the Gibson Les Paul Custom.

Grading	100%	98% MINT	95% EXC+	90% EXC	80% VG+	70% VG	60% G

Les Paul Standard — similar to Les Paul Custom, except has figured maple top, white pickguard, trapezoid fingerboard inlay, unbound peghead with model name and logo inlay, pearl tuner buttons, chrome hardware. Available in Sunburst finish. Mfd. 1991 to date.

Mfr.'s Sug. Retail	$630	$504	$378	$315	$250	$225	$205	$190

This is a Gibson authorized version of the Gibson Les Paul Standard.

S-310 — offset double cutaway maple body, black pickguard, bolt-on maple neck, 22 fret maple fingerboard with black dot inlay, standard vibrato, 6 on one side tuners, chrome hardware, 3 single coil exposed pickups, volume/2 tone controls, 5 position switch. Available in Black, Red and White finishes. Mfd. 1991 to date.

Mfr.'s Sug. Retail	$290	$232	$174	$145	$115	$105	$95	$85

SHERATON — double rounded cutaway, arched bound maple top, f holes, raised bound tortoise pickguard with stylized E logo, maple back/sides, center block maple neck, 22 fret bound rosewood fingerboard with pearl/abalone block/triangle inlay, tunomatic bridge/stop tailpiece, bound peghead with pearl vine/logo inlay, 3 per side tuners, gold hardware, 2 humbucker covered pickups with exposed screws, 2 volume/tone controls, 3 position switch. Mfd. 1959 to 1970. Reintroduced 1993 to date.

1959-1970		$1,950	$1,670	$1,395	$1,115	$1,005	$920	$835
Curr. Mfr.'s Sug. Retail	$650	$520	$390	$325	$260	$235	$215	$195

This model has laminated body and neck wood.

Earlier models have either a Frequensator or gold plated Bigsby vibrato.

USA CORONET — offset double cutaway mahogany body, white pickguard, mahogany neck, 24 fret bound rosewood fingerboard with pearl block inlay, tunomatic bridge/stop tailpiece, black face reverse peghead with logo/USA inscription, 6 on one side tuners, gold hardware, single coil/humbucker exposed pickups, volume/tone control, 5 position switch control, active electronics. Available in Black, California Coral, Cherry, Pacific Blue, Sunburst, Sunset Yellow and White finishes. Mfd. 1991 to date.

Mfr.'s Sug. Retail	$900	$720	$540	$450	$360	$325	$300	$275

Add $100 for double locking Floyd Rose vibrato, black hardware.

This model is made in the USA.

USA PRO — offset double cutaway poplar body, bolt-on maple neck, 24 fret extended ebony fingerboard with offset pearl dot inlay, "pro" inscribed pearl block inlay at 24th fret, double locking Floyd Rose vibrato, black face peghead with logo/USA inscription, 6 on one side tuners, black hardware, single coil/humbucker exposed pickups, volume/tone control, 3 position switch. Available in Black, California Coral, Cherry, Pacific Blue, Sunburst, Sunset Yellow and White finishes. Mfd. 1991 to date.

Mfr.'s Sug. Retail	$600	$480	$360	$300	$240	$215	$195	$180

This model is made in the USA.

ELECTRIC BASS

ACCU BASS — offset double cutaway maple body, black pickguard with thumb rest, bolt-on maple neck, 20 fret maple fingerboard with black dot inlay, fixed bridge, body matching peghead with logo inscription, 4 on one side tuners, chrome hardware, P-style exposed pickup, volume/tone control. Available in Black, Red and White finishes. Curr. mfr.

Mfr.'s Sug. Retail	$370	$296	$222	$185	$150	$135	$120	$110

EBM-4 — offset sweeping double cutaway basswood body, bolt-on maple neck, 24 fret rosewood fingerboard with pearl offset dot inlay, fixed bridge, black face reverse peghead, 4 on one side tuners, chrome hardware, P-style/J-style covered pickups, 2 volume/tone controls. Available in Black, Red and White finishes. Mfd. 1992 to date.

Mfr.'s Sug. Retail	$580	$464	$348	$290	$230	$205	$190	$175

EBM-5 — similar to EBM-4, except has 5 strings, 5 on one side tuners.

Mfr.'s Sug. Retail	$620	$496	$372	$310	$250	$225	$205	$190

POWER BASS — offset double cutaway maple body, bolt-on maple neck, 20 fret rosewood fingerboard with pearl dot inlay, fixed bridge, body matching peghead with logo inscription, 4 on one side tuners, black hardware, P-style/J-style exposed pickups, 2 volume/1 tone controls. Available in Black, Red and White finishes. Curr. mfr.

Mfr.'s Sug. Retail	$420	$336	$252	$210	$170	$150	$135	$125

ROCK BASS — similar to Power Bass, except has black pickguard with thumb rest and chrome controls cover, chrome hardware, 2 P-style exposed pickups.

Mfr.'s Sug. Retail	$380	$304	$228	$190	$150	$135	$120	$110

ERLEWINE

Instruments built in Austin, Texas since 1973.

Luthier Mark Erlewine began building guitars and basses with his cousin Dan (noted repairman/columnist for **Guitar Player** magazine) in Ypsilanti, Michigan in 1970. Three years later, Mark moved to Austin, Texas and continued building guitars as well as performing repairs and custom work. Erlewine Custom Guitars is still based in Austin, Texas.

Erlewine still produces three models. In 1979 Erlewine and Billy Gibbons (ZZ Top) developed the Chiquita Travel Guitar (current list price $565), a 27" long playable guitar that will fit in airplane overhead storage. The Chiquita featues a solid hardwood body and one humbucker. Later, the two developed the Erlewine Automatic (contact for price) a cross between the best features of a Strat and a Les Paul. The Automatic is currently offered as a custom built guitar. In 1982, Erlewine developed the Lazer ($1,900), a headless guitar with a reverse tuning bridge and minimal body. The Lazer model is highly favored by Johnny Winter.

ERNIE BALL'S EARTHWOOD

Instruments produced in San Luis Obispo, California in the early to mid 1970s.

After finding great success with prepackaged string sets and custom gauges, Ernie Ball founded the Earthwood company to produce a four string acoustic bass guitar. George Fullerton built the prototype, as well as helping with other work before moving to Leo Fender's CLF Research company in 1974. Earthwood offered both the acoustic bass guitar and a lacquer finished "solid body" guitar with large sound chambers in 1972, but production was short lived (through February 1973). In April of 1975, bass guitar operations resumed on a limited edition basis.

ERNIE BALL/MUSIC MAN

Instruments produced in San Luis Obispo, California under the Ernie Ball/Music Man trademark since 1984. Earlier Music Man models were produced in Fullerton, California between 1976 and 1979. Current manufacture and distribution by Ernie Ball/Music Man.

Ernie Ball was born in Cleveland, Ohio in 1930. The American Depression pressured the family to move to Santa Monica, California in 1932. By age nine Ball was practicing guitar, and this interest in music led to a twenty year career as a professional steel guitarist, music teacher, and retailer.

During the 1950s, the steel guitar was a popular instrument to play - but there was some difficulty in obtaining a matched set of strings. Early electric guitar players were also turning to "mixing" sets of strings to get the desired string gauges, but at a waste of the other strings. Ball found great success in marketing prepackaged string sets in custom gauges, and the initial mail order business expanded into a nationwide wholesale operation of strings, picks and other accessories.

In the early 1970s Ball founded the Earthwood company, and produced both electric guitars and acoustic basses for a number of years. After some production disagreements between the original Music Man company and Leo Fender's CLF Research in 1978 (See MUSIC MAN), Fender stopped building instruments exclusively for Music Man, and began designs and production for his final company (G & L). In 1984 Ernie Ball acquired the trademark and design rights to Music Man. Ball set up production in the factory that previously had built the Earthwood instruments. Ernie Ball/Music Man instruments have been in production at that location since 1984.

The first instruments that returned to production were Music Man basses, due to their popularity in the market. By 1987, the first guitar by Ernie Ball/Music Man was released. The Silhouette model was then followed by the Steve Morse model later in that year.

Since the Ernie Ball acquisition of Music Man, the first two digits in the serial number will indicate the date of construction. Ernie Ball/Music Man has retained the high level of quality from original Fender/CLF designs, and has introduced some innovative designs to their current line.

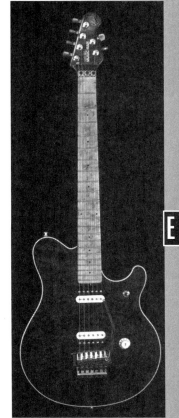

Ernie Ball/Music Man EVH
courtesy Cassi International

ELECTRIC

Grading	100%	98% MINT	95% EXC+	90% EXC	80% VG+	70% VG	60% G

ALBERT LEE — angular offset double cutaway ash body, white lam pickguard, bolt-on maple neck, 22 fret maple fingerboard with black dot inlay, strings thru fixed bridge, 4/2 per side Schaller tuners, chrome hardware, 3 single coil Seymour Duncan pickups, volume/tone control, 5 position switch. Available in Translucent Pinkburst finish. New 1994.

	100%	98%	95%	90%	80%	70%	60%
Mfr.'s Sug. Retail	$1,400	$1,120	$840	$700	$560	$505	$460	$420

The Albert Lee model was designed in conjunction with the artist.

EDWARD VAN HALEN — single cutaway basswood body, bound figured maple top, bolt-on maple neck, 22 fret maple fingerboard with black dot inlay, strings thru bridge, 4/2 per side Schaller tuners with pearl buttons, chrome hardware, 2 humbucker DiMarzio pickups, volume control, 3 position switch. Available in Translucent Gold, Translucent Purple and Translucent Red finishes. Disc. 1995.

	100%	98%	95%	90%	80%	70%	60%
	$1,145	$975	$800	$640	$575	$530	$480

Last Mfg.'s Sug. Retail was $1,650.

Edward Van Halen Tremolo — similar to Edward Van Halen, except has Floyd Rose double locking vibrato. Available in Black, Metallic Gold, Natural, Sunburst, Transparent Black, Transparent Blue, Transparent Gold, Transparent Pink, Transparent Purple and Transparent Red finishes.

	100%	98%	95%	90%	80%	70%	60%
	$2,225	$1,850	$1,275	$940	$730	$675	$575

Last Mfg.'s Sug. Retail was $1,750.

LUKE — offset double cutaway alder body, bolt-on maple neck, 22 fret rosewood fingerboard with pearl dot inlay, double locking vibrato, 4/2 per side Schaller tuners, chrome hardware, 2 single coil/1 humbucker EMG pickups, volume control, 5 position switch, active electronics. Available in Pearl Blue and Pearl Red finishes. New 1994.

	100%	98%	95%	90%	80%	70%	60%
Mfr.'s Sug. Retail	$1,600	$1,280	$960	$800	$640	$575	$530	$480

The Luke model is the signature guitar from artist Steve Lukather (Toto).

"I get to buy and sell guitars for a living. I go to shows and look at guitars. I talk to people and talk about guitars. And I get paid for it! I would do it for nothing."
—*L. Acunto on Samuel Ash*

TCG, July/Aug. 1994

Grading		100%	98% MINT	95% EXC+	90% EXC	80% VG+	70% VG	60% G

SILHOUETTE — offset double cutaway alder, ash or poplar body, white pickguard, bolt-on maple neck, 24 fret maple fingerboard with black dot inlay, strings thru bridge, 4/2 per side Schaller tuners, chrome hardware, 3 single coil DiMarzio pickups, volume/tone control, 5 position switch. Available in Black, Natural, Sunburst, Transparent Blueburst, Transparent Teal, Transparent Red and White finishes. Mfg 1987 to current.

Mfr.'s Sug. Retail	$1,050	$787	$525	$485	$370	$335	$305	$280

    The Silhouette was the first Ernie Ball/Music Man production guitar. Designed by Dudley Gimpel, and developed in part by guitarist Alvin Lee, this design was influenced by earlier CLF Research models but a number of modern refinements added.

    This model also available with 2 humbucker pickup with 3 position switch.
    Add $50 for 2 single coil/1 humbucker pickups.
    Add $75 for humbucker/single coil/humbucker pickups.

Silhouette Trem — similar to Silhouette, except has double locking vibrato.

Mfr.'s Sug. Retail	$1,150	$862	$575	$565	$455	$405	$370	$335

    This model also available with 2 humbucker pickup with 3 position switch.
    Add $50 for 2 single coil/1 humbucker pickups.
    Add $75 for humbucker/single coil/humbucker pickups.

STEVE MORSE — offset double cutaway poplar body, black pickguard, bolt-on maple neck, 22 fret rosewood fingerboard with pearl dot inlay, tunomatic bridge/stop tailpiece, 4/2 per side Schaller tuners, chrome hardware, humbucker/2 single coil/humbucker DiMarzio pickups, volume/tone control, 3 position and 2 mini switches. Available in Transparent Blueburst finish. Curr. mfr.

Mfr.'s Sug. Retail	$1,500	$1,200	$900	$750	$600	$540	$495	$450

Steve Morse Trem — similar to Steve Morse, except has double locking vibrato.

Mfr.'s Sug. Retail	$1,650	$1,320	$990	$825	$660	$595	$545	$495

ELECTRIC BASS

SILHOUETTE BASS GUITAR — offset double cutaway poplar body, bolt-on maple neck, 22 fret maple fingerboard with black dot inlay, strings thru bridge, 4/2 per side Schaller tuners, chrome hardware, 2 humbucker DiMarzio pickups, volume/tone/series-parallel control, 5 way position switch. Available in Black finish. Curr. mfr.

Mfr.'s Sug. Retail	$1,800	$1,440	$1,080	$900	$720	$650	$595	$540

STERLING — offset double cutaway alder body, white lam pickguard, bolt-on maple neck, 22 fret rosewood fingerboard with pearl dot inlay, fixed bridge, 3/1 per side Schaller tuners, chrome hardware, humbucker Ernie Ball pickup, volume/treble/mid/bass control, 3 position switch, active electronics. Available in Black, Pearl Blue, Sunburst and Translucent Red finishes. New 1994.

Mfr.'s Sug. Retail	$1,300	$1,040	$780	$650	$520	$470	$430	$390

STING RAY — offset double cutaway alder, ash or poplar body, white pickguard, bolt-on maple neck, 21 fret maple fingerboard with black dot inlay, fixed bridge, 3/1 per side Schaller tuners, chrome hardware, humbucker alnico pickup, volume/treble/bass control, active electronics. Available in Black, Natural, Sunburst, Transparent Blueburst, Transparent Teal, Transparent Red and White finishes. Curr. mfr.

Mfr.'s Sug. Retail	$1,200	$900	$600	$570	$440	$395	$365	$330

    Add $50 for treble/mid/bass control.

    This model also available with rosewood fingerboard with pearl dot inlay or pau ferro fretless fingerboard.

Sting Ray 5 — similar to Sting Ray, except has 5 strings, 4/1 per side tuners, treble/mid/bass control, 3 position switch.

Mfr.'s Sug. Retail	$1,600	$1,200	$800	$770	$600	$540	$495	$450

EROS

Instruments were produced in Japan between the early 1970s through the early 1980s.

The EROS trademark is the brandname of a UK importer. These guitars were generally entry level copies of American designs.

(Source: Tony Bacon and Paul Day, The Guru's Guitar Guide)

ESP

Instruments manufactured in Japan from the early 1980s to current. Production currently takes place at the ESP Factory 21 in Japan. Distribution in the U.S. market by the E S P Guitar Company, Inc., of Hollywood, California.

E S P was originally known as a source for high quality guitar components and replacement parts. In the early 1980s the company then focused on building Fender- and Gibson-derived designs, evolving to high quality "superstrat" models.

The ESP Guitar Company, Inc. was formed in 1985 as the USA distribution point, and custom work shop, for ESP guitars. These instruments have always been offered as custom option outfitted equipment, making the following descriptions the base models.

Grading	100%	98% MINT	95% EXC+	90% EXC	80% VG+	70% VG	60% G

ELECTRIC

In 1992, standard features were as follows: Transparent finishes have gold hardware, all other finishes have black hardware.

ECLIPSE CUSTOM — single cutaway bound mahogany body, bolt-on maple neck, 22 fret ebony fingerboard with pearl dot inlay, strings thru bridge, blackface peghead with screened logo, 6 on one side tuners, black hardware, 2 exposed humbucker pickups, volume/tone controls, 3 position switch. Available in Baby Blue, Black, Bubblegum Pink, Candy Apple Blue, Fiesta Red, Metallic Blue, Metallic Red, Midnight Black, Mint Green, Snow White, Transparent Cherry Red and Transparent Blue finishes. Mfd. 1986 to 1987.

	$805	$690	$575	$460	$415	$380	$345

Last Mfr.'s Sug. Retail was $1,150.

In 1987, Cherry Sunburst, Pearl Gold, Pearl Pink, Pearl White and Turquoise finishes were introduced. Thru body maple neck, bound fingerboard, offset pearl block fingerboard inlay, redesigned bound peghead, chrome hardware replaced original items. Baby Blue, Bubblegum Pink, Candy Apple Blue, Fiesta Red, Metallic Blue, Metallic Red, Mint Green, Snow White, Transparent Cherry Red and Transparent Blue finishes were discontinued.

Eclipse Custom T — similar to Eclipse Custom, except has thru body maple neck, offset pearl block fingerboard inlay/logo block inlay at 12th fret, double locking vibrato, body matching bound peghead. Available in Black, Cherry Sunburst, Pearl Gold, Pearl Pink, Pearl White and Turquoise finishes. Mfd. 1987 to 1988.

	$875	$750	$625	$500	$450	$415	$375

Last Mfr.'s Sug. Retail was $1,750.

In 1988, Black, Cherry Sunburst, Pearl Gold and Pearl Pink finishes were discontinued, Burgundy Mist, Brite Red, Midnight Black and Pearl Silver finishes were introduced.

Eclipse Deluxe — similar to Eclipse Custom, except has standard vibrato. Mfd. 1986 to 1988.

	$725	$620	$520	$415	$375	$340	$310

Last Mfr.'s Sug. Retail was $1,450.

In 1988, Black, Cherry Sunburst, Pearl Gold and Pearl Pink finishes were discontinued, double locking vibrato replaced original item, Burgundy Mist, Brite Red, Midnight Black and Pearl Silver finishes were introduced.

HORIZON — offset double cutaway bound ash body, bolt-on maple neck, 22 fret maple fingerboard with black dot inlay, standard vibrato, maple peghead with screened logo, 6 on one side tuners, chrome hardware, 3 single coil pickups, 1 volume/2 tone controls, 5 position switch. Available in Baby Blue, Black, Bubblegum Pink, Candy Apple Blue, Fiesta Red, Metallic Blue, Metallic Red, Midnight Black, Mint Green, Snow white, Transparent Cherry Red and Transparent Blue finishes. Disc. 1986.

	$400	$340	$285	$230	$205	$190	$170

Horizon Custom — offset double cutaway arched top ash body, thru-body maple neck, 24 fret bound ebony fingerboard, double locking vibrato, bound peghead, 6 on one side tuners, chrome hardware, single coil/humbucker EMG pickups, 1 volume/2 tone controls, 3 position switch. Available in Black, Fiesta Red, Magenta, Pearl Rose and Pearl White finishes. Mfd. 1987 to 1993.

	$1,100	$940	$785	$630	$565	$515	$470

Last Mfr.'s Sug. Retail was $2,195.

In 1988, Brite Red, Burgundy Mist, Gunmetal Blue and Midnight Black were introduced, Fiesta Red and Pearl Rose finishes were discontinued.

In 1990, Candy Apple Red and Dark Metallic Blue finishes were introduced, black hardware replaced original item, Brite Red, Burgundy Mist, Magenta and Midnight Blue finishes were discontinued.

In 1991, Dark Metallic Purple finish was introduced, bound fingerboard with 12th fret pearl logo block inlay, redesigned peghead, 3 per side tuners replaced original items.

In 1992, Metallic Green finish was introduced, Dark Metallic Blue finish was discontinued.

Horizon Deluxe — similar to Horizon Custom, except has bolt-on neck, 22 fret rosewood fingerboard with pearl dot inlay, gold hardware. Available in Black, Brite Red, Burgundy Mist, Gunmetal Blue, Magenta and Pearl White finishes. Mfd. 1989 to 1992.

	$850	$730	$610	$485	$435	$400	$365

Last Mfr.'s Sug. Retail was $1,695.

In 1990, Candy Apple Red and Dark Metallic Blue finishes were introduced, black hardware replaced original item, Brite Red, Burgundy Mist and Magenta were discontinued.

In 1991, Transparent Blue, Transparent Purple and Transparent Red finishes were introduced, bound fingerboard with 12th fret pearl logo block inlay, tunomatic bridge/stop tailpiece, redesigned peghead, 3 per side tuners replaced original items, Candy Apple Red, Dark Metallic Blue and Gunmetal Blue finishes was discontinued.

In 1992, Transparent Green finish was introduced, 24 fret fingerboard replaced original item, Cherry Sunburst finish was discontinued.

Horizon Deluxe T — similar to Horizon Custom, except has bolt-on neck, 24 fret bound rosewood fingerboard with offset pearl dot inlay/12th fret block logo inlay, black hardware. Available in Black, Pearl White, Transparent Blue, Transparent Green, Transparent Purple and Transparent Red finishes. Mfd. 1992 to 1993.

	$950	$815	$680	$545	$490	$445	$405

Last Mfr.'s Sug. Retail was $1,895.

Grading	100%	98% MINT	95% EXC+	90% EXC	80% VG+	70% VG	60% G

HORIZON CLASSIC — offset double cutaway carved mahogany body, mahogany neck, pearl dot fingerboard inlay/12th fret logo block inlay. Mfd. 1993 to 1995.

		$1,955	$1,675	$1,395	$1,115	$1,005	$920	$835

Last Mfr.'s Sug. Retail was $2,795.

Horizon Classic instruments were all handcrafted in the USA to customer specifications. ESP currently maintains a custom order workshop that can build instruments to customer specifications.

The Horizon Classic was also offered with a mahogany body and figured top with matching peghead for an additional cost of $700.

HYBRID — offset double cutaway alder body, black pickguard, metal control plate, maple neck, 22 fret rosewood fingerboard with pearl dot inlay, strings thru fixed bridge, 6 on one side tuners, chrome hardware, humbucker ESP pickup, volume/tone controls. Available in Black, Burgundy Mist, Fiesta Red, Lake Placid Blue, Metallic Gold, Pearl White, Olympic White and Turquoise finishes. Mfd 1993 to date.

Mfr.'s Sug. Retail	$895	$671	$447	$445	$360	$325	$300	$275

Hybrid 2 — similar to Hybrid, except has single coil/humbucker pickups, 3 position switch.

Mfr.'s Sug. Retail	$1,095	$821	$547	$545	$435	$395	$360	$330

HYBRID I — offset double cutaway hardwood body, metal control plate, bolt-on maple neck, 22 fret rosewood fingerboard with pearl dot inlay, standard vibrato, 6 on one side tuners, chrome hardware, 2 single coil pickups, volume/tone control, 3 position switch. Available in Baby Blue, Black, Blonde, Fiesta Red, Lake Placid Blue, Metallic Blue, Metallic Red, Natural, Olympic White, Salmon Pink, Two Tone Sunburst and Three Tone Sunburst finishes. Disc. 1986.

	$375	$320	$270	$215	$195	$180	$160

Hybrid II — similar to Hybrid I, except has 3 single coil pickups. Disc. 1986.

	$375	$320	$270	$215	$195	$180	$160

M-I CUSTOM — offset double cutaway alder body, thru body maple neck, 24 fret bound rosewood fingerboard with pearl offset block inlay/logo block inlay at 12th fret, double locking vibrato, body matching bound peghead with screened logo, 6 on one side tuners, chrome hardware, humbucker ESP pickup, volume control, coil tap switch. Available in Black, Fiesta Red, Snow White and Turquoise finishes. Mfd. 1987 to 1994.

	$395	$340	$285	$225	$205	$185	$170

In 1988, Magenta, Metallic Black, Midnight Black and Pearl Yellow were introduced, Bright Yellow and Cherry Sunburst finishes were discontinued.

In 1989, Dark Metallic Blue, Candy Apple Red and Pearl White finishes were introduced, Fiesta Red, Metallic Black, Midnight Black, Snow White and Turquoise finishes were discontinued.

M-I Deluxe — offset double cutaway alder body, black pickguard, bolt-on maple neck, 22 fret maple fingerboard with black dot inlay, double locking vibrato, 6 on one side tuners, chrome hardware, 2 single coil/1 humbucker ESP pickups, 1 volume/2 tone controls, 5 position switch. Available in Bright Yellow, Candy Apple Red, Cherry Sunburst, Dark Metallic Blue, Pearl Pink Sunburst and Pearl White finishes. Mfd. 1987 to 1989.

	$350	$300	$250	$200	$180	$165	$150

This model had rosewood fingerboard with pearl dot inlay optionally available.

In 1988, Magenta, Metallic Black, Midnight Black and Pearl Yellow were introduced, Bright Yellow and Cherry Sunburst finishes were discontinued.

M-I Standard — offset double cutaway hardwood body, bolt-on maple neck, 22 fret rosewood fingerboard with pearl dot inlay, standard vibrato, 6 on one side tuners, chrome hardware, humbucker ESP pickup, volume/tone controls. Available in Bright Yellow, Candy Apple Red, Cherry Sunburst, Dark Metallic Blue, Pearl Pink Sunburst and Pearl White finishes. Mfd. 1987 to 1990.

	$325	$280	$235	$190	$170	$155	$140

In 1988, Magenta, Metallic Black, Midnight Black and Pearl Yellow were introduced, Bright Yellow and Cherry Sunburst finishes were discontinued.

In 1990, Black and Snow White finishes were introduced, black hardware, single coil/humbucker pickups replaced original items, Dark Metallic Blue, Magenta, Metallic Black, Midnight Black, Pearl Pink Sunburst, Pearl White and Pearl Yellow were discontinued.

M-II — offset double cutaway hardwood body, bolt-on maple neck, 22 fret maple fingerboard with black offset dot inlay, double locking vibrato, reverse blackface peghead with screened logo, 6 on one side tuners, black hardware, single coil/humbucker ESP pickups, volume control, 3 position switch. Available in Black, Brite Red and Snow White finishes. Mfd. 1989 to 1994.

	$500	$430	$360	$285	$260	$235	$215

This model had rosewood fingerboard with pearl offset dot inlay optionally available.

In 1990, Candy Apple Red finish was introduced, rosewood fingerboard with pearl dot inlay replaced original item, Brite Red finish was discontinued.

"Even in the early years, once I started to know what good guitars were all about, I began to develop an appreciation for them. Before long I was as much interested in the instruments as in the music - maybe even more so."
—A. Ingram on Mark Campbell
TCG, July/Aug. 1994

M-II Custom — offset double cutaway alder body, thru body maple neck, 24 fret bound rosewood fingerboard with pearl offset block inlay/logo block inlay at 12th fret, double locking vibrato, reverse bound peghead, 6 on one side tuners, black hardware, single coil/humbucker ESP pickups, volume control, 3 position switch. Available in Black, Candy Apple Red, Gunmetal Blue, Magenta and Pearl White finishes. Mfd. 1990 to 1994.

	100%	98%	95%	90%	80%	70%	60%
	$1,465	$1,255	$1,045	$840	$755	$685	$625

Last Mfr.'s Sug. Retail was $2,095.

In 1991, Dark Metallic Blue and Dark Metallic Purple finishes were introduced, Magenta finish was discontinued.

In 1992, Metallic Green finish was introduced, Dark Metallic Blue was discontinued.

In 1993, pearl dot fingerboard inlay replaced original item.

M-II Deluxe — similar to M-II Custom, except has bolt-on neck, unbound fingerboard with pearl dot inlay/12th fret logo block inlay, unbound peghead. Available in Black, Pearl White, Transparent Blue, Transparent Green, Transparent Purple and Transparent Red finishes. Mfd. 1992 to date.

Mfr.'s Sug. Retail	$1,495	$1,121	$747	$690	$545	$465	$425	$385

This model has maple fingerboard optionally available.

M-III — offset double cutaway hardwood body, bolt-on maple neck, 22 fret rosewood fingerboard with pearl offset block dot inlay, double locking vibrato, blackface peghead with screened logo, 6 on one side tuners, black hardware, 2 single coil/1 humbucker ESP pickups, volume control, 5 position switch. Available in Black, Brite Red and Snow White finishes. Mfd. 1989 to 1994.

	100%	98%	95%	90%	80%	70%	60%
	$500	$430	$360	$285	$260	$235	$215

This model had maple fingerboard with black offset dot inlay optionally available.

MAVERICK — offset double cutaway hardwood body, bolt-on maple neck, 24 fret maple fingerboard with black offset dot inlay, double locking vibrato, blackface peghead with screened logo, 6 on one side tuners, black hardware, single coil/humbucker ESP pickups, volume control, 3 position switch. Available in Black, Brite Yellow, Candy Apple Red, Dark Metallic Blue, Fluorescent Pink and Snow White finishes. Mfd. 1989 to 1991.

	100%	98%	95%	90%	80%	70%	60%
	$385	$330	$275	$220	$200	$180	$165

This model had rosewood fingerboard with pearl dot inlay optionally available.

In 1990, Pearl White and Turquoise finishes were introduced, Brite Yellow, Fluorescent Pink and Snow White finishes were discontinued.

In 1991, Dark Metallic Purple and Gunmetal Blue finishes were introduced, Turquoise finish was discontinued.

Maverick Deluxe-1988 — offset double cutaway ash body, bolt-on maple neck, 24 fret rosewood fingerboard with pearl dot inlay, double locking vibrato, blackface peghead with screened logo, 6 on one side tuners, black hardware, 2 humbucker ESP pickups, volume control, 3 position switch. Available in Brite Red, Brite Yellow, Fluorescent Pink, Fluorescent White, Gunmetal Blue and Midnight Black finishes. Mfd. 1988 only.

	100%	98%	95%	90%	80%	70%	60%
	$400	$340	$285	$230	$205	$190	$170

The neck position pickup was a stacked humbucker.

Maverick Deluxe-1992 — offset double cutaway ash body, pearloid pickguard, bolt-on maple neck, 24 fret rosewood fingerboard with pearl dot inlay/12th fret logo block inlay, double locking vibrato, maple peghead with screened logo, 6 on one side tuners, black hardware, 2 single coil/1 humbucker ESP pickups, volume/tone controls, 5 position switch. Available in Black, Pearl White, Transparent Blue, Transparent Green, Transparent Purple and Transparent Red finishes. Mfd. 1992 only.

	100%	98%	95%	90%	80%	70%	60%
	$750	$640	$535	$430	$390	$355	$325

Last Mfr.'s Sug. Retail was $1,495.

Metal Series

METAL I — offset double cutaway alder body, bolt-on maple neck, 22 fret rosewood fingerboard with pearl dot inlay, standard vibrato, maple peghead with screened logo, 6 on one side tuners, gold hardware, exposed humbucker pickup, volume/tone control. Available in Pearl Blue, Pearl Green, Pearl Pink, Pearl White and Metallic Purple. Mfd. 1986 only.

	100%	98%	95%	90%	80%	70%	60%
	$350	$300	$250	$200	$180	$165	$150

METAL II — similar to Metal I, except has single horn cutaway V shape body. Mfd. 1986 only.

	100%	98%	95%	90%	80%	70%	60%
	$300	$260	$215	$175	$155	$140	$130

METAL III — reverse offset double cutaway asymmetrical alder body, bolt-on maple neck, 22 fret maple fingerboard with black dot inlay, standard vibrato, maple peghead with screened logo, 6 on one side tuners, gold hardware, exposed humbucker pickup, volume control. Mfd. 1986 only.

	100%	98%	95%	90%	80%	70%	60%
	$325	$280	$235	$190	$170	$155	$140

MIRAGE — offset double cutaway hardwood body, bolt-on maple neck, 22 fret bound rosewood fingerboard with pearl offset block inlay/logo block inlay at 12th fret, double locking vibrato, bound blackface peghead with screened logo, 6 on one side tuners, black hardware, 2 single coil/1 humbucker ESP pickups, volume/tone control, 5 position switch. Available in Black, Candy Apple Red, Dark Metallic Blue, Dark Metallic Purple, Gunmetal Blue and Pearl White finishes. Mfd. 1991 only.

	100%	98%	95%	90%	80%	70%	60%
	$1,185	$1,015	$845	$675	$605	$555	$505

Last Mfr.'s Sug. Retail was $1,695.

Mirage Custom — offset double cutaway mahogany body, bolt-on maple neck, 22 fret rosewood fingerboard with pearl dot inlay, strings thru bridge, blackface peghead with screened logo, 6 on one side tuners, black hardware, 2 exposed humbucker pickups, volume/tone controls, 3 position switch. Available in Baby Blue, Black, Bubblegum Pink, Candy Apple Blue, Fiesta Red, Metallic Blue, Metallic Red, Midnight Black, Mint Green, Snow White, Transparent Cherry Red and Transparent Blue finishes. Mfd. 1986 to 1990.

$450	$385	$320	$255	$230	$210	$195

In 1987, Pearl Gold, Pearl Pink, Pearl White and Turquoise finishes were introduced, thru body maple neck, 24 fret bound ebony fingerboard with offset pearl block inlay/logo block inlay at 12th fret, double locking vibrato, redesigned bound peghead, 2 single coil/1 humbucker pickups, 5 position switch replaced original items, Baby Blue, Bubblegum Pink, Candy Apple Blue, Metallic Blue, Metallic Red, Mint Green, Snow White, Transparent Cherry Red and Transparent Blue finishes were discontinued.

In 1988, Brite Red, Gunmetal Blue, Magenta, Mediterranean Blue and Pearl Silver finishes were introduced, Fiesta Red, Pearl Gold and Pearl Pink finishes were discontinued.

In 1989, Candy Apple Red and Lake Placid Blue finishes were introduced, 2 stacked coil/1 humbuckers replaced respective item, Brite Red, Mediterranean Blue and Pearl Silver finishes were discontinued.

In 1990, Magenta and Turquoise finishes were discontinued.

Mirage Deluxe — similar to Mirage Custom, except has bound rosewood fingerboard with pearl offset block inlay, double locking vibrato, stacked coil/humbucker pickups. Available in Black, Fiesta Red, Pearl Gold, Pearl Pink, Pearl White and Turquoise finishes. Mfd. 1987 to 1990.

$425	$365	$305	$240	$220	$200	$180

In 1988, Brite Red, Gunmetal Blue, Magenta, Mediterranean Blue and Pearl Silver finishes were introduced, Fiesta Red, Pearl Gold and Pearl Pink finishes were discontinued.

In 1989, Candy Apple Red and Lake Placid Blue finishes were introduced, Brite Red, Mediterranean Blue and Pearl Silver finishes were discontinued.

In 1990, Magenta and Turquoise finishes were discontinued.

Mirage Standard — offset double cutaway mahogany body, bolt-on maple neck, 22 fret rosewood fingerboard with pearl dot inlay, strings thru bridge, blackface peghead with screened logo, 6 on one side tuners, black hardware, exposed humbucker pickup, volume/tone controls. Available in Baby Blue, Black, Bubblegum Pink, Candy Apple Blue, Fiesta Red, Metallic Blue, Metallic Red, Midnight Black, Mint Green, Snow White, Transparent Cherry Red and Transparent Blue finishes. Mfd. 1986 only.

$375	$320	$270	$215	$195	$180	$160

PHOENIX — asymmetrical hourglass style mahogany body, white pickguard, thru body mahogany neck, 22 fret bound rosewood fingerboard with pearl dot inlay, double locking vibrato, bound blackface peghead with screened logo, 6 on one side tuners, black hardware, 2 covered humbucker pickups, 2 volume/2 tone controls, 3 position switch. Available in Black, Fiesta Red, Snow White and Turquoise finishes. Mfd. 1987 only.

$545	$470	$390	$315	$280	$260	$235

Last Mfr.'s Sug. Retail was $1,550.

S-454 — offset double cutaway alder body, white pickguard, bolt-on maple neck, 22 fret maple fingerboard with black dot inlay, standard vibrato, maple peghead with screened logo, 6 on one side tuners, chrome hardware, 3 single coil exposed pickups, 1 volume/2 tone controls, 5 position switch. Available in Baby Blue, Black, Blonde, Fiesta Red, Lake Placid Blue, Metallic Blue, Metallic Red, Natural, Olympic White, Salmon Pink, Two Tone Sunburst and Three Tone Sunburst finishes. Mfd. 1986 to 1987.

$350	$300	$250	$200	$180	$165	$150

S-465 — similar to S-454, except has rosewood fingerboard with pearl dot inlay. Mfd. 1986 to 1987.

$350	$300	$250	$200	$180	$165	$150

S-487 DELUXE — offset double cutaway hardwood body, black lam pickguard, bolt-on maple neck, 22 fret rosewood fingerboard with pearl dot inlay, double locking vibrato, maple peghead with screened logo, 6 on one side tuners, chrome hardware, 3 single coil exposed pickups, 1 volume/2 tone controls, 5 position switch. Available in Black, Brite Red, Burgundy Mist, Cherry Sunburst, Mediterranean Blue and Snow White finishes. Mfd. 1987 to 1988.

$445	$380	$320	$255	$230	$210	$190

S-487 Standard — similar to S-487 Deluxe, except has black pickguard, standard vibrato, black hardware. Mfd. 1987 to 1988.

$385	$330	$275	$220	$200	$180	$165

This model had maple fingerboard with black dot inlay optionally available.

S-500 — offset double cutaway ash body, bolt-on maple neck, 22 fret rosewood fingerboard with pearl dot inlay, vintage vibrato, graphite nut, 6 on one side locking Sperzel tuners, gold hardware, 2 single coil/1 humbucker ESP pickups, volume/tone control, 5 position switch. Available in Black, Pearl White, Transparent Blue, Transparent Green, Transparent Purple and Transparent Red finishes. Mfd. 1991 to 1993.

$1,045	$895	$750	$600	$540	$495	$450

Last Mfr.'s Sug. Retail was $1,495.

S-500 T — similar to S-500, except has double locking vibrato. Mfd. 1992 only.

$850	$730	$610	$485	$435	$400	$365

Last Mfr.'s Sug. Retail was $1,695.

Grading	100%	98% MINT	95% EXC+	90% EXC	80% VG+	70% VG	60% G

T-454 — single cutaway alder body, white pickguard, metal control plate, bolt-on maple neck, 22 fret maple fingerboard with black dot inlay, strings thru bridge, maple peghead with screened logo, 6 on one side tuners, chrome hardware, 2 single coil pickups, volume/tone controls, 3 position switch. Available in Baby Blue, Black, Blonde, Fiesta Red, Lake Placid Blue, Metallic Blue, Metallic Red, Natural, Olympic White, Salmon Pink, Two Tone Sunburst and Three Tone Sunburst finishes. Mfd. 1986 to 1987.

	$325	$280	$235	$190	$170	$155	$140

T-463 — similar to T-454, except has bound body, rosewood fingerboard with pearl dot inlay. Mfd. 1986 to 1987.

	$325	$280	$235	$190	$170	$155	$140

In 1987, renamed T-465.

THE MIRAGE — offset double cutaway ash body, maple neck, 22 fret rosewood fingerboard with pearl dot inlay/logo block inlay at 12th fret, double locking vibrato, reverse peghead, 6 on one side tuners, black hardware, 2 single coil/1 humbucker ESP pickups, volume/tone control, 5 position switch. Available in Black, Natural, Transparent Blue, Transparent Green, Transparent Purple and Transparent Red finishes. New 1994.

Mfr.'s Sug. Retail	$1,495	$1,196	$897	$750	$600	$540	$495	$450

TRADITIONAL — offset double cutaway alder body, bolt-on maple neck, 21 fret rosewood fingerboard with pearl dot inlay, standard vibrato, maple peghead with screened logo, 6 on one side tuners, chrome hardware, 3 single coil ESP pickups, 1 volume/2 tone controls, 5 position switch. Available in Black, Candy Apple Red, Lake Placid Blue, Olympic White, Two Tone Sunburst and Three Tone Sunburst finishes. Mfd. 1989 to 1990.

	$905	$775	$645	$515	$465	$425	$385

Last Mfr.'s Sug. Retail was $1,295.

This model had maple fingerboard with black dot inlay optionally available.

Traditional Reissue — similar to Traditional, except has pearloid pickguard, 22 fret fingerboard with pearl dot inlay, locking tuners. Available in Black, Burgundy, Candy Apple Red, Gunmetal Blue, Metallic Blue, Metallic Purple, Pearl Yellow and Pearl White finishes. Mfd. 1993 only.

	$905	$775	$645	$515	$465	$425	$385

Last Mfr.'s Sug. Retail was $1,295.

VINTAGE — offset double cutaway alder body, white lam pickguard, bolt-on maple neck, 22 fret maple fingerboard with black dot inlay, standard vibrato, 6 on one side tuners, chrome hardware, 3 single coil ESP pickups, 1 volume/2 tone controls, 5 position switch. Available in Black, Burgundy Mist, Candy Apple Red, Olympic White, 2 Tone Sunburst, 3 Tone Sunburst and Turquoise finishes. New 1994.

Mfr.'s Sug. Retail	$1,095	$821	$547	$545	$435	$395	$360	$330

This model has rosewood fingerboard with pearl dot inlay optionally available.

VINTAGE PLUS I — offset double cutaway alder body, pearloid pickguard, bolt-on maple neck, 22 fret maple fingerboard with pearl dot inlay/logo block inlay at 12th fret, standard vibrato, 6 on one side Sperzel locking tuners, chrome hardware, 3 mini humbucker rail Seymour Duncan pickups, 1 volume/2 tone controls, 5 position switch. Available in Black, Candy Apple Red, Gunmetal Blue, Pearl White, 2 Tone Sunburst, 3 Tone Sunburst, Transparent Blue, Transparent Green, Transparent Purple and Transparent Red finishes. New 1994.

Mfr.'s Sug. Retail	$1,495	$1,196	$897	$750	$600	$540	$495	$450

This model has rosewood fingerboard optionally available.

Vintage Plus II — similar to Vintage Plus I, except has double locking vibrato, 2 single coil/1 humbucker ESP pickups, volume/tone control. New 1994.

Mfr.'s Sug. Retail	$1,495	$1,196	$897	$750	$600	$540	$495	$450

Vintage Plus III — single round cutaway bound alder body, pearloid pickguard, bolt on maple neck, 22 fret maple fingerboard with pearl dot inlay/logo block inlay at 12th fret, strings thru fixed bridge, 6 on one side tuners, chrome hardware, 2 single coil Seymour Duncan pickups, volume/tone control, 3 position switch, control mounted metal plate. Available in Black, Candy Apple Red, Gunmetal Blue, Pearl White, 2 Tone Sunburst, 3 Tone Sunburst, Transparent Blue, Transparent Green, Transparent Purple and Transparent Red finishes. New 1994.

Mfr.'s Sug. Retail	$1,495	$1,196	$897	$750	$600	$540	$495	$450

This model has rosewood fingerboard optionally available.

Signature Series

All models in this series are built to their namesakes' specifications.

GEORGE LYNCH — All instruments in this group have the following items; offset double cutaway alder body, bolt-on maple neck, 22 fret fingerboard, double locking vibrato, 6 on one side tuners, black hardware, single coil/humbucker pickups, pan control.

Kamikaze I, II, III — rosewood fingerboard with pearl dot inlay, reverse peghead, Available in Kamikaze finish. Mfd. 1990 to date.

Mfr.'s Sug. Retail	$2,295	$1,836	$1,377	$1,150	$920	$825	$755	$690

Kamikaze Ltd — maple fingerboard with offset black dot inlay, reverse peghead. Available in Kamikaze finish. Mfd. 1992 to date.

Mfr.'s Sug. Retail	$2,545	$2,036	$1,527	$1,275	$1,020	$915	$840	$765

Serpent — rosewood fingerboard with pearl dot inlay/logo block inlay at 12th fret, reverse peghead with screened logo/initial. Available in Black/White Serpent finish. Mfd. 1993 to date.

Mfr.'s Sug. Retail	$2,195	$1,756	$1,317	$1,100	$880	$790	$725	$660

"There are a number of properties that wood can have that effect the tonal quality of the finished instrument. I don't think that the degree of figure is one; the top produces the sound and the rest of the body just reflects it - the influence is minimal. Figuring does have a lot to do with aesthetic quality. Visual quality can't be ignored."
—A. Ingram on Mark Campbell
TCG, July/Aug. 1994

Grading	100%	98% MINT	95% EXC+	90% EXC	80% VG+	70% VG	60% G

Skull & Snakes Ltd — rosewood fingerboard with pearl skull/swords inlay, reverse peghead. Available in Skulls/Snake finish. Mfd. 1990 to date.

Mfr.'s Sug. Retail	$2,245	$1,683	$1,122	$1,120	$890	$810	$740	$675

Sunburst Tiger — rosewood fingerboard with pearl dot inlay. Available in Tiger Sunburst finish. Mfd. 1990 to date.

Mfr.'s Sug. Retail	$2,095	$1,571	$1,047	$1,045	$840	$755	$685	$625

JAKE E. LEE — offset double cutaway alder body, white pickguard, bolt-on maple neck, 22 fret maple fingerboard with black dot inlay, fixed strings thru bridge, screened peghead signature/logo, 6 on one side tuners, chrome hardware, 2 single coil/1 humbucker pickups, volume/tone controls, 5 position switch. Available in Black, Metallic Purple and Snow White finishes. New 1994.

Mfr.'s Sug. Retail	$1,395	$1,116	$837	$700	$560	$505	$460	$420

This model has rosewood fingerboard with pearl dot inlay optionally available.

KIRK HAMMETT KH-2 — offset double cutaway alder body, bolt-on maple neck, 24 fret ebony fingerboard with pearl skull/crossbones inlay, double locking vibrato, reverse peghead with screened logo/initials, 6 on one side tuners, black hardware, 2 humbucker EMG pickups, 1 volume/2 tone controls. Curr. mfr.

Mfr.'s Sug. Retail	$1,995	$1,496	$997	$995	$795	$720	$660	$600

Kirk Hammett KH-3 — single cutaway mahogany body, mahogany neck, 24 fret rosewood fingerboard with white spider/skulls inlay, double locking vibrato, blackface peghead with screened signature/logo, 3 per side tuners, black hardware, 2 humbucker EMG pickups, 1 volume/2 tone controls, 3 position switch. Available in Black with Spider/Web graphic finish. New 1994.

Mfr.'s Sug. Retail	$2,395	$1,796	$1,197	$1,195	$955	$855	$785	$715

RONNIE WOOD — single round cutaway bound alder body, white lam pickguard, bolt on maple neck, 22 fret maple fingerboard with black dot inlay, strings thru bridge, 6 on one side tuners, chrome hardware, humbucker/single coil pickups, volume/tone control on metal plate, 3 position switch. Available in Black, Fiesta Red and Metallic Blue finishes. Curr. Mfr.

Mfr.'s Sug. Retail	$1,295	$971	$647	$645	$515	$465	$425	$385

Ronnie Wood Bend — similar to Ronnie Wood, except has pearloid pickguard, 2 humbucker pickups, Parsons-White Stringbender.

Mfr.'s Sug. Retail	$1,995	$1,496	$997	$995	$795	$720	$660	$600

ELECTRIC BASS

J-FOUR — offset double cutaway asymmetrical alder body, pearloid pickguard, bolt-on maple neck, 21 fret rosewood fingerboard with pearl dot inlay/logo block inlay at 12th fret, fixed bridge, 4 on one side tuners, chrome hardware, 2 J-style ESP pickups, 2 volume/1 tone controls mounted on metal plate. Available in Black, Candy Apple Red, Gunmetal Blue, Pearl White, 2 Tone Sunburst, 3 Tone Sunburst, Transparent Blue, Transparent Green, Transparent Purple and Transparent Red finishes. New 1994.

Mfr.'s Sug. Retail	$1,195	$956	$717	$600	$480	$430	$395	$360

J-Five — similar to J-Four, except has 5 strings, 5 on one side tuners.

Mfr.'s Sug. Retail	$1,395	$1,116	$837	$700	$560	$505	$460	$420

J-464 — offset double cutaway asymmetrical hardwood body, white pickguard, bolt-on maple neck, 21 fret rosewood fingerboard with pearl dot inlay, fixed bridge, 4 on one side tuners, chrome hardware, 2 J-style pickups, 2 volume/1 tone controls. Available in Baby Blue, Black, Blonde, Fiesta Red, Lake Placid Blue, Metallic Blue, Metallic Red, Natural, Olympic White, Salmon Pink, Two Tone Sunburst and Three Tone Sunburst finishes. Mfd. 1986 only.

			$275	$235	$195	$155	$140	$125	$115

This model had tortoise pickguard optionally available.

HORIZON — offset double cutaway mahogany body, bolt-on maple neck, 21 fret maple fingerboard with black dot inlay, fixed bridge, 4 on one side tuners, black hardware, P-style pickup, volume/tone control. Available in Baby Blue, Black, Bubblegum Pink, Candy Apple Blue, Fiesta Red, Metallic Blue, Metallic Red, Midnight Black, Mint Green, Snow White, Transparent Cherry Red and Transparent Blue finishes. Mfd. 1986 only.

			$300	$260	$215	$175	$155	$140	$130

Horizon PJ — similar to Horizon, except has rosewood fingerboard with pearl dot inlay, P-style/J-style pickups, 2 volume/1 tone controls. Mfd. 1986 only.

			$325	$280	$235	$190	$170	$155	$140

Horizon-4 — offset double cutaway maple body, bolt-on maple neck, 24 fret ebony fingerboard, fixed bridge, blackface peghead with screened logo, 2 per side tuners, chrome hardware, P-style/J-style EMG pickups, volume/bass/treble/mix controls, active electronics. Available in Black, Bright Red, Snow White and Turquoise finishes. Mfd. 1987 to 1993.

	$1,540	$1,320	$1,100	$880	$790	$725	$660

Last Mfr.'s Sug. Retail was $2,195.

In 1988, Gunmetal Blue, Mediterranean Blue, Midnight Black, Pearl Pink and Pearl Yellow finishes were introduced.

In 1989, Burgundy Mist, Cherry Sunburst were introduced, thru body maple neck, bound fingerboard with offset pearl dot inlay, bound peghead, black hardware, replaced original items, Mediterranean Blue, Midnight Black, Pearl Pink and Pearl Yellow finishes were discontinued.

In 1990, Candy Apple Red, Dark Metallic Blue and Pearl White finishes were introduced, offset pearl dot fingerboard inlay/12th logo block inlay replaced respective items, Bright Red, Burgundy Mist, Cherry Sunburst, Snow White and Turquoise finishes were discontinued.

In 1991, Dark Metallic Purple finish was introduced.

In 1992, Metallic Green finish was introduced, Dark Metallic Blue finish was discontinued.

Grading	100%	98% MINT	95% EXC+	90% EXC	80% VG+	70% VG	60% G

Horizon-5 — similar to Horizon-4, except has 5 strings, 3/2 per side tuners. Mfd. 1987 to 1993.

| | $1,675 | $1,435 | $1,195 | $955 | $855 | $785 | $715 |

Last Mfr.'s Sug. Retail was $2,395.

M-4 STANDARD — offset double cutaway alder body, bolt-on maple neck, 21 fret maple fingerboard with black dot inlay, fixed bridge, 4 on one side tuners, black hardware, P-style/J-style pickups, volume/tone controls, 3 position switch. Available in Fiesta Red, Flip Flop Pearl Blue, Flip Flop Pearl Red, Pearl White and Turquoise finishes. Mfd. 1987 to 1993.

| | $695 | $595 | $500 | $400 | $360 | $330 | $300 |

Last Mfr.'s Sug. Retail was $1,295.

In 1989, Black, Brite Red and Snow White finishes were introduced, rosewood fingerboard replaced original item, Fiesta Red, Flip Flop Pearl Blue, Flip Flop Pearl Red, Pearl White and Turquoise finishes were discontinued.

In 1990, Candy Apple Red finish was introduced, Brite Red was discontinued.

From 1990 to 1992, model was discontinued.

In 1992, model was reintroduced. Available in Black, Candy Apple Red, Gunmetal Blue, Metallic Green, Metallic Purple and Pearl White finishes.

M-4 Custom — offset double cutaway asymmetrical ash body, bolt-on maple neck, 21 fret rosewood fingerboard with pearl dot inlay, fixed bridge, 4 on one side tuners, black hardware, P-style/J-style pickups, 2 volume/1 tone controls. Available in Black, Cherry Sunburst, Pearl White, Transparent Blue, Transparent Purple and Transparent Red finishes. Mfd. 1991 only.

| | $800 | $685 | $570 | $460 | $410 | $375 | $340 |

Last Mfr.'s Sug. Retail was $1,595.

M-4 Deluxe — similar to M-4 Standard, except has rosewood fingerboard with pearl dot inlay. Available in Brite Red, Gunmetal Blue, Midnight Black, Pearl Yellow, Pearl White and Turquoise finishes. Mfd. 1988 to 1990.

| | $835 | $715 | $600 | $480 | $430 | $395 | $360 |

Last Mfr.'s Sug. Retail was $1,195.

In 1989, Black, Candy Apple Red and Magenta finishes were introduced, redesigned bound peghead, P-style/J-style stacked coil pickups replaced original items, Brite Red, Midnight Black and Turquoise finishes were discontinued.

In 1990, Pearl Yellow finish was discontinued.

M-5 STANDARD — offset double cutaway asymmetrical hardwood body, bolt-on maple neck, 21 fret rosewood fingerboard with pearl dot inlay, fixed bridge, 5 on one side tuners, chrome hardware, 2 J-style pickups, 2 volume/1 tone controls. Available in Black, Dark Metallic Blue, Flip Flop Pearl Red and Pearl White finishes. Mfd. 1987 only.

| | $300 | $260 | $215 | $175 | $155 | $140 | $130 |

M-5 Custom — offset double cutaway asymmetrical ash body, bolt-on maple neck, 21 fret rosewood fingerboard with pearl dot inlay, fixed bridge, 5 on one side tuners, black hardware, P-style/J-style pickups, 2 volume/1 tone controls. Available in Black, Candy Apple Red, Dark Metallic Blue, Dark Metallic Purple, Gunmetal Blue and Pearl White finishes. Mfd. 1991 only.

| | $850 | $730 | $610 | $485 | $435 | $400 | $365 |

Last Mfr.'s Sug. Retail was $1,695.

M-5 Deluxe — similar to M-5 Standard, except has rosewood fingerboard with pearl dot inlay. Available in Brite Red, Gunmetal Blue, Midnight Black, Pearl Yellow, Pearl White and Turquoise finishes. Mfd. 1988 only.

| | $325 | $280 | $235 | $190 | $170 | $155 | $140 |

METAL IV — offset double cutaway hardwood body, bolt-on maple neck, 21 fret maple fingerboard with black dot inlay, fixed bridge, 4 on one side tuners, gold hardware, P-style/J-style pickups, 2 volume/1 tone controls. Available in Pearl Blue, Pearl Green, Pearl Pink, Pearl White and Metallic Purple. Mfd. 1986 only.

| | $275 | $235 | $195 | $155 | $140 | $125 | $115 |

P-457 — offset double cutaway hardwood body, white pickguard, bolt-on maple neck, 21 fret maple fingerboard with black dot inlay, fixed bridge, 4 on one side tuners, chrome hardware, P-style pickup, 2 volume/1 tone controls. Available in Baby Blue, Black, Blonde, Fiesta Red, Lake Placid Blue, Metallic Blue, Metallic Red, Natural, Olympic White, Salmon Pink, Two Tone Sunburst and Three Tone Sunburst finishes. Mfd. 1986 only.

| | $300 | $260 | $215 | $175 | $155 | $140 | $130 |

P-464 — similar to P-457, except has tortoise pickguard, rosewood fingerboard with pearl dot inlay.

| | $300 | $260 | $215 | $175 | $155 | $140 | $130 |

SURVEYOR — offset double cutaway mahogany body, black pickguard, bolt-on maple neck, 21 fret ebony fingerboard with pearl dot inlay, fixed bridge, 4 on one side tuners, black hardware, P-style/J-style pickups, 2 volume/1 tone controls. Available in Black, Bright Yellow, Snow White and Transparent Cherry Red finishes. Mfd. 1987 only.

| | $300 | $260 | $215 | $175 | $155 | $140 | $130 |

Surveyor Custom — offset double cutaway mahogany body, black pickguard, bolt-on maple neck, 21 fret ebony fingerboard, fixed bridge, 4 on one side tuners, black hardware, P-style/J-style pickups, volume/tone control, 3 position switch. Available in Baby Blue, Black, Bubblegum Pink, Candy Apple Blue, Fiesta Red, Metallic Blue, Metallic Red, Midnight Black, Mint Green, Snow White, Transparent Cherry Red and Transparent Blue finishes. Mfd. 1986 to 1989.

| | $275 | $235 | $195 | $155 | $140 | $125 | $115 |

In 1988, Brite Red, Gunmetal Blue, Mediterranean Blue, Pearl Yellow, Pearl White and Turquoise finishes were introduced, redesigned body/bound peghead, thru body maple neck, 24 fret bound fingerboard with offset pearl block inlay/logo block inlay at 12th fret replaced original items, Baby Blue, Bubblegum Pink, Candy Apple Blue, Fiesta Red, Metallic Blue, Metallic Red, Mint Green, Transparent Cherry Red and Transparent Blue finishes were discontinued.

In 1989, Candy Apple Red and Magenta finishes were introduced, Brite Red, Mediterranean Blue, Snow White and Turquoise finishes were discontinued.

E

Grading	100%	98% MINT	95% EXC+	90% EXC	80% VG+	70% VG	60% G

Surveyor Deluxe — similar to Surveyor Custom, except has pearl dot fingerboard inlay. Mfd. 1986 only.

	100%	98%	95%	90%	80%	70%	60%
	$275	$235	$195	$155	$140	$125	$115

This model had rosewood fingerboard with black dot inlay optionally available.

ESPANOLA

See TEXARKANA.

Instruments are produce in Asia. Distributed by V.J. Wholesalers, Inc.

Espanola instruments are designed with the entry level beginner or student in mind.

ESTESO

Guitars were built in Spain.

The Esteso label indicated instruments built by Domingo Esteso (1882 - 1937). Originally trained at the Madrid workshop of Manuel Ramirez, Esteso later set up shop in the same town, and his instruments were widely praised.

(Source: Tony Bacon, The Ultimate Guitar Book)

GUITARRAS FRANCISCO ESTEVE

Instruments currently built in Alboraya (Valencia), Spain.

Francisco Esteve builds a range of classical and flamenco acoustic guitars. For information regarding availability and pricing, contact Guitarras Francisco Esteve via the Index of Current Manufacturers located in the back of this book.

EUGEN

Instruments currently built in Bergen, Norway.

Luthier Eugen began handcrafting solid body electric guitars in 1979, and currently offers 7 different body designs in four models (component options). For information regarding availability and pricing, contact Eugen guitars via the Index of Current Manufacturers located in the back of this book.

EUPHONON

See LARSON BROTHERS (1900-1944).

The Euphonon brand of guitars and mandolins was made by the Larson brothers of Maurer & Co. in Chicago from the mid-1930s till the demise of the company in 1944. This brand was added to the other Larson brands to accommodate the larger size guitars and mandolins the industry started producing at that time to meet the players' demand for more volume. A new style of purfling was used for this brand consisting of alternating strips of black and white woods instead of the marquetry used in the past. The top-of-the-line instruments have abalone trimmed tops.

The Larsons made Euphonon guitars in two main types: the traditional round-hole and the dreadnaught. The round-hole guitar sizes range from 15" student grade to 16", 17", 19" and a very rare 21" in the better and best grades. Many of the better and all of the best grades have laminated top braces and laminated necks. Euphonons have backs and sides made of oak, maple, mahogany, or rosewood.

Some of the fret markers used on the Euphonons and the larger Prairie State guitars are the same as the ones used on the earlier Maurers and Prairie States of the smaller body sizes. The fancier trimmed instruments often have engraved pearl fret markets along with a similar inlay on each end of the bridge. The Euphonon guitars are quite rare, of very high quality, and are sought by players and collectors.

For more information regarding other Larson-made brands, see MAURER, PRAIRIE STATE, WM. C. STAHL, W.J. DYER, and THE LARSON BROTHERS.

For more detailed information regarding all Larson brands, see The Larsons' Creations, Guitars and Mandolins, *by Robert Carl Hartman, Centerstream Publishing, P.O. Box 5450, Fullerton, CA 92635, phone/fax (714) 779-9390.*

EUROPA

Instruments built in France in the mid 1980s.

This company built high quality Fender-style solid body guitars, and offered both hardware options and choice of a graphite neck.

(Source: Tony Bacon and Paul Day, The Guru's Guitar Guide)

15" Euphonon acoustic w/Stahl label
courtesy Robert Carl Hartman

EVERETT

Instruments currently built in Atlanta, Georgia.

These high quality hand-built acoustic guitars are offered in four models: The **P** (medium body, slightly smaller than a dreadnaught), **N** (Dreadnaught), **L** (small body, Grand Concert shape), and **A.C.** (large body). All models feature an AAA Sitka Spruce top, mahogany neck, and abalone inlays. Models retail at $1,860 for Mahogany back and sides, and $1,930 with Rosewood back and sides. For further information, please contact luthier Everett through the Index of Current Manufacturers located in the back of this book.

EXCETRO

Instruments built in Japan during the mid 1970s.

The EXCETRO company featured a range of medium quality semi-hollowbody guitars based on Rickenbacher-derived designs.

(Source: Tony Bacon and Paul Day, The Guru's Guitar Guide)

E

E

F

F GUITARS

Instruments built in Hamilton, Ontario (Canada) since 1976.

F Guitars was founded by George Furlanetto (luthier/bassist) and Froc Filipetti (musician) in 1976. Their high quality basses and guitars are the result of their custom building and designing backgrounds.

Retail prices list between $1,795 (basic 4-string) up to $2,995 (6-string fretless). They also build the **Alain Caron** signature model which lists at $3,600. For further information, please contact F Guitars through the Index of Current Manufacturers located in the back of this book.

FACTORY MUSIC OUTLET

Instruments built in Kenmore, New York since 1981.

Factory Music Outlet was founded in 1981 by Carol Lund. Lund had worked in California with the late Harry Wake. The business began as a hobby, and became a full time business as the need for quality repairs required more of her time. The repair business has expanded to include violins, cellos, and all forms of stringed instruments.

As the repair business expanded, Lund realized the need for high quality, one-of-a-kind instruments. Each individual player seemed to have an idea of what their instrument should be. This evolved into a custom building segment of the business that continues today. FMO prides itself in providing cutting edge innovations for customers. FMO currently employs the use of graphite and graphite composites for structural integrity as well as tonal quality. They feature graphite reinforced wood necks, bridge plates, cello and violin boards as well as all-graphite necks. FMO is currently using the new 2-TEK bridge in many of their custom guitars and basses. The Sabine tuner is also an innovation that FMO uses frequently, in both the onboard and removeable format.

Factory Music Outlet's mission plan is simple: develop and build instruments that are one of a kind. These instruments must be functional and durable as well as aesthetically pleasing. Factory Music Outlet currently distributes at the Kenmore Avenue location in Kenmore, New York. This ensures direct control over quality and customer satisfaction.

The model name **"Black Widow"** is derived from the use of graphite components and American Black Walnut wood. The graphite is black, as is the Walnut when refinished using their "See Through Black" finish. While FMO's original guitars and basses were made exclusively of these materials, they are now building using a variety of woods and combinations of wood types. For further information on custom building options and prices, contact the Factory Music Outlet via the Index of Current Manufacturers located in the back of this book.

FMO Black Widow
courtesy Carol Lund

SIMON FARMER

Circa unknown.

In November 1991, a source close to Blue Book Publishing sent in a fax containing a picture and write up of a prototype guitar built by Simon Farmer. The "Guitube", as the prototype was named, featured a routed Canadian rock maple fingerboard, a Kent Armstrong humbucking pickup, a gas-spring dampened tremolo system (!?), and steel tubing that formed the "wings" of the guitar body. The headstock has six-on-a-side tuners, and a pronounced "droop". Needless to say, we have not heard nor seen this prototype or any "production" designs approaching this model. Anyone with information regarding the "Guitube" is encouraged to write the **Blue Book of Guitars**.

FARNELL CUSTOM GUITARS

Instruments were built in Rancho Cucamonga in the early 1990s. Distributed by Le Pik Guitar Piks of Rancho Cucamonga, California.

Farnell guitars featured synthetic bodies of fiberglass. Current correspondence has met with no response from the company, so it is assumed for this edition that the company is inactive. Further updates will be included in future editions of the **Blue Book of Guitars**.

FASCINATOR

See chapter on House Brands.

This Gibson built budget line of guitars has been identified as a "House Brand" of the Tonk Bros. company of Chicago, Illinois. While built to the same standards as other Gibson guitars, they lack the one true 'Gibson' touch: an adjustable truss rod. "House Brand" Gibsons were available to musical instrument distributors in the late 1930s and early 1940s.

(Source: Walter Carter, Gibson Guitars: 100 Years of an American Icon)

FAVILLA

Instruments built in New York City, New York between 1929 to 1973.

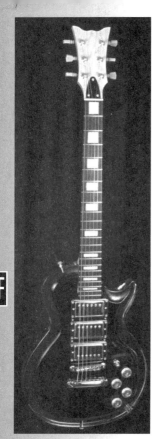

Fedden acrylic guitar
courtesy George Fedden

In 1888, brothers John and Joseph Favilla left their home country of Italy and moved to Manhattan. Two years later, they founded Favilla Brothers, which later became Favilla Guitars, Inc. The workshop moved to Brooklyn in 1929, and later back to Manhattan.

Frank Favilla (John's elder son) began running the facility in the late 1940s. The company moved to larger facilities in Brooklyn in 1959, and in 1965 moved to a 20,000 square-foot plant out in Long Island. The larger facilities employed between fifteen and twenty men, and the staff produced about 3,000 acoustic guitars a year. Higher production costs were one of the factors that led to the plant closing in 1973.

In 1970, Tom Favilla (third generation) began importing guitars from Japan. Japanese Favillas had the company name in script; American-built Favillas will have the family crest on the headstock.

(Source: Tom Wheeler, American Guitars)

FEDDEN

Instruments currently built in Port Washington, New York.

Luthier George Fedden is currently producing acrylic "see-through" guitar bodies that feature colored inlays inside the body for a stunning effect. Designs are based on classic American favorites, and feature wood bolt-on necks, gold hardware, and gold-plated Kent Armstrong pickups. Their clarity and clean wiring harnesses will definitely make you take a second look. The overall feel and body weight will make you want to play guitar!

These instruments are available directly from the builder. Contact luthier George Fedden through his listing in the Index of Current Manufacturers located in the back of this book.

FENDER

Instruments currently produced in the U.S., Mexico, Japan, and Korea. Fender will soon open new facilities in Tianjin, China. Distributed by the Fender Musical Instruments Corporation of Scottsdale, Arizona.

Trademark established circa 1948 in Fullerton, California.

Clarence Leonidas Fender was born and raised in Fullerton, California. As a teenager he developed an interest in electronics, and soon was building and repairing radios for fellow classmates. After high school, Leo Fender held a bookkeeping position while he still did radio repair at home. After holding a series of jobs, Fender opened up a full scale radio repair shop in 1939. In addition to service work, the Fender Radio Service store soon became a general electronics retail outlet. However, the forerunner to the Fender Electric Instruments company was a smaller two-man operation that was originally started as the K & F company in 1945. Leo Fender began modestly building small amplifiers and electric lap steels with his partner, Clayton Orr "Doc" Kaufman. After K & F dissolved, Fender then formed the Fender Electric Instrument company in 1946, located on South Pomona Avenue in Fullerton, California. The company sales, though slow at first, began to expand as his amplifiers and lap steel began meeting acceptance among West Coast musicians. In 1950, Fender successfully developed the first production solid body electric guitar. Originally the Broadcaster, the name was quickly changed to the Telecaster after the Gretsch company objected.

Soon Fender's inventive genius began designing new models through the early 1950s and early 1960s. The Fender "Precision" Bass guitar was unveiled in 1951. While there is some kind of an existing background for the development of an electric solid body guitar, the notion of a 34" scale instrument with a fretted neck that could replace an upright acoustic doublebass was completely new to the music industry. The Precision bass (so named because players could fret the note 'precisely') coupled with a Fender Bassman amplifier gave the bass player more projection. Fender then followed with another design in 1954, the Stratocaster. The simplicity in design, added to the popular sounds and playability, makes this design the most copied world wide. Other popular models of guitars, basses, and amplifiers soon followed.

By 1964, Fender's line of products included electric guitars, basses, steel guitars, effects units, acoustic guitars, electric pianos and a variety of accessories. Leo's faltering health was a factor in putting the company up for sale, and first offered it to Don Randall (the head of Fender Sales) for a million and a half dollars. Randall opened negotiations with the Baldwin Piano & Organ company, but when those negotiations fell through, offered it to the conglomerate CBS (who was looking to diversify the company holdings). Fender (FEIC) was purchased by CBS in early 1965 for thirteen million dollars. Leo Fender was kept on as a "special consultant" for five years, and then left when then contract was up in 1970. Due to a ten year "no complete" clause, the next Leo Fender-designed guitars did not show up in the music industry until 1976 (Music Man).

While Fender was just another division of CBS, a number of key figures left the company. Forrest White, the production manager, left in 1967 after a dispute in producing solid state amplifiers. Don Randall left in 1969, disenchanted with corporate life. George Fullerton, one of the people involved with the Stratocaster design, left in 1970. Obviously, the quality in Fender products did not drop the day Leo Fender sold the company. Dale Hyatt, another veteran of the early Fender days, figured that the quality on the products stayed relatively stable until around 1968 (Hyatt left in 1972). But a number of cost-cutting strategies, and attempts to produce more products had a deteriorating effect. This reputation leads right to the classic phrase heard at vintage guitar shows, "Pre-CBS?".

In the early 1980s, the Fender guitar empire began to crumble. Many cost-cutting factors and management problems forced CBS to try various last ditch efforts to salvage the instrument line. In March of 1982, Fender (with CBS' blessing) negotiated with Kanda Shokai and Yamano Music to establish Fender Japan. After discussions with Tokai (who built a great Fender Strat replica), Kawai, and others, Fender

Fender Telecaster
Blue Book archives

finally chose Fuji Gen Gakki (based in Matsumoto, about 130 miles northwest of Tokyo). In 1983 the **Squier** series was built in Japan, earmarked for European distribution. The Squier trademark came from a string-making company in Michigan (V.C. Squier) that CBS had acquired in 1965.

In 1984 CBS decided to sell Fender. Offers came in from IMC (Hondo, Charvel/Jackson), and the Kaman Music Corporation (Ovation). Finally, CBS sells to an investment group led by William Schultz in March for twelve and a half million dollars. This investment group formally becomes the Fender Musical Instruments Corporation (FMIC). As the sale did not include production facilities, USA guitar production ceased for most of 1985. It has been estimated that 80% of the guitars sold between late 1984 and mid-1986 were made in Japan. Soon after, a new factory was built in Corona, California, and USA production was restored in 1986 and continues to this day. Also, in 1990, the Fender (FMIC) company built an assembly facility in Mexico to offset rising costs of oriental production due to the weakening of the American dollar in the international market. Fender experimented with production based in India from 1989 to 1990. The Fender (FMIC) company currently manufactures instruments in Japan, Korea, Mexico, and the U.S. Plans have been announced for production facilities to be opened in Tianjin, China.

(Source for earlier Fender history: Richard R. Smith, Fender: The Sound Heard 'Round the World)

VISUAL IDENTIFICATION FEATURES

When trying to determine the date of an instrument's production, it is useful to know a few things about feature changes that have occurred over the years. The following information may help you to determine the approximate date of manufacture of a Fender instrument by visual observation, without having to handle (or disassemble) the instrument for serial number verification.

Fingerboard Construction

From 1950 to 1958, all necks were made out of a solid piece of maple with the frets being driven right into the neck. This is the standard design for maple necks.

From 1959 to 1962, the maple neck was planed flat and a rosewood fingerboard with frets and inlay was glued to the top of the neck. This is known as the "slab top" fingerboard.

From 1962 to 1983, the maple necks were rounded to the neck's radius and a thinner piece of rosewood was glued to the neck area. This design is called the "veneer" fingerboard.

From 1983 to date, Fender returned to the "slab top" fingerboard design of the 1959 to 1962 era.

Neckplate Identification

From 1950 to 1971, the neck was attached to the body by means of a 4 screw neckplate.

From 1971 to 1981, the neckplate was changed to 3 screws, and a micro neck adjustment device was added.

In 1981, a transition from the 3 screw design back to the 4 screw design began to occur.

By 1983, the 4 screw neckplate was back in standard production, with the micro neck adjuster remaining.

ACOUSTIC

Grading	100%	98% MINT	95% EXC+	90% EXC	80% VG+	70% VG	60% G

AG Series

AG-10 — dreadnought style, spruce top, round soundhole, black pickguard, 5 stripe bound body/rosette, mahogany back/sides/neck, 14/20 fret rosewood fingerboard with pearl dot inlay, rosewood bridge with black white dot pins, 6 on one side chrome tuners. Available in Natural finish. New 1994.

Mfr.'s Sug. Retail	$230	$172	$115	$90	$80	$75	$70	$65

AG-15 — similar to AG-10, except has high gloss finish. New 1994.

Mfr.'s Sug. Retail	$250	$187	$125	$105	$100	$90	$85	$80

AG-20 — similar to AG-10, except has rosewood back/sides. New 1994.

Mfr.'s Sug. Retail	$280	$210	$140	$110	$100	$90	$85	$80

AG-25 — single round cutaway dreadnought style, spruce top, round soundhole, black pickguard, mahogany back/sides/neck, 20 fret rosewood fingerboard with pearl dot inlay, rosewood bridge with black white dot pins, 6 on one side chrome tuners, piezo bridge pickup, volume/tone slide control. Available in Natural finish. New 1994.

Mfr.'s Sug. Retail	$335	$251	$167	$135	$120	$105	$95	$90

California Series

AVALON — folk style, spruce top, round soundhole, black pickguard, 3 stripe bound body/rosette, mahogany back/sides/neck, 14/20 fret bubinga fingerboard with pearl dot inlay, bubinga strings thru bridge, 6 on one side die-cast tuners. Available in Natural finish. Mfd. 1987 to date.

Mfr.'s Sug. Retail	$300	$225	$150	$120	$110	$100	$90	$80

Fender Concert Acoustic
19th Annual Dallas Show

Grading	100%	98% MINT	95% EXC+	90% EXC	80% VG+	70% VG	60% G

"Your instrument is special to you, and should be treated as such. Whoever does the work should handle it with respect."
—*S. B. MacDonald*
TCG, July/Aug. 1994

F

CATALINA—dreadnought style, spruce top, round soundhole, black pickguard, 3 stripe bound body/rosette, mahogany back/sides/neck, 14/20 fret rosewood fingerboard with pearl dot inlay, rosewood bridge with white black dot pins, 6 on one side die-cast tuners. Available in Black finish. Mfd. 1987 to date.

Mfr.'s Sug. Retail	$370	$277	$185	$160	$140	$130	$120	$105

CONCORD — similar to Catalina, except has bubinga fingerboard/bridge. Available in Natural finish. Mfd. 1987 to date.

Mfr.'s Sug. Retail	$300	$225	$150	$120	$110	$100	$90	$80

LA BREA — single round cutaway dreadnought style, spruce top, round soundhole, black pickguard, 3 stripe bound body/rosette, mahogany back/sides/neck, 21 fret rosewood fingerboard with pearl dot inlay, rosewood bridge with white black dot pins, 6 on one side chrome tuners, acoustic pickup, volume/tone control. Available in Natural finish. Mfd. 1987 to date.

Mfr.'s Sug. Retail	$480	$360	$240	$200	$190	$180	$175	$170

Add $10 for Black finish.
Add $20 for Sunburst finish.
Add $30 for figured maple top/back/sides.

MALIBU — dreadnought style, sycamore top, round soundhole, black pickguard, sycamore back/sides, mahogany neck, 14/20 fret rosewood fingerboard with pearl dot inlay, rosewood bridge with white black dot inlay, 6 on one side die-cast tuners. Available in Dark Violin Sunburst finish. Mfd. 1987 to date.

Mfr.'s Sug. Retail	$385	$288	$192	$170	$150	$140	$130	$115

MONTARA — single round cutaway dreadnought style, spruce top, oval soundhole, bound body, multi-ring rosette, mahogany back/sides/neck, convex back, 21 fret rosewood fingerboard with pearl dot inlay, rosewood bridge with white pins, 6 on one side die-cast tuners with pearl buttons, acoustic pickup, volume/treble/mid/bass controls. Available in Natural finish. Mfd. 1990 to date.

Mfr.'s Sug. Retail	$650	$487	$325	$290	$275	$265	$245	$235

Add $10 for Black finish.
Add $20 for Sunburst finish.
Add $80 for flame maple top/back/sides/neck.

NEWPORTER — dreadnought style, mahogany top, round soundhole, black pickguard, 3 stripe bound body/rosette, mahogany back/sides/neck, 14/20 fret rosewood fingerboard with pearl dot inlay, rosewood bridge with white black dot pins, 6 on one side die-cast tuners. Available in Natural finish. Curr. mfr.

Mfr.'s Sug. Retail	$325	$243	$162	$145	$135	$120	$110	$100

REDONDO — dreadnought style, spruce top, round soundhole, black pickguard, 3 stripe bound body/rosette, mahogany back/sides/neck, 14/20 fret rosewood fingerboard with pearl dot inlay, rosewood bridge with white black dot pins, 6 on one side die-cast tuners. Available in Natural finish. Curr. mfr.

Mfr.'s Sug. Retail	$335	$251	$167	$160	$150	$140	$130	$125

SAN LUIS REY — dreadnought style, solid spruce top, round soundhole, black pickguard, rosewood back/sides, mahogany neck, 14/20 fret rosewood fingerboard with pearl snowflake inlay, 6 on one side chrome tuners. Available in Natural finish. Mfd. 1990 to date.

Mfr.'s Sug. Retail	$445	$333	$222	$190	$175	$160	$150	$140

SANTA MARIA — dreadnought style, spruce top, round soundhole, tortoise pickguard, 3 stripe bound body/rosette, mahogany back/sides/neck, 14/20 fret rosewood fingerboard with pearl dot inlay, rosewood bridge with white black dot pins, 6 per side die-cast tuners. Available in Natural finish. Mfd. 1989 to date.

Mfr.'s Sug. Retail	$360	$270	$180	$160	$150	$140	$120	$110

SAN MARINO — dreadnought style, solid spruce top, round soundhole, black pickguard, 3 stripe bound body/rosette, mahogany back/sides/neck, 14/20 fret rosewood fingerboard with pearl dot inlay, rosewood bridge with white black dot pins, 6 on one side chrome tuners. Available in Natural finish. Mfd. 1989 to date.

Mfr.'s Sug. Retail	$370	$277	$185	$160	$150	$140	$130	$115

SAN MIGUEL — single round cutaway dreadnought style, spruce top, round soundhole, black pickguard, 3 stripe bound body/rosette, mahogany back/sides/neck, 14/20 fret rosewood fingerboard with pearl dot inlay, rosewood bridge with white black dot pins, 6 on one side tuners. Available in Natural finish. Curr. mfr.

Mfr.'s Sug. Retail	$360	$270	$180	$160	$150	$140	$130	$120

This model has left hand configuration optionally available.

Designer/Signature Series

D'AQUISTO ULTRA—single round cutaway hollow figured maple body, arched bound spruce top, bound f holes, maple neck, raised bound ebony pickguard, 20 fret bound ebony fingerboard with pearl block inlay, adjustable ebony bridge/ebony trapeze tailpiece, bound peghead with pearl fan/logo inlay, 3 per side gold tuners with ebony buttons. Available in Natural finish. New 1994.

Mfr.'s Sug. Retail	$7,000	$5,600	$4,200	$3,650	$3,500	$3,250	$3,100	$3,000

This model has pickguard mounted pickup/volume/tone controls optionally available.

Springhill Series

Retail prices listed below reflect the July 1995 price changes.

Grading	100%	98% MINT	95% EXC+	90% EXC	80% VG+	70% VG	60% G

LS-10 — dreadnought style, solid spruce top, round soundhole, tortoise pickguard, mahogany back/sides/neck, 14/20 fret bound rosewood fingerboard with pearl dot inlay, rosewood bridge with black pearl dot pins, ebony veneered peghead with pearl logo inlay, 3 per side chrome tuners. Available in Natural finish. New 1994.

Mfr.'s Sug. Retail	$1,700	$1,275	$850	$725	$650	$575	$500	$450

LS-20 — similar to LS-10, except has rosewood back/sides, ebony fingerboard/bridge, gold tuners. New 1994.

Mfr.'s Sug. Retail	$2,075	$1,556	$1,037	$840	$750	$685	$625	$550

LS-30 — similar to LS-10, except has figured maple back/sides, ebony fingerboard/bridge, bound peghead, gold tuners. New 1994.

Mfr.'s Sug. Retail	$2,000	$1,500	$1,000	$825	$750	$675	$625	$550

LS-40C — single sharp cutaway dreadnought style, solid spruce top, round soundhole, tortoise pickguard, mahogany back/sides/neck, 14/20 fret bound rosewood fingerboard with pearl dot inlay, rosewood bridge with black pearl dot pins, ebony veneered peghead with pearl logo inlay, 3 per side chrome tuners. Available in Natural finish. New 1994.

Mfr.'s Sug. Retail	$1,900	$1,425	$950	$825	$750	$675	$625	$550

LS-50C — similar to LS-40C, except has rosewood back/sides, ebony fingerboard/bridge, gold tuners. New 1994.

Mfr.'s Sug. Retail	$2,100	$1,575	$1,050	$800	$700	$600	$550	$500

LS-60C — similar to LS-40C, except has figured maple back/sides, ebony fingerboard/bridge, bound peghead, gold tuners. New 1994.

Mfr.'s Sug. Retail	$2,200	$1,650	$1,100	$800	$700	$600	$550	$500

SB-15 — jumbo style, solid spruce top, round soundhole, tortoise pickguard, mahogany back/sides/neck, 14/20 fret bound rosewood fingerboard with pearl dot inlay, rosewood bridge with black pearl dot pins, ebony veneered peghead with pearl logo inlay, 3 per side chrome tuners. Available in Natural finish. New 1994.

Mfr.'s Sug. Retail	$1,925	$1,443	$962	$765	$650	$600	$550	$500

SB-25 — similar to SB-15, except has rosewood back/sides, ebony fingerboard/bridge, gold tuners. New 1994.

Mfr.'s Sug. Retail	$2,125	$1,593	$1,062	$840	$730	$600	$550	$500

SB-35 — similar to SB-15, except has figured maple back/sides, ebony fingerboard/bridge, bound peghead, gold tuners. New 1994.

Mfr.'s Sug. Retail	$2,100	$1,575	$1,050	$825	$700	$640	$590	$520

SB-45C — single sharp cutaway jumbo style, solid spruce top, round soundhole, tortoise pickguard, mahogany back/sides/neck, 14/20 fret bound rosewood fingerboard with pearl dot inlay, rosewood bridge with black pearl dot pins, ebony veneered peghead with pearl logo inlay, 3 per side chrome tuners. Available in Natural finish. New 1994.

Mfr.'s Sug. Retail	$2,000	$1,500	$1,000	$800	$700	$600	$550	$500

SB-55C — similar to SB-45C, except has rosewood back/sides, ebony fingerboard/bridge, gold tuners. New 1994.

Mfr.'s Sug. Retail	$2,200	$1,650	$1,100	$885	$790	$700	$600	$500

SB-65C — similar to SB-45C, except has figured maple back/sides, ebony fingerboard/bridge, bound peghead, gold tuners. New 1994.

Mfr.'s Sug. Retail	$2,300	$1,725	$1,150	$890	$800	$750	$660	$550

SX Series

600SX — dreadnought style, spruce top, round soundhole, tortoise pickguard, 5 stripe bound body/rosette, nato back/sides/neck, 14/20 fret rosewood fingerboard with pearl dot inlay, rosewood bridge with white black dot pins, rosewood veneered peghead with pearl logo inlay, 3 per side chrome tuners. Available in Natural finish. New 1994.

Mfr.'s Sug. Retail	$405	$303	$202	$160	$145	$135	$120	$110

800SX — similar to 600SX, except has rosewood back/sides, gold hardware. New 1994.

Mfr.'s Sug. Retail	$460	$345	$230	$190	$170	$160	$150	$140

1000SX — dreadnought style, solid spruce top, round soundhole, 3 stripe bound body/rosette, mahogany back/sides/neck, 14/20 fret rosewood fingerboard with pearl dot inlay, strings thru rosewood bridge, bound rosewood veneered peghead with pearl logo inlay, 3 per side chrome tuners. Available in Natural finish. Mfd. 1993 to date.

Mfr.'s Sug. Retail	$645	$483	$322	$285	$245	$225	$215	$200

1100SX — similar to 1000SX, except has rosewood back/sides, ebony fingerboard/bridge, gold tuners. Mfd. 1993 to date.

Mfr.'s Sug. Retail	$780	$585	$390	$350	$305	$285	$260	$250

1105SXE — similar to 1000SX, except has rosewood back/sides, ebony fingerboard/bridge, gold tuners, piezo pickup, volume/treble/bass/mix controls. Mfd. 1993 to date.

Mfr.'s Sug. Retail	$880	$660	$440	$390	$360	$330	$305	$285

1200SX — dreadnought style, solid spruce top, round soundhole, 3 stripe bound body/rosette, mahogany back/sides/neck, 14/20 fret rosewood fingerboard with pearl dot inlay, strings thru rosewood bridge, bound rosewood veneered peghead with pearl logo inlay, 3 per side chrome tuners. Available in Natural finish. Mfd. 1993 to date.

Mfr.'s Sug. Retail	$965	$723	$482	$420	$380	$340	$320	$300

Grading	100%	98% MINT	95% EXC+	90% EXC	80% VG+	70% VG	60% G

1300SX — similar to 1200SX, except has rosewood back/sides, ebony fingerboard with pearl snowflake inlay, ebony bridge, gold tuners. Mfd. 1993 to date.

Mfr.'s Sug. Retail	$1,175	$881	$587	$500	$450	$410	$375	$350

1500SX — jumbo style, solid spruce top, round soundhole, black pickguard, rosewood back/sides, mahogany neck, 14/20 fret rosewood fingerboard with pearl block inlay, strings thru rosewood bridge, bound rosewood veneered peghead with pearl logo inlay, 3 per side gold tuners. Available in Natural finish. Mfd. 1993 to date.

Mfr.'s Sug. Retail	$965	$723	$482	$420	$400	$370	$335	$310

1505SX — similar to 1500SX, except has sycamore back/sides. Available in Sunburst top finish. Mfd. 1993 to date.

Mfr.'s Sug. Retail	$1,015	$761	$507	$410	$360	$340	$320	$300

1600SXE — similar to 1500SX, except has piezo pickup, volume/treble/bass/mix controls. Mfd. 1993 to date.

Mfr.'s Sug. Retail	$1,065	$798	$532	$425	$375	$355	$335	$305

2100SX — single round cutaway classic style, solid cedar top, round soundhole, 5 stripe bound body, wood inlay rosette, ovankol back/sides, nato neck, 19 fret rosewood fingerboard, rosewood bridge, rosewood veneered peghead, 3 per side gold tuners with pearloid buttons. Available in Natural finish. New 1994.

Mfr.'s Sug. Retail	$640	$480	$320	$280	$250	$230	$215	$200

Telecoustic Series

TELECOUSTIC STANDARD — single round cutaway style, spruce top, oval soundhole, basswood back/sides, maple neck, 22 fret rosewood fingerboard, rosewood bridge with white pins, 6 on one side chrome tuners with plastic buttons, piezo bridge pickup, volume/treble/bass slide controls. Available in Antique Burst, Black and Natural finishes. Mfd. 1993 to date.

Mfr.'s Sug. Retail	$960	$720	$480	$420	$400	$385	$350	$340

Telecoustic Custom — similar to Telecoustic Standard, except has bound solid spruce top, mahogany back/sides/neck, pau ferro fingerboard, pau ferro/ebony laminate bridge, Schaller tuners with pearl buttons, active electronics. Available in Antique Burst and Natural finishes. Mfd 1993 to date.

Mfr.'s Sug. Retail	$2,150	$1,612	$1,075	$900	$800	$775	$735	$700

Telecoustic Deluxe — similar to Telecoustic Standard, except has mahogany back/sides/neck, rosewood/ebony laminate bridge, pearl tuner buttons.

Mfr.'s Sug. Retail	$1,160	$870	$580	$515	$450	$420	$390	$375

ELECTRIC

Add 100% + to price of instrument with Custom Color finishes. The rarer the finish, the higher the price you can expect to pay for that instrument.

The most common Custom Color finishes found are Candy Apple Red, Lake Placid Blue and Olympic White. These Custom Colors may not be as highly sought as other Custom Color finishes, and therefore will not be as highly valued.

In the late 1970s, instrument bodies generally became heavier and less desirable due to their weight.

ARROW — Refer to the "Swinger" model.

BRONCO — offset double cutaway poplar body, white pickguard, bolt-on maple neck, 22 fret rosewood fingerboard with pearl dot inlay, standard vibrato, covered single coil pickup, volume/tone control. Available in Black, Red and White finishes. Mfd. 1967 to 1980.

		$500	$480	$460	$450	$435	$415	$400

Bullet Series

Models in this series have offset double cutaway alder body, white pickguard, bolt-on maple neck, 22 fret maple fingerboard with black dot inlay, fixed bridge, telecaster style peghead, 6 on one side tuners, chrome hardware, fixed bridge, volume/tone control, unless otherwise listed. Available in Ivory, Red, Metallic Red, Sunburst, Walnut and White finishes.

The Bullet model was introduced in 1983, and was designed by John Page (now with the Fender Custom shop). Originally built in Korea, production was switched back to the U.S. facilities after six months and remained there through 1983. The original design featured a Telecaster-ish body design and slim headstock, a 25 1/2" scale, and two pickups that were "leftovers" from the Mustang production line. The Bullet had a suggested list price of $189, although this amount changed as more models were introduced to the series.

BULLET — single cutaway body, 22 fret rosewood fingerboard with pearl dot inlay, 2 single coil covered pickups, 3 position switch. Mfd. 1981 to 1983.

		$250	$235	$215	$200	$195	$185	$175

This model was also available with black pickguard.

In 1983, the body was changed to offset double cutaway alder body, known as the second version of the Bullet.

Bullet Deluxe — single cutaway mahogany body, 22 fret rosewood fingerboard with pearl dot inlay, strings thru bridge, 2 single coil covered pickups, 3 position switch.

		$275	$255	$235	$225	$215	$205	$200

This model was also available with black pickguard.

F

Grading	100%	98% MINT	95% EXC+	90% EXC	80% VG+	70% VG	60% G

Bullet H-1 — covered humbucker pickup, push button coil split switch. Mfd. 1983 only.

| | $215 | $170 | $160 | $150 | $140 | $135 | $130 |

Bullet H-2 — strings thru bridge, 2 covered humbucker pickups, 3 position switch, 2 push button coil split switches. Mfd. 1983 only.

| | $230 | $210 | $190 | $160 | $150 | $140 | $135 |

Bullet S-2 — laminated plastic pickguard, strings thru bridge, 2 single coil covered pickups, 3 position switch. Mfd. 1983 only.

| | $225 | $205 | $180 | $160 | $150 | $140 | $135 |

Bullet S-3 — strings thru bridge, 3 single coil covered pickups, 5 position switch. Mfd. 1983 only.

| | $250 | $225 | $200 | $175 | $165 | $160 | $150 |

CUSTOM — offset double cutaway asymmetrical body with point on bottom bout, tortoise pickguard, bolt-on maple neck, 21 fret bound rosewood fingerboard with pearl block inlay, floating bridge/vibrato with bridge cover, droopy peghead, 3 per side tuners, chrome hardware, 2 split covered pickups, volume/tone control, 4 position rotary switch. Available in Sunburst top/Black back finish. Mfd. 1969 to 1970.

| | $1,800 | $1,700 | $1,600 | $1,500 | $1,350 | $1,175 | $1,000 |

The Custom model was devised by long time Fender employee Virgilio "Babe" Simoni as a method to use up necks and bodies left over from the Electrix XII model. The twelve string peghead was refitted to six strings, and the body was recarved into a different design. The Custom model was originally to be named the "Maverick", which appears on some pegheads. Simoni estimated production to be around 600 to 800 completed pieces.

CORONADO — double rounded cutaway semi hollow bound beech body, arched top, f holes, raised white pickguard, bolt-on maple neck, 21 fret rosewood fingerboard with pearl dot inlay, adjustable rosewood bridge/trapeze tailpiece, 6 on one side tuners, chrome hardware, single coil covered pickup, volume/tone control. Available in Cherry, Custom Colors and Sunburst finishes. Mfd. 1966 to 1970.

| | $600 | $565 | $535 | $500 | $475 | $425 | $400 |

This model was also offered with checkered binding, gold pickguard and tunomatic bridge/vibrato tailpiece.

Fender Custom
Blue Book archives

Coronado II Wildwood — similar to Coronado, except has dye-injected beechwood body, bound f holes, white pickguard with engraved Wildwood/I-VI, bound fingerboard with block inlay, tunomatic bridge/vibrato trapeze tailpiece, pearl tuner buttons, 2 single coil covered pickups, 2 volume/2 tone controls, 3 position switch. Available in Natural finish. Mfd. 1967 to 1970.

| | $800 | $725 | $660 | $600 | $575 | $530 | $500 |

The Wildwood finish was the result of a seven year process in Germany where dye was injected into a growing tree. After the tree was harvested, veneers were cut and laminated to the guitar tops. Pickguard numbers (I-VI) refer to the dye color (primary color of green, blue, and gold) and the applied finish.

Coronado XII Wildwood — similar to Coronado, except has 12 strings, dye-injected beechwood body, bound f holes, white pickguard with engraved Wildwood/I-VI, bound fingerboard with block inlay, tunomatic bridge/trapeze tailpiece, ebony tailpiece insert with pearl F inlay, 6 per side tuners with pearl buttons, 2 single coil covered pickups, 2 volume/2 tone controls, 3 position switch. Available in Natural finish. Mfd. 1967 to 1970.

| | $850 | $775 | $725 | $650 | $580 | $560 | $550 |

The Wildwood finish was the result of a seven year process in Germany where dye was injected into a growing tree. After the tree was harvested, veneers were cut and laminated to the guitar tops. Pickguard numbers (I-VI) refer to the dye color (primary color of green, blue, and gold) and the applied finish.

James D'Aquisto Signature Series

Models were designed by Master Luthier James D'Aquisto.

D'AQUISTO ULTRA — single round cutaway hollow figured maple body, carved bound spruce top, bound f-holes, maple neck, raised bound ebony pickguard, 22 fret bound ebony fingerboard with pearl block inlay, adjustable ebony bridge/ebony trapeze tailpiece, bound peghead with pearl fan/logo inlay, 3 per side tuners with ebony buttons, gold hardware, exposed humbucker pickup, volume/tone control. Available in Natural finish. Mfd. 1984, 1989 to date.

| Mfr.'s Sug. Retail | $6,000 | $4,800 | $3,600 | $3,000 | $2,850 | $2,700 | $2,600 | $2,500 |

D'AQUISTO ELITE — single round cutaway hollow figured maple body, arched bound spruce top, bound f holes, maple neck, raised bound ebony pickguard, 22 fret bound ebony fingerboard with pearl block inlay, adjustable ebony bridge/ebony trapeze tailpiece, bound peghead with pearl fan/logo inlay, 3 per side tuners with ebony buttons, gold hardware, exposed humbucker pickup, volume/tone control. Available in Natural finish. Mfd. 1989 to date.

| Mfr.'s Sug. Retail | $2,000 | $1,500 | $1,000 | $750 | $675 | $625 | $600 | $575 |

D'AQUISTO STANDARD — single round cutaway laminated maple body, laminated maple top, f-holes, maple neck, raised bound solid rosewood pickguard, 20 fret bound rosewood fingerboard with pearl block inlay, adjustable rosewood bridge/rosewood trapeze tailpiece, bound peghead with pearl fan/logo inlay, 3 per side tuners with ebony buttons, gold hardware, two exposed humbucker pickups, 2 volume and 2 tone controls. Available in Natural, Black, and Violin Sunburst finish. Mfd. 1989 to date.

| Mfr.'s Sug. Retail | $899 | $719 | $539 | $450 | $425 | $400 | $375 | $350 |

Fender D'Aquisto Ultra
courtesy Scott Chinery

Grading	100%	98% MINT	95% EXC+	90% EXC	80% VG+	70% VG	60% G

'66 Fender Electric XII
courtesy Rusty Miller

DUO-SONIC — offset double cutaway hardwood ¾ size body, metal pickguard, bolt-on maple neck, 21 fret rosewood fingerboard with pearl dot inlay, fixed bridge with cover, 6 on one side tuners with plastic buttons, chrome hardware, 2 single coil pickups, volume/tone control, 3 position switch. Available in Blond, Custom Colors and Sunburst finishes. Mfd. 1956 to 1964.

1956-1960 Long Scale	$600	$575	$550	$515	$490	$475	$460
1956-1960 Short Scale	$500	$475	$450	$415	$390	$375	$360
1960-1964	$400	$375	$360	$335	$320	$310	$300

This model was released as a student model.

In 1960, tortoise or white plastic pickguard replaced metal pickguard.

Duo-Sonic II— similar to Duo-Sonic, except has asymmetrical waist body, restyled plastic/metal pickguard, 22 fret fingerboard, enlarged peghead, 2 pickup selector slide switches. Available in Blue, Red and White finishes. Mfd. 1964 to 1969.

	$500	$480	$460	$440	$420	$410	$400

This instrument had a longer scale length than its predecessor.

Duo-Sonic Reissue — offset double cutaway poplar body, white pickguard, bolt-on maple neck, 20 fret maple neck, fixed bridge, 6 on one side tuners, chrome hardware, 2 single coil pickups, volume/tone controls, 3 position switch. Available in Black, Red and White finishes. New 1994.

Mfr.'s Sug. Retail	$270	$216	$162	$155	$145	$135	$125	$115

ELECTRIC XII — offset double cutaway asymmetrical body, tortoise pickguard, bolt-on maple neck, 21 fret rosewood fingerboard with pearl dot inlay, strings thru bridge, droopy peghead, 6 per side tuners, chrome hardware, 2 split covered pickups, volume/tone controls, 4 position rotary switch. Available in Custom Colors and Sunburst finishes. Mfd. 1965 to 1968.

	$1,000	$975	$940	$900	$870	$840	$800

In 1965, the fingerboard was bound.

In 1966, block fingerboard inlay replaced dot inlay.

ESQUIRE — single cutaway ash body, black pickguard, bolt-on maple neck, 21 fret maple fingerboard with black dot inlay, strings thru bridge with cover, 6 on one side tuners, chrome hardware, single coil pickup, volume/tone control, 3 position switch, controls mounted on metal plate. Available in Butterscotch Blonde finish. Mfd. 1950 to 1969.

1950-1954	$6,500	$4,550	$3,900	$3,250	$2,600	$2,340	$2,145
1955-1959	$4,500	$3,150	$2,700	$2,250	$1,800	$1,620	$1,485
1960-1964	$3,000	$2,095	$1,800	$1,500	$1,200	$1,080	$990
1965-1969	$1,750	$1,225	$1,050	$975	$880	$810	$790

A few early models of this instrument were produced with 2 single coil pickups. First runs on this series were sparse and no instruments were made in the latter part of 1950.

In late 1954, white pickguard replaced black pickguard.

In 1955, level pole piece pickups were standard.

In 1958, fixed bridge replaced original item.

In 1959, rosewood fingerboard with pearl dot inlay replaced original item.

In 1960, a strings thru bridge was reinstated as standard.

In 1967, maple fingerboard was optionally available.

In 1969, maple fingerboard became standard.

Esquire Custom— similar to Esquire, except has bound body, white pickguard, rosewood fingerboard with pearl dot inlay. Available in Sunburst finish. Mfd. 1960 to 1970.

1960-1964	$5,000	$3,500	$3,000	$2,500	$2,000	$1,800	$1,650
1965-1970	$2,400	$1,680	$1,440	$1,200	$960	$860	$790

JAG-STANG — offset double cutaway asymmetrical basswood body, bolt-on maple neck, 22 fret rosewood fingerboard with dot inlay, 24" scale, floating bridge/Fender "Dynamic" vibrato tailpiece, 6 on one side tuners, chrome hardware, white pickguard, 1 Vintage Stratocaster single coil/1 humbucking pickups, volume/tone controls. Available in Fiesta Red and Sonic Blue. Current production.

Mfr.'s Sug. Retail	$619	$526	$433	$400	$360	$300	$250	$200

JAGUAR — offset double cutaway asymmetrical alder body, metal/plastic pickguard, bolt-on maple neck, 22 fret rosewood fingerboard with pearl dot inlay, string mute, floating bridge/vibrato, bridge cover plate, 6 on one side tuners, chrome hardware, 2 single coil exposed pickups, volume/tone control, volume/tone roller control, preset slide switch, 3 preset slide switches. Available in Custom Colors and Sunburst finishes. Mfd. 1962 to 1975.

1962-1965	N/A	$1,300	$1,150	$1,100	$990	$905	$800
1966-1969	N/A	$1,100	$995	$950	$900	$825	$750
1970-1975	$900	$875	$825	$800	$775	$725	$700

Add 20% for ash body with gold hardware and Blonde finish.

In 1965, the fingerboard was bound.

In 1966, block fingerboard inlay replaced dot inlay.

1955 Fender Esquire
courtesy Garrie Johnson

Grading	100%	98% MINT	95% EXC+	90% EXC	80% VG+	70% VG	60% G

JAZZMASTER — offset double cutaway asymmetrical alder body, gold metal pickguard, bolt-on maple neck, 21 fret rosewood fingerboard with pearl dot inlay, floating bridge/vibrato, bridge cover plate, 6 on one side tuners, chrome hardware, 2 single coil exposed pickups, volume/tone control, volume/tone roller control, 3 position switch, preset selector slide switch. Available in Custom Colors and Sunburst finishes. Mfd. 1958 to 1980.

	100%	98%	95%	90%	80%	70%	60%
1958-1959	N/A	$2,500	$2,140	$1,785	$1,430	$1,285	$1,180
1960-1965	N/A	$1,495	$1,285	$1,070	$855	$770	$705
1966-1969	N/A	$1,000	$855	$715	$570	$510	$465
1970-1980	$750	$640	$535	$430	$390	$355	$325

Add 20% for ash body with gold hardware and Blonde finish.

In 1960, tortoise pickguard replaced metal pickguard.

In 1965, the fingerboard was bound.

In 1966, block fingerboard inlay replaced dot inlay.

In 1976, black pickguard replaced tortoise pickguard.

THE VENTURES JAZZMASTER — offset double cutaway asymmetrical light ash body, white shell pickguard, bolt-on maple neck, 22 fret rosewood fingerboard with white block inlay, floating bridge/vibrato, bridge cover plate, 6 on one side tuners, gold hardware, 2 Seymour Duncan JM single coil pickups, volume/tone control, volume/tone roller control, 3 position switch, preset selector slide switch. Available in Midnight Black Transparent finish. Current production.

	100%	98%	95%	90%	80%	70%	60%
Mfr.'s Sug. Retail	$1,344	$1,142	$940	$820	$725	$610	$550	$500

Fender Jaguar
Blue Book archives

Lead Series

LEAD I — offset double cutaway alder body, black pickguard, bolt-on maple neck, 21 fret maple fingerboard with black dot inlay, strings thru bridge, 6 on one side tuners, chrome hardware, humbucker exposed pickup, 2 two position switches. Available in Black and Brown finishes. Mfd. 1979 to 1982.

	100%	98%	95%	90%	80%	70%	60%
	$400	$390	$370	$350	$335	$315	$300

In 1981, Custom Colors became optional.

Lead II — similar to Lead I, except has 2 single coil exposed pickups.

	100%	98%	95%	90%	80%	70%	60%
	$450	$440	$410	$375	$365	$355	$350

Lead III — similar to Lead I, except has 2 humbuckers. Mfd. 1981 to 1982.

	100%	98%	95%	90%	80%	70%	60%
	$450	$440	$410	$375	$365	$355	$350

LTD — single round cutaway hollow figured maple body, arched bound spruce top, f holes, raised tortoise pickguard, bolt-on maple neck, 20 fret bound ebony fingerboard with pearl "diamond-in-block" inlay, adjustable ebony bridge/metal trapeze tailpiece, ebony tailpiece insert with pearl F inlay, bound peghead with pearl "mirrored F"/logo inlay, 3 per side tuners with pearl buttons, gold hardware, covered humbucker pickup, volume/tone control. Available in Sunburst finish. Mfd. 1968 to 1974.

	100%	98%	95%	90%	80%	70%	60%
	$2,800	$2,400	$2,250	$1,960	$1,870	$1,760	$1,680

Designed by luthier Roger Rossmeisel.

MARAUDER — offset double cutaway asymmetrical alder body, white pickguard, 3 control mounted metal plates, bolt-on maple neck, 21 fret bound rosewood fingerboard with pearl block inlay, strings thru bridge with metal cover, 6 on one side tuners, chrome hardware, 4 pickups, volume/tone controls on lower treble bout, volume/tone controls, slide switch on upper bass bout, 4 push switches on upper treble bout. Available in Custom Colors and Sunburst finishes. Mfd. 1965 to 1966.

The pickups on this instrument were set under the pickguard, making the guitar appear to have no pickups. Due to unknown circumstances, this model never went into full production. There are few of these instruments to be found and, though they were featured in 1965 sales brochures, they would have to be considered prototypes.

In the 1965-1966 catalog, the newly introduced Marauder carried a list price of $479. Compare this to the then-current list price of the Stratocaster's $281!

This model had standard vibrato optionally available.

In 1966, the "second generation" Marauder featured 3 exposed pickups (which replaced original 'hidden' pickups). According to Gene Fields, who was in the Fender R & D section at the time, 8 prototypes were built: 4 with regular frets and 4 with slanted frets. Again, the Marauder was not put into full production.

MAVERICK — Refer to the "Custom" Model.

MONTEGO I — single round cutaway hollow figured maple body, arched bound spruce top, bound f holes, raised black pickguard, bolt-on maple neck, 20 fret bound ebony fingerboard with pearl "diamond-in-block" inlay, adjustable ebony bridge/metal trapeze tailpiece, ebony tailpiece insert with pearl F inlay, bound peghead with pearl fan/logo inlay, 3 per side tuners with pearl buttons, chrome hardware, covered humbucker pickup, volume/tone control. Available in Natural and Sunburst finishes. Mfd. 1968 to 1974.

	100%	98%	95%	90%	80%	70%	60%
	$800	$560	$480	$400	$320	$290	$265

Montego II — similar to Montego I, except has 2 humbucker pickups, 2 volume/2 tone controls, 3 position switch.

	100%	98%	95%	90%	80%	70%	60%
	$1,000	$700	$600	$500	$400	$360	$330

Fender Jazzmaster
Blue Book archives

MUSICLANDER — Refer to the "Swinger" Model.

Fender's Mustang model was initially offered in both the full-scale or 3/4-scale neck. While the Mustangs were in great demand, both necks were produced; but many of the 3/4-scale models were returned from the field due to lack of popularity as compared to the full-scale neck. To salvage leftover parts, Virgilio "Babe" Simoni then redesigned the headstock (which then began to resemble a spear) while another worker redesigned the body. These changes are

Grading	100%	98% MINT	95% EXC+	90% EXC	80% VG+	70% VG	60% G

'78 Fender Musicmaster
courtesy Bill Stapelton

purely cosmetic; the Musiclander model is basically a Mustang with the 3/4-scale neck and a single pickup. Simoni estimates that all in all perhaps 250 to 300 were built, and even some of these were renamed into the **Arrow** or **Swinger**.

MUSICMASTER — offset double cutaway poplar body, metal pickguard, bolt-on maple neck, 21 fret maple fingerboard with black dot inlay, fixed bridge with cover, 6 on one side tuners, chrome hardware, single coil covered pickup, volume/tone control. Available in Blonde, Custom Colors and Sunburst finishes. Mfd. 1956 to 1964.

	100%	98%	95%	90%	80%	70%	60%
	$450	$420	$370	$325	$280	$270	$260

In 1959, rosewood fingerboard with pearl dot inlay replaced maple fingerboard.

In 1960, pickguard was changed to plastic: tortoise or white.

Musicmaster II — similar to Musicmaster, except has asymmetrical body, restyled pearloid pickguard, control mounted metal plate, enlarged peghead. Available in Blue, Red and White finishes. Mfd. 1964 to 1975.

	$350	$315	$275	$245	$230	$220	$210

In 1969, 24 fret fingerboard replaced 21 fret fingerboard.

Musicmaster, Later Mfr. — similar to Musicmaster, except has asymmetrical body, black pickguard, 22 fret fingerboard. Available in Black and White finishes. Mfd. 1975 to 1980.

	$275	$240	$215	$195	$185	$175	$165

This model was also available with alder or ash body.

MUSTANG — offset double cutaway asymmetrical ash body, pearloid or shell pickguard, bolt-on maple neck, 21 or 22 fret rosewood fingerboard with pearl dot inlay, floating bridge/vibrato with bridge cover, 6 on one side tuners with plastic buttons, chrome hardware, 2 single coil covered pickups, volume/tone control, 2 selector slide switches. Available in Black, Blonde, Blue, Natural, Sunburst, Red, Walnut and White finishes. Mfd. 1964 to 1981.

	100%	98%	95%	90%	80%	70%	60%
1964-1969	N/A	$750	$700	$650	$600	$575	$550
1970-1981	$600	$675	$630	$550	$500	$490	$475

Fender offered the Mustang model in both the full-scale or a student-sized 3/4-scale neck. The Mustang model stayed popular for a number of years with the full-scale neck, but many of the 3/4-scale models were returned from dealers due to lack of acceptance (See MUSICLANDER). As a result, the number of 3/4-scale Mustangs available in the vintage market is a small amount.

In 1969, 22 fret fingerboard became standard.

In the 1970s, Black, Blonde, Natural, Sunburst and Walnut were the standard finishes.

In 1975, tuner buttons became metal; black pickguard replaced original item.

Competition Mustang — similar to Mustang, except has Competition finishes (finishes with 3 racing stripes). Available in Blue, Burgundy, Orange and Red finishes. Mfd. 1968 to 1973.

	N/A	$800	$725	$650	$630	$610	$600

(U.S.) PRODIGY — offset double cutaway asymmetrical poplar body, black pickguard, bolt-on maple neck, 22 fret rosewood fingerboard with pearl dot inlay, standard vibrato, 6 on one side tuners, 2 single coil/1 humbucker exposed pickups, volume/tone controls, 5 position switch. Available in Arctic White, Black, Crimson Red Metallic and Lake Placid Blue finishes. Mfd. 1991 to date.

Mfr.'s Sug. Retail	$570	$427	$285	$250	$230	$220	$210	$205

This model is also available with maple fingerboard with black dot inlay.

Robben Ford Signature Series

ROBBEN FORD — double cutaway alder body, hollowed tone chambers, arched bound spruce top, maple neck, 22 jumbo fret bound ebony fingerboard with pearl split block inlay, tunomatic bridge/stop tailpiece, bound peghead with pearl stylized fan/logo inlay, 3 per side tuners with ebony buttons gold hardware, 2 exposed humbucker pickups, 2 volume/tone controls, 3 position/coil tap switches. Available in Antique Burst, Autumn Gold and Black finishes. Mfd. 1989 to 1994.

	$875	$850	$775	$700	$650	$630	$600

This model had Robben Ford's signature on the truss rod cover.

Last Mfr.'s Sug. Retail was $1,750.

Robben Ford Elite — double cutaway mahogany body with tone chambers, multibound carved figured maple top, mahogany neck, 22 fret bound ebony fingerboard with pearl dot inlay, adjustable bridge/tunable tailpiece, bound blackface peghead with pearl fan/logo inlay, 3 per side tuners with ebony buttons, chrome hardware, 2 humbucker Seymour Duncan pickups, 2 volume/2 tone controls, 3 position/coil tap switches, active electronics. Available in Sunburst finish. New 1994.

Mfr.'s Sug. Retail	$3,000	$2,250	$1,500	$1,300	$1,200	$1,150	$1,100	$1,080

This instrument was designed to Robben Ford specifications.

Robben Ford Ultra FM — similar to Robben Ford Elite, except has pearl block fingerboard inlay, gold hardware. New 1994.

Mfr.'s Sug. Retail	$4,000	$3,000	$2,000	$1,800	$1,700	$1,600	$1,500	$1,440

Robben Ford Ultra SP — similar to Robben Ford Elite, except has alder body, spruce top, pearl block fingerboard inlay, gold hardware. New 1994.

Mfr.'s Sug. Retail	$3,800	$2,850	$1,900	$1,420	$1,360	$1,305	$1,285	$1,255

Grading	100%	98% MINT	95% EXC+	90% EXC	80% VG+	70% VG	60% G

STARCASTER — offset double cutaway asymmetrical semi hollow maple body, bound arched top, f-holes, raised black pickguard, bolt-on maple neck, 22 fret maple fingerboard with black dot inlay, fixed bridge, 6 on one side tuners, chrome hardware, 2 covered humbucker pickups, master volume plus 2 volume and 2 tone controls, 3 position switch. Available in Black, Blond, Natural, Tobacco Sunburst, Walnut and White finishes. Mfd. 1976 to 1978.

| | | $1,200 | $1,100 | $1,000 | $950 | $900 | $850 | $800 |

Designed by Gene Fields, the Starcaster was Fender's answer to Gibson's popular ES-335.

SWINGER — offset double cutaway asymmetrical alder body with cutaway on bottom bout, pearloid pickguard, bolt-on maple neck, 21 fret rosewood fingerboard with pearl dot inlay, fixed bridge, pointed peghead, 6 on one side tuners, chrome hardware, single coil covered pickup, volume/tone control. Available in Black, Blue, Green and Red finishes. Mfd. 1969 only.

| | | $1,500 | $1,400 | $1,300 | $1,200 | $1,100 | $1,000 | $900 |

This model was also known as the Arrow and/or the Musiclander.

STRATOCASTER SERIES

This series has an offset double cutaway body, bolt-on maple neck, 6 on one side tuners, 3 single coil pickups, unless otherwise listed.

STRATOCASTER - STANDARD (PRE-CBS MFR.) — ash body, white pickguard, 4 screw bolt-on maple neck, 21 fret maple fingerboard with black dot inlay, strings thru bridge, nickel hardware, 3 single coil exposed pickups, 1 volume/2 tone controls, 3 position switch. Available in 3 Tone Sunburst finish. Mfd. 1954 to 1959.

	100%	98%	95%	90%	80%	70%	60%
1954	N/A	$12,000	$10,000	$8,750	$7,450	$6,650	$5,425
1955-1956	N/A	$10,750	$9,500	$8,000	$6,450	$5,400	$4,800
1957	N/A	$9,500	$8,140	$6,785	$5,325	$4,765	$4,330
1958-1959	N/A	$7,500	$6,430	$5,360	$4,150	$3,740	$3,420
1959/rosewood fingerboard	N/A	$6,500	$5,570	$4,640	$3,600	$3,210	$3,050

Add $150 for standard vibrato with cover.

During 1954, the standard vibrato back cover had round string holes.

During 1955, the standard vibrato back cover had oval string holes.

From 1954-1958, some models were made with aluminum pickguards - Black and Blonde finishes were special order items.

In 1956, gold hardware became optionally available.

In 1957, alder body replaced original item.

In 1958, Black, Dakota Red, Desert Sand, Fiesta Red, Lake Placid Blue, Olympic White and Shoreline Gold finishes became optionally available.

In 1959, 3 layer pickguard replaced original item, rosewood fingerboard became optionally available.

STRATOCASTER WITH ROSEWOOD FINGERBOARD (PRE-CBS MFR.) — similar to Stratocaster-Standard, except has rosewood fingerboard with pearl dot inlay. Mfd. 1960 to 1964.

	100%	98%	95%	90%	80%	70%	60%
1960-1962	N/A	$5,500	$4,715	$3,930	$3,100	$2,850	$2,550
1963	N/A	$5,000	$4,285	$3,570	$2,800	$2,500	$2,350
1964	N/A	$4,505	$3,860	$3,220	$2,500	$2,300	$2,100

In 1960, some models were issued with tortoise pickguards, but this was not a standard practice. Burgundy Mist, Candy Apple Red, Daphne Blue, Foam Green, Inca Silver, Shell Pink, Sonic Blue and Surf Green finishes became optionally available.

In late 1962, rosewood veneer fingerboard replaced original item.

STRATOCASTER WITHOUT TILTED NECK (CBS MFR.) — similar to Stratocaster-Standard, except has smaller body contours, large headstock. Mfd. 1965 to 1971 (referred to as CBS Mfr. because of the sale of Fender Musical Instruments Corp. to the CBS Broadcasting Co. in January, 1965).

	100%	98%	95%	90%	80%	70%	60%
1965	N/A	$4,000	$3,430	$2,860	$2,250	$2,000	$1,850
1966	N/A	$3,250	$2,790	$2,320	$1,850	$1,650	$1,500
1967	N/A	$3,000	$2,570	$2,140	$1,700	$1,510	$1,400
1968	N/A	$2,750	$2,360	$1,965	$1,530	$1,400	$1,275
1969	N/A	$2,500	$2,140	$1,785	$1,400	$1,265	$1,120
1970	$2,250	$1,575	$1,345	$1,125	$900	$800	$700
1971	$2,000	$1,400	$1,200	$1,000	$800	$700	$600

This guitar was also available with rosewood fingerboard with pearl dot inlay.

In 1965, Blue Ice, Charcoal Frost, Firemist Gold, Firemist Silver, Ocean Turquoise and Teal Green finishes became optionally available.

In 1966, enlarged peghead became standard.

In 1970, Blond, Black, Candy Apple Red, Firemist Gold, Firemist Silver, Lake Placid Blue, Ocean Turquoise, Olympic White and Sonic Blue finishes became optionally available.

Fender Starcaster
courtesy Jimmy Gravity

1957 Fender Stratocaster
courtesy Gary Beunal

Grading	100%	98% MINT	95% EXC+	90% EXC	80% VG+	70% VG	60% G

1959 Fender Stratocaster
courtesy Glenn Allan

STRATOCASTER WITH TILTED NECK AND BULLET HEADSTOCK — similar to Strato-caster-Standard, except has even smaller body contours, 3 bolt tilted neck with micro adjustment, large peghead with truss rod adjustment, black logo. Mfd. 1972 to 1980.

1972-1974	$1,350	$840	$720	$600	$480	$430	$395
1975	$750	$525	$450	$375	$300	$270	$245
1976-1977	$650	$455	$390	$325	$260	$235	$215
1978-1980	$550	$385	$330	$275	$220	$200	$180

This model was also offered with a rosewood fingerboard with pearl dot inlay.

In 1972, Natural finish became a standard item.

In 1975, pickups were installed that had flat pole pieces along the bobbin top.

From the mid to late 70's these instruments became heavier and less desirable.

Stratocaster (1983 to 1984) — alder body, white pickguard, 21 fret maple fingerboard with black dot inlay, strings thru bridge, chrome hardware, 3 single coil exposed pickups, volume/tone control, 3 position switch. Available in Black, Brown Sunburst, Ivory and Sienna Sunburst finishes. Mfd. 1983 to 1984.

	$500	$470	$430	$395	$370	$350	$320

This model had a vibrato system that was surface mounted and without a vibrato back cavity. Also, the cord receptor was mounted through the pickguard at a right angle.

Smith Strat — similar to original Stratocaster, except has an alder body, small peghead with black logo, 4 bolt neck, 21 fret rosewood fingerboard with pearl dot inlay. Mfd. 1981 to 1982.

	$750	$700	$650	$575	$525	$475	$450

AMERICAN STANDARD STRATOCASTER — alder body, white pickguard, 22 fret maple fingerboard with black dot inlay, standard vibrato, chrome hardware, 3 single coil exposed pickups, 5 position switch. Available in Arctic White, Black, Brown Sunburst, Caribbean Mist, Lipstick Red, Midnight Blue and Midnight Wine finishes. Mfd. 1984 to date.

1986-1992		$600	$585	$565	$550	$535	$515	$500
Mfr.'s Sug. Retail	$929	$696	$464	$435	$350	$315	$290	$265

Add $100 for left hand version of this model.

This model is also available with rosewood fingerboard with pearl dot inlay.

These were the first Stratocasters of the post-CBS era to be made in the U.S., at the Corona, CA, production facility.

American Classic Strat — similar to American Standard Stratocaster, except has pearloid pickguard, and reverse wound middle pickup. Available in Black Holo-flake and Olympic White finishes.

Mfr.'s Sug. Retail	$1,540	$1,155	$770	$750	$725	$700	$675	$650

Instruments with Olympic White finish have tortoise pickguard.

This instrument is a Custom Shop model.

CONTEMPORARY STRATOCASTER — alder body, white pickguard, 22 fret rosewood fingerboard with pearl dot inlay, double locking vibrato, black face peghead, chrome hardware, humbucker exposed pickup, volume control. Mfd. 1985 to 1987.

	$250	$230	$210	$195	$185	$175	$165

This model was also available with black pickguard, 2 humbucker pickups, volume/tone control, 3 position switch, coil tap configuration or 2 single coil/1 humbucker pickups, volume/tone control, 5 position switch, coil tap configuration.

This model was constructed in Japan.

1961 Fender Stratocaster
courtesy Gary S. Dick

STRATOCASTER GOLD — hardwood body, white pickguard, 21 fret maple fingerboard with black dot inlay, standard brass vibrato, brass tuners, gold hardware, 3 single coil exposed pickups, volume/2 tone controls, 5 position switch. Available in Gold finish. Mfd. 1981 to 1983.

	$1,025	$950	$840	$720	$675	$650	$620

This model has been nicknamed the "Gold/Gold" Stratocaster.

FLOYD ROSE CLASSIC STRATOCASTER — alder body, 22 fret rosewood fingerboard with pearl dot inlay, double locking Floyd Rose vibrato system, chrome hardware, 2 single coil/1 humbucker pickups, volume/2 tone controls, 5 position switch. Available in Black, Candy Apple Red, 3 Tone Sunburst and Vintage White finishes. Mfd. 1992 to date.

Mfr.'s Sug. Retail	$1,190	$952	$714	$630	$580	$540	$490	$460

This model has maple fingerboard with black dot inlay optionally available.

Floyd Rose Standard Stratocaster — similar to Floyd Rose Classic, except has poplar body. New 1994.

Mfr.'s Sug. Retail	$600	$510	$420	$380	$360	$330	$300	$280

This model has basswood body, rosewood fingerboard with Foto-Flame finish optionally available.

H.M. STRAT — basswood body, 24 fret maple fingerboard with black dot inlay, double locking Kahler vibrato, black face peghead with Strat logo, black hardware, humbucker exposed pickup, volume/tone control, coil tap. Available in Black, Blue, Red and White finishes. Mfd. 1988 to 1992.

	$285	$265	$255	$230	$215	$205	$190

Last Mfr. Sug. Retail price was $1,449.

This instrument was also available with rosewood fingerboard with pearl dot inlay and the following pickup configurations: 1 single coil/1 humbucker, 2 humbucker, 2 single coil/1 humbucker exposed pickups with volume/2 tone controls, pickup selector switch, coil tap.

Grading	100%	98% MINT	95% EXC+	90% EXC	80% VG+	70% VG	60% G

H.M. Strat Ultra — similar to H.M. Strat, except has figured maple top/back, ebony fingerboard with pearl triangle inlay, mother of pearl headstock logo, 4 single coil covered Lace Sensor pickups (2 pickups in humbucker configuration by the vibrato), volume/2 tone controls, 5 position/mini switches. Mfd. 1990 to 1992.

	$300	$280	$265	$245	$220	$200	$185

"HRR" '50s STRATOCASTER — basswood body, 22 fret maple fingerboard with black dot inlay, double locking Floyd Rose vibrato, 2 single coil/1 humbucker pickups, volume/2 tone controls, 5 position/coil split switches. Available in Black, Blue Foto Flame, Crimson Foto Flame, Olympic White and 2 Tone Sunburst finishes. Mfd. 1990 to date.

Mfr.'s Sug. Retail	$900	$720	$540	$450	$360	$325	$300	$275

This model is manufactured in Japan.

"HRR" '60s Stratocaster — similar to "HRR" '50s Stratocaster, except has rosewood fingerboard with pearl dot inlay. Available in Black, Blue Foto Flame, Crimson Foto Flame, Olympic White and 3 Tone Sunburst finishes. Mfd. in Japan, 1990 to 1994.

	$360	$345	$325	$315	$300	$290	$280

Last Mfr.'s Sug. Retail was $900.

25TH ANNIVERSARY STRATOCASTER — alder body, black pickguard, "Anniversary" logo on bass cutaway, 21 fret maple fingerboard with black dot inlay, standard vibrato, chrome hardware, 3 single coil pickups, volume/2 tone controls, 5 position switch. Available in Metallic Silver finish. Mfd. 1979 to 1980.

	$850	$790	$720	$675	$600	$550	$510

Approximately 10,000 of these instruments were produced.

Early models of this series were finished in a Pearl White finish, which checked and cracked very badly. Most models were returned to the factory to be refinished.

35TH ANNIVERSARY STRATOCASTER — quilted maple/alder body, white pickguard, birdseye maple neck, 22 fret ebony fingerboard with pearl dot inlay, standard vibrato, locking tuners, chrome hardware, 3 single coil Lace pickups, 5 position/mini switches, active electronics. Available in 3 Tone Sunburst finish. Mfd. 1990 to 1991.

	$2,000	$1,850	$1,675	$1,500	$1,400	$1,300	$1,200

This model was a Custom Shop Limited Edition with 500 instruments made.

ELITE STRATOCASTER — hardwood body, white pickguard, 21 fret maple fingerboard with black dot inlay, Freeflyte vibrato, chrome hardware, 3 single coil covered pickups, volume/2 tone controls, 3 push button pickup selectors, active electronics. Available in Aztec Gold, Candy Apple Green, Emerald Green, Mocha Brown, Pewter, Ruby Red, Sapphire Blue and Stratoburst finishes. Mfd. 1983 to 1984.

	$650	$600	$550	$500	$450	$400	$350

This instrument was also available with rosewood fingerboard with pearl dot inlay.

Gold Elite Stratocaster — similar to Elite Stratocaster, except has pearloid tuner buttons, gold hardware.

	$650	$600	$550	$500	$450	$400	$350

Walnut Elite Stratocaster — similar to Elite Stratocaster, except has walnut body/neck, ebony fingerboard, pearloid tuner buttons, gold hardware.

	$750	$690	$620	$540	$500	$475	$450

SET NECK STRATOCASTER — mahogany body, figured maple top, 22 fret ebony fingerboard with pearl dot inlay, standard vibrato, chrome hardware, 4 single coil Lace Sensor pickups (2 in humbucker configuration), volume/2 tone controls, 5 position/mini switches, active electronics. Available in Antique Burst, Natural, Transparent Crimson and Transparent Ebony finishes. Mfd. 1992 to date.

Mfr.'s Sug. Retail	$2,150	$1,720	$1,290	$1,125	$1,050	$960	$890	$840

This model has gold hardware with Brite White finish optionally available.

Set Neck Floyd Rose Strat — similar to Set Neck Stratocaster, except has double locking Floyd Rose vibrato, 2 single coil/1 humbucker pickups. Mfd. 1992 to date.

Mfr.'s Sug. Retail	$2,150	$1,612	$1,075	$900	$840	$800	$775	$750

STANDARD STRATOCASTER — poplar body, white pickguard, 22 fret maple fingerboard with black dot inlay, standard bridge, chrome hardware, 3 single coil pickups, 5 position switch. Available in Arctic White, Black, Crimson Red Metallic and Lake Placid Blue finishes. Curr. Mfr.

Mfr.'s Sug. Retail	$410	$307	$205	$185	$175	$165	$155	$145

This model also available with rosewood fingerboard with pearl dot inlay.

Standard Stratocaster-Left Handed — similar to Standard Stratocaster, except has rosewood fingerboard with pearl dot inlay. Available in Arctic White and Black finishes.

Mfr.'s Sug. Retail	$670	$536	$402	$335	$315	$280	$260	$240

U.S. CONTEMPORARY STRATOCASTER — alder body, white pickguard, 22 fret rosewood fingerboard with pearl dot inlay, double locking vibrato, chrome hardware, 2 single coil/1 humbucker exposed pickups, 5 position switch. Available in Arctic White, Black, Brown Sunburst, Gun Metal Blue, Pewter and Torino Red finishes. Mfd. 1989 to 1991.

	$475	$445	$385	$330	$300	$280	$250

1965 Fender Stratocaster
courtesy Garrie Johnson

Fender "Mary Kaye" Stratocaster
courtesy Iain Ashley Hersey

Grading	100%	98% MINT	95% EXC+	90% EXC	80% VG+	70% VG	60% G

'57 lefthanded Stratocaster
courtesy Thoroughbred Music

U.S. STRAT PLUS — alder body, 22 fret maple fingerboard with black dot inlay, standard vibrato, roller nut, locking tuners, chrome hardware, 3 single coil Lace Sensor pickups, volume/2 tone controls, 5 position switch. Available in Arctic White, Black, Black Pearl Dust, Blue Pearl Dust, Brown Sunburst, Caribbean Mist, Lipstick Red, Midnight Blue and Midnight Wine finishes. Mfd. 1987 to date.

Mfr.'s Sug. Retail	$1,195	$896	$597	$540	$505	$450	$400	$350

This model also available with rosewood fingerboard with pearl dot inlay.

U.S. Deluxe Strat Plus — similar to U.S. Strat Plus, except has ash top/back. Available in Antique Burst, Blue Burst, Crimson Burst, Mystic Black and Natural finishes.

Mfr.'s Sug. Retail	$1,280	$960	$640	$620	$580	$540	$500	$460

U.S. Strat Ultra — similar to U.S. Strat Plus, except has figured maple top/back, ebony fingerboard with pearl dot inlay, locking vibrato, 4 single coil covered Lace Sensor pickups (2 in humbucker configuration), mini switch. Available in Antique Burst, Blue Burst, Crimson Burst, and Mystic Black finishes. Mfd. 1990 to date.

Mfr.'s Sug. Retail	$1,730	$1,297	$865	$735	$680	$645	$600	$560

U.S. VINTAGE '57 STRATOCASTER — alder body, white pickguard, 21 fret maple fingerboard with black dot inlay, standard vibrato, nickel hardware, 3 single coil exposed pickups, volume/2 tone controls, 3 position switch. Available in Black, Candy Apple Red, Fiesta Red, Ocean Turquoise, 2 Tone Sunburst and Vintage White finishes. Mfd. 1982 to date.

Mfr.'s Sug. Retail	$1,330	$1,064	$798	$670	$640	$580	$560	$520

This is a replica of the Stratocaster as it appeared in 1957.
In 1982-1983, Fender produced a Fullerton-built reissue model that bring an additional $200 premium to the above price line.

Custom Shop '57 Stratocaster — similar to U.S. Vintage '57 Stratocaster, except is left hand model. Available in Black and Olympic White finishes. Curr. mfr.

Mfr.'s Sug. Retail	$2,260	$1,921	$1,582	$1,440	$1,340	$1,260	$1,100	$1,000

U.S. VINTAGE '62 STRATOCASTER — alder body, white pickguard, 21 fret rosewood fingerboard with pearl dot inlay, standard vibrato, nickel hardware, 3 single coil exposed pickups, volume/2 tone controls, 3 position switch. Available in Black, Candy Apple Red, Fiesta Red, Ocean Turquoise, 3 Tone Sunburst and Vintage White finishes. Mfd. 1982 to date.

Mfr.'s Sug. Retail	$1,399	$1,049	$699	$680	$640	$590	$540	$500

This is a replica of the Stratocaster as it appeared in 1962.
In 1982-1983, Fender produced a Fullerton-built reissue model that bring an additional $200 premium to the above price line.

Custom Shop '62 Stratocaster — similar to U.S. Vintage '62 Stratocaster, except is left hand model. Available in Black and Olympic White finishes. Curr. mfr.

Mfr.'s Sug. Retail	$2,260	$1,808	$1,356	$1,180	$1,100	$1,000	$970	$880

THE STRAT — alder body, white pickguard, 21 fret maple fingerboard with black dot inlay, standard brass vibrato, body matching peghead with Strat logo, brass tuners, gold hardware, 3 single coil pickups, volume/tone/rotary controls, 5 position switch. Available in Arctic White, Candy Apple Red and Lake Placid Blue finishes. Mfd. 1980 to 1983.

	$500	$470	$430	$400	$390	$380	$370

Walnut Strat — similar to The Strat, except has walnut body/neck, black pickguard, gold hardware. Available in Natural finish. Mfd. 1981 to 1983.

	$900	$800	$725	$650	$560	$440	$400

A few of these instruments have ebony fingerboards.

STRATOCASTER XII — alder body, white pickguard, 22 fret rosewood fingerboard with pearl dot inlay, strings thru bridge, 6 per side tuners, chrome hardware, 3 single coil exposed pickups, volume/2 tone controls, 5 position switch. Available in Candy Apple Red finish. Mfd. 1988 to 1990.

	$600	$540	$480	$420	$380	$340	$300

These instruments were built by Fender Japan.

'54 STRATOCASTER — ash body, white pickguard, figured maple neck, 21 fret maple fingerboard with black dot inlay, strings thru bridge, chrome hardware, 3 single coil pickups, volume/2 tone controls, 3 position switch. Available in Aztec Gold, 2 Tone Sunburst and Vintage Blonde finishes. Curr. mfr.

Mfr.'s Sug. Retail	$2,150	$1,720	$1,290	$1,260	$1,120	$1,050	$960	$890

This guitar is a custom order instrument.

'60 STRATOCASTER — similar to '54 Stratocaster, except has alder body, rosewood fingerboard with pearl dot inlay. Available in Burgundy Mist, Olympic White and 3 Tone Sunburst finishes.

Mfr.'s Sug. Retail	$2,150	$1,720	$1,290	$1,260	$1,120	$1,050	$960	$890

The pickguard, pickups, controls and finish are aged on this instrument.
Instruments with Olympic White finish have tortoise pickguards and body matching pegheads.
This guitar is a custom order instrument.

'83 "Bowling Ball" Stratocaster
courtesy Elliot Rubinson

Stratocaster Signature Series

Signature Series Stratocasters are designed in collaboration with the artist whose name appears on the headstock. The nature of the Signature Series is to present an instrument that contains the idiosyncrasies similar to the artist's guitar.

Grading	100%	98% MINT	95% EXC+	90% EXC	80% VG+	70% VG	60% G

JEFF BECK — alder body, 22 fret rosewood fingerboard with pearl dot inlay, standard vibrato, roller nut, Jeff Beck's signature on peghead, locking tuners, chrome hardware, 4 single coil Lace Sensor pickups (2 in humbucker configuration), coil tap switch. Available in Midnight Purple, Surf Green and Vintage White finishes. Mfd. 1991 to date.

Mfr.'s Sug. Retail	$1,430	$1,144	$858	$760	$700	$640	$600	$560

ERIC CLAPTON — alder body, 22 fret maple fingerboard with black dot inlay, standard vibrato, Eric Clapton's signature on headstock, chrome hardware, 3 single coil Lace Sensor pickups, active electronics. Available in Black, Candy Green, Pewter and Torino Red finishes. Mfd. 1988 to date.

Mfr.'s Sug. Retail	$1,530	$1,224	$918	$800	$750	$700	$650	$600

ROBERT CRAY — alder body, 21 fret rosewood fingerboard with pearl dot inlay, strings thru bridge, Robert Cray's signature on peghead, chrome hardware, 3 single coil exposed pickups. Available in Inca Silver, 3 Tone Sunburst and Violet finishes. Mfd. 1991 to date.

Mfr.'s Sug. Retail	$2,000	$1,500	$1,000	$850	$770	$740	$700	$650

This guitar is available on custom order only.

DICK DALE — alder body, rosewood fingerboard with pearl dot inlay, standard vibrato, Dick Dale's signature on reverse peghead. chrome hardware. Available in Vintage Tint finish. New 1994.

Mfr.'s Sug. Retail	$2,500	$2,000	$1,500	$1,320	$1,250	$1,120	$1,000	$940

HENDRIX LIMITED EDITION — ash body, 21 fret maple fingerboard with black dot inlay, standard vibrato, reverse headstock, chrome hardware, 3 single coil pickups. Available in White finish. Mfd. 1980 only.

		$925	$875	$825	$775	$725	$675	$625

Last Mfr.'s Sug. Retail was $1,500.

YNGWIE MALMSTEEN — alder body, 21 fret scalloped maple fingerboard with black dot inlay, standard vibrato, brass nut, Yngwie Malmsteen's signature on peghead, chrome hardware, 3 single coil pickups, active electronics. Available in Candy Apple Red, Sonic Blue and Vintage White finishes. Mfd. 1988 to date.

Mfr.'s Sug. Retail	$1,530	$1,147	$765	$560	$540	$520	$500	$480

This model is also available with rosewood fingerboard and pearl dot inlays.

This model built by Fender U.S.A.

Yngwie Malmsteen Standard — similar to Yngwie Malmsteen, except has basswood body, 70's style headstock, no active electronics. Available in Black, Sonic Blue and Vintage White finishes. Mfd. 1991 to 1994.

		$350	$340	$330	$320	$310	$300	$290

Last Mfr.'s Sug. Retail was $960.

This model built by Fender Japan.

BONNIE RAITT — alder body, 22 fret rosewood fingerboard with white dot inlay, larger (1970s-style) headstock, six on a side tuners, vintage-style vibrato, Bonnie Raitt's signature on peghead, chrome hardware, white shell pickguard, 3 Texas Special single coil pickups, 1 volume/2 tone controls. Available in Turquoiseburst and 3 color Sunburst finishes. New 1996.

Mfr.'s Sug. Retail	$1,399	$1,119	$839	$800	$740	$600	$535	$500

RICHIE SAMBORA — alder body, 22 fret maple fingerboard with abalone star inlay, double locking vibrato, Richie Sambora's signature on peghead, pearl tuner buttons, chrome hardware, 2 single coil/1 humbucker pickups, active electronics. Available in Arctic White and Cherry Sunburst finishes. Mfd. 1993 to date.

Mfr.'s Sug. Retail	$1,630	$1,222	$815	$700	$640	$600	$575	$540

Richie Sambora Standard — poplar body, 22 fret maple fingerboard with pearl dot inlay, double locking Floyd Rose II vibrato, chrome hardware, 2 single coil/1 humbucker pickup. New 1994.

Mfr.'s Sug. Retail	$600	$450	$300	$260	$240	$215	$200	$185

Richie Sambora Black Paisley Stratocaster — similar to the Richie Sambora Signature model, except features 1 custom wound humbucking/2 RS special single coil pickups and black paisley finish. New 1996.

Mfr.'s Sug. Retail	$1,369	$1,095	$821	$800	$710	$600	$535	$475

STEVIE RAY VAUGHN — alder body, black pickguard with "SRV" logo, 21 fret rosewood fingerboard with clay dot inlay, left-handed standard vibrato, Stevie Ray Vaughn's signature on peghead, gold hardware, 3 single coil pickups, volume/2 tone controls, 5 position switch. Available in 3 Tone Sunburst finish. Mfd. 1992 to date.

Mfr.'s Sug. Retail	$1,430	$1,215	$1,001	$880	$840	$790	$750	$700

Stratocaster Reissue Series

This series has offset double cutaway basswood body, white pickguard, bolt-on maple neck, 21 fret fingerboard, standard vibrato, 6 on one side tuners, nickel hardware, 3 single coil pickups, volume/2 tone controls, 5 position switch, unless otherwise listed.

'50s STRATOCASTER — maple fingerboard with black dot inlay, strings thru bridge. Available in Black, Olympic White, and 2 Tone Sunburst finishes. Mfd. 1992 to date.

Mfr.'s Sug. Retail	$560	$420	$280	$235	$215	$200	$185	$165

Fender Anniversary Stratocaster
courtesy Jason Brown

Fender Aluminum Body Custom
19th Annual Dallas Show

Grading	100%	98% MINT	95% EXC+	90% EXC	80% VG+	70% VG	60% G

1950 Fender "No-Caster"
courtesy Russell Farrow

'50s Stratocaster-Vibrato — maple fingerboard with black dot inlay. Available in Black, Blue Foto Flame, Crimson Foto Flame, Olympic White, and 2 Tone Sunburst finishes.

Mfr.'s Sug. Retail	$650	$520	$390	$345	$320	$295	$275	$255

Fender's Foto Flame finish simulated the look of a flametop guitar.

'60s STRATOCASTER — rosewood fingerboard with pearl dot inlay. Available in Black, Blue Foto Flame, Crimson Foto Flame, Olympic White, and 3 Tone Sunburst finishes. Mfd. 1992 to date.

Mfr.'s Sug. Retail	$650	$520	$390	$345	$320	$295	$275	$255

Fender's Foto Flame finish simulated the look of a flametop guitar.

'60s Strat Natural — similar to '60s Stratocaster, alder body, basswood top. Available in Foto-Flame finish. New 1994.

Mfr.'s Sug. Retail	$790	$592	$395	$345	$320	$295	$280	$260

TELECASTER SERIES

All instruments in this series have a single cutaway body, bolt-on maple neck, 6 on one side tuners, unless otherwise listed.

BROADCASTER — ash body, black pickguard, 21 fret maple fingerboard with black dot inlay, fixed bridge with cover, chrome hardware, 2 single coil pickups, 3 position switch, volume/tone control. Available in Translucent Butterscotch finish. Mfd. 1950.

$13,500	$9,450	$8,100	$6,750	$5,400	$4,860	$4,455

Prototypes and custom models did exist before 1948.

By 1951, the Broadcaster name was changed to Telecaster due to the use of the original name by Gretsch.

Certain very clean/all original models have sold for as high as $18,000. However, this should be determined on a piece-by-piece basis as opposed to the usual market.

"NO"CASTER — similar to Broadcaster, except has Fender name only on headstock.

$10,500	$7,350	$6,300	$5,250	$4,200	$3,780	$3,465

Add $200 for original case.

After Fender released the Broadcaster model, the Fred Gretsch company objected to the similarity of the name to their "Broadkaster" trademark used on Gretsch drums. Fender complied to the Gretsch request, and clipped the Broadcaster name off of labels. Models produced between the Broadcaster and Telecaster guitars have been nicknamed the "No"caster by collectors due to lack of model name after the 'Fender' logo on the headstock.

Certain very clean/all original models have sold for as high as $14,000. However, this should be determined on a piece-by-piece basis as opposed to the usual market.

TELECASTER (ORIGINAL FENDER MFR.) — ash body, black pickguard, 21 fret maple fingerboard with black dot inlay, strings thru bridge, chrome hardware, 2 single coil pickups, volume/tone controls, 3 position switch, controls mounted metal plate. Available in Blonde finish. Mfd. 1951 to 1964.

1951-1954	N/A	$8,500	$7,080	$5,665	$5,150	$4,725	$4,500
1955-1959	N/A	$5,500	$4,580	$3,665	$3,400	$3,125	$2,825
1960-1964	N/A	$3,500	$2,915	$2,335	$2,200	$1,975	$1,825

In late 1954, white pickguard replaced original item.

In 1955, level pole piece pickups became standard.

In 1958, fixed bridge replaced original item.

In 1959, rosewood fingerboard with pearl dot inlay replaced maple fingerboard.

In 1960, strings thru bridge replaced fixed bridge.

Refinished '53 Telecaster
courtesy Tom Murphy

TELECASTER (CBS MFR.) — similar to original Telecaster, except has F stamp on back of neck plates. Mfd. 1965 to 1983 (referred to as CBS Mfr. because of the sale of Fender Musical Instruments Corp. to the CBS Broadcasting Co. in early 1965.)

1965-1969	N/A	$1,750	$1,455	$1,165	$1,000	$900	$825
1970-1975	$1,000	$700	$600	$500	$400	$350	$300
1976-1979	$750	$525	$450	$375	$300	$250	$200
1980-1983	$525	$370	$315	$260	$200	$170	$160

In 1967, Bigsby vibrato tailpiece was optionally available.

From 1967-1969, maple fingerboard was optionally available.

In 1969, maple fingerboard with black dot inlay replaced original item.

In 1975, black pickguard replaced respective item.

Telecasters with a maple cap fingerboard bring a higher premium.

TELECASTER WITH BIGSBY VIBRATO — similar to original Telecaster, except has Bigsby vibrato unit. Mfd. 1967 to 1975.

1967-1969	N/A	$1,500	$1,250	$1,000	$900	$825	$750
1970-1975	$900	$770	$640	$515	$465	$425	$385

Telecasters with a maple cap fingerboard bring a higher premium.

Grading	100%	98% MINT	95% EXC+	90% EXC	80% VG+	70% VG	60% G

TELECASTER CUSTOM — bound alder body, white pickguard, 21 fret maple fingerboard with pearl dot inlay, strings thru bridge, chrome hardware, 2 single coil pickups, volume/tone controls, 3 position switch, controls mounted metal plate. Available in Custom Colors finish. Mfd. 1959 to 1972.

	100%	98%	95%	90%	80%	70%	60%
1959-1965	N/A	$4,500	$3,750	$3,000	$2,800	$2,675	$2,450
1966-1972	N/A	$2,500	$2,080	$1,665	$1,550	$1,375	$1,260

This model is also found with an ash body.

Certain very clean/all original models have sold for as high as $4,000 to $7,000. However, this should be determined on a piece-by-piece basis as opposed to the usual market.

ACOUSTIC/ELECTRIC TELECASTER — single round cutaway semi hollow basswood body, bound solid spruce top, f-hole, 22 fret rosewood fingerboard with pearl triangle inlay, double locking vibrato, 6 on one side tuners, black hardware, single coil Lace Sensor/piezo bridge pickups, volume/pan control, mini boost switch. Available in Black, Natural, Transparent Crimson and 3 Color Sunburst finishes. Curr. mfr.

	100%	98%	95%	90%	80%	70%	60%
Mfr.'s Sug. Retail	$699	$524	$349	$340	$330	$320	$310	$300

AMERICAN STANDARD TELECASTER — alder body, white pickguard, 22 fret maple fingerboard with black dot inlay, fixed bridge, chrome hardware, 2 American Standard Telecaster single coil pickups, volume/tone control, 3 position switch. Available in Black, Caribbean Mist, Lipstick Red, Midnight Blue, Midnight Wine, Sunburst and Vintage White finishes. Mfd. 1988 to date.

	100%	98%	95%	90%	80%	70%	60%
1988-1994		$575	$535	$475	$405	$380	$340	$305
Mfr.'s Sug. Retail	$929	$743	$557	$530	$500	$470	$450	$430

This model also available with rosewood fingerboard with pearl dot inlay.

Only vintage Telecasters were available in 1986 and 1987.

These were the first Telecasters of the post-CBS era to be made in the U.S., at the Corona, California, production facility.

American Standard "B-Bender" Telecaster — similar to the American Standard Telecaster, except has custom designed Parsons/White B-Bender system installed. Available in Black, Vintage White, Candy Apple Red, and Brown Sunburst. New 1996.

	100%	98%	95%	90%	80%	70%	60%
Mfr.'s Sug. Retail	$1,099	$934	$769	$680	$610	$560	$490	$420

BLACK & GOLD TELECASTER — hardwood body, black pickguard, 21 fret maple fingerboard with black dot inlay, brass strings thru bridge, black face peghead with logo, gold hardware, 2 single coil pickups, volume/tone control, 3 position switch, controls mounted metal plate. Available in Black finish. Mfd. 1981 to 1983.

	98%	95%	90%	80%	70%	60%
	$525	$500	$475	$450	$425	$400	$375

This model was also available with rosewood fingerboard with pearl dot inlay.

CONTEMPORARY TELECASTER — hardwood body, 22 fret rosewood fingerboard with pearl dot inlay, standard vibrato, black hardware, 2 single coil/1 humbucker pickup, volume/tone controls, 3 mini switches. Mfd. 1985 to 1987.

	98%	95%	90%	80%	70%	60%
	$210	$200	$190	$180	$170	$160	$150

This model was also available with 2 humbucker pickups, 3 position/coil tap switches.

This model built by Fender Japan.

CUSTOM TELECASTER — ash body, black pickguard, 21 fret maple fingerboard with black dot inlay, strings thru bridge with cover, chrome hardware, humbucker/single coil pickups, 2 volume/2 tone controls, 3 position switch. Available in Black, Blonde, Natural and Sunburst finishes. Mfd. 1972 to 1981.

	98%	95%	90%	80%	70%	60%
	$1,200	$1,140	$1,080	$1,000	$920	$840	$800

Bigsby vibrato and maple fingerboard were optional.

DELUXE TELECASTER — poplar body, black pickguard, 21 fret maple fingerboard with black dot inlay, strings thru bridge with cover, chrome hardware, 2 humbucker pickups, 2 volume/2 tone controls, 3 position switch. Available in Blonde, Custom Colors, Natural and 3 Tone Sunburst finishes. Mfd. 1973 to 1981.

	98%	95%	90%	80%	70%	60%
	$1,000	$940	$880	$800	$720	$640	$600

From 1977-1979, Antigua finish was available with matching pickguard.

ELITE TELECASTER — bound alder body, 21 fret fingerboard with black dot inlay, fixed bridge, chrome hardware, 2 covered humbuckers, 2 volume/2 tone controls, 3 position switch, active electronics. Available in Natural and Sunburst finishes. Mfd. 1983 to 1985.

	98%	95%	90%	80%	70%	60%
	$450	$415	$385	$325	$295	$260	$230

This model came with a white pickguard that could be applied with the supplied adhesive backing.

This model was also available with rosewood fingerboard with pearl dot inlay.

Elite Telecaster Gold — similar to Elite Telecaster, except has pearloid button tuners, gold hardware.

	98%	95%	90%	80%	70%	60%
	$550	$500	$450	$400	$350	$300	$275

Elite Telecaster Walnut — similar to Elite Telecaster, except has walnut body/neck, ebony fingerboard with pearl dot inlay, pearloid button tuners, gold hardware. Available in Natural finish.

	98%	95%	90%	80%	70%	60%
	$650	$455	$390	$325	$260	$235	$215

FLORAL/PAISLEY TELECASTER — ash body, floral/paisley pickguard, 21 fret maple fingerboard with black dot inlay, strings thru bridge, chrome hardware, 2 single coil pickups, volume/tone controls, 3 position switch, controls mounted metal plate. Available in Blue Floral and Pink Paisley finishes. Mfd. 1968 to 1970.

	98%	95%	90%	80%	70%	60%
	$2,500	$2,200	$1,900	$1,750	$1,600	$1,650	$1,500

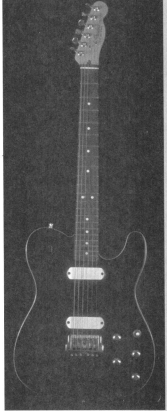

Telecaster w/Bigsby
Blue Book archives

Telecaster Elite
courtesy Fred Quann

Grading	100%	98% MINT	95% EXC+	90% EXC	80% VG+	70% VG	60% G

Fender "Cow-Caster" Custom
courtesy Thoroughbred Music

FORTIETH ANNIVERSARY TELECASTER — ash body, bound figured maple top, cream pickguard, 22 fret maple fingerboard with black dot inlay, fixed bridge, pearl tuner buttons, gold hardware, 2 single coil pickups, volume/tone control, 3 position switch. Available in Antique Two-Tone, Natural and Transparent Red finishes. Mfd. 1988 to 1990.

	100%	98%	95%	90%	80%	70%	60%
	$1,950	$1,840	$1,760	$1,650	$1,540	$1,460	$1,370

Approximately 300 of these instruments were mfd.

ROSEWOOD TELECASTER — rosewood body, black pickguard, bolt-on rosewood neck, 21 fret rosewood fingerboard with pearl dot inlay, strings thru bridge with cover, chrome hardware, 2 single coil pickups, volume/tone control, 3 position switch, controls mounted metal plate. Available in Natural finish. Mfd. 1969 to 1972.

	$2,200	$2,000	$1,800	$1,650	$1,500	$1,400	$1,300

Certain very clean/all original models have sold for as high as $4,000 to $7,000. However, this should be determined on a piece-by-piece basis as opposed to the usual market.

The Rosewood Telecaster was also offered with a hollowed (3 chambers) body between 1971 and 1972.

SET NECK TELECASTER — mahogany body, bound figured maple top, mahogany neck, 22 fret rosewood fingerboard with pearl dot inlay, strings thru bridge, locking tuners, 2 humbucker DiMarzio pickups, volume/tone control, 3 position/coil tap switches. Available in Antique Burst, Autumn Gold, Transparent Crimson, Transparent Ebony and Transparent Sapphire Blue finishes. Mfd. 1990 to date.

Mfr.'s Sug. Retail	$2,150	$1,612	$1,075	$910	$850	$800	$775	$750

This model is also available with double locking Floyd Rose vibrato, roller nut.

In 1993, pau ferro fingerboard became standard.

Set Neck Telecaster C/A — similar to Set Neck Telecaster, except has tortoise pickguard, pau ferro fingerboard, gold hardware, humbucker/single coil pickups. Available in Gold Sparkle, Natural, Silver Sparkle and Transparent Sunset Orange finishes. Mfd. 1991 to date.

Mfr.'s Sug. Retail	$2,150	$1,612	$1,075	$910	$850	$800	$775	$750

STANDARD TELECASTER — poplar body, white pickguard, 21 fret maple fingerboard with black dot inlay, strings thru bridge, chrome hardware, 2 single coil pickups, volume/tone control, 3 position switch. Available in Arctic White, Black, Crimson Red Metallic and Lake Placid Blue finishes. Curr. mfr.

Mfr.'s Sug. Retail	$410	$307	$205	$180	$170	$160	$150	$140

THINLINE TELECASTER — ash body with hollowed bass side, f hole, pearloid pickguard, 21 fret maple fingerboard with black dot inlay, strings thru bridge with cover, chrome hardware, 2 single coil pickups, volume/tone control, 3 position switch. Available in Custom Colors, Natural and Sunburst finishes. Mfd. 1968 to 1971.

	$1,800	$1,650	$1,460	$1,250	$1,140	$1,080	$960

Add $300 for Sunburst or Custom Color finishes.

In 1969, rosewood fingerboard with pearl dot inlay became optionally available.

Telecaster Thinline II — similar to Thinline Telecaster, except has 2 humbucker pickups. Mfd. 1972 to 1978.

	$1,000	$940	$860	$800	$770	$730	$700

Add $100 for Sunburst or Custom Color finishes (except Mocha Brown).

TELE PLUS — alder body, ash top/back, 22 fret rosewood fingerboard with pearl dot inlay, fixed bridge, chrome hardware, 3 single coil Lace Sensor pickups (2 in humbucker position by bridge), volume/tone control, 3 position/mini switch. Available in Antique Burst, Blue Burst, Crimson Burst and Mystic Blue finishes. Mfd. 1990 to date.

Mfr.'s Sug. Retail	$1,020	$765	$510	$430	$400	$370	$340	$300

Add $100 for solid ash body with Natural finish.

This model also available with maple fingerboard with black dot inlay.

TELE SPECIAL — poplar body, ash top, 22 fret maple fingerboard with black dot inlay, fixed strings thru bridge, chrome hardware, humbucker/single coil pickups, volume/tone controls, 3 position switch. Available in Natural finish. Mfd. 1994 to date.

Mfr.'s Sug. Retail	$510	$382	$255	$250	$200	$180	$165	$150

Telecaster Custom Classic Series Solid Bodies

BAJO SEXTO TELECASTER — ash body, black pickguard, 24 fret maple fingerboard with black dot inlay, strings thru bridge with brass saddles, nickel hardware, 2 single coil pickups, volume/tone control, 3 position switch. Available in Honey Blond and 2 Tone Sunburst finishes. Mfd. 1993 to date.

Mfr.'s Sug. Retail	$1,950	$1,462	$975	$950	$875	$825	$750	$700

This instrument is a longer scaled (baritone) instrument and custom order only.

SPARKLE TELECASTER — poplar body, white pickguard, figured maple neck, 21 fret maple fingerboard with black dot inlay, strings thru bridge with brass saddles, nickel hardware, 2 single coil pickups, volume/tone control, 3 position switch. Available in Champagne Sparkle, Gold Sparkle and Silver Sparkle finishes. Mfd. 1993 to date.

Mfr.'s Sug. Retail	$2,150	$1,827	$1,505	$1,350	$1,225	$1,175	$1,100	$1,050

This guitar is custom order only.

Telecaster Signature Series

Signature Series Telecasters are designed in collaboration with the artist whose name appears on the headstock. The nature of the Signature Series is to present an instrument that contains the idiosyncrasies similar to the artist's guitar.

Grading	100%	98% MINT	95% EXC+	90% EXC	80% VG+	70% VG	60% G

JAMES BURTON — light ash body, bolt-on maple neck, 21 fret maple fingerboard with black dot inlay, strings thru bridge, 6 on one side tuners, gold hardware, 3 single coil Lace Sensor pickups, volume/tone control, 5 position switch. Available in Black with Candy Red Paisley, Black with Gold Paisley, Frost Red and Pearl White finishes. Mfd. 1990 to date.

| Mfr.'s Sug. Retail | $1,530 | $1,147 | $765 | $650 | $600 | $550 | $500 | $450 |

This model is also available with black hardware, depending on finish.

ALBERT COLLINS — bound ash body, white pickguard, bolt-on maple neck, 21 fret maple fingerboard with black dot inlay, strings thru bridge with cover, 6 on one side tuners, chrome hardware, humbucker/single coil pickups, volume/tone control, 3 position switch, controls mounted on a metal plate. Available in Natural finish. Mfd. 1990 to date.

| Mfr.'s Sug. Retail | $2,560 | $1,920 | $1,280 | $1,100 | $1,050 | $1,000 | $950 | $900 |

This guitar is custom order only.

JERRY DONAHUE — ash body, birdseye maple top/back, black pickguard, bolt-on bird's eye maple neck, 21 fret maple fingerboard with black dot inlay, strings thru bridge, 6 on one side tuners, gold hardware, 2 single coil pickups, volume/tone control, 3 position switch. Available in 3 Tone Sunburst and Transparent Crimson finishes. Mfd. 1992 to date.

| Mfr.'s Sug. Retail | $2,150 | $1,612 | $1,075 | $1,050 | $960 | $840 | $800 | $750 |

This guitar is custom order only.

NOKIE EDWARDS — laminated ash/basswood/rock maple body with flame maple top, black pickguard, bolt-on 3-ply maple neck, 22 fret ebony fingerboard with pearloid dot inlay and zero fret, tilt back headstock, 6 on one side tuners, gold hardware, 2 Seymour Duncan humbucking pickups, volume/tone control, 3 position switch. Available in 3 Tone Sunburst and Transparent finishes. New 1996.

| Mfr.'s Sug. Retail | $1,959 | $1,567 | $1,175 | $1,080 | $940 | $830 | $760 | $720 |

DANNY GATTON — ash body, black pickguard, bolt-on maple neck, 22 fret maple fingerboard with black dot inlay, strings thru bridge, 2 single coil Barden pickups, volume/tone control, 3 position switch. Available in Frost Gold and Honey Blonde finishes. Mfd. 1990 to date.

| Mfr.'s Sug. Retail | $2,560 | $2,048 | $1,536 | $1,350 | $1,250 | $1,125 | $1,080 | $1,000 |

This guitar is custom order only.

CLARENCE WHITE — ash body, tortoise pickguard, figured maple neck, 21 fret maple fingerboard with black dot inlay, fixed strings thru bridge, Parsons-White stringbender, 2 single coil pickups, volume/tone control, 3 position switch. Available in 2 Tone Sunburst finish. Mfd. 1994 to date.

| Mfr.'s Sug. Retail | $3,500 | $2,800 | $2,100 | $1,840 | $1,750 | $1,600 | $1,500 | $1,400 |

This instrument has banjo tuners on the E strings.

This guitar is custom order only.

Telecaster Reissue Series Solid Bodies

PAISLEY TELE — basswood body, white pickguard, 21 fret maple fingerboard with black dot inlay, fixed strings thru bridge, chrome hardware, 2 single coil pickups, volume/tone controls, 3 position switch. Available in Paisley finish. New 1994.

| Mfr.'s Sug. Retail | $820 | $615 | $410 | $370 | $340 | $315 | $290 | $275 |

U.S. VINTAGE/'52 TELECASTER — ash body, black pickguard, 21 fret maple fingerboard with black dot inlay, fixed bridge with brass saddles, nickel hardware, 2 single coil pickups, volume/tone control, 3 position switch. Available in Butterscotch Blonde finish. Mfd. 1982 to 1984.

| | | $750 | $730 | $710 | $690 | $660 | $630 | $600 |

U.S. Vintage/'52 Telecaster (Reissue) — similar to U.S. Vintage/'52 Telecaster, except mfd. 1986 to date.

| Mfr.'s Sug. Retail | $1,399 | $1,119 | $839 | $760 | $750 | $735 | $715 | $700 |

This model is based upon the instrument as it appeared in 1952.

'52 Telecaster (Left-Hand Model) — similar to U.S. Vintage/'52 Telecaster, except is left handed. Available in Honey Burst and 2 Color Sunburst finishes.

| Mfr.'s Sug. Retail | $2,260 | $1,808 | $1,356 | $1,340 | $1,220 | $1,160 | $1,100 | $1,000 |

'50s TELECASTER — basswood body, white pickguard, 21 fret maple fingerboard with black dot inlay, fixed bridge with brass saddles, nickel hardware, 2 single coil pickups, volume/tone control, 3 position switch. Available in Blonde, Candy Apple Red and 2 Color Sunburst finishes. Mfd. 1990 to date.

| Mfr.'s Sug. Retail | $640 | $480 | $320 | $285 | $260 | $240 | $220 | $200 |

'62 CUSTOM TELECASTER — bound basswood body, 3 ply white pickguard, 21 fret rosewood fingerboard with pearl dot inlay, fixed bridge, chrome hardware, 2 single coil pickups, volume/tone control, 3 position switch. Available in Candy Apple Red and 3 Color Sunburst finishes. Curr. Mfr.

| Mfr.'s Sug. Retail | $740 | $592 | $444 | $370 | $350 | $320 | $300 | $280 |

Add $60 for left handed version of this model.

'69 THINLINE TELECASTER — semi hollow mahogany body, f hole, white pickguard, 21 fret maple fingerboard with black dot inlay, fixed bridge, nickel hardware, 2 single coil pickups, volume/tone control, 3 position switch. Available in Natural finish. Curr. mfr.

| Mfr.'s Sug. Retail | $820 | $656 | $492 | $425 | $400 | $375 | $350 | $325 |

Telecaster Thinline
Blue Book archives

F

Grading	100%	98% MINT	95% EXC+	90% EXC	80% VG+	70% VG	60% G

'72 TELECASTER THINLINE — similar to '69 Telecaster Thinline, except has ash body. New 1994.

Mfr.'s Sug. Retail	$890	$667	$445	$390	$360	$340	$320	$300

Limited Edition Series

All instruments in this series are custom order, limited edition instruments. Manufactured by Fender Japan.

'62 JAGUAR — offset double cutaway asymmetrical alder body, metal/plastic pickguard, bolt-on maple neck, 22 fret rosewood fingerboard with pearl dot inlay, string mute, floating bridge/vibrato, bridge cover plate, 6 on one side tuners, chrome hardware, 2 single coil exposed pickups, volume/tone control, volume/tone roller control, preset slide switch, 3 preset slide switches. Available in Candy Apple Red, Vintage White and 3 Tone Sunburst finishes. Curr. mfr.

Mfr.'s Sug. Retail	$870	$696	$522	$450	$425	$400	$375	$350

'62 JAZZMASTER — offset double cutaway asymmetrical alder body, gold metal pickguard, bolt-on maple neck, 21 fret rosewood fingerboard with pearl dot inlay, floating bridge/vibrato, bridge cover plate, 6 on one side tuners, chrome hardware, 2 single coil exposed pickups, volume/tone control, volume/tone roller control, 3 position switch, preset selector slide switch. Available in Candy Apple Red, Vintage White and 3 Tone Sunburst finishes. Curr. mfr.

Mfr.'s Sug. Retail	$870	$696	$522	$450	$425	$400	$375	$350

'68 STRATOCASTER — offset double cutaway ash body, white pickguard, bolt-on maple neck, 21 fret maple fingerboard with black dot inlay, standard vibrato, 6 on one side tuners, chrome hardware, 3 single coil pickups, 2 volume/1 tone controls, 5 position switch. Available in Vintage White and 3 Tone Sunburst finishes. Curr. mfr.

Mfr.'s Sug. Retail	$710	$532	$355	$350	$325	$300	$275	$250

Add $60 for left handed version of this model.

PAISLEY STRAT — similar to '68 Stratocaster, except has Paisley pickguard/finish.

Mfr.'s Sug. Retail	$820	$615	$410	$400	$375	$350	$325	$300

BLUE FLOWER STRAT — similar to '68 Stratocaster, except has Blue Flower pickguard/finish. Disc. 1994.

		$500	$475	$450	$425	$400	$375	$350

Last Mfr.'s Sug. Retail was $720.

'72 STRATOCASTER — offset double cutaway ash body, white pickguard, bolt-on maple neck, 21 fret maple fingerboard with black dot inlay, standard vibrato, 6 on one side tuners, chrome hardware, 3 single coil pickups, volume/2 tone controls, 5 position switch. Available in Natural and Vintage White finishes. Curr. mfr.

Mfr.'s Sug. Retail	$710	$532	$355	$350	$330	$310	$290	$270

STRAT XII — offset double cutaway alder body, white pickguard, bolt-on maple neck, 22 fret rosewood fingerboard with pearl dot inlay, strings thru bridge, 6 per side tuners, chrome hardware, 3 single coil exposed pickups, volume/2 tone controls, 5 position switch. Available in 3 Tone Sunburst finish. Curr. mfr.

Mfr.'s Sug. Retail	$920	$690	$460	$430	$400	$375	$350	$325

"SHORT SCALE" STRAT — offset double cutaway ash body, white pickguard, bolt-on maple neck, 22 fret maple fingerboard with black dot inlay, standard vibrato, 6 on one side tuners, chrome hardware, 3 single coil pickups, volume/2 tone controls, 5 position switch. Available in Arctic White, Black, Frost Red and 3 Tone Sunburst finishes. Disc. 1994.

		$350	$325	$300	$275	$250	$225	$200

Last Mfr.'s Sug. Retail was $550.

This model had rosewood fingerboard with pearl dot inlay optionally available.

J.D. TELECASTER — single cutaway bound basswood body, black pickguard, bolt-on maple neck, 21 fret maple fingerboard with black dot inlay, strings thru bridge, Jerry Donahue's signature on peghead, 6 on one side tuners, gold hardware, 2 single coil pickups, volume/tone controls, 5 position switch, controls mounted metal plate. Available in Transparent Crimson and 3 Tone Sunburst finishes. Mfd. 1992 to date.

Mfr.'s Sug. Retail	$770	$577	$385	$300	$280	$270	$260	$250

ROSEWOOD TELECASTER — single cutaway rosewood body, black pickguard, bolt-on rosewood neck, 21 fret rosewood fingerboard with pearl dot inlay, strings thru bridge with cover, chrome hardware, 2 single coil pickups, volume/tone control, 3 position switch, controls mounted metal plate. Available in Natural finish. Curr. mfr.

Mfr.'s Sug. Retail	$1,230	$984	$738	$630	$600	$570	$530	$500

'72 TELECASTER THINLINE — single cutaway ash body with hollowed bass side, f hole, pearloid pickguard, bolt-on maple neck, 21 fret maple fingerboard with black dot inlay, strings thru bridge with cover, chrome hardware, 2 humbucker pickups, volume/tone control, 3 position switch. Available in Natural finish. Curr. mfr.

Mfr.'s Sug. Retail	$890	$712	$534	$455	$415	$385	$350	$330

PAISLEY TELE — single cutaway ash body, paisley pickguard, bolt-on maple neck, 21 fret maple fingerboard with black dot inlay, strings thru bridge, 6 on one side tuners, chrome hardware, 2 single coil pickups, volume/tone controls, 3 position switch, controls mounted metal plate. Available in Paisley finish. Curr. mfr.

Mfr.'s Sug. Retail	$820	$615	$410	$400	$380	$350	$330	$305

BLUE FLOWER TELE — similar to Paisley Tele, except has Blue Floral pickguard/finish. Disc. 1994.

		$500	$480	$450	$430	$400	$350	$320

Last Mfr.'s Sug. Retail was $720.

Fender Telecaster
courtesy Dave Rodgers

Grading	100%	98% MINT	95% EXC+	90% EXC	80% VG+	70% VG	60% G

'72 TELECASTER CUSTOM — single cutaway ash body, black pickguard, bolt-on maple neck, 21 fret maple fingerboard with black dot inlay, strings thru bridge, chrome hardware, humbucker/single coil pickups, volume/tone control, 3 position switch. Available in Black and 3 Tone Sunburst finishes. Curr. mfr.

Mfr.'s Sug. Retail	$720	$540	$360	$300	$285	$255	$240	$220

'54 ESQUIRE — single cutaway ash body, black pickguard, bolt-on maple neck, 21 fret maple fingerboard with black dot inlay, strings thru bridge with cover, 6 on one side tuners, chrome hardware, single coil pickup, volume/tone control, 3 position switch, controls mounted metal plate. Available in Blonde and 2 Tone Sunburst finishes. Disc. 1994.

$285	$265	$245	$225	$205	$190	$170

Last Mfr.'s Sug. Retail was $570.

'62 Esquire Custom — similar to '54 Esquire, except has bound body, white pickguard, rosewood fingerboard with pearl dot inlay. Available in Candy Apple Red and 3 Tone Sunburst finishes. Disc. 1994.

$350	$330	$310	$290	$260	$230	$210

Last Mfr.'s Sug. Retail was $580.

'69 MUSTANG — offset double cutaway asymmetrical ash body, pickguard, bolt-on maple neck, 22 fret rosewood fingerboard with pearl dot inlay, floating bridge/vibrato with bridge cover, 6 on one side tuners with plastic buttons, chrome hardware, 2 single coil covered pickups, volume/tone control, 2 selector slide switches. Available in Sonic Blue and Vintage White finishes. Curr. mfr.

Mfr.'s Sug. Retail	$710	$568	$426	$355	$325	$300	$270	$250

ELECTRIC BASS

BASS V — offset double cutaway elongated ash body, white plastic/metal pickguard, thumb rest, bolt-on maple neck, 15 fret rosewood fingerboard with pearl dot inlay, strings thru bridge, coverplate with F logo, 5 on one side tuners, chrome hardware, single coil split covered pickup, pickup coverplate, volume/tone control. Available in Custom Colors and Sunburst finishes. Mfd. 1965 to 1970.

$1,450	$1,325	$1,190	$1,025	$930	$870	$820

Add $100 for left-hand version.

In 1966, bound fingerboard with black inlay became standard.

BASS VI — offset double cutaway asymmetrical ash body, tortoise/metal or white pickguard, bolt-on maple neck, 21 fret rosewood fingerboard with pearl dot inlay, floating bridge/vibrato with bridge cover, 6 on one side tuners, chrome hardware, 3 single coil exposed pickups with metal rings, volume/tone control, 3 two position switches. Available in Custom Color and Sunburst finishes. Mfd. 1961 to 1975.

1962-1965	$3,000	$2,570	$2,140	$1,715	$1,545	$1,415	$1,285
1966-1969	$2,000	$1,715	$1,425	$1,140	$1,030	$940	$855
1970-1975	$1,500	$1,285	$1,070	$860	$770	$710	$645

In 1963, strings mute and another 2 position switch were added, a maple fingerboard with black dot inlay was made available.

In 1966, bound fingerboard with block inlay became standard.

In 1969, Fender locking vibrato was optionally offered.

In 1974, a black pickguard became standard.

BULLET B30 — offset double cutaway alder body, white pickguard, bolt-on maple neck, 19 fret maple fingerboard with black dot inlay, fixed bridge, tele-style peghead, chrome hardware, 1 split covered pickup, volume/tone control. Available in Brown Sunburst, Custom Colors, Ivory, Red and Walnut finishes. Mfd. 1982 to 1983.

$325	$300	$260	$225	$200	$185	$165

Bullet B34 — similar to Bullet B30, except has a long scale length.

$350	$325	$285	$250	$225	$210	$190

Bullet B40 — similar to Bullet B30, except has 20 fret fingerboard.

$375	$350	$310	$275	$250	$235	$215

CORONADO BASS I — double rounded cutaway semi hollow bound maple body, arched top, f holes, 2 finger rests, bolt-on maple neck, 21 fret rosewood fingerboard with pearl dot inlay, adjustable aluminum bridge/trapeze tailpiece, ebony tailpiece insert with pearl F inlay, 4 on one side tuners, chrome hardware, single coil covered pickup, volume/tone control. Available in Cherry and Sunburst finishes. Mfd. 1966 to 1970.

$450	$410	$380	$320	$280	$240	$220

A wide variety of bridge styles was available on this model.

Coronado Bass II — similar to Coronado Bass I, except has bound f holes/fingerboard with block inlay, tunomatic bridge, string mutes, 2 single coil covered pickups, 2 volume/2 tone controls, 3 position switch. Mfd. 1967 to 1970.

$600	$560	$480	$400	$360	$320	$290

Wildwood finishes were optionally available.

The Wildwood finish was the result of a seven year process in Germany where dye was injected into a growing tree. After the tree was harvested, veneers were cut and laminated to the guitar tops. Pickguard numbers (I-VI) refer to the dye color (primary color of green, blue, and gold) and the applied finish.

Fender Telecaster
Blue Book archives

F

Grading	100%	98% MINT	95% EXC+	90% EXC	80% VG+	70% VG	60% G

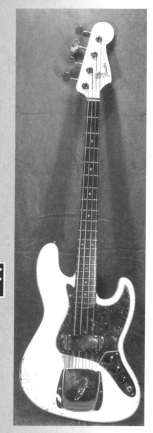

Fender Jazz Bass
Blue Book archives

Coronado Bass II Antigua — similar to Coronado Bass II, except has Antigua (black to silver sunburst) finish. Mfd. 1970 to 1972.

	$650	$610	$530	$450	$400	$360	$310

Jazz Series

Instruments in this series have an offset double cutaway asymmetrical body, bolt-on maple neck, 4 on one side tuners, unless otherwise listed.

JAZZ — alder body, tortoise/metal pickguard with finger rest, 20 fret rosewood fingerboard with pearl dot inlay, fixed bridge with string mutes, F logo bridge cover, chrome hardware, 2 J-style pickups, 2 concentric (volume/tone) controls. Available in Blonde, Custom Colors and 3 Tone Sunburst finishes. Mfd. 1960 to 1974.

	100%	98%	95%	90%	80%	70%	60%
1960-1961	N/A	$4,500	$3,750	$3,000	$2,650	$2,425	$2,225
1962-1965	N/A	$3,500	$2,915	$2,335	$2,050	$1,900	$1,700
1966-1969	N/A	$2,000	$1,665	$1,335	$1,150	$1,050	$1,000
1970-1974	$1,250	$1,070	$895	$715	$625	$575	$535

In 1962, Blonde and Custom Colors finishes were introduced, 2 volume/1 tone controls replaced original items. Blonde finish instruments have ash body. Custom Color finishes have white pickguards.

In 1963, string mutes were removed.

In 1965, bound fingerboard was added.

In 1966, block fingerboard inlay replaced dot inlay.

In 1969, black bound maple fingerboard with black block inlay was made optional.

Certain very clean/all original models in a blonde finish with concentric knobs have sold for as high as $7,000. However, this should be determined on a piece-by-piece basis as opposed to the usual market.

Jazz 3 Bolt Neck — similar to Jazz, except has a 3 bolt neck. Mfd. 1975 to 1980.

	$1,500	$1,400	$1,300	$1,200	$1,100	$1,000	$900

AMERICAN STANDARD JAZZ — alder body, white/metal pickguard, 22 fret rosewood fingerboard with pearl dot inlay, fixed bridge, chrome hardware, 2 J-style American Vintage Jazz pickups, 2 volume/1 tone controls. Available in Arctic White, Black, Brown Sunburst, Caribbean Mist, Lipstick Red, Midnight Blue and Midnight Wine finishes. Curr. mfr.

Mfr.'s Sug. Retail	$989	$741	$494	$480	$450	$410	$380	$350

This model is built in America.

In 1996, Artic White, Carribbean Mist, Lipstick Red, Midnight Blue, and Midnight Wine colors were discontinued. New colors introduced were Candy Apple Red, Vintage White, Crimson burst, and Sonic Blue.

JAZZ CONTEMPORARY — ash body, 20 fret rosewood fingerboard with pearl dot inlay, fixed bridge, chrome hardware, P-style/J-style pickups, volume/tone controls. Mfd. 1987.

	$350	$325	$290	$240	$220	$200	$190

This model also available without frets.

Jazz Gold — similar to Jazz, except has gold hardware. Available in Gold finish. Mfd. 1981 to 1984.

	$750	$700	$660	$540	$500	$475	$450

JAZZ SPECIAL — P-style basswood body, no pickguard, J-bass style neck, graphite nut, black hardware, P/J pickup configuration.

	$315	$300	$290	$270	$240	$220	$200

Jazz "Power" Special — similar to Jazz Special, except has triple laminated maple, graphite and rosewood neck, active circuitry.

	$315	$300	$290	$270	$240	$220	$200

JAZZ PLUS — alder body, 22 fret rosewood fingerboard with pearl dot inlay, fixed bridge, chrome hardware, 2 J-style Lace Sensor pickups, volume/pan control, concentric treble/bass control, active electronics. Available in Arctic White, Black, Black Pearl Burst, Blue Pearl Burst, Brown Sunburst, Caribbean Mist, Lipstick Red, Midnight Blue, Midnight Wine and Natural finishes. Mfd. in USA. Curr. mfr.

Mfr.'s Sug. Retail	$1,120	$840	$560	$490	$440	$420	$400	$385

This model has ash body, maple fingerboard with black dot inlay optionally available.

Jazz Plus V — similar to Jazz Plus, except has 5 strings, 5 on one side tuners.

Mfr.'s Sug. Retail	$1,190	$892	$595	$520	$470	$450	$430	$405

JAZZ STANDARD — poplar body, white/metal pickguard, 20 fret rosewood fingerboard with pearl dot inlay, fixed bridge, chrome hardware, 2 J-style pickups, 2 volume/1 tone controls. Available in Arctic White, Black, Crimson Red Metallic and Lake Placid Blue finishes. Mfd. in Japan. Curr. mfr.

Mfr.'s Sug. Retail	$410	$307	$205	$190	$180	$170	$160	$140

Jazz Standard Fretless — similar to Jazz Standard, except has basswood body, fretless fingerboard. Available in Arctic White and Black finishes.

Mfr.'s Sug. Retail	$660	$495	$330	$245	$230	$210	$195	$180

Jazz Standard Left Hand — similar to Jazz Standard, except has basswood body, left handed configuration. Available in 3-Color Sunburst and Vintage White finishes.

Mfr.'s Sug. Retail	$840	$630	$420	$275	$260	$250	$235	$220

Fender Jazz Bass
Blue Book archives

Grading	100%	98% MINT	95% EXC+	90% EXC	80% VG+	70% VG	60% G

REISSUE '60s JAZZ — basswood body, white/metal pickguard with finger rest, 20 fret rosewood fingerboard with pearl dot inlay, fixed bridge, chrome hardware, 2 J-style pickups, 2 volume/1 tone controls. Available in Black, Candy Apple Red, Olympic White, Sonic Blue and 3-Color Sunburst finishes. Curr. mfr.

| Mfr.'s Sug. Retail | $700 | $525 | $350 | $300 | $285 | $275 | $260 | $245 |

This model is also referred to as the '60s Jazz Bass.

Reissue '60s Jazz Natural — similar to Reissue 60's Jazz, except has Foto-Flame finish. Mfd. 1994 to date.

| Mfr.'s Sug. Retail | $800 | $600 | $400 | $360 | $325 | $315 | $300 | $285 |

JAZZ U.S. VINTAGE '62 — alder body, white/metal pickguard with finger rest, 20 fret rosewood fingerboard with pearl dot inlay, fixed bridge, chrome hardware, 2 J-style pickups, 2 concentric (volume/tone) controls. Available in Black, 3-Color Sunburst and Vintage White finishes. Current production.

| Mfr.'s Sug. Retail | $1,499 | $1,124 | $749 | $600 | $550 | $525 | $500 | $450 |

This model is also referred to as the '62 Jazz Bass.

This model has black or tortoise pickguards optionally available.

THE VENTURES JAZZ BASS — light ash body, white shell/metal pickguard with finger rest, 20 fret rosewood fingerboard with white block inlay, fixed bridge, gold hardware, 2 J-style Fender U.S.A. pickups, volume/tone controls. Available in Midnight Black Transparent finish. Current production.

| Mfr.'s Sug. Retail | $1,439 | $1,151 | $863 | $740 | $650 | $585 | $525 | $500 |

JP-90 — offset double cutaway asymmetrical poplar body, black pickguard, bolt-on maple neck, 20 fret rosewood fingerboard with pearl dot inlay, fixed bridge, 4 on one side tuners, chrome hardware, P-style/J-style pickups, volume/tone control, 3 position switch. Available in Arctic White, Black and Torino Red finishes. Mfd. 1990 to date.

| Mfr.'s Sug. Retail | $530 | $397 | $265 | $245 | $220 | $210 | $200 | $190 |

MB-4 — offset double cutaway asymmetrical basswood body, black pickguard, bolt-on maple neck, 22 fret rosewood fingerboard with pearl dot inlay, fixed bridge, 4 on one side tuners, chrome hardware, P-style/J-style pickups, concentric volume/treble/bass/mix controls, 3 position switch. Available in Black, Red and White finishes. New 1994.

| Mfr.'s Sug. Retail | $550 | $412 | $275 | $200 | $180 | $170 | $160 | $150 |

MB-5 — similar to MB-4, except has 5 strings, 5 on one side tuners. New 1994.

| Mfr.'s Sug. Retail | $620 | $465 | $310 | $225 | $200 | $180 | $170 | $160 |

This model has poplar body optionally available.

MUSICMASTER — offset double cutaway asymmetrical ash body, black pickguard, thumb rest, bolt-on maple neck, 19 fret rosewood fingerboard with pearl dot inlay, fixed bridge, 4 on one side tuners, chrome hardware, single coil covered pickup, volume/tone control. Available in Black, Blue, Red and White finishes. Mfd. 1970 to 1983.

| | | $400 | $380 | $350 | $340 | $320 | $300 | $280 |

MUSTANG — offset double cutaway poplar body, plastic/metal pickguard, thumb rest, bolt-on maple neck, 19 fret rosewood fingerboard with pearl dot inlay, fixed bridge, 4 on one side tuners, chrome hardware, P-style pickup, volume/tone control. Available in Antigua, Black, Blond, Blue, Natural, Red, Sunburst, Walnut, White and Wine finishes. Mfd. 1966 to 1983.

| | | $700 | $675 | $625 | $600 | $575 | $540 | $500 |

Add $45 for left-hand version.

Add $100 for Competition finishes.

In 1969, Competition finishes were introduced. These finishes consist of solid colors (blue, burgundy, orange and red) with racing stripes. The instrument was also referred to as Competition Mustang Bass with these finishes.

PERFORMER — offset dual cutaway asymmetrical hardwood body, white pickguard, bolt-on maple neck, 24 fret rosewood fingerboard with pearl dot inlay, fixed bridge, 4 on one side tuners, chrome hardware, 2 single coil covered pickups, 2 volume/1 tone controls, active electronics. Available in Sunburst finish. Mfd. 1987 to 1988.

| | | $280 | $260 | $240 | $200 | $190 | $170 | $150 |

Precision Series

All instruments in this series have an offset double cutaway body, bolt-on maple neck, 4 on one side tuners, unless otherwise listed.

PRECISION, EARLY DESIGN — ash body, black pickguard, 20 fret maple fingerboard with black dot inlay, strings thru bridge with cover, chrome hardware, single coil exposed pickup with cover, volume/tone controls on metal plate. Available in Blond finish. Mfd. 1951 to 1954.

| | | $3,250 | $2,275 | $1,950 | $1,625 | $1,300 | $1,170 | $1,070 |

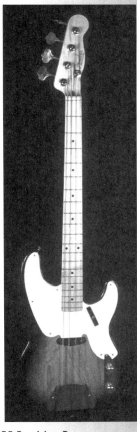

1955 Precision Bass
courtesy Thoroughbred Music

"The interest for the real fine acoustic body guitar, which is worldwide, has never dwindled down. This is certainly backed up by the amount of money people are willing to pay now for a good handcrafted guitar."
—Fred Popovich on Johnny Smith
TCG, Sept/Oct 1990

Grading	100%	98% MINT	95% EXC+	90% EXC	80% VG+	70% VG	60% G

Precision — similar to original design Precision, except has white pickguard. Available in Blond, Custom Colors, 2 Tone Sunburst and 3 Tone Sunburst finishes. Mfd. 1954 to date.

	100%	98%	95%	90%	80%	70%	60%
1954-1957	N/A	$3,000	$2,500	$2,000	$1,800	$1,650	$1,500
1957-1959	N/A	$4,000	$3,330	$2,665	$2,400	$2,200	$2,000
1960-1965	N/A	$2,000	$1,665	$1,335	$1,200	$1,100	$1,000
1966-1969	N/A	$1,250	$1,045	$835	$750	$690	$625
1970-1979	$550	$525	$500	$460	$430	$400	$370
Curr. Mfr.'s Sug. Retail	$410	$328	$246	$205	$165	$145	$135	$125

Black pickguard with Blonde finish was optionally available on this instrument.

During 1957, a redesigned aluminum pickguard, fixed bridge, strat style peghead and split pickup replaced the original items.

In 1959, rosewood fingerboard with pearl dot inlay replaced maple.

In 1968, maple fingerboard was optionally available.

In 1970, fretless fingerboard was optionally available.

By 1976, thumbrest on pickguard was standard.

Precision Contemporary — similar to Precision, except has no pickguard and a rosewood fingerboard. Mfd. 1987.

	$245	$230	$210	$190	$175	$165	$155

PRECISION ACOUSTIC/ELECTRIC — hollowed basswood body, bound solid spruce top, f hole, fretless rosewood fingerboard, strings thru acoustic style rosewood bridge, chrome hardware, P-style Lace Sensor/piezo bridge pickups, volume/tone/pan controls, active electronics. Available in Antique Burst and Natural finishes. Curr. mfr.

Mfr.'s Sug. Retail	$1,230	$922	$615	$375	$350	$325	$300	$275

This model is also available with 20 fret fingerboard.

AMERICAN STANDARD PRECISION — alder body, graphite reinforced maple neck with vintage decal, 34" scale, 20 fret rosewood fingerboard with pearl dot inlay, strings through body bridge, chrome hardware, P-style American Vintage Precision pickup, volume/tone controls. Available in Black, Brown Sunburst, Candy Apple Red, Vintage White, Crimson burst, Sonic Blue finishes. New 1996.

Mfr.'s Sug. Retail	$929	$743	$557	$480	$360	$290	$240	$220

American Standard Precision (Fretless) — similar to the American Standard Precision, except with fretless neck. Available in Black, Brown Sunburst, Candy Apple Red, and Vintage White. New 1996.

Mfr.'s Sug. Retail	$999	$799	$599	$540	$430	$360	$310	$290

American Standard Precision (Left Hand) — similar to the American Standard Precision, except in a left handed configuration. Available in Black, Brown Sunburst, Candy Apple Red, and Vintage White. New 1996.

Mfr.'s Sug. Retail	$1,049	$839	$629	$590	$480	$400	$360	$310

PRECISION CONTEMPORARY "LYTE" — basswood body, 22 fret rosewood fingerboard with pearl dot inlay, fixed bridge, gold hardware, P-style/J-style Lace Sensor covered pickups, volume/treble/bass/pan controls, active electronics. Available in Blue Foto Flame, Crimson Foto Flame, Frost White, Montego Black and Violin Burst finishes. Curr. mfr.

Mfr.'s Sug. Retail	$820	$615	$410	$270	$260	$250	$240	$220

Precision Elite Series

PRECISION ELITE I — ash body, white pickguard, 20 fret maple fingerboard with black dot inlay, fixed bridge with tuners, die-cast tuners, chrome hardware, P-style covered pickup, volume/tone control, active electronics. Mfd. 1983 to 1985.

	$370	$350	$330	$300	$280	$260	$240

Precision Elite II — similar to Precision Elite I, except has 2 P-style pickups, 2 volume/1 tone controls, 3 position mini switch.

	$375	$355	$335	$305	$285	$265	$245

Precision Gold Elite I — similar to Precision Elite I, except has gold hardware.

	$360	$340	$320	$290	$270	$250	$230

Precision Gold Elite II — similar to Precision Elite I, except has gold hardware, 2 P-style pickups, 2 volume/1 tone controls, 3 position mini switch.

	$400	$390	$360	$330	$310	$290	$260

Precision Walnut Elite I — similar to Precision Elite I, except has walnut body/neck, black pickguard, ebony fingerboard with pearl dot inlay, strings thru bridge, gold hardware, P-style exposed pickup, volume/treble/bass controls, series/parallel switch. Available in Natural finish.

	$385	$365	$345	$315	$295	$275	$255

Precision Walnut Elite II — similar to Precision Elite I, except has walnut body/neck, black pickguard, ebony fingerboard with pearl dot inlay, strings thru bridge, gold hardware, 2 P-style exposed pickups, volume/treble/bass controls, series/parallel switch. Available in Natural finish.

	$415	$405	$375	$345	$325	$305	$275

Grading	100%	98% MINT	95% EXC+	90% EXC	80% VG+	70% VG	60% G

PRECISION PLUS — alder body, 22 fret rosewood fingerboard with pearl dot inlay, fixed bridge with tuners, chrome hardware, P-style/J-style Lace Sensor pickups, volume/tone control, 3 position switch, series/parallel pushbutton, active electronics. Available in Arctic White, Black, Black Pearl Burst, Blue Pearl Burst, Brown Sunburst, Caribbean Mist, Lipstick Red, Midnight Blue, Midnight Wine and Natural finishes. Mfd. 1990 to 1994.

			$500	$475	$425	$400	$375	$350	$325

Last Mfr.'s Sug. Retail was $1,000.

Add $100 for ash body with Natural finish.

This model was also available with maple fingerboard with black dot inlay.

Precision Deluxe Plus — similar to Precision Plus, except has down-sized body style, volume/treble/bass/pan controls, redesigned active electronics.

Mfr.'s Sug. Retail	$1,200	$900	$600	$490	$440	$400	$385	$350

Precision Reissue '50s — basswood body, white pickguard, 20 fret maple fingerboard with black dot inlay, fixed bridge, chrome hardware, P-style exposed pickup, volume/tone control. Available in Black, Candy Apple Red, Olympic White, Sonic Blue and 3 Tone Sunburst finishes. Curr. mfr.

Mfr.'s Sug. Retail	$690	$517	$345	$290	$265	$250	$240	$230

Precision Reissue '60s — similar to Precision Reissue '50s, except has tortoise pickguard, rosewood fingerboard with pearl dot inlay.

Mfr.'s Sug. Retail	$690	$517	$345	$290	$265	$250	$240	$230

This model also available with white pickguard.

Precision Reissue '60s Natural — similar to Precision Reissue '50s, except has tortoise pickguard, rosewood fingerboard with pearl dot inlay. Available in Foto-Flame finish. New 1994.

Mfr.'s Sug. Retail	$800	$600	$400	$355	$330	$315	$305	$295

PRECISION SPECIAL — alder body, white pickguard, 22 fret maple fingerboard with black dot inlay, fixed bridge, brass hardware, P-style exposed pickup, volume/treble/bass controls, active electronics. Available in Candy Apple Red and Lake Placid Blue finishes. Mfd. 1982 to 1983.

			$340	$315	$295	$270	$255	$245	$235

Precision Special Walnut — similar to Precision Special, except has walnut body/neck. Available in Natural finish. Mfd. 1982 to 1983.

			$330	$305	$285	$260	$245	$235	$225

STANDARD PRECISION — poplar body, white pickguard, 20 fret rosewood fingerboard with pearl dot inlay, fixed bridge, chrome hardware, P-style pickup, volume/tone control. Available in Arctic White, Black, Crimson Red, and Lake Placid Blue finishes. Mfd. 1987 to date.

Mfr.'s Sug. Retail	$410	$307	$205	$190	$180	$160	$150	$140

U.S. VINTAGE '57 PRECISION — ash body, gold aluminum pickguard with thumbrest, 20 fret maple fingerboard with black dot inlay, fixed bridge, gold hardware, P-style pickup, volume/tone control. Available in Blond, Black, 2 Tone Sunburst and Vintage White finishes. Mfd. 1982 to date.

Mfr.'s Sug. Retail	$1,330	$997	$665	$550	$500	$475	$450	$425

This model is a replica of the Precision Bass as it appeared in 1957.

In 1989, alder body and nickel plated hardware replaced original items.

U.S. Vintage '57 Precision (Left-Hand Model) — similar to U.S. Vintage '57 Precision, except is left handed. Available in Black and Olympic white finishes. Curr. mfr.

Mfr.'s Sug. Retail	$2,460	$1,845	$1,230	$975	$900	$825	$780	$750

U.S. VINTAGE '62 PRECISION — ash body, tortoise pickguard with thumbrest, 20 fret rosewood fingerboard with pearl dot inlay, fixed bridge, chrome hardware, P-style pickup, volume/tone control. Available in Blond, Black, 3 Tone Sunburst and Vintage White finishes. Mfd. 1982 to date.

Mfr.'s Sug. Retail	$1,339	$1,071	$803	$680	$630	$590	$550	$520

This model is a replica of the Precision Bass as it appeared in 1962.

U.S. Vintage '62 Precision (Left-Hand Model) — similar to U.S. Vintage '62 Precision, except is left handed. Available in Black and Olympic white finishes. Disc. 1994.

			$1,100	$1,000	$900	$800	$750	$700	$650

Last Mfr.'s Sug. Retail was $2,200.

VINTAGE PRECISION CUSTOM — ash body, 20 fret maple fingerboard with black dot inlay, fixed bridge, nickel hardware, P-style/J-style pickups, 2 volume/2 tone controls. Available in Honey Blonde and 2 Tone Sunburst finishes. New 1993.

Mfr.'s Sug. Retail	$2,150	$1,612	$1,075	$840	$760	$710	$680	$650

PRODIGY ACTIVE BASS — offset double cutaway poplar body, bolt-on maple neck, 20 fret rosewood fingerboard with pearl dot inlay, fixed bridge, 4 on one side tuners, chrome hardware, P-style/J-style pickups, concentric volume-pan/treble-bass controls, active electronics. Available in Arctic White, Black, Crimson Red Metallic and Lake Placid Blue finishes. Mfd. 1992 to date.

Mfr.'s Sug. Retail	$600	$450	$300	$260	$240	$220	$200	$185

Grading	100%	98%	95%	90%	80%	70%	60%
	MINT	**EXC+**	**EXC**	**VG+**	**VG**	**G**	

PROPHECY I — offset double cutaway asymmetrical basswood body, bolt-on maple neck, 22 fret rosewood fingerboard with pearl dot inlay, fixed bridge, 2 per side tuners, chrome hardware, P-style/J-style pickups, volume/treble/bass/mix controls. Available in Sunburst finish. Curr. mfr.

Mfr.'s Sug. Retail	$770	$577	$385	$280	$265	$240	$230	$210

Prophecy II — similar to Prophecy I, except has ash body, gold hardware, active electronics.

Mfr.'s Sug. Retail	$870	$652	$435	$320	$300	$280	$270	$250

Prophecy III — similar to Prophecy I, except has alder/walnut/bubinga body, thru body maple neck, gold hardware, active electronics.

Mfr.'s Sug. Retail	$1,330	$997	$665	$490	$475	$450	$435	$400

TELECASTER-1st VERSION — offset double cutaway ash body, white pickguard, finger rest, bolt-on maple neck, 20 fret maple fingerboard with black dot inlay, fixed bridge with cover, 4 on one side tuners, chrome hardware, single coil exposed pickup with cover, volume/tone control. Available in Blonde and Custom Colors finishes. Mfd. 1968 to 1972.

	$1,500	$1,350	$1,100	$1,000	$950	$900	$840

In 1970, a fretless fingerboard became optionally available.

Telecaster-2nd Version — similar to Telecaster, except has redesigned pickguard, thumb rest, 2 section bridge, covered humbucker pickup with no separate cover. Available in Blonde and Sunburst finishes. Mfd. 1972 to 1979.

	$1,000	$900	$800	$700	$650	$600	$550

A 4 section single string groove bridge was available 1977-1979.

Telecaster Paisley/Floral — similar to Telecaster Bass, except available in Blue Floral and Pink Paisley finishes and had a single coil pickup. Mfd. 1968 to 1970.

	$3,000	$2,700	$2,300	$2,000	$1,900	$1,800	$1,700

URGE — offset double cutaway alder body, pearloid pickguard, bolt-on maple neck, 24 fret pau ferro fingerboard, strings thru gold bridge, Stu Hamm's signature on peghead, 4 on one side black chrome tuners, J-style/P-style/J-style pickups, concentric volume-pan/treble-bass controls, 3 position mini/rotary switches, active electronics. Available in Burgundy Mist, Lake Placid Blue, Montego Black and Sherwood Metallic finishes. Mfd. 1993 to date.

Mfr.'s Sug. Retail	$1,400	$1,050	$700	$620	$560	$530	$500	$450

This instrument was designed by Stu Hamm.

Urge Standard — similar to Urge, except has poplar body, rosewood fingerboard, 2 J-style pickups, volume/treble/bass/mix controls, active electronics. New 1994.

Mfr.'s Sug. Retail	$560	$420	$280	$240	$220	$200	$185	$160

Limited Edition Series

All instruments in this series are custom order, limited edition instruments.

'51 PRECISION — offset double cutaway ash body, black pickguard, bolt-on maple neck, 20 fret maple fingerboard with black dot inlay, strings thru bridge, chrome hardware, single coil exposed pickup with cover, volume/tone controls on metal plate. Available in Blonde and 2 Tone Sunburst finishes. Curr. mfr.

Mfr.'s Sug. Retail	$810	$607	$405	$400	$375	$340	$300	$280

'75 PRECISION — similar to '51 Precision, except has P-style pickup. Available in Natural finish. Curr. mfr.

Mfr.'s Sug. Retail	$720	$540	$360	$300	$280	$260	$240	$220

This model also available with rosewood fingerboard with pearl dot inlay.

'75 JAZZ — offset double cutaway asymmetrical ash body, white/metal pickguard with finger rest, 20 fret rosewood fingerboard with pearl dot inlay, fixed bridge with string mutes, F logo bridge cover, chrome hardware, 2 J-style pickups, 2 volume/1 tone controls. Available in Natural and 3 Tone Sunburst finishes. Curr. mfr.

Mfr.'s Sug. Retail	$880	$660	$440	$360	$320	$300	$280	$260

This model also available with maple fingerboard with black dot inlay.

FENIX

Instruments built in Korea from the late 1980s to date.

Fenix guitars were built in the same Korean factory that produced Fender's Squier models; as a result, models with the FENIX trademark tend to be copies of American designs and "superstrat" designs.

(Source: Tony Bacon and Paul Day, The Guru's Guitar Guide)

FENTON-WEILL

Instruments built in England from 1959 through the mid 1960s.

Henry Weill's company after collaboration with Jim Burns (BURNS-WEILL trademark) produced a decent range of distinctive solid body designs. While earlier models may seem similar to BURNS-WEILL models, they were soon restyled and other models of "similar character" added.

Fenton-Weill also produced fibreglass bodied guitars under the trademark of FIBRATONE.

"I seriously doubt if anybody on earth ever answered the familiar childhood query 'what do you want to be when you grow up' with the answer 'I want to sell used guitars!'"

—Skip Henderson

TCG, Sept/Oct 1990

As author Tony Bacon has noted, "Although UK-made guitars have often offered better value and quality, they apparently lack the mystique of leading USA instruments". Most English-built guitars were destined for English consumption.

(Source: Tony Bacon, The Ultimate Guitar Book)

FERNANDES

Instruments produced in Tokyo, Japan since the mid 1980s by the Fernandes Company, Ltd. Distribution in the U.S. market by Fernandes Guitars U.S.A. Inc., of Van Nuys, California.

Fernandes offers a wide range of instruments aimed at the entry level beginner up to the professional musician.

ELECTRIC

Grading	100%	98% MINT	95% EXC+	90% EXC	80% VG+	70% VG	60% G

AFR-80 — offset double cutaway maple body, bolt-on maple neck, 24 fret rosewood fingerboard with pearl dot inlay, double locking vibrato, 6 on one side tuners, black hardware, 2 stacked coil/1 humbucker pickups, volume/tone control, 5 position switch. Available in Candy Apple Red, Metallic Blue, Pearl Black and Pearl White finishes. Mfd. 1991 to 1992.

	$525	$450	$375	$300	$270	$245	$225

Last Mfr.'s Sug. Retail was $750.

This model had ash body optionally available.

AFR-85 — similar to AFR-80, except has humbucker/stacked coil/humbucker pickups.

	$560	$480	$400	$320	$290	$265	$240

Last Mfr.'s Sug. Retail was $800.

AMG-60 — double cutaway basswood body, set in maple neck, 24 fret maple fingerboard with black dot inlay, standard vibrato, 3 per side tuners, gold hardware, 2 humbucker pickups, volume/tone control, 3 position switch. Available in Fire Red, Navy Blue, Screaming Yellow and Snow White finishes. Mfd. 1991 to 1992.

	$510	$440	$365	$290	$260	$240	$220

Last Mfr.'s Sug. Retail was $730.

AMG-70 — similar to AMG-60, except has ash body, rosewood fingerboard with white dot inlay, black hardware, 2 stacked coil/1 humbucker pickups. Available in Transparent Black, Transparent Green, Transparent Purple and Transparent Red finishes. Disc. 1993.

	$525	$450	$375	$300	$270	$245	$225

Last Mfr.'s Sug. Retail was $750.

APG-80 — double cutaway bound mahogany body, maple top, set in maple neck, 24 fret rosewood fingerboard with pearl dot inlay, double locking vibrato, bound peghead, 3 per side tuners, gold hardware, stacked coil/humbucker pickups, volume/tone control, 3 position switch. Available in Lemon Drop, Transparent Blue, Transparent Purple and Transparent Red finishes. Mfd. 1991 to 1992.

	$630	$540	$450	$360	$325	$300	$275

Last Mfr.'s Sug. Retail was $900.

APG-90FS — similar to APG-80, except has arched maple top, tunomatic bridge/stop tailpiece, 2 humbucker pickups, mini switch, active electronics. Available in Lemon Drop, Transparent Black and Transparent Red finishes. Disc. 1993.

	$840	$720	$600	$480	$430	$395	$360

Last Mfr.'s Sug. Retail was $1,200.

APG-100 — similar to APG-80, except has arched maple top, tunomatic bridge/stop tailpiece and 2 humbucker pickups. Available in Cherry Sunburst, Lemon Drop, Transparent Black and Transparent Red finishes. Mfd. 1991 to date.

Mfr.'s Sug. Retail	$1,000	$800	$600	$500	$400	$360	$330	$300

FSG-60 — offset double cutaway basswood body, bolt-on maple neck, 22 fret rosewood fingerboard with pearl dot inlay, standard vibrato, 6 on one side tuners, black hardware, 2 single coil/1 humbucker pickups, 2 volume/1 tone control, 3 position switch, 2 mini switches, active electronics. Available in Black, Cobalt Blue and Cream White finishes. Mfd. 1993 to date.

Mfr.'s Sug. Retail	$800	$640	$480	$400	$320	$290	$265	$240

FSG-80 — similar to FSG-60, except has ash body. Available in Tobacco Sunburst, Transparent Black, Transparent Purple and Transparent Red finishes. New 1994.

Mfr.'s Sug. Retail	$900	$720	$540	$450	$360	$325	$300	$275

FSG-100 — similar to FSG-60, except has ash body, double locking vibrato, gold hardware. Available in Transparent Black, Transparent Purple, Transparent Red and Tobacco Sunburst finishes.

Mfr.'s Sug. Retail	$1,100	$880	$660	$550	$440	$395	$365	$330

LE-1 — offset double cutaway basswood body, white pickguard, bolt-on maple neck, 21 fret maple fingerboard with black dot inlay, standard vibrato, 6 on one side tuners, chrome hardware, 3 single coil pickups, volume/2 tone controls, 5 position switch. Available in Black, Cream White and Red finishes. Mfd. 1993 to date.

Mfr.'s Sug. Retail	$400	$320	$240	$200	$160	$145	$130	$120

This model has rosewood fingerboard with pearl dot inlay optionally available.

Grading	100%	98% MINT	95% EXC+	90% EXC	80% VG+	70% VG	60% G

LE-2 — offset double cutaway basswood body, white pickguard, bolt-on maple neck, 21 fret maple fingerboard with black dot inlay, standard vibrato, 6 on one side tuners, chrome hardware, 3 single coil pickups, volume/2 tone controls, 5 position switch. Available in Black, Candy Apple Red, Cream, Sonic Blue, 2 Tone Sunburst and 3 Tone Sunburst finishes. Mfd. 1991 to date.

Mfr.'s Sug. Retail	$470	$376	$282	$235	$190	$170	$155	$140

Add $70 for left handed version of this model (LE-2LH).

This model has alder body optionally available.

LE-2FS — similar to LE-2, except has active electronics. Disc. 1993.

	$495	$425	$355	$285	$255	$235	$215

Last Mfr.'s Sug. Retail was $710.

LE-2G — similar to LE-2, except has gold hardware. Available in Candy Apple Red, Cream White, Gold, Vintage Metallic Blue and 3 Tone Sunburst finishes.

Mfr.'s Sug. Retail	$500	$400	$300	$250	$200	$180	$165	$150

LE-2X — similar to LE-2, except has double locking vibrato, 2 single coil/1 humbucker pickups. Available in Black, Candy Apple Red, Cream, Sonic Blue and 3 Tone Sunburst finishes.

	$420	$360	$300	$240	$215	$195	$180

Last Mfr.'s Sug. Retail was $600.

This model has reverse peghead, gold hardware optionally available.

LE-3 — offset double cutaway basswood body, white pickguard, bolt-on maple neck, 21 fret maple fingerboard with black dot inlay, standard vibrato, roller nut, 6 on one side tuners, chrome hardware, 3 single coil pickups, volume/2 tone controls, 5 position switch. Available in Black, Cream White and Red finishes. Disc. 1993.

	$490	$420	$350	$280	$250	$230	$210

Last Mfr.'s Sug. Retail was $700.

LE-3FS — similar to LE-3, except has active electronics.

	$700	$600	$500	$400	$360	$330	$300

Last Mfr.'s Sug. Retail was $1,000.

TE-1 — single cutaway basswood body, white pickguard, bolt-on maple neck, 21 fret maple fingerboard with black dot inlay, thru strings bridge, 6 on one side tuners, chrome hardware, 2 single coil pickups, volume/tone control, 3 position switch. Available in Black, Candy Apple Red, Cream White and Three Tone Sunburst finishes. Mfd. 1993 to date.

Mfr.'s Sug. Retail	$470	$376	$282	$235	$190	$170	$155	$140

Add $30 for ash body (TE-1N).

This model has rosewood fingerboard with pearl dot inlay optionally available.

TE-2 — similar to TE-1, except has bound body. Available in Black, Candy Apple Red, Vintage Metallic Blue and 3 Tone Sunburst finishes.

Mfr.'s Sug. Retail	$500	$400	$300	$250	$200	$180	$165	$150

TE-3 — similar to TE-1, except has semi hollow ash body, restyled pearloid pickguard. Available in Black, Candy Apple Red, Natural and 3 Tone Sunburst finishes.

Mfr.'s Sug. Retail	$700	$560	$420	$350	$280	$250	$230	$210

ELECTRIC BASS

AMB-40 — offset double cutaway basswood body, bolt-on maple neck, 24 fret rosewood fingerboard with pearl dot inlay, fixed bridge, 2 per side tuners, chrome hardware, P-style/J-style Fernandes pickups, 2 volume/1 tone control. Available in Black, Blue Sunburst, Fire Red and Snow White finishes. Mfd. 1991 to 1993.

	$400	$340	$285	$230	$205	$190	$170

Last Mfr.'s Sug. Retail was $570.

Available in left handed style only.

AMB-60 — similar to AMB-40, except has black hardware.

Mfr.'s Sug. Retail	$600	$480	$360	$300	$240	$215	$195	$180

Available in right handed style only.

AMB-70 — similar to AMB-40, except has ash body, active pickups and gold hardware. Available in Transparent Black, Transparent Purple, Transparent White and Vintage Natural finishes. Disc. 1992.

	$560	$480	$400	$320	$290	$265	$240

Last Mfr.'s Sug. Retail was $800.

APB-80 — offset double cutaway ash body, bolt-on maple neck, 24 fret rosewood fingerboard with pearl dot inlay, fixed bridge, 2 per side tuners, gold hardware, P-style/J-style pickups, 2 volume/1 tone control. Available in Black, Fire Red, Metallic Blue and Snow White finishes. Disc. 1993.

	$490	$420	$350	$280	$250	$230	$210

Last Mfr.'s Sug. Retail was $700.

APB-90 — similar to APB-80, except has active pickups, volume/treble/bass/mix controls. Available in Transparent Blue, Transparent Purple, Transparent Red and Transparent White finishes.

Mfr.'s Sug. Retail	$900	$720	$540	$450	$360	$325	$300	$275

This model also available with maple fingerboard with black dot inlay, 2 J-style pickups (APB-90M).

This model has fretless fingerboard optionally available.

Grading	100%	98% MINT	95% EXC+	90% EXC	80% VG+	70% VG	60% G

APB-100 — similar to APB-80, except has 5 strings, 3/2 per side tuners, 2 active J-style pickups. Available in Transparent Black, Transparent Purple, Transparent White and Vintage Natural finishes.

Mfr.'s Sug. Retail	$1,000	$800	$600	$500	$400	$360	$330	$300

This model has fretless fingerboard optionally available.

TEB-1 — single cutaway basswood body, black pickguard, bolt-on maple neck, 21 fret maple fingerboard with black dot inlay, fixed bridge, 4 on one side tuners, gold hardware, P-style/J-style pickups, 2 volume/1 tone control. Available in Black and Cream White finishes. Mfd. 1993 to date.

Mfr.'s Sug. Retail	$700	$560	$420	$350	$280	$250	$230	$210

FERRINGTON

Instruments built in Santa Monica, California since 1980.

Luthier Danny Ferrington was born and raised in Louisiana. Ferrington's father, Lloyd, was a cabinet maker who had previously played guitar and bass in a local country western combo. Ferrington's first experiences with woodworking were in his father's shop in Monroe, Louisiana.

Ferrington accepted an apprenticeship in 1975 at the Old Time Pickin' Parlour in Nashville, Tennessee. He spent the next five years working with noted acoustic guitar builder Randy Woods. Ferrington's first acoustic was built in 1977, and he continued to hone his craft.

In 1980, Ferrington moved to Los Angeles, California. Ferrington spent a number of years experimenting with different designs, and tones from instruments, and continued building custom guitars. Many of the features on the custom guitars are developed through discussions with the musician commissioning the piece. It is estimated that by 1992, Ferrington had constructed over one hundred custom instruments.

(Source: Kate Geil, et al, the Ferrington Guitars book)

In the late 1980s, the Kramer guitar company was offering several models designed by Ferrington. After Kramer went under, the Ferrington Guitar Company of Long Branch, New Jersey (908.870.3800) offered essentially the same models (KFS-1, KFT-1, and KFB-1) with "Ferrington" on the headstock. These models feature a maple neck, rosewood fingerboard, acoustic body, 3-band EQ, and a thinline bridge transducer.

FIBRATONE

See FENTON-WEILL.

These semi-hollow body guitars were built of fibre-glass, and produced by the Fenton-Weill company of England in the 1960s.

FICHTER

Instruments built in Frankfurt, Germany since 1988.

Luthier/designer Thomas Fichter has been building modern electric upright basses for over seven years. While production was modest in the early years, annual production now reaches fifty instruments a year. In 1995 Fichter debuted a five string model (strung with either a high C or low B). Current musicians playing the Fichter upright are jazz bassist Marc Abrams and Alex Al (touring with Diana Ross).

The Fichter **e - kontrabasse** is minimally larger than an electric bass guitar, and can easily fit in the back seat of a mid-sized car. Weighing in at around 13 pounds, the body is constructed of maple and mahogany and has a 41" scale. The model features an ebony fingerboard, active preamp and coaxial transducer pickup system, and custom Schaller tuners. 1996 U.S. prices run $3,490 for the four string model and $3,620 for the five string (the instrument's display stand is another $98). For further information, please contact luthier Fichter through the Index of Current Manufacturers located in the rear of this book.

Fichter Kontrabasse
courtesy Thomas Fichter

FINGERBONE

Instruments were built in England from 1986 to 1989.

The 'Fastback' model was a high quality solid body guitar with an original design and different hardware options.

(Source: Tony Bacon and Paul Day, The Guru's Guitar Guide)

FIREFOX

Instruments were built in Japan since late 1980s.

These medium quality solid body guitars were based on American designs, and produced in either full size or "mini" versions.

(Source: Tony Bacon and Paul Day, the Guru's Guitar Guide)

FISHER

Instruments built in Coalport, Pennsylvania in the early 1990s.

Fisher guitars offered 2 models of solid body electric guitars that featured American components (hardware and pickups).

FITZPATRICK JAZZ GUITARS

Instruments currently built in Wickford, Rhode Island.

Luthier C. Fitzpatrick builds high quality hand-crafted guitars. For further information on pricing and availability, please contact luthier Fitzpatrick via the Index of Current Manufacturers located in the back of this book.

FIVE STAR

See chapter on House Brands.

While this trademark has been identified as a "House Brand", the retailer or distributor has not yet been identified. These smaller bodied acoustics have the logo and star position markers painted on, as opposed to the inlay work of a more expensive guitar.

(Source: Willie G. Moseley, Stellas & Stratocasters)

FLANDERS

Instruments built in New England since 1979. Distributed by Fretboard Corner of Lake Ronkonkoma, New York.

Building his first guitar in 1979, Martin Flanders has managed to walk the fine line between old world craftsmanship and modern vision. Flanders gained experience and respect for quality by restoring antique furniture in his father's shop.

Living in New England (where select tone woods exist) has afforded Flanders the thrill of harvesting his own stock. With guitars as diverse of the Model 200 (a hybrid carved guitar with tone bars), to stunning archtops, his clients cover the entire musical spectrum. Flanders holds the intent of marketing his custom built guitars at a price you would expect to pay for a production instrument.

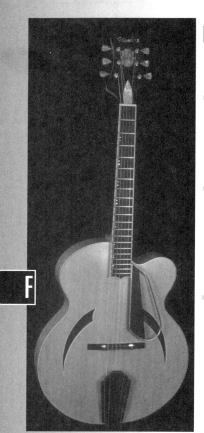

Flanders Archtop
courtesy Martin Flanders

FLEISHMAN

Instruments currently built in Boulder, Colorado.

Luthier Harry Fleishman has been designing and building high quality guitars and basses for numerous years. Fleishman is also a current columnist for the Guild of American Luthiers newsletter. For information or correspondence, please contact Mr. Fleishman through the Index of Current Manufacturers located in the back of the book.

FLETA

Instruments built in Barcelona, Spain from 1927 to 1977.

Luthier Ignacio Fleta (1897-1977) built classical guitars in Spain that reflected the influence of Antonio de Torres, but featured some of Fleta's design ideas as well. Fleta would varnish the inside of the guitar as well, with the intent of brightening the sound. Fleta also added an extra strut under the treble side of the top as a means of increasing volume.

(Source: Tony Bacon, The Ultimate Guitar Book)

FM

Instruments currently built in Austin, Texas.

Luthier Fred Murray has been building custom guitars, and repairing or modifying guitars around Austin for a number of years. Murray can be contacted at his business line at 312.292.0544.

FMO

See FACTORY MUSIC OUTLET.

Instruments built in Kenmore, New York since 1981.

The FMO trademark found on the headstock of these high quality electric guitars or basses is the logo of the Factory Music Outlet.

FM Custom
courtesy Fred Murray

FOCUS

See KRAMER.

Instruments built in Japan.

The Focus series of guitars were built overseas in the ESP factory for Kramer in the mid to late 1980s to supplement the higher end American models. The Kramer company could then offer a wider price range of models to consumers, and still maintain design and quality control over their product.

FODERA

Instruments built in Brooklyn, New York since 1983.

Luthiers Vinnie Fodera and Joseph Lauricella founded Fodera Guitars in 1983. Fodera, who had previously worked with Stuart Spector and Ned Steinberger in the late 1970s, focused directly on bass building. Fodera bass designs feature neck-through construction, active/passive circuitry, and both domestic and exotic woods. Two notable Fodera bass players are Anthony Jackson and Victor Wooten.

FOSTER

Instruments currently built in Covington, Louisiana. Distributed by Foster Guitar Manufacturing of Covington, Louisiana.

Luthier Jimmy Foster combines his musical and repair backgrounds in his current guitar designs. Models offered include an archtop guitar and the T-5 solid body. For current information, please contact luthier Foster through the Index of Current Manufacturers located in the back of this book.

FRAMUS

Instruments were produced in Germany from the late 1940s through the early 1980s.

Trademark re-introduced to Europe in 1996 by Hans-Peter Wilfer, the son of original founder Frederick Wilfer. Hans-Peter established the WARWICK trademark starting in 1982.

This West German company originally established itself in 1946, producing a range of musical instruments including violins and cellos. The first Framus electric guitars appeared in the 1950s. While the original 'Hollywood' series was Gibson-influenced, the later 'Strato' series of guitars were strikingly Fender-ish. However, the company did pioneer their own designs such as the Big 6 doubleneck model and the Melodie 9 string guitar.

Due to the presence of American servicemen stationed there, the influence of rock'n roll surfaced earlier in Germany than other European countries. As a result, German guitar builders had a headstart on answering the demand caused by the flowering of pop groups during the 1960s. Furthermore, as the German production increased, they began exporting their guitars to other countries (including the U.S.).

In order to properly date the year of issue, most Framus guitars had a separate pair of digits after the main serial number. If the separate pair is present, the two numbers will indicate the year.

(Reference source for company history: Tony Bacon and Paul Day, The Guru's Guitar Guide)

FRANCONIA

Instruments were built in Japan between 1980 and 1985.

The FRANCONIA trademark was a brandname used by a UK importer. The guitars were generally entry level to mid quality copies of American designs.

(Source: Tony Bacon and Paul Day, The Guru's Guitar Guide)

FRESHER

Instruments were produced in Japan from the late 1970s to the early 1980s.

Fresher solid body and semi-hollow body guitars were generally medium quality copies of American designs. However, viewing the "Fresher" logo on a strat-style guitar from a distance will make you check your eyesight - and finding a Fresher "Straighter" with built-in effects will make you check your blood pressure!

(Source: Michael Wright, Guitar Stories Volume One)

FRESHMAN

Instruments were built in Japan in the mid 1960s.

As an inexpensive, entry level guitar, the Freshman trademark is quite apt: a Senior, it isn't. In fact, it's not even close to a Sophomore.

(Source: Tony Bacon and Paul Day, The Guru's Guitar Guide)

FRITZ BROTHERS

Instruments were built in Mobile, Alabama since 1988.

Luthier Roger Fritz met Marc Fisher in Nashville in 1987. Together with guitarist Roy Buchanan they formed Fritz Brothers guitars, which was relocated to Alabama a year later. During 1988, the Fritz Brothers began building the Roy Buchanan Bluesmaster model; Buchanan died later that year (portion of the sales goes to Buchanan's estate).

(Source: Tom Wheeler, American Guitars)

"When you're 13 or 14 years old, you're not really at the point where you can say OK, now what factors do I want in a guitar? What happens is you see Eric Clapton play something and that's what you want."

—*R. Matuza on Tuck Andress*

TCG, July 1995

F

FROGGY BOTTOM

Instruments built in Newfane, Vermont since 1970. Instruments are available through Froggy Bottom Guitars as well as selected dealers.

Luthier Michael Millard initially began Froggy Bottom Guitars as a custom shop back in 1970, as a means to providing guitars crafted for their commissioned owners. Millard, a one-time guitar student of Reverend Gary Davis, responds to the customer's request for certain tone or feel. Although there is a "standard" for each of Millard's models, it is the customer who defines certain parameters that get built in to the player's special guitar.

Luthier Millard, who is assisted by his partner Andrew Mueller, also builds "production models" in their two-man shop. These guitars also share more in common with the specially commissioned models than the average production line acoustics.

The name "Froggy Bottom" is derived from the nickname given to land along the Mississippi Delta that is prone to flooding each year. The term was used by the sharecroppers who worked the land, and Millard seeks to capture the spirit of the place and its people in his custom guitar construction.

ACOUSTIC

Froggy Bottom guitars are offered in four style options on the standard models. Each style adds features to the preceding listing, which defines the different levels of refinement. The **Basic** style offers maple trim, a single herringbone rosette ring, 8 ply top purfling, mother-of-pearl peghead logo, a Brazilian rosewood bridge, and chrome Schaller tuners. The **Standard** options go one step up with an ebony bridge, abalone position markers, an abalone logo, 2 ring rosette, Maple end inlay and heel cap, and back and side purfling. Further options in the **Deluxe** category include an abalone rosette, Curly Maple neck heel trim, Gold Schaller tuners, a bound headstock, and a distinctive fretboard inlay. Finally, the **Limited** style option offers an abalone back seam inlay and abalone top trim inlay to the preceding steps.

All guitar models are offered in four standard back and sides materials such as Mahogany, Indian Rosewood, Curly Maple, and Curly Hawaiian Koa. Each series listed below will have a series of numbers described at the list price: the format follows the Basic/Standard/Deluxe/Limited model. For further information and clarity, please contact Michael Millard through the Index of Current Manufacturers located in the back of this book.

Concert Series

The **Model A** is the smallest standard model offered by Millard. It features a concert or "Double-O" size body with a 25" scale length and a 12 fret neck. Intended for finger style playing, this model is very light in the traditional style. The **Model H** is a 14 fret grand concert guitar. It is popular with finger style players, especially for ragtime and country blues. A variant of the Model H is the **Model H-12**, a traditional 12 fret with a slightly shorter scale length and lighter bracing pattern. The H-12 model was the best seller at Froggy Bottom Guitars in 1994, and comes standard with an Englemann spruce top.

Pricing on Models A, H, and H-12: Basic ($2,215), Standard (ranges from $2,355 to $2,780), Deluxe (ranges from $2,965 to $3,470), and Limited (ranges from $4,045 to $4,565). Pricing ranges are based on the body wood construction.

Full Size Series

The **Model D** is based on the ever popular dreadnought body developed by the Martin company. While the traditional dreadnought guitar is both powerful and bass heavy, the Froggy Bottom adds clarity, especially up the neck. The **Model F** evolved out of conversions of Martin arch tops in the New York shop of Matt Umanov. Those early conversions demonstrated the virtues of reducing the body volume of larger instruments and clearly altered the course of contemporary flat top guitar design. The Model F is available in both 12 and 14 fret configurations. The 14 fret **Model K** is similar in size to the Model D and Model F, but is more rounded in profile.

Pricing on Models D, F, and K: Basic ($2,320), Standard (ranges from $2,505 to $2,975), Deluxe (ranges from $3,160 to $3,670), and Limited (ranges from $4,300 to $4,830). Pricing ranges are based on the body wood construction.

Jumbo Series

With the revival of interest in older 12 fret guitars (i.e. where the neck joins the body) such as the Martin original D, the **Model B** is the choice of many customers. Designed as the 12 string with a long (26") scale for blues master Paul Geremia, this is THE guitar for those who love the old Stellas of Willie McTell and Leadbelly. The **Model G** is based on the beautiful Gibson L-5 profile, and is a well-balanced, powerful, jumbo guitar. The **Model J** is the original "Froggy Bottom Special", Millard's earliest jumbo model (first built in 1972). Similar to the Model G with a 17" body and 14 fret neck, the Model B has a more slender body and longer scale length. Frequently configured with a Florentine cutaway.

Pricing on Models B, G, and J: Basic ($2,600), Standard (ranges from $2,795 to $3,275), Deluxe (ranges from $3,380 to $3,895), and Limited (ranges from $4,595 to $5,130). Pricing ranges are based on the body wood construction. Pricing and specifications supplied to the **Blue Book of Guitars** were based on the February, 1995 retail price list.

FRONTIER

Instruments were produced in Japan during the early 1980s.

Frontier guitars are decent to good quality original designs as well as copies of American designs. The puzzling one is the signature model of Norris Fant. Guitar collectors or Fan club members who wish to enlighten us on Mr. Fant are invited to write to the **Blue Book of Guitars**.

(Source: Tony Bacon and Paul Day, The Guru's Guitar Guide)

FRONTLINE

Instruments were produced in Korea in the late 1980s.

Guitars under this trademark are medium quality vaguely Fender-ish solid body designs.

(Source: Tony Bacon and Paul Day, The Guru's Guitar Guide)

FURY

Instruments currently built in Saskatoon, Canada.

Fury guitars are high quality, solid body electrics. The 3 models range in price from $1,212-$1,277. For further information, please contact Fury Guitars through the Index of Current Manufacturers located in the back of this book.

FUTURAMA

Some guitars may also carry the trademark of GRAZIOSO.

Instruments were built in Czechoslovakia, then Sweden, and finally in Japan between 1958 and 1967.

The FUTURAMA trademark is the brandname of the British importer/distributor Selmer (UK). However, you can also find the GRAZIOSO trademark on some the of real early Czech-built instruments. Production of this line of solid body guitars continued in Eastern Europe until supplanted by some strat-styled models built by HAGSTROM in Sweden. Finally, the Futurama world tour ended on production of small-body model versions built in Japan.

(Source: Tony Bacon, The Ultimate Guitar Book)

FYLDE

Instruments currently built in Kirkham (Lancashire), England.

Luthier Roger Bucknall began building guitars in 1973. Bucknall has been handcrafting quality guitars for over 20 years, and Fylde currently produces 350 instruments a year. For further information on pricing and availability, please contact Fylde Guitars through the Index of Current Manufacturers located in the back of this book.

F

F

G

G & L

Instruments produced in Fullerton, California from 1980 to present. G & L is currently owned and distributed by BBE Sound of Huntington Beach, California.

In the late 1970s, the controlling interest at (pre-Ernie Ball) Music Man was making offers to purchase Leo Fender's CLF guitar production facility. Fender and George Fullerton turned down repeated offers, and Music Man began cutting production orders. The controversy settled as CLF Research stopped manufacturing instruments for Music Man in late 1979. In April of 1980 Fender and Fullerton started a new company, G & L (George & Leo), to continue producing Fender's ongoing design ideas and models. As Fender once again handled R & D in his office/workshop, George Fullerton maintained production management and Dale Hyatt (another ex-Fender/FIEC) was in charge of administrative management and sales.

Between 1980 and 1991, Leo Fender continued to refine his vision of his "Fender" guitar. Where other people saw individual models, Fender saw an ongoing project that kept getting better. Clarence Leo Fender passed away in 1991. The company was purchased a while later by John McLaren of BBE Sound, and continues to produce the affordable, quality solid body guitars that the company was known for.

(Source: Paul Bechtoldt, G&L: Leo's Legacy)

A final note from Paul Bechtoldt: "During the eleven years that Leo owned G & L, less than 27,000 guitars were produced. That is less than most companies make in half a year! With monthly production totals less than 800, Leo was making more guitars at his old company in the 1950's than at G & L! How rare are they?"

Grading		100%	98% MINT	95% EXC+	90% EXC	80% VG+	70% VG	60% G

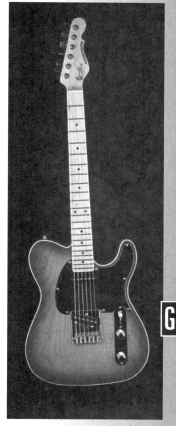

G & L Commemorative
courtesy Eugene Sharpey

ELECTRIC

Unless otherwise listed, all models in this series are available with 22 fret maple fingerboard with black dot inlay or rosewood fingerboard with pearl dot inlay and in the following finishes: Belair Green, Black, Black Swirl, Blueburst, Blue Emerald, Blue Swirl, Candy Apple Red, Cherryburst, Gold Metallic, Lake Placid Blue, Natural, Red Swirl, Silver Metallic, Sparkle Purple, Sparkle Red, Sunburst, Tobacco Sunburst, Transparent Blonde, Transparent Blue, Transparent Forest Green, Transparent Red and White.

ASAT — single cutaway alder body, black pickguard, bolt-on maple neck, fixed bridge with locking saddles, 6 on one side tuners, black hardware, 2 single coil pickups, volume/tone control, 3 position switch. Mfg. 1986 to date.

Mfr.'s Sug. Retail	$900	$720	$540	$450	$360	$325	$300	$275

ASAT Classic — similar to ASAT, except has ash body, white pickguard, standard fixed bridge, chrome hardware. Mfg. 1990 to date.

Mfr.'s Sug. Retail	$1,200	$960	$720	$600	$480	$430	$395	$360

ASAT Special — similar to ASAT, except has ash body, white pickguard.

Mfr.'s Sug. Retail	$900	$720	$540	$450	$360	$325	$300	$275

BROADCASTER — single cutaway alder body, black pickguard, bolt-on maple neck, fixed bridge with locking saddles, body color matching peghead, 6 on one side tuners, black hardware, 2 single coil pickups, volume/tone control, 3 position switch. Available in Black finish. Mfg. 1985 to 1986.

Maple fingerboard	$1,800	$1,260	$1,080	$900	$720	$650	$595
Ebony fingerboard	$1,200	$840	$720	$600	$480	$430	$395

Last Mfr.'s Sug. Retail was $706.

This model had an ebony fingerboard with pearl dot inlay optionally available.

42 of these instruments have double locking Kahler vibratos.

Two of these instruments are left handed.

A Certificate of Authenticity was issued with each instrument.

These instruments returned to Leo Fender's original Telecaster design, and once again Gretsch notified Leo that it already had rights to the name. Leo produced this instrument for one year, with all instruments being signed and dated by Leo in the neck pocket of the body.

G & L decided to manufacture a limited number of instruments, the total number being 869, 308 of these have maple fingerboards. In late 1986, the Broadcaster was renamed the ASAT.

CLIMAX — offset double cutaway ash body, bolt-on maple neck, double locking vibrato, 6 on one side tuners, black hardware, 2 single coil/1 humbucker pickups, volume/tone control, 5 position switch. Mfd. 1993 to date.

Mfr.'s Sug. Retail	$1,150	$862	$575	$520	$410	$345	$315	$285

Climax Plus — similar to Climax, except has humbucker/single coil/humbucker pickups.

Mfr.'s Sug. Retail	$1,250	$937	$625	$570	$450	$380	$345	$315

Climax XL — similar to Climax, except has 2 humbucker pickups, 3 position switch.

Mfr.'s Sug. Retail	$1,180	$885	$590	$530	$420	$355	$325	$295

G & L ASAT
1996 Tampa Vintage Show

Grading	100%	98% MINT	95% EXC+	90% EXC	80% VG+	70% VG	60% G

COMANCHE V — offset double cutaway ash body, black pickguard, bolt-on maple neck, 22 fret maple fingerboard with black dot inlay, standard vibrato, 6 on one side tuners, chrome hardware, 3 "split-coil" pickups, volume/2 tone controls, 5 position/mini switches. Available in Black, Blonde, Cherryburst and Natural finishes. Mfg. 1990 to 1991.

	$930	$795	$660	$530	$475	$435	$395

Add $60 for Leo Fender vibrato.

Last Mfr.'s Sug. Retail was $1,325.

Comanche VI — similar to Commanche V, except has 6 mini switches, no 5 position switch.

	$930	$795	$660	$530	$475	$435	$395

Add $60 for Leo Fender vibrato.

Last Mfr.'s Sug. Retail was $1,325.

F-100 — offset double cutaway mahogany body, bolt-on maple neck, 22 fret maple fingerboard with black dot inlay, standard vibrato, 6 on one side tuners, chrome hardware, 2 humbucker pickups, volume/tone control, 3 position/coil tap/preamp switches. Available in Natural finish. Mfg. 1980 to 1985.

	$750	$525	$450	$375	$300	$270	$245

LEGACY — offset double cutaway alder body, white pickguard, bolt-on maple neck, standard vibrato, 6 on one side tuners, chrome hardware, 3 single coil pickups, volume/treble/bass controls, 5 position switch. Mfd. 1992 to date.

Mfr.'s Sug. Retail	$900	$675	$450	$425	$340	$305	$280	$255

Legacy Special — similar to Legacy, except has ash body, graphite nut, locking Sperzel tuners, 3 single coil blade pickups. Mfg. 1993 to date.

Mfr.'s Sug. Retail	$1,100	$880	$660	$550	$440	$395	$365	$330

S-500 — offset double cutaway ash body, white pickguard, bolt-on maple neck, standard vibrato, 6 on one side locking Sperzel tuners, chrome hardware, 3 single coil pickups, volume/treble/bass control, 5 position/mini switch. Mfg. 1985 to date.

Mfr.'s Sug. Retail	$1,250	$1,000	$750	$625	$500	$450	$415	$375

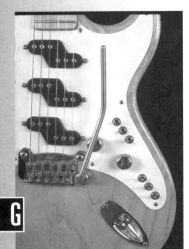

Comanche "Split-coil" pickups
courtesy Phil Willhoite

ELECTRIC BASS

All models in this series are available with 21 fret maple fingerboard with black dot inlay or rosewood fingerboard with pearl dot inlay, fixed bridge with locking saddles and in the following finishes: Belair Green, Black, Black Swirl, Blueburst, Blue Emerald, Blue Swirl, Candy Apple Red, Cherryburst, Gold Metallic, Lake Placid Blue, Natural, Red Swirl, Silver Metallic, Sparkle Purple, Sparkle Red, Sunburst, Tobacco Sunburst, Transparent Blonde, Transparent Blue, Transparent Forest Green, Transparent Red and White.

ASAT BASS — single cutaway ash body, bolt-on maple neck, 4 on one side tuners, chrome hardware, 2 humbucker pickups, volume/treble/bass controls, pickup/series-parallel/preamp switches, active electronics. Mfd. 1989 to 1994.

	$840	$720	$600	$480	$430	$395	$360

Last Mfr.'s Sug. Retail was $1,200.

CLIMAX BASS — offset double cutaway ash body, bolt-on maple neck, 4 on one side tuners, chrome hardware, humbucker pickup, volume/treble/bass controls, bypass/preamp switches. Mfd. 1993 to date.

Mfr.'s Sug. Retail	$1,100	$880	$660	$550	$440	$395	$365	$330

LEGACY BASS — offset double cutaway alder body, white pickguard, bolt-on maple neck, 4 on one side tuners, chrome hardware, P-style pickup, volume/tone control. Mfd. 1993 to 1994.

	$630	$540	$450	$360	$325	$300	$275

Last Mfr.'s Sug. Retail was $900.

In late 1993, the Legacy Bass was renamed the LB-100.

L1000 — offset double cutaway ash body, bolt-on maple neck, 4 on one side tuners, humbucker pickup, volume/treble/bass controls, series-parallel switch. Mfd. 1980 to 1994.

	$665	$570	$475	$380	$345	$315	$285

Last Mfr.'s Sug. Retail was $950.

This model had an ebony fingerboard with pearl dot inlay optionally available.

L2000 — similar to L1000, except has 2 humbucker pickups, pickup/series-parallel/preamp/treble boost switches, active electronics. Mfd. 1981 to date.

Mfr.'s Sug. Retail	$1,250	$937	$625	$600	$480	$430	$395	$360

L5000 — similar to L1000, except has 5 strings, alder body, black pickguard, 4/1 per side tuners, volume/tone control. Mfd. 1987 to 1994.

	$665	$570	$475	$380	$345	$315	$285

Last Mfr.'s Sug. Retail was $950.

L5500 — similar to L1000, except has 5 strings, alder body, black pickguard, 4/1 per side tuners, 2 humbucker pickups, volume/concentric treble-bass/mix control. New 1994.

Mfr.'s Sug. Retail	$1,500	$1,200	$900	$750	$600	$540	$495	$450

SB1 — offset double cutaway alder body, black pickguard, 4 on one side tuners, chrome hardware, P-style pickup, volume/tone control. Mfd. 1982 to date.

Mfr.'s Sug. Retail	$775	$581	$387	$350	$280	$250	$230	$210

SB2 — similar to SB1, except has P-style/J-style pickups, 2 volume controls.

Mfr.'s Sug. Retail	$875	$656	$437	$400	$320	$290	$265	$240

G & L S-500
courtesy Phil Willhoite

GALANTI

Instruments were made in Italy during the mid 1960s through the early 1970s.

The Galanti company focused on fairly straightforward original designs on their solid and semi-hollow-body guitars.

(Source: Tony Bacon, The Ultimate Guitar Book)

GEOFF GALE

Instruments were built in England through the 1970s.

Original designs were featured on these solid body guitars, and they carried model designations such as the Magnum, Quasar, Cobra, and Phasar. Anyone with information about these guitars is invited to contact the **Blue Book of Guitars** for future edition updates.

(Source: Tony Bacon and Paul Day, The Guru's Guitar Guide)

J.W. GALLAGHER & SONS

Instruments built in Wartrace, Tennessee. Distributed by J.W. Gallagher & Sons of Wartrace, Tennessee.

The Gallagher family settled in Wartrace (about 60 miles southeast of Nashville) back in the late 1820s. John William Gallagher was born in 1915, and in 1939 established a furniture making business. Don Gallagher was born in 1947, and grew up among the tools and wood in the family's woodworking shop. The furniture business converted to guitar production later in the 1960s. Gallagher and his son Don produced 24 guitars in their first year.

In 1976, Don Gallagher took over management of the business, three years before the luthier community lost J.W. Gallagher in 1979. Don Gallagher continues to build acoustic guitars in the family tradition.

(Source: Tom Wheeler, American Guitars)

Gallagher guitars have been built in very limited numbers. From the opening year of 1965 to 1990, only 2,064 guitars were made. According to the Gallagher catalog, early instruments had paper labels. The serial number on these labels indicate the year and month the guitar was made. Starting in 1970, the serialization began to reflect the number of guitars that had been built. This number, along with the model number, is stamped on the neck block inside every Gallagher guitar.

ACOUSTIC

All Gallagher guitars are meticulously handcrafted, using the finest woods available at the workshop. Gallagher acoustics can be ordered with a single cutaway (add $400) or a slotted headstock (add $400). A Fishman Acoustic Matrix system is available as an option for an additional $230, and individual models can be built as a 12 string (add $170) or finished in Sunburst (add $220). Hardshell cases are an extra charge, but well worth the investment in protecting your Gallagher guitar.

G Series

The first Gallagher guitar model was built back in 1965, and was designated the G-50 in honor of J.W. Gallagher's age at the time. The **G-50** features mahogany back and sides, a spruce top, and a soundhole edged in black and white wood strips. The rosewood fingerboard has pearl dot inlays, and the guitar has a bound peghead and body that is finished in highly polished lacquer. Retail list price is $2,000. The **G-45** is similar to the G-50, except it does not have the bound headstock and the body binding is in black. List price is also $2,000.

The **G-70** ($2,340) has a two-piece top and a body of rosewood. The bound ebony fingerboard is inlayed with mother-of-pearl diamonds and squares, and the top and the soundhole are bound in herringbone. The **G-65** ($2,180) features a bookmatched rosewood back, and rosewood sides. Black and white wood inlays surround the top and the soundhole, while the nut and saddle are constructed of bone.

In 1968 both Doc and Merle Watson began playing guitars crafted by J.W. and Don. Six years later, Doc Watson requested certain particular features in a guitar that was built for him. This model was the basis for the **Doc Watson Model**. In 1975, Merle received the first cutaway version of this model. The Doc Watson model has a spruce top, mahogany back and sides, and a bridge and fingerboard of ebony. The nut and saddles are constructed of bone, and the top and soundhole have herringbone inlays. List price is $2,165.

Modified G Series

The **G-70M** is a modified version of the G-70 model, and features a bound fingerboard, herringbone trim around the top and soundhole, a longer body design, and the neck joins at the twelfth fret. The **G-45M** is the same size as the G-70M, but features mahogany back and sides, black/white trim around the top and soundhole, and the neck joins at the twelfth fret as well. List price on the G-70M is $2,400, while the G-45M is $2,060.

Grand Concert

Model **GC-70** is similar in appointments to the G-70, except in the grand concert body size. The first GC-70 was built in 1968 for country artist Grandpa Jones. Rosewood back and sides, spruce top, bound ebony fingerboard, ebony bridge, and herringbone trim comprise this model ($2,400).

Special Series

The **71 Special** was introduced in 1970, and features a rosewood back and sides, spruce top, herringbone purfling and soundhole rosette, bound ebony fingerboard, ebony bridge, abalone snowflake inlays. List price is $2,600.

The very first **72 Special** was built by Don Gallagher in late 1977. The body is rosewood, with a spruce top and mahogany neck. Both the bridge and fingerboard are ebony, and the nut and saddle are crafted of bone. The 72 Special carries a list price of $3,100.

Auditorium Series

A more defined "waist" is featured on the **Ragtime Special**, which is an 'auditorium' size guitar. The model has mahogany back and sides, spruce top, black-bound body and peghead, ebony fingerboard and bridge. Retail list is $2,200. The **A-70** ($2,400) is similar to the GC-70 model, but has a 14 fret neck.

12 String Series

Although any model has an option to be built as a twelve string, Gallagher specifically offers 2 models designated so. The **G-70 12** ($2,510) and the **G-45 12** ($2,060) are similar in construction to their associated models, except both pegheads are equipped with the "mini" version of the standard tuning machines.

GAY

Instruments built in Edmonton, Alberta (Canada) between the early/mid 1950s and the mid 1970s.

Luthier Frank Gay maintained his guitar building and repair services for more than two decades in Edmonton. A formidable jazz and classical guitarist, his flattop acoustics were the most recognizable instrument - and oddly enough, his biggest endorsers were country western artists (one notable player was Webb Pierce). Gay guitars are recognized by the exaggerated checkerboard rosette inlays, six on a side headstocks, and the occasional heart-shaped soundhole.

(Source: Teisco Del Rey, Guitar Player magazine, August 1988)

GEMELLI

Instruments were produced in Italy during the 1960s.

Guitars bearing this trademark were built by Benito & Umberto Cingolani in Recanti, Italy. Like many other European countries, Italy experienced the 1960s pop music popularity that led to a larger demand for electric guitars. However, many electric guitar builders were also manufacturers of accordians. As a result, many guitars ended up with accordian-style finishes and touches, such as a barrage of buttons for pickup or tone selection. It is up to the individual guitar player to make the choice: play 'em or pose with 'em!

(Source: Tony Bacon, The Ultimate Guitar Book)

GHERSON

Instruments were produced in Italy from the mid 1970s to early 1980s.

The Gherson company produced a number of good quality copies of American designs in the solid body format.

(Source: Tony Bacon and Paul Day, The Guru's Guitar Guide)

G.H. RENO

See CUSTOM GUITAR WORKS.

GIANNINI

Instruments currently built in Brazil. Distributed by Music Industries Corporation of Floral Park, New York.

Giannini acoustics are offered in a wide range of entry level to professional quality instruments. For further information, contact Music Industries Corporation through the Index of Current Manufacturers in the back of this book.

GIBSON

Instruments currently produced in Nashville, Tennessee and Bozeman, Montana. Distributed by the Gibson Guitar Corporation, a division of Consolidated Musical Instruments (C M I) of Nashville, Tennessee.

Luthier Orville H. Gibson was born in Chateaugay, New York. In 1856 he "moved West" to Kalamazoo, Michigan. City records from 1896-1897 indicate a business address of "114 South Burdick" for "O.H. Gibson, Manufacturer, Musical Instruments". By 1899-1902, the city directories indicate a change to the "Second Floor of 104 East Main".

The Gibson Mandolin-Guitar Manufacturing Company, Limited was established at 2:55 p.m. on October 11, 1902. The agreement was formed by John W. Adams (pres.), Samuel H. Van Horn (treasurer), Sylvo

Gibson Harp Guitar
courtesy Tam Milano

Reams (sec., and also production mngr.), Lewis Williams (later secretary and Gen. Mngr.), and Leroy Hornbeck. Orville Gibson was not one of the founding partners, but had a separate contract to be a consultant and trainer. Gibson was also the first to purchase 500 shares of the new company's stock. In 1915, Gibson and the company negotiated a new agreement in which Orville was to be paid a monthly salary for the rest of his life. Orville, who had some troubles with his health back in 1911, was treated in 1916 at the pyschiatric center of St. Lawrence State hospital in Ogdensburg, New York. Orville Gibson died of endocarditis on August 21, 1918.

In 1906 the company moved to 116 East Exchange Place, and the name was changed to Gibson Mandolin Guitar Company. Chicago Musical Instruments (CMI) acquired controlling interest in Gibson, Inc. in 1944. Maurice H. Berlin (president of CMI) became general secretary and treasurer of Gibson. From this date, the Gibson Sales Department became located in Chicago while the Kalamazoo plant concentrated on poduction. Gibson acquired Epiphone in 1957, and production of Gibson-made Epiphones began in 1959. Ten years later, as the Epiphone name was being run down, production moved to Japan (or, the Epiphone name was applied to imported instruments). In December of 1969, E.C.L. Industries, Inc., took control of CMI. Gibson, Inc. stayed under control of CMI until 1974, when it became a subsidiary of NORLIN Industries (Norlin is the named after H. Norton Stevens, pres. of E.C.L. and Maurice H. Berlin, pres. of CMI). A new factory is opened in Nashville, Tennessee the same year.

In 1980, Norlin decided to sell Gibson. Norlin also relocated some of the sales, marketing, administration, and finance personnel from Chicago to the Nashville plant. Main Gibson production was then handled in Nashville, and Kalamazoo became a specialist factory for "custom orders". In 1983, then-Gibson president Marty Locke informed Jim Deurloo that the Kalamazoo plant would close. Final production was June 1984, and the plant closed three months later. [Rather than give up on the 65 year old facilities, Jim Deurloo, Marv Lamb, and J.P. Moats started the Heritage Guitar Company in April of 1985. The company is located in the ground floor of the 1917 building.]

In January of 1986, Henry Juskiewicz (pres), David Berryman (VP of finance and accounting), and Gary Zebrowski (electronics business) bought Gibson for an unspecified amount. Since the late 1980s, the Gibson company has been at work to return to the level of quality the company had reached earlier. Expansion of the acoustic guitar production at the Bozeman, Montana facilities, as well as the level of quality at Gibson's Custom Shop, indicate that the company is once again on its way.

(Source: Tom Wheeler, American Guitars; Walter Carter, Gibson Guitars: 100 Years of an American Icon)

Gibson "Orville" Custom LP
courtesy Gibson Custom Shop

Identifying Features on Gibson Musical Instruments

The most consistent and easily found feature that goes across all models of Gibson production is the logo, or lack of one, found on the peghead. The very earliest instruments made are generally found with a star inside a crescent design, or a blank peghead, and labels inside the body. This lasted until approximately 1902.

From 1902 to the late 1920s, "The Gibson", inlaid in pearl and placed at a slant, is found on the peghead. In the late 1920s, this style of logo was changed to having "The Gibson" read straight across the peghead as opposed to being slanted. Flat top acoustics production began at approximately this time and these instruments generally do not have "The" on the inlay, it just has "Gibson" in script writing. By 1933, this was the established peghead logo for Gibson. Just before WWII, Gibson began making the lettering on the logo thicker and this became standard on most prewar instruments. Right after WWII, the styling of the logo remained but it became slanted once again.

In 1947, the logo that is still in use today made its debut. This logo has a block styling with the "G" having a tail, the "i" dot is touching the "G", the "b" and "o" are open and the "n" is connected at the bottom. The logo is still slanted. By 1951, the dot on the "i" was no longer connected to the "G". In 1967, the logo styling became even more squared (pentographed) with the "b" and "o" becoming closed and the "i" dot being removed.

In 1970, Gibson replaced the black tinted piece of wood that had been used on peghead face with a black fiber that the logo and other peghead inlay were placed into. With the change in peghead facing came a slightly smaller logo lettering. In 1972, the "i" dot reappeared on the peghead logo. In 1981, the "n" is connected at the top of the "o". There are a few models through the years that do not follow this timeline, ie: reissues and limited editions, but most of the production instruments can be found with the above feature changes.

The configuration of the Kluson tuners used on Gibson instruments can be used to date an instrument. Before 1959, all Kluson tuners with plastic buttons had a single ring around the stem end of the button. In 1960, this was changed to a double ring configuration.

Another dating feature of Gibsons is the use of a peghead volute found on instruments between 1970 and 1973. Also, in 1965 Gibson switched from 17 degrees to 14 degrees on the tilt of the peghead. Before 1950, peghead thickness varied, getting narrower towards the top of the peghead. After 1950, pegheads all became one uniform thickness, from bottom to top.

Common Gibson Abbreviations

C - Cutaway

D - Dreadnought or Double

E - Electric

ES - Electric (Electro) Spanish

GS - Gut String

J - Jumbo

LE - Limited Edition

S - Spanish, Solid Body, Special or Super

SG - Solid Guitar

T - Tremolo or Thinline

Gibson "Hard Rock" Custom LP
courtesy Gibson Custom Shop

Grading	100% MINT	98% EXC+	95% EXC+	90% EXC	80% VG+	70% VG	60% G

V - Venetian or Vibrato

Gibson B-25-12-N
courtesy Jason Crisp

ACOUSTIC

BLUE RIDGE — dreadnought style, solid spruce top, round soundhole, black pickguard, 3 stripe bound body/rosette, laminated rosewood back/sides, mahogany neck, 14/20 fret rosewood fingerboard with pearl dot inlay, reverse belly rosewood bridge with black white dot pins, blackface peghead with screened logo, 3 per side chrome tuners. Available in Natural finish. Mfg. 1968 to 1979.

	$650	$600	$525	$430	$360	$260	$215

In 1969, standard bridge replaced original item.

In 1973, low impedance pickup became optionally available.

Blue Ridge 12 — similar to Blue Ridge, except has 12 strings, 6 per side tuners. Mfg. 1970 to 1978.

	$600	$515	$425	$340	$310	$280	$255

B Series

B-15 — dreadnought student style, spruce top, round soundhole, tortoise pickguard, 1 stripe rosette, bound top, mahogany back/sides/neck, 14/20 fret rosewood fingerboard with pearl dot inlay, rosewood bridge with white pins, 3 per side tuners with plastic buttons. Available in Natural finish. Mfg. 1967 to 1971.

	$300	$260	$215	$175	$155	$140	$130

B-25 — dreadnought style, spruce top, round soundhole, tortoise pickguard, 3 stripe bound body/rosette, mahogany back/sides/neck, 14/20 fret rosewood fingerboard with pearl dot inlay, reverse belly rosewood bridge with white pins, blackface peghead with decal logo, 3 per side tuners with plastic buttons. Available in Cherry Sunburst and Natural finishes. Mfg. 1962 to 1977.

	$500	$430	$360	$285	$260	$235	$215

In 1965, plastic bridge replaced original item.

In 1968, wood bridge replaced respective item.

In 1969, standard bridge replaced respective item.

B-25 3/4 — similar to B-25, except is 3/4 size body. Mfg. 1962 to 1968.

	$400	$280	$240	$200	$160	$145	$130

In 1966, Natural finish was discontinued.

B-25-12 — dreadnought style, spruce top, round soundhole, tortoise pickguard, bound body/rosette, mahogany back/sides/neck, 14/20 fret rosewood fingerboard with pearl dot inlay, reverse belly rosewood bridge with white pins, blackface peghead with decal logo, 6 per side tuners with plastic buttons. Available in Cherry Sunburst and Natural finishes. Mfg. 1962 to 1977.

	$425	$365	$305	$240	$220	$200	$180

In 1963, strings thru bridge replaced original item, no bridge pins.

In 1965, redesigned reverse bridge replaced respective item, trapeze tailpiece added.

In 1970, standard bridge with white pins replaced respective item, no trapeze tailpiece, Cherry Sunburst finish discontinued.

B-45-12 — bell shape dreadnought style, spruce top, round soundhole, tortoise pickguard, 2 stripe bound body/rosette, mahogany back/sides/neck, 14/20 fret rosewood fingerboard with pearl dot inlay, rosewood bridge with adjustable saddle, trapeze tailpiece, blackface peghead with pearl split diamond inlay/logo decal, 6 per side nickel tuners with plastic buttons. Available in Cherry Sunburst finish. Mfg. 1961 to 1979.

	$650	$555	$465	$370	$335	$305	$280

In 1962, standard dreadnought style, reverse belly bridge with pins, adjustable saddle replaced original items.

In 1964, string thru reverse belly bridge replaced respective item, Natural finish (B-45-12N) optionally available.

In 1965, rectangular bridge/trapeze tailpiece replaced respective item.

In 1970, redesigned pickguard, 12/20 fret fingerboard, standard bridge with pins, Tobacco Sunburst finish replaced original items.

Blues Series

BLUES KING ELECTRO — single round cutaway jumbo style, spruce top, round soundhole, tortoise pickguard, multistripe bound body/rosette, flame maple back/sides, mahogany neck, 20 fret bound rosewood fingerboard with pearl parallelogram inlay, rosewood bridge with white pins, bound blackface peghead with pearl vase/logo inlay, 3 per side nickel tuners, transducer pickups/preamp system. Available in Heritage Cherry Sunburst, Natural top/Antique Chocolate back/sides and Vintage Sunburst finishes. New 1994.

Mfr.'s Sug. Retail	$1,800	$1,440	$1,080	$900	$720	$650	$595	$540

Blues King L-00 — parlor style, spruce top, round soundhole, tortoise pickguard, 3 stripe bound body/rosette, mahogany back/sides/neck, 14/20 fret rosewood fingerboard with pearl dot inlay, straight rosewood bridge with white pins, blackface peghead with pearl logo inlay, 3 per side nickel tuners. Available in Antique Ebony, Natural top/Antique Walnut back/sides and Vintage Sunburst finishes. Mfg. 1994 to date.

Mfr.'s Sug. Retail	$1,400	$1,050	$700	$550	$525	$500	$460	$420

Blues King Special — similar to Blues King L-00, except has Indian rosewood back/sides, bound ebony fingerboard with pearl block inlay, ebony belly bridge with white pins, bound blackface peghead with pearl vase/logo inlay, transducer pickup/preamp system. Available in Antique Natural and Vintage Sunburst finishes. New 1994.

Mfr.'s Sug. Retail	$2,500	$2,000	$1,500	$1,250	$1,000	$900	$825	$750

Grading	100%	98% MINT	95% EXC+	90% EXC	80% VG+	70% VG	60% G

CHICAGO 35 — bell shape dreadnought style, spruce top, round soundhole, tortoise pickguard, 3 stripe bound body/rosette, mahogany back/sides/neck, 14/19 fret rosewood fingerboard with pearl cross inlay, rosewood straight bridge with white pins, blackface peghead with screened logo, 3 per side nickel tuners, transducer pickup/preamp system. Available in Antique Natural and Special Vintage Sunburst finishes. New 1994.

	100%	98%	95%	90%	80%	70%	60%
Mfr.'s Sug. Retail	$2,000	$1,600	$1,200	$1,000	$800	$720	$660	$600

GOSPEL — bell shape dreadnought style, spruce top, round soundhole, tortoise pickguard, multistripe bound body/rosette, mahogany back/sides/neck, 14/20 fret rosewood fingerboard with pearl dot inlay, rosewood bridge with white pins, blackface peghead with screened vase/logo, 3 per side nickel tuners with pearloid buttons. Available in Antique Natural and Natural top/Antique Walnut back/sides finishes. New 1994.

	100%	98%	95%	90%	80%	70%	60%
Mfr.'s Sug. Retail	$1,050	$840	$630	$525	$420	$380	$345	$315

Gospel AV — similar to Gospel, except has transducer pickup/preamp system. Available in Antique Natural, Natural top/Antique Walnut back/sides and Vintage Sunburst finishes. New 1994.

	100%	98%	95%	90%	80%	70%	60%
Mfr.'s Sug. Retail	$1,350	$1,080	$810	$675	$540	$485	$445	$405

C Models

C-0 — classic style, spruce top, round soundhole, bound body, rosette decal, mahogany back/sides/neck, 12/19 fret rosewood fingerboard, rosewood wraparound bridge, 3 per side chrome tuners with plastic buttons. Available in Natural finish. Mfg. 1957 to 1971.

	$350	$275	$200	$160	$125	$95	$85

C-1 — classic style, spruce top, round soundhole, bound body, 2 stripe rosette, mahogany back/sides/neck, 12/19 fret rosewood fingerboard, rosewood wraparound bridge, 3 per side nickel tuners with plastic buttons. Available in Natural finish. Mfg. 1957 to 1971.

	$350	$275	$200	$160	$125	$95	$85

In 1966, wooden inlay rosette, chrome tuners replaced original items.

C-1 E — similar to C-1, except has ceramic bridge pickup. Mfg. 1960 to 1968.

	$350	$275	$200	$150	$125	$100	$75

C-1 S — similar to C-1, except has student size body. Mfg. 1961 to 1967.

	$275	$200	$150	$125	$100	$75	$70

C-1 D — similar to C-1, except has rounded peghead. Mfg. 1963 to 1971.

	$275	$200	$150	$125	$100	$75	$70

C-2 — classic style, spruce top, round soundhole, bound body, 2 stripe rosette, maple back/side, mahogany neck, 12/19 fret rosewood fingerboard, rosewood wraparound bridge with pearl block inlay, 3 per side nickel tuners with plastic buttons. Available in Natural Top/Mahogany Back/Side finish. Mfg. 1960 to 1970.

	$350	$275	$200	$150	$125	$100	$75

In 1966, redesigned rosette, peghead replaced original item.

C-4 — similar to C-2, except has gold tuners. Available in Natural Top/Rosewood Back/Sides finish. Mfg. 1962 to 1968.

	$650	$525	$450	$375	$300	$225	$175

C-6 RICHARD PICK CUSTOM — classic style, spruce top, round soundhole, tortoise bound body, wooden inlay rosette, rosewood back/sides, mahogany neck, 12/19 fret ebony fingerboard, wraparound rosewood bridge, rosewood veneered peghead, 3 per side gold tuners. Available in Natural finish. Mfg. 1958 to 1971.

	$1,075	$920	$770	$615	$555	$505	$460

In 1966, pearl block bridge inlay was added.

C-8 — similar to C-6, except has different rosette pattern, narrow peghead. Mfg. 1962 to 1969.

	$925	$850	$700	$625	$500	$375	$300

CF-100 — single sharp cutaway dreadnought style, spruce top, round soundhole, tortoise pickguard, bound body, 1 stripe rosette, mahogany back/sides/neck, 20 fret bound rosewood fingerboard with pearl trapezoid inlay, rosewood reverse bridge with pearl dot inlay, white bridge pins, blackface peghead with logo decal, 3 per side nickel tuners. Available in Golden Sunburst finish. Mfg. 1950 to 1959.

	$1,200	$1,030	$860	$685	$615	$565	$515

In 1952, pearl crown/logo inlay replaced original item.

In 1957, redesigned pickguard replaced original item.

CF-100E — similar to CF-100, except has 1 single coil pickup, volume/tone control. Mfg. 1951 to 1959.

	$1,950	$1,670	$1,395	$1,115	$1,005	$920	$835

CITATION — single round cutaway hollow multi-bound body, carved spruce top, bound f-holes, raised multi-bound flamed maple pickguard, figured maple back/sides/neck, 20 fret multi-bound pointed fingerboard with pearl cloud inlay, adjustable ebony bridge with pearl fleur-de-lis inlay on wings, gold trapeze tailpiece with engraved model name, multi-bound ebony veneered peghead with abalone fleur-de-lis/logo inlay, abalone fleur-de-lis inlay on back of peghead, 3 per side gold engraved tuners. Available in Faded Cherry Sunburst, Honeyburst and Natural finishes.

In 1972, Gibson produced only 15 Citation guitars. Ten years later, Gibson produced 3 more (by customer request). These 18 guitars have not traded sufficiently to quote pricing. Gibson currently produces a Historical Collection version of the Citation.

Grading	100%	98% MINT	95% EXC+	90% EXC	80% VG+	70% VG	60% G

DOVE — dreadnought style, spruce top, round soundhole, tortoise pickguard with dove inlay, 3 stripe bound body/rosette, figured maple 14/20 fret bound rosewood fingerboard with pearl parallelogram inlay, enlarged rosewood bridge with black pearl dot pins, pearl dove inlay on bridge wings, blackface peghead with pearl plant/logo inlay, 3 per side gold tuners with pearl buttons. Available in Antique Cherry finish. Mfg. 1962 to date.

1962-1968		$1,200	$1,030	$860	$685	$615	$565	$515
1969-1975		$1,000	$855	$715	$570	$510	$465	$425
1976-1985		$900	$770	$640	$515	$465	$425	$385
Mfr.'s Sug. Retail	$2,450	$1,837	$1,225	$1,200	$960	$860	$790	$720

In 1969, adjustable bridge replaced original item.

In 1970, non-adjustable bridge replaced respective item.

In 1975, ebony fingerboard replaced original item.

Current model features rosewood fingerboard.

EVERLY BROTHERS — jumbo style, spruce top, round soundhole, 2 tortoise pickguards, 2 stripe bound body/rosette, maple back/sides, 1 piece mahogany neck, 14/20 fret rosewood fingerboard with pearl star inlay, reverse belly adjustable bridge with pearl dot inlay, blackface peghead with pearl star/logo inlay, 3 per side gold tuners. Available in Black, Cherry Sunburst, Natural Top/Red Back/Sides and Natural Top/Walnut Back/Sides finishes. Mfg. 1962 to 1973.

$5,000	$4,300	$4,100	$3,425	$3,085	$2,825	$2,570

This model also known as J-180.

In 1962, two models with Cherry Sunburst finish were produced.

In 1963, 102 with Cherry Sunburst finish and 46 with Natural Top/Red Back/Sides finish were produced.

In 1968, black pickguards, Natural Top/Walnut Back/Sides finish replace original items.

The Everly — jumbo style, spruce top, round soundhole, 2 black pickguards, multistripe bound body/rosette, figured maple back/sides/neck, 14/20 fret bound rosewood fingerboard with pearl star inlay, rosewood mustache bridge with pearl star inlay/white pins, multibound blackface peghead with pearl star/logo inlay, 3 per side nickel tuners. Available in Antique Ebony and Heritage Cherry Sunburst finishes. New 1994.

Mfr.'s Sug. Retail	$2,000	$1,600	$1,200	$1,000	$800	$720	$660	$600

Everly Cutaway — similar to The Everly, except has single sharp cutaway, tortoise pickguards, gold tuners, transducer pickups/preamp system. Available in Antique Ebony and Heritage Cherry Sunburst finishes. New 1994.

Mfr.'s Sug. Retail	$2,300	$1,840	$1,380	$1,150	$920	$830	$760	$690

F-25 (Folksinger) — folk style, spruce top, round soundhole, 2 white pickguards, 2 stripe bound body/rosette, mahogany back/sides/neck, 12/18 fret rosewood fingerboard with pearl dot inlay, rosewood reverse belly bridge with white pins/2 pearl dot inlay, blackface peghead with screened logo, 3 per side nickel tuners with plastic buttons. Available in Natural finish. Mfg. 1963 to 1970.

$750	$640	$535	$430	$390	$355	$325

In 1969, redesigned body/peghead, standard bridge replaced original items, white pickguards were discontinued.

FJ-N (Folksinger Jumbo) — dreadnought style, spruce top, round soundhole, 2 white pickguards, 3 stripe bound body/rosette, mahogany back/sides/neck, 12/18 fret bound rosewood fingerboard with pearl trapezoid inlay, rosewood reverse bridge with white pins/2 pearl dot inlay, blackface peghead with pearl crown/logo inlay, 3 per side nickel tuners with plastic buttons. Available in Natural finish. Mfg. 1963 to 1968.

$800	$685	$575	$460	$410	$380	$345

FLAMENCO 2 — classic style, spruce top, round soundhole, 2 white pickguards, tortoise bound body, wooden inlay rosette, cypress back/side, mahogany neck, 12/19 fret rosewood fingerboard, rosewood wraparound bridge with pearl block inlay, rosewood veneered peghead with logo decal, 3 per side nickel tuners with plastic buttons. Available in Natural Top/Mahogany Back/Side finish. Mfg. 1963 to 1968.

$475	$350	$275	$225	$175	$150	$125

GOSPEL — dreadnought style, spruce top, round soundhole, tortoise pickguard, 3 stripe bound body/rosette, maple back/sides/neck, 14/20 fret ebony fingerboard with pearl dot inlay, ebony bridge with black pearl dot pins, blackface peghead with dove/logo decals, 3 per side chrome tuners. Available in Natural finish. Mfg. 1972 to 1980.

$650	$555	$465	$370	$335	$305	$280

GS-1 — classic style, round soundhole, bound body, 3 stripe rosette, bound body, 2 stripe rosette, mahogany back/sides/neck, 12/19 fret rosewood fingerboard, rosewood tied bridge with pearl cross inlay, blackface peghead with screened logo, 3 per side tuners with plastic buttons. Available in Natural finish. Mfg. 1950 to 1956.

$650	$555	$465	$370	$335	$305	$280

GS-2 — similar to GS-1, except has maple back/sides. Mfg. 1954 to 1959.

$700	$600	$500	$400	$360	$330	$300

GS-5 (Custom Classic) — similar to GS-1, except has rosewood back/sides. Mfg. 1954 to 1959.

$850	$700	$525	$450	$375	$300	$250

GS-35 — classical style, spruce top, round soundhole, bound body, 2 stripe rosette, mahogany back/sides/neck, 12/19 fret ebony fingerboard, rosewood tied bridge, solid blackface peghead with screened logo, 3 per side tuners with plastic buttons. Available in Natural finish. Mfg. 1939 to 1943.

$750	$625	$550	$475	$300	$250	$200

Grading	100%	98% MINT	95% EXC+	90% EXC	80% VG+	70% VG	60% G

GS-85 — similar to GS-35, except has rosewood back/sides, pearl bridge inlay. Mfg. 1939 to 1943.

		$1,050	$925	$800	$650	$525	$400	$325

HERITAGE — dreadnought style, round soundhole, tortoise pickguard, 2 stripe bound body/rosette, rosewood back/sides, mahogany neck, 14/20 fret ebony fingerboard with pearl dot inlay, reverse ebony bridge with white pins, adjustable saddle, blackface peghead with logo decal, 3 per side nickel tuners. Available in Natural finish. Mfg. 1965 to 1982.

		$1,000	$855	$715	$570	$510	$465	$425

In 1968, standard bridge replaced original item.

In 1969, black pickguard, pearl diamond/curlicue/logo peghead inlay replaced original items.

In 1971, pearl block fingerboard inlay replaced original item, redesigned bridge with pearl curlicue inlay replaced respective item.

In 1973, bound fingerboard replaced original item.

Heritage 12 — similar to Heritage, except has 12 strings, 6 per side tuners. Mfg. 1968 to 1970.

		$850	$730	$610	$485	$435	$400	$365

HUMMINGBIRD — dreadnought style, spruce top, round soundhole, tortoise pickguard with engraved floral/hummingbird pattern, 3 stripe bound body/rosette, mahogany back/sides/neck, 14/20 fret bound rosewood fingerboard with pearl parallelogram inlay, rosewood bridge with black pearl dot pins, blackface peghead with pearl plant/logo inlay, 3 per side nickel tuners with pearl buttons. Available in Vintage Cherry Sunburst finish. Mfg. 1963 to date.

1960-1962		$2,500	$2,100	$1,850	$1,625	$1,375	$1,050	$750
1963-1968		$1,500	$1,285	$1,070	$860	$770	$710	$645
1969-1975		$750	$640	$535	$430	$390	$355	$325
1976-1985		$1,100	$940	$785	$630	$565	$515	$470
Mfr.'s Sug. Retail	$1,950	$1,462	$975	$950	$760	$685	$625	$570

In 1962-1963, some models were produced with maple back/sides.

In 1969, adjustable saddle replaced original item.

In 1970, non-adjustable saddle replaced respective item.

In 1973, block fingerboard inlay replaced original item.

In 1984, parallelogram fingerboard inlay replaced respective item.

JUBILEE — ¾ size dreadnought style, spruce top, round soundhole, black pickguard, bound body/rosette, mahogany back/sides/neck, 14/20 fret rosewood fingerboard with pearl dot inlay, adjustable rosewood bridge, 3 per side tuners. Available in Natural finish. Mfg. 1970 to 1971.

		$625	$535	$445	$360	$325	$300	$275

Jubilee 12 String — similar to Jubilee, except has 12 strings, 6 per side tuners.

		$600	$515	$430	$345	$310	$285	$260

Jubilee Deluxe — similar to Jubilee, except has multi-wooden binding/purfling, rosewood back/sides.

		$750	$640	$535	$430	$390	$355	$325

J Series

JUMBO — bell shape jumbo style, round soundhole, tortoise pickguard, stripe bound body/rosette, mahogany back/sides/neck, 14/19 fret rosewood fingerboard with pearl dot inlay, rectangular rosewood bridge with white pins, blackface peghead with pearl logo inlay, 3 per side nickel tuners. Available in Sunburst finish. Mfg. 1934 to 1936.

		$3,500	$3,100	$2,600	$2,000	$1,400	$1,000	$900

Advanced Jumbo — similar to Jumbo, except has rosewood back/sides, pearl diamond/arrow fingerboard inlay, white black dot bridge pins, pearl diamond/arrow peghead inlay. Available in Sunburst finish. Mfg. 1936 to 1940.

		$3,500	$3,100	$2,700	$2,100	$1,450	$1,050	$950

J-25 — dreadnought style, laminated spruce top, round soundhole, tortoise pickguard, bound body/rosette, synthetic back/sides bowl, mahogany neck, 14/20 fret rosewood fingerboard with pearl dot inlay, rosewood bridge with white pins, blackface peghead with screened logo, 3 per side nickel tuners with pearloid buttons. Available in Natural finish. Mfg. 1984 to 1987.

		$550	$470	$395	$315	$285	$260	$235

J-30 — dreadnought style, spruce top, round soundhole, tortoise pickguard, 3 stripe bound body/rosette, mahogany back/sides/neck, 14/20 fret rosewood fingerboard with pearl dot inlay, blackface peghead with pearl banner/logo inlay, rosewood bridge with black pins, 3 per side nickel tuners with pearloid buttons. Available in Antique Walnut and Vintage Sunburst finishes. Mfg. 1985 to date.

Mfr.'s Sug. Retail	$1,400	$1,050	$700	$500	$480	$450	$420	$390

In 1994, reverse bridge with rosewood pins replaced original item.

J-30 Cutaway — similar to J-30, except has single round cutaway, reverse belly bridge with rosewood pins, transducer pickup/preamp system. Available in Antique Walnut and Vintage Sunburst finishes. Mfd. 1994 to date.

Mfr.'s Sug. Retail	$1,750	$1,312	$875	$500	$480	$450	$420	$390

"You can never be guaranteed that you're going to get your guitar on the plane when you carry it on. So I carry on a little backup, a little travel guitar, an Austin Hatchett, which I've got out-fitted to be identical to this electronically and feel wise."
—R. Matuza on Tuck Andress
TCG, July 1995

G

Grading	100%	98% MINT	95% EXC+	90% EXC	80% VG+	70% VG	60% G

1970s Gibson acoustic
courtesy Cassi International

Jumbo 35 — bellshape jumbo style, spruce top, round soundhole, tortoise shell pickguard, bound body, 1 stripe rosette, mahogany back/sides/neck, 14/19 fret rosewood fingerboard with pearl dot inlay, rosewood straight bridge with pearl dot inlay, white bridge pins, blackface peghead with screened logo, 3 per side tuners with plastic buttons. Available in Sunburst finish. Mfg. 1936 to 1942.

	$2,200	$2,050	$1,800	$1,500	$1,200	$1,000	$900

Last Mfr.'s Sug. Retail was $42 for Natural finish, $47.25 for Sunburst finish.

In 1939, Natural finish replaced original item.

In 1941, Natural and Sunburst finishes were available.

J-35 — jumbo style, spruce top, round soundhole, tortoise pickguard, 3 stripe bound body/rosette, maple back/sides/neck, 14/20 fret rosewood fingerboard with pearl dot inlay, rosewood reverse bridge with white black dot pins, blackface peghead with screened logo, 3 per side tuners with plastic buttons. Available in Cherry Sunburst finish. Mfg. 1985 to 1987.

	$800	$685	$575	$460	$410	$380	$345

J-40 — jumbo style, spruce top, round soundhole, black pickguard, bound body, 3 stripe rosette, mahogany back/sides/neck, 14/20 fret rosewood fingerboard with pearl dot inlay, rosewood strings thru bridge, screened peghead logo, 3 per side chrome tuners. Available in Natural finish. Mfg. 1971 to 1982.

	$950	$815	$680	$545	$490	$445	$405

This model had Cherry Sunburst finish optionally available.

In 1973, 3 piece maple neck replaced original item.

J-45 — vintage dreadnought style, spruce top, round soundhole, tortoise shell pickguard, 3 stripe bound body/rosette, mahogany back/sides/neck, 14/20 fret rosewood fingerboard with pearl dot inlay, rosewood bridge with black pins, 3 per side nickel tuners with pearl buttons. Available in Sunburst finish. Mfg. 1942 to 1982.

1942-1945	$1,675	$1,435	$1,195	$955	$855	$785	$715
1946-1950	$1,400	$1,200	$1,000	$800	$720	$660	$600
1951-1959	$1,325	$1,135	$950	$760	$685	$625	$570
1960-1964	$1,250	$1,070	$895	$715	$645	$590	$535
1965-1968	$850	$730	$610	$485	$435	$400	$365
1969-1974	$750	$640	$535	$430	$390	$355	$325
1975-1982	$700	$600	$500	$400	$360	$330	$300

This model was originally released with one stripe body binding.

In 1950, upper belly on bridge, 3 stripe body binding replaced original items.

In 1955, redesigned pickguard replaced original item.

In 1956, adjustable bridge became optionally available.

In 1962, Cherry Sunburst finish was offered.

In 1968, belly under bridge replaced respective item.

In 1969, redesigned body/pickguard replaced respective items.

In 1971, non-adjustable saddle became standard.

In 1975, redesigned pickguard, 4 stripe top purfling, tortoise body binding replaced respective items.

In 1981, 3 stripe top purfling replaced respective item.

J-45 Celebrity — similar to J-45, except has rosewood back/sides, fern peghead inlay. Mfg. 1985 only.

	$1,000	$855	$715	$570	$510	$465	$425

J-45 Reissue — similar to J-45, except has bell shape dreadnought body. Available in Ebony, Natural and Sunburst finishes. Mfg. 1984 to date.

Mfr.'s Sug. Retail	$1,500	$1,125	$750	$700	$560	$505	$460	$420

J-50 — similar to J-45, except has Natural finish. Mfg. 1947 to 1982.

1947-1954	$1,700	$1,550	$1,375	$1,150	$1,000	$925	$875
1955-1960	$1,500	$1,350	$1,175	$950	$800	$725	$675
1960-1964	$1,350	$1,200	$1,025	$800	$650	$575	$525
1965-1968	$1,100	$1,050	$925	$785	$575	$445	$400
1969-1982	$650	$600	$550	$500	$450	$400	$350

JUMBO 55 — bell shape jumbo, spruce top, round soundhole, tortoise pickguard, bound body, 1 stripe rosette, mahogany back/sides/neck, 14/20 fret bound coffeewood fingerboard with pearl dot inlay, coffeewood mustache bridge with pearl dot inlay, white bridge pins, blackface stairstep peghead with pearl logo inlay, 3 per side tuners with amber buttons. Available in Sunburst finish. Mfg. 1939 to 1942.

	$4,000	$3,600	$3,300	$2,800	$2,500	$1,900	$1,600

In 1940, standard peghead replaced original item.

In 1941, rosewood fingerboard, wings shaped rosewood bridge with pearl dot inlay replaced original items.

As a historical note, the last manufacturer's suggested retail for this model was $68.25.

J-55 — jumbo style, spruce top, round soundhole, tortoise pickguard, bound body, 3 stripe rosette, arched mahogany back/sides, maple neck, 14/20 fret rosewood fingerboard with pearl dot inlay, rosewood bridge with black white dot pins, blackface peghead with pearl logo inlay, 3 per side chrome tuners. Available in Natural finish. Mfg. 1973 to 1982.

	$550	$470	$395	$315	$285	$260	$235

Grading	100%	98% MINT	95% EXC+	90% EXC	80% VG+	70% VG	60% G

J-60 — dreadnought style, spruce top, round soundhole, tortoise pickguard, 3 stripe bound body/rosette, rosewood back/sides, mahogany neck, 14/20 fret rosewood fingerboard with pearl dot inlay, rosewood bridge with black pins, 3 per side nickel tuners with pearl buttons. Available in Antique Natural and Vintage Sunburst finishes. Curr. mfr.

Mfr.'s Sug. Retail	$1,700	$1,360	$1,020	$850	$680	$610	$560	$510

J-100 — jumbo style, spruce top, round soundhole, black pickguard, 2 stripe bound body/rosette, maple back/sides/neck, 14/20 fret rosewood fingerboard with pearl dot inlay, rosewood bridge with black pins, 3 per side nickel tuners with pearl buttons. Available in Natural finish. Mfg. 1985 to 1991.

		$900	$770	$640	$515	$465	$425	$385

This model had cedar top optionally available.

J-100 XTRA — jumbo style, spruce top, round soundhole, black pickguard, 2 stripe bound body/rosette, mahogany back/sides/neck, 14/20 fret rosewood fingerboard with pearl dot inlay, rosewood bridge with black pins, blackface peghead with pearl crown/logo inlay, 3 per side nickel tuners with pearloid buttons. Available in Antique Walnut and Vintage Sunburst finishes. Curr. mfr.

Mfr.'s Sug. Retail	$1,500	$1,125	$750	$700	$560	$505	$460	$420

In 1994, tortoise pickguard, mustache bridge with rosewood pins replaced original items.

J-100 Xtra Cutaway — similar to J-100 Xtra, except has single round cutaway, tortoise pickguard, mustache bridge with rosewood pins, transducer pickup/preamp system. Available in Antique Walnut and Vintage Sunburst finishes. New 1994.

Mfr.'s Sug. Retail	$1,850	$1,480	$1,110	$925	$740	$670	$610	$555

J-180 — jumbo style, spruce top, round soundhole, 2 tortoise pickguards, 3 stripe bound body/rosette, maple back/sides, 1 piece mahogany neck, 14/20 fret rosewood fingerboard with pearl star inlay, reverse belly bridge with black white dot pins, blackface peghead with pearl star/logo inlay, 3 per side nickel tuners with pearloid buttons. Available in Black finish. Mfg. 1986 to 1991.

		$1,025	$880	$735	$585	$525	$485	$440

J-185 — jumbo style, spruce top, round soundhole, tortoise pickguard, 2 stripe bound body/rosette, figured maple back/sides, mahogany neck, 14/20 fret rosewood fingerboard with pearl parallelogram inlay, upper belly rosewood bridge with white pins, pearl cross bridge wings inlay, blackface peghead with pearl crown/logo inlay, 3 per side nickel tuners. Available in Cremona Brown Burst and Natural finishes. Mfg.1951 to 1958.

		$4,200	$3,600	$3,000	$2,400	$2,160	$1,980	$1,800

J-200 — jumbo style, spruce top, round soundhole, black pickguard with engraved floral pattern, figured maple back/sides/neck, 14/20 bound rosewood fingerboard with pearl crown inlay, rosewood mustache bridge with pearl block inlay, black pearl dot pins, bound peghead with pearl plant/logo inlay, 3 per side gold tuners with pearl buttons. Available in Antique Walnut, Natural and Vintage Sunburst finishes. Mfg. 1946 to date.

1946-1950		$5,250	$4,500	$3,750	$3,000	$2,700	$2,475	$2,250
1951-1959		$4,250	$3,640	$3,035	$2,430	$2,185	$2,005	$1,820
1960-1964		$3,450	$2,960	$2,465	$1,970	$1,775	$1,625	$1,480
1965-1968		$2,650	$2,270	$1,895	$1,515	$1,365	$1,250	$1,135
1969-1974		$1,500	$1,285	$1,070	$860	$770	$710	$645
1975-1985		$1,000	$855	$715	$570	$510	$465	$425
Mfr.'s Sug. Retail	$2,700	$2,025	$1,350	$1,275	$1,020	$920	$840	$765

This model was known as the Super Jumbo (SJ-200) from 1936-1945. Some pre-war models with rosewood construction have sold for as high as $25,000. Instruments should be determined on a piece-by-piece basis as opposed to the usual market.

Original release of this instrument had single peghead binding.

In 1948, Natural finish became optionally available.

In 1960, adjustable saddle bridge became an option.

In 1961, tunomatic bridge with pearl block inlay replaced original items.

In 1969, adjustable saddle became standard.

In 1971, ebony fingerboard replaced original item, non-adjustable bridge replaced respective item.

In 1979, rosewood fingerboard replaced respective item.

In 1985, mustache bridge with pearl block inlay replaced respective item, multi-bound peghead replaced original item.

In 1994, Antique Ebony finish was introduced, pearl crown fingerboard inlay, gold hardware replaced respective items.

J-200 12 String — similar to J-200, except has 12 strings, 6 per side tuners. Curr. mfr.

Mfr.'s Sug. Retail	$3,200	$2,560	$1,920	$1,600	$1,280	$1,150	$1,055	$960

J-200 Celebrity — similar to J-200, except has ornate scroll type fingerboard inlay, fern peghead inlay. Mfg. 1985 only.

		$1,950	$1,700	$1,525	$1,275	$1,000	$775	$625

J-200 Deluxe — jumbo style, spruce top, round soundhole, black pickguard with engraved floral pattern/abalone dot inlay, abalone bound body/rosette, figured maple back/sides/neck, 14/20 bound ebony fingerboard with abalone crown inlay, ebony mustache bridge with abalone block inlay/white abalone dot pins, bound blackface peghead with abalone crown/logo inlay, 3 per side gold Grover Imperial tuners. Available in Antique Natural and Vintage Sunburst finishes. New 1994.

Mfr.'s Sug. Retail	$5,200	$4,160	$3,120	$2,600	$2,080	$1,870	$1,715	$1,560

This model has rosewood back/sides/neck optionally available.

1953 Gibson J-200
19th Annual Dallas Show

Grading	100%	98% MINT	95% EXC+	90% EXC	80% VG+	70% VG	60% G

J-200 Jr. — similar to J-200, except has smaller body, nickel tuners. Disc. 1994.

	$1,260	$1,080	$900	$720	$650	$595	$540

Last Mfr.'s Sug. Retail was $1,800.

J-250R — jumbo style, spruce top, round soundhole, black pickguard with engraved floral pattern, rosewood back/sides, mahogany neck, 14/20 bound rosewood fingerboard with pearl crown inlay, rosewood mustache bridge with pearl block inlay, black pearl dot pins, bound peghead with pearl crown/logo inlay, 3 per side gold tuners with pearl buttons. Available in Natural finish. Mfg. 1972 to 1978.

	$850	$725	$600	$450	$375	$300	$250

J-300 — similar to J-250R, except has 12 Strings, 6 per side tuners. Mfg. 1973 only.

	$725	$600	$450	$375	$300	$250	$175

J-1000 — rounded single cutaway jumbo style, spruce top, round soundhole, 3 stripe bound body/rosette, rosewood back/sides, mahogany neck, 20 bound rosewood pointed fingerboard with pearl diamond inlay, rosewood mustache bridge with black pearl dot pins, bound blackface peghead with pearl diamond/logo inlay, 3 per side gold tuners. Available in Natural finish. Mfg. 1992 only.

	$1,400	$1,200	$1,000	$800	$720	$660	$600

Last Mfr.'s Sug. Retail was $1,999.

J-1500 — rounded single cutaway jumbo style, spruce top, round soundhole, 3 stripe bound body, abalone rosette, rosewood back/sides, mahogany neck, 20 fret bound ebony pointed fingerboard with abalone varied diamond inlay, ebony mustache bridge with white black dot pins, bound blackface peghead with abalone fleur-de-lis/logo inlay, 3 per side gold tuners. Available in Natural finish. Mfg. 1992 only.

	$1,925	$1,650	$1,375	$1,100	$990	$905	$825

Last Mfr.'s Sug. Retail was $2,750.

J-2000/CUSTOM — single round cutaway jumbo style, spruce top, round soundhole, abalone bound body/rosette, rosewood back/sides, mahogany neck, 20 fret bound ebony point fingerboard with abalone leaf inlay, ebony bridge with white abalone dot pins, abalone leaf bridge wings inlay, bound peghead with leaf/logo inlay, 3 per side gold tuners with pearl buttons, piezo bridge pickup, endpin pickup jack. Available in Antique Natural and Vintage Sunburst finishes. Disc. 1994.

	$2,800	$2,400	$2,000	$1,600	$1,440	$1,320	$1,200

Last Mfr.'s Sug. Retail was $4,010.

JG-0 — jumbo style, spruce top, round soundhole, bound body, 1 stripe rosette, mahogany back/sides/neck, 14/20 fret rosewood fingerboard with pearl dot inlay, rosewood bridge with white pins, logo peghead decal, 3 per side tuners. Available in Natural finish. Mfg. 1970 to 1972.

	$550	$400	$325	$275	$225	$175	$150

JG-12 — similar to JG-0, except has 12 strings, 6 per side tuners. Mfg. 1970 only.

	$500	$375	$300	$250	$175	$125	$100

SJ (SOUTHERNER JUMBO) — vintage dreadnought style, spruce top, round soundhole, black pickguard, 2 stripe bound body/rosette, mahogany back/sides/neck, 14/20 fret bound rosewood fingerboard with pearl parallelogram inlays, rosewood bridge with white pins, blackface peghead with pearl banner logo inlay, 3 per side nickel tuners. Available in Sunburst finish. Mfg. 1942 to 1978.

	100%	98%	95%	90%	80%	70%	60%
1942-1945	$1,725	$1,480	$1,235	$985	$890	$815	$740
1946-1950	$1,500	$1,285	$1,070	$860	$770	$710	$645
1951-1959	$1,300	$1,115	$930	$740	$670	$610	$555
1960-1964	$1,125	$965	$805	$640	$580	$530	$480
1965-1968	$800	$685	$575	$460	$410	$380	$345
1969-1978	$700	$600	$500	$400	$360	$330	$300

A few early models are found with rosewood back/sides.

In 1946, no peghead logo appeared.

In 1949, upper belly bridge replaced original item.

In 1954, Natural finish became optionally available.

In 1955, redesigned pickguard replaced original item.

In 1961, adjustable saddle replaced original item.

In 1963, redesigned body/pickguard replaced respective items.

In 1969, standard style bridge replaced respective item.

In 1970, non-adjustable saddle replaced respective item.

In 1974, 4 stripe body/2 stripe neck binding replaced original items.

SJN (Country Western) — similar to SJ (Southern Jumbo), except has tortoise pickguard. Available in Natural finish. Mfg. 1956 to 1978.

	100%	98%	95%	90%	80%	70%	60%
1956-1964	$950	$815	$680	$545	$490	$445	$405
1965-1968	$700	$600	$500	$400	$360	$330	$300
1969-1978	$500	$430	$360	$285	$260	$235	$215

Grading	100%	98% MINT	95% EXC+	90% EXC	80% VG+	70% VG	60% G

SJ-45 DELUXE — bellshape dreadnought style, spruce top, round soundhole, tortoise pickguard, abalone bound body, 3 stripe rosette, rosewood back/sides, mahogany neck, 14/20 fret bound rosewood fingerboard with pearl flower inlay, rosewood bridge with white pins, blackface peghead with pearl banner/logo inlay, 3 per side gold tuners. Available in Antique Natural and Special Vintage Sunburst finishes. New 1994.

Mfr.'s Sug. Retail	$3,000	$2,400	$1,800	$1,500	$1,200	$1,080	$990	$900

L Series

STYLE L — folk style, arched spruce top, round soundhole, bound body, wood inlay rosette, maple back/sides/neck, 13/19 fret ebony fingerboard with pearl dot inlay, ebony bridge/trapeze tailpiece, blackface peghead, 3 per side tuners. Available in Orange Top finish. Mfg. approx. 1903.

		$1,250	$925	$800	$675	$500	$375	$250

L-0 — folk style, spruce top, round soundhole, mottled pickguard, bound body, 2 stripe rosette, maple back/sides, mahogany neck, 12/19 fret ebonized fingerboard with pearl dot inlay, ebony pyramid bridge with black pins, blackface peghead with screened logo, 3 per side tuners with plastic buttons. Available in Amber Brown finish. Mfg. 1926 to 1933.

		$1,300	$1,100	$950	$860	$750	$640	$575

A few of these instruments are found with black tuner buttons.

In 1928, mahogany top/back/sides, bound soundhole, rosewood fingerboard, rosewood standard bridge with extra white pin replaced original items.

In 1929, straight bridge with no extra pin replaced respective item.

In 1932, 14/19 fret fingerboard replaced original item.

L-0 Reissue — similar to L-0, except has Ebony finish. Mfg. 1937 to 1942.

		$1,300	$1,100	$950	$860	$750	$640	$575

A few of these instruments are found with white pickguards.

L-00 — folk style, spruce top, round soundhole, mottled pickguard, bound body, 2 stripe rosette, mahogany back/sides/neck, 14/19 fret rosewood fingerboard with pearl dot inlay, rosewood straight bridge with black white dot pins, blackface peghead with screened logo, 3 per side tuners with plastic buttons. Available in Ebony, Natural and Sunburst finishes. Mfg. approx. 1930 to 1945.

		$1,500	$1,300	$1,100	$950	$850	$750	$675

A few of these instruments are found with white pickguards.

Early models of this line have 12/19 fret fingerboards.

In 1934, Sunburst finish became available.

In 1937, ¾ size body became optionally available.

In 1941, Natural finish became optionally available, Ebony finish was discontinued.

In 1942, banner peghead logo found on a few instruments.

L-00 1936 REISSUE — folk style, spruce top, round soundhole, 2 stripe bound body/rosette, mahogany back/sides/neck, 14/19 fret bound rosewood fingerboard with pearl dot inlay, rosewood bridge with white pins, 3 per side nickel tuners with plastic buttons. Available in Antique Walnut and Vintage Sunburst finishes. Mfg. 1992 to date.

Mfr.'s Sug. Retail	$1,300	$1,040	$780	$650	$520	$470	$430	$390

L-1 - ARCHTOP — hollow style, carved spruce top, bound round soundhole, raised tortoise pickguard, bound body, 2 rope pattern rosette, birch back/sides, maple neck, 13/19 fret ebony fingerboard with pearl dot inlay, ebony bridge/trapeze tailpiece, slotted peghead, 3 per side tuners with plastic buttons. Available in Orange Top/Mahogany finish. Mfg. 1903 to 1925.

		$1,000	$925	$850	$775	$675	$625	$575

This model was also produced with maple back/sides.

This instrument was available in standard, concert and grand concert sizes.

In 1918, Sheraton Brown finish replaced original item.

In 1920, 5 ring rosette replaced original item.

While earlier models may bring in as little as $700 (95%), models with an adjustable bridge and neck command a higher premium.

L-1 - Flat Top — concert style, spruce top, round soundhole, bound body, 3 ring rosette, mahogany back/sides, maple neck, 12/19 fret ebony fingerboard with pearl dot inlay, ebony pyramid bridge with black pins, painted peghead logo, 3 per side tuners with plastic buttons. Available in Sheraton Brown finish. Mfg. 1926 to 1937.

		$1,100	$940	$785	$630	$565	$515	$470

By 1928, bound rosewood fingerboard, 3 stripe bound body/rosette, rosewood belly bridge with white pins, Brown Sunburst finish replaced original items, extra bridge pin was added.

In 1929, straight bridge replaced respective item, extra bridge pin was discontinued.

In 1931, the body and bridge were redesigned, unbound fingerboard replaced respective item.

In 1932, single bound body, 14/19 fret fingerboard replaced respective items.

In 1933, a tortoise pickguard and peghead logo were added.

Grading	100%	98% MINT	95% EXC+	90% EXC	80% VG+	70% VG	60% G

L-1 (Current Manufacture) — folk style, spruce top, round soundhole, 2 stripe bound body/rosette, mahogany back/sides/neck, 14/19 fret bound rosewood fingerboard with pearl dot inlay, rosewood bridge with white pins, 3 per side nickel tuners with plastic buttons. Available in Vintage Cherry Sunburst finish. Current production.

Mfr.'s Sug. Retail	$1,400	$1,120	$840	$700	$560	$505	$460	$420

L-2 - ARCHTOP, 1st STYLE — hollow style, carved spruce top, round soundhole, raised tortoise pickguard, bound body, 3 rope pattern rosette, birch back/sides, maple neck, 13/19 fret ebony fingerboard with pearl dot inlay, adjustable ebony bridge/trapeze tailpiece, snakehead peghead with pearl logo inlay, 3 per side tuners with plastic buttons. Available in Orange Top finish. Mfg. 1902 to 1908.

		$825	$705	$585	$470	$425	$390	$355

This instrument was available in standard, concert and grand concert sizes.

L-2 - Archtop, 2nd Style — concert style, carved spruce top, round soundhole, raised tortoise pickguard, bound body, 2 ring rosette, maple back/sides, mahogany neck, 13/19 fret bound ebony fingerboard with pearl dot inlay, adjustable ebony bridge/trapeze tailpiece, snakehead peghead with pearl logo inlay, 3 per side tuners with plastic buttons. Available in Amber finish. Mfg. 1924 to 1926.

	$1,100	$1,000	$900	$800	$700	$600	$500

L-2 - Flat Top — concert style, spruce top, round soundhole, 3 stripe body/rosette, bound body, rosewood back/sides, mahogany neck, 13/19 fret bound ebony fingerboard with pearl dot inlay, ebony pyramid bridge, blackface peghead with pearl logo inlay, 3 per side tuners with plastic buttons. Available in Natural and Sunburst finish. Mfg. 1929 to 1934.

	$2,200	$2,000	$1,800	$1,450	$1,200	$1,000	$800

This model was also available with adjustable ebony bridge/trapeze tailpiece.

In 1931, mahogany back/sides, 12/19 fret fingerboard replaced original items, gold sparkle inlay rosette/body, pearl flame peghead inlay were added.

In 1932, rosewood back/sides, 13/19 fret fingerboard adjustable ebony bridge/trapeze tailpiece replaced respective items, raised pickguard was added, gold sparkle inlay no longer available.

In 1933, top glued pickguard, ebony bridge with black pins replaced respective items.

In 1934, 14/19 fret fingerboard replaced respective item.

There is a rare version of the L-2 Flat Top that was available with a mahogany body, sparkle binding, and a green-to-yellow sunburst.

L-3 — hollow style, carved spruce top, bound round soundhole, raised tortoise pickguard, bound body, 3 ring wooden inlay rosette, birch back/sides, maple neck, 13/19 fret bound ebony fingerboard with pearl dot inlay, ebony bridge/trapeze tailpiece, blackface peghead with pearl logo inlay, 3 per side tuners with plastic buttons. Available in Orange Top/Mahogany finish. Mfg. 1902 to 1933.

	$1,025	$880	$735	$585	$525	$485	$440

This instrument was available in standard, concert and grand concert sizes.

L-4 — grand concert style, arched carved spruce top, oval soundhole, wooden inlay rosette, raised tortoise pickguard, bound soundhole/body, maple back/sides, mahogany neck, 12/20 fret bound ebony pointed fingerboard with pearl dot inlay, ebony bridge/trapeze tailpiece with black pins, bound blackface peghead with pearl logo inlay, 3 per side tuners with buttons. Available in Black finish. Mfg. 1912 to 1956.

	$1,500	$1,350	$1,160	$965	$770	$690	$630

In 1914, 3 ring rosette, Mahogany finish replaced original items, Black and Orange finishes optionally available.

In 1918, Mahogany Sunburst finish replaced respective item.

By 1920, rosette and peghead logo inlay were redesigned.

In 1923, tailpiece pins were removed.

In 1927, rosette was redesigned.

In 1928, round soundhole 14/20 fret unbound fingerboard, unbound peghead replaced original items, redesigned peghead logo replaced respective items, 2 ring rosette.

By 1933, bound fingerboard replaced respective item, pearl diamond peghead inlay was added.

In 1935, f-holes, bound pickguard, redesigned fingerboard inlay, redesigned trapeze tailpiece, bound peghead with lily inlay replaced respective items.

In 1937, unbound pickguard replaced respective item, round soundhole was optionally available.

In 1940, Natural finish optionally available.

In 1941, unbound peghead replaced respective item.

In 1946, bound pickguard, multi bound body replaced respective items.

In 1947, laminated pickguard, parallelogram fingerboard inlay replaced respective items.

L-4 models with the truss rod command a higher premium.

L-4 C — pointed cutaway concert style, arched spruce top, f-holes, raised laminated pickguard, bound body, carved maple back/sides, mahogany neck, 19 fret bound rosewood fingerboard with pearl parallelogram inlay, adjustable rosewood bridge/trapeze tailpiece, blackface peghead with pearl flowerpot/logo inlay, 3 per side tuners with plastic buttons. Available in Natural and Sunburst finishes. Mfg. 1949 to 1971.

1949-1962	$1,750	$1,600	$1,400	$1,250	$1,000	$925	$850
1963-1971	$1,400	$1,200	$1,075	$950	$840	$760	$700

Grading	100%	98% MINT	95% EXC+	90% EXC	80% VG+	70% VG	60% G

L-5 — orchestra style, carved spruce top, f-holes, raised multi bound pickguard, multi bound body, carved figured maple back/sides, figured maple/ebony neck, 14/20 fret bound ebony pointed fingerboard with pearl dot inlay, adjustable ebony bridge/trapeze tailpiece, multi bound blackface snakehead peghead with pearl flowerpot/logo inlay, 3 per side silver plate tuners with pearl buttons, Master Model/Loyd Loar signature labels. Available in Cremona Brown Sunburst finish. Mfg. 1922 to 1958.

1922-1924	$15,000	$13,500	$11,000	$9,200	$7,600	$6,100	$5,500
1925-1933	$2,550	$2,100	$1,825	$1,575	$1,250	$1,000	$775
1934-1942	$3,750	$3,300	$2,950	$2,525	$1,975	$1,500	$1,175
1943-1958	$2,975	$2,650	$2,225	$1,900	$1,550	$1,200	$950

Some early versions of this instrument have birch back/sides.

In 1924, Loar signature label discontinued.

In 1925, gold tuners replaced original item.

In 1927, Master Model label was discontinued.

In 1929, flat fingerboard with block inlay replaced original items, individual tuners replaced respective item.

In 1934, larger body (17 inches across bottom bout), binding, tailpiece, peghead replaced original items, redesigned fingerboard replaced respective item.

In 1936, bound f-holes replaced original item.

In 1937, gold tailpiece with silver insert, Grover Imperial tuners replaced respective items.

In 1939, redesigned tailpiece replaced respective item, pearloid pickguard, Natural finish optionally available.

In 1948, 1 or 2 pickguard mounted pickups became optionally available.

L-5 Premiere — single round cutaway grand auditorium style, arched spruce top, bound f-holes, raised multi bound pearloid pickguard, multi bound body, carved figured maple back/sides, figured maple neck, 14/20 fret multi bound ebony pointed fingerboard with pearl block inlay, adjustable ebony bridge/gold trapeze tailpiece with silver insert, multi bound blackface peghead with pearl flowerpot/logo inlay, 3 per side gold tuners. Available in Natural and Sunburst finishes. Mfg. 1939 to 1989.

1939-1941	$12,000	$10,000	$8,500	$6,500	$5,500	$4,500	$3,900
1942-1949	$8,050	$6,900	$5,750	$4,600	$4,140	$3,795	$3,450
1950-1962	$5,050	$4,750	$4,200	$3,750	$3,000	$2,550	$2,200
1963-1989	$3,000	$2,750	$2,225	$1,900	$1,650	$1,225	$950

Though not officially out of production, these instruments are sporadically produced.

In 1948, renamed L-5C, 1 or 2 pickguard mounted pickups became optionally available.

L-5CT — similar to L-5C, except has thin body, shorter scale length. Available in Red finish. Mfg. 1959 to 1961.

	$20,000	$18,500	$17,500	$15,000	$10,000	$8,000	$7,500

Also referred to as the George Gobel model. 2 humbucker pickups, 2 volume/tone controls, and a 3 position switch were optionally available.

L-7 — orchestra style, arched spruce top, f-holes, raised bound black pickguard, bound body, carved maple back/sides, mahogany neck, 14/19 fret bound rosewood fingerboard with pearl multi design inlay, adjustable rosewood bridge/trapeze tailpiece, bound blackface peghead with pearl fleur-de-lis/logo inlay, 3 per side tuners with plastic buttons. Available in Sunburst finish. Mfg. 1932 to 1956.

	$1,900	$1,700	$1,400	$1,100	$980	$890	$800

In 1934, redesigned body, fingerboard/peghead inlay, trapeze tailpiece replaced original items.

In 1937, redesigned trapeze tailpiece replaced respective item.

In 1939, Natural finish became available.

In 1942, multi bound body, parellogram fingerboard inlay, crown peghead inlay replaced respective items.

In 1944, redesigned trapeze tailpiece replaced respective item.

In 1948, laminated pickguard replaced respective item, 1 or 2 pickguard mounted pickups became optionally available.

L-7C — single round cutaway grand auditorium style, arched spruce top, f-holes, raised black laminated pickguard, bound body, carved maple back/sides, mahogany neck, 14/19 fret bound rosewood fingerboard with pearl parallelogram inlay, adjustable rosewood bridge/trapeze tailpiece, bound blackface peghead with pearl crown/logo inlay, 3 per side tuners with plastic buttons. Available in Natural and Sunburst finishes. Mfg. 1948 to 1972.

	$2,350	$2,015	$1,675	$1,340	$1,200	$1,100	$1,000

This model had 1 or 2 pickguard mounted pickups optionally available.

In 1957, redesigned trapeze tailpiece replaced original item.

L-10 — orchestra style, arched spruce top, f-holes, raised black pickguard, bound body, carved maple back/sides, mahogany neck, 14/19 fret bound ebony fingerboard with pearl dot inlay, adjustable ebony bridge/wrarover trapeze tailpiece, blackface peghead with pearl logo inlay, 3 per side nickel tuners. Available in Black finish. Mfg. 1931 to 1939.

	$1,850	$1,590	$1,325	$1,060	$950	$875	$795

In 1934, redesigned body, bound pickguard, checkered top binding, double triangle fingerboard inlay, redesigned trapeze tailpiece, bound peghead with pearl vase inlay, Red Mahogany finish replaced original items.

In 1935, redesigned tailpiece, redesigned peghead inlay replaced respective items.

1937 Gibson L-7
courtesy Southworth Guitars

Grading	100%	98% MINT	95% EXC+	90% EXC	80% VG+	70% VG	60% G

L-12 — orchestra style, arched spruce top, f-holes, raised bound black pickguard, bound body, carved maple back/sides, mahogany neck, 14/19 fret bound ebony fingerboard with pearl flowers inlay, adjustable ebony bridge/trapeze tailpiece, bound blackface peghead with pearl vase/logo inlay, 3 per side gold tuners. Available in Red Mahogany Sunburst finish. Mfg. 1932 to 1955.

	$2,150	$1,840	$1,535	$1,230	$1,105	$1,015	$920

In 1934, grand auditorium style body, multi bound pickguard/top/peghead, parallelogram fingerboard inlay, diamond/star peghead inlay replaced original items.

In 1937, redesigned tailpiece replaced original item.

In 1941, bound pickguard/peghead, crown peghead inlay replaced respective items.

L-12 Premiere — similar to L-12, except has single round cutaway. Mfg. 1947 to 1950.

	$2,150	$1,840	$1,535	$1,230	$1,105	$1,015	$920

L-20 SPECIAL — folk style, spruce top, round soundhole, 2 stripe bound body/rosette, rosewood back/sides/neck, 14/19 fret bound rosewood fingerboard with pearl dot inlay, rosewood bridge with white pins, 3 per side gold tuners with plastic buttons, piezo bridge pickup, endpin pickup jack. Available in Antique Natural and Vintage Sunburst finishes. Curr. mfr.

Mfr.'s Sug. Retail	$2,000	$1,600	$1,200	$1,000	$800	$720	$660	$600

L-30 — dreadnought style, arched spruce top, f-holes, raised black pickguard, bound body, maple back/sides, mahogany neck, 14/19 fret ebony fingerboard with pearl dot inlay, adjustable ebony bridge/trapeze tailpiece, blackface peghead with screened logo, 3 per side tuners with plastic buttons. Available in Black finish. Mfg. 1935 to 1943.

	$600	$425	$365	$305	$245	$220	$200

In 1936, Dark Mahogany Sunburst finish replaced original item.

In 1938, rosewood bridge replaced original item.

L-37 — similar to L-30, except has Red Mahogany Sunburst finish. Mfg. 1935 to 1941.

	$725	$620	$520	$415	$375	$340	$310

In 1936, Brown Sunburst finish replaced original item.

L-47 — dreadnought style, arched spruce top, f-holes, raised bound pickguard, tortoise bound body, maple back/sides, mahogany neck, 14/19 fret ebony fingerboard with pearl dot inlay, adjustable ebony bridge/trapeze tailpiece, blackface peghead with screened logo, 3 per side tuners with plastic buttons. Available in Natural and Sunburst finishes. Mfg. 1940 to 1943.

	$650	$555	$465	$370	$335	$305	$280

L-48 — orchestra style, arched mahogany top, f-holes, raised black pickguard, bound body, mahogany back/sides/neck, 14/19 fret rosewood fingerboard with pearl dot inlay, adjustable rosewood bridge/trapeze tailpiece, blackface peghead with screened logo, 3 per side tuners. Available in Cremona Brown Sunburst finish. Mfd. 1946 to 1971.

	$700	$650	$600	$550	$500	$450	$400

A few early instruments have spruce tops, trapezoid fingerboard inlay.

In 1952, spruce top, maple back, mahogany sides replaced original items.

In 1957, mahogany top replaced respective item, some instruments found with mahogany back also.

L-50 — hollow body style, arched spruce top, round soundhole, black pickguard, bound body, maple back/sides, mahogany neck, 14/19 fret ebony fingerboard with pearl dot inlay, adjustable ebony bridge/trapeze tailpiece, blackface peghead with screened logo, 3 per side tuners with plastic buttons. Available in Dark Mahogany Sunburst finish. Mfg. 1932 to 1971.

	$900	$850	$800	$750	$700	$650	$600

In 1934, redesigned body, raised pickguard, redesigned tailpiece replaced original items.

In 1935, orchestra style body replaced respective item, arched back replaced original item.

In 1936, redesigned tailpiece replaced respective item.

In 1943, redesigned tailpiece replaced original item, 3 per side plate mounted tuners replaced original item.

In 1946, bound pickguard/fingerboard with pearl trapezoid inlay replaced original items, redesigned tailpiece, 3 per side tuners with plastic buttons replaced respective items.

In 1949, laminated pickguard replaced respective item.

L-75 — hollow body style, arched spruce top, f-holes, bound body, mahogany back/sides, mahogany neck, 14/19 fret pearloid fingerboard with pearl multi-design inlay in blocks of rosewood, adjustable rosewood bridge/trapeze tailpiece, pearloid veneered peghead, rosewood diamond peghead inlay with pearl logo, 3 per side tuners with plastic buttons. Available in Natural finish. Mfg. 1932 to 1939.

	$1,500	$1,285	$1,070	$860	$770	$710	$645

In 1934, redesigned body/tailpiece, bound rosewood fingerboard with pearl dot inlay, blackface peghead with pearl vase logo inlay replaced original items.

In 1935, carved back replaced original item, orchestra style body, redesigned peghead inlay replaced respective items, raised pickguard added.

Grading	100%	98% MINT	95% EXC+	90% EXC	80% VG+	70% VG	60% G

L-C (Century) — folk style, spruce top, round soundhole, tortoise pickguard, bound body, 1 stripe rosette, curly maple back/sides, mahogany neck, 14/19 fret bound pearloid fingerboard, rosewood block with pearl diamonds fingerboard inlay, rosewood straight bridge with white pins, bound peghead with pearloid veneer, rosewood wedge with pearl slotted diamond/logo inlay, 3 per side tuners with plastic buttons. Available in Sunburst finish. Mfg. 1933 to 1940.

	$2,025	$1,740	$1,450	$1,160	$1,040	$955	$870

> In 1938, 2 types of rosewood peghead veneer replaced original item; one featured pearl diamond inlay, the other was bound with pearl slotted diamond/logo inlay.

L Junior — concert style, carved spruce top, round bound soundhole, birch back/sides, maple neck, 13/19 fret ebony fingerboard with pearl dot inlay, ebony bridge/trapeze tailpiece, tortoise plate with black pins on trapeze tailpiece, slotted peghead, 3 per side tuners with plastic buttons. Available in Brown finish. Mfg. 1919 to 1926.

	$650	$600	$500	$430	$360	$285	$260

> L Junior models with truss rod or factory black finish command a higher premium.

LG Series

LG-0 — folk style, mahogany top, round soundhole, black pickguard, bound body, 1 stripe rosette, mahogany back/sides/neck, 14/20 fret rosewood fingerboard with pearl dot inlay, rosewood straight bridge with pearl dot inlay, white bridge pins, blackface peghead with screened logo, 3 per side nickel tuners with plastic buttons. Available in Natural finish. Mfg. 1958 to 1974.

	$350	$300	$250	$200	$150	$125	$100

> In 1962, plastic screw-on bridge replaced original item.
> In 1963, redesigned tortoise pickguard replaced original item.
> In 1966, rosewood reverse bridge replaced respective item.
> In 1969, spruce top, standard bridge replaced respective items.
> In 1970, veneerless peghead replaced original item, black pickguard replaced respective item.

LG-1 — folk style, spruce top, round soundhole, tortoise pickguard, bound body, 1 stripe rosette, mahogany back/sides/neck, 14/19 fret rosewood fingerboard with pearl dot inlay, rosewood straight bridge with pearl dot inlay, black bridge pins, blackface peghead with screened logo, 3 per side nickel tuners with plastic buttons. Available in Sunburst finish. Mfg. 1947 to 1968.

	$500	$430	$360	$285	$260	$235	$215

> In 1955, redesigned pickguard, 14/20 fret fingerboard replaced original items.
> In 1962, plastic screw-on bridge replaced original item.

LG-2 — folk style, red spruce top, round soundhole, tortoise shell pickguard, bound body, 1 stripe rosette, mahogany back/sides/neck, 14/19 fret rosewood fingerboard with pearl dot inlay, rosewood straight bridge with pearl dot inlay, black bridge pins, blackface peghead with screened logo, 3 per side nickel tuners with plastic buttons. Available in Cherry Sunburst and Golden Sunburst finishes. Mfg. 1942 to 1962.

	$700	$600	$500	$400	$360	$330	$300

> Early models are found with banner/logo peghead decals. During WWII, Gibson used whatever materials were available to construct instruments. Consequently, there are LG-2's found with mahogany tops, maple back/sides/neck, no truss rods and other little differences from other production models found before and after the war.
> In 1955, redesigned pickguard, 14/20 fret fingerboard replaced original items.
> In 1961, Cherry Sunburst finish replaced original item.

LG-2 ¾ — similar to LG-2, except has ¾ size body. Mfg. 1949 to 1968.

	$500	$430	$360	$285	$260	$235	$215

LG-3 — folk style, spruce top, round soundhole, tortoise shell pickguard, 3 stripe bound body/rosette, mahogany back/sides/neck, 14/19 fret rosewood fingerboard with pearl dot inlay, rosewood straight bridge with pearl dot inlay, white bridge pins, blackface peghead with banner/logo decal, 3 per side nickel tuners with plastic buttons. Available in Natural finish. Mfg. 1945 to 1963.

	100%	98%	95%	90%	80%	70%	60%
1945-1960	$900	$850	$775	$700	$625	$550	$480
1961-1963	$750	$640	$535	$430	$390	$355	$325

> In 1947, banner peghead decal was removed.
> In 1955, redesigned pickguard, 14/20 fret fingerboard replaced original items.
> In 1961, adjustable bridge replaced original item.
> In early 1962, reverse rosewood bridge with adjustable saddle replaced respective item.
> In late 1962, plastic screw-on bridge replaced respective item.

Mark Series

All of the following instruments have these features: dreadnought style spruce top, round soundhole, removable pickguard, bound body, mahogany neck, 14/20 fret fingerboard, fan bridge, 3 different replaceable saddles, blackface snakehead peghead, 3 per side tuners. Available in Natural and Sunburst finishes, unless otherwise noted. Mfg. 1975 to 1979.

MK-35 — spruce top, 2 stripe rosewood soundhole cap, mahogany back/sides, rosewood fingerboard with pearl dot inlay, nickel tuners.

	$550	$470	$395	$315	$285	$260	$235

"I'm more into instruments as instruments, not so much the collector game."

—L. Acunto on Steve Miller

TCG, Mar/Apr 1993

G

Grading	100%	98% MINT	95% EXC+	90% EXC	80% VG+	70% VG	60% G

MK-35-12 — similar to MK-35, except has 12 strings, 6 per side tuners. Mfg. 1977 only.

| | $600 | $515 | $430 | $345 | $310 | $285 | $260 |

12 of these instruments were produced.

MK-53 — spruce top, multi-bound body, 2 stripe rosewood soundhole cap, maple back/sides, rosewood fingerboard with pearl dot inlay, nickel tuners.

| | $650 | $555 | $465 | $370 | $335 | $305 | $280 |

MK-72 — spruce top, 3 stripe rosette, rosewood back/sides, 3 piece ebony/rosewood/ebony fingerboard with pearl dot inlay, nickel tuners.

| | $700 | $600 | $500 | $400 | $360 | $330 | $300 |

MK-81 — spruce top, 3 stripe rosewood rosette cap, multi-bound body, rosewood back/sides, ebony fingerboard with block abalone inlays, gold tuners.

| | $750 | $640 | $535 | $430 | $390 | $355 | $325 |

MK-99 — dreadnought style, spruce top, round soundhole with 2 stripe rosewood soundhole cap, red stripe bound body, purple stained rosewood back/sides, purple stained maple neck, 14/20 fret red stripe bound ebony fingerboard with abalone bowtie inlay, ebony fan bridge with silver red dot pins, blackface red bound peghead, 3 per side gold tuners. Available in Natural finish. Mfg. 1975 to 1979.

| | $2,550 | $1,900 | $1,725 | $1,500 | $1,225 | $975 | $750 |

This model was handcrafted and signed by Gibson's Master Luthier, Richard Schneider. Only 12 instruments are known to have been made.

Roy Smeck Series

RADIO GRANDE — bell shape dreadnought style, spruce top, round soundhole, tortoise pickguard, bound body, 1 stripe rosette, rosewood back/sides, mahogany neck, 12/19 fret bound rosewood fingerboard with pearl varying diamond inlay, rosewood straight bridge with black pearl dot pins, blackface peghead with screened model name/logo, 3 per side tuners with plastic buttons. Available in Natural finish. Mfg. 1934 to 1939.

| | $2,250 | $1,930 | $1,605 | $1,285 | $1,155 | $1,060 | $965 |

Stage Deluxe — similar to Radio Grande, except has mahogany back/sides, pearl dot fingerboard inlay, white pearl dot bridge pins. Available in Sunburst finish. Mfg. 1934 to 1942.

| | $1,750 | $1,500 | $1,250 | $1,000 | $900 | $825 | $750 |

Two styles of this model were available; Standard and Hawaiian. The Standard model had the logo only screened on the peghead. The Hawaiian model featured inlaid ivoroid pieces instead of frets. The ivoroid pieces were usually replaced by frets, making the original ivoroid inlay configuration more desired by purists.

In 1935, bound fingerboard with pearl varying diamond inlay replaced original item.

STYLE O — hollow style, arched spruce top, oval soundhole, bound body, wood inlay rosette, walnut back/sides, mahogany neck, 12/20 fret bound pointed rosewood fingerboard with pearl dot inlay, rosewood bridge/trapeze tailpiece with black pearl dot pins, bound blackface peghead with pearl logo inlay, friction tuners. Available in Black Top finish. Mfg. 1902 to 1907.

| | $1,225 | $950 | $800 | $725 | $575 | $450 | $325 |

This model was available in standard, concert and grand concert sizes.

There are several different variants of this instrument to be found. Some have slotted peghead, some solid. Standard fixed bridge with no trapeze tailpiece, metal tuners, various peghead inlay are also found.

STYLE O ARTIST — single sharp cutaway grand concert style, carved spruce top, scrolled upper bass bout, oval soundhole, raised tortoise pickguard, bound body, wood inlay rosette, maple back/sides, mahogany neck, 15/22 fret bound extended ebony fingerboard with pearl dot inlay, ebony bridge/trapeze tailpiece with black pearl dot pins, bound blackface peghead with pearl fleur-de-lis/logo inlay, 3 per side diecast tuners. Available in Amber, Black, Mahogany Stain and Mahogany Sunburst finishes. Mfg. 1908 to 1923.

| | $2,750 | $2,275 | $1,925 | $1,750 | $1,500 | $1,325 | $1,175 |

In 1914, Amber and Mahogany finishes replaced original finishes.

In 1918, redesigned pickguard/peghead inlay replaced original items. Mahogany Sunburst finish replaced respective finish.

SUPER 300 — grand auditorium style body, arched spruce top, f-holes, raised multi-ply black pickguard, figured maple back/sides, multiple bound body, 3 piece figured maple/mahogany neck, 14/20 fret bound Brazilian rosewood fingerboard with pearl parallelogram inlay, adjustable rosewood bridge/nickel trapeze tailpiece, multi-bound blackface peghead with pearl crown/logo inlay, 3 per side nickel tuners. Available in Golden Sunburst finish. Mfg. 1948 to 1955.

| | $2,500 | $2,140 | $1,785 | $1,430 | $1,285 | $1,180 | $1,070 |

Super 300 C — similar to Super 300, except has a single round cutaway. Mfg. 1957 to 1958.

| | $3,500 | $2,500 | $2,000 | $1,500 | $1,200 | $1,000 | $800 |

Grading	100%	98% MINT	95% EXC+	90% EXC	80% VG+	70% VG	60% G

SUPER 400 — grand auditorium style body, carved spruce top, bound f-holes, raised multi-bound mottled plastic pickguard, carved maple back/sides, multiple bound body, 3 piece figured maple neck, model name engraved into heel cap, 20 fret bound ebony fingerboard with point on bottom, pearl split block fingerboard inlay, adjustable rosewood bridge with pearl triangle wings inlay, gold trapeze tailpiece with engraved model name, multi-bound blackface peghead with pearl 5 piece split diamond/logo inlay, pearl 3 piece split diamond inlay on back of peghead, 3 per side engraved gold tuners. Available in Brown Sunburst and Natural finishes. Mfg. 1934 to 1955.

1934-1939	$12,000	$10,000	$7,000	$6,000	$5,000	$4,000	$3,600
1945-1955	$5,000	$4,500	$4,000	$3,000	$2,500	$2,000	$1,800

The lower bout on this instrument measures 18 inches across.

Natural finish instruments have become highly desirable pieces.

From 1934 to 1938, Varitone tailpiece replaced respective item.

In 1936, upper bouts were widened.

In 1937, Grover Imperial tuners became optionally available.

In 1938, Kluson Sealfast tuners replaced original item.

In 1939, Natural finish became optionally available.

In 1941, engraved heel cap and rosewood bridge with pearl inlay were discontinued.

Super 400 Premier (400C) — similar to Super 400, except has a single round cutaway, multi-bound pearloid pickguard, unhinged Varitone tailpiece. Available in Brown Sunburst and Natural finishes. Mfg. 1937 to 1983.

1937-1942	$16,000	$12,200	$9,600	$6,800	$6,400	$5,760	$5,280
1944-1968	$10,500	$8,750	$6,500	$5,000	$4,250	$3,100	$2,750
1969-1983	$5,000	$4,800	$4,200	$3,400	$3,200	$2,880	$2,640

Prewar models with Natural finish have become highly desirable pieces.

Some early models were produced with solid metal tuners.

In 1942, no model name was indicated on heel cap.

In 1949, rosewood fingerboard replaced original item.

In 1953, ebony fingerboard replaced respective item.

By 1957, metal tuners replaced original item.

ACOUSTIC ELECTRIC

BOSSA NOVA — single round cutaway dreadnought style, spruce top, round soundhole, 2 stripe bound body/rosette, rosewood back/sides, mahogany neck, 20 fret rosewood fingerboard, rosewood tied bridge, classical style slotted peghead, 3 per side nickel tuners with plastic buttons, ceramic bridge pickup. Available in Natural finish. Mfg. 1971 to 1973.

	$1,050	$900	$750	$600	$540	$495	$450

This model was a nylon strings instrument.

Chet Atkins Series

CHET ATKINS CE/CEC — classic style single round cutaway mahogany body with hollow sound chambers, solid spruce top, round soundhole with plastic bowl insert, 2 stripe bound body, wood inlay rosette, mahogany neck, 19 fret rosewood fingerboard, tied rosewood bridge, rosewood veneer on slotted peghead, 3 per side gold tuners with pearl buttons, Gibson piezo bridge pickups, volume/tone control, active electronics. Available in Alpine White, Ebony and Wine Red finishes. Curr. mfr.

Mfr.'s Sug. Retail	$1,479	$1,109	$739	$675	$540	$485	$445	$405

In 1994, Alpine White and Ebony finishes were discontinued.

Chet Atkins CE/CEC-CD — similar to Chet Atkins CE/CEC, except has solid cedar top. Available in Antique Natural finish. Curr. mfr.

Mfr.'s Sug. Retail	$1,579	$1,184	$789	$750	$600	$540	$495	$450

CHET ATKINS SST — single round cutaway mahogany body with hollow sound chamber, 5 stripe bound solid spruce top with Chet Atkins' signature, mahogany neck, 21 fret ebony fingerboard with pearl star inlay, ebony bridge with black pearl dot pins, pearl star bridge wings inlay, blackface peghead with pearl star/logo inlay, 3 per side gold tuners, transducer bridge pickup, volume/treble/bass controls, active electronics. Available in Alpine White, Ebony and Wine Red finishes. Mfg. 1987 to date.

Mfr.'s Sug. Retail	$1,679	$1,259	$839	$750	$625	$500	$450	$415

In 1994, Wine Red finish was discontinued.

Chet Atkins SST-AN — similar to Chet Atkins SST, except has Antique Natural, Heritage Cherry Sunburst and Translucent Red finishes.

Mfr.'s Sug. Retail	$2,349	$1,761	$1,174	$970	$825	$780	$620	$575

In 1994, Translucent Red finish was discontinued.

Chet Atkins SST Flame Top — similar to Chet Atkins SST, except has figured maple top. Available in Antique Natural, Heritage Cherry Sunburst and Translucent Red finishes.

Mfr.'s Sug. Retail	$2,179	$1,634	$1,089	$925	$800	$640	$575	$530

In 1994, Translucent Amber finish was introduced, Translucent Red finish was discontinued.

Gibson Super 400
courtesy Dr. Tom Van Hoose

G

Grading	100%	98% MINT	95% EXC+	90% EXC	80% VG+	70% VG	60% G

Chet Atkins SST 12 — similar to Chet Atkins SST, except has 12 string configuration, 6 per side tuners. Available in Ebony and Wine Red finishes. Disc. 1994.

| | $875 | $750 | $625 | $500 | $450 | $415 | $375 |

Add $250 for Antique Natural finish.

Last Mfr.'s Sug. Retail was $1,250.

Chet Atkins SST 12 Flame Top — similar to Chet Atkins SST, except has 12 string configuration, flame maple top, 6 per side tuners. Available in Antique Natural, Heritage Cherry Sunburst and Translucent Red finishes. Disc. 1994.

| | $1,120 | $960 | $800 | $640 | $575 | $530 | $480 |

Last Mfr.'s Sug. Retail was $1,600.

EAS STANDARD — single round cutaway flat-top body, solid spruce top, round soundhole, tortoise pickguard, bound body, 2 multi-stripe rings rosette, maple back/sides/neck, 20 fret rosewood fingerboard with pearl dot inlay, rosewood reverse bridge with white pins, blackface peghead with screened logo, 3 per side chrome tuners, bridge pickup, 3 band EQ. Available in Antique Natural, Cherry and Vintage Sunburst finishes. Mfg. 1992 to 1994.

| | $910 | $780 | $650 | $520 | $470 | $430 | $390 |

Last Mfr.'s Sug. Retail was $1,300.

EAS Deluxe — similar to EAS Standard, except has figured maple top, white pickguard, bound fingerboard with trapezoid inlay, pearl crown/logo peghead inlay, nickel tuners with plastic buttons. Available in Vintage Cherry Sunburst finish. Mfg. 1992 to 1994.

| | $1,050 | $900 | $750 | $600 | $540 | $495 | $450 |

Last Mfr.'s Sug. Retail was $1,500.

J-160 E — bell shape dreadnought style, spruce top, round soundhole, tortoise pickguard, 2 stripe bound body/rosette, mahogany back/sides/neck, 15/19 fret bound rosewood fingerboard with pearl block/trapezoid inlay, rosewood bridge with white pins, adjustable saddle, blackface peghead with pearl crown/logo inlay, 3 per side nickel tuners, single coil pickup, volume/tone control. Available in Sunburst finish. Mfg. 1954 to 1979.

1954-1959	$1,850	$1,590	$1,325	$1,060	$950	$875	$795
1960-1964	$1,125	$965	$805	$645	$575	$530	$480
1965-1968	$1,500	$1,285	$1,070	$860	$770	$710	$645
1969-1979	$850	$730	$610	$485	$435	$400	$365

J-160 E Reissue — similar to J-160 E, except has regular saddle. Available in Vintage Sunburst finish. Mfg. 1991 to date.

| Mfr.'s Sug. Retail | $1,900 | $1,425 | $950 | $900 | $720 | $650 | $595 | $540 |

LES PAUL JUMBO — single round cutaway dreadnought style, spruce top, round soundhole, tortoise pickguard, 2 stripe bound body/rosette, rosewood back/sides, mahogany neck, 19 fret rosewood fingerboard with pearl dot inlay, rosewood bridge with black white dot pins, 3 per side chrome tuners, single coil pickup, volume/treble/mid/bass controls, 2 position switch. Available in Natural finish. Mfg. 1970 only.

| | $1,200 | $1,030 | $860 | $685 | $615 | $565 | $515 |

Gibson Byrdland
courtesy Thoroughbred Music

ELECTRIC

BYRDLAND — single round cutaway multi-bound hollow body, solid spruce top, raised bound tortoise pickguard, black pickguard, bound f-holes, maple back/sides/neck, 22 fret multi-bound ebony pointed fingerboard with pearl block inlay, tunomatic bridge/rosewood base, trapeze tailpiece, multi-bound blackface peghead with pearl flower-pot/logo inlay, 3 per side tuners, gold hardware, 2 single coil Alnico pickups, 2 volume/2 tone controls, 3 position switch. Available in Natural and Sunburst finishes. Mfg. 1955 to 1985.

1955-1957	$2,950	$2,500	$2,225	$1,650	$1,225	$1,100	$1,025
1958-1959	$4,000	$3,600	$2,800	$2,325	$1,950	$1,800	$1,625
1960-1961	$4,000	$3,500	$2,750	$2,300	$1,950	$1,750	$1,525
1962-1968	$2,500	$2,150	$2,025	$1,725	$1,550	$1,200	$975
1969-1985	$1,500	$1,400	$1,200	$1,025	$950	$825	$775

The Byrdland model was designed in conjunction with Billy Byrd and Hank Garland.

In 1958, 2 covered P.A.F. humbucker pickups replaced original item.

In 1959, Stereo-Varitone electronics optionally offered.

In 1960, single sharp cutaway replaced original item.

In 1962, Patent Number humbucker pickups replaced the previous P.A.F. humbuckers.

In 1969, single round cutaway replaced respective item.

Byrdland models in a blond finish with a high degree of "flame" command higher premiums.

CHALLENGER I — single cutaway mahogany body, black pickguard, bolt-on maple neck, 22 fret rosewood fingerboard with pearl dot inlay, tunomatic stud tailpiece, 3 per side tuners, chrome hardware, humbucker pickup, volume/tone control. Available in Cherry Red finish. Mfg. 1983 to 1985.

| | $275 | $235 | $195 | $155 | $140 | $125 | $115 |

Challenger II — similar to Challenger I, except has 2 humbucker pickups, 2 volume controls.

| | $300 | $260 | $215 | $175 | $155 | $140 | $130 |

Gibson ES-5
courtesy Lloyd Bennett

Grading	100%	98% MINT	95% EXC+	90% EXC	80% VG+	70% VG	60% G

CHET ATKINS TENNESSEAN — single round cutaway semi hollow bound maple body, f-holes, raised pickguard with engraved "Tennessean", arm rest on bottom bass bout, 3 piece maple neck, 22 fret rosewood fingerboard with offset pearl dot inlay, tunomatic bridge/stop tailpiece, blackface peghead with signature/pearl logo inlay, 3 per side tuners with pearl buttons, chrome hardware, 2 covered humbucker pickups, master volume on upper treble bout, 2 volume/1 tone controls, 3 position switch. Available in Ebony finish. Curr. mfr.

Mfr.'s Sug. Retail	$3,489	$2,616	$1,744	$1,675	$1,250	$1,000	$900	$825

In 1994, Country Gentleman Brown, Sunrise Orange and Wine Red finishes became standard, Ebony finish was discontinued.

CORVUS I — can opener style hardwood body, black pickguard, bolt-on maple neck, 22 fret rosewood fingerboard with white dot inlay, tunomatic stud tailpiece, 6 on one side tuners, chrome hardware, covered humbucker pickup, volume/tone control. Available in Silver finish. Mfg. 1983 to 1985.

		$200	$170	$145	$115	$105	$95	$85

Corvus II — similar to Corvus I, except has 2 covered humbucker pickups, 3 position switch.

		$225	$195	$160	$130	$115	$105	$95

Corvus III — similar to Corvus I, except has 3 exposed single coil pickups, 5 position switch.

		$250	$215	$180	$145	$130	$120	$110

Doubleneck Models

Gibson 4/6 Doubleneck
19th Annual Dallas Show

DOUBLE TWELVE — double cutaway hollow maple body, carved spruce top, 2 stripe bound body, double neck configuration, 2 bound black pickguards, 3 position neck selector switch, each mahogany neck has 20 fret bound rosewood fingerboard with pearl parallelogram inlay, tunomatic bridge/fixed tailpiece, 6 per side/3 per side tuners with pearl buttons, chrome hardware, 2 covered humbucker pickups, volume/tone control, 3 position switch. Available in Black, Sunburst and White finishes. Mfg. 1958 to 1962.

	$20,000	$18,000	$15,000	$12,500	$10,000	$8,000	$6,500

EDS 1275 — double cutaway mahogany body, double neck configuration, 2 black tri-lam pickguards, 3 position neck/pickup selector switches, 2 volume/2 tone controls, each mahogany neck has 20 fret bound rosewood fingerboard with pearl parallelogram inlay, tunomatic bridge/fixed tailpiece, 6 per side/3 per side tuners with pearl buttons, chrome hardware, 2 covered humbucker pickups. Available in Jet Black, Sunburst and White finishes. Mfg. 1963 to 1968.

		$2,450	$2,100	$1,750	$1,400	$1,260	$1,150	$1,050

EBSF 1250 — similar to EDS 1275, except has bass configuration instead of twelve string configuration on upper neck, built-in fuzztone. Mfd. 1962 to 1967.

		$2,050	$1,760	$1,465	$1,170	$1,050	$965	$880

EDS 1275 Reissue — similar to EDS 1275, except available in Alpine White, Cherry, Heritage Cherry, Cherry Sunburst, Sunburst, Walnut and White finishes. Mfg. 1977 to date.

1977-1985		$1,250	$1,070	$895	$715	$645	$590	$535
Mfr.'s Sug. Retail	$2,350	$1,880	$1,410	$1,175	$940	$845	$775	$705

In 1984, Cherry Sunburst, Walnut and White finishes became standard items.

In 1987, Cherry finish was optionally available.

In 1990, Alpine White and Heritage Cherry finishes became standard items.

ES Series

ES-5 — single round cutaway hollow body, arched figured maple top, bound f-holes, raised layered black pickguard, 3 stripe bound body, figured maple back/sides/neck, 20 fret multi-bound pointed fingerboard with pearl block inlay, adjustable ebony bridge/trapeze tailpiece, bound blackface peghead with pearl crown/logo inlay, 3 per side tuners with plastic buttons, gold hardware, 3 single coil pickups, tone control on cutaway bout, 3 volume controls. Available in Natural and Sunburst finishes. Mfg. 1949 to 1962.

1949-1956		$3,500	$2,950	$2,450	$2,025	$1,875	$1,600	$1,225
1957-1962		$6,525	$5,590	$4,660	$3,730	$3,355	$3,075	$2,795

Add $1,200 for Natural finish.

Subtract $750 for 2 pickup versions.

A few early models can be found with unbound f-holes.

In 1955, model renamed "ES-5 Switchmaster", tunomatic bridge, 3 volume/3 tone controls, 4 position switch replaced respective items.

In 1957, humbucker pickups replaced original items.

In 1960, sharp cutaway replaced original item.

ES-100 — folk style body, arched maple top, f-holes, raised black pickguard, bound body, maple back, mahogany sides/neck, 14/20 fret rosewood fingerboard with pearl dot inlay, adjustable rosewood bridge/trapeze tailpiece, blackface peghead with pearl logo inlay, 3 per side tuners, nickel hardware, single coil pickup, volume/tone control. Available in Sunburst finish. Mfg. 1938 to 1941.

1938-1939		$1,000	$855	$715	$570	$510	$465	$425
1940-1941		$650	$555	$465	$370	$335	$305	$280

1951 Gibson ES-5
courtesy Jim Colclasure

Grading	100%	98% MINT	95% EXC+	90% EXC	80% VG+	70% VG	60% G

ES-120T — dreadnought style thin body, arched maple top, molded black pickguard, f-hole, maple back, mahogany sides/neck, 14/20 fret rosewood fingerboard with pearl dot inlay, adjustable rosewood bridge/trapeze tailpiece, 3 per side tuners with plastic buttons, chrome hardware, single coil pickup, volume/tone control. Available in Sunburst finish. Mfg. 1962 to 1971.

		$375	$320	$270	$215	$195	$180	$160

Add $100 for 2 pickup versions (ES-120 TD).

ES-125 — folk style body, arched maple top, f-holes, raised black pickguard, bound body, maple back, mahogany sides/neck, 14/20 fret rosewood fingerboard with pearl dot inlay, adjustable rosewood bridge/trapeze tailpiece, blackface peghead with pearl logo inlay, 3 per side tuners, nickel hardware, single coil pickup, volume/tone control. Available in Sunburst finish. Mfg. 1946 to 1970.

	$800	$715	$645	$580	$535	$500	$475

Some production occurred in 1941, though the majority of production was post-World War II.

In 1946, a few models were produced with an all mahogany body.

ES-125 T — similar to ES-125, except has a thin body. Mfg. 1956 to 1969.

	$950	$815	$675	$575	$500	$450	$400

ES-125 T ¾ — similar to ES-125 T, except has a ¾ size body. Mfg. 1957 to 1969.

	$450	$385	$325	$260	$230	$215	$195

ES-135 — dreadnought style thin body, arched maple top, layered black pickguard, f-hole, maple back, mahogany sides/neck, 14/20 fret bound rosewood fingerboard with pearl block inlay, adjustable rosewood bridge/trapeze tailpiece, 3 per side tuners with plastic buttons, nickel hardware, single coil pickup, volume/tone control. Available in Sunburst finish. Mfg. 1954 to 1958.

	$600	$565	$500	$460	$425	$390	$340

ES-135D — similar to ES-135, except had 2 single coil pickups, 2 volume/2 tone controls.

	$1,000	$855	$715	$570	$510	$465	$425

ES-135 (CURRENT MANUFACTURE) — single sharp cutaway semi hollow bound maple body, f-holes, raised black pickguard, maple neck, 22 fret rosewood fingerboard with pearl dot inlay, tunomatic bridge/trapeze tailpiece, 3 per side tuners with pearl buttons, chrome hardware, 2 single coil pickups, 2 volume/2 tone controls, 3 position switch. Available in Ebony finish. Curr. mfr.

Mfr.'s Sug. Retail	$1,339	$1,004	$669	$645	$500	$400	$360	$330

Add $140 for Cherry and Vintage Sunburst finishes.

ES-140 ¾ — single sharp cutaway folk style, arched maple top, raised black pickguard, f-holes, bound body, maple back/sides, mahogany neck, 19 fret rosewood fingerboard with pearl dot inlay, adjustable rosewood bridge/trapeze tailpiece, 3 per side tuners with plastic buttons, nickel hardware, single coil pickup, volume/tone control. Available in Natural and Sunburst finishes. Mfg. 1950 to 1957.

	$825	$705	$585	$470	$425	$390	$355

ES-140 T ¾ — similar to ES-140 ¾, except had a thin body. Mfg. 1957 to 1968.

	$675	$580	$485	$385	$350	$320	$290

ES-150, PREWAR — folk style body, spruce top, f-holes, bound black pickguard, bound body, maple back, mahogany sides/neck, 14/19 fret bound rosewood fingerboard with pearl dot inlay, adjustable rosewood bridge/trapeze tailpiece, pearl peghead logo inlay, 3 per side tuners, nickel hardware, single coil pickup, volume/tone control. Available in Sunburst finish. Mfg. 1936 to 1942.

	$2,450	$2,125	$1,800	$1,650	$1,525	$1,275	$950

This guitar was known as the "Charlie Christian" model.

In 1940, arched back and unbound fingerboard replaced original items.

ES-150, POST-WAR — similar to ES-150, prewar, except has slightly larger body, layered black pickguard, silkscreen peghead logo. Mfg. 1946 to 1956.

	$950	$800	$725	$600	$525	$450	$375

In 1950, bound fingerboard with trapezoid inlay replaced original item.

ES-150DC — double cutaway semi hollow style, arched maple top, f-holes, raised layered black pickguard, bound body, maple back/sides, mahogany neck, 22 fret rosewood fingerboard with pearl block inlay, tunomatic bridge/trapeze tailpiece, 3 per side tuners, chrome hardware, 2 covered humbucker pickups, master volume control on upper treble bout, 2 volume/2 tone controls, 3 position switch. Available in Cherry, Natural and Walnut finishes. Mfg. 1969 to 1975.

1969-1970	$1,200	$1,050	$940	$860	$750	$675	$600
1971-1975	$825	$705	$585	$470	$425	$390	$355

ES-175 — single sharp cutaway dreadnought style, arched maple top, f-holes, raised layered black pickguard, bound body, maple back/sides, mahogany neck, 20 fret bound rosewood fingerboard with pearl parallelogram inlay, adjustable rosewood bridge/trapeze tailpiece, black face peghead with pearl crown/logo inlay, nickel hardware, single coil pickup, volume/tone control. Available in Natural and Sunburst finishes. Mfg. 1949 to 1971.

1949-1956	$1,950	$1,750	$1,500	$1,225	$950	$800	$650
1957-1962	$2,750	$1,925	$1,650	$1,375	$1,100	$950	$875
1963-1971	$1,550	$1,200	$1,050	$900	$750	$675	$575

In 1957, P.A.F. humbucker pickup replaced original item.

In 1962, Pat. No. humbucker pickups replaced respective item.

Grading		100%	98% MINT	95% EXC+	90% EXC	80% VG+	70% VG	60% G

ES-175D — similar to ES-175, except has 2 single coil pickups, 2 volume/2 tone controls, 3 position switch. Mfg. 1953 to date.

1953-1956		$2,450	$2,100	$1,950	$1,750	$1,625	$1,450	$1,300
1957-1962		$4,500	$4,000	$3,650	$3,325	$2,900	$2,650	$2,200
1963-1971		$1,950	$1,700	$1,550	$1,225	$1,050	$925	$750
1972-1985		$1,450	$1,225	$950	$800	$675	$575	$450
Mfr.'s Sug. Retail	$2,725	$2,043	$1,362	$1,245	$985	$875	$760	$690

Currently Mfg. instruments are produced on a limited run basis.

In 1957, P.A.F. humbucker pickups replaced original item.

In 1962, Pat. No. humbucker pickups replaced respective item.

In 1974, neck volute was introduced.

By 1977, tunomatic bridge replaced original item.

In 1981, neck volute was discontinued.

In 1983, mahogany back/sides replaced original items.

In 1990, maple back/sides replaced respective items.

ES-175D Reissue — similar to ES-175, except has 2 single coil pickups, 2 volume/2 tone controls, 3 position switch. Available in Antique Natural finish. Curr. mfr.

Mfr.'s Sug. Retail	$3,839	$3,071	$2,303	$2,260	$1,935	$1,615	$1,295	$1,165

ES-225T — single sharp cutaway thin body style, arched maple top, f-holes, raised layered black pickguard, bound body, maple back/sides, mahogany neck, 20 fret bound rosewood fingerboard with pearl dot inlay, trapeze wrapover tailpiece, blackface peghead with pearl logo inlay, single coil pickup, volume/tone control. Available in Sunburst finish. Mfg. 1955 to 1959.

$950	$800	$700	$525	$400	$350	$275

ES-225TD — similar to ES-225T, except has 2 pickups, 2 volume/2 tone controls. Mfg. 1956 to 1959.

$1,250	$1,070	$895	$715	$645	$590	$535

ES-250 — jumbo style, spruce top, raised bound black pickguard, 3 stripe bound body, maple back/sides/neck, 14/20 fret bound rosewood fingerboard with pearl open book inlay, adjustable rosewood bridge/trapeze tailpiece, blackface stairstep peghead with pearl logo inlay, 3 per side tuners, nickel hardware, single coil pickup, volume/tone control. Available in Natural and Sunburst finishes. Mfg. 1938 to 1940.

$5,250	$4,500	$3,750	$3,000	$2,700	$2,475	$2,250

In 1940, standard style peghead, split half circle fingerboard inlay replaced original items.

ES-295 — single sharp cutaway hollow body, multi-bound maple top, f-holes, raised white pickguard with etched flowers, maple back/sides/neck, 19 fret bound rosewood fingerboard with pearl parallelogram inlay, trapeze wrapover tailpiece, blackface peghead with pearl plant/logo inlay, 3 per side tuners with pearl buttons, gold hardware, 2 single coil pickups, 2 volume/2 tone controls, 3 position switch. Available in Gold finish. Mfg. 1952 to 1959.

$3,450	$2,960	$2,465	$1,970	$1,775	$1,625	$1,480

In 1955, 20 fret fingerboard replaced original item.

In 1958, humbucker pickups replaced original items.

	90%	80%	70%	60%	50%	40%	20%

ES-300, PREWAR — jumbo style, spruce top, bound black pickguard, multi-bound body, maple back/sides/neck, 14/20 fret rosewood fingerboard with pearl parallelogram inlay, adjustable rosewood bridge/trapeze tailpiece, bound peghead with pearl crown/logo inlay, 3 per side tuners, nickel hardware, single coil pickup, volume/tone control. Available in Natural and Sunburst finishes. Mfg. 1940 to 1942.

$1,800	$1,700	$1,500	$1,250	$1,050	$960	$850

This model was also found with split diamond peghead inlay.

Grading	100%	98%	95%	90%	80%	70%	60%

ES-300, Post-war — similar to ES-300 Prewar, except has layered black pickguard, bound fingerboard. Mfg. 1946 to 1952.

$1,800	$1,650	$1,450	$1,200	$1,000	$920	$810

In 1948, 2 single coil pickups, 2 volume controls replaced original items. Tone control moved to upper treble bout.

ES-320TD — double round cutaway semi hollow bound body, arched maple top, f-holes, raised black pickguard, maple back/sides/neck, 22 fret rosewood fingerboard with pearl dot inlay, fixed tunomatic bridge with logo engraved cover, 3 per side tuners, nickel hardware, 2 single coil pickups, volume/tone control, 2 slide switches. Available in Cherry, Natural and Walnut finishes. Mfg. 1971 to 1975.

$500	$430	$360	$285	$260	$235	$215

ES-325TD — double round cutaway semi hollow bound body, arched maple top, f-holes, raised layered black pickguard, maple back/sides/neck, 22 fret rosewood fingerboard with pearl dot inlay, tunomatic bridge/trapeze tailpiece, 3 per side tuners with plastic buttons, nickel hardware, 2 mini humbucker pickups, 2 volume/2 tone controls, 3 position switch, control mounted on black plastic plate. Available in Cherry, Walnut and Wine Red finishes. Mfg. 1972 to 1979.

$650	$555	$465	$370	$335	$305	$280

"Many people have come to believe that old is always better. Some old guitars are worth collecting, some are worth playing, and some are worth forgetting."

—B. Blackburn, Ph.D.

on Richard Smith

TCG, Mar/Apr 1992

Grading	100%	98% MINT	95% EXC+	90% EXC	80% VG+	70% VG	60% G

1964 Gibson ES-335
courtesy Garrie Johnson

ES-330T — double round cutaway hollow bound body, arched maple top, raised bound black pickguard, f-holes, maple back/sides, 22 fret bound rosewood fingerboard with pearl dot inlay, tunomatic bridge/trapeze tailpiece, blackface peghead with pearl logo inlay, 3 per side tuners with plastic buttons, nickel hardware, single coil pickup, volume/tone control. Available in Cherry, Natural and Sunburst finishes. Mfg. 1959 to 1963.

	$850	$730	$610	$485	$435	$400	$365

In 1962, block fingerboard inlay, chrome covered pickups replaced original items, Cherry finish optionally available, Natural finish discontinued.

ES-330TD — similar to ES-330T, except has 2 single coil pickups, 2 volume/2 tone controls, 3 position switch. Mfg. 1959 to 1972.

	$2,025	$1,740	$1,450	$1,160	$1,040	$955	$870

In 1962, pearl block fingerboard inlay replaced original item.

Between 1967-1969, Sparkling Burgundy finish optionally available.

In 1968, Walnut finish optionally available.

ES-335T — double round cutaway semi hollow bound body, arched maple top, f-holes, raised layered black pickguard, maple back/sides, mahogany neck, 22 fret rosewood fingerboard with pearl dot inlay, tunomatic bridge/stop tailpiece, blackface peghead with pearl crown/logo inlay, 3 per side tuners, nickel hardware, 2 covered humbucker PAF pickups, 2 volume/2 tone controls, 3 position switch. Available in Cherry, Blonde and Sunburst finishes. Mfg. 1958 to 1982.

	100%	98%	95%	90%	80%	70%	60%
1958-1959	$13,500	$11,570	$9,640	$7,715	$6,940	$6,365	$5,785
1960-1961	$10,000	$8,570	$7,145	$5,715	$5,145	$4,715	$4,285
1962-1964	$5,500	$4,715	$3,930	$3,140	$2,830	$2,590	$2,355
1965-1968	$1,525	$1,310	$1,090	$870	$785	$720	$655
1969-1974	$850	$730	$610	$485	$435	$400	$365
1975-1982	$1,025	$880	$735	$585	$525	$485	$440

Add 20%-30% for Blonde finish.

In 1958, some models found unbound.

In 1959, Cherry finish optionally available.

In 1960, the name changed to **ES-335TD**, smaller pickguard replaced original item.

In 1962, block fingerboard inlay, Pat. No. pickups replaced original items.

In 1964, trapeze tailpiece replaced original item.

In 1969, Walnut finish became optionally available, some models with slanted block fingerboard inlay.

From 1969 to 1970, neck volute was available.

In 1977, coil tap switch was added.

Gibson also produced the ES-335TD 12, a 12-string version of the ES-335.

ES-335 Studio — similar to ES-335T, except has no f-holes. Mfg. 1987 to 1994.

	$630	$540	$450	$360	$325	$300	$275

Last Mfr.'s Sug. Retail was $900.

ES-335 REISSUE — double round cutaway semi hollow bound maple body, f-holes, raised black pickguard, mahogany neck, 22 fret bound rosewood fingerboard with pearl dot inlay, tunomatic bridge/stop tailpiece, blackface peghead with pearl plant/logo inlay, 3 per side tuners, nickel hardware, 2 covered humbucker pickups, 2 volume/2 tone controls, 3 position switch. Available in Cherry, Ebony and Vintage Sunburst finishes. Curr. mfr.

Mfr.'s Sug. Retail	$3,299	$2,474	$1,649	$1,580	$1,330	$1,095	$825	$740

Add $435 for Natural finish.

In 1994, Ebony finish was discontinued.

ES-340TD — double round cutaway semi hollow bound body, arched maple top, f-holes, raised layered black pickguard, maple back/sides/neck, 22 fret rosewood fingerboard with pearl dot inlay, tunomatic bridge/stop tailpiece, blackface peghead with pearl crown/logo inlay, 3 per side tuners, nickel hardware, 2 covered humbucker pickups, volume/mixer/2 tone controls, 3 position switch. Available in Natural and Walnut finishes. Mfg. 1969 to 1974.

	$1,750	$1,500	$1,250	$1,000	$900	$825	$750

ES-345TD — double round cutaway semi hollow bound body, arched maple top, f-holes, raised layered black pickguard, maple back/sides, mahogany neck, 22 fret bound rosewood fingerboard with pearl parallelogram inlay, tunomatic bridge/trapeze tailpiece, blackface peghead with pearl crown/logo inlay, 3 per side tuners with plastic buttons, gold hardware, 2 covered humbucker pickups, 2 volume/2 tone controls, 3 position/Vari-tone switches, stereo output. Available in Cherry, Natural, Sunburst and Walnut finishes. Mfg. 1959 to 1982.

	100%	98%	95%	90%	80%	70%	60%
1959-1964	$5,500	$4,715	$3,930	$3,140	$2,830	$2,590	$2,355
1965-1974	$1,300	$1,115	$930	$740	$670	$610	$555
1975-1982	$1,050	$900	$750	$600	$540	$495	$450

In 1959, Cherry finish became optionally available.

In 1969, Walnut finish became optionally available.

In 1982, stop tailpiece replaced original item.

ES-347TD — double round cutaway semi hollow bound body, arched figured maple top, f-holes, raised layered black pickguard, maple back/sides/neck, 22 fret bound ebony fingerboard with pearl block inlay, tunomatic bridge/tunable stop tailpiece, bound blackface peghead with pearl crown/logo inlay, 3 per side tuners, gold hardware, 2 covered humbucker pickups, 2 volume/2 tone controls, 3 position/coil tap switches. Available in Sunburst finish. Mfg. 1978 to 1991.

	$1,800	$1,540	$1,285	$1,025	$925	$845	$770

Grading	100%	98% MINT	95% EXC+	90% EXC	80% VG+	70% VG	60% G

ES-350 — single round cutaway hollow bound body, arched figured maple top, bound f-holes, raised layered black pickguard, maple back/sides/neck, 22 fret bound rosewood fingerboard with pearl parallelogram inlay, adjustable rosewood bridge/trapeze tailpiece, bound blackface peghead with pearl crown/logo inlay, 3 per side tuners with plastic buttons, gold hardware, covered single coil pickup, volume/tone controls. Available in Natural and Sunburst finishes. Mfg. 1947 to 1956.

1947-1949	$2,650	$2,270	$1,895	$1,515	$1,365	$1,250	$1,135
1950-1956	$2,500	$2,200	$1,750	$1,440	$1,225	$1,000	$900

> In 1948, 2 single coil pickups, tone control on cutaway bout, 2 volume controls replaced original items.
>
> In 1952, 2 volume/2 tone controls 3 position switch replaced respective items.
>
> In 1956, tunomatic bridge replaced original item.

ES-350 T — similar to ES-350, except has thin body, short scale length. Mfg. 1955 to 1963.

	$3,500	$3,250	$2,725	$2,335	$1,950	$1,550	$1,400

> In 1957, P.A.F. humbucker pickups replaced original item.
>
> In 1960, sharp cutaway replaced original item.
>
> ES-350 T models with PAF pickups and/or a blond finish command a premium.

ES-355TD-SV — double round cutaway semi hollow bound body, arched maple top, bound f-holes, raised layered black pickguard, maple back/sides, mahogany neck, 22 fret bound ebony fingerboard with pearl block inlay, tunomatic bridge/Bigsby vibrato tailpiece, bound blackface peghead with pearl split diamond/logo inlay, 3 per side tuners, gold hardware, 2 covered P.A.F. humbucker pickups, 2 volume/2 tone controls, 3 position/Vari-tone switches, stereo output. Available in Cherry and Walnut finishes. Mfg. 1958 to 1982.

1958-1962	$2,850	$2,440	$2,035	$1,630	$1,465	$1,345	$1,220
1963-1968	$1,950	$1,750	$1,500	$1,325	$1,050	$875	$700
1969-1974	$1,250	$1,070	$895	$715	$645	$590	$535
1975-1982	$1,000	$855	$715	$570	$510	$465	$425

> In 1961, side-pull vibrato replaced original item.
>
> In 1962, Pat. No. humbucker pickups replaced original item.
>
> In 1963, Vibrola tailpiece with engraved lyre/logo replaced respective item.
>
> In 1969, Bigsby vibrato replaced respective item, Walnut finish became optionally available.
>
> In 1974, neck volute was introduced.
>
> In 1981, neck volute was discontinued.

ES-369 — double round cutaway semi hollow bound body, arched maple top, f-holes, raised cream pickguard, maple back/sides, mahogany neck, 22 fret bound rosewood fingerboard with pearl trapezoid inlay, tunomatic bridge/tunable stop tailpiece, blackface peghead with pearl logo inlay, 3 per side tuners, chrome hardware, 2 exposed humbucker pickups, 2 volume/2 tone controls, 3 position/coil tap switches. Available in Cherry, Natural, Sunburst and Walnut finishes. Mfg. 1982 only.

	$750	$640	$535	$430	$390	$355	$325

ES-775 — single sharp cutaway hollow bound maple body, f-holes, raised bound black pickguard, 3 piece figured maple neck, 20 fret bound ebony fingerboard with pearl block inlay, tunomatic metal/ebony bridge/trapeze tailpiece, ebony block tailpiece insert, bound peghead with pearl stylized bird/logo inlay, 3 per side Grover Imperial tuners, gold hardware, 2 covered humbucker pickups, 2 volume/2 tone controls, 3 position switch. Available in Ebony finish. Curr. mfr.

Mfr.'s Sug. Retail	$2,400	$1,920	$1,440	$1,200	$960	$860	$790	$720

> Add $400 for Antique Natural and Vintage Sunburst finishes.

ES ARTIST ACTIVE — double round cutaway semi hollow bound body, arched maple top, raised layered black pickguard, maple back/sides, mahogany neck, 22 fret bound ebony fingerboard with pearl offset dot inlay, tunomatic bridge/tunable stop tailpiece, blackface peghead with pearl winged-f/logo inlay, 3 per side tuners, gold hardware, 2 covered humbucker pickups, 2 volume/1 tone controls, 3 position switch, 3 mini switches, active electronics, stereo output. Available in Cherry, Natural, Sunburst and Walnut finishes. Mfg. 1979 to 1986.

	$915	$785	$655	$520	$470	$430	$390

Explorer Series

EXPLORER (KORINA) — radical offset hourglass korina body, white pickguard, korina neck, 22 fret rosewood fingerboard with pearl dot inlay, tunomatic bridge/stop tailpiece, blackface peghead with pearl logo inlay, 6 on one side tuners, gold (1958-59) or nickel (1962-63) hardware, 2 P.A.F. (1958-59) or patent number (1962-63) humbucker pickups, 2 volume/1 tone controls, 3 position switch. Available in Natural finish, brown case 1958-59, black case 1962-63. Mfg. 1958 to 1959 and 1962 to 1963.

> A few early specimens were produced with a V-shaped peghead and a raised plastic logo. The first prototype was dubbed the "Futura".

> The Explorer model was introduced shortly after the Flying V and had a 1958 retail price of $247.50. A modernistic concept guitar from Gibson, this model had very limited manufacture (estimated to be under 100 instruments). Original Explorers exhibiting some wear and no problems are currently priced in the $45,000-$55,000 range, and upwards to $75,000. Even though the 1962-1963 period of manufacture was mostly a clean-up of earlier bodies and related parts that were never finished, values seem to be the same for both periods. Until someone finds and documents a Moderne, the Explorer (Korina) will continue to be Gibson's most desirable and rarest electric instrument.

1958 Gibson Explorer
courtesy Dave Rodgers

Grading	100%	98% MINT	95% EXC+	90% EXC	80% VG+	70% VG	60% G

Explorer Reissue — similar to Explorer (Korina), except has mahogany body/neck, Available in Black, Natural and White finishes. Mfg. 1975 to 1980.

	$1,500	$1,285	$1,070	$860	$770	$710	$645

Explorer II — similar to Explorer (Korina), except has 5 piece laminated walnut/maple body, maple neck, ebony fingerboard with dot inlay, tunable stop tailpiece, gold hardware, 2 exposed humbucker pickups. Available in Natural finish. Mfg. 1979 to 1984.

	$400	$340	$285	$230	$205	$190	$170

This model was also available with maple neck.

Body woods on this model were interchangeable (ie. walnut or maple used on top).

EXPLORER KORINA REISSUE — radical offset hourglass korina body, black pickguard, korina neck, 22 fret rosewood fingerboard with pearl dot inlay, tunomatic bridge/stop tailpiece, blackface peghead with pearl logo inlay, stamped serial number on peghead, 6 on one side Schaller tuners, gold hardware, 2 humbucker pickups, 2 volume/1 tone controls, 3 position switch. Available in Antique Natural, Candy Apple Red, Ebony and Ivory finishes. Mfg. 1983 only.

	$2,000	$1,715	$1,425	$1,140	$1,030	$940	$855

This was Gibson's first Explorer Korina reissue (a Limited Edition re-issue of 1958 Explorer).

Explorer Heritage — similar to Explorer Korina Reissue, except has inked serial number on peghead, plastic single ring tuner buttons, black control knobs. Available in Antique Natural, Ebony and Ivory finishes. Mfg. 1981 to 1983.

	$3,500	$3,000	$2,500	$2,000	$1,800	$1,650	$1,500

100 of these instruments were manufactured.

Custom Shop Explorer Heritage — similar to Explorer Korina Reissue, except has stamped serial number on peghead, black pickguard, gold hardware. Available in Antique Natural, Ebony and Ivory finishes. Mfg. 1983 only.

	$1,500	$1,285	$1,070	$860	$770	$710	$645

1981 Gibson Explorer II
courtesy Bart Labowitz

500 of these instruments were manufactured.

EXPLORER III — radical offset hourglass alder body, white pickguard, korina neck, 22 fret rosewood fingerboard with pearl dot inlay, tunomatic bridge/stop tailpiece, blackface peghead with pearl logo inlay, 6 on one side tuners, chrome hardware, 3 single coil pickups, volume/tone controls, 3 position switch. Available in Natural finish. Mfg. 1984 to 1985.

	$275	$235	$195	$155	$140	$125	$115

This model was also available with black hardware in 1985 only.

EXPLORER 425 — radical offset hourglass mahogany body/neck, white pickguard, 22 fret ebony fingerboard with pearl dot inlay, double locking vibrato, blackface peghead with pearl logo inlay, 6 on one side tuners, black hardware, 2 single coil/1 humbucker pickups, volume/tone controls, 3 mini switch. Available in Natural finish. Mfg. 1986 only.

	$750	$640	$535	$430	$390	$355	$325

EXPLORER '76 — radical offset hourglass mahogany body/neck, white pickguard, 22 fret rosewood fingerboard with pearl dot inlay, tunomatic bridge/stop tailpiece, blackface peghead with pearl logo inlay, 6 on one side tuners, chrome hardware, 2 exposed humbucker pickups, 2 volume/1 tone controls, 3 position switch. Available in Cherry, Classic White, Ebony and Vintage Sunburst finishes. Curr. mfr.

Mfr.'s Sug. Retail	$1,110	$832	$555	$500	$400	$360	$330	$300

In 1994, Vintage Sunburst finish was discontinued.

EXPLORER 90 DOUBLE — radical offset hourglass mahogany body/neck, white pickguard, 22 fret rosewood fingerboard with pearl dot inlay, tunomatic bridge/stop tailpiece, blackface peghead with pearl split diamond/logo inlay, 6 on one side tuners, gold hardware, 2 humbucker pickups, 2 volume/1 tone controls, 3 position switch. Available in Natural finish. Mfg. 1989 to 1991.

	$950	$815	$675	$540	$490	$450	$405

Firebird Reverse Series

Firebird guitars were offered in custom colors as well as standard Gibson finishes. The custom colors command a 25% to 50% premium above regular trading prices (depending on rarity of the custom color). The Firebirds were available in these Custom Colors: Amber Red, Cardinal Red, Frost Blue, Golden Mist, Heather, Inverness Green, Kelly Green, Pelham Blue, Polaris Blue, and Silver Mist finishes.

FIREBIRD I — asymmetrical hourglass style mahogany body, layered white pickguard, thru body mahogany neck, 22 fret Brazilian rosewood fingerboard with pearl dot inlay, wrapover stop tailpiece, partial blackface reverse peghead with pearl logo inlay, 6 on one side banjo tuners, nickel hardware, covered humbucker pickup, volume/tone control. Available in Sunburst finish. Mfg. 1963 to 1965.

	$3,250	$2,790	$2,320	$1,860	$1,670	$1,535	$1,395

A few of these guitars were produced with vibratos.

In 1965, peghead design changed to bass side tuner array.

In 1965, some models found with perpendicular to peghead tuners, single coil pickups.

FIREBIRD III — similar to Firebird I, except has bound fingerboard, tunomatic bridge/vibrato tailpiece, 2 humbucker pickups, 2 volume/2 tone controls, 3 position switch.

	$3,000	$2,625	$2,100	$1,890	$1,730	$1,575	$1,200

Gibson Explorer Custom
courtesy Bruce Hastell

In 1965, peghead design changed to bass side tuner array, some models found with perpendicular to peghead tuners, single coil pickups.

Grading	100%	98% MINT	95% EXC+	90% EXC	80% VG+	70% VG	60% G

FIREBIRD V — similar to Firebird I, except has bound fingerboard with trapezoid inlay, tunomatic bridge/vibrato with engraved cover, 2 humbucker pickups, 2 volume/2 tone controls, 3 position switch.

	$4,500	$3,780	$3,050	$2,360	$2,070	$1,860	$1,640

In 1965, peghead design changed to bass side tuner array.

FIREBIRD V REISSUE — asymmetrical hourglass style mahogany body, white pickguard with engraved Firebird symbol, thru body 9 piece mahogany/walnut neck, 22 fret rosewood fingerboard with pearl trapezoid inlay, tunomatic bridge/stop tailpiece, partial blackface peghead with pearl logo inlay, 6 on one side banjo tuners, chrome hardware, 2 covered pickups, 2 volume/2 tone controls, 3 position switch. Available in Cardinal Red, Classic White, Ebony, Heritage Cherry and Vintage Sunburst finishes. Mfg. 1990 to date.

Mfr.'s Sug. Retail	$1,575	$1,181	$787	$745	$560	$505	$460	$420

Circa 1975, the Firebird V Reissue was briefly offered in a "gold coil" finish. Examples of these guitars are generally priced around $2,000.

In 1994, Cardinal Red, Classic White, Ebony and Heritage Cherry finishes were discontinued.

FIREBIRD VII — asymmetrical hourglass style mahogany body, layered white pickguard, thru body mahogany neck, 22 fret bound ebony fingerboard with pearl block inlay, tunomatic bridge/vibrato tailpiece with engraved cover, partial blackface reverse peghead with pearl logo inlay, 6 on one side banjo tuners, gold hardware, 3 covered humbucker pickups, 2 volume/2 tone controls, 3 position switch. Available in Sunburst finish. Mfg. 1963 to 1965.

	$8,570	$7,145	$5,715	$5,145	$4,715	$4,285	$3,750

In 1965, peghead design changed to bass side tuner array.

FIREBIRD '76 — similar to Firebird VII, except has red/white/blue Firebird emblem on pickguard, pearl dot fingerboard inlay, 2 humbucker pickups. Available in Black, Mahogany, Sunburst and White finishes. Mfg. 1976 only.

	$750	$640	$535	$430	$390	$355	$325

Firebird Non-Reverse Series Solid Bodies

FIREBIRD I — asymmetrical hourglass style mahogany body, layered white pickguard with engraved Firebird logo, mahogany neck, 22 fret Brazilian rosewood fingerboard with pearl dot inlay, compensated bridge/vibrato tailpiece, 6 on one side tuners, chrome hardware, 2 single coil pickups, 2 volume/2 tone controls, 3 position switch. Available in Custom Color and Sunburst finishes. Mfg. 1965 to 1969.

	$1,300	$1,230	$1,050	$960	$850	$770	$630

FIREBIRD III — similar to Firebird I, except has 3 pickups.

	$1,600	$1,450	$1,285	$1,155	$1,060	$965	$900

FIREBIRD V — similar to Firebird I, except has tunomatic bridge/vibrato tailpiece with engraved cover, 2 covered original style Firebird humbucking pickups.

	$2,000	$1,850	$1,685	$1,470	$1,260	$1,040	$950

Firebird V 12 — similar to Firebird I, except has 12 strings, blackface peghead with pearl split diamond inlay, tunomatic bridge/fixed tailpiece, 6 on one side tuners. Mfg. 1966 to 1967.

	$1,100	$940	$785	$630	$565	$515	$470

FIREBIRD VII — similar to Firebird I, except has tunomatic bridge/vibrato tailpiece with engraved cover, gold hardware, 3 original style Firebird humbucking pickups.

	$2,500	$2,300	$1,950	$1,775	$1,550	$1,380	$1,100

Flying V Series

FLYING V (KORINA) — V shape korina body, layered white pickguard, rubber strip on treble side of body, korina neck, 22 fret rosewood fingerboard with pearl dot inlay, tunomatic bridge, strings thru anchoring with V shaped metal plate, raised plastic lettering on peghead, 3 per side tuners with amber buttons, gold (1958-59) or nickel (1962-63) hardware, 2 PAF (1958-59) or patent number (1962-63) humbucker pickups, 2 volume/1 tone controls. Available in Natural finish, brown case 1958-59, black case 1962-63. Mfg. 1958 to 1959 and 1962 to 1963.

A few models had black pickguards.

The Flying V model was introduced in 1958 and had an original retail price of $247.50 plus $75 for the case. A modernistic concept guitar (along with the Explorer and Moderne) from Gibson, this model had very limited manufacture (estimated to be under 100 instruments). Original Flying Vs exhibiting some wear and no problems are currently priced in the $35,000-$45,000 range, up to $50,000. Even though the 1962-1963 period of manufacture was mostly a clean-up of earlier bodies and related parts that were never finished, values seem to be the same for both periods.

Flying V Reissue — similar to Flying V, except has mahogany body/neck, no rubber strip on body, stop tailpiece, redesigned peghead. Available in Cherry and Sunburst finishes. Mfg. 1966 to 1970.

	$4,500	$3,860	$3,215	$2,570	$2,315	$2,120	$1,930

Flying V Medallion — similar to Flying V Reissue, except has Limited Edition medallion on top, redesigned peghead. Mfg. 1971 only.

	$3,000	$2,570	$2,140	$1,715	$1,545	$1,415	$1,285

Flying V 2nd Reissue — similar to Flying V Reissue, except has Black, Natural, Tobacco Sunburst and White finishes. Mfg. 1975 to 1980.

	$1,000	$855	$715	$570	$510	$465	$425

1972 Gibson Firebird
19th Annual Dallas Show

G

1958 Gibson Flying V
courtesy Southworth Guitars

Grading	100%	98% MINT	95% EXC+	90% EXC	80% VG+	70% VG	60% G

Gibson Flying V II
courtesy Bill Stapelton

Gibson Invader
courtesy Judy Hill

THE V (1980) — V shape mahogany body, bound figured maple top, mahogany neck, 22 fret ebony fingerboard with pearl dot inlay, tunomatic bridge/stop tailpiece, 3 per side tuners, chrome hardware, 2 humbucker pickups, 2 volume/1 tone controls, 3 position switch. Available in Antique Natural, Antique Sunburst and Vintage Cherry Sunburst finishes. Mfg. 1980.

	$500	$430	$360	$285	$260	$235	$215

FLYING V II — V shape 5 piece laminated walnut/maple body, layered black pickguard, walnut neck, 22 fret ebony fingerboard with pearl dot inlay, tunomatic bridge, strings thru anchoring with V shaped metal plate, blackface peghead with pearl logo, 3 per side tuners, gold hardware, 2 V shaped humbucker pickups, 2 volume/1 tone controls, 3 position switch. Available in Natural finish. Mfg. 1979 to 1982.

	$650	$555	$465	$370	$335	$305	$280

This model was also available with maple neck.

Body woods on this model were interchangeable, ie. walnut or maple were used for top.

FLYING V HERITAGE — V shape korina body, layered white pickguard, rubber strip on treble side of body, korina neck, 22 fret rosewood fingerboard with pearl dot inlay, tunomatic bridge, strings thru anchoring with V shaped metal plate, raised plastic lettering on peghead, 3 per side tuners with plastic single ring buttons, gold hardware, 2 humbucker PAF pickups, 2 volume/1 tone gold controls. Available in Antique Natural, Candy Apple Red, Ebony and White finishes. Mfg. 1981 to 1984.

	$2,500	$2,140	$1,785	$1,430	$1,285	$1,180	$1,070

Subtract 20% for White finish.

Add 60% for Candy Apple Red finish.

In 1983, renamed Flying V (Reissue); black control knobs replaced original item.

THE V (1983) — similar to original Flying V, except has a curly maple top. Available in Antique Natural, Antique Sunburst or Cherry finishes. Mfg. 1983 only.

	$750	$640	$535	$430	$390	$355	$325

Flying V CMT — similar to Flying V, except has curly maple top. Available in Antique Sunburst or Vintage Cherry Sunburst finishes. Mfg. 1984 only.

	$700	$600	$500	$400	$360	$330	$300

FLYING V XPL — "V" shape mahogany body, layered white pickguard, mahogany neck, 22 fret rosewood fingerboard with pearl dot inlay, tunomatic bridge/stop tailpiece, 6 on one side tuners, black hardware, 2 humbucker pickups, 2 volume/1 tone controls. Available in Night Violet and Plum Wineburst finishes. Mfg. 1984 to 1987.

	$500	$430	$360	$285	$260	$235	$215

This model was also available with double locking vibrato.

FLYING V (Mfg. 1988 to 1989) — similar to original Flying V, except has a 24 fret ebony fingerboard, Steinberger KB-X vibrato or string thru body design, 1 double coil pickup.

	$600	$515	$430	$345	$310	$285	$260

FLYING V 90 DOUBLE — similar to Flying V XPL, except has 24 fret ebony fingerboard with pearl split diamond inlay, strings thru anchoring with V shaped metal plate, blackface peghead with pearl logo inlay, single coil/humbucker pickups, volume/tone control, 3 position switch. Available in Black finish. Mfg. 1989 to 1992.

	$790	$675	$565	$455	$405	$370	$335

FLYING V '67 — "V" shape mahogany body, white pickguard, mahogany neck, 22 fret rosewood fingerboard with pearl dot inlay, tunomatic bridge/stop tailpiece, arrow style peghead, 3 per side tuners with pearl buttons, chrome hardware, 2 exposed humbucker pickups, 2 volume/1 tone controls, 3 position switch. Available in Cherry, Classic White, Ebony and Vintage Sunburst finishes. Curr. mfr.

Mfr.'s Sug. Retail	$1,110	$832	$555	$500	$400	$360	$330	$300

In 1994, Vintage Sunburst finish was discontinued.

FUTURA — can opener style hardwood body, black tri-lam pickguard, thru body maple neck, 22 fret rosewood fingerboard with white dot inlay, tunomatic bridge/stop tailpiece, 6 on one side tuners, chrome hardware, 2 covered humbucker pickups, 2 volume/1 tone controls, 3 position/rotary coil tap switches. Available in Ebony, Ultraviolet and White finish. Mfg. 1983 to 1985.

	$225	$195	$160	$130	$115	$105	$95

GK-55 — single cutaway mahogany body, bolt-on mahogany neck, 22 fret rosewood fingerboard with pearl dot inlay, tunomatic bridge/stop tailpiece, 3 per side tuners, chrome hardware, 2 exposed humbucker pickups, 2 volume/2 tone controls, 3 position switch. Available in Tobacco Sunburst finish. Mfg. 1979 only.

	$300	$260	$215	$175	$155	$140	$130

INVADER — single cutaway mahogany body/neck, 22 fret ebony fingerboard with dot inlay, double locking vibrato, 6 on one side tuners, black hardware, 2 exposed "dirty finger" humbucker pickups, 2 volume/2 tone controls, 3 position switch. Available in Black finish. Mfg. 1983 to 1989.

	$350	$300	$250	$200	$180	$165	$150

Grading	100%	98% MINT	95% EXC+	90% EXC	80% VG+	70% VG	60% G

L-5 CES — single round cutaway bound hollow body, carved spruce top, layered tortoise pickguard, bound f-holes, maple back/sides/neck, 20 fret bound pointed ebony fingerboard with pearl block inlay, ebony bridge with pearl inlay on wings, model name engraved trapeze tailpiece with chrome insert, multibound blackface peghead with pearl flame/logo inlay, 3 per side tuners, gold hardware, 2 single coil pickups, 2 volume/2 tone controls, 3 position switch. Available in Sunburst finish. Mfg. 1951 to date.

1951-1959	$15,000	$12,858	$10,715	$8,570	$7,715	$7,070	$6,430
1960-1964	$11,375	$9,750	$8,125	$6,500	$5,850	$5,365	$4,875
1965-1968	$7,500	$6,430	$5,360	$4,285	$3,860	$3,535	$3,215
1969-1974	$4,500	$3,860	$3,220	$2,575	$2,315	$2,120	$1,930
1975-1981	$6,000	$5,145	$4,280	$3,425	$3,085	$2,825	$2,570

Currently manufactured instruments are part of the Historic Collection Series, found at the end of this section.

This model has Natural finish optionally available.

In 1957, humbucker pickups replaced original item.

In 1960, sharp cutaway replaced original item.

In 1962, Pat. No. humbucker pickups replaced P.A.F. humbuckers.

In 1969, round cutaway replaced respective item.

In 1974, neck volute was introduced.

In 1981, neck volute was discontinued.

L-5S — single sharp cutaway multi bound maple body, carved figured maple top, maple neck, 22 fret bound ebony pointed-end fingerboard with abalone block inlay, tunomatic bridge/trapeze tailpiece, silver center tailpiece insert with engraved model name, multi bound blackface peghead vase/logo inlay, 3 per side tuners, gold hardware, 2 covered single coil pickups, 2 volume/2 tone controls, 3 position switch. Available in Cherry Sunburst finish. Mfg. 1972 to 1985.

	$1,800	$1,600	$1,450	$1,285	$1,055	$960	$840

In 1974, covered humbucker pickups replaced original items.

In 1975, stop tailpiece replaced original item.

In 1976, tunable stop tailpiece replaced respective item.

L-6S — single sharp cutaway maple body, black pickguard, maple neck, 24 fret maple fingerboard with pearl block inlay, tunable bridge/stop tailpiece, blackface peghead, 3 per side tuners, chrome hardware, 2 covered humbucker pickups, 2 volume/1 tone controls, rotary switch. Available in Cherry and Natural finishes. Mfg. 1973 to 1980.

Gibson L-5 Custom
courtesy Elliot Rubinson

	$400	$340	$285	$230	$205	$190	$170

This model was available with ebony fingerboard in Tobacco Sunburst finish.

In 1975, pearl dot inlay replaced block inlay, instrument renamed L-6S Custom.

L-6S Deluxe — similar to L6-S, except has bolt-on maple neck, pearl dot fingerboard inlay, strings thru anchoring, volume/tone control, 3 position switch. Mfg. 1975 to 1980.

	$450	$385	$325	$260	$230	$215	$195

A few of these instruments have set necks.

This instrument was also available with rosewood fingerboard.

LE GRAND — single round cutaway hollow style, spruce top, bound f-holes, raised bound tortoise pickguard, figured maple back/sides/neck, 19 fret bound ebony fingerboard with abalone/pearl split block inlay, adjustable ebony bridge with pearl inlay/finger tailpiece, bound blackface peghead with pearl split diamond/logo inlay, 3 per side tuners, gold hardware, floating single coil pickup. Available in Chablis, Sunrise Orange and Translucent Amber finishes. New 1994.

Mfr.'s Sug. Retail	$6,300	$5,040	$3,780	$3,150	$2,520	$2,270	$2,080	$1,890

LES PAUL SERIES

Original Les Paul Series

LES PAUL MODEL — single sharp cutaway solid mahogany body, bound carved maple top, raised cream pickguard, one piece mahogany neck, 22 fret bound rosewood fingerboard with pearl trapezoid inlays, trapeze bridge/tailpiece, blackface peghead with holly veneer/pearl logo inlay, silkscreen model name on peghead, 3 per side Kluson tuners with plastic single ring buttons, nickel hardware, 2 single coil P-90 pickups, 2 volume/2 tone controls, 3 position switch. Available in Gold Top/Natural back finish. Mfg. 1952 to 1958.

1952-1953 Trapeze	N/A	$3,500	$3,200	$2,870	$2,460	$2,180	$1,840
1953-1955 Stop Tailpiece	N/A	$5,500	$4,310	$3,495	$2,740	$2,405	$2,165
1956-1957	N/A	$7,500	$6,420	$5,335	$4,900	$4,575	$4,250
1958	N/A	$15,00	$13,800	$12,370	$11,800	$10,200	$9,700

Originally, bridge tailpieces were used with the strings traveling under the bar of the bridge. During 1952 and through most of 1953, the strings were changed to travel over the bridge bar.

This was Gibson's first production solid body. Early models are without binding around the fingerboard and do not have a plastic ring around the selector switch. Some models are noted to have Gold finish on sides and back in addition to the top. Original finish on the Gold Top models can usually be determined by a greenish hue around the lower bouts of the instrument where the player's arm(s) has rubbed off the clear and/or color coat (the color coat was

1953 Gibson Les Paul Goldtop
courtesy Dave Hinson

Grading	100%	98% MINT	95% EXC+	90% EXC	80% VG+	70% VG	60% G

originally mixed with bronze powder), producing a green oxidation that can even be noticed on the metal parts occasionally. Horizontal weather checking striations are also normal on original Gold Top finishes.

Special order instruments have Dark Brown back finish.

In 1952, these models were not serialized.

In 1953, ink stamped serial numbers on back of peghead were introduced, wrapover bridge/tailpiece replaced original item.

In 1955, tunomatic bridge/stop tailpiece replaced respective item.

In 1957, humbucker PAF pickups replaced original item.

Les Paul models in very clean/all original condition have sold for as high as $20,000. Instruments should be determined on a piece-by-piece basis as opposed to the usual market.

LES PAUL STANDARD — single sharp cutaway mahogany body, bound carved flame maple top, raised cream pickguard, one piece mahogany neck, 22 fret rosewood fingerboard with pearl trapezoid inlay, tunomatic bridge/stop tailpiece, blackface peghead with holly veneer/pearl logo inlay, 3 per side Kluson tuners with single ring plastic buttons, nickel hardware, 2 covered humbucker PAF pickups, 2 volume/2 tone controls, 3 position switch. Available in Cherry Sunburst finish. Mfg. 1958 to 1960.

This model has achieved awe among guitar collectors (and investors) throughout the world. The flametop's popularity and stratospheric price appreciation have launched a wave of vintage nostalgia and reissues that have created an independent, significant marketplace. The value of a flame top Gibson Les Paul Standard depends on two factors: the degree of "flame" in the maple top and the degree of original condition. It's hard to believe that two killer bookmatched pieces of flame maple that no one paid much attention to in 1959 will cost you $35,000 EXTRA today. These instruments in average (60%-80%) original condition without much flame start in the $20,000-$25,000 area. 80%-90% condition with nicely flamed tops weigh in at the $30,000-$35,000 range. And a really mint, spectacular flamed instrument in original condition could cost you more than the roof over your head. Stories of flame top sales in the $60,000 to $80,000 range have circulated, and some collectors hypothesized that the price could reach $100,000. This model, more than any other, proves what turbo-charged desirability can do to an instrument's price tag. In 1959, they retailed for $279 - if you had a new one in the case today and advertised it as best-offer, you would soon have to change your phone number to unlisted. The **Blue Book of Guitars** fully recommends that several professional appraisals be secured before purchasing a collectible guitar of this magnitude. Certainly, a crown jewel of any guitar collection.

In 1959, large frets replaced original item.

In 1960, thin neck, double ring tuner buttons replaced original items.

LES PAUL (SG BODY STYLE) — double sharp cutaway mahogany body, layered black pickguard, mahogany neck, 22 fret bound rosewood fingerboard with pearl trapezoid inlay, tunomatic bridge/side-pull vibrato, blackface peghead with pearl logo inlay, 3 per side Kluson tuners with double ring plastic tuners, nickel hardware, 2 covered humbucker pickups, 2 volume/2 tone controls, 3 position switch. Available in Cherry finish. Mfg. 1960 to 1963.

	$2,500	$2,250	$1,930	$1,605	$1,285	$1,155	$1,060

In late 1960, the body style was changed to what is now known as the "SG" body style. Les Paul logo still found on peghead (see submodel description directly below).

In 1961, the Les Paul name was put on truss rod cover, and did not have a model name on the peghead. Pearl crown peghead inlay.

In 1962, some models were produced with ebony tailblock and pearl inlay.

In 1963, renamed SG Standard. See SG Series later in text.

Les Paul Standard (1968-1969 Mfr.) — single sharp cutaway solid mahogany body, deeper cutaway binding, bound carved maple top, raised cream pickguard, mahogany neck, 22 fret bound rosewood fingerboard with pearl trapezoid inlay, tunomatic bridge/stop tailpiece, blackface peghead with pearl logo inlay, 3 per side Kluson tuners with double ring plastic buttons, nickel hardware, 2 single coil P-90 pickups, 2 volume/2 tone controls, 3 position switch. Available in Gold Top/Natural Back finish. Mfg. 1968 to 1969.

1968	$2,400	$2,100	$1,800	$1,625	$1,240	$1,050	$960
1969	$1,800	$1,600	$1,400	$1,200	$1,050	$980	$890

This was Gibson's first Gold Top reissue.

Les Paul Standard (1971 Mfr.) — single sharp cutaway solid mahogany body, bound carved maple top, raised cream pickguard, mahogany neck, 22 fret bound rosewood fingerboard with pearl trapezoid inlay, wrapover bridge tailpiece, blackface peghead with pearl logo inlay, 3 per side Kluson tuners with plastic double ring buttons, nickel hardware, 2 single coil P-90 pickups, 2 volume/2 tone controls, 3 position switch. Available in Gold Top finish. Mfg. 1971 to 1973.

	$1,700	$1,460	$1,215	$970	$870	$800	$730

This model did not have a neck volute.

This model was a reissue of the 1954 Les Paul.

Les Paul Standard (Current Manufacture) — single sharp cutaway 3 piece mahogany/maple body, deeper cutaway binding, bound carved 3 piece maple top, cream pickguard, 22 fret bound rosewood fingerboard with pearl trapezoid inlay, tunomatic bridge/stop tailpiece, blackface peghead with pearl logo inlay, "Standard" engraved on truss rod cover, 3 per side tuners with pearloid buttons, chrome hardware, 2 covered humbucker pickups, 2 volume/2 tone controls, 3 position switch. Available in Cherry Sunburst, Dark Sunburst, Ebony, Gold Top, Heritage Sunburst, Honey Burst, Natural, Tobacco Sunburst, TV Yellow, Vintage Sunburst and Wine Red finishes. Mfg. 1974 to date.

Mfr.'s Sug. Retail	$2,399	$1,919	$1,439	$1,250	$1,000	$925	$850	$800

Add $75 for Wine Red finish.

Add $250 for Heritage Cherry Sunburst, Honey Burst and Vintage Sunburst finishes.

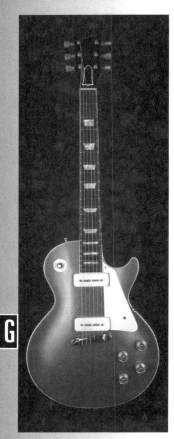

Gibson Les Paul Goldtop
courtesy Guitarville

G

Grading	100% MINT	98% EXC+	95% EXC	90% VG+	80% VG	70% VG	60% G

In 1971, neck volute was introduced, slab cut body replaced original item.

In 1978, one-piece body replaced original item.

In 1981, carved top replaced respective item, neck volute was discontinued.

In 1990, TV Yellow finish became standard.

In 1994, Cherry Sunburst, Dark Sunburst, Gold Top, Heritage Sunburst, Natural, Tobacco Sunburst and TV Yellow finishes were discontinued.

Gibson also offers the Les Paul Standard Plus model (LPS+) with a current retail price of $3,500 (1996).

Gibson has offered a twelve-string version of the Les Paul in the past. However, these instruments have either been very, very low production batches, or specialty productions, or custom shop orders.

Les Paul Standard Birdseye — similar to Les Paul Standard, except has birdseye maple top. Available in Heritage Sunburst, Honey Burst and Vintage Sunburst finishes. Mfg. 1993 to date.

Mfr.'s Sug. Retail	$2,699	$2,024	$1,349	$1,140	$860	$775	$710	$645

In 1994, Vintage Sunburst finish was discontinued.

LES PAUL DELUXE — single sharp cutaway 3 piece mahogany/maple body, deeper cutaway binding, bound carved maple top, raised cream pickguard, mahogany neck, 22 fret bound rosewood fingerboard with pearl trapezoid inlay, tunomatic bridge/stop tailpiece, widened blackface peghead with pearl logo inlay, 3 per side Kluson tuners with plastic double ring buttons, nickel hardware, 2 mini humbucker pickups, 2 volume/2 tone controls, 3 position switch. Available in Blue Sparkle Top, Cherry, Cherry Sunburst, Gold Top, Red Sparkle Top, Tobacco Sunburst, Walnut and Wine Red finishes. Mfg. 1969 to 1985.

1969-1971		$1,200	$1,030	$860	$685	$615	$565	$515
1972-1985		$850	$730	$610	$485	$435	$400	$365

A few of these models were produced with 2 single coil P-90 pickups.

In 1971, neck volute was introduced, Cherry, Cherry Sunburst and Walnut finishes became standard.

In 1972, the Walnut finish was discontinued, and the Tobacco Sunburst finish became standard.

In 1975, Natural and Wine Red finishes became options.

In 1977, 2-piece mahogany body replaced original item.

In 1981, neck volute was discontinued.

Les Paul Pro-Deluxe — similar to Les Paul Deluxe, except has ebony fingerboard, chrome hardware. Available in Black, Cherry Sunburst, Gold Top and Tobacco Sunburst finishes. Mfg. 1978 to 1982.

Gibson Les Paul Deluxe
courtesy John Miller

		$750	$640	$535	$430	$390	$355	$325

KALAMAZOO CUSTOM ORDER '59 REISSUE LES PAUL — circa 1978-79, a few companies including Leo's in CA, Guitar Trader in NJ, and Jimmy Wallace through Arnold and Morgan Music in TX, custom ordered Les Paul's that were patterned exactly after Gibson's original 1959 Standard Model (and feature individualized truss rod covers). These guitars are noted for their ebonized holly veneered pegheads, original inked serialization, highly figured (flame or quilted) maple tops and other '59 Standard features.

These instruments are very desirable because they duplicated the original 1959 Les Paul Standard almost exactly. Because of this and limited manufacture (less than 250 exist), asking prices today are in the $5,000- $6,000 range.

LES PAUL KALAMAZOO — single sharp cutaway solid mahogany body, bound carved maple top, raised cream pickguard, mahogany neck, 22 fret bound rosewood fingerboard with pearl trapezoid inlay, Nashville tunomatic bridge/stop tailpiece, large blackface peghead with pearl logo inlay, "Les Paul K.M." engraved on truss cover, 3 per side Grover tuners, nickel hardware, 2 cream colored covered humbucker pickups, 2 volume/2 tone controls, 3 position switch. Available in Antique Sunburst, Cherry Sunburst and Natural finishes. Mfg. 1979 only.

		$1,200	$1,030	$860	$685	$615	$565	$515

This was Gibson's first nationally distributed flame top reissue.

The first production run of these instruments exhibited a metal plate with engraved "Custom Made" logo below the tailpiece. Approximately 1,500 of this model were manufactured in Gibson's Kalamazoo plant.

LES PAUL HERITAGE 80 — single sharp cutaway mahogany body, bound carved flame maple top, raised cream pickguard, 3 piece mahogany neck, 22 fret rosewood fingerboard with pearl trapezoid inlay, tunomatic bridge/stop tailpiece, blackface peghead with pearl logo inlay, "Heritage 80" on truss cover, 3 per side Grover tuners, nickel hardware, 2 covered humbucker pickups, 2 volume/2 tone controls, 3 position switch. Available in Cherry Sunburst and Honey Sunburst finishes. Mfg. 1980 to 1982.

		$3,000	$2,570	$2,140	$1,715	$1,545	$1,415	$1,285

A few of these instruments were produced with Ebony finish and are very rare.

Les Paul Heritage 80 Elite — similar to Les Paul Heritage 80, except has quilted maple top, one piece neck, ebony fingerboard.

		$3,000	$2,570	$2,140	$1,715	$1,545	$1,415	$1,285

LES PAUL SPOTLIGHT SPECIAL — single sharp cutaway mahogany body, bound carved 3 piece maple/mahogany/maple top, raised cream pickguard, mahogany neck, 22 fret rosewood fingerboard with pearl trapezoid inlay, tunomatic bridge/stop tailpiece, blackface peghead with pearl logo inlay, 3 per side tuners with plastic buttons, chrome hardware, 2 covered humbucker pickups, 2 volume/2 tone controls, 3 position switch. Available in Natural finish. Mfg. 1980 to 1985.

		$2,250	$1,930	$1,605	$1,285	$1,155	$1,060	$965

LES PAUL 1985 REISSUE — similar specifications to the current Gibson Historic Collection Les Paul '59 Flametop Reissue, this was Gibson's first authorized 1959 Les Paul reissue.

		$3,000	$2,890	$2,600	$2,380	$2,170	$1,850	$1,640

Gibson Les Paul Corvette
courtesy Elliot Rubinson

Grading	100%	98% MINT	95% EXC+	90% EXC	80% VG+	70% VG	60% G

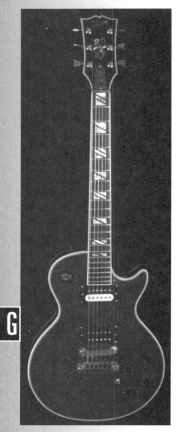

Gibson Les Paul 25/50
courtesy Thoroughbred Music

LES PAUL CMT — similar to Les Paul Spotlight Special, except has maple/walnut/maple body, curly maple top. Mfg. 1986 to 1989.

	$2,500	$2,140	$1,785	$1,430	$1,285	$1,180	$1,070

Les Paul 25/50 Anniversary — mahogany body, carved maple top, slashed block fingerboard inlay, 25/50 peghead inlay, 2 humbuckers. Mfg. 1979 only.

	$1,500	$1,200	$925	$790	$660	$530	$475

Last Mfr.'s Sug. Retail was $1,250.

This guitar commemorated 25 years of the Les Paul model, and 50 years of Les Paul's continuing career.

LES PAUL STANDARD THIRTIETH ANNIVERSARY — single sharp cutaway mahogany body, bound carved maple top, raised cream pickguard, mahogany neck, 22 fret rosewood fingerboard with pearl trapezoid inlay, pearl "Thirtieth Anniversary" inlay at 15th fret, tunomatic bridge/stop tailpiece, blackface peghead with pearl logo inlay, 3 per side tuners with plastic buttons, nickel hardware, 2 covered humbucker pickups, 2 volume/2 tone controls, 3 position switch. Available in Gold Top finish. Mfg. 1982 to 1984.

	$1,950	$1,725	$1,500	$1,050	$900	$750	$575

Les Paul Standard Fortieth Anniversary — similar to Les Paul Standard Thirtieth Anniversary, except has ebony fingerboard, gold hardware, 2 stacked humbucker pickups. Mfg. 1992 only.

	$1,500	$1,285	$1,070	$860	$770	$710	$645

LES PAUL LP-XPL — single sharp cutaway solid mahogany body, bound carved maple top, raised cream pickguard, mahogany neck, 22 fret bound ebony fingerboard with pearl dot inlay, tunomatic bridge/stop tailpiece, blackface peghead with pearl logo inlay, 6 on one side tuners, chrome hardware, 2 single coil pickups, 2 volume/2 tone controls, 3 position switch. Available in Cherry Sunburst finish. Mfg. 1984 to 1987.

	$500	$430	$360	$285	$260	$235	$215

This model was also available with double cutaway body.

This model was also available with 2 single coil/1 humbucker pickups configuration.

LES PAUL CLASSIC — single sharp cutaway mahogany body, bound carved maple top, cream pickguard with engraved "1960", bound rosewood fingerboard with pearl trapezoid inlay, tunomatic bridge/stop tailpiece, blackface peghead with pearl logo inlay, pearloid button tuners, nickel hardware, 2 exposed humbucker pickups. Available in Bullion Gold, Ebony, Honey Burst, Heritage Cherry Sunburst and Vintage Sunburst finishes. Mfg. 1990 to date.

Mfr.'s Sug. Retail	$2,600	$1,950	$1,300	$1,200	$1,000	$900	$850	$800

In 1994, Ebony and Vintage Sunburst finishes were discontinued.

Les Paul Classic Plus — similar to Les Paul Classic, except has curly maple top. Available in Honey Burst, Heritage Cherry Sunburst, Translucent Amber, Translucent Purple, Translucent Red and Vintage Sunburst finishes. Curr. mfr.

Mfr.'s Sug. Retail	$2,675	$2,006	$1,337	$1,220	$965	$810	$740	$675

In 1994, Translucent Purple, Translucent Red and Vintage Sunburst finishes were discontinued.

Les Paul Classic Premium Plus — similar to Les Paul Classic, except has highest quality curly maple top. Available in Honey Burst, Heritage Cherry Sunburst, Translucent Amber, Translucent Purple, Translucent Red and Vintage Sunburst finishes. Curr. mfr.

Mfr.'s Sug. Retail	$5,099	$3,824	$2,549	$2,380	$1,930	$1,690	$1,450	$1,200

In 1994, Translucent Purple, Translucent Red and Vintage Sunburst finishes were discontinued.

Les Paul Classic Birdseye — similar to Les Paul Classic, except has birdseye maple top. Available in Honey Burst, Heritage Cherry Sunburst, Translucent Amber, Translucent Purple, Translucent Red and Vintage Sunburst finishes. Disc. 1994.

	$1,820	$1,560	$1,300	$1,040	$935	$860	$780

Last Mfr.'s Sug. Retail was $2,600.

Les Paul Classic Premium Birdseye — similar to Les Paul Classic, except has highest quality birdseye maple top. Available in Honey Burst, Heritage Cherry Sunburst, Translucent Amber, Translucent Purple, Translucent Red and Vintage Sunburst finishes. Disc. 1994.

	$3,290	$2,820	$2,350	$1,880	$1,690	$1,550	$1,410

Last Mfr.'s Sug. Retail was $4,700.

LES PAUL XR-I — single cutaway mahogany body, carved maple top, 22 fret rosewood fingerboard with pearl dot inlay, tunomatic bridge/stop tailpiece, 3 per side tuners with pearloid buttons, chrome hardware, 2 exposed humbucker pickups, 2 volume/2 tone controls, 3 position/coil tap switches. Available in Cherry Sunburst, Goldburst and Tobacco Sunburst finishes. Mfg. 1981 to 1983.

	$600	$515	$430	$345	$310	$285	$260

Refinished Gibson LP Custom
courtesy Garrie Johnson

Grading	100%	98% MINT	95% EXC+	90% EXC	80% VG+	70% VG	60% G

Les Paul XR-II — similar to Les Paul XR-I, except has bound figured maple top, "Gibson" embossed pickup covers. Available in Honey Sunburst finish.

	$750	$640	$535	$430	$390	$355	$325

Les Paul Custom Series

LES PAUL CUSTOM — single sharp cutaway multi-bound mahogany body with carved top, raised bound black pickguard, mahogany neck, 22 fret bound ebony fingerboard with pearl block inlay, tunomatic bridge/stop tailpiece, multi-bound peghead with pearl split diamond/logo inlay, 3 per side Deluxe Kluson tuners with plastic single ring buttons, gold hardware, 2 single coil pickups, 2 volume/2 tone controls, 3 position switch. Available in Black finish. Mfg. 1954 to 1960.

1954-1957		$5,500	$4,715	$3,930	$3,145	$2,830	$2,595	$2,360
1958-1960		$8,500	$7,290	$6,075	$4,860	$4,370	$4,010	$3,645

This guitar was nicknamed the "Black Beauty" and also the "Fretless Wonder".

In 1957, 3 humbucker PAF pickups replaced 2 pickup configuration. A few models found with 2 humbucker pickups.

In 1959, Grover tuners replaced original item.

LES PAUL CUSTOM (SG BODY STYLE) — double sharp cutaway mahogany body, white layered pickguard, mahogany neck, 22 fret bound ebony fingerboard with pearl block inlay, tunomatic bridge/side-pull vibrato, multi-bound peghead with pearl split diamond inlay, 3 per side tuners, gold hardware, 3 covered humbucker pickups, 2 volume/2 tone controls, 3 position switch. Available in Black or White finishes. Mfg. 1961 to 1963.

	$3,500	$3,250	$2,790	$2,320	$1,860	$1,670	$1,535

In 1962, some models were produced with pearl inlaid ebony tailpiece insert.

In 1963, renamed SG Custom. See SG Series later in text.

Models in black finish are very rare.

LES PAUL CUSTOM 1968 REISSUE — single sharp cutaway mahogany body, multi-bound carved maple top, raised bound black pickguard, one piece mahogany neck, 22 small fret bound ebony fingerboard with pearl block inlay, tunomatic bridge/stop tailpiece, multi-bound peghead with pearl split diamond/logo inlay, no neck volute, 3 per side Grover tuners, gold hardware, 2 humbucker Pat. No. pickups, 2 volume/2 tone controls, 3 position switch. Available in Black finish. Mfg. 1968 only.

	$2,000	$1,870	$1,570	$1,400	$1,250	$1,140	$1,020

This instrument was a reissue of 1957 version of the Les Paul Custom.

Les Paul Custom 1969 Reissue — similar to Les Paul Custom 1968 Reissue, except has 3 piece mahogany/maple body, 3 piece neck. Available in Alpine White, Black, Cherry, Cherry Sunburst, Heritage Sunburst, Honeyburst, Natural, Tobacco Sunburst, Vintage Sunburst, Walnut, White, and Wine Red finishes. Mfg. 1969 to date.

1969		$2,000	$1,715	$1,430	$1,145	$1,030	$945	$860
1970		$1,400	$1,200	$1,000	$800	$720	$660	$600
1971-1985		$1,200	$1,030	$860	$685	$615	$565	$515
Mfr.'s Sug. Retail	$3,599	$2,699	$1,799	$1,650	$1,250	$1,100	$1,000	$950

In 1971, neck volute was introduced, Cherry and Cherry Sunburst finishes became optionally available.

From 1971-1973, 3 humbucker pickup configuration became optionally available.

In 1972, Tobacco Sunburst became optionally available.

In 1975, jumbo frets replaced original item, Natural and White finishes became optionally available.

In 1976, Wine Red finish became available.

In 1977, one piece mahogany body replaced original item, Walnut finish became available.

In 1981, neck volute was discontinued.

In 1988, Alpine White, Ebony, Heritage Sunburst and Vintage Sunburst finishes became available.

In 1990, Honey Burst finish became available.

In 1994, Black, Cherry, Cherry Sunburst, Heritage Sunburst, Honeyburst, Tobacco Sunburst, Vintage Sunburst, Walnut and White finishes were discontinued.

Les Paul Custom Plus — similar to Les Paul Custom, except has bound figured maple top. Available in Dark Wineburst, Honeyburst, Heritage Cherry Sunburst and Vintage Sunburst finishes. Curr. mfr.

Mfr.'s Sug. Retail	$4,439	$3,329	$2,219	$1,965	$1,645	$1,345	$1,160	$1,050

In 1994, Dark Wineburst finish was discontinued.

Les Paul Custom Premium Plus — similar to Les Paul Custom, except has highest quality bound figured maple top. Available in Dark Wineburst, Honey Burst, Heritage Cherry Sunburst and Vintage Sunburst finishes. Disc. 1994.

	$2,095	$1,800	$1,500	$1,200	$1,080	$990	$900

Last Mfr.'s Sug. Retail was $3,000.

Les Paul Custom Reissue '54 — similar to original Les Paul Custom. Mfg. 1972 to 1977.

	$1,150	$985	$825	$660	$590	$545	$495

In 1977, this model was available with a maple fingerboard.

LES PAUL CUSTOM TWENTIETH ANNIVERSARY — single sharp cutaway multi-bound mahogany body with carved top, raised bound black pickguard, mahogany neck, 22 fret bound ebony fingerboard with pearl block inlay, "Twentieth Anniversary" engraved into block inlay at 15th fret, tunomatic bridge/stop tailpiece, multi-bound peghead with pearl split diamond/logo inlay, 3 per side tuners with plastic buttons, gold hardware, 2 single coil pickups, 2 volume/2 tone controls, 3 position switch. Available in Black and White finishes. Mfg. 1974 only.

	$1,800	$1,540	$1,285	$1,025	$925	$845	$770

'61 Gibson LP Custom SG
courtesy Garrie Johnson

G

Grading	100%	98% MINT	95% EXC+	90% EXC	80% VG+	70% VG	60% G

Les Paul Custom Thirty-Fifth Anniversary — similar to original Les Paul Custom Twentieth Anniversary, except has "Thirty-Fifth Anniversary" etched on peghead inlay, 3 humbucker pickups. Mfg. 1989 only.

| | $1,600 | $1,370 | $1,145 | $915 | $825 | $755 | $685 |

THE LES PAUL — single sharp cutaway body, rosewood bound carved 2 piece bookmatched flame maple top/back/sides, mahogany core, raised rosewood pickguard, maple neck, 22 fret bound 3 piece ebony/rosewood/ebony/ fingerboard with abalone block inlay, tunomatic bridge/stop tailpiece, pearl split diamond/logo peghead inlay, 3 per side Schaller tuners with pearl buttons, serial number engraved pearl plate on peghead back, gold hardware, 2 Super humbucker pickups with rosewood surrounds, 2 volume/2 tone rosewood control knobs, 3 position switch, rosewood control plate on back. Available in Natural and Wine Red finishes. Mfg. 1976 to 1980.

> Due to extreme rarity (71 were produced, #61-#68 were made without their rosewood parts) accurate price evaluation is difficult for this model. Since this variation was perhaps Gibson's most elaborate and ornate (not to mention most expensive) L.P., most of these instruments were not played. As a result, remaining specimens are usually in 95% + condition. Current asking prices for this condition factor are presently in the $11,000-$13,500 price range, though some instruments have been seen to go as high as $20,000.
>
> A few early models had solid figured maple bodies.
>
> In 1978, Schaller tunomatic bridge/tunable stop tailpiece replaced original items.
>
> In 1979, Wine Red finish was discontinued.

LES PAUL ARTISAN — single sharp cutaway mahogany body, multi-bound carved maple top, raised bound black pickguard, mahogany neck, 22 fret bound ebony fingerboard with pearl flowers/heart inlay, tunomatic bridge/tunable stop tailpiece, multi-bound peghead with pearl split flowers/heart/logo inlay, 3 per side tuners, gold hardware, 2 single coil pickups, 2 volume/2 tone controls, 3 position switch. Available in Ebony, Tobacco Sunburst and Walnut finishes. Mfg. 1976 to 1982.

| | $1,525 | $1,310 | $1,090 | $870 | $785 | $720 | $655 |

> Originally offered with 3 humbuckers pickups optional.
>
> In 1979, 3 humbucker pickup configuration replaced original item.
>
> In 1980, larger tunomatic bridge replaced original item.

LES PAUL ARTIST — single cutaway mahogany body, multi-bound carved maple top, raised black pickguard, mahogany neck, 22 fret bound ebony fingerboard with pearl block inlay, tunomatic bridge/tunable stop tailpiece, multibound blackface peghead with pearl script "LP"/logo, 3 per side tuners, gold hardware, 2 covered humbucker pickups, volume/treble/bass controls, 3 position selector/3 mini switches, active electronics. Available in Sunburst finish. Mfg. 1979 to 1981.

| | $850 | $730 | $610 | $485 | $435 | $400 | $365 |

> In 1980, Ebony and Fireburst finishes became optionally available.

LES PAUL CUSTOM LITE — single sharp cutaway multi-bound mahogany body with carved top, raised bound black pickguard, mahogany neck, 22 fret bound ebony fingerboard with pearl block inlay, tunomatic bridge/stop tailpiece, multi-bound peghead with pearl split diamond/logo inlay, 3 per side tuners with chrome buttons, gold hardware, 2 covered humbucker pickups, volume/tone control, 3 position switch, mini coil tap switch. Available in Black finish. Mfg. 1987 to 1990.

| | $900 | $770 | $640 | $515 | $465 | $425 | $385 |

> This model was also available with double locking vibrato.

Les Paul Studio Series

LES PAUL STUDIO — single sharp cutaway mahogany body, carved maple top, raised black pickguard, 22 fret rosewood fingerboard with pearl dot inlay, tunomatic bridge/stop tailpiece, 3 per side tuners, gold hardware, 2 covered humbucker pickups, 2 volume/2 tone controls, 3 position switch. Available in Ebony, White and Wine Red finishes. Mfg. 1984 to date.

| Mfr.'s Sug. Retail | $1,439 | $1,151 | $863 | $740 | $650 | $560 | $500 | $450 |

> Add $50 for gold hardware with Alpine White finish.
>
> In 1987, ebony fingerboard replaced rosewood fingerboard.
>
> In 1990, trapezoid fingerboard inlay replaced dot inlay.
>
> In 1994, White finish was discontinued.
>
> In 1996, the Les Paul Studio Gem series was introduced. These models have different color options and a retail price of $1,639.

Les Paul Studio Custom — similar to Les Paul Studio, except has multi-bound body, bound fingerboard, multi-bound peghead. Available in Cherry Sunburst, Ebony and Sunburst finishes. Mfg. 1984 to 1987.

| | $675 | $580 | $485 | $385 | $350 | $320 | $290 |

Les Paul Studio Standard — similar to Les Paul Studio, except has bound body. Available in Cherry Sunburst, Sunburst and White finishes. Mfg. 1984 to 1987.

| | $675 | $580 | $485 | $385 | $350 | $320 | $290 |

Les Paul Studio Lite — similar to Les Paul Studio, except has no pickguard, ebony fingerboard with trapezoid inlay, black chrome hardware, exposed pickups. Available in Translucent Black, Translucent Blue and Translucent Red finishes. Curr. mfr.

| Mfr.'s Sug. Retail | $1,220 | $915 | $610 | $550 | $440 | $395 | $365 | $330 |

> Add $130 for gold hardware with Heritage Cherry Sunburst and Vintage Sunburst finishes.
>
> In 1994, Translucent Black and Translucent Red finishes were discontinued.

Grading	100%	98% MINT	95% EXC+	90% EXC	80% VG+	70% VG	60% G

Les Paul Studio Lite/M III — similar to Les Paul Studio, except has no pickguard, exposed humbucker/single coil/humbucker pickups, volume/tone control, 5 position switch. Curr. mfr.

Mfr.'s Sug. Retail	$1,350	$1,012	$675	$600	$480	$430	$395	$360

Les Paul Junior Series

LES PAUL JUNIOR — single cutaway mahogany body, black pickguard, mahogany neck, 22 fret rosewood fingerboard with dot inlay, wrapover stop tailpiece, 3 per side tuners with plastic buttons, nickel hardware, single coil pickup, volume/tone control. Available in Brown Sunburst and Cherry finishes. Mfg. 1954 to 1963.

	$1,750	$1,480	$1,170	$1,060	$970	$810	$740

In 1958, double round cutaway body, tortoise pickguard replaced original items, Cherry finish became available, Sunburst finish was discontinued.

LES PAUL JUNIOR (SG BODY STYLE) — double cutaway mahogany body, black pickguard, mahogany neck, 22 fret rosewood fingerboard with pearl dot inlay, tunomatic bridge/stop tailpiece, silkscreened model name on peghead, 3 per side tuners with plastic buttons, nickel hardware, single coil pickup, volume/tone control. Available in Cherry finish. Mfg. 1961 to 1963.

	$1,050	$900	$750	$600	$540	$495	$450

In 1962, Maestro vibrato became optionally available.

In 1963, renamed SG Junior. See SG Series later in text.

Les Paul TV — similar to Les Paul Junior, except has Limed Mahogany finish. Mfg. 1954 to 1959.

	$2,750	$2,400	$1,900	$1,800	$1,680	$1,500	$1,350

A few of these guitars were made with a ¾ size body.

In 1958, double round cutaway body and multi-layer pickguard replaced original items.

Les Paul TV (SG Body Style) — double cutaway mahogany body, black pickguard, mahogany neck, 22 fret rosewood fingerboard with pearl dot inlay, stop tailpiece, silkscreened model name on peghead, 3 per side tuners with plastic buttons, nickel hardware, single coil pickup, volume/tone control. Available in Limed Mahogany finish. Mfg. 1959 to 1963.

	$2,500	$2,140	$1,715	$1,545	$1,415	$1,285	$1,070

In 1962, Maestro vibrato became optionally available.

In 1963, renamed SG TV. See SG Series later in text.

Les Paul Junior ¾ — similar to Les Paul Junior, except has ¾ size body, shorter neck. Mfg. 1956 to 1961.

	$1,100	$940	$785	$630	$565	$515	$470

Les Paul Junior II — similar to Les Paul Junior, except has 2 P-100 pickups. Mfg. 1989 only.

	$800	$685	$575	$460	$410	$380	$345

This model is also available in a dual cutaway version.

Les Paul Junior Reissue — similar to Les Paul Junior. Available in Cherry, Tobacco Sunburst, TV Yellow or White finishes. Mfg. 1986 to date.

Mfr.'s Sug. Retail	$900	$720	$540	$450	$360	$325	$300	$275

Les Paul Special Series

LES PAUL SPECIAL — single cutaway mahogany body, multi-layer black pickguard, mahogany neck, 22 fret bound rosewood fingerboard with dot inlay, wrapover stop tailpiece, 3 per side tuners with plastic buttons, nickel hardware, 2 single coil pickups, 2 volume/2 tone controls, 3 position switch. Available in Limed Mahogany finish. Mfg. 1955 to 1959.

	$3,000	$2,650	$2,230	$1,900	$1,680	$1,240	$1,060

In 1959, double round cutaway body replaced original item, Cherry finish became available.

LES PAUL SPECIAL (SG BODY STYLE) — double cutaway mahogany body, black pickguard, mahogany neck, 22 fret rosewood fingerboard with pearl dot inlay, tunomatic bridge/stop tailpiece, silkscreened model name on peghead, 3 per side tuners with plastic buttons, nickel hardware, single coil pickup, volume/tone control. Available in Cherry finish. Mfg. 1961 to 1963.

	$1,350	$1,175	$950	$800	$725	$650	$575

Add $1,000 for TV finish.

In 1962, Maestro vibrato became optionally available.

In 1963, renamed SG Special. See SG Series later in text.

Les Paul Special ¾ — similar to Les Paul Special, except has a ¾ size body, shorter neck. Available in Cherry Red finish. Mfg. 1959 to 1961.

	$1,250	$950	$825	$750	$675	$600	$525

1955 Gibson TV Junior
courtesy Vallis Kolbeck

G

Grading		100%	98% MINT	95% EXC+	90% EXC	80% VG+	70% VG	60% G

Les Paul Special Reissue — similar to Les Paul Special, except has tunomatic bridge/stop tailpiece, stacked humbucker pickups. Available in Ebony, Heritage Cherry, Tobacco Sunburst and TV Yellow finishes. Mfg. 1989 to date.

Mfr.'s Sug. Retail	$1,239	$1,053	$867	$775	$680	$545	$500	$485

The Les Paul Special is also offered in a double cutaway body style. Current retail is $1,339.

Low-Impedance Les Paul Series

LES PAUL PERSONAL — single cutaway multi-bound mahogany body, carved top, raised bound pickguard, mahogany neck, 22 fret bound ebony fingerboard with pearl block inlay, tunomatic bridge/stop tailpiece, multi-bound blackface peghead with pearl diamond/logo inlay, 3 per side tuners with plastic buttons, gold hardware, 2 low impedance pickups, mic volume control on upper bass bout, volume/decade/treble/bass controls, two 3 position switches, phase slide switch. Available in Walnut finish. Mfg. 1969 to 1971.

	$1,250	$1,070	$895	$715	$645	$590	$535

This instrument had a Bigsby vibrato optionally available.

LES PAUL PROFESSIONAL — single cutaway bound mahogany body, raised black pickguard, mahogany neck, 22 fret rosewood fingerboard with pearl trapezoid inlay, tunomatic bridge/stop tailpiece, blackface peghead with pearl logo inlay, 3 per side tuners, nickel hardware, 2 low impedance pickups, volume/decade/treble/bass controls, two 3 position switches, phase slide switch. Available in Walnut finish. Mfg. 1969 to 1971.

	$900	$770	$640	$515	$465	$425	$385

This instrument had Bigsby vibrato optionally available.

LES PAUL RECORDING — single cutaway bound mahogany body, carved top, raised multi-layer pickguard, mahogany neck, 22 fret bound rosewood fingerboard with pearl block inlay, tunomatic bridge/stop tailpiece, multi-bound peghead with pearl split diamond/logo inlay, 2 covered low impedance pickups, "Gibson" formed on pickup covers, volume/decade/treble/bass controls, two 3 position switches, impedance/phase slide switches, built-in transformer. Available in Walnut finish. Mfg. 1971 to 1980.

	$750	$640	$535	$430	$390	$355	$325

In 1975, White finish became optionally available.

In 1978, Ebony and Cherry Sunburst finishes became optionally available.

LES PAUL SIGNATURE — offset double cutaway, arched maple top, raised cream pickguard, f-holes, maple back/sides, mahogany neck, 22 fret bound rosewood fingerboard with pearl trapezoid inlay, tunomatic bridge/stop tailpiece, blackface peghead with pearl logo inlay, 3 per side tuners with plastic buttons, chrome hardware, 2 low impedance humbucker pickups, plastic pickup covers with stamped logo, volume/tone control, 3 position/phase/level switches. Available in Gold Top and Sunburst finishes. Mfg. 1973 to 1978.

	$950	$815	$675	$540	$490	$450	$405

This model has walnut back/sides with Gold Top finish.

After 1976, high and low impedance humbuckers became available.

The Paul Series

THE PAUL STANDARD — single sharp cutaway walnut body/neck, 22 fret ebony fingerboard with pearl dot inlay, tunomatic bridge/stop tailpiece, 3 per side tuners, chrome hardware, 2 exposed humbucker pickups, 2 volume/2 tone controls, 3 position switch. Available in Natural finish. Mfg. 1978 to 1982.

	$425	$365	$305	$240	$220	$200	$180

In 1980, this guitar was renamed Firebrand, with the Firebrand logo burned into the peghead.

The Paul Deluxe — similar to original The Paul Standard, except has mahogany body/neck. Available in Antique Natural, Ebony, Natural and Wine Red finishes. Mfg. 1980 to 1986.

	$450	$385	$325	$260	$230	$215	$195

In 1985, Ebony and Wine Red finishes replaced original items.

M Series

M III DELUXE — offset double cutaway poplar/maple/walnut body, tortoise pickguard with engraved "M III" logo, maple neck, 24 fret maple fingerboard with wood arrow inlay, double locking Floyd Rose vibrato, reverse blackface peghead with screened logo, 6 on one side tuners, black chrome hardware, exposed humbucker/single coil/humbucker pickups, volume/tone control, 5 position/tone selector switches. Available in Antique Natural finish. Disc. 1994.

	$910	$780	$650	$520	$470	$430	$390

Last Mfr.'s Sug. Retail was $1,300.

M III Standard — similar to M III Deluxe, except has solid poplar body. Available in Alpine White, Candy Apple Red and Ebony finishes. Curr. mfr.

Mfr.'s Sug. Retail	$1,080	$810	$540	$500	$400	$360	$330	$300

Add $55 for Translucent Amber and Translucent Red finishes, no pickguard.

In 1994, Alpine White and Candy Apple Red finishes were discontinued.

M IV S DELUXE — offset double cutaway black limba body, maple neck, 24 fret ebony fingerboard with pearl arrow inlay, Steinberger vibrato, reverse blackface peghead with screened logo, 6 on one side Steinberger locking tuners, black chrome hardware, exposed humbucker/single coil/humbucker pickups, volume/tone control, 5 position/tone selector switches. Available in Natural finish. New 1994.

Mfr.'s Sug. Retail	$2,375	$1,781	$1,187	$1,185	$950	$850	$780	$710

Grading	100%	98% MINT	95% EXC+	90% EXC	80% VG+	70% VG	60% G

M IV S Standard — similar to M IV S Deluxe, except has poplar body, pearl dot fingerboard inlay. Available in Ebony finish. New 1994.

Mfr.'s Sug. Retail	$2,100	$1,680	$1,260	$1,050	$840	$755	$690	$630

MAP — United States shaped mahogany body, 3 piece maple neck, 22 fret bound rosewood fingerboard with pearl dot inlay, tunomatic bridge/stop tailpiece, blackface peghead with pearl logo inlay, chrome hardware, 2 covered humbucker pickups, 2 volume/2 tone controls, 3 position switch. Available in Natural finish. Mfg. 1983 only.

	$1,250	$800	$700	$500	$400	$360	$330

MARAUDER — single cutaway alder body, white pickguard, bolt-on maple neck, 22 fret rosewood fingerboard with pearl dot inlay, tunomatic bridge/stop tailpiece, 3 per side tuners, chrome hardware, humbucker/single coil pickups, volume/tone control, rotary switch. Available in Black and Natural finishes. Mfg. 1975 to 1980.

	$400	$340	$285	$230	$205	$190	$170

Black pickguards were also available on this instrument.

In 1978, maple fingerboard replaced original item.

Marauder Custom — similar to Marauder, except has bound fingerboard with block inlay, 3 position switch, no rotary switch. Available in Sunburst finish. Mfg. 1976 to 1977.

	$450	$385	$325	$260	$230	$215	$195

Melody Maker Series

All notes on original Melody Maker apply to all instruments in this section, unless otherwise noted.

MELODY MAKER — single cutaway mahogany body, black pickguard with model name stamp, mahogany neck, 22 fret rosewood fingerboard with pearl dot inlay, wrapover stop tailpiece, 3 per side tuners with plastic buttons, nickel hardware, covered single coil pickup, volume/tone control. Available in Sunburst finish. Mfg. 1959 to 1971.

	100%	98%	95%	90%	80%	70%	60%
1959-1960	$750	$625	$550	$400	$325	$275	$245
1961-1965	$500	$430	$360	$285	$260	$235	$215
1966-1969	$450	$385	$325	$260	$230	$215	$195
1970-1971	$400	$340	$285	$230	$205	$190	$170

In 1960, redesigned narrower pickup replaced original item.

In 1961, double round cutaway body replaced original item.

In 1962, Maestro vibrato became optionally available.

In 1963, Cherry finish became available.

In 1966, double sharp cutaway body, white pickguard, vibrato tailpiece, Fire Engine Red and Pelham Blue finishes replaced respective items.

In 1967, Sparkling Burgundy finish became optionally available.

In 1970, only Walnut finish was available.

Melody Maker ¾ — similar to Melody Maker, except has ¾ size body. Available in Golden Sunburst finish. Mfg. 1959 to 1970.

1959-1960	$525	$460	$410	$380	$345	$300	$240
1961-1970	$400	$340	$285	$230	$205	$190	$170

Melody Maker-D — similar to Melody Maker, except has 2 mini humbucker pickups. Available in Golden Sunburst finish. Mfg. 1960 to 1971.

1960	$900	$800	$725	$635	$575	$500	$425
1961-1965	$600	$515	$450	$375	$300	$275	$225
1966-1969	$450	$375	$300	$250	$200	$175	$150
1970-1971	$425	$365	$305	$240	$220	$200	$180

Melody Maker III — similar to Melody Maker, except has 3 pickups. Available in Pelham Blue and Sparkling Burgundy finishes. Mfg. 1968 to 1971.

	$525	$450	$375	$300	$270	$245	$225

Melody Maker-12 — similar to original Melody Maker, except has twelve strings, 6 per side tuners, 2 mini humbuckers. Mfg. 1967 to 1971.

	$650	$525	$450	$375	$300	$250	$200

Add $250 for Pelham Blue and Sparkling Burgundy finishes.

In 1970, Pelham Blue and Sparkling Burgundy finishes only.

MELODY MAKER, CURR. MFR. — single cutaway mahogany body, black pickguard, mahogany neck, 22 fret rosewood fingerboard with pearl dot inlay, tunomatic bridge/stop tailpiece, 3 per side tuners with pearloid buttons, chrome hardware, covered humbucker pickup, volume/tone control. Available in Alpine White, Ebony and Frost Blue finishes. Curr. mfr.

Mfr.'s Sug. Retail	$750	$600	$450	$375	$300	$270	$245	$225

Gibson Moderne Reissue
1996 Tampa Vintage Show

Grading	100%	98%	95%	90%	80%	70%	60%
		MINT	EXC+	EXC	VG+	VG	G

'95 Gibson Nighthawk
courtesy Thoroughbred Music

Gibson SG
courtesy Garrie Johnson

MODERNE — originally designed as one of three Gibson modernistic concept guitars (with the Explorer and Flying V), this instrument was blue-printed in 1958. A debate still rages over whether or not they were actually built, as a 1958 Moderne has not yet been seen. There is some vague mention on a shipping list (that could also apply to the Explorer model). Tom Wheeler, in his book **American Guitars**, suggests that some were built - and when the music retailers responded in a negative way, Gibson sold some at a cut rate price to employees and destroyed others. Ted McCarty, who was president of Gibson at the time (and part designer of the three models), has guessed that a handful were built as prototypes.

It's hard to hang a price tag on something that hasn't been seen. Until one actually shows up, and can be authenticated by experts (materials, construction techniques, parts) can there be an intelligent conversation about a price.

MODERNE HERITAGE — single cutaway sharkfin style korina body, black pickguard, korina neck, 22 fret rosewood fingerboard with pearl dot inlay, tunomatic bridge/stop tailpiece, tulip blackface peghead with pearl logo inlay, inked serial number on peghead, 3 per side tuners with plastic single ring buttons, gold hardware, 2 humbucker pickups, 2 volume/1 tone controls, 3 position switch. Available in Natural finish. Mfg. 1982 only.

| | $1,500 | $1,285 | $1,070 | $860 | $770 | $710 | $645 |

This is a reissue of a 1958 Moderne from the blueprint. An actual specimen has not yet been seen.

Nighthawk Series

NIGHTHAWK CST — single cutaway mahogany body, bound figured maple top, mahogany neck, 22 fret bound ebony fingerboard with pearl crown inlay, strings thru bridge, bound blackface peghead with pearl plant/logo inlay, 3 per side tuners with pearl buttons, gold hardware, 2 humbucker pickups, volume/push-pull tone controls, 5 position switch. Available in Antique Natural, Dark Wineburst, Fireburst, Translucent Red and Vintage Sunburst finishes. Curr. mfr.

| Mfr.'s Sug. Retail | $1,770 | $1,327 | $885 | $810 | $600 | $540 | $495 | $450 |

In 1994, Translucent Amber finish was introduced, Dark Wineburst, Translucent Red and Vintage Sunburst finishes were discontinued.

Nighthawk CST 3 — similar to Nighthawk CST, except has humbucker/single coil/humbucker pickups. Curr. mfr.

| Mfr.'s Sug. Retail | $1,880 | $1,410 | $940 | $865 | $640 | $575 | $530 | $480 |

Nighthawk CST 3 FG — similar to Nighthawk CST, except has double locking Floyd Rose vibrato, humbucker/single coil/humbucker pickups. New 1994.

| Mfr.'s Sug. Retail | $2,025 | $1,620 | $1,215 | $1,015 | $810 | $730 | $670 | $610 |

NIGHTHAWK SP — single cutaway mahogany body, bound maple top, mahogany neck, 22 fret rosewood fingerboard with pearl dot inlay, strings thru bridge, blackface peghead with pearl logo inlay, 3 per side tuners, gold hardware, 2 humbucker pickups, volume/push-pull tone controls, 5 position switch. Available in Ebony, Heritage Cherry and Vintage Sunburst finishes. Curr. mfr.

| Mfr.'s Sug. Retail | $925 | $693 | $462 | $400 | $320 | $290 | $265 | $240 |

Nighthawk SP 3 — similar to Nighthawk SP, except has humbucker/single coil/humbucker pickups. Curr. mfr.

| Mfr.'s Sug. Retail | $1,025 | $768 | $512 | $450 | $360 | $325 | $300 | $275 |

NIGHTHAWK ST — single cutaway mahogany body, bound figured maple top, mahogany neck, 22 fret bound rosewood fingerboard with pearl parallelogram inlay, strings thru bridge, bound blackface peghead with pearl plant/logo inlay, 3 per side tuners with pearl buttons, gold hardware, 2 humbucker pickups, volume/push-pull tone controls, 5 position switch. Available in Fireburst, Translucent Amber, Translucent Red and Vintage Sunburst finishes. Curr mfr.

| Mfr.'s Sug. Retail | $1,250 | $937 | $625 | $550 | $440 | $395 | $365 | $330 |

In 1994, Translucent Red finish was discontinued.

Nighthawk ST 3 — similar to Nighthawk ST, except has humbucker/single coil/humbucker pickups. Curr. mfr.

| Mfr.'s Sug. Retail | $1,350 | $1,012 | $675 | $600 | $480 | $430 | $395 | $360 |

Nighthawk ST 3 FG — similar to Nighthawk ST, except has double locking Floyd Rose vibrato, humbucker/single coil/humbucker pickups. New 1994.

| Mfr.'s Sug. Retail | $1,600 | $1,280 | $960 | $800 | $640 | $575 | $530 | $480 |

RD Series

RD STANDARD — single cutaway asymmetrical hourglass style maple body, black pickguard, maple neck, 22 fret rosewood fingerboard with pearl dot inlay, tunomatic bridge/stop tailpiece, blackface peghead with logo decal, 3 per side tuners, nickel hardware, 2 covered humbucker pickups, 2 volume/2 tone controls, 3 position switch. Available in Cherry Sunburst, Ebony, Natural and Tobacco Sunburst finishes. Mfg. 1977 to 1979.

| | $500 | $430 | $360 | $285 | $260 | $235 | $215 |

RD Artist — similar to RD Standard, except has an ebony fingerboard with block inlay, multi bound peghead with pearl stylized f-hole/logo inlay, gold hardware, mini switch, active electronics.

| | $750 | $640 | $535 | $430 | $390 | $355 | $325 |

In 1978, tunable stop tailpiece replaced original item.

RD Custom — similar to RD Standard, except has maple fingerboard, active electronics, mini switch.

| | $600 | $515 | $430 | $345 | $310 | $285 | $260 |

Grading	100%	98% MINT	95% EXC+	90% EXC	80% VG+	70% VG	60% G

S-1 — single cutaway ash body, black tri-lam pickguard, bolt-on maple neck, 22 fret rosewood fingerboard with pearl dot inlay, tunomatic bridge/stop tailpiece, 3 per side tuners, chrome hardware, 3 single coil bar pickups, volume/tone control, 3 position/rotary switches. Available in Blonde finish. Mfg. 1976 to 1980.

	$400	$340	$285	$230	$205	$190	$170

SG Series

In 1961, these instruments were originally intended to bring a new style to the Les Paul line, but without Les Paul's approval they were renamed the "SG", in 1963. The first two years of instruments in this series have "Les Paul" logos on their pegheads or the area below the fingerboard.

SG STANDARD — double sharp cutaway mahogany body, layered black pickguard, one piece mahogany neck, 22 fret bound rosewood fingerboard with pearl trapezoid inlay, tunomatic bridge/side-pull vibrato, blackface peghead with pearl logo inlay, 3 per side tuners, nickel hardware, 2 covered humbucker pickups, 2 volume/2 tone controls, 3 position switch. Available in Cherry finish. Mfg. 1963 to 1971.

1963-1965	$2,025	$1,740	$1,450	$1,160	$1,040	$955	$870
1966-1971	$1,200	$1,030	$860	$685	$615	$565	$515

In 1963, some models were produced with ebony tailblock with pearl inlay.

SG Standard Reissue I — similar to SG Standard, except has pearl block fingerboard inlay, stop tailpiece, pearl crown peghead inlay, chrome hardware. Available in Cherry finish. Mfg. 1972 to 1981.

	$575	$490	$410	$325	$295	$270	$245

In 1976, Bigsby vibrato became standard, stop tailpiece optionally available, Cherry, Tobacco Sunburst and White finishes became available.

In 1977, stop tailpiece became standard, Bigsby vibrato became optionally available.

SG Standard Reissue II — same as SG Standard Reissue I. Available in Cherry and Sunburst finishes. Mfg. 1983 to 1987.

	$525	$450	$375	$300	$270	$245	$225

SG Standard Reissue III — similar to SG Standard Reissue I, except has trapezoid fingerboard inlay. Available in Ebony and Wine Red finishes. Mfg. 1989 to 1990.

	$500	$430	$360	$285	$260	$235	$215

SG STANDARD (CURRENT MANUFACTURE) — double cutaway mahogany body, layered black pickguard, mahogany neck, 22 fret bound rosewood fingerboard with pearl trapezoid inlay, tunomatic bridge/stop tailpiece, blackface peghead with pearl crown/logo inlay, 3 per side tuners with plastic buttons, chrome hardware, 2 covered humbucker pickups, 2 volume/2 tone controls, 3 position switch. Available in Candy Apple Blue, Candy Apple Red, Ebony, Heritage Cherry and TV Yellow finishes. Curr. mfr.

Mfr.'s Sug. Retail	$1,200	$900	$600	$525	$420	$380	$345	$315

In 1994, Candy Apple Blue, Candy Apple Red and TV Yellow finishes were discontinued.

SG Deluxe — double cutaway mahogany body, raised layered black pickguard, mahogany neck, 22 fret bound rosewood fingerboard with pearl block inlay, tunomatic bridge/Bigsby vibrato tailpiece, blackface peghead with pearl crown/logo inlay, 3 per side tuners, chrome hardware, 2 covered humbucker pickups, 2 volume/2 tone controls mounted on layered black plate, 3 position switch. Available in Cherry, Natural and Walnut finishes. Mfg. 1971 to 1974.

	$450	$385	$325	$260	$230	$215	$195

THE SG (STANDARD) — double cutaway walnut body, layered black pickguard, walnut neck, 22 fret ebony fingerboard with pearl dot inlay, tunomatic bridge/stop tailpiece, blackface peghead with pearl crown/logo inlay, 3 per side tuners, chrome hardware, 2 covered humbucker pickups, 2 volume/2 tone controls, 3 position switch. Available in Natural finish. Mfg. 1979 to 1981.

	$450	$385	$325	$260	$230	$215	$195

In 1980, renamed "Firebrand" with new name burned into top.

The SG (Deluxe) — similar to The SG (Standard), except has mahogany body/neck. Available in Antique Mahogany, Ebony, Natural and Wine Red finishes. Mfg. 1979 to 1985.

	$450	$385	$325	$260	$230	$215	$195

In 1980, renamed "Firebrand" with new name burned into top.

SG Exclusive — similar to the the SG (Standard), except has mahogany body, black finish, cream binding on neck, cream pickguard, cream pickup covers, gold knobs, quail tap switch, TP-6 stop tailpiece, and truss rod cover that reads "Exclusive". Mfd. 1979 only.

Model has not traded sufficiently to quote pricing.

SG CUSTOM — double sharp cutaway mahogany body, white layered pickguard, mahogany neck, 22 fret bound ebony fingerboard with pearl block inlay, tunomatic bridge/side-pull vibrato, multi-bound peghead with pearl split diamond inlay, 3 per side tuners, gold hardware, 3 covered humbucker pickups, 2 volume/2 tone controls, 3 position switch. Available in Black, Cherry, Tobacco Sunburst, Walnut, White and Wine Red finishes. Mfg. 1963 to 1980.

1963-1966	$1,750	$1,500	$1,250	$1,000	$900	$825	$750
1967-1972	$1,250	$1,070	$895	$715	$645	$590	$535
1973-1975	$1,000	$855	$715	$570	$510	$465	$425
1976-1980	$800	$685	$575	$460	$410	$380	$345

In 1963, Maestro vibrato replaced original item.

In 1972, stop tailpiece replaced respective item.

In 1976, Bigsby vibrato replaced respective item.

1972 Gibson SG Deluxe
courtesy David West

G

Gibson SG
courtesy Thoroughbred Music

Grading	100%	98% MINT	95% EXC+	90% EXC	80% VG+	70% VG	60% G

SG SPECIAL — double sharp cutaway mahogany body, black pickguard, maple neck, 22 fret rosewood fingerboard with pearl dot inlay, tunomatic bridge/stop tailpiece, blackface peghead with pearl logo inlay, 3 per side tuners, chrome hardware, 2 covered humbucker pickups, 2 volume/2 tone controls, 3 position switch. Available in Alpine White, Ebony, Ferrari Red and TV Yellow finishes. Curr. mfr.

	100%	98%	95%	90%	80%	70%	60%
Mfr.'s Sug. Retail	$825	$618	$412	$375	$300	$270	$245	$225

In 1994, TV Yellow finish was discontinued.

'62 SG REISSUE — double cutaway mahogany body, layered black pickguard, mahogany neck, 22 fret bound rosewood fingerboard with pearl trapezoid inlay, tunomatic bridge/stop tailpiece, blackface peghead with pearl plant/logo inlay, 3 per side tuner with pearl buttons, nickel hardware, 2 covered humbucker pickups, 2 volume/2 tone controls, 3 position switch. Available in Heritage Cherry finish. Mfg. 1986 to date.

	100%	98%	95%	90%	80%	70%	60%
Mfr.'s Sug. Retail	$1,775	$1,331	$887	$800	$640	$575	$530	$480

SG-100 — double cutaway mahogany body, black pickguard, mahogany neck, 22 fret rosewood fingerboard with dot inlay, tunable stop tailpiece, 3 per side tuners, nickel hardware, single coil pickup, volume/tone control. Available in Cherry and Walnut finishes. Mfg. 1971 to 1972.

		$250	$215	$180	$145	$130	$120	$110

SG-200 — similar to SG-100, except has 2 single coil pickups, slide switch.

		$275	$235	$195	$155	$140	$125	$115

SG-250 — similar to SG-100, except has 2 single coil pickups, 2 slide switches. Available in Cherry Sunburst finish.

		$300	$260	$215	$175	$155	$140	$130

SG I — double cutaway mahogany body, black pickguard, mahogany neck, 22 fret rosewood fingerboard with dot inlay, tunable stop tailpiece, 3 per side tuners, nickel hardware, single coil pickup, volume/tone control. Available in Cherry and Walnut finishes. Mfg. 1972 to 1979.

		$250	$215	$180	$145	$130	$120	$110

SG II — similar to SG I, except has 2 single coil pickups, slide switch.

		$275	$235	$195	$155	$140	$125	$115

SG III — similar to SG I, except has 2 single coil pickups, 2 slide switches. Available in Cherry Sunburst finish.

		$300	$260	$215	$175	$155	$140	$130

SG JUNIOR — double cutaway mahogany body, black pickguard, mahogany neck, 22 fret rosewood fingerboard with pearl dot inlay, tunomatic bridge/stop tailpiece, 3 per side tuners with plastic buttons, nickel hardware, single coil pickup, volume/tone control. Available in Cherry finish. Mfg. 1963 to 1971.

	100%	98%	95%	90%	80%	70%	60%
1963-1965	$750	$675	$550	$475	$405	$340	$270
1966-1971	$600	$525	$400	$340	$285	$230	$205

This model had optionally available vibrato.

In 1965, vibrato became standard.

SG TV — double round cutaway mahogany body, black pickguard, mahogany neck, 22 fret rosewood fingerboard with pearl dot inlay, tunomatic bridge/stop tailpiece, 3 per side tuners with plastic buttons, nickel hardware, single coil pickup, volume/tone control. Available in Lime Mahogany and White finishes. Mfg. 1963 to 1968.

		$1,000	$880	$740	$650	$555	$465	$370

SG SPECIAL — double cutaway mahogany body, layered black pickguard, mahogany neck, 22 fret rosewood fingerboard with pearl dot inlay, stop tailpiece, blackface peghead with pearl logo inlay, 3 per side tuners with plastic buttons, nickel hardware, 2 single coil pickups, 2 volume/2 tone control, 3 position switch. Available in Cherry and White finishes. Mfg. 1963 to 1971.

	100%	98%	95%	90%	80%	70%	60%
1963-1965	$1,400	$1,250	$1,000	$900	$800	$685	$575
1966-1971	$800	$665	$575	$490	$410	$325	$295

Add $200 for a 1963-1965 manufacture in a white finish.

This model had optionally available vibrato.

In 1965, vibrato became standard.

SG Special 3/4 — similar to SG Special, except has 3/4 size body, 19 fret fingerboard. Available in Cherry Red finish. Mfg. 1959 to 1961.

		$650	$555	$465	$370	$335	$305	$280

SG Professional — similar to SG Special, except has a pearl logo, 2 black soap bar P-90 pickups. Available in Cherry, Natural and Walnut finishes. Mfg. 1971 to 1974.

		$475	$405	$340	$270	$245	$225	$205

SG Studio — similar to SG Special, except has no pickguard, 2 humbucker pickups, 2 volume/1 tone controls. Available in Natural finish. Mfg. 1978 only.

		$450	$385	$325	$260	$230	$215	$195

SG '90 SINGLE — double sharp cutaway mahogany body, pearloid pickguard, maple neck, 24 fret bound ebony fingerboard with pearl split diamond inlay, strings thru anchoring, blackface peghead with pearl crown/logo inlay, 3 per side tuners, black chrome hardware, humbucker pickups, volume/tone control, 3 position switch. Available in Alpine White, Heritage Cherry and Metallic Turquoise finishes. Mfg. 1989 to 1990.

		$725	$620	$520	$415	$375	$340	$310

This model had double locking vibrato optionally available.

'94 Gibson Lucille
courtesy Tracy Cooley

Gibson Sonex-180 Deluxe
courtesy Michelle Oleck

G

Grading	100%	98% MINT	95% EXC+	90% EXC	80% VG+	70% VG	60% G

SG '90 Double — similar to SG '90 Single, except has single coil/humbucker pickups. Mfg. 1989 to 1992.

| | $675 | $580 | $485 | $385 | $350 | $320 | $290 |

SONEX-180 CUSTOM — single cutaway composite body, black pickguard, bolt-on maple neck, 22 fret ebony fingerboard with dot inlay, tunomatic bridge/stop tailpiece, blackface peghead with decal logo, 3 per side tuners, chrome hardware, 2 exposed humbucker pickups, 2 volume/2 tone controls, 3 position switch. Available in Ebony and White finishes. Mfg. 1981 to 1982.

| | $325 | $280 | $235 | $190 | $170 | $155 | $140 |

Sonex-180 Deluxe — similar to Sonex-180 Custom, except has 2 ply pickguard, rosewood fingerboard. Available in Ebony finish. Mfg. 1981 to 1984.

| | $325 | $280 | $235 | $190 | $170 | $155 | $140 |

In 1982, a left handed version of this instrument became available.

Sonex Artist — similar to Sonex-180 Custom, except has rosewood fingerboard, tunable stop tailpiece, 3 mini switches, active electronics. Available in Candy Apple Red and Ivory finishes. Mfg. 1981 to 1984.

| | $375 | $320 | $270 | $215 | $195 | $180 | $160 |

SPIRIT I — double cutaway mahogany body, bound figured maple top, tortoise shell pickguard, mahogany neck, 2 fret rosewood fingerboard with pearl dot inlay, tunable wrapover bridge, blackface peghead with logo decal, 3 per side tuners with plastic buttons, chrome hardware, 1 exposed humbucker pickup, volume/tone control. Available in Natural, Red and Sunburst finishes. Mfg. 1982 to 1988.

| | $300 | $260 | $215 | $175 | $155 | $140 | $130 |

In 1983, 6 per side tuner peghead replaced original item, figured maple top was removed.

SPIRIT II — similar to Spirit I, except has no pickguard, 2 exposed humbuckers pickups, 2 volume/1 tone controls.

| | $325 | $280 | $235 | $190 | $170 | $155 | $140 |

Spirit II XPL — similar to Spirit I, except has bound fingerboard, Kahler vibrato, 6 on one side tuners, 2 exposed humbuckers pickups, 2 volume/1 tone controls. Mfg. 1985 to 1987.

| | $450 | $385 | $325 | $260 | $230 | $215 | $195 |

SR-71 — offset double cutaway, 2 single coil/1 humbucker pickups. Mfg. 1989 only.

| | $600 | $515 | $430 | $345 | $310 | $285 | $260 |

SUPER 400 CES — single round cutaway grand auditorium style body, arched spruce top, bound f-holes, raised multi-bound mottled plastic pickguard, figured maple back/sides, multiple bound body, 3 piece figured maple/mahogany neck, model name engraved into heel cap, 14/20 fret bound ebony fingerboard with point on bottom, pearl split block fingerboard inlay, adjustable rosewood bridge with pearl triangle wings inlay, gold trapeze tailpiece with engraved model name, multi-bound blackface peghead with pearl split diamond/logo inlay, pearl split diamond inlay on back of peghead, 3 per side tuners, gold hardware, 2 single coil pickups, 2 volume/2 tone controls, 3 position switch. Available in Ebony, Natural, Sunburst and Wine Red finishes. Mfg. 1951 to 1994.

1951-1954	$13,000	$11,140	$9,285	$7,430	$6,685	$6,130	$5,570
1955-1959	$12,500	$10,715	$8,930	$7,145	$6,430	$5,895	$5,360
1960-1969	$10,625	$9,110	$7,590	$6,070	$5,465	$5,010	$4,555
1970-1974	$5,500	$3,850	$3,300	$2,750	$2,200	$1,980	$1,815
1975-1985	$5,000	$4,285	$3,570	$2,860	$2,570	$2,360	$2,145
1986-1994	$3,500	$3,000	$2,500	$2,000	$1,800	$1,650	$1,500

Last Mfr.'s Sug. Retail was $5,000.

Current production instruments are part of the Historic Collection Series, found at the end of this section.

In 1957, humbucker pickups replaced original item.

In 1960, sharp cutaway replaced original item.

In 1962, Pat. No. humbucker pickups replaced respective item.

In 1969, round cutaway replaced respective item.

In 1974, neck volute was introduced.

In 1981, neck volute was discontinued.

Super 400 CES models with PAF pickups (1957-1962) have sold for as high as $15,000. Instruments should be determined on a piece-by-piece basis as opposed to the usual market.

U-2 — offset double cutaway basswood body, maple neck, rosewood fingerboard, Kahler vibrato, 6 on one side tuners, black hardware, 2 single coil/1 humbucker pickups. Mfg. 1987 to date.

| Mfr.'s Sug. Retail | $949 | $759 | $569 | $475 | $380 | $345 | $315 | $285 |

US-1 — offset double cutaway basswood body, bound maple top/back, balsa wood core, ebony fingerboard, 6 on one side tuners, 1 humbucker/2 stacked coil humbuckers. Available in Natural top finish. Mfg. 1987 to date.

| Mfr.'s Sug. Retail | $1,575 | $1,181 | $787 | $785 | $630 | $565 | $515 | $470 |

VICTORY MV-2 — offset double cutaway, rosewood fingerboard, 6 on one side tuners, 2 humbuckers. Available in Antique Sunburst or Candy Apple Red finishes. Mfg. 1981 to 1984.

| | $325 | $280 | $235 | $190 | $170 | $155 | $140 |

Restored 1961 Gibson Super 400 courtesy Harry Harris

G

Gibson Barney Kessel courtesy Tam Milano

Grading	100%	98% MINT	95% EXC+	90% EXC	80% VG+	70% VG	60% G

Victory MV-10 — similar to Victory MV-2, except has an ebony fingerboard, stacked coil pickup, coil tap switch. Available in Apple Red and Twilight Blue finishes.

	$450	$385	$325	$260	$230	$215	$195

Professional Series

B.B. KING STANDARD — double round cutaway semi hollow bound body, arched maple top, raised layered black pickguard, maple back/sides/neck, 22 fret bound rosewood fingerboard with pearl dot inlay, tunomatic bridge/tunable stop tailpiece, blackface peghead with pearl "Lucille"/logo inlay, 3 per side tuners, chrome hardware, 2 covered humbucker pickups, 2 volume/2 tone controls, 3 position switch, stereo output. Available in Cherry and Ebony finishes. Mfg. 1980 to 1985.

	$1,200	$1,030	$860	$685	$615	$565	$515

B.B. King Lucille — similar to B.B. King Standard, except has bound pickguard, bound ebony fingerboard with pearl block inlay, bound peghead, gold hardware, Vari-tone switch. Available in Cherry and Ebony finishes. Mfg. 1980 to date.

Mfr.'s Sug. Retail	$2,756	$2,067	$1,378	$1,230	$1,005	$810	$635	$555

From 1980 to 1988, this model was named the B.B. King Custom.

BARNEY KESSEL REGULAR — double sharp cutaway semi hollow bound body, arched maple top, bound f-holes, raised layered black pickguard, maple back/sides, mahogany neck, 22 fret bound rosewood fingerboard with pearl block inlay, adjustable rosewood bridge/trapeze tailpiece, wood tailpiece insert with pearl model name inlay, bound blackface peghead with pearl crown/logo inlay, 3 per side tuners, nickel hardware, 2 covered humbucker pickups, 2 volume/2 tone controls, 3 position switch. Available in Cherry Sunburst finish. Mfg. 1961 to 1974.

	$2,250	$1,930	$1,605	$1,285	$1,155	$1,060	$965

Barney Kessel Custom — similar to Barney Kessel Regular, except has bowtie fingerboard inlay, musical note peghead inlay, gold hardware.

	$2,500	$2,140	$1,785	$1,430	$1,285	$1,180	$1,070

CHET ATKINS COUNTRY GENTLEMAN — single round cutaway semi hollow bound maple body, bound f-holes, raised bound tortoise pickguard, bound arm rest on bottom bass bout, 3 piece maple neck, 22 fret rosewood fingerboard with offset red block inlay, tunomatic bridge/Bigsby vibrato tailpiece, blackface peghead with pearl plant/logo inlay, 3 per side tuners, gold hardware, 2 covered humbucker pickups, master volume on upper treble bout, 2 volume/1 tone controls, 3 position switch. Available in Country Gentleman Brown, Ebony, Sunrise Orange and Wine Red finishes. Mfg. 1987 to date.

Mfr.'s Sug. Retail	$4,339	$3,471	$2,603	$2,450	$2,025	$1,355	$1,130	$925

In 1994, Ebony finish was discontinued.

ES-165 HERB ELLIS — single sharp cutaway hollow bound maple body, f-holes, raised black pickguard, mahogany neck, 20 fret bound rosewood fingerboard with pearl parallelogram inlay, tunomatic metal/rosewood bridge/trapeze tailpiece, peghead with pearl plant/logo inlay, 3 per side tuners with pearl buttons, gold hardware, 2 covered humbucker pickups, 2 volume/2 tone controls, 3 position switch. Available in Cherry, Ebony and Vintage Sunburst finishes. Curr. mfr.

Mfr.'s Sug. Retail	$2,867	$2,150	$1,433	$1,270	$1,030	$830	$645	$560

In 1994, Cherry and Ebony finishes were discontinued.

HOWARD ROBERTS ARTIST — single sharp cutaway dreadnought style, arched maple top, oval soundhole, raised multi-bound tortoise pickguard, 3 stripe bound body/rosette, maple back/sides/neck, 22 fret bound ebony fingerboard with pearl slot block inlay, adjustable ebony bridge/trapeze tailpiece, wood tailpiece insert with pearl model name inlay, bound peghead with pearl flower/logo inlay, 3 per side tuners, gold hardware, humbucker pickup, volume/treble/mid controls. Available in Natural, Red Wine and Sunburst finishes. Mfg. 1976 to 1981.

	$1,025	$880	$735	$585	$525	$485	$440

In 1979, 2 pickups became optionally available.

Howard Roberts Custom — similar to Howard Roberts Artist, except has rosewood fingerboard, chrome hardware. Available in Cherry, Sunburst and Wine Red finishes. Mfg. 1974 to 1981.

	$1,000	$855	$715	$570	$510	$465	$425

Howard Roberts Fusion III — single sharp cutaway semi hollow bound maple body, f-holes, raised black pickguard, maple neck, 20 fret bound rosewood fingerboard with pearl dot inlay, tunomatic bridge/adjustable tailpiece, peghead with pearl plant/logo inlay, 3 per side tuners, gold hardware, 2 covered humbucker pickups, 2 volume/2 tone controls, 3 position switch. Available in Ebony and Fireburst finishes. Mfg. 1979 to date.

Mfr.'s Sug. Retail	$2,199	$1,649	$1,099	$940	$785	$600	$480	$430

Add $425 for Vintage Sunburst finish.

In 1990, 6 finger tailpiece replaced original item.

In 1994, Cherry and Ebony finishes were discontinued.

JOHNNY SMITH — single round cutaway bound hollow body, carved spruce top, bound f-holes, raised bound tortoise pickguard, figured maple back/sides/neck, 20 fret bound ebony fingerboard with pearl split block inlay, adjustable rosewood bridge/trapeze tailpiece, multi-bound peghead with split diamond/logo inlay, 3 per side tuners, gold hardware, mini humbucker pickup, pickguard mounted volume control. Available in Natural and Sunburst finishes. Mfg. 1961 to 1989.

1961-1968	$6,500	$5,900	$4,750	$4,225	$3,775	$3,100	$2,750
1969-1973	$5,050	$4,500	$4,125	$3,550	$3,125	$2,500	$1,750
1974-1989	$3,025	$2,590	$2,160	$1,730	$1,555	$1,425	$1,295

Add $500 for Blond finish.

Grading	100%	98% MINT	95% EXC+	90% EXC	80% VG+	70% VG	60% G

In 1963, 2 pickup model was introduced.

By 1979, 6 finger tailpiece replaced original item.

TAL FARLOW — single round cutaway bound hollow body, arched figured maple top, bound f-holes, scroll style inlay on cutaway, raised black bound pickguard, maple back/sides/neck, 20 bound rosewood fingerboard with pearl reverse crown inlay, tunomatic bridge/trapeze tailpiece, rosewood tailpiece insert with pearl engraved block inlay, bound peghead with pearl crown/logo inlay, 3 per side tuners, chrome hardware, 2 covered humbucker pickups, 2 volume/2 tone controls, 3 position switch. Available in Brown Sunburst finish. Mfg. 1962 to 1971.

| | $6,000 | $5,140 | $4,285 | $3,430 | $3,085 | $2,830 | $2,570 |

TRINI LOPEZ STANDARD — double round cutaway semi hollow bound body, arched maple top, bound diamond holes, raised layered black pickguard, maple back/sides, mahogany neck, 22 fret bound rosewood fingerboard with pearl split diamond inlay, tunomatic bridge/trapeze tailpiece, ebony tailpiece insert with pearl model name inlay, 6 on one side tuners, chrome hardware, 2 covered humbucker pickups, 2 volume/2 tone controls, 3 position switch. Available in Cherry finish. Mfg. 1964 to 1971.

| | $750 | $640 | $535 | $430 | $390 | $355 | $325 |

Trini Lopez Deluxe — similar to Trini Lopez Standard, except has sharp cutaway, tortoise pickguard, 20 fret ebony fingerboard. Available in Cherry Sunburst finish.

| | $1,025 | $880 | $735 | $585 | $525 | $485 | $440 |

GIBSON HISTORICAL COLLECTION

The instruments in this series are reproductions of Gibson classics. The instruments are manufactured to the exact specifications of their original release and in several cases, use the same tooling when available.

ACOUSTIC

CITATION — single round cutaway hollow multi-bound body, carved spruce top, bound f-holes, raised multi-bound flamed maple pickguard, figured maple back/sides/neck, 20 fret multi-bound pointed fingerboard with pearl cloud inlay, adjustable ebony bridge with pearl fleur-de-lis inlay on wings, gold trapeze tailpiece with engraved model name, multi-bound ebony veneered peghead with abalone fleur-de-lis/logo inlay, abalone fleur-de-lis inlay on back of peghead, 3 per side gold engraved tuners. Available in Faded Cherry Sunburst, Honeyburst and Natural finishes. Curr. mfr.

| Mfr.'s Sug. Retail | $18,000 | $15,840 | $13,860 | $12,860 | $10,290 | $9,255 | $8,485 | $7,715 |

Gibson Historic Reissue Explorer
courtesy Ronn David

1934 L-5CES — multi-bound grand auditorium style body, carved spruce top, layered tortoise pickguard, bound f-holes, maple back/sides/neck, 20 fret bound pointed ebony fingerboard with pearl block inlay, ebony bridge with pearl inlay on wings, model name engraved trapeze tailpiece with chrome insert, multi-bound blackface peghead with pearl flame/logo inlay, 3 per side gold tuners. Available in Cremona Brown Sunburst finish. Curr. mfr.

| Mfr.'s Sug. Retail | $3,800 | $3,344 | $2,926 | $2,715 | $2,170 | $1,955 | $1,790 | $1,630 |

1939 SUPER 400 — grand auditorium style body, arched spruce top, bound f-holes, raised multi-bound mottled plastic pickguard, figured maple back/sides, multiple bound body, 3 piece figured maple/mahogany neck, model name engraved into heel cap, 14/20 fret bound ebony fingerboard with point on bottom, pearl split block fingerboard inlay, adjustable rosewood bridge with pearl triangle wings inlay, gold trapeze tailpiece with engraved model name, multi-bound blackface peghead with pearl 5 piece split diamond/logo inlay, pearl 3 piece split diamond inlay on back of peghead, 3 per side gold Grover Imperial tuners. Available in Natural finish. Curr. mfr.

| Mfr.'s Sug. Retail | $14,000 | $12,320 | $10,780 | $10,000 | $8,000 | $7,200 | $6,600 | $6,000 |

1939 Super 400 — with Cremona Brown Burst finish.

| Mfr.'s Sug. Retail | $13,000 | $11,440 | $10,010 | $9,285 | $7,430 | $6,685 | $6,130 | $5,570 |

1939 SUPER 400 PREMIER — single round cutaway grand auditorium style body, arched spruce top, bound f-holes, raised multi-bound pearloid pickguard, figured maple back/sides, multiple bound body, 3 piece figured maple/mahogany neck, model name engraved into heel cap, 14/20 fret bound ebony fingerboard with point on bottom, pearl split block fingerboard inlay, adjustable rosewood bridge with pearl triangle wings inlay, gold unhinged "PAF" trapeze tailpiece with engraved model name, multi-bound blackface peghead with pearl 5 piece split diamond/logo inlay, pearl 3 piece split diamond inlay on back of peghead, 3 per side gold Grover Imperial tuners. Available in Natural finish. Curr. mfr.

| Mfr.'s Sug. Retail | $14,000 | $12,320 | $10,780 | $10,000 | $8,000 | $7,200 | $6,600 | $6,000 |

1939 Super 400 Premier — with Cremona Brown Burst finish.

| Mfr.'s Sug. Retail | $13,000 | $11,440 | $10,010 | $9,285 | $7,430 | $6,685 | $6,130 | $5,570 |

ELECTRIC

ES-295 — single sharp cutaway hollow bound maple body, f-holes, raised white pickguard with etched flowers, maple neck, 20 fret bound rosewood fingerboard with pearl parallelogram inlay, tunomatic metal/rosewood bridge/Bigsby vibrato tailpiece, blackface peghead with pearl plant/logo inlay, 3 per side tuners with pearl buttons, chrome hardware, 2 covered stacked humbucker pickups, 2 volume/2 tone controls, 3 position switch. Available in Bullion Gold finish. Curr. mfr.

| Mfr.'s Sug. Retail | $2,050 | $1,804 | $1,578 | $1,465 | $1,170 | $1,050 | $965 | $880 |

Gibson Historic Reissue Flying V
courtesy Ronn David

Gibson Historic Reissue Les Paul
courtesy Ronn David

Gibson Super 400-CES
courtesy Scott Chinery

Grading	100%	98% MINT	95% EXC+	90% EXC	80% VG+	70% VG	60% G

1958 KORINA EXPLORER — radical offset hourglass korina body, white pickguard, korina neck, 22 fret rosewood fingerboard with pearl dot inlay, tunomatic bridge/trapeze tailpiece, 6 on one side tuners, gold hardware, 2 humbucker pickups, 2 volume/1 tone controls, 3 position switch. Available in Natural finish. Curr. mfr.

Mfr.'s Sug. Retail	$10,000	$8,800	$7,700	$7,145	$5,715	$5,145	$4,715	$4,285

1958 KORINA FLYING V — V shaped korina body, white pickguard, korina neck, 22 fret rosewood fingerboard with pearl dot inlay, tunomatic bridge/stop tailpiece, 3 per side tuners with plastic buttons, gold hardware, 2 humbucker pickups, 2 volume/1 tone controls, 3 position switch. Available in Natural finish. Curr. mfr.

Mfr.'s Sug. Retail	$10,000	$8,800	$7,700	$7,145	$5,715	$5,145	$4,715	$4,285

LES PAUL CUSTOM BLACK BEAUTY '54 REISSUE — single sharp cutaway multi-bound mahogany body with carved top, raised bound black pickguard, mahogany neck, 22 fret bound ebony fingerboard with pearl block inlay, tunomatic bridge/stop tailpiece, multi-bound peghead with pearl split diamond/logo inlay, 3 per side tuners with plastic buttons, gold hardware, 2 single coil pickups, 2 volume/2 tone controls, 3 position switch. Available in Ebony finish. Curr. mfr.

Mfr.'s Sug. Retail	$2,500	$2,200	$1,925	$1,785	$1,430	$1,285	$1,180	$1,070

LES PAUL CUSTOM BLACK BEAUTY '57 REISSUE — single sharp cutaway multi-bound mahogany body with carved top, raised bound black pickguard, mahogany neck, 22 fret bound ebony fingerboard with pearl block inlay, tunomatic bridge/stop tailpiece, multi-bound peghead with pearl split diamond/logo inlay, 3 per side tuners with plastic buttons, gold hardware, 2 humbucker pickups, 2 volume/2 tone controls, 3 position switch. Available in Ebony finish. Curr. mfr.

Mfr.'s Sug. Retail	$2,475	$2,178	$1,905	$1,770	$1,415	$1,275	$1,165	$1,060

This model also available with 3 humbucker pickups configuration.

LES PAUL '56 GOLD TOP REISSUE — single sharp cutaway solid mahogany body, bound carved maple top, raised cream pickguard, mahogany neck, 22 fret bound rosewood fingerboard with pearl trapezoid inlays, tunomatic bridge/trapeze tailpiece, blackface peghead with pearl logo inlay, 3 per side tuners with plastic buttons, nickel hardware, 2 single coil pickups, 2 volume/2 tone controls, 3 position switch. Available in Antique Gold Top finish. Mfg. 1990 to date.

Mfr.'s Sug. Retail	$2,600	$2,288	$2,002	$1,860	$1,485	$1,335	$1,225	$1,115

LES PAUL '57 GOLD TOP REISSUE — single sharp cutaway solid mahogany body, bound carved maple top, raised cream pickguard, mahogany neck, 22 fret bound rosewood fingerboard with pearl trapezoid inlays, tunomatic bridge/stop tailpiece, blackface peghead with pearl logo inlay, 3 per side tuners with plastic buttons, nickel hardware, 2 humbucker pickups, 2 volume/2 tone controls, 3 position switch. Available in Antique Gold Top finish. Curr. mfr.

Mfr.'s Sug. Retail	$2,700	$2,376	$2,079	$1,930	$1,540	$1,390	$1,270	$1,155

LES PAUL '59 FLAMETOP REISSUE — single sharp cutaway solid mahogany body, bound carved curly maple top, raised cream pickguard, mahogany neck, 22 fret bound rosewood fingerboard with pearl trapezoid inlays, tunomatic bridge/stop tailpiece, blackface peghead with pearl logo inlay, 3 per side tuners with plastic buttons, nickel hardware, 2 humbucker pickups, 2 volume/2 tone controls, 3 position switch. Available in Heritage Darkburst and Heritage Cherry Sunburst finishes. Curr. mfr.

Mfr.'s Sug. Retail	$5,400	$4,752	$4,158	$3,860	$3,085	$2,775	$2,545	$2,315

LES PAUL '60 FLAMETOP REISSUE — single sharp cutaway mahogany body, bound carved flame maple top, raised cream pickguard, mahogany neck, 22 fret rosewood fingerboard with pearl trapezoid inlay, tunomatic bridge/stop tailpiece, blackface peghead with pearl logo inlay, 3 per side tuners with plastic buttons, nickel hardware, 2 covered humbucker pickups, 2 volume/2 tone controls, 3 position switch. Available in Heritage Darkburst and Heritage Cherry Sunburst finishes. Curr. mfr.

Mfr.'s Sug. Retail	$5,400	$4,752	$4,158	$3,860	$3,085	$2,775	$2,545	$2,315

L-4CES — single sharp cutaway bound hollow body, carved spruce top, layered black pickguard, f-holes, mahogany back/sides/neck, 20 fret bound ebony fingerboard with pearl parallelogram inlay, tunomatic bridge on ebony base with pearl inlay on wings, trapeze tailpiece, blackface peghead with pearl crown/logo inlay, 3 per side tuners with plastic buttons, gold hardware, 2 covered humbucker pickups, 2 volume/2 tone controls, 3 position switch. Available in Natural finish. Mfg. 1987 to date.

Mfr.'s Sug. Retail	$3,800	$3,344	$2,926	$2,715	$2,170	$1,955	$1,790	$1,630

L-4CES — with Vintage Sunburst finish.

Mfr.'s Sug. Retail	$2,725	$2,725	$2,335	$1,950	$1,555	$1,395	$1,280	$1,165

L-4CES — with Ebony and Wine Red finishes.

Mfr.'s Sug. Retail	$2,100	$2,100	$1,800	$1,500	$1,200	$1,080	$990	$900

L-5CES — single round cutaway bound hollow body, carved spruce top, layered tortoise pickguard, bound f-holes, maple back/sides/neck, 20 fret bound pointed ebony fingerboard with pearl block inlay, ebony bridge with pearl inlay on wings, model name engraved trapeze tailpiece with chrome insert, multi-bound blackface peghead with pearl flame/logo inlay, 3 per side tuners, gold hardware, 2 covered humbucker pickups, 2 volume/2 tone controls, 3 position switch. Available in Natural finish. Curr. mfr.

Mfr.'s Sug. Retail	$9,500	$9,500	$8,140	$6,785	$5,430	$4,885	$4,480	$4,070

L-5CES — with Vintage Sunburst finish.

Mfr.'s Sug. Retail	$7,625	$6,710	$5,871	$5,445	$4,355	$3,925	$3,595	$3,270

L-5CES — with Ebony and Wine Red finishes.

Mfr.'s Sug. Retail	$5,300	$4,505	$3,710	$3,180	$2,650	$2,120	$1,910	$1,750

Grading	100%	98% MINT	95% EXC+	90% EXC	80% VG+	70% VG	60% G

SG LES PAUL CUSTOM — double sharp cutaway mahogany body, white layered pickguard, mahogany neck, 22 fret bound ebony fingerboard with pearl block inlay, model tunomatic bridge/stop tailpiece, multi-bound peghead with pearl split diamond inlay, 3 per side tuners, gold hardware, 3 covered humbucker pickups, 2 volume/2 tone controls, 3 position switch. Available in Classic White finish. Curr. mfr.

Mfr.'s Sug. Retail	$1,800	$1,584	$1,386	$1,285	$1,025	$925	$845	$770

TAL FARLOW — single round cutaway bound hollow body, arched figured maple top, bound f-holes, scroll style inlay on cutaway, raised black bound pickguard, maple back/sides/neck, 20 fret bound rosewood fingerboard with pearl reverse crown inlay, tunomatic bridge/trapeze tailpiece, rosewood tailpiece insert with pearl engraved block inlay, bound peghead with pearl crown/logo inlay, 3 per side tuners, chrome hardware, 2 covered humbucker pickups, 2 volume/2 tone controls, 3 position switch. Available in Vintage Sunburst finish. Curr. mfr.

Mfr.'s Sug. Retail	$3,100	$2,728	$2,387	$2,215	$1,770	$1,595	$1,460	$1,330

Tal Farlow — with Wine Red finish. Curr. mfr.

Mfr.'s Sug. Retail	$2,375	$2,090	$1,828	$1,695	$1,360	$1,225	$1,120	$1,025

SUPER 400 CES — single sharp cutaway grand auditorium style body, arched spruce top, bound f-holes, raised multi-bound mottled plastic pickguard, figured maple back/sides, multiple bound body, 3 piece figured maple/mahogany neck, model name engraved into heel cap, 14/20 fret bound ebony fingerboard with point on bottom, pearl split block fingerboard inlay, adjustable rosewood bridge with pearl triangle wings inlay, gold trapeze tailpiece with engraved model name, multi-bound blackface peghead with pearl 5 piece split diamond/logo inlay, pearl 3 piece split diamond inlay on back of peghead, 3 per side tuners, gold hardware, 2 pickups, 2 volume/2 tone controls, 3 position switch. Available in Natural finish. Curr. mfr.

Mfr.'s Sug. Retail	$12,000	$10,560	$9,240	$8,575	$6,860	$6,270	$5,660	$5,145

Super 400 CES — with Vintage Sunburst finish.

Mfr.'s Sug. Retail	$9,550	$8,404	$7,353	$6,825	$5,460	$4,910	$4,505	$4,095

Super 400 CES — with Ebony and Wine Red finishes.

Mfr.'s Sug. Retail	$6,350	$5,588	$4,889	$4,535	$3,630	$3,265	$2,990	$2,720

WES MONTGOMERY — single round cutaway hollow body, carved spruce top, bound f-holes, raised bound tortoise pickguard, multibound body, carved flame maple back/sides, 5 piece maple neck, 20 fret multibound ebony fingerboard with pearl block inlay, tunomatic bridge on ebony base with pearl leaf inlay, engraved trapeze tailpiece with silver engraved insert, multibound blackface peghead with pearl torch/logo inlay, 3 per side tuners, gold hardware, humbucker pickup, volume/tone control. Available in Vintage Sunburst finish. New 1994.

Mfr.'s Sug. Retail	$4,625	$4,070	$3,561	$3,305	$2,640	$2,380	$2,180	$1,980

Wes Montgomery — With Wine Red finish.

Mfr.'s Sug. Retail	$4,125	$3,630	$3,176	$2,950	$2,360	$2,125	$1,945	$1,770

ELECTRIC BASS

EB Series

EB — double sharp cutaway maple body, tortoise pickguard, maple neck, 20 fret maple fingerboard with pearl dot inlay, bar bridge, blackface peghead with logo decal, 2 per side tuners, chrome hardware, covered humbucker pickup, volume/tone control. Available in Natural finish. Mfg. 1970 only.

$675	$580	$485	$385	$350	$320	$290

EB-O — double round cutaway mahogany body, black pickguard, mahogany neck, 20 fret rosewood fingerboard with pearl dot inlay, bar bridge, blackface peghead with pearl crown/logo inlay, 2 per side Kluson banjo tuners, nickel hardware, covered humbucker pickup, volume/tone control. Available in Cherry Red finish. Mfg. 1959 to 1979.

1959-1960	$1,250	$1,070	$895	$715	$645	$590	$535
1961-1979	$600	$515	$430	$345	$310	$285	$260

In 1961, double sharp cutaway body, laminated pickguard, standard tuners replaced original items.

In 1963, metal handrest added, metal covered pickup replaced original item.

EB-OF — similar to EB-O, except has double sharp cutaway body, laminated pickguard, metal handrest, built-in fuzztone electronics with volume/attack controls and on/off switch. Mfg. 1962 to 1965.

$500	$430	$360	$285	$260	$235	$215

EB-OL — similar to EB-O, except has long scale length. Mfg. 1969 to 1979.

$450	$385	$325	$260	$230	$215	$195

EB-1 — violin shaped mahogany body, arched top with painted f-hole/purfling, raised black pickguard, mahogany neck, 20 fret rosewood fingerboard with pearl dot inlay, bar bridge, blackface peghead with pearl logo inlay, 2 per side Kluson banjo tuners, nickel hardware, covered alnico pickup, volume/tone control. Available in Dark Brown finish. Mfg. 1953 to 1958.

$2,025	$1,740	$1,450	$1,160	$1,040	$955	$870

EB-1 Reissue — similar to EB-1, except has standard tuners, 1 covered humbucker pickup. Mfg. 1970 to 1972.

$1,500	$1,285	$1,070	$860	$770	$710	$645

Gibson EB-0F
courtesy Thoroughbred Music

Grading	100% MINT	98% EXC+	95% EXC+	90% EXC	80% VG+	70% VG	60% G

EB-2 — double round cutaway semi hollow body, arched maple top, raised laminated pickguard, f-holes, bound body, maple back/sides, mahogany neck, 20 fret rosewood fingerboard with pearl dot inlay, bar bridge, blackface peghead with pearl crown/logo inlay, 2 per side Kluson banjo tuners, nickel hardware, covered humbucker pickup, volume/tone control. Available in Natural and Sunburst finishes. Mfg. 1958 to 1961.

	$1,300	$850	$730	$610	$485	$435	$400

In 1959, baritone switch added.

In 1960, string mute added, standard tuners, redesigned pickup replaced original items.

EB-2 models in blond finishes command a premium.

EB-2, Reissue — similar to EB-2, except has standard tuners, metal covered humbucker pickup. Available in Sunburst finish. Mfg. 1964 to 1970.

	$850	$730	$610	$485	$435	$400	$365

In 1965, Cherry finish became optionally available.

EB-2D — similar to EB-2, except has standard tuners, 2 metal covered humbucker pickups. Available in Cherry and Sunburst finishes. Mfg. 1966 to 1972.

	$925	$790	$660	$530	$475	$435	$395

EB-3 — double sharp cutaway mahogany body, laminated black pickguard with finger rest, metal hand rest, mahogany neck, 20 fret rosewood fingerboard with pearl dot inlay, bar bridge, blackface peghead with pearl crown/logo inlay, 2 per side Kluson tuners, nickel hardware, 2 covered humbucker pickups, 2 volume/tone controls, rotary switch. Available in Cherry finish. Mfg. 1961 to 1979.

	$625	$535	$445	$360	$325	$300	$275

In 1963, metal pickup covers were added.

In 1969, metal bridge cover added, slotted peghead replaced original item, handrest, crown peghead inlay were removed.

In 1971, Natural finish became available, Walnut finish became optionally available.

In 1972, crown peghead inlay added, solid peghead replaced respective item.

In 1976, White finish became available.

EB-3L — similar to EB-3, except has a long scale length. Mfg. 1969 to 1972.

	$675	$580	$485	$385	$350	$320	$290

EB-4L — double sharp cutaway mahogany body/neck, black laminated pickguard, 20 fret rosewood fingerboard with pearl dot inlay, bar bridge with metal cover, covered humbucker pickup, volume/tone control, 3 position switch. Available in Cherry and Walnut finishes. Mfg. 1972 to 1979.

	$450	$385	$325	$260	$230	$215	$195

EB-6 - Thinline — double round cutaway semi hollow body, arched maple top, raised laminated pickguard, f-holes, bound body, maple back/sides, mahogany neck, 20 fret rosewood fingerboard with pearl dot inlay, bar bridge, blackface peghead with pearl crown/logo inlay, 3 per side Kluson tuners with plastic buttons, nickel hardware, covered humbucker pickup, volume/tone control, pushbutton switch. Available in Sunburst finish. Mfg. 1958 to 1961.

	$3,000	$2,700	$2,100	$1,600	$1,250	$1,070	$895

EB-6 - Solid Body — similar to EB-6 - Thinline, except has double sharp cutaway solid mahogany body, all metal tuners.

	$1,750	$1,500	$1,250	$1,000	$900	$825	$750

In 1962, hand rest and string mute added, 2 covered humbucker pickups, 2 volume/tone controls, 3 position switch replaced original items, pushbutton switch removed.

EB 650 — single sharp cutaway semi hollow bound maple body, arched top, diamond soundholes, maple neck, 21 fret rosewood fingerboard with pearl dot inlay, adjustable rosewood bridge/trapeze tailpiece, blackface peghead with pearl vase/logo inlay, 2 per side tuners, chrome hardware, 2 covered humbucker pickups, 2 volume/2 tone controls. Available in Translucent Amber, Translucent Black, Translucent Blue, Translucent Purple and Translucent Red finishes. Curr. mfr.

Mfr.'s Sug. Retail	$2,100	$1,680	$1,260	$1,050	$840	$755	$690	$630

EB 750 — similar to EB 650, except has deeper body, f-holes, figured maple back/sides, abalone inlay, gold hardware, 2 Bartolini pickups, volume/treble/bass/pan controls, active electronics. Available in Ebony finish. Curr mfr.

Mfr.'s Sug. Retail	$2,200	$1,760	$1,320	$1,100	$880	$790	$725	$660

Add $400 for Antique Natural and Vintage Sunburst finishes.

EXPLORER — radical offset hourglass alder body, maple neck, 21 fret rosewood fingerboard with pearl dot inlay, fixed bridge, blackface peghead with logo decal, 4 on one side tuners, chrome hardware, 2 humbucker pickups, 2 volume/1 tone controls. Available in Ebony and Ivory finishes. Mfg. 1984 to 1987.

	$550	$470	$395	$315	$285	$260	$235

In 1985 only, a Custom Graphics finish was available.

GIBSON IV — offset double cutaway alder body, maple neck, 22 fret ebony fingerboard with offset pearl dot inlay, fixed bridge, blackface peghead with logo decal, 2 per side tuners, black hardware, 2 humbucker pickups, 2 volume/1 tone controls. Available in Black, Red and White finishes. Mfg. 1987 to 1989.

	$700	$600	$500	$400	$360	$330	$300

GIBSON V — similar to Gibson IV, except has 5 strings, 3/2 per side tuners.

	$800	$685	$575	$460	$410	$380	$345

Grading		100%	98% MINT	95% EXC+	90% EXC	80% VG+	70% VG	60% G

GRABBER — offset double cutaway alder body, tortoise pickguard, bolt-on maple neck, 20 fret maple fingerboard with pearl dot inlay, tunomatic bridge with metal cover, string thru body tailpiece, logo peghead decal, 2 per side tuners, chrome hardware, 1 movable pickup, volume/tone control. Available in Natural finish. Mfg. 1973 to 1982.

		$275	$235	$195	$155	$140	$125	$115

> In 1975, Ebony and Wine Red finishes became available.
>
> In 1976, Black and White finishes became available.
>
> In 1977, Walnut finish became available.

G-3 — similar to Grabber, except has black pickguard, rosewood fingerboard, fixed bridge with cover, blackface peghead with logo decal, 3 single coil pickups, 3 position switch. Available in Natural and Sunburst finishes. Mfg. 1975 to 1982.

		$275	$235	$195	$155	$140	$125	$115

> In 1976, Ebony and Wine Red finishes became available.
>
> In 1977, Walnut finish became available.

L9-S — offset double cutaway alder body, black pickguard, bolt-on maple neck, 20 fret maple fingerboard with pearl dot inlay, tunomatic bridge with metal cover, string thru body tailpiece, blackface peghead with logo decal, 2 per side tuners, chrome hardware, 2 humbucker pickups, volume/treble/bass controls, rotary switch. Available in Ebony and Natural finishes. Mfg. 1973 to 1982.

		$375	$320	$270	$215	$195	$180	$160

> Add $75 for fretless ebony fingerboard with Sunburst finish.
>
> In 1974, this model was renamed the **Ripper**.
>
> In 1975, fretless ebony fingerboard with Sunburst finish became available.
>
> In 1976, Tobacco Sunburst became available.

Les Paul Series

LES PAUL BASS — single sharp cutaway mahogany body, bound body, control plate, mahogany neck, 24 fret bound rosewood fingerboard with pearl block inlay, fixed bridge with metal cover, bound peghead with pearl split diamond/logo inlay, 2 per side tuners, chrome hardware, 2 humbucker pickups with metal rings, volume/treble/bass controls, 3 position pickup/tone switches, impedance/phase switches. Available in Walnut finish. Mfg. 1969 to 1976.

		$650	$555	$465	$370	$335	$305	$280

LES PAUL SIGNATURE — offset double cutaway, arched maple top, raised cream pickguard, f-holes, maple back/sides, mahogany neck, 22 fret rosewood fingerboard with pearl trapezoid inlay, fixed bridge with cover, 2 per side tuners, chrome hardware, humbucker pickup, plastic pickup cover with stamped logo, volume/tone controls, level switch. Available in Gold Top and Sunburst finishes. Mfg. 1973 to 1979.

		$825	$705	$585	$470	$425	$390	$355

> This model had walnut back/sides with Gold Top finish.

LES PAUL TRIUMPH — single sharp cutaway mahogany body, bound body, control plate, mahogany neck, 24 fret bound rosewood fingerboard with pearl block inlay, fixed bridge with metal cover, bound peghead with pearl split diamond/logo inlay, 2 per side tuners, chrome hardware, 2 humbucker pickups with metal rings, volume/treble/bass controls, 3 position pickup/tone switches, impedance/phase switches. Available in Natural and White finishes. Mfg. 1975 to 1979.

		$650	$555	$465	$370	$335	$305	$280

LPB Series

LPB-1 — single cutaway mahogany body/neck, 20 fret ebony fingerboard with pearl dot inlay, fixed bridge, blackface peghead with pearl logo inlay, 2 per side tuners, black hardware, 2 covered humbucker pickups, volume/treble/bass/pan controls, active electronics. Available in Ebony, Classic White, Heritage Cherry and Translucent Amber finishes. Mfg. 1992 to date.

Mfr.'s Sug. Retail	$1,050	$840	$630	$525	$420	$380	$345	$315

> In 1994, Translucent Amber finish was discontinued.

LPB-1/5 — similar to LPB-1, except has 5 strings, 2/3 per side tuners.

Mfr.'s Sug. Retail	$1,050	$840	$630	$525	$420	$380	$345	$315

LPB-2 — similar to LPB-1, except has figured maple top, trapezoid fingerboard inlay, Bartolini pickups. Available in Heritage Cherry Sunburst, Translucent Amber, Translucent Black, Translucent Blue and Translucent Red finishes. Curr. mfr.

Mfr.'s Sug. Retail	$1,475	$1,180	$885	$800	$640	$575	$530	$480

> In 1994, Translucent Amber, Translucent Black, Translucent Blue and Translucent Red finishes were discontinued.

LPB-2/5 — similar to LPB-2, except has 5 strings, 2/3 per side tuners. Available in Heritage Cherry Sunburst and Translucent Amber finishes. Curr. mfr.

Mfr.'s Sug. Retail	$1,560	$1,248	$936	$780	$625	$560	$515	$470

LPB-2 Premium — similar to LPB-1, except has figured maple top, trapezoid fingerboard inlay, Bartolini pickups. Available in Heritage Cherry Sunburst, Honey Burst, Translucent Amber and Vintage Sunburst finishes. Curr. mfr.

Mfr.'s Sug. Retail	$1,560	$1,248	$936	$850	$680	$610	$560	$510

> In 1994, Honey Burst and Vintage Sunburst finishes were discontinued.

G

Grading	100%	98% MINT	95% EXC+	90% EXC	80% VG+	70% VG	60% G

LPB-3 — similar to LPB-1, except has bound maple top, abalone trapezoid fingerboard inlay, chrome hardware. Available in Ebony finish. Curr. mfr.

Mfr.'s Sug. Retail	$1,650	$1,320	$990	$825	$660	$595	$545	$495

Add $200 for Heritage Cherry Sunburst, Honey Burst and Vintage Sunburst finishes.

LPB-3 Plus — similar to LPB-1, except has bound figured maple top, abalone trapezoid fingerboard inlay, chrome hardware. Available in Heritage Cherry Sunburst, Honey Burst, Translucent Amber and Vintage Sunburst finishes. Disc. 1994.

		$1,500	$1,290	$1,075	$860	$775	$710	$645

Last Mfr.'s Sug. Retail was $2,150.

LPB-3 Premium Plus — similar to LPB-1, except has bound highest quality figured maple top, abalone trapezoid fingerboard inlay, chrome hardware. Available in Heritage Cherry Sunburst, Honey Burst, Translucent Amber and Vintage Sunburst finishes. Curr. mfr.

Mfr.'s Sug. Retail	$2,400	$1,920	$1,440	$1,200	$960	$860	$790	$720

In 1994, Translucent Amber finish was discontinued.

LPB-3/5 Premium Plus — similar to LPB-1, except has 5 strings, bound highest quality figured maple top, abalone trapezoid fingerboard inlay, 2/3 per side tuners, chrome hardware. Available in Heritage Cherry Sunburst, Honey Burst and Vintage Sunburst finishes. New 1994.

Mfr.'s Sug. Retail	$2,400	$1,920	$1,440	$1,200	$960	$860	$790	$720

Q-80 — offset double cutaway asymmetrical alder body, bolt-on maple neck, 22 fret rosewood fingerboard with pearl dot inlay, fixed bridge, blackface peghead with screened logo, 4 on one side tuners, chrome hardware, 2 humbucker pickups, 2 volume/1 tone controls. Available in Ebony, Red and Black finishes. Mfg. 1987 to 1992.

	$650	$555	$465	$370	$335	$305	$280

In 1988, this model was renamed Q-90.

In 1989, fretless fingerboard became available.

RD STANDARD BASS — radical hourglass maple body, layered black pickguard, maple neck, 20 fret maple fingerboard with pearl dot inlay, tunomatic bridge/strings thru anchoring, blackface peghead with pearl logo inlay, 2 per side tuners, nickel hardware, 2 pickups, 2 volume/2 tone controls. Available in Ebony and Natural finishes. Mfg. 1979 to 1980.

	$375	$320	$270	$215	$195	$180	$160

This model had an ebony fingerboard with Ebony finish only.

RD Artist Bass — similar to RD Standard Bass, except has winged "f" peghead inlay, 3 mini switches, active electronics. Available in Ebony, Fireburst, Natural and Sunburst finishes. Mfg. 1979 to 1982.

	$475	$405	$340	$270	$245	$225	$205

SB Series

SB 300 — double sharp cutaway mahogany body/neck, 20 fret rosewood fingerboard with pearl dot inlay, fixed bridge with metal cover, blackface peghead with screened logo, 2 per side tuners, chrome hardware, 2 single coil pickups with metal rings, volume/tone control, 3 position switch, control plate. Available in Walnut finish. Mfg. 1971 to 1973.

	$300	$260	$215	$175	$155	$140	$130

SB 400 — similar to SB 300, except has a long scale length. Available in Cherry finish.

	$350	$300	$250	$200	$180	$165	$150

SB 350 — double sharp cutaway mahogany body/neck, thumbrest, 20 fret rosewood fingerboard with pearl dot inlay, bar bridge with metal cover, blackface peghead with pearl logo inlay, 2 covered humbucker pickups, volume/tone control, 2 on/off switches. Available in Cherry, Natural and Walnut finishes. Mfg. 1972 to 1975.

	$325	$280	$235	$190	$170	$155	$140

SB 450 — similar to SB 350, except has a long scale length. Mfg. 1972 to 1976.

	$375	$320	$270	$215	$195	$180	$160

THUNDERBIRD II — asymmetrical hourglass style mahogany body, layered white pickguard with engraved Thunderbird logo, thumb rest, thru body mahogany neck, 20 fret rosewood fingerboard with pearl dot inlay, tunomatic bridge/stop tailpiece, 6 on one side tuners, chrome hardware, single coil pickups with cover, volume/tone controls. Available in Custom Color and Sunburst finishes. Mfg. 1963 to 1969.

1963-1965	$2,250	$1,930	$1,605	$1,285	$1,155	$1,060	$965
1966-1969	$1,500	$1,350	$1,200	$1,070	$950	$820	$670

In 1965, body/neck were redesigned and replaced original items.

Thunderbird IV — similar to Thunderbird II, except has 2 pickups.

1963-1965	$2,500	$2,140	$1,785	$1,430	$1,285	$1,180	$1,070
1966-1969	$1,700	$1,550	$1,400	$1,270	$1,150	$1,020	$870

In 1965, body/neck were redesigned and replaced original items.

Thunderbird 1976 Bicentennial — similar to Thunderbird, except has a red/white/blue engraved logo on white pickguard. Available in Black, Natural and Sunburst finishes. Mfg. 1976 only.

	$1,500	$1,285	$1,070	$860	$770	$710	$645

Grading	100%	98% MINT	95% EXC+	90% EXC	80% VG+	70% VG	60% G

THUNDERBIRD IV REISSUE — asymmetrical hourglass style mahogany body, white pickguard with engraved Thunderbird symbol, thru body 9 piece mahogany/walnut neck, 20 fret ebony fingerboard with pearl dot inlay, fixed bridge, partial blackface peghead with pearl logo inlay, 4 on one side tuners, black hardware, 2 covered pickups, 2 volume/1 tone controls. Available in Cardinal Red, Classic White, Ebony and Vintage Sunburst finishes. Mfg. 1987 to date.

Mfr.'s Sug. Retail	$1,600	$1,200	$800	$700	$560	$505	$460	$420

    In 1994, Cardinal Red, Classic White and Ebony finishes were discontinued.

Victory Series

VICTORY ARTIST — offset double cutaway asymmetrical alder body, black pickguard, bolt-on maple neck, 24 fret extended rosewood fingerboard with offset pearl dot inlay, fixed bridge, blackface peghead with screened logo, 4 on one side tuners, chrome hardware, 2 humbucker pickups, volume/treble/bass controls, electronics/phase switches, active electronics. Available in Antique Fireburst and Candy Apple Red finishes. Mfg. 1981 to 1986.

		$625	$535	$445	$360	$325	$300	$275

Victory Custom — similar to Victory Artist, except has no active electronics. Mfg. 1982 to 1984.

		$525	$450	$375	$300	$270	$245	$225

Victory Standard — similar to Victory Artist, except has 1 humbucker pickup, volume/tone control, phase switch, no active electronics. Available in Candy Apple Red and Silver finishes. Mfg. 1981 to 1987.

		$425	$365	$305	$245	$220	$200	$185

GILBERT

Instruments are built outside San Francisco, California.

Luthier John Gilbert began building acoustic guitars in 1966, and has been concentrating on the classical design, coupled with a louder, yet responsive projection of volume in his models.

(Source: Tony Bacon, The Ultimate Guitar Book)

GITTLER

Instruments originally handbuilt by Allan Gittler in New York from mid-1970s to mid-1980s. Between 1986 and 1987 the Astron company of Israel produced commercial versions based on the original unique design.

Designer Allan Gittler introduced an electric guitar that expressed its design through function. Gittler produced the first 60 instruments himself and entered into an agreement with an American company that built an additional 100 instruments (which Gittler considers flawed). In 1982, Gittler moved to Israel and took the Hebrew name of Avraham Bar Rashi. Bar Rashi currently offers a new, innovative, wood constructed design that further explores his guitar concepts.

(Information courtesy of Brian Gidyk, Vancouver, Canada)

ROBERT L. GIVENS

Instruments built circa 1960-1993.

Luthier Robert L. Givens (1944-1993) began building guitars in 1960, and continued through until his untimely death in March of 1993. He built around 1,500 mandolins (about 700 of those for Tut Taylor's GTR company), around 200 guitars, and nearly 750 custom 5 string tenor banjo necks. According to Greg Boyd of the Stringed Instrument Division (Missoula, Montana), Givens built one mandolin a week except during his yearly two week vacation. Givens eschewed modern conveniences like telephones, and business was generally done face to face. Luthier Givens sometimes had one or two part time workers assisting him.

GLF

Instruments built in Rogers, Minnesota. Distributed by the GLF Custom Shop of Rogers, Minnesota.

Luthier Kevin Smith began building and "messing around" with guitars since his high school days. Born in Fosston, Minnesota in 1961, Smith later attended the Redwing Technical College. He spent a number of years as a lighting and guitar tech for the regional band "Encounter", which was based out of Chicago, Illinois.

Smith opened the GLF Custom Shop in 1984. Although the original focus was on both lighting and guitars, he soon focused on guitar repair and custom building. A custom ordered guitar may range between $1,200 and $1,500, but for further details on models and components contact the GLF shop. Smith holds the patent on the 'Combo Rack', a guitar stand that attaches to the player's amplifier and holds the instrument when not in use. In addition to his busy schedule, he also provides custom finishes for the Benedict Guitar company.

GLOBE

See chapter on House Brands.

This trademark has been identified as a "House Brand" of the Goodman Community Discount Center, circa 1958-1960. See also GOODMAN.

Gittler Guitar
courtesy Brian Gidyk

G

Gittler "fretless" Bass
courtesy Brian Gidyk

(Source: Willie G. Moseley, Stellas & Stratocasters)

G M P GUITARS

Instruments currently built in San Dimas, California. Distributed by G M Precision Products, Inc. of San Dimas, California.

G M P produces a number of fine, high quality guitars and basses. For further information, please contact G M Precision Products, Inc. through the Index of Current Manufacturers located in the back of the book.

GODIN

Since 1987, all instruments built in La Patrie and Princeville, Quebec, in Canada; and Berlin, New Hampshire. Distributed by La Si Do, Inc. of St. Laurent, Canada.

Although the trademark and instruments bearing his name are relatively new, Robert Godin has been a mainstay in the guitar building industry since 1972. Godin got his first guitar at age seven and never looked back. By the time he was 15, he was working at La Tosca Musique in Montreal selling guitars and learning about minor repairs and set up work. Before long, Robert's passion for guitar playing was eclipsed by his fascination with the construction of the instruments themselves. In 1968 Godin set up a custom guitar shop in Montreal called Harmonilab. Harmonilab quickly became known for it's excellent work and musicians were coming from as far away as Quebec City to have their guitars adjusted. Harmonilab was the first guitar shop in Quebec to use professional strobe tuners for intonating guitars.

Although Harmonilab's business was flourishing, Robert was full of ideas for the design and construction of acoustic guitars. So in 1972, the **Norman Guitar Company** was born. From the beginning the Norman guitars showed signs of the innovations that Godin would eventually bring to the guitar market. Perhaps the most significant item about the Norman history is that it represented the beginning of guitar building in the village of La Patrie, Quebec. La Patrie has since become an entire town of guitar builders - more on that later.

By 1978, Norman guitars had become quite successful in Canada and France, while at the same time the people in La Patrie were crafting replacement necks and bodies for the electric guitar market. Before long there was a lineup at the door of American guitar companies that wanted Godin's crew to supply all their necks and bodies.

In 1980 Godin introduced the Seagull guitar. With many innovations like a bolt-on neck (for consistent neck pitch), pointed headstock (straight string pull) and a handmade solid top, the Seagull was designed for an ease of play for the entry level to intermediate guitar player. Most striking was the satin lacquer finish. Godin borrowed the finishing idea that was used on fine violins, and applied it to the acoustic guitar. When the final version of the Seagull guitar went into production, Godin went about the business of finding a sales force to help introduce the Seagull into the U.S. market. Several independent U.S. sales agents jumped at the chance to get involved with this new guitar, and armed with samples off they went into the market. A couple of months passed, and not one guitar was sold. Rather than retreat back to Harmonilab, Godin decided that he would have to get out there himself and explain the Seagull guitar concept. So he bought himself an old Ford Econoline van and stuffed it full of about 85 guitars, and started driving through New England visiting guitar shops and introducing the Seagull guitar. Acceptance of this new guitar spread, and by 1985 La Si Do was incorporated and the factory in La Patrie expanded to meet the growing demand. Godin introduced the La Patrie brand of classical acoustic guitars in 1982. The La Patrie trademark was used to honor the town's tradition of luthiery that had developed during the first ten years since the inception of the Norman guitars trademark. In 1985, Godin also introduced the Simon & Patrick line (named after his two sons) for people interested in a more traditional instrument. Simon & Patrick guitars still maintained a number of Seagull innovations.

Since Godin's factory had been producing necks and bodies for various American guitar companies since 1978, he combined that knowledge with his backround in acoustic guitar design for an entirely new product. The 'Acousticaster' was debuted in 1987, and represented the first design to be under the Godin name. The Acousticaster was designed to produce an acoustic sound from an instrument that was as easy to play as the player's favorite electric guitar. This was achieved through the help of a patented mechanical harp system inside the guitar. Over the past few years, the Godin name has become known for very high quality and innovative designs. Robert Godin is showing no signs of slowing down, having recently introduced the innovative models Multiac, LGX, and LGX-SA.

Today, La Si Do Inc. employs close to 500 people in four factories located in La Patrie and Princeville, Quebec (Canada), and Berlin, New Hampshire. Models of the La Si Do guitar family are in demand all over the world, and Godin is still on the road teaching people about guitars. In a final related note, the Ford Econoline van "died" with about 300,000 miles on it about 14 years ago.

(Company History courtesy Robert Godin and Katherine Calder [Artist Relations], La Si Do, Inc., June 5, 1996)

> "In the short time we have on this earth, you could do a lot more harmful things than buying old guitars."
>
> —L. Acunto on Elliot Easton
>
> TCG, May/June 1991

Grading		100%	98% MINT	95% EXC+	90% EXC	80% VG+	70% VG	60% G

ACOUSTIC ELECTRIC

ACOUSTICASTER — single cutaway routed out maple body, bound spruce top, maple neck, 24 fret rosewood fingerboard with offset dot inlay, rosewood bridge with white black dot pins, 6 on one side gold tuners, tuned bridge harp, piezo bridge pickup, 4 band EQ. Available in Aqua, Black and White finishes. Curr. mfr.

Mfr.'s Sug. Retail	$860	$688	$516	$430	$345	$310	$285	$260

This model has maple fingerboard optionally available.

Grading	100%	98% MINT	95% EXC+	90% EXC	80% VG+	70% VG	60% G

Acousticaster 12 — similar to Acousticaster, except has 12 strings, 6 per side tuners. Available Black and White finishes.

Mfr.'s Sug. Retail	$960	$768	$576	$480	$385	$350	$320	$290

ACOUSTICASTER DELUXE — similar to Acousticaster, except has routed out mahogany body. Available in Cherryburst, Cognacburst and Natural finishes. Curr. mfr.

Mfr.'s Sug. Retail	$920	$736	$552	$460	$370	$335	$305	$280

Acousticaster Deluxe 12 — similar to Acousticaster, except has routed out mahogany body, 12 strings, 6 per side tuners. Available in Cognacburst and Natural finishes.

Mfr.'s Sug. Retail	$1,020	$816	$612	$510	$410	$370	$340	$310

ACOUSTICLASSIC — single cutaway routed out maple body, bound cedar top, mahogany neck, 24 fret rosewood fingerboard with offset dot inlay, rosewood tied bridge, slotted peghead, 3 per side gold tuners with pearloid buttons, tuned bridge harp, piezo bridge pickup, 4 band EQ. Available in Black finish. Curr. mfr.

Mfr.'s Sug. Retail	$955	$764	$573	$480	$380	$345	$315	$285

Acousticlassic Deluxe — similar to Acousticlassic, except has routed out mahogany body. Available in Natural finish. Mfg. 1993 to date.

Mfr.'s Sug. Retail	$1,015	$812	$609	$510	$405	$365	$335	$305

MULTIAC — single cutaway routed out mahogany body, bound spruce top, multiple soundholes on upper bass bout, mahogany neck, 22 fret ebony fingerboard with offset dot inlay, rosewood tied bridge, slotted peghead with R. Godin signature, 3 per side gold tuners with pearloid buttons, 6 bridge sensor pickups, 5 band EQ, tone switch, 2 program push buttons, preamp. Available in Black finish. Curr. mfr.

Mfr.'s Sug. Retail	$1,595	$1,196	$797	$795	$635	$575	$525	$475

Add $100 for Natural finish.

This instrument is specially designed to play with MIDI.

ACOUSTIC ELECTRIC BASS

ACOUSTIBASS — single cutaway routed out maple body, bound spruce top, thumb rest, bolt-on maple neck, fretless ebony fingerboard, ebony strings thru bridge, 4 on one side gold tuners, piezo bridge pickup, 4 band EQ. Available in Aqua, Black and White finishes. Curr. mfr.

Mfr.'s Sug. Retail	$1,060	$848	$636	$530	$425	$385	$350	$320

Acoustibass Deluxe — similar to Acoustibass, except has routed out mahogany body. Available in Cherryburst, Cognacburst and Natural finishes. Curr. mfr.

Mfr.'s Sug. Retail	$1,105	$828	$552	$550	$440	$400	$365	$330

ELECTRIC

Artisan Series

ST 1 — offset double cutaway maple body, carved figured maple top, bolt-on maple neck, 22 fret ebony fingerboard with offset dot inlay, 21st fret pearl block inlay, standard Wilkinson vibrato, 6 on one side locking Schaller tuners, gold hardware, 3 twin blade Godin pickups, volume/tone controls, 5 position switch. Available in Cognacburst, Transparent Black and Transparent Purple finishes. Curr. mfr.

Mfr.'s Sug. Retail	$1,100	$880	$660	$550	$440	$395	$365	$330

ST IV — similar to ST 1, except has rosewood fingerboard with 21st fret block inlay, standard Schaller vibrato, 2 twin blade/1 humbucker pickups. Available in Cognacburst and Transparent Black finishes. Curr. mfr.

Mfr.'s Sug. Retail	$960	$768	$576	$480	$385	$350	$320	$290

This model has maple fingerboard with black inlay optionally available.

ST VI — similar to ST 1, except has longer bass/shorter treble horns body, rosewood fingerboard without 21st block inlay, double locking vibrato, non locking tuners, black hardware, humbucker/twin blade/humbucker pickups. Available in Transparent Amber, Transparent Blue and Transparent Green finishes. Curr. mfr.

Mfr.'s Sug. Retail	$990	$792	$594	$500	$400	$360	$330	$300

This model has maple fingerboard with black inlay optionally available.

JEFF COOK SIGNATURE — offset double cutaway maple body, carved figured maple top, bolt-on maple neck, 22 fret maple fingerboard with offset black dot inlay, strings thru fixed bridge, 6 on one side tuners, black hardware, 2 twin blade/1 humbucker Godin pickups, volume/tone controls, 5 position switch. Available in Cognacburst and Transparent Black finishes. Curr. mfr.

Mfr.'s Sug. Retail	$1,190	$952	$714	$595	$475	$430	$390	$360

TC 1 — single cutaway maple body, carved figured maple top, bolt-on maple neck, 22 fret ebony fingerboard with offset dot inlay, 21st fret pearl block inlay, strings thru fixed bridge, 6 on one side tuners, gold hardware, 2 twin blade Godin pickups, volume/tone controls, 3 position switch. Available in Cognacburst, Transparent Black and Transparent Purple finishes. Curr. mfr.

Mfr.'s Sug. Retail	$990	$792	$594	$500	$400	$360	$330	$300

GODWIN

Instruments were built in Italy in the mid 1970s.

In 1966 the Vox company fused a Phantom model guitar with a Continental model organ and produced the first commercially available guitar that made organ sounds. Following Bob Murrell's GuitOrgan, the Godwin company apparently thought that the third time was the charm as they introduced the Godwin Organ model guitar. The instrument featured a double cutaway wood body, 2 independent single coil pickups, and 13 knobs **plus** 19 switches! Even with a large amount of wood removed for the organ circuitry, the fairly deep-bodied guitar is still heavy. Still a bargain if bought by the pound (not by the sound!), the Godwins were only produced for about a year.

(Source: Tony Bacon, The Ultimate Guitar Book)

GOLDENTONE

Instruments were produced in Japan during the 1960s.

The Goldentone trademark was used by U.S. importers Elger and its partner Hoshino Gakki Ten as one of the brandnames used in their joint guitar producing venture. Hoshino in Japan was shipping Fuji Gen Gakki-built guitars marketed in the U.S. as Goldentone, Elger, and eventually Ibanez. These solid body guitars featured original body designs in the early to mid 1960s.

(Source: Michael Wright, Guitar Stories Volume One)

GOODALL

Instruments currently built in Kailua-Kona, Hawaii.

Luthier James Goodall builds several models of high quality acoustic guitars. Instruments are constructed of Alaskan Sitka spruce tops and choice of maple, walnut, koa back and sides. For further information on pricing, specifications, and availability, please contact luthier Goodall through the Index of Current Manufacturers located in the back of this book.

GOODFELLOW

See LOWDEN GUITARS.

Instruments built in Northern Ireland. Distributed in the U.S. market by Quality First Products of Forest City, North Carolina.

Goodfellow basses were introduced in the 1980s, and caught the eye of Lowden Guitars' Andy Kidd during an exhibit in Manchester. Kidd, originally offering to further "spread the word" and help subcontract some of the building, eventually acquired the company. These high quality basses feature select figured and exotic wood construction, as well as active tone circuitry and humbucking pickups designed by Kent Armstrong. Available in 4, 5 or 6 string models, the ebony fingerboard spans a two octave neck.

GOODMAN

See chapter on House Brands.

This trademark has been identified as a "House Brand" of the Goodman Comunity Discount Center, circa 1961-1964. Previously, the company used the trademark of GLOBE. Additional information on this company or guitars produced for their trademark would be welcomed for upcoming editions of the **Blue Book of Guitars**.

(Source: Willie G. Moseley, Stellas & Stratocasters)

GORDON SMITH

Instruments were produced in England from 1979 to current.

This company built both original designs and Fender/Gibson-esque designed solid and semi-hollow body guitars. Models feature company's own pickups and hardware, but hardware options changed through the years. Though information is still lacking in model differences, the names remain the same: The Gypsy, Galaxi, Graduate, Gemini, and GS. Fans of Gordon Smith guitars or the letter **G** are invited to send any information to the **Blue Book of Guitars** for future updates.

(Source: Tony Bacon and Paul Day, The Guru's Guitar Guide)

GORDY

Instruments were built in England from the mid 1980s on.

Luthier Gordon Whitham, the "Gordon" of GORDON SMITH fame, is producing a series of high quality instruments. These original design solid body guitars carry such model designations as the Red Shift, 1810, and Xcaster.

(Source: Tony Bacon and Paul Day, The Guru's Guitar Guide)

GOSPEL

Instruments were built in Bakersfield, California in the late 1960s; a second series was produced in Jonah's Ridge, North Carolina in the early 1980s.

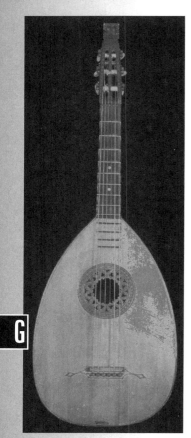

Goldklang acoustic
courtesy Hal Hammer

Moseley Gospel
courtesy Hal Hammer

In 1969, luthier Semie Moseley trademarked the Gospel brandname separate from his Mosrite company. Only a handful of late '60s Gospels were produced and featured a design based on Mosrite's Celebrity model guitar. In the early '80s, Moseley again attempted to offer guitars to the gospel music industry. The Gospel guitars represent Semie Moseley's love of gospel music and his attempt to furnish gospel musicians with quality instruments.

(Information courtesy of Andy Moseley and Hal Hammer, 1996).

GOYA

Instruments were originally produced in Sweden. Instruments are currently distributed by The Martin Guitar Company, located in Nazareth, Pennsylvania.

Although not too much is known about the early Goya company, some of the earlier models were built by Levin of Sweden for an American distributor. Goya was later sold to Avnet (see Guild), who then sold to the trademark to Kustom Electronics. The C. F. Martin company later acquired the Levin company, and bought the rights to the Goya trademark from a company named Dude, Inc. in 1976.

The Goya company featured a number of innovations that most people are not aware of. Goya was the first classic guitar line to put the trademark name on the headstock, and also created the ball end classic guitar string.

While Goya currently offers acoustic guitars, the first electrics debuted in the early '60s. The second series of electrics, named **Range Masters**, were produced from 1967-1969 and featured pushbutton controls. Goya also produced a number of electric guitar amplifiers.

Grading	100%	98% MINT	95% EXC+	90% EXC	80% VG+	70% VG	60% G

ACOUSTIC

G-120 — classic style, spruce top, round soundhole, bound body, wood inlay rosette, mahogany back/sides/neck, 12/18 fret rosewood fingerboard, rosewood tied bridge, 3 per side chrome tuners. Available in Natural finish. Curr. mfr.

Mfr.'s Sug. Retail	$260	$208	$156	$130	$100	$90	$80	$75

G-125 — classic style, spruce top, round soundhole, bound body, wood inlay rosette, mahogany back/sides/neck, 12/19 fret rosewood fingerboard, rosewood tied bridge, 3 per side chrome tuners. Available in Natural finish. Curr. mfr.

Mfr.'s Sug. Retail	$290	$232	$174	$145	$115	$105	$95	$85

G-145 — classic style, cedar top, round soundhole, bound body, wood inlay rosette, rosewood mahogany back/sides, mahogany neck, 12/19 fret rosewood fingerboard, rosewood tied bridge, 3 per side gold tuners. Available in Natural finish. Curr. mfr.

Mfr.'s Sug. Retail	$350	$280	$210	$175	$140	$125	$115	$105

G-145S — similar to G-145, except has solid cedar top. Curr. mfr.

Mfr.'s Sug. Retail	$510	$382	$255	$250	$200	$180	$165	$150

G-215 — grand concert style, spruce top, round soundhole, black pickguard, 3 stripe bound body/rosette, mahogany back/sides/neck, 14/20 fret rosewood fingerboard with pearl dot inlay, rosewood bridge with white black dot pins, rosewood veneered peghead with screened logo, 3 per side chrome tuners. Available in Natural finish. Curr. mfr.

Mfr.'s Sug. Retail	$330	$264	$198	$165	$130	$120	$110	$100

Add $20 for left hand version (G-215L).

G-230S — similar to G-215, except has solid spruce top, tortoise pickguard, gold tuners. Curr. mfr.

Mfr.'s Sug. Retail	$405	$303	$202	$200	$160	$145	$130	$120

G-300 — dreadnought style, spruce top, round soundhole, black pickguard, bound body, 3 stripe rosette, mahogany back/sides/neck, 14/20 fret rosewood fingerboard with pearl dot inlay, rosewood bridge with black white dot pins, screened peghead logo, 3 per side diecast tuners. Available in Natural finish. Curr. mfr.

Mfr.'s Sug. Retail	$300	$240	$180	$150	$120	$110	$100	$90

Add $20 for left hand version (G-300L).
Add $30 for Sunburst finish (G-300SB).

G-312 — dreadnought style, spruce top, round soundhole, black pickguard, 3 stripe bound body/rosette, mahogany back/sides/neck, 14/20 fret rosewood fingerboard with pearl dot inlay, rosewood bridge with black white dot pins, screened peghead logo, 3 per side chrome tuners. Available in Natural finish. Curr. mfr.

Mfr.'s Sug. Retail	$360	$288	$216	$180	$145	$130	$120	$110

Add $20 for Sunburst finish (G-312SB).

G-312E — similar to G-312, except has piezo bridge pickup, volume/tone controls. Curr. mfr.

Mfr.'s Sug. Retail	$475	$356	$237	$235	$190	$170	$155	$140

G-316H — dreadnought style, spruce top, round soundhole, tortoise pickguard, herringbone bound body/rosette, rosewood back/sides, mahogany neck, 14/20 fret rosewood fingerboard with pearl dot inlay, rosewood bridge with white black dot pins, screened peghead logo, 3 per side chrome tuners. Available in Natural finish. Curr. mfr.

Mfr.'s Sug. Retail	$480	$384	$288	$240	$190	$170	$155	$145

Grading	100%	98% MINT	95% EXC+	90% EXC	80% VG+	70% VG	60% G

G-318C — single round cutaway dreadnought style, spruce top, round soundhole, black pickguard, 3 stripe bound body/rosette, mahogany back/sides/neck, 14/20 fret rosewood fingerboard with pearl dot inlay, rosewood bridge with black white dot pins, screened peghead logo, 3 per side chrome tuners. Available in Natural finish. Curr. mfr.

Mfr.'s Sug. Retail	$375	$281	$187	$185	$150	$135	$120	$110

G-318CE — similar to G-318C, except has piezo bridge pickup, volume/tone control. Curr. Mfr.

Mfr.'s Sug. Retail	$515	$412	$309	$260	$205	$185	$170	$155

G-330S — dreadnought style, solid spruce top, round soundhole, tortoise pickguard, multibound body/rosette, rosewood back/sides/neck, 14/20 fret bound ebonized rosewood fingerboard with pearl dot inlay, rosewood bridge with white black dot pins, bound peghead with pearl torch inlay, 3 per side gold tuners. Available in Natural finish. Curr. mfr.

Mfr.'s Sug. Retail	$555	$444	$333	$280	$220	$200	$185	$165

G-335S — dreadnought style, solid spruce top, round soundhole, tortoise pickguard, herringbone bound body/rosette, rosewood back/sides, mahogany neck, 14/20 fret bound rosewood fingerboard with pearl snowflake/tree of life inlay, rosewood bridge with white black dot pins, bound peghead with pearl torch inlay, 3 per side gold tuners. Available in Natural finish. Curr. mfr.

Mfr.'s Sug. Retail	$580	$464	$348	$290	$230	$205	$190	$175

G-415 — dreadnought style, spruce top, round soundhole, black pickguard, multibound body/rosette, mahogany back/sides/neck, 14/20 fret rosewood fingerboard with pearl dot inlay, rosewood bridge with black white dot pins, screened peghead logo, 6 per side chrome tuners. Available in Natural finish. Curr. mfr.

Mfr.'s Sug. Retail	$390	$312	$234	$195	$155	$140	$125	$115

G-600 — single sharp cutaway dreadnought style, spruce top, round soundhole, black pickguard, multibound body/rosette, mahogany back/sides/neck, 14/20 fret bound rosewood fingerboard with pearl dot inlay, rosewood bridge with white black dot pins, bound peghead with screened logo, 3 per side chrome tuners, piezo bridge pickup, 3 band EQ. Available in Black and Natural finishes. Curr. mfr.

Mfr.'s Sug. Retail	$580	$464	$348	$290	$230	$205	$190	$175

G Series

G-1 — classic style, spruce ply top, round soundhole, bound body, rosette decal, mahogany stain ply back/sides, nato neck, 12/19 fret ebonized fingerboard, ebonized tied bridge, 3 per side chrome tuners with white buttons. Available in Natural finish. Curr. mfr.

Mfr.'s Sug. Retail	$115	$92	$69	$60	$45	$40	$35	$30

G-2 — classic style, spruce ply top, round soundhole, bound body, rosette decal, rosewood stain ply back/sides, nato neck, 12/19 fret ebonized fingerboard, ebonized tied bridge, 3 per side chrome tuners with pearloid buttons. Available in Natural finish. Curr. mfr.

Mfr.'s Sug. Retail	$155	$116	$77	$75	$60	$55	$50	$45

G-3 — dreadnought style, spruce ply top, round soundhole, black pickguard, bound body, rosette decal, mahogany stain ply back/sides, nato neck, 14/20 fret ebonized fingerboard with pearl dot inlay, ebonized bridge with white pins, screened peghead logo, 3 per side chrome diecast tuners. Available in Natural finish. Curr. mfr.

Mfr.'s Sug. Retail	$135	$108	$81	$70	$55	$50	$45	$40

G-4 — dreadnought style, spruce ply top, round soundhole, black pickguard, bound body, rosette decal, rosewood stain ply back/sides, nato neck, 14/20 fret ebonized fingerboard with pearl dot inlay, rosewood bridge with white pins, screened peghead logo, 3 per side chrome diecast tuners. Available in Natural finish. Curr. mfr.

Mfr.'s Sug. Retail	$170	$127	$85	$80	$65	$60	$55	$45

ACOUSTIC ELECTRIC

G-500 — single round cutaway hollow style, round soundhole, multibound body/rosette, mahogany back/sides/neck, 20 fret bound rosewood fingerboard with pearl dot inlay, rosewood bridge with white black dot pins, bound peghead with screened logo, 3 per side chrome tuners, piezo bridge pickup, 3 band EQ. Available in Black, Blueburst and Natural finishes. Curr. mfr.

Mfr.'s Sug. Retail	$600	$480	$360	$300	$240	$215	$195	$180

OSKAR GRAF

Instruments currently built in Clarendon, Ontario (Canada).

Luthier Oscar Graf has been handcrafting classical and steel-string acoustic guitars for the past 25 years. Instruments feature cedar and spruce tops, and rosewood and koa backs and sides. Graf has built flamenco style guitars and lutes through the years, and estimates that he has produced maybe 250 guitars (mostly as commissioned pieces). For further information, please contact luthier Graf via the Index of Current Manufacturers located in the back of this book.

GRAFFITI

Instruments built in England from the early to late 1980s.

Grammer G-10
courtesy John Miller

While the instruments were indeed **constructed** in the UK, the parts themselves were from Italy or Japan. The guitars were medium-to-good quality Fender-styled solid body instruments.

(Source: Tony Bacon and Paul Day, The Guru's Guitar Guide)

GRAMMER

Instruments were built in Nashville, Tennessee circa 1960s.

Grammer Guitars was founded in part by country singer Billy Grammer's investment (after Grammer succeeded R.G.&G. Musical Instrument Company).

(Source: Tom Wheeler, American Guitars)

GRANDE

Instruments built in Japan during the mid to late 1970s. Imported by Jerry O'Hagan of St. Louis Park, Minnesota.

Between 1975 and 1979, Jerry O'Hagan imported the Japanese-built Grande acoustic guitars to the U.S. market. O'Hagan later went on to produce the American-built solid body electric O'Hagan guitars (1979 to 1983).

(Source: Michael Wright, Guitar Stories Volume One, pg. 277)

GRANT

Instruments produced in Japan from the 1970s through the 1980s.

The GRANT trademark was the brandname of a UK importer, and the guitars were medium quality copies of American designs.

(Source: Tony Bacon and Paul Day, The Guru's Guitar Guide)

GRANTSON

Instruments produced in Japan during the mid 1970s.

These entry level guitars featured designs based on popular American models.

(Source: Tony Bacon and Paul Day, The Guru's Guitar Guide)

Kevin Gray Zebra
courtesy Kevin Gray

G

KEVIN GRAY

Instruments currently built in Dallas, Texas.

Luthier Kevin Gray has been building custom guitars, as well as performing repairs and restorations on instruments for a number of years. Gray blends state of the art technology with handcrafted exotic wood tops. Standard features include a solid mahogany body and neck, 24 fret rosewood or ebony fingerboard, choice of 24 3/4" or 25 1/2" scale, and mother of pearl or abalone inlays. Gray also features gold-plated hardware, Sperzel locking tuners, Seymour Duncan or Lindy Fralin pickups, and hand-rubbed lacquer finishes.

ELECTRIC

Gray offers four different variations of his custom guitars. The **Carved Top** ($2,995) features an exotic wood top over the mahogany body, and has a set-neck. A **Marquetry Flat Top** (also $2,995) has designs or scenes formed from exotic hardwoods, body binding, and a set-neck. An unsculpted exotic hardwood top and body binding is offered on the **Flat Top** ($2,795). Gray also builds a **Contoured Top/Bolt-on** design ($2,495) with a carved maple top, maple neck, and either a maple, alder, or basswood body.

GRAZIOSO

See FUTURAMA.

G R D

Instruments built in Stafford, Vermont circa 1970s.

In 1972, designer/luthier Charles Fox founded the School of Guitar Research and Design Center (G R D) in Stafford, Vermont. G R D offered numerous innovatively designed guitars during the 1970s.

(Source: Tom Wheeler, American Guitars)

GRECO

Instruments produced in Japan during the 1960s.

Greco instruments were imported to the U.S. through Goya Guitars/Avnet. Avnet was the same major company that also acquired Guild in 1966.

(Source: Michael Wright, Guitar Stories Volume One, pg. 76)

Greco
courtesy Mike Coulson

GREEN MOUNTAIN GUITARS

Instruments built in Tumalo, Oregon by the Breedlove Guitar Company. Distribution is handled by the Breedlove company in Tumalo, Oregon.

Breedlove's Green Mountain Guitars offers an acoustic guitar with an interchangeable neck system for beginning (and growing) guitar students. As the student physically matures, the graduated necks can be changed to match the student's growth. For further information, contact Breedlove Guitar Company via the Index of Current Manufacturers located in the back of this book.

GREMLIN

See ARBOR/MIDCO INT'L.

Gremlin guitars are designed for the entry level or student guitarist.

GRENN

Instruments were built in Japan during the late 1960s.

Grenn guitars were a series of entry level semi-hollow body designs.

(Source: Tony Bacon and Paul Day, The Guru's Guitar Guide)

GRETSCH

Original production of instruments took place in New York City, New York from the early 1900s to 1970. Production was moved to Booneville, Arkansas from 1970 to 1979; however, Gretsch (under control of the D. H. Baldwin Company) ceased production in 1981.

Instruments currently produced in Japan since 1989. There are also three current models that are built in the U.S. Distribution is handled by the Fred Gretsch Company of Savannah, Georgia.

Friedrich Gretsch was born in 1856, and emigrated to America when he was 16. In 1883 he founded a musical instrument shop in Brooklyn which prospered. The Fred Gretsch Company began manufacturing instruments in 1883 (while Friedrich maintained his proper name, he "americanized" it for the company). Gretsch passed away unexpectedly (at age 39) during a trip to Germany in April 1895, and his son Fred (often referred to as Fred Gretsch, Sr. in company histories) took over the family business (at 15!). Gretsch Sr. expanded the business considerably by 1916. Beginning with percussion, ukeleles, and banjos, Gretsch introduced guitars in the early 1930s, developing a well respected line of archtop orchestra models. In 1926 the company acquired the rights to K. Zildjian Cymbals, and debuted the Gretsch tenor guitar. During the Christmas season of 1929, the production capabilities was reported to be 100,000 instruments (stringed instruments and drums); and a new midwestern branch was opened in Chicago, Illinois. In March of 1940 Gretsch acquired the B & D trademark from the Bacon Banjo Corporation. Fred Gretsch, Sr. retired in 1942.

William Walter Gretsch assumed the presidency of the company until 1948, and then Fred Gretsch, Jr. took over the position. Gretsch, Jr. was the primary president during the great Gretsch heyday, and was ably assisted by such notables as Jimmy Webster and Charles "Duke" Kramer (Kramer was involved with the Gretsch company from 1935 to his retirement in 1980, and was even involved after his retirement!). During the 1950s, the majority of Gretsch's guitar line was focused on electric six string Spanish instruments. With the endorsement of Chet Atkins and George Harrison, Gretsch electrics became very popular with both country and rock-n-roll musicians through the 1960s.

Outbid in their attempt to buy Fender in 1965, the D. H. Baldwin company bought Gretsch in 1967, and Gretsch, Jr. was made a director of Baldwin. Baldwin had previously acquired the manufacturing facilities of England's James Ormstron Burns (Burns Guitars) in September 1965, and Baldwin was assembling the imported Burns parts in Booneville, Arkansas. In a business consolidation, The New York Gretsch operation was moved down to the Arkansas facility in 1970. Production focused on Gretsch, and Burns guitars are basically discontinued.

Charles "Duke" Kramer
19th Annual Dallas Show

In January of 1973 the Booneville plant suffered a serious fire. Baldwin made the decision to discontinue guitar building operations. Three months later, long-time manager Bill Hagner formed the Hagner Musical Instruments company and formed an agreement with Baldwin to build and sell Gretsch guitars to Baldwin from the Booneville facility. Baldwin would still retain the rights to the trademark. Another fire broke out in December of the same year, but the operation recovered. Baldwin stepped in and regained control of the operation in December of 1978, the same year that they bought the Kustom Amplifier company in Chanute, Kansas. Gretsch production was briefly moved to the Kansas facility, and by 1982 they moved again to Gallatin, Tennessee. 1981 was probably the last date of guitar production, but Gretsch drum products were continued at Tennessee. In 1983 the production had again returned to Arkansas.

Baldwin had experimented briefly with guitar production at their Mexican organ facilities, producing perhaps 100 "Southern Belle" guitars (renamed Country Gentlemans) between 1978 and 1979. When Gretsch production returned to Arkansas in 1983, the Baldwin company asked Charles Kramer to come out of retirement and help bring the business back (which he did). In 1984, Baldwin also sold off their rights to Kustom amps. In 1985 Kramer brokered a deal between Baldwin and Fred Gretsch III that returned the trademark back to the family. Kramer and Gretsch III developed the specifications for the reissue models that are being built by the Terada company in Japan. In 1995, three models were introduced that are currently built in the U.S: **Country Club 1955** (model G6196-1955), **Nashville 1955** (model G6120-1955), and the **White Falcon I - 1955** (model G6136-1955).

(Later company history courtesy Michael Wright, Guitar Stories Volume One, pgs. 209-217)

When Charles "Duke" Kramer first retired in 1980, he formed D & F Products. In late 1981, when Baldwin lost a lease on one of their small production plants, Kramer went out and bought any existing guitar parts (about three 42-foot semi-trailers worth!). While some were sold back to the revitalized Gretsch company in 1985, Kramer still makes the parts available through his D & F Products company, and can be reached via the Index of Current Manufacturers located in the back of this book (underneath the Gretsch listing).

ACOUSTIC

MODEL 35 — carved spruce top, f-holes, raised bound black pickguard, bound body, maple back/sides, 3 piece maple/rosewood neck, 14/20 fret ebony fingerboard with pearloid dot inlay, ebony bridge/trapeze tailpiece, rosewood peghead veneer with pearl logo inlay, 3 per side diecast tuners. Available in Dark Red Sunburst finish. Mfg. 1933 to 1949.

$400	$340	$285	$230	$205	$190	$170

Original Mfr.'s Sug. Retail was $35.

This instrument measures 16 inches across bottom bout.

In 1936, adjustable maple bridge and black plastic peghead veneer replaced original items.

By 1939, 3 stripe body binding, rosewood fingerboard, tortoise shell tuner buttons, nickel plated hardware, and Brown Sunburst finish became standard.

MODEL 50 — carved spruce top, f-holes, raised black pickguard, bound body, avoidire back, figured maple sides/neck, 14/20 fret bound ebony pointed end fingerboard with pearloid diamond inlay, adjustable maple bridge/trapeze tailpiece, black face peghead with pearl scroll inlay, 3 per side nickel tuners with tortoise buttons. Available in Brown Sunburst finish. Mfg. 1936 to 1949.

$425	$365	$305	$240	$220	$200	$180

Original Mfr.'s Sug. Retail was $50.

This instrument measures 16 inches across bottom bout.

This model also available with round soundhole (50R), which was discontinued by 1940.

By 1940, rosewood fingerboard with dot inlay replaced ebony fingerboard with diamond inlay.

MODEL 75 — arched spruce top, raised bound tortoise pickguard, f-holes, bound body, figured maple back/sides, 3 piece maple neck, 14/20 fret bound rosewood pointed end fingerboard with pearloid block inlay, adjustable rosewood stairstep bridge/nickel trapeze tailpiece, black face peghead with large floral/logo inlay, 3 per side nickel tuners. Available in Brown Sunburst finish. Mfg. 1939 to 1949.

$550	$470	$395	$315	$285	$260	$235

Original Mfr.'s Sug. Retail was $75.

This instrument measures 16 inches across bottom bout.

Early models had bound pegheads.

By 1940, 3 stripe bound pickguard/body replaced original items, pickguard was also enlarged.

MODEL 100 — arched spruce top, raised bound tortoise pickguard, f-holes, 2 stripe bound body, curly maple back/sides, 3 piece curly maple/rosewood neck, 14/20 fret bound rosewood fingerboard with pearl block inlay, adjustable rosewood stairstep bridge/step tailpiece, bound blackface peghead with pearl floral/logo inlay, 3 per side gold tuners. Available in Natural and Sunburst finishes. Mfg. 1939 to 1955.

$650	$475	$400	$325	$275	$225	$200

Original Mfr.'s Sug. Retail was $100.

This instrument measures 16 inches across bottom bout.

MODEL 150 — carved spruce top, raised bound tortoise pickguard, f-holes, multibound body, curly maple back/sides, curly maple neck, 14/20 fret bound ebony fingerboard with pearl block inlay, adjustable ebony stairstep bridge/step tailpiece, bound blackface peghead with pearl "Artist"/logo inlay, 3 per side gold tuners. Available in Natural and Sunburst finishes. Mfg. 1935 to 1939.

$750	$600	$525	$450	$375	$300	$225

Original Mfr.'s Sug. Retail was $100.

This instrument measures 16 inches across bottom bout.

MODEL 250 — arched spruce top, raised bound tortoise pickguard, bound catseye soundholes, 3 stripe bound body, arched maple back/sides, 14/20 fret bound ebony fingerboard with pearl block inlay, adjustable stylized ebony bridge/step trapeze tailpiece, bound blackface peghead with 2 pearl quarter notes/logo inlay, 3 per side gold tuners with pearloid buttons. Available in Sunburst finish. Mfg. 1936 to 1939.

$950	$775	$600	$450	$400	$325	$275

Original Mfr.'s Sug. Retail was $250.

This instrument measures 16 inches across bottom bout.

BURL IVES — folk style, spruce top, round soundhole, tortoise pickguard, 2 stripe bound body/rosette, mahogany back/sides/neck, 14/19 fret rosewood fingerboard with pearloid dot inlay, rosewood bridge with black pins, black peghead face with Burl Ives/logo, 3 per side tuners with plastic buttons. Available in Natural finish. Mfg. 1952 to 1955.

$525	$450	$375	$300	$270	$245	$225

Grading	100%	98% MINT	95% EXC+	90% EXC	80% VG+	70% VG	60% G

CONSTELLATION — single round cutaway hollow style, arched spruce top, 2 stripe bound f-holes, raised bound tortoise pickguard, 2 stripe bound body, laminated maple back/sides, 3 piece maple/rosewood neck, 19 fret bound rosewood fingerboard with pearloid block inlay, adjustable rosewood stairstep bridge/gold trapeze tailpiece, bound black face peghead with pearl logo inlay, 3 per side gold tuners. Available in Natural and Sunburst finishes. Mfg. 1951 to 1960.

	$1,750	$1,500	$1,250	$1,000	$900	$825	$750

Originally released as the Synchromatic, it was later known as the Constellation.

By 1955, hump top block fingerboard inlay and ebony bridge/G logo trapeze tailpiece replaced original items.

CRIMSON FLYER — single round cutaway dreadnought style, solid spruce top, triangle soundhole, multi bound body, floral pattern rosette, chestnut back/sides, 2 piece mahogany neck, 22 fret rosewood fingerboard with pearl dot inlay, pearl scroll inlay at 12th fret, rosewood bridge with black pearl pins, pearl floral bridge wing inlay, bound body matching peghead with pearl logo inlay, 3 per side gold tuners, active ceramic pickup, volume/tone control. Available in Cherry Sunburst finish. Mfg. 1991 to date.

Mfr.'s Sug. Retail	$1,350	$1,080	$810	$675	$540	$485	$445	$405

Crimson Flyer V — similar to Crimson Flyer, except has rosewood/metal tunomatic bridge/Bigsby vibrato.

Mfr.'s Sug. Retail	$1,650	$1,320	$990	$825	$660	$595	$545	$495

ELDORADO — single round cutaway hollow style, arched spruce top, f-holes, raised pickguard, 3 stripe bound body, maple back/sides/neck, 21 fret bound ebony fingerboard with pearloid humptop block inlay, adjustable ebony stairstep bridge/gold G logo trapeze tailpiece, bound black face peghead with logo inlay, 3 per side gold tuners. Available in Natural and Sunburst finishes. Mfg. 1955 to 1970.

	$1,750	$1,500	$1,250	$1,000	$900	$825	$750

By 1968, Natural finish was discontinued.

FLEETWOOD — similar to Eldorado, except has smaller body, Synchromatic/logo on peghead. Available in Natural and Sunburst finishes. Mfg. 1955 to 1968.

	$1,950	$1,670	$1,395	$1,115	$1,005	$920	$835

In 1959, the thumbnail fingerboard inlays replaced block inlays.

FOLK — folk style, spruce top, round soundhole, tortoise pickguard, 3-stripe bound body/rosette, mahogany back/sides/neck, 14/19 fret rosewood fingerboard with pearloid dot inlay, rosewood bridge with black pins, black peghead face with logo, 3 per side tuners with plastic buttons. Available in Natural finish. Mfg. 1951 to 1975.

	$375	$320	$270	$215	$195	$180	$160

By 1955, this model was named Grand Concert and had slanted peghead logo.

In 1959, this was renamed Jimmy Rogers Model.

In 1963, this was renamed Folk Singing Model.

In 1965, this was renamed Folk Model.

In 1967, straight across peghead logo was added.

In 1969, mahogany top and Sunburst finish became optional.

RANCHER — jumbo style, spruce top with stylized G brand, triangle soundhole, tortoise pickguard with engraved longhorn steer head, 3 stripe bound body/rosette, maple arched back/sides/neck, 14/21 fret bound rosewood fingerboard with pearloid block inlay, adjustable rosewood bridge/stop tailpiece mounted on triangular rosewood base, black face bound peghead with pearl steer head/logo inlay, 3 per side gold tuners. Available in Golden Red finish. Mfg. 1954 to 1973.

1954-1959	$2,575	$2,210	$1,840	$1,470	$1,325	$1,215	$1,100
1960-1964	$2,010	$1,720	$1,435	$1,150	$1,030	$945	$860
1965-1969	$1,650	$1,415	$1,175	$940	$845	$775	$705
1970-1973	$950	$815	$680	$545	$490	$445	$405

G brand was on bass side of top, fingerboard inlay was inscribed with cows and cactus.

By 1957, gold pickguard and hump top fingerboard inlay with no engraving replaced original items.

In 1959, tan pickguard, thumbnail fingerboard inlay replaced respective items.

In 1961, no G brand on top, and horseshoe peghead inlay replaced original items.

Rancher-Reissue — similar to Rancher, except has block fingerboard inlay with engraved cows and cactus, rosewood bridge with white pins, horseshoe peghead inlay. Mfg. 1975 to 1980.

	$950	$815	$680	$545	$490	$445	$405

In 1978, tri-saddle bridge with white pins replaced respective item.

RANCHER - 2nd REISSUE (Model 6022) — jumbo style, spruce top with "G" brand, bound triangle soundhole, tortoise pickguard with engraved steerhead, 3 stripe bound body, maple back/sides/neck, 14/21 fret bound rosewood fingerboard with western motif engraved pearl block inlays, rosewood bridge with black white dot pins, bound peghead with pearl steerhead/logo inlay, 3 per side gold tuners. Available in Transparent Orange finish. Mfg. 1991 to date.

Mfr.'s Sug. Retail	$1,050	$840	$630	$525	$420	$380	$345	$315

Rancher C — similar to Rancher-2nd Reissue, except has single round cutaway, single coil pickup, volume/tone control.

Mfr.'s Sug. Retail	$1,500	$1,200	$900	$750	$600	$540	$495	$450

Rancher CV (Model 6022CV) — similar to Rancher-2nd Reissue, except has single round cutaway, no pickguard, adjustamatic metal bridge with rosewood base/Bigsby vibrato, single coil pickup, volume/tone control.

Mfr.'s Sug. Retail	$1,750	$1,400	$1,050	$875	$700	$630	$575	$525

Grading	100%	98% MINT	95% EXC+	90% EXC	80% VG+	70% VG	60% G

Rancher 12 — similar to Rancher-2nd Reissue, except has 12 strings, 6 per side tuners.
Mfr.'s Sug. Retail $1,500 $1,200 $900 $750 $600 $540 $495 $450

Rancher C12 — similar to Rancher-2nd Reissue, except has 12 strings, single round cutaway, 6 per side tuners, single coil pickup, volume/tone control.
Mfr.'s Sug. Retail $1,600 $1,280 $960 $800 $640 $575 $530 $480

SUN VALLEY — dreadnought style, spruce top, round soundhole, tortoise pickguard, 3 stripe bound body/rosette, mahogany back/sides/neck, 14/20 fret bound rosewood fingerboard with dot inlay, rosewood bridge with black pins, bound peghead, 3 per side chrome tuners. Available in Natural and Sunburst finishes. Mfg. 1959 to 1977.
1959-1964 $750 $640 $535 $430 $390 $355 $325
1965-1969 $625 $535 $445 $360 $325 $300 $275
1970-1977 $550 $470 $395 $315 $285 $260 $235

By 1973, Sunburst finish was optional.

Sun Valley-Reissue — dreadnought style, solid spruce top, triangle soundhole, 3 stripe bound body, floral pattern rosette, rosewood back/sides, mahogany neck, 14/20 fret bound rosewood fingerboard with pearl diamond inlay, pearl scroll inlay at 12th fret, rosewood bridge with black pearl dot pins, pearl floral bridge wing inlay, bound blackface peghead with pearl floral/logo inlay, 3 per side gold tuners. Available in Natural finish. Mfg. 1991 to date.
Mfr.'s Sug. Retail $1,250 $1,000 $750 $625 $500 $450 $415 $375

WAYFARER JUMBO — dreadnought style, spruce top, round soundhole, lucite pickguard with engraved sailboat/logos, 3 stripe bound body/rosette, red maple back/sides/neck, 14/21 fret bound rosewood fingerboard with pearl split block inlay, rosewood bridge with white pins, black face peghead with logo inlay, 3 per side Grover chrome tuners. Available in Natural finish. Mfg. 1969 to 1972.
$525 $450 $375 $300 $270 $245 $225

WHITE FALCON RANCHER — single round cutaway jumbo style, solid spruce top with "G" brand, tortoise pickguard, bound triangle soundhole, gold sparkle bound body, maple back/sides/neck, 21 fret gold sparkle bound rosewood fingerboard with western motif engraved pearl block inlays, rosewood bridge with black white dot pins, gold sparkle bound peghead with gold sparkle inlay, 3 per side gold tuners, internal acoustic pickup, volume/3 band EQ controls. Available in White finish. New 1994.
Mfr.'s Sug. Retail $2,500 $2,000 $1,500 $1,250 $1,000 $900 $825 $750

Synchromatic Series

Early Synchromatic models have bulb shape pegheads. Fingerboard inlay listed is the standard, though models are also found with split block, thumb print and other inlay styles.

MODEL 160 — carved spruce top, raised bound tortoise pickguard, bound catseye soundholes, tortoise bound body, carved curly maple back, curly maple sides, 5 piece maple neck, 14/20 fret bound rosewood fingerboard with pearl block inlay, adjustable stylized rosewood bridge/trapeze tailpiece, bound blackface peghead with pearl model name/logo inlay, 3 per side chrome Grover tuners. Available in Sunburst finish. Mfg. 1939 to 1951.
$1,050 $900 $775 $650 $525 $400 $325
This instrument measures 17 inches across the bottom bouts.
In 1942, Natural finish became available.

MODEL 200 — carved spruce top, raised bound tortoise pickguard, bound catseye soundholes, 2 stripe bound body, carved flame maple back, curly maple sides, 5 piece maple neck, 14/20 fret bound rosewood fingerboard with pearl humpblock inlay, adjustable stylized rosewood bridge/trapeze tailpiece, bound blackface peghead with pearl model name/logo inlay, 3 per side gold Grover tuners. Available in Natural and Sunburst finishes. Mfg. 1939 to 1949.
$1,250 $1,100 $950 $825 $700 $550 $475
This instrument measures 17 inches across the bottom bouts.

MODEL 300 — carved spruce top, raised bound tortoise pickguard, bound catseye soundholes, multibound body, carved flame maple back, curly maple sides, 5 piece maple/rosewood neck, 14/20 fret bound ebony fingerboard with pearl humpblock inlay, adjustable stylized Brazilian rosewood bridge/trapeze tailpiece, bound blackface peghead with pearl model name/logo inlay, 3 per side gold Grover tuners. Available in Natural and Sunburst finishes. Mfg. 1939 to 1959.
$1,900 $1,650 $1,400 $1,225 $1,050 $925 $750
This instrument measures 17 inches across the bottom bouts.

MODEL 400 — carved spruce top, raised bound tortoise pickguard, multibound catseye soundholes, multibound body with gold inner stripe, carved flame maple back, curly flame sides, 3 piece curly maple neck, 14/20 fret multibound ebony fingerboard with pearl humpblock with gold stripe inlay, adjustable stylized ebony bridge/trapeze tailpiece, multibound blackface peghead with pearl catseye-stairstep/logo inlay, 3 per side gold Grover Imperial tuners. Available in Natural and Sunburst finishes. Mfg. 1939 to 1955.
$4,000 $3,300 $2,900 $2,625 $2,300 $2,050 $1,775
This instrument measures 18 inches across the bottom bouts.

SYNCHROMATIC — jumbo style, arched spruce top, raised bound tortoise pickguard, bound catseye soundholes, 3 stripe bound body, arched maple back, maple sides/neck, 14/20 fret bound rosewood fingerboard with pearl split humpblock inlay, adjustable stylized ebony bridge/step trapeze tailpiece, bound blackface peghead with pearl model name/logo inlay, 3 per side gold tuners. Available in Sunburst finish. Mfg. 1991 to date.
Mfr.'s Sug. Retail $1,500 $1,200 $900 $750 $600 $540 $495 $450

Gretsch Synchromatic
courtesy Thoroughbred Music

Grading	100%	98% MINT	95% EXC+	90% EXC	80% VG+	70% VG	60% G

Synchromatic C — similar to Synchromatic, except has single round cutaway. Available in Sunburst finish. Mfg. 1991 to date.

Mfr.'s Sug. Retail	$1,750	$1,400	$1,050	$875	$700	$630	$575	$525

Add $100 for Natural finish.

SYNCHROMATIC JUMBO 125F — jumbo style, arched spruce top, triangle soundhole, tortoise shell pickguard, 2 stripe bound body/rosette, figured maple back/sides/neck, 14/21 fret bound rosewood fingerboard with pearloid block inlay, adjustable rosewood bridge/stop tailpiece mounted on triangular rosewood base, black face peghead with pearl logo inlay, 3 per side diecast tuners. Available in Natural top, Sunburst back/side finish. Mfg. 1947 to 1954.

	$1,250	$1,070	$895	$715	$645	$590	$535

Some models had tortoise binding all around, other models came with single body binding.

SYNCHROMATIC 300F — auditorium style, spruce top, triangle soundhole, raised pickguard, 3 stripe body/rosette, maple arched back/sides/neck, 14/21 fret bound rosewood fingerboard with pearloid slashed humptop block inlay, adjustable rosewood stairstep bridge/gold trapeze tailpiece, bound cloud peghead with silkscreened Synchromatic/logo, 3 per side gold tuners. Available in Natural top, Dark back/side finish. Mfg. 1947 to 1955.

	$1,750	$1,500	$1,250	$1,000	$900	$825	$750

Synchromatic 400F — similar to Synchromatic 300F, except has grand auditorium style body. Available in Sunburst back/side finish.

	$3,250	$2,790	$2,320	$1,860	$1,670	$1,535	$1,395

ACOUSTIC ELECTRIC

NIGHTBIRD — single round cutaway jumbo style, solid spruce top, triangle soundhole, 3 stripe bound body, floral pattern rosette, maple back/sides, 2 piece mahogany neck, 21 fret bound rosewood fingerboard with pearl dot inlay, pearl scroll inlay at 12th fret, rosewood bridge with black pearl dot pins, pearl floral pattern bridge wing inlay, bound blackface peghead with pearl logo inlay, 3 per side gold tuners, active ceramic pickup, volume/tone control. Available in Ebony finish. Curr. mfr.

Mfr.'s Sug. Retail	$1,200	$960	$720	$600	$480	$430	$395	$360

Nightbird V — similar to Nightbird, except has rosewood/metal tunomatic bridge/Bigsby vibrato tailpiece.

Mfr.'s Sug. Retail	$1,500	$1,200	$900	$750	$600	$540	$495	$450

ACOUSTIC ELECTRIC BASS

ACOUSTIC BASS — single round cutaway jumbo style, spruce top, triangle soundhole, 3 stripe bound body, floral pattern rosette, maple back/sides/neck, 23 fret bound rosewood fingerboard with pearl dot inlay, pearl scroll inlay at 12th fret, rosewood strings thru bridge, bound blackface peghead with pearl logo inlay, 2 per side gold tuners, active ceramic pickup, volume/tone control. Available in Transparent Orange finish. Curr. mfr.

Mfr.'s Sug. Retail	$1,400	$1,120	$840	$700	$560	$505	$460	$420

This model has fretless fingerboard optionally available.

ELECTRIC

The Gretsch company assigned a name and a four digit number to each guitar model. However, they would also assign another number to the same model in a different color or component assembly. This system helped "expedite the ordering system", says Charles "Duke" Kramer, "you could look at an invoice and know exactly which model and color from one number." References in this section, while incomplete, will list variances in the model designations.

ANNIVERSARY (Model 6124) — single round cutaway semi-hollow maple body, arched top, bound body, f-holes, raised white pickguard with logo, mahogany neck, 21 fret ebony fingerboard with pearloid thumbnail inlay, roller bridge/G logo trapeze tailpiece, blackface peghead with logo inlay, peghead mounted nameplate with engraved diamond, 3 per side tuners, chrome hardware, covered pickup, volume control on cutaway bout, 3 position tone switch. Available in Sunburst (model 6124), Two Tone Green (model 6125), and Two Tone Tan finishes. Mfg. 1958 to 1972.

1958-1964	$750	$640	$535	$430	$390	$355	$325
1965-1972	$600	$515	$425	$340	$310	$280	$255

In 1960, rosewood fingerboard replaced ebony fingerboard.

In 1963, the Two Tone Tan was also designated as model 6125.

Double Anniversary (Model 6117) — similar to Anniversary, except has 2 covered pickups, 2 volume controls, 3 position selector switch. Available in Sunburst (model 6117) and Two Tone Green (model 6118) finishes. Mfg. 1958 to 1975.

1958-1964	$1,500	$1,285	$1,070	$860	$770	$710	$645
1965-1975	$750	$640	$535	$430	$390	$355	$325

In 1961, stereo output was optional. The Anniversary Stereo model was offered in Sunburst (model 6111) and Two Tone Green (model 6112) until 1963.

In 1963, bound fingerboard was added, palm vibrato optional, stereo output was discontinued.

In 1963, Two Tone Brown was also designated at model 6118.

In 1972, f-holes were made smaller, adjustable bridge replaced roller bridge, peghead nameplate was removed.

In 1974, block fingerboard inlay replaced thumbnail inlay, and the sunburst finish designation became model 7560.

Gretsch Malcolm Young Signature model
courtesy Fred Gretsch Company

Grading	100%	98% MINT	95% EXC+	90% EXC	80% VG+	70% VG	60% G

Anniversary-Reissue — similar to Anniversary, except has rosewood fingerboard. Available in Sunburst (model 6124) and 2 Tone Green (model 6125) finishes. Curr. mfr.

Mfr.'s Sug. Retail	$1,500	$1,200	$900	$750	$600	$540	$495	$450

Double Anniversary-Reissue — similar to Anniversary, except has rosewood fingerboard, 2 pickups, 2 volume controls, 3 position switch. Available in Sunburst (model 6117) and 2 Tone Green (model 6118) finishes. Curr. mfr.

Mfr.'s Sug. Retail	$1,700	$1,360	$1,020	$850	$680	$610	$560	$510

ASTRO-JET (Model 6126) — offset double cutaway asymmetrical hardwood body, black pickguard, metal rectangle plate with model name/serial number on bass side cutaway, maple neck, 21 fret bound ebony fingerboard with thumbnail inlay, adjustamatic bridge/Burns vibrato, asymmetrical blackface peghead with silkscreen logo, 4/2 per side tuners, chrome hardware, 2 exposed pickups, 3 controls, 3 switches. Available in Red top/Black back/side finish. Mfg. 1965 to 1968.

		$1,025	$880	$735	$585	$525	$485	$440

ATKINS AXE (Model 7685) — single sharp cutaway bound hardwood body, white pickguard with logo, maple neck, 22 fret bound ebony fingerboard with white block inlay, tunomatic stop bridge, bound black face peghead with logo, 3 per side tuners, chrome hardware, 2 covered humbucker pickups, 2 volume/2 tone controls, 3 position switch. Available in Dark Grey (model 7685) and Rosewood Stain (model 7686) finishes. Mfg. 1976 to 1981.

		$1,025	$880	$735	$585	$525	$485	$440

Atkins Super Axe (Model 7680) — similar to Atkins Axe, except has black plate with mounted controls, volume/3 effects controls, 2 effects switches, active electronics. Available in Red (model 7680), Dark Grey (model 7681), and Sunburst (model 7682).

		$1,075	$920	$770	$615	$555	$505	$460

Gretsch Astro
courtesy Thoroughbred Music

BST ("Beast") Series

Baldwin-owned Gretsch introduced the solid body BST series from 1979 to 1981, and originally they carried a price range from $299 (single pickup, bolt-on neck) up to $695 (two pickup, neck-through design).

The **BST-1000** had a single cutaway solid body, bolt-on 24 fret neck, single humbucker, and volume/tone controls. The BST-1000 was available in Brown (model 8210) or Red (model 8216). The same model designation was also used for the two pickup version, except that Brown was model 8215 and Red was model 8211. Both models featured 2 humbucking pickups, and a 3-way selector switch as extras to the basic single pickup model. In 1981, another single pickup model dubbed the BST-1500 was offered in Brown as model 8217.

The **BST-2000** was offered in 1979 and 1980 as an offset double cutaway solid body guitar with a 22 fret bolt-on neck in Brown (model 8220) and Red (model 8221). The top of the BST line was the **BST-5000** with a laminated neck-through design, and carved edges on the body. The BST-5000 had a 24 fret neck, and was available in Red (model 8250).

BST series guitars at 80% to 90% range in price between $175 and $300.

BIKINI (Model 6023) — double cutaway slide-and-lock poplar body with detachable poplar center block, raised white pickguard with logo, bolt-on maple neck, 22 fret maple fingerboard with black dot inlay, adjustable ebony bridge/trapeze tailpiece, black face peghead with logo, 3 per side tuners, chrome hardware, exposed pickup, volume/tone control. Available in Black finish. Mfg. 1961 to 1963.

	$700	$600	$500	$400	$360	$330	$300

The slide-and-lock body is named a "Butterfly" back and is interchangeable with 6 string or bass shafts. There is also a "double Butterfly", able to accommodate both necks (model 6025). Controls for this instrument are located on top of detachable center block.

BLACK FALCON 1955 SINGLE CUTAWAY — single round cutaway semi hollow bound maple body, raised gold pickguard with flying falcon, bound f-holes, maple neck, 22 fret bound rosewood fingerboard with pearl block inlay, ebony/metal tunomatic bridge/Cadillac tailpiece, bound peghead with pearl gold sparkle logo inlay, 3 per side tuners, gold hardware, 2 humbucker pickups, master volume/2 volume/1 tone controls, selector switch. Available in Black finish. Curr. mfr.

Mfr.'s Sug. Retail	$3,250	$2,600	$1,950	$1,625	$1,300	$1,170	$1,070	$975

Black Falcon I (Model 7594BK) — similar to Black Falcon, except has a Bigsby vibrato tailpiece.

Mfr.'s Sug. Retail	$3,200	$2,560	$1,920	$1,600	$1,280	$1,150	$1,055	$960

This model also available in double round cutaway body (Black Falcon II - Model 7594).

BLACKHAWK (Model 6100) — double round cutaway bound maple body, f-holes, raised silver pickguard with logo, maple neck, 22 fret bound fingerboard with thumbnail inlay, dot inlay above the 12th fret, tuning fork bridge, roller bridge/G logo Bigsby vibrato tailpiece, black face peghead with logo inlay, peghead mounted nameplate, 3 per side tuners, chrome hardware, 2 covered pickups, volume control on upper bout, 2 volume controls, two 3 position switches. Available in Black (model 6101) and Sunburst (model 6100) finishes. Mfg. 1967 to 1972.

	$1,250	$1,070	$895	$715	$645	$590	$535

BRIAN SETZER MODEL (6120SSL) — single round cutaway hollow style, arched flamed maple top, bound f-holes, raised gold pickguard with artist signature/model name/logo, bound body, flame maple back/sides, maple neck, 22 fret bound ebony fingerboard with pearl thumbnail inlay, adjustamatic metal bridge with ebony base/Bigsby vibrato tailpiece, bound flame maple veneered peghead with pearl horseshoe/logo inlay, 3 per side tuners, gold hardware, 2 humbucker Gretsch pickups, master volume/2 volume controls, 3 position/tone switches. Available in Western Orange Lacquer finish. New 1994.

Mfr.'s Sug. Retail	$3,350	$2,680	$2,010	$1,675	$1,340	$1,200	$1,100	$1,000

This model has dice volume control knobs optionally available.

Gretsch Super Axe
courtesy Elliot Rubinson

G

Grading	100%	98% MINT	95% EXC+	90% EXC	80% VG+	70% VG	60% G

Brian Setzer Model (6120SSU) — similar to Brian Setzer Model - SSL, except has Western Orange polyurethane finish. New 1994.

Mfr.'s Sug. Retail	$2,900	$2,320	$1,740	$1,450	$1,160	$1,040	$955	$870

BROADKASTER HOLLOW BODY (Model 7607) — double round cutaway semi hollow bound maple body, f-holes, raised black pickguard with logo, maple neck, 22 fret rosewood fingerboard with white dot inlay, adjustable bridge/G logo trapeze tailpiece, blackface peghead with logo, 3 per side tuners, chrome hardware, 2 covered pickups, master volume/2 volume/2 tone controls, 3 position switch. Available in Natural (model 7607) and Sunburst (model 7608) finishes. Mfg. 1975 to 1980.

	$725	$620	$520	$415	$375	$340	$310

This model was also available with Bigsby vibrato tailpiece as model 7603 (Natural) and model 7604 (Sunburst).

In 1976, tunomatic stop tailpiece, 2 covered humbucker DiMarzio pickups replaced respective items.

Between 1977 and 1979, a Red finish was offered as model 7609.

BROADKASTER SOLID BODY (Model 7600) — offset double cutaway maple body, white pickguard, bolt-on maple neck, 22 fret maple fingerboard with black dot inlay, fixed bridge, 3 per side tuners, chrome hardware, 2 exposed pickups, 2 volume controls, pickup selector/tone switch. Available in Natural (model 7600) and Sunburst (model 7601) finishes. Mfg. 1975 to 1980.

	$550	$470	$395	$315	$285	$260	$235

CHET ATKINS — single cutaway routed mahogany body, bound maple top, raised gold pickguard with signature/logo, G brand on lower bout, tooled leather side trim, maple neck, 22 fret bound rosewood fingerboard with pearl block inlay with engraved western motif, adjustable bridge/Bigsby vibrato tailpiece, bound peghead with maple veneer and pearl steer's head/logo inlay, 3 per side tuners, gold hardware, 2 exposed DeArmond pickups, control on cutaway bout, 2 volume/tone controls, 3 position switch. Available in Red Orange finish. Mfg. 1954 to 1963.

1954-1960	$4,500	$3,860	$3,215	$2,570	$2,315	$2,120	$1,930
1961-1963	$3,250	$2,800	$2,375	$1,950	$1,725	$1,500	$1,225

The Bigsby vibrato was available with or without gold-plating.

This model was originally issued with a jeweled Western styled strap.

In 1957, an ebony fingerboard with humptop block inlay was introduced, Filter-tron pickups replaced original item,"G" brand and tooled leather side trim were discontinued.

In 1958, thumbnail fingerboard inlays replaced block inlays, steer's head peghead inlay replaced horseshoe inlay, tone control replaced by 3-position switch and placed by the pickup selector switch.

In 1961, the body was changed to double cutaway style.

In 1962, a standby switch was added.

Gretsch Chet Atkins Country Gentleman
courtesy Charlie Wirtz

CHET ATKINS COUNTRY GENTLEMAN (Model 6122) — single round cutaway hollow bound maple body, simulated f-holes, gold pickguard with logo, maple neck, 22 fret bound ebony fingerboard with pearl thumbnail inlay, adjustable bridge/Bigsby vibrato tailpiece, bound blackface peghead with logo inlay, peghead mounted nameplate, 3 per side tuners, gold hardware, 2 covered humbucker pickups, master volume/2 volume controls, two 3 position switches. Available in Mahogany and Walnut finishes. Mfg. 1957 to 1981.

1957-1959	$3,225	$2,765	$2,300	$1,840	$1,655	$1,520	$1,380
1960-1969	$1,525	$1,310	$1,090	$870	$785	$720	$655
1970-1981	$1,050	$900	$750	$600	$540	$495	$450

A few of the early models had the Chet Atkins signpost signature on the pickguard, but this was not a standard feature.

The f-holes on this model were inlaid in early production years, then they were painted on, sometimes being painted as if they were bound. A few models produced during 1960-1961 did have actual f-holes in them, probably special order items.

The Bigsby vibrato tailpiece was not gold-plated originally.

In 1961, double round cutaway body, bridge mute, standby switch and padded back became available.

By 1962, gold-plated vibrato was standard.

In 1972, this model became available with open f-holes.

Between 1972 to 1980, a Brown finish was offered as model 7670.

In 1975, a tubular arm was added to the Bigsby vibrato.

In 1979, vibrato arm was returned to a flat bar.

Grading	100% MINT	98% EXC+	95% EXC+	90% EXC	80% VG+	70% VG	60% G

CHET ATKINS HOLLOW BODY,

CHET ATKINS NASHVILLE (Model 6120) — single round cutaway bound maple body, arched top with stylized G brand, bound f-holes, raised gold pickguard with Chet Atkins' sign post signature/logo, maple neck, 22 fret bound rosewood fingerboard with pearl Western motif engraved block inlay, adjustable bridge/Bigsby vibrato tailpiece, bound blackface peghead with steerhead/logo inlay, 3 per side tuners, gold hardware, 2 exposed DeArmond pickups, volume control on cutaway bout, 2 volume/tone controls, 3 position switch. Available in Red, Red Amber and Western Orange finishes. Mfg. 1954 to 1980.

1954-1961	$6,750	$5,785	$4,825	$3,860	$3,470	$3,185	$2,895
1962-1967	$1,500	$1,285	$1,070	$860	$770	$710	$645
1968-1980	$800	$685	$575	$460	$410	$380	$345

'60/'61 Gretsch 6120
courtesy Dave Hinson

Some models were available with body matching pegheads.

In 1956, engraved fingerboard inlay was discontinued, horseshoe peghead inlay replaced steer's head, vibrato unit was nickel plated.

In 1957, humptop fingerboard inlay, Filter-tron pickups replaced original items, G brand on top discontinued.

In 1958, ebony fingerboard with thumbnail inlay and adjustable bar bridge replaced respective items. The tone control changed to a 3 position switch and was placed next to the pickup selector switch.

In 1961, body was changed to a double round cutaway semi-hollow style with painted f-holes, pickguard had no signpost around Chet Atkins' signature, string mute, mute/standby switches (a few models were produced with a mute control) and back pad were added.

In **1967**, this model was renamed the **Nashville**, with Chet Atkins Nashville on pickguard and peghead mounted nameplate.

In 1972, tunomatic bridge and elongated peghead were added, string mute and switch, nameplate were removed.

Between 1972 to 1979, a Red finish was offered as model 7660.

In 1973, real f-holes were added.

In 1975, tubular arm added to vibrato, hardware became chrome plated and the standby switch was removed.

In 1979, flat vibrato arm replaced tubular arm.

CHET ATKINS TENNESSEAN (Model 6119) — single round cutaway hollow bound maple body, arched top, f-holes, raised black pickguard with Chet Atkins' signpost signature/logo, maple neck, 22 fret ebony fingerboard with pearl thumbnail inlay, adjustable bar bridge/Bigsby vibrato tailpiece, 3 per side tuners, chrome hardware, exposed pickup, volume control, 3 position switch. Available in Cherry, Dark Cherry Stain, Mahogany and Walnut finishes. Mfg. 1958 to 1980.

1958-1961	$2,500	$2,140	$1,785	$1,430	$1,285	$1,180	$1,070
1962-1968	$1,250	$1,070	$895	$715	$645	$590	$535
1969-1980	$1,000	$855	$715	$570	$510	$465	$425

In 1961, solid maple top with painted f-holes, grey pickguard with logo, bound rosewood fingerboard, tuners with plastic buttons replaced respective items; exposed pickup, 2 volume controls, tone switch were added.

In 1962, Chet Atkins signature on pickguard, standby switch were added.

In 1963, painted bound f-holes, padded back were added.

In 1964, peghead nameplate became available.

In 1970, real f-holes were added.

In 1972, adjustamatic bridge replaced bar bridge, peghead nameplate was removed.

Between 1972 to 1979, a Dark Red finish was offered as model 7655.

CLIPPER (Model 6186) — single round cutaway bound maple body, arched top, f-holes, raised pickguard with logo, maple neck, 21 fret ebony fingerboard with white dot inlay, adjustable ebony bridge/trapeze tailpiece, blackface peghead with logo, 3 per side tuners with plastic buttons, chrome hardware, exposed DeArmond pickup, volume/tone control. Available in Natural (model 6188), Beige/Grey (model 6187), and Sunburst (model 6186) finishes. Mfg. 1958 to 1975.

	$650	$555	$465	$370	$335	$305	$280

The original release of this model had a deep, full body. By 1958, the body had a thinner, 335 style thickness to it.

In 1963, a palm vibrato was offered as standard, though few models are found with one.

In 1968, vibrato was no longer offered.

In 1972, 2 pickup models became available.

Between 1972 to 1975, a Sunburst/Black finish was offered as model 7555.

COMMITTEE (Model 7628) — double cutaway walnut body, clear pickguard, thru body maple/walnut neck, 22 fret rosewood fingerboard with pearl dot inlay, fixed bridge, bound peghead with burl walnut veneer and pearl logo inlay, 3 per side tuners, chrome hardware, 2 covered humbucker pickups, 2 volume/2 tone controls, 3 position switch. Available in Natural finish. Mfg. 1975 to 1981.

	$425	$365	$305	$245	$220	$200	$185

Gretsch Chet Atkins Tennessean
courtesy Bill Ferrell

Grading	100%	98% MINT	95% EXC+	90% EXC	80% VG+	70% VG	60% G

CONVERTIBLE (Model 6199) — single round cutaway hollow maple body, spruce top, gold pickguard with logo, bound body/f-holes, maple neck, 21 fret bound rosewood fingerboard with pearl humptop block inlay, adjustable rosewood bridge/G logo trapeze tailpiece, bound blackface peghead with logo inlay, 3 per side Grover Imperial tuners, gold hardware, 1 exposed DeArmond pickup, volume/tone control. Available in Bamboo Yellow and Ivory top with Copper Mist and Sunburst body/neck finishes. Mfg. 1955 to 1968.

1955-1959	$2,750	$2,360	$1,965	$1,570	$1,415	$1,295	$1,180
1960-1968	$1,750	$1,500	$1,250	$1,000	$900	$825	$750

The pickup and controls were pickguard mounted on this instrument.

In 1957, ebony fingerboard with thumbnail inlay replaced original fingerboard/inlay.

In 1958, this model was renamed Sal Salvador.

In 1965, block fingerboard inlay replaced thumbnail fingerboard inlay, controls were mounted into the instrument's top.

CORVETTE (Model 6183) — non-cutaway semi-hollow mahogany body, tortoiseshell pickguard, mahogany neck, 20 fret rosewood fingerboard with pearl dot inlay, 2 f-holes, adjustable rosewood bridge/trapeze tailpiece, black face peghead with logo, 3 per side tuners with plastic buttons, chrome hardware, single coil pickup, volume/tone control. Available in Natural (model 6183), Sunburst (model 6182), and Gold (model 6184) finishes. Mfg. 1954 to 1956.

	$725	$650	$575	$500	$470	$415	$325

The semi-hollow Corvette was originally issued as the Electromatic Spanish model. Some models have necks with 21 frets instead of 20.

CORVETTE (Model 6132) — offset double cutaway mahogany body, 2 piece pickguard, mahogany neck, 21 fret rosewood fingerboard with pearl dot inlay, adjustable rosewood bridge/trapeze tailpiece, black face peghead with logo, 3 per side tuners with plastic buttons, chrome hardware, exposed pickup, volume/tone control. Available in Natural (model 6132) and Platinum Grey (model 6133) finishes. Mfg. 1961 to 1978.

	$525	$450	$375	$300	$270	$245	$225

In 1963, cutaways were sharpened and changed, pickguard styling changed, metal bridge replaced ebony bridge, 1 pickup with vibrato (model 6134) or 2 pickups (extra tone control and 3 position switch) with vibrato (model 6135) became optional, Cherry finish added, and Platinum Grey finish discontinued.

In 1964, peghead shape became rounded with 2/4 tuners per side.

In 1966, Silver Duke with Silver Glitter finish and Gold Duke with Gold Glitter finish were offered. Few of these models exist.

COUNTRY CLASSIC I (Model 6122) — single round cutaway semi-hollow bound maple body, raised gold pickguard with model name/logo, bound f-holes, 3 piece maple neck, 22 fret bound ebony fingerboard with pearl thumbnail inlay, ebony/metal tunomatic bridge/Bigsby vibrato tailpiece, bound blackface peghead with pearl logo inlay, peghead mounted metal nameplate, 3 per side tuners, gold hardware, 2 humbucker pickups, master volume/2 volume/1 tone controls, selector switch. Available in Walnut Stain finish. Curr. mfr.

Mfr.'s Sug. Retail	$2,200	$1,760	$1,320	$1,100	$880	$790	$725	$660

This model also available with double round cutaway (Country Classic II - Model 6122-1962).

COUNTRY CLUB (Model 6192) — single round cutaway hollow body, arched laminated maple top, bound body, bound f-holes, raised bound tortoise pickguard, laminated figured maple back/sides, maple neck, 21 fret bound rosewood fingerboard with ivoroid block inlay, Melita bridge/"G" trapeze tailpiece, bound black face peghead with logo, 3 per side Grover Statite tuners, gold hardware, 2 DeArmond single coil pickups, master volume/2 volume/1 tone controls, 3 position switch. Available in Cadillac Green (model 6196), Natural (model 6193), and Sunburst (model 6192) finishes. Mfd. 1954 to 1981.

1954-1957	$2,500	$2,150	$1,875	$1,540	$1,180	$990	$900
1958-1959	$3,200	$2,850	$2,400	$2,080	$1,825	$1,450	$1,050
1960-1969	$3,800	$3,400	$3,000	$2,600	$2,350	$1,950	$1,240
1970-1981	$1,500	$1,180	$1,020	$940	$880	$800	$750

This model measures 17 inches across the bottom bout.

In 1955, raised gold pickguard with logo replaced original item. Raised black pickguards may also be found.

In 1956, peghead truss rod cover was introduced.

In 1958, PAF Filter'Tron humbucker pickups, master/2 volume controls, pickup/tone 3 position switches.

In 1959, Grover Imperial tuners replaced original item.

By 1960, zero fret was introduced, Pat. Num. Filter'Tron pickups replaced respective item.

In 1961, thinline body replaced original item.

In 1962, padded back, string mute with dial knob, standby switch was introduced.

In 1964, Grover "kidney button" tuners replaced respective item, padded back, string mute/dial was discontinued.

In 1965, deep body replaced respective item.

In 1968, Cadillac Green finish was discontinued.

By 1972, raised grey pickguard with engraved logo, block fingerboard inlay, adjustamatic/rosewood bridge, trapeze tailpiece with logo engraved black plastic insert replaced original item.

Between 1972 to 1974, the sunburst designation was changed to model 7575, and Natural was changed to model 7576.

In 1974, master volume/2 volume/2 tone controls, 3 position switch replaced respective items.

In 1975, Antique Stain (model 7577) finish was introduced, Sunburst finish was discontinued.

In 1979 only, Walnut finish was available.

Gretsch USA Country Club (6192-1955)
courtesy Fred Gretsch Company

G

Grading	100%	98% MINT	95% EXC+	90% EXC	80% VG+	70% VG	60% G

Country Club Project-O-Sonic (Model 6101) — similar to Country Club, except has bound ebony fingerboard with pearl thumbnail inlay, Grover Imperial tuners, PAF P.O.S. Filter'Tron "stereo" pickups, treble/bass volume controls, 3 position treble/bass/closing switches. Available in Cadillac Green (model 6103), Natural (model 6102), and Sunburst (model 6101) finishes. Mfd. 1958 to 1967.

$3,000 $2,700 $2,300 $1,900 $1,600 $1,250 $1,040

In 1959, zero nut, standard Pat. Num. Filter'Tron pickups begin to replace original items, 3 tone/1 pickup select, 3 position switches replaced original items.

COUNTRY ROC (Model 7620) — single cutaway routed mahogany body, bound arched maple top, raised pickguard with logo, G brand on lower bout, tooled leather side trim, maple neck, 22 fret bound ebony fingerboard with pearl block inlay with engraved western motif, adjustamatic bridge/"G" trapeze tailpiece with western motif belt buckle, bound peghead with figured maple veneer and pearl horseshoe logo/inlay, 3 per side tuners, gold hardware, 2 exposed pickups, master volume/2 volume/2 tone controls, 3 position switch. Available in Red Stain finish. Mfg. 1974 to 1979.

$2,250 $1,875 $1,650 $1,525 $1,250 $1,000 $850

DELUXE CHET (Model 7680) — single round cutaway semi-hollow bound maple body, bound f-holes, raised black pickguard with model name/logo, 3 piece maple neck, 22 fret bound ebony fingerboard with pearl thumbnail inlay, tunomatic bridge/Bigsby vibrato tailpiece, bound black face peghead with pearl logo inlay, 3 per side tuners, chrome hardware, 2 exposed pickups, master volume/2 volume/2 tone controls, 3 position switch. Available in Dark Red (model 7680) and Walnut (model 7681) finishes. Mfg. 1973 to 1975.

$1,250 $1,050 $900 $750 $625 $550 $475

In 1976, this model was renamed the Super Axe, and was discontinued in 1980.

Duo-Jet Series

These guitars have a single cutaway body, unless otherwise noted. The body is constructed by placing a top on a highly routed body made of pine, maple, mahogany, spruce or plastic drum material, with rosewood fingerboard, mahogany neck and 2 DeArmond Dynasonic pickups, unless noted otherwise.

DUO-JET (Model 6128) — single cutaway routed mahogany body, bound maple top, raised white pickguard with logo, mahogany neck, 22 fret bound rosewood fingerboard with pearloid block inlay, adjustable bridge/G logo trapeze tailpiece, bound black face peghead with logo, 3 per side tuners, chrome hardware, 2 exposed DeArmond pickups, master volume/2 volume/1 tone control, 3 position switch. Available in Black and Sparkle finishes. Mfg. 1953 to 1971.

1953-1960	$2,850	$2,440	$2,035	$1,630	$1,465	$1,345	$1,220
1961-1964	$1,550	$1,330	$1,110	$885	$795	$730	$665
1965-1971	$1,025	$880	$735	$585	$525	$485	$440

This model was available as a custom order instrument with Green finish and gold hardware.

In 1956, humptop fingerboard inlay replaced block inlay.

In 1957, Filter-tron pickups replaced original item.

In 1958, thumbnail fingerboard inlay and roller bridge replaced the respective items, 3 position switch replaced tone control and placed by the other switch.

In 1961, double cutaway body became available.

In 1962, gold pickguard, Burns vibrato, gold hardware and standby switch replaced, or were added, items.

From 1963-1966, Sparkle finishes were offered.

In 1968, Bigsby vibrato replaced existing vibrato/tailpiece, treble boost switch added.

Duo Jet - Reissue — single round cutaway mahogany body, bound arched maple top, raised white pickguard with logo, mahogany neck, 22 fret bound rosewood fingerboard with pearl humpblock inlay, adjustamatic bridge/G logo trapeze tailpiece, bound blackface peghead with pearl horseshoe/logo inlay, 3 per side tuners, chrome hardware, 2 humbucker pickups, master/2 volume/1 tone controls, selector switch. Available in Jet Black top finish. Mfg. 1990 to date.

Mfr.'s Sug. Retail	$1,500	$1,200	$900	$750	$600	$540	$495	$450

Duo Jet 1957 Reissue — single round cutaway mahogany body, bound arched maple top, raised white pickguard with logo, mahogany neck, 22 fret bound rosewood fingerboard with pearl humpblock inlay, adjustamatic metal bridge with rosewood base/Bigsby vibrato tailpiece, bound blackface peghead with pearl logo inlay, 3 per side tuners, chrome hardware, 2 humbucker pickups, master volume/2 volume/1 tone controls, 3 position switch. Available in Black finish. New 1994.

Mfr.'s Sug. Retail	$1,950	$1,560	$1,170	$975	$780	$700	$645	$580

This model has G logo trapeze tailpiece optionally available.

JET FIREBIRD (Model 6131) — similar to Duo Jet, except has black pickguard with logo, 22 fret bound rosewood fingerboard with pearloid block inlay, adjustable bridge/G logo trapeze tailpiece, bound black face peghead with logo, 3 per side tuners, chrome hardware, 2 exposed pickups, master/2 volume/1 tone control, 3 position switch. Available in Red top/Black back/sides/neck finish. Mfg. 1955 to 1971.

1955-1960	$2,250	$1,930	$1,605	$1,285	$1,155	$1,060	$965
1961-1964	$1,550	$1,330	$1,110	$885	$795	$730	$665
1965-1971	$1,500	$1,285	$1,070	$860	$770	$710	$645

A few models were produced without the logo on the pickguard.

Jet Firebird - Reissue — similar to Duo Jet, except has gold pickguard, gold hardware. Available in Cherry Red top finish.

Mfr.'s Sug. Retail	$1,600	$1,280	$960	$800	$640	$575	$530	$480

Gretsch Sparkle Jet
19th Annual Dallas Show

G

Gretsch Fire Jet
Guitarville

Grading	100%	98% MINT	95% EXC+	90% EXC	80% VG+	70% VG	60% G

ELECTROMATIC SPANISH (Model 6182) — hollow bound maple body, arched spruce top, f-holes, raised tortoise pickguard, maple neck, 14/20 fret rosewood fingerboard with white dot inlay, adjustable rosewood bridge/trapeze tailpiece, blackface peghead with engraved logo, Electromatic vertically engraved onto peghead, 3 per side tuners with plastic buttons, chrome hardware, exposed DeArmond pickup, volume/tone control. Available in Natural (model 6185N) and Sunburst (model 6185) finishes. Mfg. 1940 to 1959.

	$350	$300	$250	$200	$180	$165	$150

The original (1940) version of this model had a larger body style. By 1949, the body style was 16 inches across the bottom bouts.

In 1952, the Sunburst finish was redesignated model 6182, and the Natural finish was redesignated model 6183.

In 1955, this model was renamed Corvette, with a new peghead design.

In 1957, a single round cutaway body became available.

Electro II (Model 6187) — similar to Electromatic, except has 2 DeArmond pickups. Available in Natural (model 6188) and Sunburst (model 6187) finishes. Mfd. 1951 to 1955.

	$500	$430	$360	$285	$260	$235	$215

Electro IIC (Model 6193) — similar to Electromatic, except has single round cutaway, gold hardware, 2 DeArmond pickups. Available in Natural (model 6193) and Sunburst (model 6192) finishes. Mfg. 1951 to 1953.

	$500	$430	$360	$285	$260	$235	$215

This model is 17 inches across bottom bout.

In 1953, a truss rod was introduced, Melita bridge repaced original item.

In 1954, this model was renamed Country Club.

MONKEES' ROCK-N-ROLL MODEL (Model 6123) — double round cutaway bound maple body, arched top, bound f-holes, raised white pickguard with Monkees/logo, maple neck, 22 fret bound rosewood fingerboard with pearl double thumbnail inlay, adjustable bridge/Bigsby vibrato tailpiece, blackface peghead with pearl logo inlay, peghead mounted nameplate, 3 per side tuners, chrome hardware, 2 covered pickups, volume control on cutaway bout, 2 volume controls, pickup selector/2 tone switches. Available in Red finish. Mfg. 1966 to 1968.

	$1,295	$1,110	$925	$740	$670	$610	$555

The Monkees' name appears on the truss rod cover and pickguard.

NASHVILLE 1955 CUSTOM (Model 6120) — single round cutaway semi-hollow bound maple body, raised gold pickguard with logo, bound f-holes, 3 piece maple neck, 22 fret bound ebony fingerboard with pearl block inlay, adjustamatic metal bridge with ebony base/Bigsby vibrato tailpiece, bound blackface peghead with pearl horseshoe/logo inlay, 3 per side tuners, gold hardware, 2 humbucker pickups, master/2 volume/1 tone controls, selector switch. Available in Transparent Orange finish. Mfg. 1991 to date.

Mfr.'s Sug. Retail	$1,750	$1,400	$1,050	$875	$700	$630	$575	$525

Add $225 for Blue Sunburst finish.

Nashville Western — similar to Nashville, except has stylized "G" brand on lower bass bout, model name in fence post on pickguard, engraved western motif fingerboard inlay.

Mfr.'s Sug. Retail	$1,875	$1,500	$1,125	$940	$750	$675	$615	$560

Nashville Tiger Maple — similar to Nashville, except has figured maple body/neck.

Mfr.'s Sug. Retail	$2,200	$1,760	$1,320	$1,100	$880	$790	$725	$660

PRINCESS (Model 6106) — offset double cutaway mahogany body, pickguard with "Princess" logo, mahogany neck, 21 fret rosewood fingerboard with pearl dot inlay, adjustable bridge/trapeze tailpiece, Tone Twister vibrato, body matching peghead with logo, 3 per side tuners with plastic buttons, gold hardware, exposed pickup, volume/tone control. Available in Blue, Pink and White finishes. Mfg. 1962 to 1964.

	$2,200	$1,890	$1,575	$1,260	$1,130	$1,040	$945

Pickguard color on this model was dependent on body color.

RALLY (Model 6104) — double round cutaway bound maple body, arched top, f-holes, raised pickguard with sportstripes/logo, maple neck, 22 fret bound rosewood fingerboard with pearl thumbnail inlay, dot inlay above 12th fret, adjustable bar bridge/Bigsby vibrato tailpiece, blackface peghead with logo inlay, 3 per side tuners, chrome hardware, 2 exposed pickups, volume control on cutaway bout, 2 volume/tone controls, pickup selector/treble boost/standby switches. Available in Bamboo Yellow top/Copper Mist back/side (model 6105) and Rally Green (model 6104) finishes. Mfd. 1967 to 1970.

	$950	$815	$680	$545	$490	$445	$405

RAMBLER (Model 6115) — single sharp cutaway ¾ size hollow bound maple body, f-holes, raised black pickguard with logo, maple neck, 20 fret rosewood fingerboard with white dot inlay, adjustable rosewood bridge/G logo trapeze tailpiece, bound blackface peghead with logo inlay, 3 per side tuners with plastic buttons, chrome hardware, 1 exposed DeArmond pickup, volume/tone control. Available in Ivory top/Black body/neck finish. Mfg. 1957 to 1961.

	$550	$470	$395	$315	$285	$260	$235

In 1960, a round cutaway replaced original style cutaway.

ROC JET (Model 6127) — single cutaway mahogany body, arched bound top, raised silver pickguard with logo, mahogany neck, 22 fret bound ebony fingerboard with pearloid halfmoon inlay and zero fret, adjustable bridge/G logo trapeze tailpiece, bound black face peghead with "Roc Jet"logo, 3 per side tuners, chrome hardware, model nameplate on peghead, 2 humbucking pickups, 2 volume/2 tone controls, 3 position switch. Available in Black (model 6130) and Orange (model 6127) finishes. Mfg. 1969 to 1972.

	$1,150	$945	$875	$740	$690	$550	$405

Gretsch USA Nashville (6120-1955)
courtesy Fred Gretsch Company

Grading	100%	98% MINT	95% EXC+	90% EXC	80% VG+	70% VG	60% G

ROC JET (Model 7610) — single cutaway mahogany body, arched bound top, raised silver pickguard with logo, mahogany neck, 22 fret bound rosewood fingerboard with pearloid thumbnail inlay, adjustable bridge/G logo trapeze tailpiece, bound black face peghead with logo, nameplate with serial number attached to peghead, 3 per side tuners, chrome hardware, 2 exposed pickups, master volume on cutaway bout, 2 volume/2 tone controls, 3 position switch. Available in Black (model 7610), Porsche Pumpkin (model 7611), Red (model 7612), and Walnut Stain (model 7613) finishes. Mfg. 1970 to 1980.

| | $950 | $815 | $675 | $540 | $490 | $450 | $405 |

In 1972, the pickguard was redesigned, peghead nameplate was removed.

In 1978, tunomatic stop tailpiece and covered humbucker DiMarzio pickups replaced original items.

ROUNDUP (Model 6130) — single cutaway routed mahogany body, bound knotty pine top, raised tortoise pickguard with engraved steer's head, "G" brand on lower bout, tooled leather side trim, maple neck, 22 fret bound rosewood fingerboard with pearl block inlay with engraved western motif, adjustable bridge/G logo trapeze tailpiece with western motif belt buckle, bound peghead with pine veneer and pearl steer's head/logo inlay, 3 per side tuners, gold hardware, 2 exposed DeArmond pickups, control on cutaway bout, 2 volume/tone controls, 3 position switch. Available in Orange Stain finish. Mfg. 1954 to 1960.

| | $4,250 | $3,640 | $3,035 | $2,430 | $2,185 | $2,005 | $1,820 |

This model was also available with mahogany and maple tops.

This model was originally issued with a jeweled Western styled strap.

ROUNDUP REISSUE (Model 6121) — single round cutaway mahogany body, bound arched maple top, raised gold pickguard with logo, stylized "G" brand on lower bass bout, mahogany neck, 22 fret bound rosewood fingerboard with pearl engraved western motif block inlay, adjustamatic metal bridge with ebony base/Bigsby vibrato tailpiece, bound peghead with pearl horseshoe/logo inlay, 3 per side tuners, gold hardware, 2 humbucker pickups, master/2 volume/1 tone controls, selector switch. Available in Transparent Orange finish. Curr. mfr.

| Mfr.'s Sug. Retail | $1,750 | $1,400 | $1,050 | $875 | $700 | $630 | $575 | $525 |

Gretsch Roundup
19th Annual Dallas Show

SILVER JET (Model 6129) — single cutaway routed mahogany body, bound Nitron plastic top, raised white pickguard with logo, mahogany neck, 22 fret bound rosewood fingerboard with pearloid block inlay, adjustable bridge/G logo trapeze tailpiece, bound black face peghead with logo, 3 per side tuners, chrome hardware, 2 exposed pickups, master/2 volume/1 tone control, 3 position switch. Available in Silver Sparkle finish. Mfg. 1955 to 1963.

| 1955-1960 | $8,500 | $7,290 | $6,075 | $4,860 | $4,370 | $4,010 | $3,645 |
| 1961-1963 | $4,000 | $3,430 | $2,860 | $2,285 | $2,060 | $1,885 | $1,715 |

Any models with Silver Sparkle finish found after 1963 are Duo Jets with Sparkle finish (see Duo Jet earlier in this section).

Silver Jet — single round cutaway mahogany body, bound arched maple top, raised white pickguard with logo, mahogany neck, 22 fret bound rosewood fingerboard with pearl humpblock inlay, adjustamatic bridge/G logo trapeze tailpiece, bound blackface peghead with pearl horseshoe/logo inlay, 3 per side tuners, chrome hardware, 2 humbucker pickups, master/2 volume/1 tone controls, selector switch. Available in Silver Sparkle top finish. Curr. mfr.

| Mfr.'s Sug. Retail | $1,700 | $1,360 | $1,020 | $850 | $680 | $610 | $560 | $510 |

In 1994, Bigsby vibrato tailpiece became optionally available.

SILVER JET 1957 REISSUE — single round cutaway mahogany body, bound arched maple top, raised white pickguard with logo, mahogany neck, 22 fret bound rosewood fingerboard with pearl humpblock inlay, adjustamatic metal bridge with rosewood base/Bigsby vibrato tailpiece, bound blackface peghead with pearl logo inlay, 3 per side tuners, chrome hardware, 2 humbucker pickups, master volume/2 volume/1 tone controls, 3 position switch. Available in Silver Sparkle finish. New 1994.

| Mfr.'s Sug. Retail | $2,150 | $1,720 | $1,290 | $1,075 | $860 | $775 | $710 | $645 |

SILVER JET REISSUE (Model 6129) — single round cutaway mahogany body, bound arched maple top, raised silver pickguard with logo, mahogany neck, 22 fret bound rosewood fingerboard with pearl humpblock inlay, adjustamatic bridge/G logo trapeze tailpiece, bound blackface peghead with pearl horseshoe/logo inlay, 3 per side tuners, chrome hardware, 2 humbucker pickups, master volume/2 volume/1 tone controls, selector switch. Available in Sparkle Silver finish. Curr. mfr.

| Mfr.'s Sug. Retail | $1,600 | $1,280 | $960 | $800 | $640 | $575 | $530 | $480 |

STREAMLINER (Model 6190) — Single cutaway hollow bound body, arched top, f-holes, maple neck, 21 fret bound rosewood fingerboard with pearl 'hump-back' inlay, roller bridge/G logo trapeze tailpiece, blackface peghead with nameplate, 3 per side tuners with plastic buttons, chrome hardware, plastic pickguard, 1 single coil pickup, volume/tone controls. Available in Natural (6191), Yellow/Brown (model 6189), Gold (model 6189), and Sunburst (model 6190) finishes. Mfg. 1954 to 1959.

| | $1,050 | $955 | $880 | $745 | $690 | $545 | $425 |

In 1958, a humbucker replaced the single coil pickup.

STREAMLINER (Model 6102) — double round cutaway bound maple body, arched top, f-holes, maple neck, 22 fret bound rosewood fingerboard with pearl thumbnail inlay, dot inlay above 12th fret, roller bridge/G logo trapeze tailpiece, blackface peghead with nameplate, 3 per side tuners with plastic buttons, chrome hardware, 2 covered pickups, master volume/2 volume controls, pickup selector/treble boost/standby switches. Available in Cherry Red (model 6103) and Sunburst (model 6102) finishes. Mfg. 1969 to 1975.

| | $950 | $815 | $680 | $545 | $490 | $445 | $405 |

In 1972, dot fingerboard inlay and nameplate were removed, tunomatic bridge replaced roller bridge.

Between 1972 to 1975, the Red finish was redesignated model 7566, and the Sunburst finish was redesignated model 7565.

1975 Gretsch Streamliner
courtesy Bobby Chandler

Grading	100%	98% MINT	95% EXC+	90% EXC	80% VG+	70% VG	60% G

SUPER CHET (Model 7690) — single round cutaway hollow bound maple body, bound f-holes, raised black pickguard with engraved model name/logo, maple neck, 22 fret bound ebony fingerboard with abalone floral inlay, adjustamatic bridge/trapeze tailpiece with ebony insert with abalone floral inlay, bound blackface peghead with abalone floral/logo inlay, 3 per side tuners, gold hardware, 2 exposed humbucker pickups, master volume/2 volume/2 tone controls all mounted on the pickguard. Available in Red (model 7690) and Walnut (model 7691) finishes. Mfg. 1972 to 1980.

	$2,200	$1,890	$1,575	$1,260	$1,130	$1,040	$945

This model was also available with Bigsby vibrato tailpiece.

SYNCHROMATIC — single round cutaway jumbo style, arched maple top, bound fang soundholes, raised bound tortoise pickguard, 3 stripe bound body, arched maple back, maple sides/neck, 14/20 fret bound rosewood fingerboard with pearl split humpblock inlay, adjustamatic metal bridge with ebony base/Bigsby vibrato tailpiece, bound blackface peghead with pearl model name/logo inlay, 3 per side tuners, gold hardware, humbucker pickup, volume/tone control, pickguard mounted pickup/controls. Available in Natural finish. Mfg. 1991 to date.

Mfr.'s Sug. Retail	$2,500	$2,000	$1,500	$1,250	$1,000	$900	$825	$750

SYNCHROMATIC JAZZ — single round cutaway multi-bound auditorium style, carved spruce top, raised bound flame maple pickguard, f-holes, flame maple back/sides/neck, 20 fret multi-bound ebony fingerboard with pearl split hump block inlay, adjustable ebony stairstep bridge/trapeze tailpiece, multi-bound blackface peghead with pearl logo inlay, 3 per side Imperial tuners, gold hardware, humbucker pickup, volume control, pickguard mounted pickup/control. Available in Natural and Shaded finishes. Mfg. in USA. New 1993.

Mfr.'s Sug. Retail	$5,700	$4,560	$3,420	$2,850	$2,280	$2,050	$1,880	$1,710

TENNESSEE ROSE (Model 6119) — single round cutaway semi hollow bound maple body, raised silver pickguard with model name/logo, bound f-holes, maple neck, 22 fret bound rosewood fingerboard with pearl thumbnail inlay, ebony/metal tunomatic bridge/Bigsby vibrato tailpiece, black face peghead with pearl logo inlay, 3 per side tuners, chrome hardware, 2 humbucker pickups, master volume/2 volume/1 tone controls, selector switch. Available in Dark Cherry Red Stain finish. Curr. mfr.

Mfr.'s Sug. Retail	$1,495	$1,196	$897	$750	$600	$540	$495	$450

1975 Gretsch Super Chet
courtesy Dave Hinson

TK-300 — offset double cutaway solid body, white pickguard, bolt-on maple neck, 22 fret rosewood fingerboard with dot inlay, stop bridge, "hockey stick" peghead, 6 on a side tuners, chrome hardware, 2 humbucker pickups, volume/tone controls, 3-way pickup selector switch. Available in Red (model 7624) and Natural (model 7625) finishes. Mfg. 1977 to 1981.

	$325	$300	$250	$215	$185	$155	$125

VAN EPS (Model 6079) — single round cutaway hollow bound maple body, bound f-holes, raised white pickguard with logo, maple neck, 21 fret bound ebony fingerboard with pearl thumbnail inlay, tuning fork bridge, roller bridge/G logo trapeze tailpiece, bound blackface asymmetrical peghead with pearl logo inlay, peghead mounted nameplate, 4/3 per side tuners, gold hardware, 2 covered humbucker pickups, master volume/2 volume controls, pickup selector/tone/standby switches. Available in Sunburst (model 6079) and Walnut (model 6080) finishes. Mfg. 1968 to 1979.

	$1,950	$1,670	$1,395	$1,115	$1,005	$920	$835

The above model was a 7-string version. A **6-string version** was also offered with 3 per side tuners in Sunburst (model 6081) and Brown (model 6082), though it was discontinued in 1972.

In 1972, peghead nameplate, tuning fork bridge and standby switch were removed, ebony bridge and chrome hardware replaced respective items.

Between 1972 to 1979, the Brown finish was redesignated model 7581, and the Sunburst finish was redesignated model 7580.

VIKING (Model 6187) — double round cutaway hollow bound maple body, f-holes, raised pickguard with Viking/logo, 21 fret bound ebony fingerboard with pearl thumbnail inlay, offset dot inlay above 12th fret, string mute, roller bridge/Bigsby vibrato tailpiece with telescoping arm, bound blackface peghead with pearl logo inlay, peghead mounted nameplate, 3 per side tuners, gold hardware, 2 covered humbucker rail pickups, master volume/2 volume controls, pickup selector/tone/mute/standby switches, leatherette back pad. Available in Cadillac Green (model 6189), Natural (model 6188), and Sunburst (model 6187) finishes. Mfg. 1964 to 1974.

	$1,250	$1,070	$895	$715	$645	$590	$535

Early models had a Viking ship on the pickguard as well as the logos.

In 1966, tuning fork bridge was added.

In 1968, flat arm vibrato unit replaced original item.

In 1972, string mute, tuning fork and back pad were removed.

Between 1972 to 1974, the Natural finish was redesignated model 7586, and the Sunburst finish was redesignated model 7585.

Gretsch Viking
courtesy Elliot Rubinson

Grading	100%	98% MINT	95% EXC+	90% EXC	80% VG+	70% VG	60% G

WHITE FALCON (Model 6136) — single round cutaway hollow bound maple body, arched spruce top, bound f-holes, raised gold pickguard with falcon/logo, maple neck, 21 fret bound ebony fingerboard with pearl "feather engraved" humptop block inlay, adjustable bridge/G logo tubular trapeze tailpiece, bound V styled whiteface peghead with vertical Gold Sparkle wings/logo, 3 per side Grover Imperial tuners, gold hardware, 2 exposed DeArmond pickups, master volume on cutaway bout, 2 volume/1 tone control, 3 position switch. Available in White finish. Mfg. 1955 to 1981.

1955-1958	$13,000	$11,140	$9,285	$7,430	$6,685	$6,130	$5,570
1959-1961	$17,000	$14,570	$12,145	$9,715	$8,745	$8,015	$7,285
1962-1963	$5,750	$4,930	$4,110	$3,285	$2,960	$2,710	$2,465
1964	$4,000	$3,430	$2,860	$2,285	$2,060	$1,885	$1,715
1965-1981	$2,300	$1,970	$1,645	$1,315	$1,185	$1,085	$985

Art Wiggs
19th Annual Dallas Show

This instrument had Gold Sparkle binding and jeweled control knobs. The Gold Sparkle binding was not on all bound edges on the earliest models and it was sometimes omitted during this instruments production run.

In 1957, Filter-tron pickups replaced original item.

In 1958, arched maple top, thumbnail fingerboard inlay, horizontal peghead logo, roller bridge and tone switch (placed by pickup selector control) replaced original items, peghead mounted nameplate was added, though it was not placed on all instruments produced. Stereo output became optionally available (as Model 6137).

In 1959, second version of stereo output offered with 3 tone switches placed by pickup selector switch.

In 1960, double mute with 2 controls and back pad were added.

In 1962, double round cutaway body and Bigsby vibrato tailpiece became standard, it was offered as an option up to this time. Some models had a "G" logo tubular trapeze tailpiece. Stereo models had master volume control removed and pickup selector switch put in its place.

In 1963, mute controls were changed to switches.

In 1964, Gretsch G logo vibrato trapeze tailpiece and oval button tuners replaced respective items.

In 1965, offset dot fingerboard inlay above 12th fret was added, stereo tone switches were moved to lower bout and controls/switches were reconfigured.

In 1966, tuning fork bridge was added.

In 1972, Bigsby vibrato unit replaced Gretsch vibrato unit.

Between 1972 to 1981, the model was redesignated model 7594.

In 1980, non-stereo models were discontinued, double round cutaway stereo model (model 7595) available as special order item.

White Falcon Reissue — reissue of original White Falcon design. Available in White finish. Mfg. 1972 to 1981.

	$4,300	$3,685	$3,075	$2,460	$2,210	$2,030	$1,845

WHITE FALCON 1955 SINGLE CUTAWAY — single round cutaway semi-hollow bound maple body, raised gold pickguard with flying falcon, bound f-holes, maple neck, 22 fret bound rosewood fingerboard with pearl block inlay, ebony/metal tunomatic bridge/Cadillac tailpiece, bound peghead with pearl gold sparkle logo inlay, 3 per side tuners, gold hardware, 2 humbucker pickups, master volume/2 volume/1 tone controls, selector switch. Available in White finish. Mfg. 1991 to date.

Mfr.'s Sug. Retail	$3,250	$2,600	$1,950	$1,625	$1,300	$1,170	$1,070	$975

White Falcon I 1955 Custom (Model 6136-1955) — similar to White Falcon 1955 Single Cutaway, except has Bigsby vibrato tailpiece.

Mfr.'s Sug. Retail	$3,000	$2,400	$1,800	$1,500	$1,200	$1,080	$990	$900

This model also available in double round cutaway body (White Falcon II).

WHITE PENGUIN (Model 6134) — single cutaway mahogany body, bound arched top, raised gold pickguard with penguin/logo, mahogany neck, 22 fret bound ebony fingerboard with pearl "feather engraved" humptop block inlay, adjustable bridge/G logo tubular trapeze tailpiece, bound V styled white face peghead with vertical Gold Sparkle wings/logo, 3 per side Grover Imperial tuners, gold hardware, 2 exposed DeArmond pickups, master/2 volume/1 tone control, 3 position switch. Available in White finish. Mfg. 1955 to 1963.

	$60,000	$55,200	$50,000	$43,800	$38,500	$29,800	$21,000

Originally released with banjo armrest attached to bass lower bout.

This guitar is ultra rare; and of the 50 manufactured, only 19 are accounted for.

This instrument had gold sparkle binding and jeweled control knobs.

In 1957, Filter-tron pickups replaced original item.

In 1958, thumbnail fingerboard inlay, roller bridge replaced the respective items, 3 position switch replaced tone control and was placed by the other switch.

In 1959, horizontal logo/metal nameplate was applied to peghead.

In 1961, double cutaway body became available.

ELECTRIC BASS

BIKINI — double cutaway slide-and-lock poplar body with detachable poplar center block, bolt-on maple neck, 17 fret maple fingerboard with black dot inlay, adjustable ebony bridge/stop tailpiece, black face peghead with logo, 2 per side tuners, chrome hardware, humbucker pickup, volume/tone control. Available in Black finish. Mfg. 1961 to 1963.

	$500	$430	$360	$285	$260	$235	$215

The slide-and-lock body is called a "Butterfly" back and is interchangeable with 6 string or bass shafts. There was also a "double Butterfly", able to accommodate both necks. Controls for this instrument are located on top of detachable center block.

1960 Gretsch White Penguin
courtesy Art Wiggs

Grading	100%	98% MINT	95% EXC+	90% EXC	80% VG+	70% VG	60% G

Grimes Archtop
courtesy Stephen Grimes

BROADKASTER — offset double cutaway maple body, white pickguard, bolt-on maple neck, 20 fret maple fingerboard with black dot inlay, fixed bridge with cover, 2 per side tuners, chrome hardware, exposed pickup, volume/tone control. Available in Natural and Sunburst finishes. Mfg. 1975 to 1979.

	$525	$450	$375	$300	$270	$245	$225

Broadkaster - Reissue — single round cutaway semi hollow bound maple body, bound f-holes, maple neck, 20 fret bound rosewood fingerboard with pearl thumbnail inlay, adjustamatic metal bridge with ebony base/trapeze tailpiece, blackface peghead with pearl logo inlay, 2 per side tuners, chrome hardware, 2 humbucker pickups, 2 volume/1 tone controls, selector switch. Available in Natural and Transparent Orange finishes. Current production.

Mfr.'s Sug. Retail	$1,875	$1,500	$1,125	$940	$750	$675	$615	$560

COMMITTEE — double cutaway walnut body, clear pickguard, thru body maple/walnut neck, 22 fret rosewood fingerboard with pearl dot inlay, fixed bridge, bound peghead with burl walnut veneer and pearl logo inlay, 2 per side tuners, chrome hardware, exposed pickup, volume/tone control. Available in Natural finish. Mfg. 1977 to 1981.

	$425	$365	$305	$245	$220	$200	$185

MODEL 6070 — double round cutaway hollow bound maple body, arched top with painted bound f-holes, finger rests, maple neck, 20 fret rosewood fingerboard with white dot inlay, string mute with switch, roller bridge/G logo trapeze tailpiece, bound blackface peghead with metal nameplate, 2 per side tuners, gold hardware, covered pickup, volume control, tone/standby switches, padded back. Available in Amber Red and Sunburst finishes. Mfg. 1962 to 1972.

	$500	$430	$360	$285	$260	$235	$215

This instrument was also called the Country Gentleman Bass.

MODEL 6071 — single round cutaway hollow bound maple body, painted bound f-holes, finger rests, maple neck, 21 fret rosewood fingerboard with white dot inlay, string mute with switch, roller bridge/G logo trapeze tailpiece, blackface peghead with logo, 4 on one side tuners, gold hardware, covered pickup, volume control, tone/standby switches. Available in Mahogany finish. Mfg. 1964 to 1972.

	$400	$340	$285	$230	$205	$190	$170

In 1967, chrome hardware replaced gold hardware.

MODEL 6072 — double round cutaway hollow bound maple body, arched top with painted bound f-holes, finger rests, maple neck, 20 fret rosewood fingerboard with white dot inlay, string mute with switch, roller bridge/G logo trapeze tailpiece, bound blackface peghead with metal nameplate, 2 per side tuners, gold hardware, 2 covered pickups, master/2 volume controls, pickup selector/tone/standby switches, padded back. Available in Sunburst finish. Mfg. 1964 to 1972.

	$650	$555	$465	$370	$335	$305	$280

MODEL 6073 — single round cutaway hollow bound maple body, painted bound f-holes, finger rests, maple neck, 21 fret rosewood fingerboard with white dot inlay, string mute with switch, roller bridge/G logo trapeze tailpiece, blackface peghead with logo, 4 on one side tuners, gold hardware, 2 covered pickups, master/2 volume controls, pickup selector/tone/standby switches. Available in Mahogany finish. Mfg. 1964 to 1972.

	$450	$385	$325	$260	$230	$215	$195

In 1967, chrome hardware replaced gold hardware.

MODEL 7615 — offset double cutaway asymmetrical mahogany body treble bout cutout, rosewood pickguard with finger rests, mahogany neck, 22 fret bound rosewood fingerboard with white dot inlay, fixed bridge, bound peghead with logo, 2 per side tuners, chrome hardware, 2 exposed pickups, 2 controls, 3 position switch. Available in Mahogany finish. Mfg. 1972 to 1975.

	$275	$235	$195	$155	$140	$125	$115

TK 300 7626 — offset double cutaway maple body with divot in bottom, white pickguard, bolt-on maple neck, 20 fret rosewood fingerboard, fixed bridge with cover, chrome hardware, 4 on one side tuners, exposed pickup, volume/tone control. Available in Autumn Red Stain and Natural finishes. Mfg. 1977-1981.

	$300	$260	$215	$175	$155	$140	$130

Grimes Jazz Laureate
courtesy Scott Chinery

GRIMES

Instruments built in Kula, Hawaii since 1974.

Luthier Stephen Grimes originally apprenticed with a violin maker and set up his own mandolin shop in 1972. Two years later, Grimes focused on handcrafting archtop guitars. Grimes continues to build high quality guitars out of personally selected woods. For more information regarding models, pricing, and availability, please contact luthier Grimes through the Index of Current Manufacturers at the back of this book.

GRIMSHAW

Instruments produced in England from the 1950s through the late 1970s.

While this company is best known for its high quality archtop guitars, they also produced a notable semi-hollowbody design in the mid 1950s called the Short-Scale. In the early 1960s, Emil Grimshaw introduced the Meteor solid body guitar. The company then focused on both original and copies of American designs from the late 1960s on.

(Source: Tony Bacon and Paul Day, The Guru's Guitar Guide)

GROSSMAN

See chapter on House Brands.

Before World War II, the majority of guitars were sold through mail-order distributors. The Grossman company distributed a number of guitars built for them with their trademark on the headstock.

(Source: Tom Wheeler, American Guitars)

GROWLER

See PALMER.

GRUGGETT

Instruments originally built in Bakersfield, California circa 1960s. Instruments currently produced by the Gruggett Mfg. Company in Bakersfield, California. Distributed by Stark-Marquadt of Bakersfield, California or Jacobson's Service in Denver, Colorado.

Luthier Bill Gruggett originally worked at the Mosrite plant for Semie Moseley beginning in 1962. Gruggett worked his way up to a management position at Mosrite, but when he returned from a vacation in 1966 found that he had been replaced. Gruggett then went to work for another ex-Mosrite employee named Joe Hall, who produced a limited amount of Hallmark "Sweptwing" guitars.

In 1967, Gruggett started his own **Gruggett Guitars**. He built the first forty models of the "Stradette" guitar in his garage, and then moved to a factory in downtown Bakersfield and hired four employees. Between 1967 and 1968, the company started around 300 guitars but only finished 120 of them. During that same year, Gruggett built thirty-five ES-335-style guitars for Ed Pregor of Hollywood (which carried Pregor's **EPCORE** label). From 1969 to 1974, Gruggett ran the family's pipe and cable business. Two years later, when Semie Moseley returned to Bakersfield to reopen Mosrite, he called on Gruggett to manage the plant. Unfortunately, Semie's venture ran out of operating capital four months later - and Gruggett was back to building his own models again. Gruggett Guitars is still in full operation, and luthier Bill Gruggett is building a variety of designs from traditional solid body to hand carved custom guitars.

(Source: Peter Jacobson, Jacobson's Service; and Hal Hammer)

Gruggett Stradette
courtesy Bill Gruggett

GTX

Instruments are currently produced in Korea and distributed by the Kaman Music Corporation of Bloomfield, Connecticut.

The GTX trademark is the brandname of the Kaman Corporation for this series of Fender-ish and 'superstrat' solid body models. Imported from Korea since the late 1980s, The GTX line offers comfortable feeling and good sounding guitars at reasonable prices.

GUDELSKY MUSICAL INSTRUMENTS

Instruments were built in Vista, California from 1985 to 1996. Distribution was handled by Gudelsky Musical Instruments of Vista, California.

Luthier Harris Paul Gudelsky (1964-1996) had apprenticed to James D'Aquisto before starting Gudelsky Musical Instruments. Gudelsky's personal goal was to try to build a more modern version of the archtop guitar. Gudelsky offered a small line of instruments exclusively on a customer order basis that included hollow body archtops (acoustic and electric/acoustic) ranged between $4,290 and $5,500; semi hollow bodies ranged from $4,235 to $4,400; and set-neck solid bodies ranged from $2,450 to $3,500. Paul Gudelsky was found fatally shot at his Vista, California home in May, 1996.

GUGINO

Instruments built in Buffalo, New York between the 1930s and 1940s.

Luthier Carmino Gugino built instruments that featured high quality conventional building (the frets, finish, carving, etc.) combined with very unconventional design ideas. As detailed by Jay Scott, certain models feature necks that screw on to the body, or have asymetrical bodies, or an archtop that has a detachable neck/body joint/bridge piece that is removable from the body. Anyone with further information is invited to write to the **Blue Book of Guitars** for updates in future editions.

(Source: Teisco Del Rey, Guitar Player magazine, October 1985)

GUILD

Manufactured by Guild Guitars of Westerly, Rhode Island. Guild was recently purchased in 1995 by the Fender Musical Instrument Corporation of Scottsdale, Arizona. Distribution of Guild Guitars is handled through FMIC.

Contrary to stories of a "guild of old world-style craftsmen" gathering to build these exceptional guitars, Guild was founded in 1952 by Alfred Dronge. Dronge, a Jewish emigrant from Europe, grew up in New York City and took jobs working for various music stores on Park Row. Dronge became an accomplished musician who played both banjo and guitar, and loved jazz music. His experience in teaching music and performing in small orchestras led to the formation of the Sagman and Dronge music store.

Gruggett Velvet Touch
courtesy Bill Gruggett

After World War II, Dronge gave up the music store in favor of importing and distributing Italian accordions. The Sonola Accordion Company was successful enough to make Dronge a small fortune. It is with this reputation and finances that Dronge formed Guild Guitars, Inc. with ex-Ephiphone sales manager George Mann. Incidentally, the "Guild" name came from a third party who was involved with a guitar amplifier company that was going out of business. As the plant was closing down Dronge and Gene Detgen decided to keep the name. The Guild company was registered in 1952.

As the original New York-based Epiphone company was having problems with the local unions, they decided to move production down to Philadelphia. Dronge took advantage of this decision and attracted several of their ex-luthiers to his company. Some of the workers were of Italian ancestry, and felt more comfortable remaining in the "Little Italy" neighborhood rather than moving to Pennsylvania.

The company was originally located in a New York loft from 1952 through 1956. They expanded into a larger workshop in Hoboken, New Jersey, in late 1956. Finally, upon completion of new facilities, Guild moved to its current home in Westerly, Rhode Island, in 1969.

As pop music in the 1960s spurred on a demand for guitars, musical instrument companies expanded to meet the business growth. At the same time, large corporations began to diversify their holdings. Most people are aware of the CBS decision to buy Fender in 1965, or Baldwin Piano's purchase of the Burns trademark and manufacturing equipment in 1967. In 1966 electronic parts producer Avnet Inc. bought Guild Musical Instruments, and Alfred Dronge stayed on as president. Dronge also hired Jim Deurloo (of Gibson and later Heritage fame) as plant manager in December 1969. Deurloo's commitment to quality control resulted in better consistency of Guild products.

Tragedy occurred in 1972 as Alfred Dronge was killed in an aircraft crash. The relationships he built with the members of the company dissipated, and the driving force of twenty years since the inception was gone. However, Leon Tell, Guild's vice president from 1963 to 1973 became the company president in 1973 and maintained that position until 1983.

In mid August of 1986, Avnet sold Guild to a management/investment group from New England and Tennessee. Officers of the newly formed Guild Music Corporation included company President Jerre R. Haskew (previously Chief Executive Officer and President of the Commerce Union Bank of Chattanooga Tennessee), Executive Vice President of Plant and Operations George A. Hammerstrom, and Executive Vice President of Product Development and Artist Relations George Gruhn (noted authority on vintage stringed instruments). Gruhn later left the company in early 1988.

Unfortunately, the remaining members of the investment group defaulted on bank obligations in November of 1988, leading to a court supervised financial restructuring. The Faas Corporation of New Berlin, Wisconsin (now U.S. Musical Corporation) bought Guild on January 1989. Solid body guitar production was discontinued in favor of acoustic and acoustic-electric production (a company strength) although some electric models were "reissued" in the mid 1990s.

Most recently, the Guild company was purchased by Fender Musical Instrument Corporation in 1995. A recent 1996 catalog shows an arrangement of acoustic and acoustic-electric models, as well as some semi-hollowbody guitars and one solid body electric. All current production is distributed through Fender Musical Instrument Corporation of Scottsdale, Arizona.

(Reference source for early Guild history: Hans Moust, The Guild Guitar Book; contemporary history courtesy Jay Pilzer)

Identifying Features on Guild Instruments

According to noted authority and Guild enthusiast Jay Pilzer, there are identifying features on Guild instruments that can assist in dating them.

Knobs on Electrics:

1953-58 transparent barrel knobs; 1959-63 transparent yellowish top hat knobs with Guild logo in either chrome or gold; 1964-72 black top hat knobs, Guild logo, tone or vol; circa 1990-present black top hat with Guild logo, no numbers or tone/vol.

Electric Pickguards:

Except for the Johnny Smith/Artist Award (which used the stairstep pickguard), Guild pickguards were rounded, following the shape of the guitar until 1963 when the stairstep became standard on archtop electrics.

Acoustic Pickguards:

Most models have distinct Guild shape in either tortoise or black with rounded edges that follow the line of guitar, except the F-20, M-20, and new "A" series which have teardrop pickguards.

Headstock Inlays:

The earliest were simple Guild inverted "V" with triangular insert, with "G" logo below, later the triangular insert disappears, Chesterfield introduced on some models by 1957. In general the more elaborate the headstock, the higher price the instrument.

Grading	100%	98% MINT	95% EXC+	90% EXC	80% VG+	70% VG	60% G

ACOUSTIC ARCHTOPS

Archtop Models

A-50 GRANADA — hollow non-cutaway style bound body (16¼ inch at lower bout), laminated arched spruce top, f-holes, raised black pickguard, mahogany back/sides/neck, 14/20 fret rosewood fingerboard with pearl dot inlay, adjustable rosewood bridge/trapeze tailpiece, blackface peghead with screened logo, 3 per side nickel tuners. Available in Sunburst finish. Mfd. 1952 to 1968.

| | $450 | $425 | $375 | $325 | $275 | $200 | $150 |

A-150 — hollow single round cutaway style bound body (17 inch at lower bout), carved solid spruce top, f-holes, raised black pickguard, laminated maple back and sides, 20 fret rosewood fingerboard with block inlay, 24¾ inch scale, adjustable rosewood bridge/trapeze tailpiece, blackface peghead with screened logo, 3 per side nickel tuners. Available in Sunburst finish. Mfd. 1953 to 1973.

| | $1,350 | $1,275 | $1,200 | $1,150 | $1,075 | $1,000 | $925 |

A-350 STRATFORD — single round cutaway hollow style, arched spruce top, raised black laminated pickguard, 2 bound f-holes, multibound body, maple back/sides/neck, 20 fret bound rosewood fingerboard with pearl block inlay, adjustable rosewood bridge/harp tailpiece, multibound blackface peghead with pearl shield/logo inlay, 3 per side gold tuners. Available in Sunburst finish. Mfg. 1952 to 1972.

| | $1,200 | $1,100 | $950 | $825 | $700 | $575 | $525 |

A-500 STUART — single round cutaway hollow style, bound arched solid spruce top, 2 bound f-holes, bound tortoise pickguard, maple back/sides/neck, 20 fret bound ebony fingerboard with pearl block/abalone wedge inlay, adjustable ebony bridge, stylized trapeze tailpiece, bound peghead with pearl shield/logo inlay, 3 per side gold Imperial tuners. Available in Natural and Sunburst finishes. Mfg. 1952 to 1966.

| | $1,600 | $1,550 | $1,450 | $1,200 | $900 | $850 | $800 |

ARTIST AWARD — single round cutaway hollow style, bound solid spruce archtop, 2 bound f-holes, bound tortoise pickguard, German maple back/sides, 5 piece maple neck, 20 fret bound ebony fingerboard with pearl block/abalone wedge inlay, adjustable ebony bridge, stylized trapeze tailpiece, bound peghead with pearl/abalone inscribed block/logo inlay, 3 per side Imperial tuners, gold hardware, special design pickup. Available in Blonde and Sunburst finishes. Mfg. 1954 to date.

| Mfr.'s Sug. Retail | $5,500 | $4,125 | $2,750 | $2,745 | $2,195 | $1,975 | $1,810 | $1,645 |

This instrument began life as the "Johnny Smith Model", though shortly after its debut Mr. Smith discontinued his association with Guild.

CA-100 CAPRI — single sharp cutaway hollow style, arched bound spruce top, raised bound black pickguard, 2 f-holes, maple back/sides/neck, 20 fret bound rosewood fingerboard with pearl block inlay, adjustable rosewood bridge/trapeze tailpiece, blackface peghead with pearl shield/logo inlay, 3 per side chrome tuners. Available in Sunburst finish. Mfg. 1956 to 1972.

| | $650 | $600 | $550 | $450 | $375 | $300 | $275 |

In 1954, harp tailpiece replaced original item.

ACOUSTIC

A Series

A-25HR — concert size body, spruce top, mahogany back and sides, rosewood fingerboard with dot inlays, rosewood bridge, 3+3 headstock, tortoise shell pickguard. Curr. production.

| Mfr.'s Sug. Retail | $899 | $674 | $449 | $435 | $380 | $300 | $260 | $200 |

A-25HG — similar to the A-25HR, except has a high gloss finish.

| Mfr.'s Sug. Retail | $1,099 | $879 | $659 | $650 | $570 | $500 | $450 | $375 |

A-50 — similar to the A-25HR, except has rosewood back and sides, abalone rosette, ebony fingerboard and bridge.

| Mfr.'s Sug. Retail | $1,499 | $1,274 | $1,049 | $950 | $845 | $760 | $675 | $535 |

The A-50 steel string design is not to be confused with the earlier A-50 archtop.

Dreadnought Series

All models in this series have dreadnought style bodies.

D-4 — solid spruce top, round soundhole, tortoise pickguard, 3 stripe bound body/rosette, mahogany back/sides/neck, 14/20 fret rosewood fingerboard with pearl dot inlay, rosewood bridge with white black dot pins, 3 per side chrome tuners. Available in Natural finish. Curr. mfr.

| Mfr.'s Sug. Retail | $730 | $547 | $365 | $345 | $260 | $235 | $215 | $195 |

D-4 HG — similar to D-4, except has high gloss finish. Disc. 1994.

| | $625 | $535 | $445 | $360 | $325 | $300 | $275 |

Last Mfr.'s Sug. Retail was $895.

D-4/12 — similar to D-4, except has 12 strings, 6 per side tuners. Curr. mfr.

| Mfr.'s Sug. Retail | $900 | $675 | $450 | $405 | $320 | $270 | $245 | $225 |

D-6 — similar to D-4, except has gold hardware. Available in Natural finish. Curr. mfr.

| Mfr.'s Sug. Retail | $950 | $712 | $475 | $430 | $340 | $280 | $260 | $235 |

Grading	100%	98% MINT	95% EXC+	90% EXC	80% VG+	70% VG	60% G

D-6 HG — similar to D-4, except has gold hardware, high gloss finish. Curr. mfr.

Mfr.'s Sug. Retail	$1,100	$825	$550	$525	$415	$360	$330	$300

D-15 — mahogany top/back/sides/neck, round soundhole, tortoise pickguard, 3 stripe rosette, 14/20 fret rosewood fingerboard with pearl dot inlay, rosewood bridge with white black dot pins, 3 per side chrome tuners. Available in Black, Natural and Woodgrain Red finishes. Mfg. 1987 to 1994.

		$595	$510	$425	$340	$305	$280	$255

Last Mfr.'s Sug. Retail was $850.

D-25 — solid spruce top, round soundhole, tortoise pickguard, black bound body, 3 stripe rosette, mahogany back/sides/neck, 14/20 fret rosewood fingerboard with pearl dot inlay, rosewood bridge with white black dot pins, 3 per side chrome tuners. Available in Black, Natural and Sunburst finishes. Mfg. 1979 to date.

Mfr.'s Sug. Retail	$950	$760	$570	$500	$400	$360	$330	$300

D-25 M — similar to D-25, except has mahogany top.

		$595	$525	$450	$400	$360	$330	$300

D-25/12 — similar to D-25 except has 12 strings, 6 per side tuners. Curr. mfr.

Mfr.'s Sug. Retail	$1,100	$825	$550	$545	$435	$395	$360	$330

D-35 — solid spruce top, round soundhole, tortoise pickguard, bound body, 1 stripe rosette, mahogany back/sides/neck, 14/20 fret rosewood fingerboard with pearl dot inlay, rosewood bridge with white black dot pins, screened peghead logo, 3 per side chrome tuners. Available in Natural finish.

		$750	$730	$700	$650	$600	$500	$400

D-40 — solid spruce top, round soundhole, tortoise pickguard, bound body, 3 stripe rosette, mahogany back/sides/neck, 14/20 fret rosewood fingerboard with pearl dot inlay, rosewood bridge with white black dot pins, pearl Chesterfield/logo peghead inlay, 3 per side chrome tuners. Available in Natural finish. Disc. 1991.

		$905	$775	$645	$515	$465	$425	$385

Last Mfr.'s Sug. Retail was $1,295.

This model had single sharp cutaway (D4C) optionally available.

D-44 — solid spruce top, round soundhole, tortoise pickguard, 5 stripe bound body/rosette, pearwood back/sides, mahogany neck, 14/20 fret ebony fingerboard with pearl dot inlay, ebony bridge with white black dot pins, pearl Chesterfield/logo peghead inlay, 3 per side chrome tuners. Available in Natural and Sunburst finishes. Mfg. 1964 to 1979.

		$850	$800	$750	$650	$550	$500	$450

In 1974, maple back/sides (D44M) replaced original item.

D-46 — similar to the D-44, except has ash back and sides.

		$900	$850	$800	$750	$700	$625	$550

D-50 — solid spruce top, round soundhole, tortoise pickguard, 5 stripe bound body/rosette, rosewood back/sides, mahogany neck, 14/20 fret ebony fingerboard with pearl dot inlay, ebony bridge with white black dot pins, pearl Chesterfield/logo peghead inlay, 3 per side chrome tuners. Available in Natural and Sunburst finishes. Disc. 1994.

		$975	$835	$700	$560	$505	$460	$420

Last Mfr.'s Sug. Retail was $1,395.

D-55 — solid spruce top, round soundhole, tortoise pickguard, 3 stripe bound body/rosette, rosewood back/sides, 3 piece mahogany neck, 14/20 fret bound ebony fingerboard with pearl block/abalone wedge inlay, ebony bridge with white abalone dot pins, maple endpin wedge, bound peghead with pearl shield/logo inlay, 3 per side gold tuners. Available in Natural and Sunburst finishes. Curr. mfr.

Mfr.'s Sug. Retail	$1,800	$1,350	$900	$895	$715	$645	$590	$540

D-100 — spruce top, round soundhole, black pickguard, maple bound body, abalone purfling/rosette, rosewood back/sides, 3 piece mahogany/maple neck, 14/20 fret maple bound ebony fingerboard with abalone crown inlay, ebony bridge with white abalone dot pins, maple endpin wedge, maple bound peghead with abalone shield/logo inlay, 3 per side gold tuners. Available in Natural and Sunburst finishes. Curr. mfr.

Mfr.'s Sug. Retail	$3,600	$2,700	$1,800	$1,795	$1,435	$1,290	$1,185	$1,075

D-100 C — similar to D-100, except has handcarved heel. Curr. mfr.

Mfr.'s Sug. Retail	$3,900	$3,120	$2,340	$1,950	$1,555	$1,395	$1,280	$1,165

DCE-1 — single cutaway flat-top body, solid spruce top, round soundhole, black pickguard, bound body, 3 stripe rosette, mahogany back/sides/neck, 20 fret rosewood fingerboard with dot inlay, rosewood bridge with white black dot pins, 3 per side gold tuners, transducer pickup, preamp. Available in Natural finish. New 1994.

Mfr.'s Sug. Retail	$1,000	$800	$600	$500	$400	$360	$330	$300

DCE-5 — similar to DCE1, except has rosewood back/sides, ebony fingerboard. Available in Natural and Sunburst finishes. New 1994.

Mfr.'s Sug. Retail	$1,400	$1,120	$840	$700	$560	$505	$460	$420

DK-70 — dreadnought, limited edition koa, ebony fingerboard with cloud inlays, Guild logo in abalone.

		$1,700	$1,600	$1,500	$1,300	$1,200	$1,100	$1,000

Guild D-25 M
courtesy Mark Humphrey

D-25 M label (closeup)
courtesy Mark Humphrey

Grading	100%	98% MINT	95% EXC+	90% EXC	80% VG+	70% VG	60% G

DV-6 — dreadnought size, spruce top, mahogany back and sides, scalloped bracing, abalone rosette, rosewood fingerboard, 3+3 headstock. Current production.

	$825	$750	$700	$625	$550	$500	$450

DV-52 — solid spruce top, round soundhole, scalloped bracing, tortoise pickguard, 3 stripe bound body, herringbone rosette, rosewood back/sides, mahogany neck, 14/20 fret ebony fingerboard with pearl dot inlay, ebony bridge with white black dot pins, pearl Chesterfield/logo peghead inlay, 3 per side gold tuners. Available in Natural and Sunburst finishes. Curr. mfr.

Mfr.'s Sug. Retail	$1,100	$825	$550	$545	$435	$395	$360	$330

DV-52 HG — similar to DV-52, except has high gloss finish. Disc. 1994.

		$910	$780	$650	$520	$470	$430	$390

Last Mfr.'s Sug. Retail was $1,300.

DV-62 — solid spruce top, round soundhole, tortoise pickguard, herringbone bound body/rosette, rosewood back/sides, mahogany neck, 14/20 fret ebony fingerboard with pearl dot inlay, ebony bridge with white black dot pins, pearl shield/logo peghead inlay, 3 per side gold tuners. Available in Natural and Sunburst finishes. New 1994.

Mfr.'s Sug. Retail	$1,500	$1,200	$900	$750	$600	$540	$495	$450

DV-74 — limited edition dreadnought, spruce top, rosewood back and sides, Southwestern motif. Current production.

Mfr.'s Sug. Retail	$2,499	$1,999	$1,499	$1,400	$1,200	$1,100	$1,000	$925

G-37 — solid spruce top, round soundhole, tortoise pickguard, bound body, 3 stripe rosette, maple back/sides/neck, 14/20 fret rosewood fingerboard with pearl dot inlay, rosewood bridge with white black dot pins, pearl Chesterfield/logo peghead inlay, 3 per side chrome tuners. Available in Black, Natural and Sunburst finishes. Introduced 1972.

	$910	$775	$645	$515	$465	$425	$385

The G-37 is nearly the same guitar as the D-30, but features chrome tuners (which some D-30s have as well).

G-41 — dreadnought shape (but larger at 17 inches across bout), solid spruce top, mahogany back and sides, rosewood fingerboard with dot inlay, 26¼ inch scale. Introduced 1974.

Model has not traded in sufficient quantities to quote pricing.

G-75 — dreadnought shape (¾ size - 15 inches across bout), solid spruce top, rosewood back and sides, ebony fingerboard, 25½ inch scale. Introduced 1975.

Model has not traded in sufficient quantities to quote pricing.

GV-52 — bellshape flat-top body, solid spruce top, round soundhole, tortoise pickguard, bound body, herringbone rosette, rosewood back/sides, mahogany neck, 14/20 fret ebony fingerboard with pearl dot inlay, ebony bridge with white black dot pins, blackface peghead with pearl Chesterfield/logo inlay, 3 per side gold tuners. Available in Natural finish. New 1994.

Mfr.'s Sug. Retail	$1,150	$920	$690	$575	$460	$415	$380	$345

F Series

F-20 TROUBADOR — flat-top body, solid spruce top, round soundhole, tortoise pickguard, bound body, single rosette, maple back/sides, mahogany neck, 14/20 fret rosewood fingerboard with pearl dot inlay, rosewood bridge with white pins, blackface peghead with screened logo, 3 per side chrome tuners. Available in Natural top/Mahogany Stain back/sides finish. Mfg. 1952 to 1973.

1952-1956	$700	$675	$650	$600	$525	$450	$350
1957-1973	$700	$650	$600	$575	$500	$400	$325

This model had the following features: body length - 18 inches, lower bout width - 13⅓ inches, body depth - 4¼ inches.

In 1957, mahogany back/sides replaced original items.

M-20 — similar to F-20, except has mahogany top. Mfg. 1964 to 1973.

	$500	$450	$400	$375	$350	$300	$275

F-30 ARAGON — flat-top body, solid spruce top, round soundhole, black pickguard, bound body, single rosette, maple back/sides, mahogany neck, 14/20 fret rosewood fingerboard with pearl dot inlay, rosewood bridge with white pins, blackface peghead with screened logo, 3 per side chrome tuners. Available in Natural top/Mahogany Stain back/sides finish. Mfg. 1952 to 1985.

1952-1956	$850	$800	$750	$700	$600	$500	$450
1957-1985	$800	$750	$700	$650	$550	$450	$400

This model had the following features: body length - 19 1/4 inches, lower bout width - 15 1/2 inches, body depth - 4 1/4 inches.

F-30 R — similar to the F-30, except this limited edition featured rosewood back and sides.

	$1,150	$1,100	$1,050	$950	$900	$850	$800

M-30 — similar to F-30 Aragon, except has mahogany top, black pickguard. Mfg. 1952-1985.

	$750	$700	$650	$500	$400	$350	$300

G

Grading	100%	98% MINT	95% EXC+	90% EXC	80% VG+	70% VG	60% G

F-40 VALENCIA — flat-top body, solid spruce top, round soundhole, black pickguard, multibound body, 2 stripe rosette, maple back/sides, mahogany neck, 14/20 fret bound rosewood fingerboard with pearl block inlay, rosewood bridge with white pins, blackface peghead with pearl shield/logo inlay, 3 per side chrome tuners. Available in Natural and Sunburst finishes. Mfg. 1952 to 1964.

| | $1,000 | $900 | $850 | $800 | $725 | $700 | $550 |

This model had the following features: Body Length - 19 1/4 inches, Lower Bout Width - 16 inches, Body Depth - 4 1/4 inches.

M-40 Reissue — similar to F-40, except has pearl Chesterfield/logo peghead inlay. Mfg. 1973 to circa 1985.

| | $850 | $800 | $750 | $650 | $600 | $500 | $400 |

F-42 — 16 inch folk style body, spruce top, mahogany back and sides, rosewood fingerboard with dot inlays, circa late 1980s.

| | $900 | $850 | $775 | $700 | $650 | $575 | $500 |

F-44 — similar to the F-42, except has maple back and sides, multiple bindings, and a bound fingerboard. Mfd. 1984 to 1988.

| | $1,250 | $1,175 | $1,100 | $1,000 | $900 | $800 | $700 |

F-48 — flat-top body, solid spruce top, round soundhole, black pickguard, multibound body, 3 stripe rosette, mahogany back/sides, mahogany neck, 14/20 fret bound rosewood fingerboard with pearl block inlay, rosewood bridge with white black dot pins, bound blackface peghead with pearl shield/logo inlay, 3 per side gold tuners. Available in Natural and Sunburst finishes. Mfg. 1973 to 1975.

| | $850 | $800 | $725 | $675 | $600 | $525 | $475 |

This model had the following features: Body Length - 21 inches, Lower Bout Width - 17 inches, Body Depth - 5 inches.

F-50 — flat-top body, solid spruce top, round soundhole, black pickguard, multibound body, 3 stripe rosette, figured maple back/sides, mahogany neck, 14/20 fret bound ebony fingerboard with pearl block/abalone wedge inlay, ebony bridge with white black dot pins, bound blackface peghead with pearl shield/logo inlay, 3 per side gold tuners. Available in Natural and Sunburst finishes. Mfg. 1952 to circa 1990.

| | $1,250 | $1,200 | $1,150 | $1,100 | $1,000 | $800 | $600 |

This model has the following features: Body Length - 21 inches, Lower Bout Width - 17 inches, Body Depth - 5 inches.

F-50 R — similar to F-50, except has rosewood back/sides. Mfg. 1964 to circa 1990.

| | $1,500 | $1,450 | $1,400 | $1,350 | $1,000 | $850 | $700 |

F-47 — similar to the F-50 model, except has mahogany construction, rosewood fingerboard with block inlays, and chrome tuners.

| | $900 | $850 | $800 | $750 | $700 | $625 | $575 |

F-64 — similar to the F-42, but has rosewood back and sides, bound ebony fingerboard, and bound headstock. Produced in the late 1980s.

| | $1,250 | $1,175 | $1,100 | $1,000 | $900 | $800 | $700 |

GF-30 — solid spruce top (16 inch folk model), arched maple back, and maple sides, rosewood fingerboard with dot inlays, 3+3 headstock, chrome hardware. Mfd. circa late 1980s.

| | $825 | $775 | $700 | $625 | $550 | $475 | $425 |

GF-50 — similar to the F-64, except featured dot inlays on the ebony fingerboard, and ebony bridge. Mfd. circa late 1980s.

| | $900 | $850 | $775 | $700 | $625 | $550 | $500 |

GF-60 — similar to the F-64, the original model was renamed. Mfd. circa late 1980s.

| | $1,250 | $1,175 | $1,100 | $1,000 | $900 | $800 | $700 |

STUDIO 24 — double cutaway flattop design, spruce top, maple back and sides, redesigned neck joint that allows access to upper frets. Mfd. circa late 1980s.

| | $2,600 | $2,500 | $2,350 | $2,200 | $2,150 | $2,000 | $1,850 |

Designed in conjunction with noted vintage guitar expert George Gruhn.

12 String Series

F-112 — flat-top body, solid spruce top, round soundhole, tortoise pickguard, tortoise bound body, single rosette, mahogany back/sides/neck, 14/20 fret rosewood fingerboard with pearl dot inlay, rosewood bridge with white pins, blackface peghead with screened logo, 6 per side chrome tuners. Available in Natural finish. Mfg. 1968 to 1982.

| | $600 | $575 | $550 | $525 | $475 | $425 | $350 |

This model had the following features: body length - 19 1/4 inches, lower bout width - 15 1/4 inches, body depth - 4 1/2 inches.

F-212 — flat-top body, solid spruce top, round soundhole, tortoise pickguard, multibound body, single rosette, mahogany back/sides/neck, 14/20 fret rosewood fingerboard with pearl dot inlay, rosewood bridge with white pins, blackface peghead with screened logo, 6 per side chrome tuners. Available in Natural finish. Mfg. 1963-1985.

| | $800 | $750 | $725 | $675 | $650 | $600 | $550 |

This model had the following features: Body Length - 20 inches, Lower Bout Width - 15 7/8 inches, Body Depth - 5 inches.

Grading	100%	98% MINT	95% EXC+	90% EXC	80% VG+	70% VG	60% G

F-212 XL — similar to F-212, except has larger body. Mfg. 1970 to 1985.

	$900	$850	$825	$750	$725	$700	$625

This model had the following features: Body Length - 21 inches, Lower Bout Width - 17 inches, Body Depth - 5 inches.

F-312 — similar to F-212, except has multibound body, rosewood back/sides, ebony fingerboard. Mfg. 1964 to 1974.

	$900	$850	$825	$750	$725	$700	$625

This model had the following features: Body Length - 21 inches, Lower Bout Width - 17 inches, Body Depth - 5 inches.

F-412 — flat-top body, solid spruce top, round soundhole, black pickguard, multibound body, 3 stripe rosette, maple back/sides, mahogany neck, 14/20 fret bound ebony fingerboard with pearl block inlay, ebony bridge with white pins, bound blackface peghead with pearl shield/logo inlay, 6 per side gold tuners. Available in Natural finish. Mfg. 1970 to circa 1990.

	$1,050	$1,000	$950	$900	$750	$600	$550

This model had the following features: Body Length - 21 inches, Lower Bout Width - 17 inches, Body Depth - 5 inches.

F-512 — flat-top body, solid spruce top, round soundhole, black pickguard, wood bound body, multistripe purfling/rosette, rosewood back/sides, mahogany neck, 14/20 fret bound/purfled ebony fingerboard with pearl block/abalone wedge inlay, ebony bridge with white black dot pins, bound blackface peghead with pearl shield/logo inlay, 6 per side gold tuners. Available in Natural finish. Mfg. 1970 to circa 1990.

	$1,500	$1,400	$1,350	$1,300	$1,225	$1,025	$825

This model had the following features: Body Length - 21 inches, Lower Bout Width - 17 inches, Body Depth - 5 inches.

Jumbo Series

All models in this series have jumbo style bodies, round soundholes and tortoise pickguards.

JF-4 — solid spruce top, bound body, 3 stripe rosette, mahogany back/sides/neck, 14/20 fret rosewood fingerboard with pearl dot inlay, rosewood bridge with white black dot pins, 3 per side chrome tuners. Available in Natural finish. Curr. mfr.

Mfr.'s Sug. Retail	$880	$660	$440	$415	$325	$280	$260	$235

Add $200 for high gloss finish (JF4-HG).

JF-4/12 S — similar to JF-4, except has 12 strings, 6 per side tuners. Disc. 1994.

	$695	$595	$500	$400	$360	$330	$300

Last Mfr.'s Sug. Retail was $995.

JF-30 — solid spruce top, bound body, 3 stripe rosette, maple back/sides/neck, 14/20 fret rosewood fingerboard with pearl dot inlay, rosewood bridge with white black dot pins, pearl Chesterfield/logo peghead inlay, 3 per side gold tuners. Available in Natural and Sunburst finishes. Curr. mfr.

Mfr.'s Sug. Retail	$1,300	$975	$650	$645	$515	$465	$425	$385

JF-30/12 — similar to JF-30, except has 12 strings, 6 per side tuners.

Mfr.'s Sug. Retail	$1,400	$1,120	$840	$700	$560	$505	$460	$420

JF-55 — solid spruce top, 3 stripe bound body/rosette, rosewood back/sides, mahogany neck, 14/20 fret bound ebony fingerboard with pearl block/abalone wedge inlay, ebony bridge with white abalone dot pins, maple endpin wedge, bound peghead with pearl shield/logo inlay, 3 per side gold tuners. Available in Natural finish. Curr. mfr.

Mfr.'s Sug. Retail	$1,900	$1,520	$1,140	$950	$760	$685	$625	$570

This model also available in 12 string version (JF55-12) with Natural and Sunburst finishes.

JF-65/12 — solid spruce top, 3 stripe bound body/rosette, maple back/sides/neck, 14/20 fret bound ebony fingerboard with pearl block/abalone wedge inlay, ebony bridge with white abalone dot pins, maple endpin wedge, bound peghead with pearl shield/logo inlay, 6 per side gold tuners. Available in Blonde and Sunburst finishes. Curr. mfr.

Mfr.'s Sug. Retail	$1,900	$1,520	$1,140	$950	$760	$685	$625	$570

JF-100 — solid spruce top, maple bound body, abalone purfling/rosette, rosewood back/sides, 3 piece mahogany neck with maple center strip, 14/20 fret maple bound ebony fingerboard with abalone crown inlay, ebony bridge with white abalone pins, maple endpin wedge, ebony endpin, maple bound peghead with abalone shield/logo inlay, 3 per side tuners. Available in Natural finish. Curr. mfr.

Mfr.'s Sug. Retail	$3,700	$2,960	$2,220	$1,945	$1,565	$1,435	$1,315	$1,195

JF-100C — similar to JF-100, except has hand carved heel. New 1994.

Mfr.'s Sug. Retail	$4,000	$3,200	$2,400	$2,000	$1,600	$1,440	$1,320	$1,200

JF-100/12 — similar to JF-100, except has 12 strings, 6 per side tuners.

Mfr.'s Sug. Retail	$4,000	$3,200	$2,400	$2,000	$1,600	$1,440	$1,320	$1,200

JF-100/12C — similar to JF-100, except has 12 strings, hand carved heel, 6 per side tuners. New 1994.

Mfr.'s Sug. Retail	$4,300	$3,440	$2,580	$2,150	$1,720	$1,550	$1,420	$1,290

G

Grading	100%	98% MINT	95% EXC+	90% EXC	80% VG+	70% VG	60% G

JV-52 — jumbo style, solid spruce top, round soundhole, tortoise pickguard, bound body, herringbone rosette, rosewood back/sides, mahogany neck, 14/20 fret ebony fingerboard with pearl dot inlay, ebony bridge with white black dot pins, blackface peghead with pearl Chesterfield/logo inlay, 3 per side gold tuners. Available in Natural finish. New 1994.

Mfr.'s Sug. Retail	$1,250	$1,000	$750	$625	$500	$450	$415	$375

Mark Series

Instruments in this series are classically styled.

MARK I — mahogany top, round soundhole, simple marquetry rosette, mahogany back/sides/neck, 12/19 fret rosewood fingerboard, tied rosewood bridge, 3 per side nickel tuners. Available in Natural finish. Mfg. 1960 to 1973.

	$400	$350	$325	$300	$275	$225	$200

Mark II — similar to Mark I, except has spruce top, bound body. Mfg. 1960 to 1988.

	$450	$400	$350	$325	$300	$275	$225

Mark III — similar to Mark I, except has spruce top, multibound body, floral rosette marquetry. Mfg. 1960 to 1988.

	$500	$475	$425	$400	$350	$325	$300

Mark IV — spruce top, round soundhole, multi bound body, marquetry rosette, figured pearwood back/sides, mahogany neck, 12/19 fret ebony fingerboard, tied ebony bridge, 3 per side chrome tuners with pearloid buttons. Available in Natural finish. Mfg. 1960-1985.

	$625	$600	$550	$525	$500	$450	$425

This model had figured maple back/sides optionally available.

Mark V — similar to Mark IV, except has ebony bound body, elaborate marquetry rosette, figured maple back/sides, gold tuners with engraved buttons. Mfg. 1960 to 1988.

	$750	$725	$700	$650	$625	$600	$575

This model had rosewood back/sides optionally available.

Mark VI — similar to Mark IV, except has ebony bound body, elaborate marquetry rosette, Brazilian rosewood back/sides, gold tuners with engraved buttons. Mfg. 1966 to 1968.

	$950	$900	$850	$750	$650	$500	$450

ACOUSTIC BASS

B-30 — grand concert style, spruce top, round soundhole, tortoise pickguard, 3 stripe bound body/rosette, mahogany back/sides/neck, 14/20 fret rosewood fingerboard with pearl dot inlay, rosewood bridge with white pins, pearl Chesterfield/logo peghead inlay, 2 per side chrome tuners. Available in Natural and Sunburst finishes. Mfg. 1987 to date.

Mfr.'s Sug. Retail	$1,400	$1,120	$840	$700	$560	$505	$460	$420

B-500C — similar to B-30, except has single round cutaway, maple back/sides, transducer bridge pickup, volume/concentric treble/bass control, preamp. Available in Natural and Sunburst finishes. Disc. 1994.

	$1,185	$1,015	$845	$675	$605	$555	$505

Last Mfr.'s Sug. Retail was $1,695.

ACOUSTIC ELECTRIC

CCE-100 — single round cutaway classic style, oval soundhole, bound body, wood inlay rosette, mahogany back/sides/neck, 24 fret rosewood fingerboard, rosewood bridge, 3 per side chrome tuners, transducer pickup, 4 band EQ with preamp. Available in Natural finish. New 1994.

Mfr.'s Sug. Retail	$1,200	$960	$720	$600	$480	$430	$395	$360

CCE-100 HG — similar to CCE-100, except has gold hardware. Disc. 1995.

	$980	$835	$700	$560	$505	$460	$420

Last Mfr.'s Sug. Retail was $1,400.

F Series

All models in this series have single round cutaway folk style body, oval soundhole, tortoise pickguard, 3 stripe bound body/rosette, transducer pickup, volume/4 band EQ preamp system with built in phase reversal, unless otherwise listed.

F-4 CE — solid spruce top, mahogany back/sides/neck, 24 fret rosewood fingerboard with pearl dot inlay, rosewood bridge with white black dot pins, 3 per side chrome tuners. Available in Natural finish. Curr. mfr.

Mfr.'s Sug. Retail	$1,000	$750	$500	$470	$375	$325	$300	$275

In 1994, Black and Vintage White high gloss finishes were introduced.

F-4 CEMH — similar to F-4CE, except has mahogany top. Available in Amber finish. Curr. mfr.

Mfr.'s Sug. Retail	$1,050	$787	$525	$500	$395	$345	$315	$285

F-5 CE — solid spruce top, rosewood back/sides, mahogany neck, 24 fret rosewood fingerboard with pearl dot inlay, rosewood bridge with white black dot pins, 3 per side chrome Grover tuners. Available in Black, Natural and Sunburst finishes. Curr. mfr.

Mfr.'s Sug. Retail	$1,200	$960	$720	$600	$480	$430	$395	$360

Add $100 for deep body version of this model (FF5-CE).

Grading	100%	98% MINT	95% EXC+	90% EXC	80% VG+	70% VG	60% G

F-25 CE — solid spruce top, mahogany back/sides/neck, 24 fret rosewood fingerboard with pearl dot inlay, rosewood bridge with white black dot pins, 3 per side chrome Grover tuners, volume control, concentric treble/bass control, active preamp. Available in Black, Natural and Sunburst finishes. Disc. 1992.

		$835	$715	$600	$480	$430	$395	$360

Last Mfr.'s Sug. Retail was $1,195.

F-30 CE — solid spruce top, flame maple back/sides, mahogany neck, 24 fret rosewood fingerboard with pearl dot inlay, rosewood bridge with white black dot pins, pearl Chesterfield/logo peghead inlay, 3 per side gold Grover tuners. Available in Black, Blonde, Natural and Sunburst finishes. Curr. mfr.

Mfr.'s Sug. Retail	$1,495	$1,196	$897	$750	$600	$540	$495	$450

F-65 CE — solid spruce top, figured maple back/sides, mahogany neck, 24 fret bound ebony fingerboard with pearl block/abalone wedge inlay, ebony bridge with white abalone dot pins, bound peghead with pearl shield/logo inlay, 3 per side gold Grover tuners. Available in Natural and Sunburst finishes. Curr. mfr.

Mfr.'s Sug. Retail	$1,900	$1,520	$1,140	$950	$760	$685	$625	$570

This model has figured maple top with Amber and Sunburst finishes optionally available.

In 1994, transducer pickup, preamp were introduced.

FS-48 DECEIVER — single cutaway body style, maple fingerboard, pointed headstock design, with piezo pickup and humbucker hidden between the soundhole and bridge. Mfd. circa 1984.

Model has not traded sufficiently to quote pricing.

Songbird Series

S-4 CE — routed out Les Paul style mahogany body, solid spruce top, round soundhole, tortoise pickguard, 3 stripe bound body/rosette, mahogany neck, 22 fret rosewood fingerboard with pearl dot inlay, rosewood bridge with white black dot pins, 3 per side chrome tuners, transducer bridge pickup, volume/concentric treble/bass control, preamp. Available in Natural finish. Curr. mfr.

Mfr.'s Sug. Retail	$1,000	$800	$600	$500	$400	$360	$330	$300

SONGBIRD — similar S-4CE, except has pearl Chesterfield/logo peghead inlay, gold tuners. Available in Black, Natural and White finishes. Curr. mfr.

Mfr.'s Sug. Retail	$1,300	$975	$650	$645	$515	$465	$425	$385

ACOUSTIC ELECTRIC BASS

B-4 E — single round cutaway folk style, spruce top, oval soundhole, tortoise pickguard, 3 stripe bound body/rosette, mahogany back/sides/neck, 22 fret rosewood fingerboard with pearl dot inlay, rosewood bridge with white black dot pins, 2 per side chrome tuners, transducer pickups, volume/4 band EQ control with preamp. Available in Natural finish. Curr. mfr.

Mfr.'s Sug. Retail	$1,100	$825	$550	$525	$415	$360	$330	$300

This model has fretless fingerboard optionally available.

B-4 EHG — similar to B-4E, except has high gloss finish. New 1994.

Mfr.'s Sug. Retail	$1,150	$920	$690	$575	$460	$415	$380	$345

B-4 EMH — similar to B-4E, except has mahogany top. New 1994.

Mfr.'s Sug. Retail	$1,150	$920	$690	$575	$460	$415	$380	$345

B-30 E — grand concert style, spruce top, round soundhole, tortoise pickguard, 3 stripe bound body/rosette, mahogany back/sides/neck, 14/20 fret rosewood fingerboard with pearl dot inlay, rosewood bridge with white pins, pearl Chesterfield/logo peghead inlay, 2 per side chrome tuners, transducer bridge pickup, volume/concentric treble/bass control, preamp. Available in Natural and Sunburst finishes. Curr. mfr.

Mfr.'s Sug. Retail	$1,600	$1,200	$800	$795	$635	$575	$525	$475

B-30 ET — similar to B-30E, except has thinline body style. Disc. 1992.

	$1,115	$955	$795	$635	$575	$525	$475

Last Mfr.'s Sug. Retail was $1,595.

ELECTRIC ARCHTOPS

CE-100 CAPRI — single sharp cutaway hollow style, arched bound spruce top, raised bound black pickguard, 2 f-holes, maple back/sides/neck, 20 fret bound rosewood fingerboard with pearl block inlay, adjustable rosewood bridge/trapeze tailpiece, blackface peghead with pearl shield/logo inlay, 3 per side tuners, chrome hardware, single coil pickup, volume/tone control. Available in Black, Blonde and Sunburst finishes. Mfg. 1952 to 1984.

		$800	$750	$700	$625	$600	$500	$400

This model had Bigsby vibrato optionally available.

In 1954, harp tailpiece replaced original item.

In 1962, humbucker pickup replaced original item.

CE-100 D — similar to CE-100, except has 2 single coil pickups, 2 volume/2 tone controls, 3 position switch. Mfg. 1952 to 1975.

		$850	$800	$750	$700	$650	$550	$450

In 1962, 2 humbucker pickups replaced original item.

Grading	100%	98% MINT	95% EXC+	90% EXC	80% VG+	70% VG	60% G

CROSSROADS (CR 1) — single cutaway semi-hollow mahogany body, bound figured maple top, figured maple neck, 22 fret bound rosewood fingerboard with pearl dot inlay, rosewood bridge with white black dot pins, blackface peghead with pearl shield/logo inlay, 3 per side tuners, chrome hardware, 1 humbucker/1 piezo bridge pickups, 2 volume/1 tone controls, 3 position switch. Available in Amber, Black and Natural finishes. New 1994.

Mfr.'s Sug. Retail	$1,300	$1,040	$780	$650	$520	$470	$430	$390

CROSSROADS DOUBLE E — double neck configuration, mahogany body with acoustic side routed out, bound spruce top, mahogany neck, bound blackface peghead with pearl Chesterfield/logo inlay, 3 per side tuners, chrome hardware; acoustic side features: round soundhole, 22 fret rosewood fingerboard with pearl dot inlay, rosewood bridge with white black dot pins, piezo bridge pickups; electric side features: 22 fret bound ebony fingerboard with abalone/pearl wedge/block inlay, tunomatic bridge/stop tailpiece, 2 exposed Seymour Duncan humbucker pickups, 2 volume/2 tone controls, two 3 position switches. Available in Black and Natural finishes. Mfg. 1993 to date.

Mfr.'s Sug. Retail	$2,995	$2,246	$1,497	$1,495	$1,195	$1,075	$985	$895

DUANE EDDY 400 — single round cutaway semi-hollow body, arched bound spruce top, f-holes, raised black pickguard with Duane Eddy's signature, maple back/sides, mahogany neck, 20 fret bound rosewood fingerboard with pearl block inlay, adjustable bridge/Bigsby vibrato, bound peghead with pearl Chesterfield/logo inlay, 3 per side tuners, chrome hardware, 2 covered humbuckers, 2 volume/2 tone controls, 3 position switch, mix control. Available in Natural finish. Mfg. 1963 to 1969.

	$1,500	$1,050	$900	$750	$600	$540	$495

DUANE EDDY 500 — similar to Duane Eddy 400, except has figured maple back/sides/neck, ebony fingerboard, gold hardware.

	$2,100	$1,475	$1,260	$1,050	$840	$755	$690

BERT WHEEDON — similar to the Duane Eddy 400, except has a double cutaway and pickguard reads "Bert Wheedon". Mfd. 1963 to 1965.

Model has not traded sufficiently to quote pricing.

This model was produced for U.K. distribution.

GEORGE BARNES ACOUSTI-LECTRIC — single round cutaway hollow style, arched bound spruce top, bound pickup holes, raised black pickguard with logo, figured maple back/sides/neck, 20 fret bound rosewood fingerboard with pearl block inlay, adjustable rosewood bridge/harp style tailpiece, bound peghead with pearl shield/logo inlay, 3 per side tuners with pearl buttons, chrome hardware, 2 covered humbucker pickups, 2 volume/2 tone controls, 3 position switch, pickguard mounted controls. Available in Natural finish. Mfg. 1964-1967.

Too few of these exist for accurate statistical representation.

Bound slots were placed into the top of this instrument so that the pickups would not touch it.

GEORGE BARNES "Guitar in F" — single round cutaway hollow small body, spruce top, bound pickup holes, raised black pickguard with logo, mahogany back/sides/neck, 20 fret bound rosewood fingerboard with pearl block inlay, adjustable rosewood bridge/harp tailpiece, bound blackface peghead with pearl f/logo inlay, 3 per side tuners, chrome hardware, 2 humbucker pickups, 2 volume/2 tone pickguard mounted controls, 3 position switch. Mfg. 1963 to 1965.

Too few of these exist for accurate statistical representation.

The pickups in this instrument were held in place by a lengthwise support and did not touch the top of the guitar.

M-65 — single round cutaway hollowed mahogany body, bound spruce top, 2 f-holes, raised black laminated pickguard, mahogany neck, 22 fret bound rosewood fingerboard with pearl block inlay, adjustable metal bridge/harp tailpiece, blackface peghead with pearl logo inlay, 3 per side tuners, nickel hardware, single coil pickup, volume/tone controls. Available in Sunburst finish. Mfg. 1962 to 1968.

	$700	$625	$600	$550	$500	$425	$450

M-65 3/4 — similar to M-65, except has smaller body/scale length. Mfg. 1962 to 1970.

	$525	$500	$475	$425	$375	$350	$325

M-75 ARISTOCRAT — single round cutaway hollow mahogany body, bound spruce top, raised black laminated pickguard, mahogany neck, 22 fret bound rosewood fingerboard with pearl block inlay, adjustable metal bridge/harp tailpiece, blackface peghead with pearl logo inlay, 3 per side tuners, gold hardware, 2 single coil pickups, 2 volume/2 tone controls, 3 position switch. Available in Natural and Sunburst finishes. Mfg. 1952 to 1963.

	$1,600	$1,300	$1,250	$1,150	$1,050	$900	$850

The Aristocrat model was often called the "Bluesbird".

M-75 Bluesbird — similar to M-75 Aristocrat, except has pearl Chesterfield/logo inlay, chrome hardware, 2 humbucker pickups. Mfg. 1968 to 1974.

	$1,000	$950	$900	$800	$725	$675	$600

M-75 G Bluesbird — similar to M-75 Aristocrat, except has pearl Chesterfield/logo inlay, 2 humbucker pickups, gold hardware.

	$1,000	$950	$900	$800	$725	$675	$600

M-75 CS BLUESBIRD — single round cutaway bound mahogany solid body, raised black laminated pickguard, mahogany neck, 22 fret bound rosewood fingerboard with pearl block inlay, tunomatic bridge/fixed tailpiece, blackface peghead with pearl Chesterfield/logo inlay, 3 per side tuners, chrome hardware, 2 humbucker pickups, master volume/2 volume/2 tone controls, 3 position switch. Available in Sunburst finish. Mfg. 1970 to circa 1984.

	$600	$550	$525	$500	$475	$425	$375

M-75 GS — similar to M-75CS Bluesbird, except has gold hardware.

	$650	$600	$550	$525	$500	$450	$400

Grading	100%	98% MINT	95% EXC+	90% EXC	80% VG+	70% VG	60% G

BLUESBIRD — similar to the M-75 CS Bluesbird, except had 3 single coils or 1 humbucker and 2 single coils with coil tap switch. Mfd. 1985 to 1988.

	$650	$600	$550	$525	$500	$450	$400

Starfire Series

STARFIRE I — single sharp cutaway thin hollow bound maple body, arched top, f-holes, raised black pickguard with star/logo, maple neck, 20 fret bound rosewood fingerboard with pearl dot inlay, adjustable rosewood bridge/harp trapeze tailpiece, bound blackface peghead with pearl Chesterfield/logo inlay, 3 per side tuners, chrome hardware, single coil pickup, volume/tone controls. Available in Cherry Red, Ebony, Emerald Green and Honey Amber finishes. Mfg. 1961 to 1966.

	$600	$515	$425	$340	$310	$280	$255

A mahogany body was also offered.

In 1962, humbucker pickup replaced original item.

Starfire II — similar to Starfire I, except has 2 single coil pickups, 2 volume/2 tone controls. Mfg. 1961 to 1972.

	$725	$700	$650	$600	$550	$500	$425

In 1962, 2 humbucker pickups replaced original item.

Starfire III — similar to Starfire I, except has Guild Bigsby vibrato, 2 single coil pickups, 2 volume/2 tone controls. Mfg. 1961 to 1970.

	$950	$900	$850	$775	$725	$650	$550

Starfire IV — double round cutaway semi-hollow bound maple body, raised black pickguard, 2 f-holes, 3 piece maple neck, 22 fret bound rosewood fingerboard with pearl dot inlay, tunomatic bridge/harp trapeze tailpiece, pearl Chesterfield/logo peghead inlay, 3 per side tuners, gold hardware, 2 humbucker pickups, 2 volume/2 tone controls, 3 position switch. Available in Black, Blonde, Blue, Green, Red and Walnut finishes. Mfg. 1963 to date.

Mfr.'s Sug. Retail	$1,900	$1,520	$1,140	$950	$760	$685	$625	$570

In 1972, master volume control was introduced.

In approx. 1980, ebony fingerboard, stop tailpiece replaced original item, master volume control was discontinued.

Starfire V — similar to Starfire IV, except has pearl block fingerboard inlay, Guild Bigsby vibrato, master volume control. Available in Cherry Red, Ebony, Emerald Green and Honey Amber finishes. Mfg. 1963 to 1972.

	$1,050	$950	$900	$850	$800	$750	$650

Starfire VI — similar to Starfire IV, except has bound f-holes, ebony fingerboard with pearl block/abalone wedge inlay, Guild Bigsby vibrato, bound peghead with pearl shield/logo inlay, gold hardware, master volume control. Available in Cherry Red, Ebony, Emerald Green and Honey Amber finishes. Mfg. 1963 to 1979.

	$1,250	$1,100	$1,050	$1,000	$925	$875	$825

Starfire XII — similar to Starfire IV, except has 12 strings, 6 per side tuners. Available in Cherry Red, Ebony, Emerald Green and Honey Amber finishes. Mfg. 1966 to 1975.

	$900	$850	$800	$725	$675	$600	$525

T-100 — single sharp cutaway semi hollow style, arched bound spruce top, raised bound black pickguard, 2 f-holes, mahogany back/sides/neck, 20 fret bound rosewood fingerboard with pearl dot inlay, adjustable rosewood bridge/harp tailpiece, blackface peghead with pearl shield/logo inlay, 3 per side tuners, chrome hardware, single coil pickup, volume/tone control. Available in Blonde and Sunburst finishes. Mfg. 1960 to 1972.

	$625	$575	$525	$450	$425	$375	$300

T-100 D — similar to T-100, except had 2 single coil pickups, 2 volume/2 tone controls, 3 position switch.

	$725	$700	$650	$600	$550	$425	$350

ST Series

Studio ST 301 — double cutaway archtop laminated maple body (similar to the T-100 with a double cutaway), 16⅜ inches wide x 1⅞ inches deep, 1 single coil or humbucking pickup.

	$750	$700	$650	$600	$525	$450	$375

Studio ST 302 — similar to the ST 301, except has 2 pickups.

	$850	$800	$750	$700	$625	$550	$475

Studio ST 303 — similar to the ST 301, except has 2 pickups and a Bigsby tremolo.

	$900	$850	$800	$750	$675	$600	$525

Studio ST 304 — similar to the ST 301, except has 2 pickups and a thicker body (2⅞ inches deep).

	$950	$900	$850	$800	$725	$650	$575

X-50 GRANADA — hollow style body, arch spruce top, f-holes, raised black pickguard, bound body, mahogany back/sides/neck, 14/20 fret rosewood fingerboard with pearl dot inlay, adjustable rosewood bridge/trapeze tailpiece, blackface peghead with screened logo, 3 per side tuners, humbucker pickup, volume/tone controls. Available in Sunburst finish. Mfg. 1952 to 1970.

	$650	$600	$550	$500	$425	$400	$375

T-50 — similar to X-50, except had thinline body. Mfg. 1962 to 1982.

	$550	$500	$450	$400	$325	$300	$275

Grading	100%	98% MINT	95% EXC+	90% EXC	80% VG+	70% VG	60% G

X-160 SAVOY — single round cutaway hollow style, bound curly maple archtop, 2 f-holes, bound black pickguard, curly maple back/sides/neck, 20 fret rosewood fingerboard with pearl dot inlay, adjustable rosewood bridge/Bigsby vibrato tailpiece, pearl Chesterfield/logo peghead inlay, 3 per side tuners, chrome hardware, 2 humbucker pickups, 2 volume/2 tone controls, 3 position switch. Available in Black, Blonde and Sunburst finishes. Mfg. 1991 to date.

Mfr.'s Sug. Retail	$1,600	$1,200	$800	$795	$635	$575	$525 $475

X-170 MANHATTAN — single round cutaway hollow style, bound curly maple archtop, 2 f-holes, bound black pickguard, curly maple back/sides/neck, 20 fret bound rosewood fingerboard with pearl block inlay, adjustable rosewood bridge, stylized trapeze tailpiece, pearl Chesterfield/logo peghead inlay, 3 per side tuners, gold hardware, 2 humbucker pickups, 2 volume/2 tone controls, 3 position switch. Available in Blonde and Sunburst finishes. Mfg. 1988 to date.

Mfr.'s Sug. Retail	$1,800	$1,350	$900	$895	$715	$645	$590 $540

X-175 MANHATTAN — single round cutaway hollow style, bound spruce archtop, 2 f holes, black laminated pickguard, maple back/sides, mahogany neck, 20 fret bound rosewood fingerboard with pearl block inlay, adjustable rosewood bridge/harp tailpiece, blackface peghead with pearl logo inlay, 3 per side tuners, chrome hardware, 2 single coil "Soap Bar" pickups, volume/tone controls, 3 position switch. Available in Blonde and Sunburst finishes. Mfg. 1954 to 1984.

1954-1962		$1,650	$1,600	$1,500	$1,400	$1,250	$1,100 $950
1963-1984		$1,500	$1,450	$1,350	$1,250	$1,000	$900 $800

Until 1958, models had 1 volume and 1 tone controls.

In 1962, 2 humbucker pickups replaced original item.

X-150 — similar to the X-175, but has 1 pickup in the neck position.

		$1,300	$1,200	$1,150	$1,050	$975	$900 $800

X-60 — similar to the X-150, except has gold finish.

		$1,300	$1,200	$1,150	$1,050	$975	$900 $800

X-350 STRATFORD — single round cutaway hollow style, arched spruce top, raised black laminated pickguard, 2 bound f-holes, multibound body, maple back/sides/neck, 20 fret bound rosewood fingerboard with pearl block inlay, adjustable rosewood bridge/harp tailpiece, blackface peghead with pearl shield/logo inlay, 3 per side tuners, gold hardware, 3 single coil pickups, volume/tone controls, 6 pickup pushbutton switches. Available in Natural and Sunburst finishes. Mfg. 1952 to 1973.

		$2,200	$2,100	$2,000	$1,900	$1,800	$1,700 $1,600

In 1962, 2 single coil pickups, 3 position switch replaced original items.

X-400 — similar to the X-175, except had 2 volume/2 tone controls and an early sunburst finish.

		$1,650	$1,600	$1,500	$1,400	$1,150	$1,050 $950

X-440 — similar to the X-400, except had blond finish.

		$1,650	$1,600	$1,500	$1,400	$1,150	$1,050 $950

X-500 STUART — single round cutaway hollow style, bound arched solid spruce top, 2 bound f-holes, bound tortoise pickguard, German maple back/sides, 5 piece maple neck, 20 fret bound ebony fingerboard with pearl block/abalone wedge inlay, adjustable ebony bridge, stylized trapeze tailpiece, bound peghead with pearl shield/logo inlay, 3 per side Imperial tuners, gold hardware, 2 humbucker pickups, 2 volume/2 tone controls, 3 position switch. Available in Blonde and Sunburst finishes. Mfg. 1988 to date.

Mfr.'s Sug. Retail	$3,500	$2,975	$2,450	$2,200	$2,100	$2,000	$1,800 $1,700

X-700 — single round cutaway hollow style, bound arched solid spruce top, 2 bound f-holes, bound tortoise pickguard, maple back/sides/neck, 20 fret bound ebony fingerboard with pearl block/abalone wedge inlay, adjustable ebony bridge, stylized trapeze tailpiece, bound peghead with pearl shield/logo inlay, 3 per side Imperial tuners, gold hardware, 2 humbucker pickups, 2 volume/2 tone controls, 3 position switch. Available in Blonde and Sunburst finishes. Mfg. 1983 to 1985.

		$2,400	$2,200	$2,000	$1,750	$1,450	$1,200 $1,000

Last Mfr.'s Sug. Retail was $3,300.

ELECTRIC

In the late 1980s Guild imported a number of solid body electrics as entry level instruments that had "Burnside by Guild" on the headstock. Further information on these models can be found under the BURNSIDE listing elsewhere in the **Blue Book of Guitars**.

Brian May Series

BRIAN MAY — offset double cutaway bound mahogany body, black laminated pickguard, 24 fret ebony fingerboard with pearl dot inlay, tunomatic bridge/Brian May vibrato, blackface peghead with pearl logo inlay, 3 per side tuners, chrome hardware, 3 single coil Seymour Duncan pickups, volume/tone controls, 6 slide switches. Available in Black, Transparent Green, Transparent Red and White finishes. Mfg. 1984 to 1988.

		$1,600	$1,500	$1,400	$1,300	$1,100	$950 $800

Grading	100%	98% MINT	95% EXC+	90% EXC	80% VG+	70% VG	60% G

BRIAN MAY SIGNATURE — offset double cutaway bound mahogany body, black laminated pickguard, 24 fret ebony fingerboard with pearl dot inlay, tunomatic bridge/Brian May vibrato, blackface peghead with pearl logo inlay, 3 per side tuners, chrome hardware, 3 single coil pickups, volume/tone controls, 6 slide switches. Available in Transparent Red finish. Mfg. 1994.

> In 1994, this model was offered in a limited edition of only 1,000 guitars.

> Model has not traded sufficiently to quote pricing.

BRIAN MAY PRO — offset double cutaway mahogany body, bound mahogany top, black multilaminated pickguard, 24 fret ebony fingerboard with pearl dot inlay, tunomatic bridge/Brian May vibrato, mahogany peghead with pearl logo inlay, 3 per side Schaller tuners, chrome hardware, 3 single coil Seymour Duncan pickups, volume/tone controls, 6 slide switches. Available in Black, Transparent Green, Transparent Red and White finishes. Mfg. 1994 to 1995.

	$1,260	$1,080	$900	$720	$650	$595	$540

> Last Mfr.'s Sug. Retail was $1,800.

Brian May Special — similar to Brian May Pro, except has rosewood fingerboard, tunomatic bridge/stop tailpiece. Available in Natural finish. Mfg. 1994 to 1995.

	$1,050	$900	$750	$600	$540	$495	$450

> Last Mfr.'s Sug. Retail was $1,500.

Brian May Standard — offset double cutaway mahogany body, black multilaminated pickguard, 24 fret rosewood fingerboard with pearl dot inlay, tunomatic bridge/stop tailpiece, mahogany peghead with pearl logo inlay, 3 per side Schaller tuners, chrome hardware, 3 single coil pickups, volume/tone controls, 6 slide switches. Available in Black, Green, Red and White finishes. Mfg. 1994 to 1995.

	$700	$600	$500	$400	$360	$330	$300

> Last Mfr.'s Sug. Retail was $1,000.

> This model has either 1 single coil/1 humbucker pickups or 2 humbucker pickups (both with coil tap). These pickup configurations were optionally available.

DETONATOR (1ST SERIES) — offset double cutaway poplar body, bolt-on maple neck, 22 fret rosewood fingerboard with dot inlays, black hardware, 6 on a side headstock, 2 active EMG single coils and 1 humbucker, Floyd Rose locking vibrato. Mfd. 1987 to 1988.

	$495	$450	$425	$375	$350	$325	$300

> In 1988, this model changed designation to the Detonator II.

Detonator — offset double cutaway poplar body, bolt on maple neck, 22 fret rosewood fingerboard with dot inlays, black hardware, 6 on a side headstock, 2 DiMarzio single coils and 1 humbucker, Guild/Mueller locking vibrato. Mfd. 1988.

	$395	$350	$325	$275	$250	$225	$200

LIBERATOR — offset double cutaway poplar body, bolt on maple neck, 22 fret rosewood fingerboard with dot inlays, black hardware, 6 on a side headstock, 2 DiMarzio single coils and 1 humbucker, Guild/Mueller locking vibrato. Mfd. 1988.

	$395	$350	$325	$275	$250	$225	$200

Liberator II — offset double cutaway poplar body, bolt on maple neck, 22 fret rosewood fingerboard with dot inlays, black hardware, 6 on a side headstock, 2 active EMG single coils and 1 humbucker, Floyd Rose locking vibrato. Mfd. 1987 to 1988.

	$495	$450	$425	$375	$350	$325	$300

Liberator Elite — similar to the Liberator II, except had a flamed maple top, bound ebony fingerboard with rising sun inlays, gold hardware, active Bartolini pickups. Mfd. 1988.

	$595	$550	$425	$475	$450	$425	$400

M-80 — double round cutaway bound mahogany body, raised black laminated pickguard, mahogany neck, 22 fret bound rosewood fingerboard with pearl block inlay, tunomatic bridge/fixed tailpiece, blackface peghead with pearl Chesterfield/logo inlay, 3 per side tuners, chrome hardware, 2 humbucker pickups, master volume/2 volume/2 tone controls, 3 position switch. Available in Black, Natural, Red and White finishes. Mfg. 1975 to 1983.

	$600	$550	$525	$500	$475	$425	$375

M-85 CS — similar to the M-80. Mfd. 1975 to 1980.

	$650	$600	$575	$550	$525	$475	$425

NIGHTBIRD — single cutaway bound chambered mahogany body and carved Sitka spruce or maple top, mahogany neck, 22 fret bound ebony fingerboard with diamond shaped inlays, finetune bridge/stop tailpiece. Mfd. 1985 to 1987.

	$1,250	$1,100	$1,000	$900	$800	$700	$550

> Designed in conjunction with vintage guitar expert George Gruhn.

NIGHTBIRD I — similar to the original Nightbird design, except has spruce top, unbound rosewood fingerboard, and unbound headstock, two DiMarzio pickups, separate coil tap and phase switches, and chrome hardware. Mfg. 1987 to 1988.

	$850	$725	$675	$625	$575	$550	$525

NIGHTBIRD II — similar to the original Nightbird design with carved Sitka spruce top and ebony fingerboard, except has gold hardware. Mfg. 1987 to 1988.

	$900	$775	$725	$675	$625	$600	$575

G

Grading	100%	98% MINT	95% EXC+	90% EXC	80% VG+	70% VG	60% G

S-25 — offset double cutaway mahogany body, set neck, unbound top, 2 humbuckers, 1 volume and 1 tone control. Mfd. 1981 to 1983.

> Model has not traded sufficiently to quote pricing.

S-26 — similar to the S-25, except very low production. Mfd. 1983 only.

> Model has not traded sufficiently to quote pricing.

S-50 JET STAR — offset double cutaway mahogany body with concave bottom bout, black pickguard, built-in stand, mahogany neck, 22 fret rosewood fingerboard with pearl dot inlay, adjustable metal bridge/vibrato tailpiece, 3 per side tuners, chrome hardware, single coil pickup, volume/tone controls. Available in Amber, Black, Cherry Red, Green and Sunburst finishes. Mfg. 1963 to 1967.

	$525	$450	$400	$375	$325	$300	$250

> The S-50 Jet Star was the first model of Guild's solid body guitars.

S-56 D — similar to the S-60, except has DiMarzio pickups. Mfd. 1979 to 1982.

> Model has not traded sufficiently to quote pricing.

S-60 — offset double cutaway mahogany body, black pickguard, mahogany neck, 24 fret rosewood fingerboard with pearl dot inlay, tunomatic bridge/fixed tailpiece, 3 per side tuners, chrome hardware, single pickup, volume/tone controls. Available in Black, Red and White finishes. Mfg. 1977 to 1989.

	$375	$350	$300	$275	$225	$200	$175

S-60 D — similar to S-60, except has 2 single coil DiMarzio pickups, 2 volume/2 tone controls, 3 position switch.

	$375	$350	$300	$275	$225	$200	$175

S-70 — similar to S-60, except has 3 single coil pickups, 3 position/2 mini switches.

	$450	$400	$350	$300	$250	$200	$175

S-70 AD — similar to S-70, except has an ash body and DiMarzio pickups. Mfd. 1978 to 1982.

	$450	$400	$350	$300	$250	$200	$175

S-90 — similar to the S-50, except featured a humbucker and a covered bridge/tailpiece assembly. Mfd. 1970 to 1976.

	$525	$450	$400	$375	$325	$300	$250

S-100 POLARA — offset double cutaway mahogany body with concave bottom bout, black laminated pickguard, built-in stand, mahogany neck, 22 fret rosewood fingerboard with pearl dot inlay, adjustable metal bridge/vibrato tailpiece, 3 per side tuners, chrome hardware, 2 single coil pickups, 2 volume/2 tone controls, 3 position switch. Available in Amber, Black, Cherry Red, Green and Sunburst finishes. Mfg. 1963 to 1968.

	$725	$650	$600	$550	$500	$450	$400

S-100 — offset double cutaway mahogany body, black pickguard with logo, mahogany neck, 22 fret bound rosewood fingerboard with pearl block inlay, adjustable metal bridge/vibrato tailpiece, blackface peghead with pearl Chesterfield/logo inlay, 3 per side tuners, chrome hardware, 2 humbucker pickups, 2 volume/2 tone controls, 3 position switch. Available in Amber, Black, Cherry Red, Green and White finishes. Mfg. 1970 to 1974.

	$600	$500	$450	$400	$350	$325	$300

> In 1973, phase switch was introduced.

S-100 C — similar to S-100, except has carved acorn/leaves top, clear pickguard with logo, tunomatic bridge/fixed tailpiece, phase switch, stereo output. Available in Natural finish. Mfg. 1974 to 1976.

	$650	$550	$500	$475	$425	$400	$375

S-100 Deluxe — similar to S-100, except has Bigsby vibrato tailpiece. Mfg. 1973 to 1975.

	$575	$525	$475	$450	$400	$375	$350

S-100 REISSUE — double cutaway mahogany body, black pickguard, mahogany neck, 22 fret bound rosewood fingerboard with pearl block inlay, tunomatic bridge/fixed tailpiece, blackface peghead with pearl Chesterfield/logo inlay, 3 per side tuners, chrome hardware, 2 humbucker Guild pickups, 2 volume/2 tone controls, 3 position/coil tap switches. Available in Black, Green Stain, Natural, Red Stain, Vintage White and White finishes. New 1994.

Mfr.'s Sug. Retail	$1,000	$800	$600	$500	$400	$360	$330	$300

S-100 G — similar to S-100 Reissue, except has gold hardware. New 1994.

Mfr.'s Sug. Retail	$1,200	$960	$720	$600	$480	$430	$395	$360

S-200 THUNDERBIRD — offset double cutaway asymmetrical mahogany body with concave bottom bout, black pickguard, built-in stand, mahogany neck, 22 fret bound rosewood fingerboard with pearl block inlay, adjustable metal bridge/vibrato tailpiece, bound blackface peghead with pearl eagle/logo inlay, 3 per side tuners, chrome hardware, 2 single coil pickups (some with humbuckers), 2 volume/2 tone controls, 3 pickup/1 tone slide switches. Available in Amber, Black, Cherry Red, Green and Sunburst finishes. Mfd. 1963 to 1970.

	$1,400	$1,200	$1,100	$1,000	$900	$800	$750

> The Thunderbird model featured a folding stand built into the back of the body. While a unique feature, the stand was less than steady and prone to instability. Be sure to inspect the headstock/neck joint for any indications of previous problems due to the guitar falling over.

S Series

While the following models have no accurate pricing information, there is increased interest in the Guild solid bodies and most of the 1980s models sell in the range between $325 and $550.

S-250 — offset double cutaway mahogany body, set neck, bound top, chrome hardware, 2 humbuckers, 2 volume and 2 tone controls. Mfg. 1981 to 1983.

S-260 — similar to the S-250, except produced in low numbers. Mfg. 1983.

S-270 FLYER (also RUNAWAY or SPRINT) — offset double cutaway body, bolt-on neck, 6 on one side "Blade" headstock, 1 EMG pickup, locking tremolo. Mfg. 1983 to 1985.

S-271 Sprint (may also be Flyer) — similar to S-270, except different pickup configuration. Mfg. 1983 to 1985.

S-275 — offset double cutaway body, set neck, bound top, gold hardware, 2 humbuckers, 2 volume/1 tone control, 1 phase (or coil tap) switch. Mfg. 1983 to 1987.

> In 1987, pickup configuration changed to 1 humbucker and 2 single coils.

S-280 FLYER — offset double cutaway body, bolt-on neck, 22 fret fingerboard, 6 on one side headstock, 2 humbuckers, 2 volume/2 tone controls. Mfg. 1983 to 1986.

S-281 FLYER — similar to S-280 FLYER, except has a locking tremolo and 1 volume/1 tone control. Mfg. 1983 to 1986.

S-284 AVIATOR — symmetrical double cutaway body, set neck, 6 on one side "pointed" headstock, locking tremolo, 2 single/1 humbucking EMG pickups, 1 volume/1 tone control. Mfg. 1984 to 1988.

S-285 Aviator — similar to S-284 Aviator, except has bound fingerboard and headstock, fancy fingerboard inlays. Mfg. 1986 to 1987.

S-300 — offset double cutaway mahogany body, distinctly rounded tail end, black pickguard, mahogany neck, 24 fret ebony fingerboard with pearl dot inlay, tunomatic bridge/fixed tailpiece, blackface peghead with pearl Chesterfield/logo inlay, 3 per side tuners, chrome hardware, 2 single coil pickups, 2 volume/2 tone controls, 3 position/phase switches. Available in Black, Red and White finishes. Mfg. 1976-1989.

		$375	$350	$325	$300	$250	$225	$200

S-300 A — similar to S-300, except has an ash body and maple neck. Mfg. 1977 to 1982.

		$375	$350	$325	$300	$250	$225	$200

S-300 D — similar to S-300, except has a 2 DiMarzio humbucker pickups.

		$375	$350	$325	$300	$250	$225	$200

S-400 — similar to the S-300, except has set neck and active electronics. Mfg. 1979 to 1982.

		$375	$350	$325	$300	$250	$225	$200

S-400 A — similar to S-400, except ash body and maple neck. Mfg. 1979 to 1982.

		$375	$350	$325	$300	$250	$225	$200

T-200 — similar to the T-250.

		$600	$575	$525	$475	$425	$400	$375

> The T-200 is sometimes called the "Roy Buchanan" model.

T-250 — single cutaway ash body, black pickguard, controls mounted on metal plate, bolt-on maple neck, 22 fret maple fingerboard with black dot inlay, fixed bridge, 6 on one side tuners, gold hardware, 2 single coil EMG pickups, volume/tone controls, 3 position switch. Available in Black, Blue, Red and White finishes. Mfg. 1986 to circa 1990.

		$600	$575	$525	$475	$425	$400	$375

> The T-250 is sometimes called the "Roy Buchanan" model.

X-79 — offset double cutaway asymmetrical mahogany body with fin like bottom bout, black pickguard, mahogany neck, 24 fret rosewood fingerboard with pearl dot inlay, tunomatic bridge/stop tailpiece, blackface peghead with pearl logo inlay, 3 per side tuners, chrome tuners, 2 single coil pickups, 2 volume/1 tone controls, 3 position switch. Available in Black, Green, Red, Sparkle and White finishes. Mfg. 1981 to 1985.

		$325	$300	$275	$250	$225	$200	$150

> This model had 3 single coil pickups, volume/tone controls, 3 mini switches optionally available.

X-80 SWAN — possibly related to either the X-79 or X-82. Mfg. 1983 to 1985.

> Model has not traded sufficiently to quote pricing.
> Guild records show only 172 models produced.

X-82 — asymmetrical angular body, 3 point headstock, chrome hardware, stop tailpiece, 2 humbuckers, 2 volume/2 tone controls, phase (or coil tap) switch. Mfg. 1981 to 1984.

		$450	$425	$400	$350	$325	$300	$275

> In 1983, a locking tremolo system was added.

X-84 V — bolt neck, Guild or Kahler tremolo. Mfg. 1983.

> Model has not traded sufficiently to quote pricing.
> In 1983, Guild announced a new line of bolt neck, solid body electrics. To date, research has not indicated further specifications. Future updates will appear in subsequent editions of the **Blue Book of Guitars**.

Grading	100%	98% MINT	95% EXC+	90% EXC	80% VG+	70% VG	60% G

Guild 2-3 Nova prototype
courtesy Hal Hammer

X-88 FLYING STAR — "Flying Star" asymmetrical angular body with sharp points, bolt-on neck, locking tremolo, 2 octave fingerboard with star inlays, 1 EMG pickup. Mfg. 1984 to 1985.

	$550	$500	$450	$400	$375	$350	$325

Guitar design was inspired by members of the rock band Motley Crue. Some literature may refer to this model as the Crue Flying Star.

X-88 D Flying Star — similar to X-88 Flying Star, except has DiMarzio pickups. Mfg. 1984 to 1985.

	$550	$500	$450	$400	$375	$350	$325

X-92 CITRON BREAKAWAY — offset solid body (bass side removable for travel), 3 single coil pickups, tremolo, 1 volume/1 tone control, 5 way selector switch. Mfg. 1984 to 1986.

	$425	$385	$345	$315	$285	$265	$235

Designed by luthier Harvey Citron, originally of Veillette-Citron; now currently Citron Enterprises (see CITRON). The X-92 came with a travel/gig bag.

X-97 V — bolt neck, Guild or Kahler tremolo. Mfg. 1983.

Model has not traded sufficiently to quote pricing.

In 1983, Guild announced a new line of bolt neck, solid body electrics. To date, research has not indicated further specifications. Future updates will appear in subsequent editions of the **Blue Book of Guitars**.

X-100 BLADERUNNER — asymmetrical angular body that featured triangular sections removed, bolt-on neck, 6 on one side pointed headstock, locking tremolo, humbucking pickup, 1 volume/1 tone control. Mfg. 1984 to 1985.

	$475	$450	$425	$400	$360	$330	$310

Designed by California luthier David Andrews (See DAVID ANDREWS GUITAR RESEARCH). One year after production of this model ceased, the body design became the basis for Schecter's Genesis Series.

X-108 V — bolt neck, Guild or Kahler tremolo. Mfg. 1983.

Model has not traded sufficiently to quote pricing.

In 1983, Guild announced a new line of bolt neck, solid body electrics. To date, research has not indicated further specifications. Future updates will appear in subsequent editions of the **Blue Book of Guitars**.

X-2000 NIGHTBIRD — single cutaway routed out mahogany body, bound figured maple top, bound tortoise pickguard, mahogany neck, 22 fret bound ebony fingerboard with pearl block/abalone wedge inlay, tunomatic bridge/stop tailpiece, bound peghead with pearl shield/logo inlay, 3 per side tuners, gold hardware, 2 humbucker pickups, volume/tone control, 3 position/single coil switches. Available in Amberburst, Black, Cherry Sunburst and Natural finishes. Disc. 1994.

	$1,200	$1,100	$1,000	$900	$850	$800	$750

Last Mfr.'s Sug. Retail was $1,995.

X-3000 Nightingale — similar to X-2000, except has 2 f-holes. Disc. 1994.

	$1,200	$1,100	$1,000	$900	$850	$800	$750

Last Mfr.'s Sug. Retail was $1,995.

ELECTRIC BASS

Early Guild basses have a specially designed Guild single coil pickup that is often mistaken for a humbucker. These basses are easily identified by the extra switch that activated a passive circuit and eliminated the hum associated with single coil pickups. This feature makes the basses more desirable and collectible.

ASBORY — small curved teardrop body, neck-through design, 4 on one side tuners, chrome hardware, piezo pickup under bridge, 1 volume/1 tone control. Mfg. 1986 to 1988.

	$375	$350	$325	$300	$260	$230	$190

This compact bass had surgical rubber tubing for strings, and, oddly enough, can approximate the sound of an upright bass.

B-301 — offset double cutaway mahogany body, black laminated pickguard, mahogany neck, 20 fret rosewood fingerboard with pearl dot inlay, fixed bridge, blackface peghead with pearl Chesterfield/logo inlay, 2 per side tuners, chrome hardware, single coil pickup, volume/tone controls. Available in Black, Natural, White and Red finishes. Mfg. 1977 to 1981.

	$550	$500	$475	$425	$400	$375	$350

In 1980, mahogany body/neck instruments were discontinued.

B-301A — similar to B-301, except instrument featured an ash body and maple neck. Mfg. circa 1979 to 1981.

	$550	$500	$475	$425	$400	$375	$350

B-302 — similar to B-301, except has 2 single coil pickups, 2 volume/2 tone controls, 3 position switch. Mfg. 1977 to 1981.

	$600	$550	$500	$450	$425	$400	$375

In 1980, mahogany body/neck instruments were discontinued.

B-302A — similar to B-302, except instrument featured an ash body and maple neck. Mfg. circa 1979 to 1981.

	$550	$500	$475	$425	$400	$375	$350

Grading	100%	98% MINT	95% EXC+	90% EXC	80% VG+	70% VG	60% G

B-401 — rounded double cutaway body, set neck, 1 pickup. Mfg. 1980 to 1981.

	$550	$500	$475	$425	$400	$375	$350

Total production for both the B-401 and B-402 was 335 instruments.

B-402 — similar to the B-401, except has 2 pickups. Mfg. 1980 to 1981.

	$550	$500	$475	$425	$400	$375	$350

Total production for both the B-401 and B-402 was 335 instruments.

JS BASS I — offset double cutaway mahogany body/neck, 21 fret rosewood fingerboard with pearl dot inlay, fixed bridge, blackface peghead with pearl Chesterfield/logo inlay, 2 per side tuners, chrome hardware, humbucker pickup, volume/tone controls. Available in Black, Natural and Sunburst finishes. Mfg. 1970-1978.

	$450	$425	$400	$375	$350	$325	$300

This model had fretless fingerboard optionally available.

In 1972, tone switch was introduced, redesigned humbucker pickup replaced original item.

JS Bass I LS — similar to JS Bass I, except has long scale length. Mfg. 1976 to 1978.

	$450	$400	$375	$350	$325	$300	$275

JS BASS II — similar to JS Bass I, except has 2 humbucker pickups, 2 volume/2 tone controls, 3 position switch. Mfg. 1970 to 1978.

	$450	$425	$400	$375	$350	$325	$300

In 1972, tone switch was introduced, redesigned humbucker pickups replaced original item.

In 1974 through 1976, a hand carved acorn/leaves body was offered.

JS Bass II LS — similar to JS Bass I, except has long scale length, 2 humbucker pickups, 2 volume/2 tone controls, 3 position switch. Mfg. 1976 to 1978.

	$350	$325	$275	$250	$225	$200	$175

M-85 I — similar to the JS Bass I, except has a carved top, single cutaway semi-solid design, rosewood fingerboard with dot inlays, 30¾ inch scale, 1 Hagstrom single coil pickup. Mfg. 1970 to 1980.

	$800	$750	$675	$600	$525	$450	$400

M-85 II — similar to the M-85 I, except has 2 pickups, 2 volume/2 tone controls. Mfg. 1970 to 1980.

	$950	$900	$825	$750	$675	$600	$550

Pilot Series

All models in the Pro series were available fretless at no extra cost.

PRO 4 — offset double cutaway asymmetrical maple body, bolt-on maple neck, 22 fret rosewood fingerboard with pearl dot inlay, fixed bridge, 4 on one side tuners, black hardware, 2 J-style active EMG pickups, 2 volume/tone controls, active preamp. Available in Amber, Black, Natural and White finishes. Mfg. 1994 to 1995.

	$750	$630	$525	$415	$360	$330	$300

Last Mfr.'s Sug. Retail was $1,100.

PRO 5 — similar to Pro 4, except has 5 strings, 4/1 per side tuners. Disc. 1995.

	$820	$690	$570	$450	$395	$360	$330

Last Mfr.'s Sug. Retail was $1,200.

SB-600 PILOT — similar to the Pro 4, except has a poplar body and 2 DiMarzio pickups. Mfg. 1983 to 1988.

	$500	$450	$400	$375	$350	$325	$300

SB-601 Pilot — similar to SB-600 Pilot, except has 1 pickup. Mfg. 1983 to 1988.

	$450	$400	$350	$325	$300	$275	$250

SB-602 Pilot — similar to SB-600 Pilot, except has 2 EMG pickups and a bass vibrato. Mfg. 1983 to 1988.

	$575	$525	$475	$450	$425	$400	$375

SB-603 Pilot — similar to SB-600 Pilot, except has 3 pickups. Mfg. 1983 to 1988.

	$500	$450	$400	$375	$350	$325	$300

SB-604 Pilot — similar to SB-600 Pilot, except has different headstock design and EMG pickups. Mfg. 1983 to 1988.

	$550	$500	$450	$425	$400	$375	$350

SB-605 Pilot — similar to SB-600 Pilot, except has 5 strings and EMG pickups. Mfg. 1986 to 1988.

	$600	$550	$500	$475	$450	$425	$400

SB-902 ADVANCED PILOT — similar to the SB-600 Pilot, except has a flamed maple body, ebony fingerboard, and Bartolini pickups and preamp. Mfg. 1987 to 1988.

	$700	$650	$600	$575	$550	$525	$500

SB-905 Advanced Pilot — similar to SB-902 Advanced Pilot, except has 5 strings. Mfg. 1987 to 1988.

	$750	$700	$650	$625	$600	$575	$550

SB Series

Prior to the introduction of the Pilot Bass and subsequent models in 1983, the four models in the SB series sported a vaguely Fenderish body design.

Grading	100%	98% MINT	95% EXC+	90% EXC	80% VG+	70% VG	60% G

SB-201 — offset double cutaway body, set neck, 2+2 headstock, 21 fret fingerboard, Chesterfield logo, 1 split coil pickup, 1 volume/1 tone control. Mfg. 1982 to 1983.

	$375	$350	$300	$275	$250	$225	$200

SB-202 — similar to SB-201, except features 2 pickups, 2 volume/2 tone controls, phase switch. Mfg. 1982 to 1983.

	$425	$400	$350	$325	$300	$275	$250

SB-203 — similar to SB-201, except has 1 split coil pickup and 2 single coils, 1 volume/1 tone controls, 3 mini-switches for pickup selection. Mfg. 1982 to 1983.

	$435	$410	$360	$335	$310	$285	$260

SB-502 E — similar to SB-201, except has active electronics. Mfg. 1982 to 1983.

	$425	$400	$350	$325	$300	$275	$250

SB-666 BLADERUNNER BASS — a companion piece to the X-100 Bladerunner guitar, the SB-666 bass shares similar body design features, but only 1 pickup. Mfg. 1984 to 1985.

	$525	$500	$475	$450	$410	$380	$360

SB-608 FLYING STAR BASS — a companion piece to the X-88 Flying Star guitar, the SB-608 bass shares similar body design features, but only 1 pickup. Mfg. 1984 to 1985.

	$525	$500	$475	$450	$410	$380	$360

SB-608 E — similar to the SB-608 Flying Star, except has active EMG pickups. Mfg. 1984 to 1985.

	$525	$500	$475	$450	$410	$380	$360

ST 4 — offset double cutaway asymmetrical poplar body, bolt-on maple neck, 22 fret rosewood fingerboard with pearl dot inlay, fixed bridge, 4 on one side tuners, black hardware, P-style/J-style pickups, 2 volume/tone controls. Available in Black, Natural and White finishes. Disc. 1994.

	$555	$475	$395	$315	$280	$260	$235

This model also offered a mahogany body.

Last Mfr.'s Sug. Retail was $795.

ST 5 — similar to ST 4, except has 5 strings, 4/1 per side tuners. Disc. 1994.

	$625	$535	$445	$360	$325	$300	$275

Last Mfr.'s Sug. Retail was $895.

STARFIRE BASS I — double round cutaway semi hollow bound maple body, thumb/finger rests, 2 f-holes, 3 piece maple neck, 20 fret rosewood fingerboard with pearl dot inlay, fixed bridge, pearl Chesterfield/logo peghead inlay, 2 per side tuners, chrome hardware, humbucker pickup, volume/tone controls. Available in Cherry Red, Ebony, Emerald Green and Honey Amber finishes. Mfg. 1964 to 1975.

	$600	$550	$500	$425	$400	$375	$325

In 1970, Hagstrom-made single coil pickups were featured.

This model also offered a mahogany body.

Starfire Bass II — similar to Starfire Bass I, except has 2 humbucker pickups, master volume control, bass boost switch. Mfg. 1964 to 1977.

	$675	$625	$550	$525	$500	$475	$425

GUITORGAN

Instruments were built in Waco, Texas between 1969 and 1984.

Inventor Bob Murrell introduced the GuitOrgan prototype at the 1967 Chicago NAMM show, along with partner Bill Mostyn and demonstrator Bob Wiley. The finished product was marketed in 1969, and the instrument allowed players the option of either or both sounds of a guitar and the on-board organ. Murrel combined the circuitry of an organ inside a wide Japanese hollowbody (such as a Ventura, Ibanez, or Yamaha), and then wired each segmented fret (six segments, one per string) to the internal controls. As a result, when a note or notes are fretted, the organ is triggered - and the note will sustain as long as the note stays fretted.

(Source: Teisco Del Rey, Guitar Player magazine, October and November 1993)

The GuitOrgan had a list price of $995 in 1969, and the price rose up to $2,495 new by 1984. It is estimated that 3,000 instruments were produced in the fifteen years, although Murrell did offer to build custom orders after 1984. Models include the M-3000, B-300, and M-35-B.

GURIAN

Instruments built in New York, New York between 1965 and 1982.

Luthier Michael Gurian built quality classical and steel string acoustic guitars, as well as being a major American wood supplier. He debuted his classical designs in 1965 and offered steel string designs four years later. In 1971, at the encouragement of vintage retailer Matt Umanov, Gurian designed a cutaway model that later became a regular part of the product line. Disaster struck in 1979 as a fire consumed their current stock of guitars as well as tooling and machinery. However, Gurian rebuilt by later that year and continued producing guitars for an additional three years. Gurian closed his business doors in 1982.

(Source: Tom Wheeler, American Guitars)

GUYA

Instruments were produced in Japan during the 1960s.

These instruments were generally entry level to good quality guitars based on Rickenbacker designs. Guya was the forerunner to Guyatone labeled guitars, and was built by the same company (see GUYATONE).

(Source: Michael Wright, Guitar Stories Volume One)

GUYATONE

Instruments were built in Japan from late 1950s to the mid 1970s.

The original company was founded by Mitsou Matsuki, an apprentice cabinet maker in the early 1930s. Matsuki, who studied electronics in night classes, was influenced by listening to Hawaiian music. A friend and renowned guitar player, Atsuo Kaneko, requested that Matsuki build a Hawaiian electric guitar. The two entered into business as a company called Matsuki Seisakujo, and produced guitars under the **Guya** trademark.

In 1948, a little after World War II, Matsuki founded his new company, Matsuki Denki Onkyo Kenkyujo. This company produced electric Hawaiian guitars, amplifiers, and record player cartridges. In 1951, this company began using the Guyatone trademark for its guitars. By the next year the corporate name evolved into Tokyo Sound Company. They produced their first solid body electric in the late 1950s. Original designs dominated the early production, albeit entry level quality. Later quality improved, but at the sacrifice of originality as Guyatone began building medium quality designs based on Fender influences. Some Guyatone guitars also were imported under such brandnames as STAR or ANTORIA.

While traditional stringed instruments have been part of the Japanese culture, the guitar was first introduced to Japan in 1890. Japan did not even begin to open trade or diplomatic relations with the West until U.S. President Millard Fillmore sent Commodore Matthew C. Perry in 1850. In 1929 Maestro Andres Segovia made his first concert tour in Japan, sparking an interest in the guitar that has been part of the "subculture" since then. Japanese fascination with the instrumental rock group the Ventures also indicates that not all American design influences would be strictly Fender or Gibson; Mosrite guitars by Semie Moseley also were a large influence, among others.

Classic American guitar designs may have been an influence on the early Japanese models, but the "influence" was incorporated into original designs. The era of copying designs and details began in the early 1970s, but was not the basis for Japanese guitar production. As the entry level models began to get better in quality and meticulous attention to detail, then the American market began to take notice. But to use the trite phrase "Japanese copy" as a derogatory statement applied overall merely indicates ignorance on behalf of the user.

(Source: Tom Wheeler, American Guitars)

G

HAGSTROM

Instruments were produced in Sweden from the late 1950s through the early 1980s.

Hagstrom first began building good quality guitars in 1957, although many models appeared under the FUTURAMA trademark in England during the 1960s. Hagstrom instruments were also imported to the U.S., and distributed by or through the original Ampeg company. Ampeg's attempt at guitar synthesis in the Patch 2000 system involved a Hagstrom guitar (even though the bass model was listed, it is unlikely that it was produced). Hagstrom produced both solid body and semi-hollowbody electrics, including a design by luthier James D'Aquisto in the 1970s and a solid body electric 8-string bass.

HALLMARK

Instruments originally built in Arvin, California during the 1960s. The Hallmark trademark and design was recently re-introduced in January 1995 on a custom order basis. These custom order Hallmark guitars are built in Bakersfield, California. Distribution by Front Porch Music of Bakersfield, California.

The Hallmark company was founded by Joe Hall, an ex-Mosrite employee, around 1967. The Sweptwing design, in its original dual cutaway glory, is strikingly reminiscent of a Flying V built backwards. According to ads run in **Guitar Player** magazine back in 1967, the model was availble in a six string, 12 string, bass, semi-hollowbody six string, and doubleneck configurations. The suggested list price of the semi-hollowbody six string was $265 in the same ad. According to luthier Bill Gruggett, Hallmark produced perhaps 40 guitars before the company ran out of money.

Models generally featured a 3+3 headstock, two humbuckers, a triangular pickguard with the pickup selector mounted in the horn corner, 1 volume and 1 tone knob, and a stop tailpiece. The doubleneck version has to be rarer than the standard six string, although vintage Hallmarks don't turn up every day.

If you're still smitten by the original design, the good news is that they're available again! Custom order Hallmarks that feature hardware by the EPM company are now being distributed by Front Porch Music. Interested players are urged to contact the company via the Index of Current Manufacturers that is located in the back of this book.

Hagstrom Patch 2000
courtesy Steve Burgess

HAMATAR

Instruments built in Spicewood, Texas since the early 1990s.

Luthier/designer Curt Meyers has been working on an innovative design that features primary and secondary guitar bodies that share a similar neck. A central fret replaces the conventional nut, and there is a separate scale length for the left hand and the right hand. Dubbed the model **X-15**, this new guitar can produce two notes on a single string. Retail prices on the X-15 run from $499 up to $4,000.

Meyers also produces a guitar called the "**J.H. model**" that is designed for players that favor the Jeff Healy fretting technique. The guitar consists of a central body and a pair of necks that share the same set of strings. Retail prices range from $1,400 to $4,000. For further information, contact designer Curt Meyers through the Index of Current Manufacturers located in the back of this book.

HAMBURGUITAR

Instruments built in Westland, Michigan since 1981.

These guitars are custom built by Bernie Hamburger of Westland, Michigan. The instruments are available in four different body configurations, and feature a large number of configurations and options. The base price begins at $1,550, with prices increasing depending upon options chosen. For further information, please contact luthier Hamburger through the Index of Current Manufacturers located in the rear of this book.

HAMER

Instruments produced in Arlington Heights, Illinois. The Hamer company also has an entry level series of USA-designed guitars and basses built in Asia. Hamer guitars are distributed by the Kaman Music Corporation of Bloomfield, Connecticut.

Hamer Guitars was cofounded by Paul Hamer and Jol Dantzig in 1976. In the early 1970s, the two were partners in Northern Prairie Music, a Chicago-based store that specialized in stringed instrument repair and used guitars. The repair section had been ordering so many supplies and parts from the Gibson facilities that the two were invited to a tour of the Kalamazoo plant. Later, Nothern Prairie was made the first American Gibson authorized warranty repair shop.

Hamer, a regular gigging musician at the time, built a Les Paul-shaped short scale bass with Gibson parts that attracted enough attention for custom orders. By 1973, the shop was taking orders from some professional musicians as well. Hamer and Dantzig were both Gibson enthusiasts. Their early custom guitars were Flying V-based in design, and then later they branched out in Explorer-styled guitars. These early models were basically prototypes for the later production guitars, and featured Gibson hardware, Larry DiMarzio-wound pickups, figured tops, and lacquer finishes.

In the mid 1970s, the prices of vintage Fenders and Gibsons began to rise, and those companies weren't offering any quality instruments at reasonable prices - so Hamer and Dantzig saw a market niche. They incorporated **Hamer USA** and set up the first shop in Palatine, Illinois. Their first catalog from Fall 1975 shows only the Explorer-shaped guitar (no model name) dubbed "The Hamer Guitar" (later, it became the Standard) for the retail list price of $799. Hamer USA built perhaps 50 Standards between 1975 and 1978, an estimated 10 to 15 a year. In contrast, Gibson reissued the Explorer from 1976 to 1978 and shipped 3,300 of them! In 1978, Hamer debutted their second model, the Les Paul-ish**Sunburst**. While the Standard had jumped up to a retail price of $1,199, the Sunburst's lower price created new demands. In 1980, The company expanded into larger facilities in Arlington Heights, Illinois (where they still are today). Paul Hamer left Hamer USA in 1987. A year later, Hamer was acquired by the Kaman Music Corporation, but are still run as a separate entity from the East Coast Ovation production lines.

Model designations for the Gibson-based 1970s models run as follows: Special, Sunburst ('58 LP Special), Standard (Explorer), and Vector (Flying V).

Early Hamer models such as the Standard and Sunburst in 80% to 90% now command $1,000 on the vintage market.

In the 1980s, Hamer offered some quality original body designs such as the Phantom (A5 was developed in 1983 in conjunction with Andy Summers, then with the Police - the later A7 model came equipped to interface with Roland Guitar Synth gear), Prototype, Steve Stevens, Chaparral, and Californian. Hamer currently pushes the barriers of guitar design by offering the DuoTone, a hybrid stereo acoustic/electric model.

Early 1980s original body models in 80% to 90% range in price between $350 to $600. While the quality still remains first rate, the body profile on certain models may be at odds with the retro-design driven market.

Hamer Standard
courtesy Hyatt W. Finley

ELECTRIC

Hamer USA Series

All instruments are made in Arlington Heights, Illinois, and display the USA logo on the headstock.

Grading	100%	98%	95%	90%	80%	70%	60%
	MINT	**EXC+**	**EXC**	**VG+**	**VG**	**G**	

ARCHTOP CUSTOM — double cutaway mahogany body, arched bound maple top, mahogany neck, 22 fret bound rosewood fingerboard with abalone crown inlay, tunomatic bridge/stop tailpiece, 3 per side tuners, gold hardware, 2 single coil pickups, 1 volume/2 tone controls, 3 position switch. Available in Black and Gold Top finishes. Mfd. 1992 to date.

Mfr.'s Sug. Retail	$1,500	$1,200	$900	$750	$600	$540	$495	$450

Archtop Standard — similar to Archtop Custom, except has unbound fingerboard with pearl dot inlay, chrome hardware.

Mfr.'s Sug. Retail	$1,300	$1,040	$780	$650	$520	$470	$430	$390

CALIFORNIAN DELUXE — double offset cutaway alder body, bolt-on maple neck, 27 fret ebony fingerboard with offset pearl dot inlay, pearl boomerang inlay 3rd/12th fret, double locking vibrato, 6 on one side tuners, gold hardware, stacked coil/humbucker EMG pickups, 3 position switch, volume/tone control, coil split in volume control, active electronics. Available in Aztec Gold, Black, Emerald Green and Transparent Cherry finishes. Disc. 1993.

	$1,260	$1,080	$900	$720	$650	$595	$540

Last Mfr.'s Sug. Retail was $1,800.

Californian Elite — similar to Californian Deluxe, except has mahogany body, pearl boomerang fingerboard inlay, 2 humbucker Seymour Duncan pickups, no tone control/active electronics. Available in Aztec Gold, Black, Emerald Green and Transparent Cherry finishes. Curr. mfr.

Mfr.'s Sug. Retail	$1,400	$1,120	$840	$785	$680	$610	$560	$510

This model has 12 strings, figured maple top, 6 per side tuners, black hardware optionally available.

Californian Doubleneck — similar to Californian Elite, except has doubleneck construction with a variety of configurations, 12/6 strings are the most popular. The necks on this model are glued in rather than bolt-on. The base price is $2,700.

CENTAURA — double offset cutaway ash body, bolt-on maple neck, 24 fret pau ferro fingerboard with pearl offset inlay, double locking vibrato, 6 on one side Schaller tuners, black hardware, Seymour Duncan 2 single coil/1 humbucker pickups, volume/tone control, 5-position switch, active electronics with bypass switch. Available in Aztec Gold, Black, Emerald Green and Transparent Cherry finishes. Mfd. 1992 to date.

Mfr.'s Sug. Retail	$1,350	$1,080	$810	$715	$600	$540	$495	$450

This model has black hardware optionally available.

Centaura Deluxe — similar to Centaura, except has alder body, ebony fingerboard, pearl boomerang inlay at 3rd/12th fret, chrome hardware, EMG pickups. Disc. 1993.

	$1,260	$1,080	$900	$720	$650	$595	$540

Last Mfr.'s Sug. Retail was $1,800.

CHAPARRAL ELITE — offset double cutaway alder body, bolt-on maple neck, 24 fret ebony fingerboard with pearl boomerang inlay, double locking vibrato, 6 on one side tuners, chrome hardware, humbucker/single coil/humbucker pickups, volume/tone control, 5 position/2 mini switches, active electronics. Available in Aztec Gold, Black, Emerald Green, Natural and Transparent Cherry finishes. Curr. mfr.

Mfr.'s Sug. Retail	$1,400	$1,120	$840	$700	$560	$505	$460	$420

This model has black hardware optionally available.

Grading	100%	98% MINT	95% EXC+	90% EXC	80% VG+	70% VG	60% G

DAYTONA — offset double cutaway alder body, white pickguard, bolt-on maple neck, 22 fret maple fingerboard with black dot inlay, standard vibrato, 6 on one side locking tuners, chrome hardware, 3 single coil Seymour Duncan pickups, 5 position switch, 1 volume/2 tone controls. Available in Daphne Blue, Emerald Green, Seafoam Green, Transparent Blue, Transparent Cherry, Transparent Red, Transparent White, 2 Tone Sunburst and Vintage White finishes. New 1994.

	100%	98%	95%	90%	80%	70%	60%
Mfr.'s Sug. Retail	$1,000	$800	$600	$500	$400	$360	$330	$300

Daytona SV — similar to Daytona, 3 single coil active EMG pickups. New 1994.

Mfr.'s Sug. Retail	$1,200	$960	$720	$600	$480	$430	$395	$360

DIABLO — offset double cutaway alder body, bolt-on maple neck, 24 fret rosewood fingerboard with pearl dot inlay, double locking vibrato, blackface reverse peghead with screened logo, 6 on one side tuners, chrome hardware, 2 exposed humbucker Seymour Duncan pickups, volume/tone control, 5 position switch. Available in Aztec Gold, Black, Emerald Green, Natural, Transparent Cherry and Transparent Red finishes. Curr. mfr.

Mfr.'s Sug. Retail	$950	$760	$570	$475	$380	$345	$315	$285

This model has black hardware optionally available.

DUOTONE — double cutaway semi hollow mahogany body, bound spruce top, 3 round soundholes, mahogany neck, 22 fret bound rosewood fingerboard with pearl dot inlay, strings thru rosewood bridge, blackface peghead with screened logo, 3 per side tuners, chrome hardware, 2 exposed humbucker/1 piezo bridge pickups, 2 volume controls, two 3-position switches, 3 band EQ, active electronics. Available in Black, '59 Sunburst and Natural finishes. New 1994.

Mfr.'s Sug. Retail	$1,800	$1,440	$1,080	$900	$720	$650	$595	$540

MIRAGE — offset double cutaway mahogany body/neck, carved figured koa top, 22 fret rosewood fingerboard with pearl dot inlay, standard Wilkinson vibrato, 3 per side Sperzel locking tuners, chrome hardware, 3 single coil Seymour Duncan rail pickups, volume/tone controls, 5 position/bypass switches. Available in Natural finish. New 1994.

Mfr.'s Sug. Retail	$1,400	$1,120	$840	$700	$560	$505	$460	$420

SPECIAL — double cutaway mahogany body, mahogany neck, 22 fret rosewood fingerboard with pearl dot inlay, tunomatic bridge/stop tailpiece, blackface peghead with screened logo, 3 per side tuners, chrome hardware, 2 single coil Seymour Duncan pickups, 1 volume/2 tone controls, 3 position switch. Available in Black, Natural, Transparent Cherry, 2 Tone Sunburst, TV Blonde and Vintage White finishes. New 1994.

Mfr.'s Sug. Retail	$950	$760	$570	$475	$380	$345	$315	$285

Add $100 for 2 exposed humbucker Seymour Duncan pickups.

Special FM — similar to Special, except has figured maple top. Available in Aztec Gold, Blue Burst, Emerald Green, '59 Burst, Natural, Salmon Burst, Transparent Blue, Transparent Cherry and Vintage Orange finishes.

Mfr.'s Sug. Retail	$1,150	$920	$690	$575	$460	$415	$380	$345

SUNBURST ARCHTOP CUSTOM — double cutaway mahogany body, arched bound figured maple top, mahogany neck, 22 fret bound rosewood fingerboard with abalone crown inlay, tunomatic bridge/stop tailpiece, 3 per side tuners, gold hardware, 2 humbucker Seymour Duncan pickups, 1 volume/2 tone controls, 3 position switch. Available in Aztec Gold, Blue Burst, Emerald Green, '59 Burst, Natural, Salmon Blush, Transparent Blue, Transparent Cherry and Vintage Orange finishes. Mfd. 1992 to date.

Mfr.'s Sug. Retail	$1,800	$1,440	$1,080	$925	$760	$685	$625	$570

Sunburst Archtop Standard — similar to Sunburst Archtop Custom, except has unbound fingerboard with pearl dot inlay, chrome hardware.

Mfr.'s Sug. Retail	$1,600	$1,280	$960	$825	$680	$610	$560	$510

Sunburst Archtop Studio — similar to Sunburst Archtop Custom, except has unbound figured maple top, unbound rosewood fingerboard with pearl dot inlay, chrome hardware. New 1994.

Mfr.'s Sug. Retail	$1,400	$1,120	$840	$700	$560	$505	$460	$420

T-51 — single cutaway alder body, black pickguard, bolt-on maple neck, 22 fret maple fingerboard with black dot inlay, strings thru bridge, 6 on one side tuners, chrome hardware, 2 single coil Seymour Duncan pickups, volume/tone control, 3 position switch, controls mounted metal plate. Available in Black, Butterscotch, Natural, Transparent White and Vintage Orange finishes. New 1994.

Mfr.'s Sug. Retail	$950	$760	$570	$475	$380	$345	$315	$285

TRAD '62 (formerly T-62) — double offset cutaway alder body, white pickguard, bolt-on bird's eye maple neck, 22 fret pau ferro fingerboard with pearl dot inlay, standard vibrato, Lubritrak nut, 6 on one side locking Sperzel tuners, 3 single coil Alnico pickups, volume control, 5-position switch, 3 band EQ with bypass switch. Available in Daphne Blue, Emerald Green, Seafoam Green, 2 Tone Sunburst, 3 Tone Sunburst, Transparent Blue, Transparent White and Vintage White finishes. Mfd. 1992 to date.

Mfr.'s Sug. Retail	$1,450	$1,160	$870	$795	$680	$610	$560	$510

In 1994, 3 Tone Sunburst was discontinued, Daphne Blue, Emerald Green, 2 Tone Sunburst, Transparent Blue and Transparent White finishes were introduced.

Grading	100%	98% MINT	95% EXC+	90% EXC	80% VG+	70% VG	60% G

'92 Hamer 12 String Bass (Short Scale)
courtesy Steve Burgess

VINTAGE S — similar to T-62, except has figured maple body, no pickguard, and tone control. Available in Amberburst, Aztec Gold, Cherry Sunburst, Natural, '59 Burst, Salmon Burst and 3 Tone Sunburst finishes.

Mfr.'s Sug. Retail	$1,800	$1,440	$1,080	$975	$820	$745	$675	$615

In 1994, Aztec Gold, Natural and Salmon Burst finishes were introduced, Cherry Sunburst finish was discontinued.

Hamer Slammer Series

All instruments in this series are manufactured overseas and distributed by Hamer located in Arlington Heights, IL. The specifics on these models are the same as those featured in the USA Series (see above) with corresponding names, but the materials and components are not of the similar quality.

CALIFORNIAN — locking vibrato. Available in Aztec Gold, Black, Natural, 3 Tone Sunburst and Transparent Cherry finishes. Curr. mfr.

Mfr.'s Sug. Retail	$700	$525	$350	$325	$260	$235	$215	$195

In 1994, Aztec Gold, Black, 3 Tone Sunburst and Transparent Cherry finishes were introduced, Natural finish was discontinued.

DAYTONA — rosewood fingerboard. Available in Aztec Gold Stain finish. New 1994.

Mfr.'s Sug. Retail	$500	$400	$300	$250	$200	$180	$165	$150

This model has maple fingerboard with 2 Tone Sunburst finish optionally available.

DIABLO — locking vibrato. Available in Black, Emerald Green and Light Brown Sunburst finishes. Curr. mfr.

Mfr.'s Sug. Retail	$650	$520	$390	$325	$260	$235	$215	$195

In 1994, Black and Emerald Green finishes were introduced.

Diablo II — locking vibrato, humbucker/single coil/humbucker pickups. Available in Aztec Gold, Black and Candy Apple Red finishes. New 1994.

Mfr.'s Sug. Retail	$650	$520	$390	$325	$260	$235	$215	$195

Diablo SV — standard vibrato, 3 single coil pickups. Available in Black, Candy Apple Red and Light Brown Sunburst finishes. New 1994.

Mfr.'s Sug. Retail	$550	$440	$330	$275	$220	$200	$180	$165

SPECIAL — 2 humbucker pickups. Available in Black, 3 Tone Sunburst and Transparent Cherry finishes. New 1994.

Mfr.'s Sug. Retail	$650	$520	$390	$325	$260	$235	$215	$195

SUNBURST ARCH TOP — Available in Black and Vintage White finishes. Curr. mfr.

Mfr.'s Sug. Retail	$700	$560	$420	$350	$280	$250	$230	$210

In 1994, Vintage White finish was introduced.

Sunburst Flat Top — Available in Aztec Gold, Black, Cherry Sunburst and Transparent Cherry finishes. Curr. mfr.

Mfr.'s Sug. Retail	$700	$560	$420	$350	$280	$250	$230	$210

In 1994, Aztec Gold, Black and Transparent Cherry finishes were introduced.

T-51 — maple fingerboard. Available in Light Brown Sunburst finish. New 1994.

Mfr.'s Sug. Retail	$500	$400	$300	$250	$200	$180	$165	$150

Centaura Series

These Centura models are also part of the overseas Hamer Slammer Series.

CENTAURA — maple fingerboard, standard vibrato, reverse headstock. Available in Black, Blood Red, Candy Apple Red, 3 Tone Sunburst and Vintage White finishes. Curr. mfr.

Mfr.'s Sug. Retail	$500	$400	$300	$250	$200	$180	$165	$150

In 1994, Candy Apple Red and Vintage White finishes were introduced, Blood Red finish was discontinued.

Centaura C — locking vibrato, reverse headstock. Available in Amber Burst, Black Metalflake, Black Pearl, Candy Red, Cherry Metalflake, Transparent Cherry, Vintage White and 3 Tone Sunburst finishes. Disc. 1994.

			$420	$360	$300	$240	$215	$195	$180

Last Mfr.'s Sug. Retail was $600.

Centaura Deluxe — curly sycamore body, locking vibrato, regular headstock. Available in Transparent Purple and Transparent Walnut finishes. New 1994.

Mfr.'s Sug. Retail	$540	$432	$324	$270	$215	$195	$180	$165

Centaura RC — locking vibrato, regular headstock. Available in Black and Transparent Cherry finishes. Curr. mfr.

Mfr.'s Sug. Retail	$650	$520	$390	$325	$260	$235	$215	$195

In 1994, Black finish was introduced.

Grading	100%	98% MINT	95% EXC+	90% EXC	80% VG+	70% VG	60% G

ELECTRIC BASS

CHAPARRAL BASS — offset double cutaway alder body, bolt-on maple neck, 21 fret rosewood fingerboard with pearl dot inlay, fixed bridge, 4 on one side tuners, chrome hardware, EMG P-style/J-style pickups, 1 volume/2 tone controls, active electronics. Available in Aztec Gold, Black, Candy Red, Natural, 3 Tone Sunburst, transparent Cherry, Vintage White and White finishes. Mfd. 1992 to date.

Mfr.'s Sug. Retail	$1,400	$1,120	$840	$725	$600	$540	$495	$450

This model has black hardware optionally available.

Chaparral Bass (Set Neck) — similar to Chaparral, except has glued in (set) neck. Disc. 1993.

	$1,120	$960	$800	$640	$575	$530	$480

Last Mfr.'s Sug. Retail was $1,600.

Chaparral 5-String Bass — similar to Chaparral Bass, except has set in 5 string neck, reverse headstock, 2 EMG pickups, mix control.

Mfr.'s Sug. Retail	$1,500	$1,200	$900	$805	$680	$610	$560	$510

IMPACT BASS — offset double cutaway rosewood body, African sapelle/purpleheart thru body 5 string neck, 24 fret pau ferro fingerboard with abalone boomerang inlay, fixed bridge, 2/3 per side tuners, gold hardware, 2 EMG/1 transducer bridge pickups, 2 volume/1 treble/1 bass controls, active electronics. Mfd. 1991 to 1993.

	$1,750	$1,500	$1,250	$1,000	$900	$825	$750

Last Mfr.'s Sug. Retail was $2,500.

TWELVE STRING BASS (Short Scale) — double cutaway figured maple body, set in maple neck, 21 fret rosewood fingerboard with pearl dot inlay, fixed bridge, 6 per side tuners, chrome hardware, 2 EMG pickups, 2 volume/1 tone controls, active electronics. Available in Aztec Gold, Black, Candy Red, '59 Burst, Natural, Transparent Cherry and White finishes. Mfd. 1991 to date.

Mfr.'s Sug. Retail	$2,000	$1,600	$1,200	$1,055	$880	$790	$725	$660

Twelve String Bass (Long Scale) — similar to Twelve String Bass (Short Scale) except has long scale fingerboard.

Mfr.'s Sug. Retail	$2,200	$1,760	$1,320	$1,100	$880	$790	$725	$660

Hamer Slammer Series

All instruments in this series are manufactured overseas and distributed by Hamer located in Arlington Heights, IL. The specifics on these models are the same as those featured in the USA Series (see above) with corresponding names, but the materials and components are not of the similar quality.

CENTAURA — bolt-on neck. Available in Black, Blood Red, Candy Apple Red, 3 Tone Sunburst and Vintage White finishes. Curr. mfr.

Mfr.'s Sug. Retail	$500	$400	$300	$275	$240	$215	$195	$180

In 1994, Candy Apple Red and Vintage White finishes were introduced. Blood Red finish was discontinued.

CENTAURA 5 — bolt-on neck. Available in Black, Black Metalflake, Black Pearl, Blue Metalflake, Candy Apple Red, Candy Red, 3 Tone Sunburst and Vintage White finishes. Curr. mfr.

Mfr.'s Sug. Retail	$580	$464	$348	$320	$280	$250	$230	$210

In 1994, Black and 3 Tone Sunburst finishes were introduced. Black Metalflake, Black Pearl, Blue Metalflake and Candy Red finishes were discontinued.

CHAPARRAL — Available in Black, Candy Apple Red, 3 Tone Sunburst and Vintage White finishes. Curr. mfr.

Mfr.'s Sug. Retail	$600	$480	$360	$325	$280	$250	$230	$210

In 1994, Black, Candy Apple Red and Vintage White finishes were introduced.

HANEWINCKEL

Instruments currently built in Artesia, California.

Hanewinckel currently offers custom built bass guitars. Retail prices begin at $1,450 (4-string classic) to $1,600 (5-string classic) and up to $2,050 (6-string pro). For further information, contact Hanewinckel Guitars through the Index of Current Manufacturers located in the back of this book.

HANG-DON

Instruments built in Vietnam during the 1970s.

These entry level guitars displayed a Fender-ish lean in design, although the composition and materials are basic.

(Source: Tony Bacon, The Ultimate Guitar Book)

HARDBODY COMPOSITE GUITARS

Instruments built in Escondido, California. Distributed by Bi-Mar International of Escondido, California.

Designer George M. Clayton is an expert in composite (graphite) materials, and has a background in the aerospace field as well as yacht (Catamaran) building. Clayton was a former vice president and head

Hang-Don
courtesy Steve Steinbauer

H

Hardbody Composite STS-1
courtesy George M. Clayton

Harmony Rocket
courtesy Paul Jameson

designer for the Rainsong Guitar Company and currently offers the STS-1 solid body, graphite electric guitar.

The **STS-1** ($1,750 new) features a neck-through molded design, ebony fingerboard, abalone inlays, active EMG 89 humbucking pickups, and three custom colors (red, white, or black). For distribution and availability information, please contact Bi-Mar International via the Index of Current Manufacturers located in the back of this book.

HARMONY

U.S. production of Harmony stringed instruments from 1890s to mid 1970s was localized in Chicago, Illinois. Harmony, along with Kay, were the two major producers for instrument wholesalers for a number of years (see chapter on House Brands). When U.S. manufacture stopped, the Harmony trademark was then applied to Korean-built instruments from the mid 1970s to the late 1980s.

The Harmony Company of Chicago, Illinois was one of the largest American musical instrument manufacturers. Harmony has the historical distinction of being the largest "jobber" house in the nation, and at one time the amount of instruments being produced by Harmony made up the largest percentage of stringed instruments being manufactured (archtops, flat-tops, electric Spanish, Hawaiian bodies, ukeleles, banjos, mandolins, violins and more). Individual dealers or distributors could get an instrument with their brandname on it, as long as they ordered a minimum of 100 pieces.

Harmony was founded by Wilhelm J.F. Schultz in 1892. Schultz, a German immigrant and former foreman of Lyon & Healy's drum division, started his new company with four employees. By 1984, the number of employees had grown to forty, and Shultz continued to expand into larger and larger factories through 1904. Shultz built Harmony up to a 125 employee workforce (and a quarter of a million dollars in annual sales) by 1915.

In 1916, the Sears, Roebuck Company purchased Harmony, and seven years later the company had annual sales of 250,000 units. Max Adler, a Sears executive, appointed Jay Kraus as vice-president of Harmony in 1925. The following year Jay succeeded founder Wilhelm Schultz as president, and continued expanding production. In 1930, annual sales were reported to be 500,000 units sold, with 35 to 40 percent being sold to Sears (catalog sales). Harmony had no branch offices, territorial restrictions, or dealer "reps" - wholesalers purchased the musical instruments and aggressively sold to music stores.

Harmony bought several trademarks from the bankrupt Oscar Schmidt Company in 1939, and their Sovereign and Stella lines were Harmony's more popular guitars. In 1940, Krause bought Harmony by acquiring the controlling stock, and continued to expand the company's production to meet the market boom during the 1950s and 1960s. Mr. Kraus remained president until 1968, when he died of a heart attack. Charles Rubovits (who had been with Harmony since 1935) took over as president, and remained in that position for two years. Kraus' trust still maintained control over Harmony, and trust members attempted to form a conglomerate by purchasing Chicago-based distributor Targ & Dinner and a few other companies. Company indebtedness led to a liquidation auction to satisfy creditors, although Harmony continued to turn in impressive annual sales figures right up until the company was dissolved in 1974.

(Source: Tom Wheeler, American Guitars)

Harmony reportedly made 57 "different" brands throughout their productive years. Early models featured the Harmony trademark, or remained unlabeled for the numerous wholesalers. In 1928 Harmony introduced the **Roy Smeck Vita** series, and two years later the **Grand Concert** and **Hawaiian** models debuted. The **Vagabond** line was introduced in 1931, **Cremona** series the following year, and **Patrician** guitars later in 1938.

As Harmony was purchased by Sears, Roebuck in 1916, Harmony built a number of **Silvertone** models. Harmony continued to sell to Sears even after Kraus bought the company. Harmony bought a number of trademarks from the bankrupt Oscar Schmidt Company in 1939 (**La Scala, Stella, Sovereign**), as well as expanding their own brandnames with **Valencia, Monterey, Harmony Deluxe, Johnny Marvin, Vogue**, and many that are being researched today! Although the Kay company built most of the **Airline** guitars for the Montgomery Ward stores, Harmony would sometimes be subcontracted to build Airlines to meet the seasonal shopping rush. National (Valco) supplied resonator cones for some Harmony resonator models, and probably bought guitar parts from Harmony in return.

In general, Harmony made student grade instruments. The average Harmony is of player's value, 80% of them would fall in the under $200 range. There is not a lot of collector desirability placed on these instruments.

The Silvertone series, offered by Sears, is probably the most popular. Silvertone guitars, depending on configuration and condition, range in price between $275 to $450. The Silvertone "Black Model", a single cutaway hollow body instrument with a pickguard and 2 humbuckers (easily identified by the huge aluminum binding), will bring $500 in the cleanest of conditions.

HARPER'S

Instruments currently built in Apple Valley, California.

Harper's Guitars are high quality, custom built, solid body electric guitars. Retail prices begin at $1,595 (Monterey and Sierra) up to $1,895 (Mojave) and options are available at additional cost. For further information contact Harper's Guitars through the Index of Current Manufacturers located in the back of this book.

HARPTONE

Instruments built in Newark, New Jersey 1966 to mid-1970s.

The Harptone company was a commercial successor to the Felsberg Company (circa 1893). During the 1930s, Harptone was more known for musical instrument accessories, although a few guitars were built between 1924 and 1942. In the early 1960s, Harptone's main guitar designer was Stan Koontz (who also designed Standel and his own signature guitars). Harptone's guitar product line consisted of mainly acoustic and a few electric guitar models.

When Micro-Frets closed operations in Maryland in either 1974 or 1975, the company assets were purchased by David Sturgill. Sturgill, who served as the company president of Grammer Guitars for three years, let his sons John and Danny gain access to leftover Micro-Frets parts. In addition to those parts, they had also purchased the remains of New Jersey's Harptone guitar company. The two assembled a number of solid body guitars which were then sold under the 'Diamond-S' trademark. Unfortunately, that business venture did not catch on, and dissipated sometime in 1976.

(Source: Tom Wheeler, American Guitars)

HAUSER

Instruments built in Munich, Germany since the early 1900s.

Luthier Hermann Hauser (1882-1952) built a variety of stringed instruments throughout his career. While earlier models did not share the same designs as the "Spanish school", Hauser soon adopted designs introduced by Antonio de Torres. In the late 1930s Maestro Andres Segovia moved from a Ramirez guitar to a Hauser built classical, which he played until 1970.

Hermann Hauser was succeeded by a son and grandson who also share his name and desire to build guitars.

(Source: Tony Bacon, The Ultimate Guitar Book)

HAWK

See FRAMUS.

See also KLIRA.

Instruments were built in West Germany during the early 1960s.

The Hawk trademark was a brandname used by a UK importer. Instruments imported into England were built by either Framus or Klira in Germany, and are identical to their respective builder's models.

(Source: Tony Bacon and Paul Day, The Guru's Guitar Guide)

HAYMAN

Instruments built in England during the mid 1970s.

In 1969, luthier Jim Burns (ex-Burns, Burns-Weill) was invited into the Dallas-Arbiter organization to develop a new line of guitars under the 'Hayman' trademark. He began working with Bob Pearson (ex-Vox) that ultimately developed designs for three guitars and one bass. Woodworking and truss rod work were done by Jack Golder and Norman Holder, who had been with Jim Burns previously.

Instruments were produced from 1970 through 1973. Jim Burns moved on from Dallas-Arbiter in 1971, leaving Pearson to continue developing new ideas. When Dallas-Arbiter folded in the mid 1970s, Pearson joined with Golder and Holder to form the Shergold company. Hayman instruments, while not as flashy as their Burns predecessors, were still solid instruments, and also a link to formation of the later Shergolds.

According to authors Tony Bacon and Paul Day, the last two digits of a Hayman serial number indicate the year of manufacture. This practice began in 1974.

(Source: Paul Day, The Burns Book)

HAYNES

Instruments manufactured in Boston, Massachusetts from 1865 to the early 1900s.

The Oliver Ditson Company, Inc. was formed in 1835 by music publisher Oliver Ditson (1811-1888). Ditson was a primary force in music merchandising, distribution, and retail sales on the East Coast. He also helped establish two musical instrument manufacturers: The John Church Company of Cincinnati, Ohio, and Lyon & Healy (Washburn) in Chicago, Illinois.

In 1865, Ditson established a manufacturing branch of his company under the supervision of John Haynes, called the John C. Haynes Company. This branch built guitars for a number of trademarks, such as Bay State, Tilton, and Haynes Excelsior.

(Source: Tom Wheeler, American Guitars)

HEART

Renamed HEARTWOOD in 1988.

Instruments built in England during the mid to late 1980s.

Early models of these high quality original and Fender-style guitars had heart-shaped fretboard and headstock inlays.

(Source: Tony Bacon and Paul Day, The Guru's Guitar Guide)

HEARTFIELD

Instruments were produced in Japan from 1989 through 1994. Distributed by the Fender Musical Instruments Corporation located in Scottsdale, Arizona.

As part of a reciprocal agreement, the Japanese Fuji Gen Gakki company that produced various Fender models received distribution assistance from FMIC for the Heartfield line. During the mid to late 1980s, various companies such as Jackson/Charvel popularized the "superstrat" concept: different pickup combinations and locking tremolos that updated the original Fender Stratocaster design. As Fender never had much success straying from the original Stratocaster design (like the Katana or Performer models), the Heartfield models filled a niche in promotion of designs "too radical" for the Fender trademark.

Heartfields (designed both at Fender USA and Fender Japan) were solid, playable solid body electrics. Some models feature active electronics or other 'non-Fender' associated designs. Later production models may also have 'Heartfield by Fender' on the headstock instead of Heartfield.

Grading		100%	98% MINT	95% EXC+	90% EXC	80% VG+	70% VG	60% G

ELECTRIC

Elan Series

From 1991 to 1992, this series featured ivoroid bound figured maple top, bound fingerboard with triangle inlay, humbucker/single coil/humbucker pickups. The descriptions below are for currently manufactured instruments.

ELAN I — double offset cutaway mahogany body, bookmatched figured maple top, mahogany neck, 22 fret ebony fingerboard with pearl dot inlay, fixed bridge, 3 per side tuners with pearl buttons, gold hardware, 2 humbucker pickups, volume/tone control, 5 position switch. Available in Amber, Antique Burst, Crimson Transparent and Sapphire Blue Transparent finishes. Mfd. 1991 to 1993.

		$785	$670	$560	$450	$405	$370	$335

Last Mfr.'s Sug. Retail was $1,120.

Elan II — similar to Elan I, except has locking Floyd Rose vibrato, locking tuners, chrome hardware.

		$835	$715	$595	$475	$430	$390	$360

Last Mfr.'s Sug. Retail was $1,190.

Elan III — similar to Elan I, except has double locking Floyd Rose vibrato, black hardware, humbucker/single coil/humbucker pickups.

		$980	$840	$700	$560	$505	$460	$420

Last Mfr.'s Sug. Retail was $1,400.

EX Series

This series was produced 1992 only.

EX I — double offset cutaway basswood body, mahogany neck, 22 fret rosewood fingerboard with pearl dot inlay, double locking Floyd Rose vibrato, 3 per side tuners, black hardware, 3 single coil pickups, 2 in a humbucker configuration in bridge position, volume/tone/boost control, 5 position switch, series/parallel mini switch, active electronics. Available in Black, Chrome Red, Frost Red, Midnight Blue, Montego Black and Mystic White finishes.

		$575	$405	$345	$285	$230	$205	$190

EX II — similar to EX I, except has figured maple top. Available in Amber, Antique Burst, Crimson Transparent and Sapphire Blue Transparent finishes.

		$600	$420	$360	$300	$240	$215	$195

RR Series

RR 8 — offset double shorthorn cutaway alder body, white pickguard, mahogany neck, 22 fret rosewood fingerboard with pearl dot inlay, fixed bridge, 3 per side tuners, chrome hardware, humbucker pickup, volume/tone control, 3 mini switches with LED's, active electronics. Available in Blue Sparkle, Brite White, Frost Red and Yellow Sparkle finishes. Mfd. 1991 to 1993.

		$490	$345	$295	$245	$195	$175	$160

RR 9 — similar to RR 8, except has standard vibrato.

		$540	$380	$325	$270	$215	$195	$180

RR 58 — offset double shorthorn cutaway mahogany body, black pickguard, mahogany neck, 22 fret rosewood fingerboard with abalone dot inlay, fixed bridge, 3 per side tuners, chrome hardware, 2 humbucker pickups, volume/tone control, 5 position switch. Available in Blond, Crimson transparent and Emerald Green Transparent finishes. Mfd. 1991 to 1993.

		$700	$490	$420	$350	$280	$250	$230

Grading	100%	98% MINT	95% EXC+	90% EXC	80% VG+	70% VG	60% G

RR 59 — similar to RR 58, except has standard vibrato, locking tuners, 2 humbucker pickups.

| | $770 | $540 | $460 | $385 | $310 | $280 | $255 |

Talon Series

TALON — double offset cutaway basswood body, black pickguard, bolt-on maple neck, 22 fret rosewood fingerboard with pearl dot inlay, double locking Floyd Rose vibrato, 6 on one side tuners, black hardware, 2 single coil/1 humbucker pickups, volume/tone control, 5 position switch. Available in Black, Chrome Red, Frost Red, Midnight Blue, Montego Black and Mystic White finishes. Mfd. 1991 to 1993.

| | $480 | $335 | $290 | $240 | $190 | $170 | $155 |

Talon I — similar to Talon, except has humbucker/single coil/humbucker pickups.

| | $600 | $420 | $360 | $300 | $240 | $215 | $195 |

Talon II — similar to Talon, except has 24 fret fingerboard, 2 humbucker DiMarzio pickups.

| | $650 | $455 | $390 | $325 | $260 | $235 | $215 |

Talon III — similar to Talon, except has humbucker/single coil/humbucker pickups.

| | $800 | $560 | $480 | $400 | $320 | $290 | $265 |

This model is also available without a pickguard and a reverse headstock as a Talon IIIR.

TALON IV — double offset cutaway basswood body, black pickguard, bolt-on maple neck, 24 fret rosewood fingerboard with triangle inlay, 12th and 24th frets have additional red triangle inlay, double locking Floyd Rose vibrato, 6 on one side tuners, black hardware, humbucker/single coil/humbucker pickups, volume/tone control, 5 position switch. Available in Black, Chrome Red, Frost Red, Midnight Blue, Montego Black and Mystic White finishes. Mfd. 1991 to 1993.

| | $930 | $650 | $555 | $465 | $370 | $335 | $305 |

This model is available with reverse peghead as a Talon V.

ELECTRIC BASS

DR Series

This series has offset double cutaway alder body, bolt-on 3 piece maple/graphite neck, rosewood fingerboard with offset pearl dot inlay, fixed bridge, 2 J-style pickups, volume/tone/balance controls, 2 position switch, active electronics. Mfd. 1991 to 1993.

DR 4 — 22 fret fingerboard, 2 per side tuners, chrome hardware. Available in Black Pearl Burst, Blue Pearl Burst, Mystic White and Red Pearl Burst finishes.

| | $1,000 | $700 | $600 | $500 | $400 | $360 | $330 |

DR 5 — 5 strings, 24 fret fingerboard, 2/3 per side tuners, chrome hardware.

| | $1,100 | $770 | $660 | $550 | $440 | $395 | $365 |

DR 6 — 6 strings, 24 fret fingerboard, 3 per side tuners, gold hardware, 2 humbucker pickups. Available in Black, Chrome Red, Frost Red, Midnight Blue and Mystic White finishes.

| | $1,380 | $965 | $830 | $690 | $550 | $495 | $455 |

DR C Series

This series has offset double cutaway figured hardwood body, thru body 3 piece maple/graphite neck, 24 fret rosewood fingerboard with offset pearl dot inlay, fixed bridge, gold hardware, 2 J-style pickups, volume/tone/balance controls, 2 position switch, active electronics. This series is custom made. Available in Antique Burst, Crimson Stain, Ebony Stain and Natural finishes. Mfd. 1991 to 1993.

DR 4 C — 2 per side tuners.

| | $1,700 | $1,190 | $1,020 | $850 | $680 | $610 | $560 |

DR 5 C — 5 strings, 2/3 per side tuners.

| | $1,800 | $1,260 | $1,080 | $900 | $720 | $650 | $595 |

DR 6 C — 6 strings, 3 per side tuners.

| | $2,100 | $1,475 | $1,260 | $1,050 | $840 | $755 | $690 |

Prophecy Series

PR I — double cutaway basswood body, bolt-on maple neck, 22 fret rosewood fingerboard with pearl dot inlay, fixed bridge, graphite nut, 4 on one side tuners, chrome hardware, P-style/J-style pickups, volume/balance control. Available in Black, Chrome Red, Frost Red, Midnight Blue and Mystic White finishes. Mfd. 1991 to 1993.

| | $650 | $455 | $390 | $325 | $260 | $235 | $215 |

PR II — similar to PR I, except has ash body, gold hardware, volume/treble/bass controls, active electronics. Available in Antique Burst, Crimson Transparent, Natural and Sapphire Blue Transparent finishes.

| | $750 | $525 | $450 | $375 | $300 | $270 | $245 |

PR III — similar to PR I, except has laminated ash body, thru body laminated maple neck, gold hardware, volume/treble/bass controls, active electronics. Available in Antique Burst, Crimson Transparent, Natural and Sapphire Blue Transparent finishes.

| | $1,150 | $805 | $690 | $575 | $460 | $415 | $380 |

HEARTWOOD

See HEART.

Instruments built in England during the mid to late 1980s.

Heart guitar builders decided to change the trademark in 1988.

HEIT DELUXE

Instruments produced in Japan circa 1960s.

The Heit Deluxe trademark is a brandname applied to guitars imported into the U.S. market. At this time, the U.S. importer is unknown. According to recent research, certain Heit Deluxe models share similarities with Teisco Del Rey-labeled guitars, prompting the notion that the two were built in the same Japanese factory.

(Source: Michael Wright, Guitar Stories, Volume One, page 76)

HERITAGE

Instruments built in Kalamazoo, Michigan since 1985.

In 1978 Jim Deurloo was named plant manager at Gibson's original Kalamazoo facility. Deurloo had been working at Gibson since 1958 (except for a five year managing stint at Guild from 1969 to 1974), and had been involved with the opening and tooling up of the newer Nashville facility in 1974. However, financial troubles led Norlin, Gibson's parent corporation, to consider shutting down either the Kalamazoo or Nashville facilitites in the early 1980s. Even though the Kalamazoo plant was Gibson's home since 1917, the decision was made in July of 1983 by Norlin to close the plant. The doors at 225 Parsons Street closed in the fall of 1984.

However, Jim Deurloo, Marvin Lamb, and J. P. Moats elected to stay in Kalamazoo and start a new company. Heritage Guitar, Inc. opened in 1985 in the original Gibson building. Members of the original trio were joined by Bill Paige (another long time Gibson worker) later.

Grading		100%	98% MINT	95% EXC+	90% EXC	80% VG+	70% VG	60% G

ACOUSTIC

HFT-445 (formerly H-445) — dreadnought style, solid spruce top, round soundhole, white bound body and wooden inlay rosette, black pickguard, mahogany back/sides, maple neck, 14/20 fret rosewood fingerboard with pearl dot inlay, rosewood bridge with white pins, 3 per side chrome tuners. Available in Antique Sunburst and Natural finishes. Mfd. 1989 to date.

Mfr.'s Sug. Retail	$1,045	$783	$522	$500	$400	$360	$330	$300

HFT-475 — single sharp cutaway jumbo style, solid spruce top, round soundhole, 5 stripe bound body and rosette, black pickguard, mahogany back/sides/neck, 20 fret bound rosewood fingerboard with pearl block inlay, rosewood bridge with white pins, bound peghead, 3 per side chrome tuners. Available in Antique Sunburst and Natural finishes. Curr. mfr.

Mfr.'s Sug. Retail	$1,680	$1,260	$840	$815	$640	$575	$530	$480

Add $150 for DeArmond pickup.

HFT-485 — jumbo style, solid spruce top, round soundhole, 3 stripe bound body/rosette, rosewood pickguard, rosewood back/sides, mahogany neck, 14/21 fret bound rosewood fingerboard with pearl block inlay, rosewood bridge with white pins, bound peghead, 3 per side chrome tuners. Available in Antique Sunburst and Natural finishes. Curr. mfr.

Mfr.'s Sug. Retail	$1,890	$1,417	$945	$920	$730	$650	$595	$540

Add $150 for DeArmond pickup.

ACOUSTIC ELECTRIC

SAE CUSTOM — single cutaway mahogany body with carved maple top, f-holes, bound body, mahogany neck, 22 fret bound rosewood with pearl dot inlay, tunomatic bridge/stop tailpiece, 3 per side tuners, chrome hardware, 2 humbucker/1 transducer bridge pickups, 2 volume/1 tone controls, 3 mini toggle switches. Available in Antique, Transparent Almond, Transparent Amber, Transparent Blue, Transparent Cherry and Transparent Emerald Green finishes. Mfd. 1992 to date.

Mfr.'s Sug. Retail	$1,375	$1,031	$687	$650	$515	$440	$405	$370

SAE Cutaway — similar to SAE Custom, except electronics consist of transducer bridge pickup and volume/tone control. Disc. 1994.

$670	$575	$480	$385	$350	$320	$290

Last Mfr.'s Sug. Retail was $965.

Grading	100%	98% MINT	95% EXC+	90% EXC	80% VG+	70% VG	60% G

ELECTRIC

ACADEMY CUSTOM — single round cutaway style, bound curly maple top, f-holes, bound maple pickguard, curly maple back/sides, mahogany neck, 22 fret bound rosewood fingerboard with pearl crown inlay, tunomatic bridge/stop tailpiece, bound peghead, 3 per side tuners, gold hardware, 2 humbuckers, 2 volume/tone controls, 3 position switch. Available in Almond Sunburst and Antique Sunburst finishes. Mfd. 1992 to date.

Mfr.'s Sug. Retail	$1,630	$1,222	$815	$790	$620	$560	$515	$465

Add $100 for Natural or Transparent Color finishes.

ALVIN LEE MODEL — 335 style, bound curly maple top/back/sides, f-holes, black pickguard, mahogany neck, 22 fret bound ebony fingerboard with pearl dot inlay, tunomatic bridge/stop tailpiece, 3 per side tuners, chrome hardware, humbucker/single coil/humbucker pickup, 3 volume/2 tone controls, 3 position switch. Available in Transparent Cherry finish. Curr. mfr.

Mfr.'s Sug. Retail	$1,710	$1,282	$855	$830	$650	$585	$535	$490

H-127 CUSTOM — single cutaway mahogany body, bound arch maple top, maple neck, 22 fret maple fingerboard with pearl dot inlay, tunomatic bridge/stop tailpiece, 6 on one side tuners, chrome hardware, 2 single coil pickups, volume/tone control, 3 position switch. Available in Antique Sunburst and Sunsetburst finishes. Mfd. 1992 to date.

Mfr.'s Sug. Retail	$1,250	$937	$625	$605	$475	$430	$390	$360

H-127 Standard — similar to H-127 Custom, except has solid mahogany body. Disc. 1992.

		$705	$605	$505	$405	$365	$335	$305

Last Mfr.'s Sug. Retail was $1,010.

H-140CM — single sharp cutaway mahogany body, bound curly maple top, white pickguard, mahogany neck, 22 fret rosewood fingerboard with pearl dot inlay, tunomatic bridge/stop tailpiece, 3 per side tuners, chrome hardware, 2 volume/ tone controls, 3 position switch. Available in Antique Sunburst and Antique Cherry Sunburst finishes. Mfd. 1989 to date.

Mfr.'s Sug. Retail	$990	$742	$495	$470	$375	$340	$310	$280

Add $50 for Natural or Transparent Color finishes.
Add $50 for Var-i-phase electronics (H-140CMV).
Also available with plain maple top in a Gold finish (H-140 Gold Top).

H-147 — similar to H-140CM, except has plain maple top, bound ebony fingerboard with pearl block inlay, bound peghead and gold hardware. Mfd. 1989 to 1992.

		$855	$730	$605	$485	$435	$400	$365

Last Mfr.'s Sug. Retail was $1,215.

H-150CM — single sharp cutaway mahogany body, bound carved curly maple top, white pickguard, mahogany neck, 22 fret bound rosewood fingerboard with pearl crown inlay, tunomatic bridge/stop tailpiece, 3 per side tuners, chrome hardware, 2 humbucker pickups, 2 volume/2 tone controls, 3 position switch. Available in Antique Sunburst and Antique Cherry Sunburst finishes. Mfd. 1989 to date.

Mfr.'s Sug. Retail	$1,275	$956	$637	$620	$485	$435	$400	$365

Add $50 for Natural or Transparent Color finishes.

H-150CM Classic — similar to H-150CM, except has 2 humbucker Seymour Duncan pickups. Curr. mfr.

Mfr.'s Sug. Retail	$1,445	$1,083	$722	$705	$550	$495	$455	$415

H-150CM Deluxe — similar to H-150CM, except has bound body matching peghead and gold hardware. Available in Almond Sunburst, Antique Sunburst and Antique Cherry Sunburst finishes. Mfd. 1992 to date.

Mfr.'s Sug. Retail	$1,925	$1,443	$962	$935	$735	$660	$605	$550

H-150P — similar to H-150CM, except has solid hardwood body. Available in Blue, Red and White finishes. Mfd. 1992 to date.

Mfr.'s Sug. Retail	$875	$656	$437	$435	$350	$315	$290	$265

Add $100 for Gold finish.

H-150 Special — single sharp cutaway hardwood body, bound carved maple top, mahogany neck, 22 fret bound rosewood fingerboard with pearl crown inlay, tunomatic bridge/stop tailpiece, 3 per side tuners, chrome hardware, 2 humbucker pickups, 2 volume/2 tone controls, 3 position switch. Available in Black and Orange Sunburst finishes. New 1994.

Mfr.'s Sug. Retail	$1,075	$806	$537	$535	$430	$390	$355	$325

H-157 — single sharp cutaway mahogany body, bound carved maple top, black pickguard, mahogany neck, 22 fret bound rosewood fingerboard with pearl block inlay, tunomatic bridge/stop tailpiece, bound blackface peghead with pearl diamond/logo inlay, 3 per side tuners, gold hardware, 2 humbucker pickups, 2 volume/2 tone controls, 3 position switch. Available in Black and White finishes. Mfd. 1989 to date.

Mfr.'s Sug. Retail	$1,435	$1,076	$717	$700	$550	$495	$450	$410

H-357 — single round cutaway asymmetrical hourglass style mahogany body, white pickguard, thru body mahogany neck, 22 fret rosewood fingerboard with pearl dot inlay, tunomatic bridge/stop tailpiece, 6 on one side tuners, chrome hardware, 2 humbucker pickups, 2 volume/2 tone controls, 3 position switch. Available in Antique Sunburst, Black, Blue, Red and White finishes. Mfd. 1989 to date.

Mfr.'s Sug. Retail	$1,350	$1,012	$675	$650	$500	$450	$415	$375

Also available with black pickguard and reverse headstock.

Grading	100%	98% MINT	95% EXC+	90% EXC	80% VG+	70% VG	60% G

Heritage Sweet 16
courtesy Jay Wolfe

LITTLE-001 — small size asymmetrical double cutaway curly maple body/neck, 22 fret bound rosewood fingerboard with pearl dot inlay, tunomatic bridge/stop tailpiece, 3 per side tuners, chrome hardware, humbucker pickup, volume control. Available in Transparent Amber, Transparent Black and Transparent Cherry finishes. Mfd. 1992 to 1994.

	$635	$545	$455	$365	$330	$300	$275

Last Mfr.'s Sug. Retail was $910.

MARK SLAUGHTER ROCK — radical single cutaway mahogany body/neck, 22 fret rosewood fingerboard with pearl dot inlay, tunomatic bridge/stop tailpiece, reverse headstock, 6 on one side tuners, chrome hardware, 2 single coil/1 humbucker pickups, volume/tone control, 5 position switch. Available in Black, Red and White finishes. Mfd. 1989 to date.

Mfr.'s Sug. Retail	$1,135	$851	$567	$550	$430	$390	$355	$325

Mark Slaughter Rock T — similar to Mark Slaughter Rock, except has double locking Kahler vibrato.

Mfr.'s Sug. Retail	$1,335	$1,001	$667	$655	$510	$460	$420	$380

PARSONS STREET — asymmetrical double cutaway solid mahogany body, curly maple top, mahogany neck, 22 fret bound rosewood fingerboard with pearl block inlay, tunomatic bridge/stop tailpiece, 3 per side tuners, chrome hardware, 2 single coil/1 humbucker pickups, volume/tone control, 5 position and Var-i-phase switch. Available in Antique Sunburst, Antique Cherry Sunburst and Natural finishes. Mfd. 1989 to 1992.

	$945	$810	$670	$535	$480	$440	$400

Last Mfr.'s Sug. Retail was $1,345.

PROSPECT STANDARD — 335 style, bound curly maple top/back/sides, f-holes, white pickguard, mahogany neck, 20 fret bound rosewood fingerboard with pearl dot inlay, tunomatic bridge/stop tailpiece, 3 per side tuners, chrome hardware, 2 humbucker pickups, 2 volume/tone controls, 3 position switch. Available in Almond Sunburst and Antique Sunburst finishes. Mfd. 1992 to date.

Mfr.'s Sug. Retail	$1,300	$975	$650	$640	$495	$445	$410	$370

Add $100 for Natural or Transparent Color finishes.

ROY CLARK MODEL — single round cutaway thin style, bound curly maple top/back/sides, bound f-holes, bound maple pickguard, mahogany neck, 22 fret bound rosewood fingerboard with split block inlay, tunomatic bridge/stop tailpiece, bound peghead, 3 per side tuners, gold hardware, 2 humbuckers, 2 volume/tone controls, 3 position switch. Available in Almond Sunburst and Antique Sunburst finishes. Mfd. 1992 to date.

Mfr.'s Sug. Retail	$1,870	$1,402	$935	$910	$710	$640	$585	$530

Add $100 for Natural or Transparent Color finishes.

JOHNNY SMITH — single round cutaway hollow style, solid spruce top, bound body and f-holes, bound curly maple pickguard, curly maple back/sides/neck, 20 fret ebony fingerboard with abalone block inlay, ebony bridge, trapeze tailpiece, bound peghead with abalone/pearl rose inlay, 3 per side tuners, black hardware, pickguard mounted humbucker pickup, pickguard mounted volume control. Available in Antique Sunburst finish. Mfd. 1992 to date.

Mfr.'s Sug. Retail	$4,390	$3,292	$2,195	$2,135	$1,700	$1,505	$1,380	$1,255

This model is personally signed by Johnny Smith.

STAT — double offset cutaway bound curly maple/mahogany body, mahogany neck, 22 fret rosewood fingerboard with pearl dot inlay, tunomatic bridge/stop tailpiece, 6 on one side tuners, chrome hardware, 2 single coil/1 humbucker pickups, volume/tone control, 3 mini toggle and coil split switch. Available in Antique Sunburst, Antique Cherry Sunburst and Cherry finishes. Mfd. 1989 to 1991.

	$545	$470	$390	$315	$280	$260	$235

Last Mfr.'s Sug. Retail was $785.

SWEET 16 — single sharp cutaway hollow style, solid spruce top, bound body and f-holes, bound curly maple pickguard, curly maple back/sides/neck, 20 fret ebony fingerboard with pearl split block inlay, ebony bridge with pearl 16 inlay, trapeze tailpiece, bound peghead with pearl Sweet 16 and logo inlay, 3 per side tuners, gold hardware, pickguard mounted humbucker pickup, pickguard mounted volume control. Available in Almond Sunburst and Antique Sunburst finishes. Mfd. 1989 to date.

Mfr.'s Sug. Retail	$2,995	$2,246	$1,497	$1,445	$1,150	$1,010	$925	$840

Add $300 for Natural or Transparent Color finishes.

Eagle Series

AMERICAN EAGLE — single round cutaway hollow style, solid spruce top, bound body and f-holes, bound flame maple pickguard with pearl space shuttle inlay, solid figured maple back/sides, 5 piece figured maple neck, 20 fret bound ebony fingerboard with pearl/abalone American heritage inlay, ebony/rosewood bridge with pearl star inlay, Liberty Bell shaped trapeze tailpiece, bound peghead with pearl eagle, stars, American Flag and Heritage logo inlay, pearl truss rod cover with engraved owner's name, 3 per side Kluson tuners, gold hardware, pickguard mounted Heritage pickup with 3 star inlay on cover, volume control on pickguard. Available in Natural finish. Mfd. 1989 to date.

Mfr.'s Sug. Retail	$9,500	$7,125	$4,750	$4,420	$3,480	$3,000	$2,750	$2,500

EAGLE — single round cutaway hollow style, solid mahogany top/pickguard, f-holes, bound body, mahogany back/sides/neck, 20 fret rosewood fingerboard with pearl dot inlay, rosewood bridge/trapeze tailpiece block, 3 per side tuners, chrome hardware, pickguard mounted Heritage pickup, volume control on pickguard. Available in Antique Sunburst finish. Mfd. 1989 to date.

Mfr.'s Sug. Retail	$1,875	$1,406	$937	$915	$725	$640	$585	$530

Add $200 for Natural or Transparent Color finishes.
Add $100 for gold hardware.

Grading		100%	98% MINT	95% EXC+	90% EXC	80% VG+	70% VG	60% G

Eagle Classic — single round cutaway hollow style, solid spruce top, f-holes, bound maple pickguard, bound body, solid curly maple back/sides, 5 piece maple neck, 20 fret bound ebony fingerboard, ebony/metal bridge/trapeze tailpiece, bound peghead, 3 per side tuners, gold hardware, 2 humbucker pickups, 2 volume/tone controls, 3 position switch. Available in Almond Sunburst and Antique Sunburst finishes. Mfd. 1992 to date.

Mfr.'s Sug. Retail	$2,815	$2,111	$1,407	$1,370	$1,090	$965	$885	$805

> Add $300 for Natural or Transparent Color finishes.
> Subtract $100 for Black or White finishes.

Eagle TDC — similar to Eagle, except has thin body style, tunomatic bridge, 2 humbucker pickups, 2 volume/tone controls and 3 position switch.

Mfr.'s Sug. Retail	$1,990	$1,492	$995	$960	$770	$680	$620	$565

GOLDEN EAGLE — single round cutaway hollow style, solid spruce top, bound body and f-holes, bound maple pickguard, curly maple back/sides/neck, 20 fret bound ebony fingerboard with pearl cloud inlay, ebony bridge with pearl V inlay, trapeze tailpiece, bound peghead with pearl eagle on tree and logo inlay, pearl truss rod cover with owner's name, 3 per side Kluson tuners, gold hardware, pickguard mounted humbucker pickup, pickguard mounted volume control. Available in Antique Sunburst finish. Mfd. 1989 to date.

Mfr.'s Sug. Retail	$3,520	$2,640	$1,760	$1,710	$1,365	$1,200	$1,100	$1,000

> Add $300 for Natural or Transparent Color finishes.

SUPER EAGLE — similar to Golden Eagle, except has pearl split block fingerboard inlay, 2 humbucker pickups, 2 volume/tone controls and 3 position switch.

Mfr.'s Sug. Retail	$3,980	$2,985	$1,990	$1,940	$1,545	$1,365	$1,250	$1,135

500 Series

H-535 — double round cutaway semi hollow body, bound curly maple top/back/sides, f-holes, bound curly maple pickguard, mahogany neck, 22 fret bound rosewood fingerboard with pearl dot inlay, tunomatic bridge/stop tailpiece, 3 per side tuners, chrome hardware, 2 humbucker pickups, 2 volume/tone controls, 3 position switch. Available in Antique Sunburst finish. Mfd. 1989 to date.

Mfr.'s Sug. Retail	$1,300		$975	$650	$630	$495	$445	$410	$370

> Add $100 for Natural or Transparent Color finishes.
> Add $50 for Var-i-phase and coil splitting capabilities.

H-535 Custom — similar to H-535, except has pearl diagonal inlay and bound peghead with pearl logo inlay. Available in Antique Sunburst and Transparent Black finishes. Mfd. 1991 to 1992.

		$1,040	$890	$745	$595	$535	$490	$445

> Last Mfr.'s Sug. Retail was $1,490.

H-550 — single round cutaway hollow style, bound curly maple top/back/sides, bound f-holes, bound curly maple pickguard, curly maple neck, 20 fret bound ebony fingerboard with pearl split block inlay, tunomatic bridge/trapeze tailpiece, bound peghead with pearl split block and logo inlay, 3 per side tuners, chrome hardware, 2 humbucker pickups, 2 volume/tone controls, 3 position switch. Available in Antique Sunburst finish. Mfd. 1989 to 1991.

	$1,210	$1,040	$865	$690	$620	$570	$520

> Last Mfr.'s Sug. Retail was $1,725.

> Add $100 for Natural or Transparent Color finishes.

H-555 — similar to H-535, except has bound f-holes, curly maple neck, ebony fingerboard with abalone/pearl diamond/arrow inlay with block after 17th fret, bound peghead with abalone/pearl diamond/arrow and logo inlay, gold hardware. Available in Almond Sunburst and Antique Sunburst finishes.

Mfr.'s Sug. Retail	$1,815	$1,361	$907	$885	$690	$625	$570	$520

> Add $100 for Natural or Transparent Color finishes.

H-574 — single round cutaway hollow style, bound curly maple top/back/sides, f-holes, white pickguard, mahogany neck, 20 fret rosewood fingerboard with pearl dot inlay, tunomatic bridge/stop tailpiece, 3 per side tuners, chrome hardware, 2 humbuckers, 2 volume/tone controls, 3 position switch. Available in Antique Sunburst finish. Mfd. 1989 to 1991.

	$875	$750	$625	$500	$450	$415	$375

> Last Mfr.'s Sug. Retail was $1,250.

> Add $50 for Natural finish.

H-575 — single sharp cutaway hollow style, bound curly maple top/back/sides, f-holes, bound maple pickguard, mahogany neck, 20 fret rosewood fingerboard with pearl dot inlay, rosewood bridge/trapeze tailpiece, 3 per side tuners, chrome hardware, 2 humbuckers, 2 volume/tone controls, 3 position switch. Available in Antique Sunburst finish. Mfd. 1989 to date.

Mfr.'s Sug. Retail	$1,525	$1,143	$762	$735	$580	$520	$475	$435

> Add $200 for Natural or Transparent Color finishes.

H-575 Custom — similar to H-575, except has bound fingerboard with pearl diagonal inlay, bound peghead with pearl logo inlay and gold hardware. Available in Sunsetburst finishes.

Mfr.'s Sug. Retail	$1,950	$1,462	$975	$955	$740	$670	$610	$555

> Add $200 for Natural or Transparent Color finishes.
> Subtract $100 for Black or White finishes.

H

Grading		100%	98% MINT	95% EXC+	90% EXC	80% VG+	70% VG	60% G

Dennis Hill
courtesy Hal Hammer

H-576 — similar to H-575, except has a bound fingerboard with pearl block inlay, bound peghead with curly maple veneer. Available in Antique Sunburst finish. Mfd. 1989 to date.

Mfr.'s Sug. Retail	$1,660	$1,245	$830	$805	$630	$570	$520	$475

Add $100 for Natural or Transparent Color finishes.

ELECTRIC BASS

CHUCK JACOBS MODEL — offset double cutaway asymmetrical maple body, thru body maple neck, 24 fret bound rosewood fingerboard with pearl dot inlay, fixed bridge, bound peghead, 2 per side tuners, black hardware, 2 J-style active EMG pickups, 2 volume/2 tone controls. Available in Black, Red and White finishes. Curr. mfr.

Mfr.'s Sug. Retail	$2,150	$1,612	$1,075	$1,050	$815	$735	$675	$615

Add $100 for flame maple top. Available in Sunsetburst, Transparent Black, and Transparent Cherry finishes (Chuck Jacobs CM Model).

HB-IV — offset double cutaway maple body, thru body maple neck, 24 fret rosewood fingerboard with pearl dot inlay, fixed bridge, 2 per side tuners, black hardware, 2 active EMG pickups, 2 volume/2 tone/bass expander controls. Available in Black, Red and White finishes. Curr. mfr.

Mfr.'s Sug. Retail	$1,650	$1,237	$825	$800	$630	$565	$515	$470

Add $100 for curly maple top. Available in Antique Sunburst, Transparent Black and Transparent Cherry finishes.

HB-V — similar to HB-IV, except has 5 strings, 3/2 per side tuners.

Mfr.'s Sug. Retail	$1,750	$1,312	$875	$850	$670	$600	$550	$500

HERNANDEZ y AGUADO

Instruments were built in Madrid, Spain during the 1960s.

Luthiers Manuel Hernandez and Victoriano Aguado combined guitar making skills to build world class classical guitars.

(Source: Tony Bacon, The Ultimate Guitar Book)

H.G. LEACH

Instruments currently built in Cedar Ridge, California.

H.G. Leach builds fine custom guitars. For further information contact H.G. Leach through the Index of Current Manufacturers located in the back of this book.

HILL

Instruments built in Cleveland, Ohio since 1989.

Originally established in Vermilion, Ohio in October of 1989, by founder and chief luthier Jon Hill. Hill has an extensive backround in custom lutherie and design. In 1994, Hill Guitars entered into a joint venture deal with Dean Guitars, which prompted luthier Hill to move to Florida (current location of Dean production). Hill Guitars offers eight models of U.S. built guitars that range in price from $799 to $2,999; and four models of basses (each available in 4-, 5-, and 6-string configurations) that range from $1,197 to $2,120. For further information, please contact Hill Guitar Company through the Index of Current Manufacturers located in the back of this book.

DENNIS HILL

Instruments currently built in Panama City, Florida. Distributed by Leitz Music, Inc. of Panama City, Florida.

Dennis Hill has a tradition of music in his life that reaches back to his father, who was a dance band musician. After a five year career in the U.S. Navy (Hill received his Honorable Discharge in 1969), Hill became the student to classical guitar teacher Ernesto Dijk. As Hills' interest in guitars grew, he met Augustino LoPrinzi in 1987. Hill finally became a sales representative for LoPrinzi's guitars, and studied his guitarmaking at LoPrinzi'z shop. Their agreement was that Hill could observe anytime, on any day, but not to disturb LoPrinzi during construction. Questions and answers were reserved for breakfast and lunch; and Hill had to build in his apartments after hours. In 1992, Hill moved to Panama City and established his own shop. Hill currently builds both classical and flamenco acoustic guitars in the traditional Spanish style, and constructs them with Englemann or European Spruce tops, Cedar necks, Cypress or Maple back and sides, Ebony fingerboards, and Rosewood bridge and bindings. For further information contact Leitz Music, Inc. through the Index of Current Manufacturers located in the back of this book.

(Source: Hal Hammer)

H M L GUITARS

HML Custom
courtesy Howard Leese

Instruments built in Seattle, Washington since 1994.

Founded in 1994 by Howard Leese (25 year veteran with Heart). Designed by Leese, the standard features include a unique set of five hollow chambers placed throughout the body, in areas of acoustical sensitivity to better project "true" sound dissipation. All instruments are totally handbuilt. Customers can even select their own choice of tops from Howard's personal stock of aged, exotic woods. For the fretboards, Leese prefers to use figured cocabola wood on the entire HML line due to its beauty, sound and feel. Leese participates in all aspects of construction as overall quality control inspector. He also allows every customer to help co-design their instruments for a more personal touch. Built in Seattle by luthier Jack Pimentel, the customer list includes such notables as Bruce Hastell, Mike Soldano, Val Kolbeck, Billy Gibbons, Jim Fiske, and (of course) Howard Leese himself.

Further information and pricing can be obtained through **Crosstown Management**, P.O. Box 580, Milton, Washington (98354).

(Courtesy Howard Leese and Bruce Hastell, May 29, 1996)

HOFNER

Instruments are produced in Bubenreuth, Germany. Hofner basses and products are exclusively distributed in the U.S. by the Entertainment Music Marketing Corporation of Deer Park, New York.

The Hofner instrument making company was originally founded by Karl Hofner in 1887. Originally located in Schonbach, in the area now called Czechoslovakia, Hofner produced fine stringed instruments such as violins, cellos, and doublebasses. Production of guitars began in 1925, in the area that was to become East Germany during the "Cold War" era. Following World War II, the Hofner family moved to West Germany and established a new factory in Bubenreuth in 1948. Their first electric archtop debuted in the 1950s. The concept of a violin-shaped bass was developed by Walter Hofner (Karl's son), and was based on family design traditions. While the Hofner company is mostly recognized for the "Beatle Bass" popularized by Paul McCartney, the company produced a wide range of solid, semi-hollow, and archtop designs that were good solid instruments.

Hofner produced a selection of guitars based on popular American designs from the late 1960s to the early 1980s. In the late 1970s Hofner also built a number of better quality original models such as Alpha, Compact, and Razorwood through the mid 1980s. Hofner is still currently producing instruments, although their solid body guitars remain a custom order.

(Hofner history source: Tony Bacon, The Ultimate Guitar Book)

Grading		100%	98% MINT	95% EXC+	90% EXC	80% VG+	70% VG	60% G

1956 Hofner bass
courtesy Rick King

ELECTRIC GUITARS

Between the late 1950s and early 1970s, Hofner produced a number of semi-hollow or hollowbody electric guitars and basses that were in demand in England. English distribution was handled by Selmer of London, and they specified models that were imported in. In some cases, English models were certainly different from the 'domestic' models offered in Germany.

There will always be interest in Hofners; either Paul McCartney's earlier association with the "Beatle Bass" or the thrill of a Committee or "Golden Hofner". Used clean big-body hollowbody guitars had been advertised nationally for $750 to $950, with the more ornate models carrying an asking price of $1,500 to $2,200. However, you have to "know 'em before you tag 'em". The **Blue Book of Guitars** recommends discussions with your local vintage dealers (it's easier to figure them out when you can see them). However, members of the **Blue Book** staff will handle inquires as to models and market value. Contact the staff through the address listed in the front of this book.

ELECTRIC BASS

500/1 REISSUE — violin hollow style, arched spruce top, raised pearloid pickguard with engraved logo, bound body, maple back/sides/neck, 22 fret bound rosewood fingerboard with pearl dot inlay, tunomatic bridge/trapeze tailpiece, bound blackface peghead with pearl logo inlay, 2 per side tuners, chrome hardware, 2 humbucker pickups, 2 volume controls, 3 tone slide switches, controls mounted on a pearloid plate. Available in Sunburst finish. Current production.

Mfr.'s Sug. Retail $2,495 $1,871 $1,247 $1,185

500/1LH Reissue — similar to 500/1, except is left handed version.

Mfr.'s Sug. Retail $2,695 $2,156 $1,617 $1,450

5000/1 '63 REISSUE — violin hollow style, arched maple top, raised black pickguard with engraved logo, tortoise bound body, figured maple back/sides, maple neck, 22 fret bound rosewood fingerboard with pearl dot inlay, vintage style tunomatic bridge/trapeze tailpiece, bound blackface peghead with pearl flower inlay/logo, 2 per side tuners, gold hardware, 2 humbucker pickups, volume/tone/bass vintage style knobs, 3 position/bass selector switches, controls mounted on a black plate. Available in Natural finish. Current production.

Mfr.'s Sug. Retail $2,995 $2,545 $2,096 $1,850

HOHNER

Instruments currently produced in Korea, although earlier models from the 1970s were built in Japan. Currently distributed in the U.S. by HSS (a Division of Hohner, Inc.), located in Richmond, Virginia.

Hohner offers a wide range of solidly constructed musical instruments. The company has stayed contemporary with the current market by licensing designs and parts from Ned Steinberger, Claim Guitars (Germany), and Wilkerson hardware.

Hofner bass
courtesy Thoroughbred Music

Grading	100%	98% MINT	95% EXC+	90% EXC	80% VG+	70% VG	60% G

ACOUSTIC

HAG294 — small body, spruce top, round soundhole, bound body, 5 stripe rosette, black pickguard, mahogany back/sides/neck, 12/18 fret ebonized fingerboard with white dot inlay, ebonized bridge, 3 per side diecast tuners. Available in Natural finish. Mfd. 1991 to date.

Mfr.'s Sug. Retail	$110	$88	$66	$55	$45	$40	$35	$30

HAG294C — similar to HAG294, except has classical body styling.

Mfr.'s Sug. Retail	$110	$88	$66	$55	$45	$40	$35	$30

HMC10 — classical style, spruce top, round soundhole, bound body, wooden inlay rosette, mahogany back/sides/neck, 14/19 fret ebonized fingerboard/bridge, 3 per side diecast tuners. Available in Natural finish. Mfd. 1991 to date.

Mfr.'s Sug. Retail	$220	$176	$132	$110	$90	$80	$70	$65

HMC30 — similar to HMC10, except has rosewood back/sides.

Mfr.'s Sug. Retail	$300	$240	$180	$150	$120	$110	$100	$90

HMW400 — dreadnought style, spruce top, round soundhole, bound body, 5 stripe rosette, black pickguard, mahogany back/sides/neck, 14/20 fret ebonized fingerboard with white dot inlay, ebonized bridge with white pins, 3 per side diecast tuners. Available in Natural and Sunburst finishes. Mfd. 1990 to date.

Mfr.'s Sug. Retail	$225	$168	$112	$100	$80	$70	$65	$60

Add $25 for left hand configuration.

This model has turquoise pickguard with Sunburst finish.

HMW600 — similar to HMW400, except has herringbone binding and rosette and enclosed chrome tuners. Available in Black and Natural finishes.

Mfr.'s Sug. Retail	$290	$217	$145	$130	$105	$95	$85	$80

HMW1200 — similar to HMW400, except has 12 strings.

Mfr.'s Sug. Retail	$325	$243	$162	$150	$120	$110	$100	$90

HW-300CM — dreadnought style, mahogany top, round soundhole, bound body, 5 stripe rosette, black pickguard, mahogany back/sides/neck, 14/20 fret ebonized fingerboard with white dot inlay, ebonized bridge with white pins, 3 per side diecast tuners. Available in Natural and Sunburst finishes. New 1994.

Mfr.'s Sug. Retail	$170	$127	$85	$80	$65	$60	$55	$45

ACOUSTIC ELECTRIC

HAG21 — single round cutaway classic style, solid maple body, spruce top, round soundhole, bound body, wooden inlay rosette, mahogany neck, 20 fret rosewood fingerboard with white dot inlay, rosewood bridge with white pins, 3 per side chrome tuners, piezo bridge pickup, volume/tone control. Available in Natural finish. Mfd. 1990 to 1992.

		$350	$300	$250	$200	$180	$165	$150

Last Mfr.'s Sug. Retail was $500.

HAG22 — similar to HAG21, except has dreadnought style body. Available in Sunburst finish.

		$350	$300	$250	$200	$180	$165	$150

Last Mfr.'s Sug. Retail was $500.

TWP600 — single flat cutaway dreadnought style, spruce top, triangle soundhole, bound body, 3 stripe rosette, mahogany back/sides/neck, 20 fret rosewood fingerboard with white dot inlay, rosewood bridge with white pins, 3 per side chrome tuners, piezo bridge pickup, 3 band EQ system. Available in Black, Blue Sunburst, Natural and Pumpkin Burst finishes. Mfd. 1992 to date.

Mfr.'s Sug. Retail	$550	$412	$275	$250	$200	$180	$165	$150

In 1993, Blue Sunburst finish was discontinued.

In 1994, Black finish was introduced. Pumpkin Sunburst finish was discontinued.

ACOUSTIC ELECTRIC BASS

TWP600B — single flat cutaway dreadnought style, spruce top, triangle soundhole, bound body, 3 stripe rosette, mahogany back/sides/neck, 20 fret rosewood fingerboard with white dot inlay, strings thru rosewood bridge, 2 per side chrome tuners, piezo electric bridge pickup, 3 band EQ system. Available in Black, Blue Sunburst, Natural, Pumpkin Burst and Transparent Red finishes. Mfd. 1992 to date.

Mfr.'s Sug. Retail	$650	$487	$325	$300	$240	$215	$195	$180

In 1993, Blue Sunburst finish was discontinued.

In 1994, Black and Transparent Red finishes were introduced.

ELECTRIC

G3T — Steinberger style maple body, thru body maple neck, 24 fret rosewood fingerboard with white dot inlay, Steinberger vibrato, black hardware, 2 single coil/1 humbucker EMG pickups, volume/tone control, 3 mini switches, passive filter in tone control. Available in Black and White finishes. Mfd. 1990 to date.

Mfr.'s Sug. Retail	$700	$525	$350	$325	$260	$235	$215	$195

Add $60 for left handed version (G3TLH).

In 1994, White finish was discontinued.

Grading	100%	98% MINT	95% EXC+	90% EXC	80% VG+	70% VG	60% G

THE JACK GUITAR — similar to G3T, except has asymmetrical double cutaway body. Available in Black and Metallic Red finishes. Disc. 1994.

		$530	$455	$380	$305	$275	$250	$230

Last Mfr.'s Sug. Retail was $765.

JT60— offset double cutaway maple body, tortoise pickguard, bolt-on maple neck, 22 fret rosewood fingerboard with pearl dot inlay, standard vibrato, 6 on one side tuners, chrome hardware, 3 single coil pickups, 2 volume/1 tone controls, 5 position switch, advance tone passive electronics. Available in Ivory and Seafoam Green finishes. Mfd. 1992 to date.

Mfr.'s Sug. Retail	$480	$360	$240	$200	$160	$145	$130	$120

In 1994, Seafoam Green finish was introduced.

L59 — single sharp cutaway solid maple body, bound figured maple top, black pickguard, mahogany neck, 22 fret bound rosewood fingerboard with pearl crown inlay, tunomatic bridge/stop tailpiece, bound peghead with pearl pineapple/logo inlay, 3 per side tuners, chrome hardware, 2 humbucker pickups, 2 volume/tone controls, 3 position switch. Available in Black, Cherry Sunburst, Gold Top, Ivory and Violin finishes. Mfd. 1990 to date.

Mfr.'s Sug. Retail	$625	$468	$312	$285	$230	$205	$190	$175

Add $35 for left handed version (L59LH).

This model is available with gold hardware.

In 1994, Black, Gold Top, Ivory and Violin finishes were discontinued.

L60 — single sharp cutaway maple body, black pickguard, mahogany neck, 22 fret bound rosewood fingerboard with pearl dot inlay, tunomatic bridge/stop tailpiece, blackface peghead with pearl coconut/logo inlay, 3 per side tuners, chrome hardware, 2 single coil pickups, 2 volume/2 tone controls, 3 position switch. Available in Cherry Red finish. New 1994.

Mfr.'s Sug. Retail	$575	$431	$287	$285	$230	$205	$190	$175

LP75 — similar to LP59, except has white pickguard, bolt-on neck, diamond peghead inlay. Available in Antique Sunburst and Black finishes. Mfd. 1990 to 1991.

		$260	$220	$185	$150	$135	$120	$110

Last Mfr.'s Sug. Retail was $375.

L90 — single sharp cutaway bound maple/mahogany body, white pickguard, mahogany neck, 22 fret bound rosewood fingerboard with pearl crown inlay, tunomatic bridge/stop tailpiece, bound peghead with pearl diamond/logo inlay, 3 per side tuners, chrome hardware, 2 PAF pickups, 2 volume/tone controls, 3 position switch. Available in Gold Top finish. Mfd. 1992 to date.

Mfr.'s Sug. Retail	$690	$517	$345	$315	$250	$225	$205	$190

SE35 — 335 style maple bound top/back/sides, black pickguard, mahogany neck, 22 fret rosewood fingerboard with pearl dot inlay, tunomatic bridge/stop tailpiece, pearl pineapple/logo peghead inlay, chrome hardware, 2 humbucker pickups, 2 volume/tone controls, 3 position switch. Available in Black, Natural, Sunburst, Tobacco Sunburst and White finishes. Mfd. 1990 to date.

Mfr.'s Sug. Retail	$600	$450	$300	$275	$220	$200	$180	$165

This model has gold hardware optionally available.

In 1994, Black, Sunburst and White finishes were discontinued.

SE400 — single round cutaway hollow body, maple bound top/back/sides, f-holes, black pickguard, mahogany neck, 22 fret bound rosewood fingerboard with pearl block inlay, tunomatic bridge/trapeze tailpiece, bound peghead with pearl pineapple/logo inlay, 2 humbucker pickups, 2 volume/tone controls, 3 position switch. Available in Tobacco Sunburst finish. Mfd. 1992 to date.

Mfr.'s Sug. Retail	$740	$555	$370	$350	$280	$250	$230	$210

ST59 — double offset cutaway alder body, white pickguard, bolt-on maple neck, 22 fret maple fingerboard with black dot inlay, standard vibrato, 6 on one side tuners, chrome hardware, 3 single coil pickups, volume/2 tone controls, 5 position switch. Available in Black, Blue, Red, Transparent Blue, Transparent Red and 2 Tone Sunburst finishes. Mfd. 1990 to date.

Mfr.'s Sug. Retail	$440	$330	$220	$210	$170	$150	$135	$125

Add $10 for left handed version with Sunburst finish (ST59LH).

Add $40 for active electronics with Black and Sunburst finishes.

In 1994, Transparent Blue and Transparent Red finishes were introduced. Black, Blue, Red and 2 Tone Sunburst finishes were discontinued.

ST CUSTOM — double offset cutaway flame maple body, bolt-on maple neck, 22 fret rosewood fingerboard with abalone dot inlay, double locking vibrato, 6 on one side tuners, black hardware, 2 single coil/1 humbucker EMG pickups, volume/tone control, 3 mini switches. Available in Cherry Sunburst finish. Mfd. 1990 to 1991.

		$735	$630	$525	$420	$380	$345	$315

Last Mfr.'s Sug. Retail was $1,050.

ST LYNX — double offset cutaway maple body, bolt-on maple neck, 24 fret rosewood fingerboard with white dot inlay, double locking vibrato, 6 on one side tuners, black hardware, single coil/humbucker EMG pickups, volume/tone control, 3 position switch. Available in Metallic Blue and Metallic Red finishes. Mfd. 1990 to date.

Mfr.'s Sug. Retail	$740	$555	$370	$350	$280	$250	$230	$210

H

Grading	100%	98% MINT	95% EXC+	90% EXC	80% VG+	70% VG	60% G

ST METAL S — double offset cutaway maple body, bolt-on maple neck, 22 fret rosewood fingerboard with white sharktooth inlay, double locking vibrato, 6 on one side tuners, black hardware, 2 single coil/1 humbucker EMG pickups, volume/tone control, 3 mini switches. Available in Black, Black Crackle and Pearl White finishes. Mfd. 1990 to 1991.

| | $440 | $380 | $315 | $250 | $225 | $205 | $190 |

Last Mfr.'s Sug. Retail was $630.

ST VICTORY — double offset cutaway maple body, black pickguard, bolt-on maple neck, 22 fret rosewood fingerboard with white dot inlay, reverse headstock, double locking vibrato, 6 on one side tuners, black hardware, humbucker pickup, volume/tone control. Available in Metallic Dark Purple and Metallic Red finishes. Mfd. 1990 to 1991.

| | $405 | $345 | $285 | $230 | $205 | $190 | $175 |

Last Mfr.'s Sug. Retail was $575.

TE CUSTOM — single cutaway bound maple body, white pickguard, bolt-on maple neck, 21 fret rosewood fingerboard with white dot inlay, fixed bridge, 6 on one side tuners, chrome hardware, 2 single coil pickups, volume/tone control, 3 position switch. Available in 3 Tone Sunburst finish. Mfd. 1992 to date.

| Mfr.'s Sug. Retail | $500 | $375 | $250 | $225 | $180 | $160 | $150 | $135 |

TE Custom XII — similar to TE Custom, except has 12 strings, black pickguard and 2 humbucker pickups. Available in Black finish. Mfd. 1990 to 1993.

| | $385 | $330 | $275 | $220 | $200 | $180 | $165 |

Last Mfr.'s Sug. Retail was $550.

TE PRINZ — single cutaway bound flamed maple body, tortoise pickguard, bolt-on maple neck, 21 fret maple fingerboard with black dot inlay, fixed bridge, 6 on one side tuners, chrome hardware, pickups, volume/tone control, 3 position switch. Available in Natural finish. Mfd. 1990 to date.

| Mfr.'s Sug. Retail | $565 | $423 | $282 | $260 | $205 | $185 | $170 | $155 |

Revelation Series

RTS — offset double cutaway asymmetrical poplar body, black pickguard, bolt-on maple neck, 24 fret rosewood fingerboard with offset pearl dot inlay, locking Wilkinson vibrato, roller nut, 6 on one side Schaller tuners, chrome hardware, 3 single coil pickups, volume/2 tone controls, 5 position switch. Available in Black, Marble Red, Marble White, Red, Sunburst, Transparent Blue, Transparent Honey and Transparent Red finishes. Curr. mfr.

| Mfr.'s Sug. Retail | $900 | $720 | $540 | $450 | $360 | $325 | $300 | $275 |

RTX — similar to RTS, except has middle and bridge pickups in humbucker configuration and has active tone electronics.

| Mfr.'s Sug. Retail | $900 | $720 | $540 | $450 | $360 | $325 | $300 | $275 |

Rockwood Series

LX100G — double offset cutaway maple body, black pickguard, bolt-on maple neck, 22 fret rosewood fingerboard with pearl dot inlay, standard vibrato, 6 on one side tuners, chrome hardware, 3 single coil pickups, 2 volume/1 tone controls, 5 position switch. Available in Black and Red finishes. Mfd. 1992 to date.

| Mfr.'s Sug. Retail | $260 | $195 | $130 | $125 | $100 | $90 | $80 | $75 |

LX200G — similar to LX100G, except has white pickguard, 2 single coil/1 humbucker pickups, volume/tone control, coil split switch. Available in Black and White finishes. Mfd. 1992 to date.

| Mfr.'s Sug. Retail | $330 | $264 | $198 | $165 | $130 | $120 | $110 | $100 |

In 1994, Black finish was introduced, White finish was discontinued.

LX250G — single sharp cutaway bound maple body, white pickguard, mahogany neck, 22 fret bound rosewood fingerboard with pearl crown inlay, tunomatic bridge/stop tailpiece, 3 per side tuners, chrome hardware, 2 humbucker pickups, 2 volume/2 tone controls, 3 position switch. Available in Antique Sunburst and Black finishes. Mfd. 1992 to date.

| Mfr.'s Sug. Retail | $375 | $281 | $187 | $175 | $140 | $125 | $115 | $105 |

ELECTRIC BASS

B2 — Steinberger style maple body, thru body maple neck, 24 fret rosewood fingerboard with white dot inlay, Steinberger bridge, black hardware, 2 humbucker pickups, 2 volume/1 tone controls. Available in Black and Red finishes. Mfd. 1990 to 1992.

| | $385 | $330 | $275 | $220 | $200 | $180 | $165 |

Last Mfr.'s Sug. Retail was $550.

B2A — Steinberger style maple body, thru body maple neck, 24 fret rosewood fingerboard with white dot inlay, Steinberger bridge, black hardware, 2 humbucker pickups, 2 volume/1 tone controls, mini switch, active electronics, LED. Available in Black and Red finishes. Mfd. 1990 to 1992.

| | $440 | $375 | $310 | $250 | $225 | $205 | $190 |

Add $35 for left handed version.

Last Mfr.'s Sug. Retail was $625.

B2ADB — similar to B2A, except has Steinberger DB bridge. Available in Black and Metallic Red finishes. Mfd. 1992 to date.

| Mfr.'s Sug. Retail | $800 | $600 | $400 | $385 | $310 | $280 | $255 | $230 |

B2AFL — similar to B2A, except is fretless with an ebonol fingerboard. Mfd. 1990 to 1992.

| | $485 | $415 | $350 | $280 | $250 | $230 | $210 |

Last Mfr.'s Sug. Retail was $695.

Grading	100%	98% MINT	95% EXC+	90% EXC	80% VG+	70% VG	60% G

B2B — Steinberger style maple body, bolt-on maple neck, 24 fret rosewood fingerboard with white dot inlay, Steinberger bridge, black hardware, P-style/J-style pickups, 2 volume/1 tone controls. Available in Black finish. Mfd. 1992 to date.

Mfr.'s Sug. Retail	$540	$405	$270	$245	$195	$175	$160	$150

B2V — similar to B2B, except is a 5 string. Available in Black finish. Mfd. 1990 to 1992.

		$475	$405	$340	$270	$245	$225	$205

Last Mfr.'s Sug. Retail was $675.

B BASS — offset double cutaway maple body, thru body maple neck, 24 fret rosewood fingerboard with white dot inlay, Steinberger DB bridge, 2 per side tuners, black hardware, 2 J-style pickups, 2 volume/1 tone controls, active tone electronics with switch and LED. Available in Black, Natural and Transparent Red finishes. Mfd. 1990 to date.

Mfr.'s Sug. Retail	$800	$600	$400	$375	$300	$270	$245	$225

This model is available in 5 string at no additional cost (BBASSV).

B Bass (B) — similar to B Bass, except has bolt-on maple neck. Available in Lake Placid Blue, Transparent Black and Transparent Red finishes. New 1994.

Mfr.'s Sug. Retail	$600	$480	$360	$300	$240	$215	$195	$180

HP — offset double cutaway hardwood body, white pickguard, bolt-on maple neck, 20 fret maple fingerboard with black dot inlay, fixed bridge, 4 on one side tuners, chrome hardware, P-style pickup, volume/tone control. Available in Black and Red finishes. Mfd. 1990 to 1992.

		$260	$220	$185	$150	$135	$120	$110

Last Mfr.'s Sug. Retail was $370.

THE JACK BASS CUSTOM — offset double cutaway maple body, thru body headless maple neck, 24 fret rosewood fingerboard with white dot inlay, Steinberger bridge, black hardware, 2 J-style pickups, 2 volume/1 tone controls, active tone electronics with switch and LED. Available in Black, Metallic Red and Natural finishes. Mfd. 1990 to date.

Mfr.'s Sug. Retail	$875	$656	$437	$415	$330	$300	$275	$250

Add $75 for 5 string (Jack Bass Custom 5) version.

JJ — offset double cutaway asymmetrical maple body, bolt-on maple neck, 20 fret rosewood fingerboard with white dot inlay, fixed bridge, 4 on one side tuners, chrome hardware, 2 volume/1 tone controls, active tone electronics with switch and LED. Available in Black and Vintage Sunburst finishes. Mfd. 1990 to date.

Mfr.'s Sug. Retail	$630	$472	$315	$275	$220	$200	$180	$165

In 1994, Black finish was discontinued.

JBFL (formerly JJFL) — similar to JJ, except has tortoise pickguard, fretless fingerboard. Available in Ivory and Sunburst finishes. Mfd. 1992 to date.

Mfr.'s Sug. Retail	$440	$352	$264	$220	$175	$160	$145	$135

In 1994, tortoise pickguard was discontinued.

JBASS — offset double cutaway asymmetrical maple body, tortoise pickguard, bolt-on maple neck, 20 fret rosewood fingerboard with white dot inlay, fixed bridge, 4 on one side tuners, chrome hardware, 2 volume/1 tone controls. Available in Ivory finish. New 1994.

Mfr.'s Sug. Retail	$470	$376	$282	$235	$190	$170	$155	$140

PJB — offset double cutaway maple body, white pickguard, bolt-on maple neck, 20 fret maple fingerboard with black dot inlay, fixed bridge, 4 on one side tuners, chrome hardware, P-style/J-style pickups, 2 volume/1 tone controls. Available in Black, Metallic Red and White finishes. Mfd. 1990 to date.

Mfr.'s Sug. Retail	$470	$352	$235	$210	$170	$150	$135	$125

Add $10 for left handed version (JBLH).

In 1994, Black finish was discontinued.

PJFL — similar to PJB, except has fretless ebonol fingerboard. Available in Black finish. Disc. 1992.

		$310	$265	$220	$175	$160	$145	$135

Last Mfr.'s Sug. Retail was $440.

PJSX — similar to PJB, except has rosewood fingerboard with white dot inlay. Available in Black and Metallic Red finishes.

		$295	$250	$210	$170	$150	$135	$125

Subtract $35 for left handed version (Black finish only).

Last Mfr.'s Sug. Retail was $425.

Rockwood Series

LX100B — offset double cutaway hardwood body, bolt-on maple neck, 21 fret rosewood fingerboard with white dot inlay, fixed bridge, 4 on one side tuners, chrome hardware, P-style pickup, volume/tone control. Available in Black and Red finishes. Mfd. 1992 to date.

Mfr.'s Sug. Retail	$300	$240	$180	$150	$120	$110	$100	$90

LX200B — similar to LX100B, except has short scale neck.

Mfr.'s Sug. Retail	$270	$216	$162	$135	$110	$100	$90	$80

Hollenbeck Ebony and Blue
courtesy Scott Chinery

Bill Hollenbeck
courtesy Hal Hammer

Grading	100%	98% MINT	95% EXC+	90% EXC	80% VG+	70% VG	60% G

LX300B — similar to LX100B, except has white pickguard, P-style/2 J-style pickups and 2 volume/1 tone control. Disc. 1994.

	$260	$220	$185	$150	$135	$120	$110

Last Mfr.'s Sug. Retail was $370.

Hollenbeck 18" Time Traveller
courtesy Bill Hollenbeck

HOLIDAY

See chapter on House Brands.

This trademark has been identified as a "House Brand" distributed by Montgomery Wards and Alden's department stores. Author/researcher Willie G. Moseley also reports seeing a catalog reprint showing Holiday instruments made by Harmony, Kay, and Danelectro. Additional information in regards to instruments with this trademark will be welcome, especially any Danelectro with a 'HOLIDAY' logo on the headstock. Future updates will be included in upcoming editions of the **Blue Book of Guitars**.

(Source: Willie G. Moseley, Stellas & Stratocasters)

HOLLENBECK

Instruments currently built in Lincoln, Illinois.

Luthier Bill Hollenbeck took a serious interest in guitars as a youth, and used to modify his own instruments in his attempt to improve it. Hollenbeck received a Bachelor's Degree in Industrial Arts, and taught electronics to high school students for twenty-five years. During his teaching years, Hollenbeck met well-known midwestern luthier Bill Barker in 1970, and served as Barker's apprentice as he learned the art of guitar construction. In 1990, Hollenbeck left education to devote himself full-time to guitar building, restoration, and repair. Hollenbeck currently handcrafts archtop guitars from aged Sitka Spruce and Birdseye Maple, and each instrument is customized for the purchaser. Prices range from $5,200 to $6,800. For further information regarding specifications, pricing, and availablity, please contact luthier Bill Hollenbeck through the Index of Current Manufacturers located in the back of this book.

(Source: Hal Hammer)

HOLLISTER

Instruments currently built in South Harwich, Massachusetts.

Luthier Kent Hollister is currently offering high quality, custom built archtop ($2,800), semi-hollow body ($1,900), and carved top, solid body ($1,400) guitars. For further information contact luthier Kent Hollister through the Index of Current Manufacturers located in the back of this book.

HOLMAN

Instruments built in Neodesha, Kansas during the late 1960s. Distributed by Holman-Woodell, Inc. of Neodesha, Kansas.

The Holman-Woodell company built guitars during the late 1960s in Neodesha, Kansas (around 60 miles due south from Topeka). While they were producing guitars for Wurlitzer, they also built their own Holman brand as well as instruments trademarked Alray and 21st Century. The Holman-Woodell company is also famous for building the La Baye "2 x 4" guitars for Wisconsin-based inventor Dan Helland. The Holman-Woodell company also released a number of faux "2 x 4"s built from leftover parts with the "Holman" logo after the La Baye company went under.

(Source: Michael Wright, Guitar Stories Volume One, pg. 162)

TOM HOLMES

Instruments built in Tennessee circa 1970s to 1980s.

Luthier Tom Holmes custom built numerous high quality, solid body guitars for a number of years for artists such as ZZ Top and others. Holmes is currently building humbucking pickups styled after Gibson's PAFs. A large collection of Holmes' custom guitars can be found at Larry Henricksen's Ax-in-Hand Guitar Shop (Dekalb, Illinois). Further updates on Holmes' guitars will be featured in future editions of the **Blue Book of Guitars**. For further information on Holmes' pickups, contact Tom Holmes through the Index of Current Manufacturers located in the rear of this book.

(Collector's tip courtesy David Larson at Audio Restoration)

HONDO

Instruments are currently produced in Korea; however, a number of the better Hondos were built in Japan between 1974 to early 1980s. The Hondo Guitar Company is now a division of MBT International of Charleston, South Carolina.

The Hondo guitar company was originally formed in 1969 between Jerry Freed and Tommy Moore of the International Music Corporation (IMC) of Fort Worth, Texas, and the recently formed Samick company. The Hondo concept was to offer an organized product line and solid entry level market instruments for a good price. The original Korean products were classical and steel-string acoustic guitars. In 1972, the first crudely built Hondo electrics were built. However, two years later the product line took a big leap forward in quality (although still at the entry level in the market) under the new Hondo II logo. Hondo had distributors in 70 countries worldwide, and had expanded to producing stringed

Hollister Custom
courtesy Kent Hollister

instruments at the time. A number of Hondo II models featured designs based on classic American favorites. In 1985, IMC acquired major interest in the Charvel/Jackson company, and began dedicating more time and interest in the higher end guitar market. The Hondo trademark went into mothballs in 1987, and IMC was sold in 1988.

In 1989 Jerry Freed started Jerry Freed International, and acquired the rights to the Hondo trademark in 1991. Freed began distribution of a new line of Hondo guitars. In 1993, the revamped company was relocated to Stuart, Florida. Recently, The Hondo Guitar Company was purchased by the MBT International, who also distributes J.B. Player instruments.

Hondo guitars generally carried a new retail price range between $179 and $349 (up to $449). While their more unusual-designed model may command a slghtly higher price, the average used price may range between $119 (good condition) up to $199 (clean condition, with case, DiMarzio pickups).

(Source: Michael Wright, Guitar Stories Volume One, pgs. 189-208)

ELECTRIC

Hondo was one of the first overseas guitar builders to feature American-built DiMarzio pickups on the import instruments beginning in the mid 1970s.

All Star Series

The All Star models debuted in the fall of 1983, and featured Fender-based models with a slimmed down Telecaster-ish headstock.

The Paul Dean Series

Paul Dean (Loverboy) endorsed and had a hand in designing two solid body models in 1983. The Hondo version could even be seen as a "dry run" for Dean's later association with the Kramer company. The Dean II had a stop tailpiece and two humbuckers, and the Dean III featured three single coils and a standard tremolo.

Deluxe Series

The Deluxe Series was first offered in the early 1980s, and featured 11 classical and 22 steel string acoustic models. The electric line featured 9 variations on the Les Paul theme, including the H-752 double cutaway LP. A Strat of sorts carried the designation H-760, a B.C. Rich inspired model with humbuckers and three mini-switches was the H-930, and a 335 repro was designated the H-935. Many carried a new list price between $229 and $299.

Erlewine Series

Texas luthier/designer Mark Erlewine licensed a pair of designs to Hondo during the early 1980s. His Chiquita 'travel guitar' had a scale of 19" and an overall 27 1/2" length; and the headless 'Lazer' was a full scale (25 1/2") guitar with an overall length of 31". A third model, named the 'Automatic' was offered as well. List prices ranged from $199 to $349.

Fame Series

Unvieled in late 1984, the Fame Series featured Fender-based reproductions with the "Fame" logo in a "spaghetti" looking lettering. However, the spelling and outline would be a give-away from a distance (if their intention was so bold...).

Harry Fleishman Series

In 1985, noted luthier/designer Harry Fleishman licensed the "Flash" bass, a headless, bodiless, 2 octave neck, Schaller Bridge equipped, magnetic and piezo-driven electric bass that was based on one of his high quality original designs. Fleishman also designed a Tele-ish acoustic/electric similar to the Kramer Ferrington models that were available.

MasterCaster Series

These mid 1980s models were advertised as having solid ash bodies, Kahler "Flyer" locking tremolos, and Grover tuners.

Professional Series

The Professional Series was introduced in 1982, and had a number of classical and steel string models. More importantly, there was a number of electric Strat-style guitars that were presumably built by Tokai in Japan. Tokai was one of the "reproduction" companies of the mid-to-late 1970s that built pretty good "Strats" - much to Fender's displeasure.

Standard Series

Standard Series guitars were also introduced in the early 1980s, and were Hondo's single or double pickup entry level guitars. The acoustic models were beginner's guitars as well. The Standard line did offer 11 banjo models of different add-ons, and 4 distinct mandolins.

HOOTENANNY

See chapter on House Brands.

Hondo Erlewine Lazer
courtesy Thoroughbred Music

Hopf Saturn G-3
courtesy Jimmy Gravity

This trademark has been identified as a "sub-brand" from the budget line of CHRIS guitars by the Jackson-Guldan company. However, another source suggests that the trademark was marketed by the Monroe Catalog House. Could this be a situation of "You're both right?" Break the tie by sending any information to "The Hootenanny Dilemma" c/o **Blue Book of Guitars**.

(Source: Willie G. Moseley, Stellas & Stratocasters)

HOPF

Instruments made in Germany from the late 1950s through the mid 1980s.

The Hopf name was established back in 1669, and lasted through the mid 1980s. The company produced a wide range of good quality solid body, semi-hollow, and archtop guitars from the late 1950s on. While some of the designs do bear an American design influence, the liberal use of local woods (such as beech, sycamore, or European pine) and certain departures from conventional styling give them an individual identity.

(Source: Tony Bacon, The Ultimate Guitar Book)

Grading	100%	98% MINT	95% EXC+	90% EXC	80% VG+	70% VG	60% G

ELECTRIC GUITAR

SATURN G 3 — semi-hollow body, six on one side tuners, two pickups, clear raised pickguard inscribed with 'Hopf', tremolo, one pickup selector switch, one tone switch, and volume knob. Mfd. circa 1950s.

$450 $375 $350 $280 $220 $180 $160

Guitar is equipped with a 3 pin DIN plug instead of a 1/4" jack on control panel. Make sure the original cable is <u>with the guitar when it is purchased!</u>

HOWARD

Instruments built in New York, New York circa 1930s.

The construction technique and overall appearance indicate the possibility that Epaminondas "Epi" Stathopoulos' Epiphone company built instruments under the Howard trademark for a dealer or distributor. Models that have appeared in the vintage guitar market have the "Howard" brandname and fleur-de-lis inlaid on the headstock. The dealer or distributor involved in the "Howard" trademark has yet to be identified.

(Source: Paul Bechtoldt, Vintage Guitar Magazine, February 1996)

HOYER

Instruments built in West Germany from the late 1950s through the late 1980s.

The Hoyer company produced a wide range of good to high quality solid body, semi-hollow body, and archtop guitars, with some emphasis on the later during the 1960s. During the early 1970s, there was some production of solid bodied guitars with an emphasis on classic American designs.

(Source: Tony Bacon and Paul Day, The Guru's Guitar Guide)

HUMAN BASE

Instruments currently built in Waldems, Germany.

Human Base produces high quality, bolt neck, solid body, 4-string bass guitars (Base X) that have a retail price of $1,900. The Base X is also available as a 5-string ($2,200) and a 6-string ($3,400), and is also built as a neck-through design with high grade hardware. For further information contact Human Base through the Index of Current Manufacturers located in the rear of this book.

THOMAS HUMPHREY

Instruments currently produced in New York City, New York.

Luthier Thomas Humphrey has been building classical guitars for the past 26 years. In 1985, Humphrey startled the lutherie world when he introduced the "Millennium" models, which featured an innovative, tapered body design. Though initially questioned for two years, the new design has since been accepted. Humphrey presently produces twenty-one guitars a year.

HURRICANE

Instruments were produced in Japan during the late 1980s.

The Hurricane trademark shows up on medium quality "superstrat" and solid body guitars based on popular American designs.

(Source: Tony Bacon and Paul Day, The Guru's Guitar Guide)

Howard acoustic
19th Annual Dallas Show

H

"According to Sotheby's, this honor is held by the Strat played by Jimi Hendrix at Woodstock which sold at Sotheby's in London earlier this year for the equivalent of $320,000.00."

—Lawrence Acunto

TCG, Sept/Oct 1990

HUSKEY

Instruments currently built in Hillsboro, Missouri.

Huskey Guitar Works offers several models of high quality, custom built guitars that feature original designs and neck-through construction. Retail prices range from $2,400 to $2,500. For further information contact Huskey Guitar Works through the Index of Current Manufacturers located in the rear of this book.

HUTTL

Instruments were built in Germany in the early 1980s.

The Huttl trademark may not be as well known as other German guitar builders such as Framus, Hopf, or Klira. While their designs may be as original as the others, the quality of workmanship is still fairly rough in comparison. Anyone possessing more information on Huttl guitars is invited to correspond for updates in future editions of the **Blue Book of Guitars**.

HY-LO

Instruments produced in Japan during the mid to late 1960s.

These entry level solid body guitars feature designs based on classic American favorites. One such model (designation unknown) featured an offset double cutaway body and six on a side tuners like a strat, but two single coil pickups and volume and tone controls.

HYUNDAI

Instruments currently built in Korea, and are distributed in the U.S. through Hyundai Guitars of West Nyack, New York.

Hyndai offers a range of medium quality guitars designed for beginning students that have designs based on popular American classics. For further information contact Hyundai Guitars through the Index of Current Manufacturers located in the back of this book.

H

H

IBANEZ

'70s Ibanez 12/6 Doubleneck
courtesy Eddie Welsh

Instruments produced in Japan since the early 1960s, and some models produced in Korea since the 1980s. Ibanez guitars are distributed in the U.S. by Ibanez USA (Hoshino) in Bensalem, Pennsylvania. Other distribution offices include Quebec (for Canada), Sydney (for Australia), and Auckland (for New Zealand).

The Ibanez trademark originated from the Fuji plant in Matsumoto, Japan. In 1932, the Hoshino Gakki Ten, Inc. factory began producing instruments under the Ibanez trademark. The factory and offices were burned down during World War II, and were revived in 1950. By the mid 1960s, Hoshino was producing instruments under various trademarks such as Ibanez, Star, King's Stone, Jamboree, and Goldentone.

In the mid-1950s, Harry Rosenbloom opened the Medley Music store outside Philadelphia. As the Folk Music boom began in 1959, Rosenbloom decided to begin producing acoustic guitars and formed the Elger company (named after Rosenbloom's children, Ellen and Gerson). Elger acoustics were produced in Ardmore, Pennsylvania between 1959 and 1965.

In the 1960s, Rosenbloom travelled to Japan and found a number of companies that he contracted to produce the Elger acoustics. Later, he was contacted by Hoshino to form a closer business relationship. The first entry level solid body guitars featuring original designs first surfaced in the mid 1960s, some bearing the Elger trademark, and some bearing the Ibanez logo. One of the major keys to the perceived early Ibanez quality is due to Hoshino shipping the guitars to the Elger factory in Ardmore. The arriving guitars would be re-checked, and set up prior to shipping to the retailer. Many distributors at the time would just simply ship "product" to the retailer, and let surprises occur at the unboxing. By reviewing the guitars in a separate facility, Hoshino/Ibanez could catch any problems before the retailer - so the number of perceived flawed guitars was reduced at the retail/sales end. In England, Ibanez was imported by the Summerfield Brothers, and sometimes had either the "CSL" trademark or no trademark at all on the headstock. Other U.K. distributors used the Antoria brandname, and in Australia they were rebranded with a "Jason" logo.

In the early 1970s, the level of quality rose as well as the level of indebtedness to classic American designs. It has been argued that Ibanez' reproductions of Stratocasters and Les Pauls may be equal to or better than the quality of Norlin era Gibsons or CBS era Fenders. While the **Blue Book of Guitars** would rather stay neutral on this debate (we just list them, not rate them), it has been suggested by outside sources that next time "close your eyes and let your hands and ears be the judge". In any event, the unathorized reproductions eventually led to Fender's objections to Tokai's imports (the infamous "headstock sawing" rumour), and Norlin/Gibson taking Hoshino/Ibanez/Elger into court for patent infringement.

When Ibanez began having success basically reproducing Gibson guitars and selling them at a lower price on the market, Norlin (Gibson's owner at the time) sent off a cease-and-desist warning. Norlin's lawyers decided that the best way to proceed was to defend the decorative (the headstock) versus the functional (body design), and on June 28th, 1977 the case of Gibson vs. Elger Co. opened in Philadelphia Federal District Court. In early 1978, a resolution was agreed upon: Ibanez would stop reproducing Gibsons if Norlin would stop suing Ibanez. The case was officially closed on February 2, 1978.

The infringement lawsuit ironically might have been the kick in the pants that propelled Ibanez and other Japanese builders to get back into original designs. Ibanez stopped building Gibson exact reproductions, and moved on to other designs. By the early 1980s, certain guitar styles began appealing to other areas of the guitar market (notably the Hard Rock/Heavy Metal genre), and Ibanez's use of famous endorsers probably fueled the appeal. Ibanez's continuing program of original designs and artist involvement continued to work in the mid to late 1980s, and continues to support their position in the market today.

(Source: Michael Wright, Guitar Stories Volume One, pgs. 85-145)

ACOUSTIC

Grading		100%	98% MINT	95% EXC+	90% EXC	80% VG+	70% VG	60% G

AS Series

AE20 — single round cutaway dreadnought style, spruce top, bound body, 3 stripe rosette, nato back/sides, mahogany neck, 22 fret rosewood fingerboard with pearl dot inlay, rosewood bridge with white black dot pins, blackface peghead with screened plant/logo, 3 per side chrome diecast tuners, piezo bridge pickup, 4 band EQ/volume/tone control. Available in Natural finish. New 1994.

Mfr.'s Sug. Retail	$700	$560	$420	$350	$280	$250	$230	$210

AE20N — similar to AE20, except has classic style body/peghead, no fingerboard inlay, rosewood tied bridge, 3 per side tuners with pearloid buttons.

Mfr.'s Sug. Retail	$700	$560	$420	$350	$280	$250	$230	$210

Grading	100%	98% MINT	95% EXC+	90% EXC	80% VG+	70% VG	60% G

AE40 — single round cutaway dreadnought style, figured maple top, bound body, 3 stripe rosette, nato back/sides, mahogany neck, 22 fret bound rosewood fingerboard with abalone/pearl block inlay, rosewood bridge with white black dot pins, bound body matching peghead with screened plant/logo, 3 per side gold diecast tuners with pearloid buttons, piezo bridge pickup, 4 band EQ/volume/tone control. Available in Honey Sunburst, Red Sunburst and Transparent Blue finishes. New 1994.

Mfr.'s Sug. Retail	$900	$720	$540	$450	$360	$325	$300	$275

AE60S — single round cutaway dreadnought style, solid spruce top, bound body, 3 stripe rosette, ovankol back/sides, mahogany neck, 22 fret bound rosewood fingerboard with abalone/pearl block inlay, rosewood bridge with white black dot pins, bound blackface peghead with screened plant/logo, 3 per side gold diecast tuners with pearloid buttons, piezo bridge pickup, 4 band EQ/volume/tone control. Available in Natural finish. New 1994.

Mfr.'s Sug. Retail	$1,000	$800	$600	$500	$400	$360	$330	$300

Charleston Series

CR80 — auditorium style, spruce top, bound f-holes, black tri-laminated pickguard, nato back/sides, mahogany neck, 14/22 fret bound rosewood fingerboard with pearl dot inlay, rosewood bridge with white black dot pins, blackface peghead with screened logo, 3 per side chrome tuners. Available in Brown Sunburst and Cherry Sunburst finishes. New 1994.

Mfr.'s Sug. Retail	$500	$400	$300	$250	$200	$180	$165	$150

CR100E — similar to CR80, except has thinner body, piezo bridge pickup, 4 band EQ.

Mfr.'s Sug. Retail	$700	$560	$420	$350	$280	$250	$230	$210

GA Series

GA10 — classic style, spruce top, round soundhole, bound body, wood inlay rosette, nato back/sides, mahogany neck, 12/19 fret rosewood fingerboard, rosewood tied bridge, rosewood peghead veneer, 3 per side chrome tuners with pearloid buttons. Available in Natural Matte finish. New 1994.

Mfr.'s Sug. Retail	$250	$200	$150	$125	$100	$90	$80	$75

GA30 — similar to GA10, except has Natural Gloss finish. New 1994.

Mfr.'s Sug. Retail	$270	$216	$162	$135	$110	$100	$90	$80

Performance Series

PF3 — dreadnought style, spruce top, round soundhole, black pickguard, bound body, 3 stripe rosette, nato back/sides, mahogany neck, 14/20 fret rosewood fingerboard with pearl dot inlay, rosewood bridge with black white dot pins, 3 per side chrome tuners. Available in Natural finish. New 1994.

Mfr.'s Sug. Retail	$220	$176	$132	$110	$90	$80	$70	$65

PF5 — dreadnought style, spruce top, round soundhole, bound body, 5 stripe rosette, nato back/sides, mahogany neck, 14/20 fret rosewood fingerboard with pearl dot inlay, rosewood bridge with white black dot pins, 3 per side chrome tuners. Available in Natural finish. Mfd. 1992 to date.

Mfr.'s Sug. Retail	$260	$195	$130	$100	$80	$70	$65	$60

Add $40 for left handed version.

In 1994, black pickguard was introduced.

PF5-12 — similar to PF5, except has 12 strings, black pickguard, 6 per side tuners. New 1994.

Mfr.'s Sug. Retail	$320	$256	$192	$160	$130	$115	$105	$95

PF5CE — similar to PF5, except has single round cutaway, piezo bridge pickup, 2 band volume/tone control. New 1994.

Mfr.'s Sug. Retail	$410	$328	$246	$205	$165	$145	$135	$125

PF5S — similar to PF5, except has solid spruce top, pearl snowflake fingerboard inlay. New 1994.

Mfr.'s Sug. Retail	$390	$312	$234	$195	$155	$140	$125	$115

PF10 — dreadnought style, spruce top, round soundhole, bound body, 5 stripe rosette, mahogany back/sides/neck, 14/20 fret rosewood fingerboard with pearl dot inlay, rosewood bridge with black white dot pins, 3 per side chrome tuners. Available in Natural finish. Mfd. 1991 to date.

Mfr.'s Sug. Retail	$290	$217	$145	$120	$95	$85	$80	$75

Add $40 for left handed version.

Add $50 for Black finish (PF10BK).

In 1994, black pickguard was introduced.

PF10-12 — similar to PF10, except has 12 strings, 6 per side tuners.

Mfr.'s Sug. Retail	$360	$270	$180	$135	$110	$100	$90	$80

PF10CE — similar to PF10, except has single cutaway, 3 per side chrome diecast tuners, piezo electric pickup, volume/tone control. Mfd. 1992 to date.

Mfr.'s Sug. Retail	$450	$337	$225	$185	$150	$135	$120	$110

PF18S — dreadnought style, solid spruce top, round soundhole, bound body, 5 stripe rosette, mahogany back/sides/neck, 14/20 fret rosewood fingerboard with pearl dot inlays, rosewood bridge with black white dot pins, 3 per side chrome diecast tuners. Available in Natural gloss finish. Mfd. 1992 to date.

Mfr.'s Sug. Retail	$440	$330	$220	$185	$150	$135	$120	$110

Ibanez Semi-Hollowbody Prototype
courtesy Hoshino/Ibanez USA

Grading	100%	98% MINT	95% EXC+	90% EXC	80% VG+	70% VG	60% G

PF18SCE — similar to PF18S, except has single round cutaway, piezo bridge pickup, 2 band volume/tone control. New 1994.
Mfr.'s Sug. Retail $600 $480 $360 $300 $240 $215 $195 $180

PF20 — dreadnought style, flame maple top, round soundhole, bound body, 5 stripe rosette, mahogany back/sides/neck, 14/20 fret rosewood fingerboard with pearl dot inlay, rosewood bridge with black white dot pins, 3 per side chrome enclosed tuners. Available in Traditional Violin finish. Mfd. 1991 to date.
Mfr.'s Sug. Retail $370 $277 $185 $150 $120 $110 $100 $90

In 1994, black pickguard was introduced.

PF25 — dreadnought style, spruce top, round soundhole, black pickguard, herringbone bound body, 5 stripe rosette, oak back/sides, mahogany neck, 14/20 fret rosewood fingerboard with pearl snowflake inlay, rosewood bridge with black white dot pins, 3 per side chrome diecast tuners. Available in Natural finish. New 1994.
Mfr.'s Sug. Retail $360 $288 $216 $180 $145 $130 $120 $110

PF30 — dreadnought style, cedar top, round soundhole, bound body, 5 stripe rosette, mahogany back/sides/neck, 14/20 fret rosewood fingerboard with pearl dot inlay, rosewood bridge with black white dot pins, 3 per side chrome enclosed tuners. Available in Natural finish. Mfd. 1991 to 1992.
$205 $175 $145 $115 $105 $95 $85
Last Mfr.'s Sug. Retail was $290.

PF40 — dreadnought style, flame maple top, round soundhole, bound body, 5 stripe rosette, mahogany back/sides/neck, 14/20 fret rosewood fingerboard with pearl dot inlay, rosewood bridge with white black dot pins, 3 per side chrome diecast tuners. Available in Natural finish. Mfd. 1991 to date.
Mfr.'s Sug. Retail $430 $322 $215 $175 $140 $125 $115 $105

In 1994, black pickguard was introduced, spruce top, flame maple back/sides replaced original items.

PF40FM — similar to PF40, except has flame maple top. Available in Natural and Transparent Blue finishes. New 1994.
Mfr.'s Sug. Retail $500 $400 $300 $250 $200 $180 $165 $150

PF50 — dreadnought style, spruce top, round soundhole, herringbone bound body and rosette, rosewood back/sides, mahogany neck, 14/20 fret bound rosewood fingerboard with abalone dot inlay, rosewood bridge with black abalone dot pins, bound peghead, 3 per side chrome diecast tuners. Available in Natural finish. Mfd. 1991 to 1994.
$300 $260 $215 $175 $155 $140 $130
Last Mfr.'s Sug. Retail was $430.

PF50-12 — similar to PF50, except has 12 strings.
$335 $290 $240 $190 $170 $155 $145
Last Mfr.'s Sug. Retail was $480.

PF50S — similar to PF50, except has solid spruce top.
$385 $330 $275 $220 $200 $180 $165
Last Mfr.'s Sug. Retail was $550.

PF75M — dreadnought style, spruce top, round soundhole, herringbone bound body and rosette, flame maple back/sides, maple neck, 14/20 fret bound maple fingerboard with black dot inlays, rosewood bridge with white abalone dot pins, bound peghead with abalone Ibanez logo inlay, 3 per side chrome diecast tuners. Available in Natural finish. Mfd. 1992 to date.
$385 $330 $275 $220 $200 $180 $165
Last Mfr.'s Sug. Retail was $550.

PF8OV — dreadnought style, ovankol top, round soundhole, black pickguard, bound body, 5 stripe rosette, ovankol back/sides, mahogany neck, 14/20 fret rosewood fingerboard with pearl dot inlay, rosewood bridge with black white dot pins, 3 per side chrome tuners. Available in Natural finish. New 1994.
Mfr.'s Sug. Retail $320 $256 $192 $160 $130 $115 $105 $95

Nomad Series

N600 — single cutaway classical style, cedar top, round soundhole, 5 stripe bound body, wooden inlay rosette, mahogany back/sides/neck, 21 fret rosewood fingerboard with pearl dot inlays, rosewood bridge with white black dot pins, 3 per side chrome diecast tuners, piezo electric pickup with 3-band EQ. Available in Natural finish. Mfd. 1992 to 1994.
$420 $360 $300 $240 $215 $195 $180
Last Mfr.'s Sug. Retail was $600.

N601N — single cutaway classic style, cedar top, round soundhole, 5 stripe bound body, wooden inlay rosette, mahogany back/sides/neck, 21 fret rosewood fingerboard/tied bridge, classical style peghead, 3 per side open classic gold tuners, piezo electric pickup with 3-band graphic equalizer. Available in Natural finish. Mfd. 1992 to 1994.
$475 $405 $340 $270 $245 $225 $205
Last Mfr.'s Sug. Retail was $680.

N700D — single cutaway deeper dreadnought style, spruce top, round soundhole, 5 stripe bound body, wooden inlay rosette, ovankol back/sides, mahogany neck, 21 fret rosewood fingerboard with snowflake inlays, rosewood bridge with white black dot pins, 3 per side gold diecast tuners, piezo pickup, 3 band graphic equalizer. Available in Natural finish. Mfd. 1992 to 1994.
$490 $420 $350 $280 $250 $230 $210
Last Mfr.'s Sug. Retail was $700.

"The audience looked up in disbelief at the large tote board placed high above the stage which registered the bids. $200,000.00 from the floor. $210,000 from the phone."
—Lawrence Acunto
TCG, Sept/Oct 1990

Grading	100%	98% MINT	95% EXC+	90% EXC	80% VG+	70% VG	60% G

N800 — single cutaway jumbo style, flame maple top, round soundhole, abalone bound body and rosette, flame maple back/sides, mahogany neck, 21 fret bound rosewood fingerboard with abalone block inlays, rosewood bridge with black white dot pins, bound peghead, 3 per side chrome diecast tuners, piezo pickup, Matrix 4 band EQ. Available in Transparent Blue and Transparent Violin finishes. Mfd. 1992 to 1994.

	$595	$510	$425	$340	$305	$280	$255

Last Mfr.'s Sug. Retail was $850.

N900S — similar to N800, except has solid spruce top and gold diecast tuners.

	$770	$660	$550	$440	$395	$365	$330

Last Mfr.'s Sug. Retail was $1,100.

Ragtime Series

R001 — parlor style, solid spruce top, round soundhole, wooden inlay binding and rosette, rosewood back/sides/neck, 14/20 fret rosewood fingerboard, rosewood bridge with white black dot pins, 3 per side gold diecast tuners. Available in Natural finish. Mfd. 1992 to 1994.

	$420	$360	$300	$240	$215	$195	$180

Last Mfr.'s Sug. Retail was $600.

R300 — parlor style, cedar top, round soundhole, wooden inlay binding and rosette, mahogany back/sides/neck, 14/20 fret rosewood fingerboard, rosewood bridge with white black dot pins, 3 per side chrome diecast tuners. Available in Natural finish. Mfd. 1992 to 1994.

	$280	$240	$200	$160	$145	$130	$120

Last Mfr.'s Sug. Retail was $400.

R302 — similar to R300, except has 12 strings.

	$315	$270	$225	$180	$160	$150	$135

Last Mfr.'s Sug. Retail was $450.

R350 — similar to R300, except for ovankol back/sides.

	$315	$270	$225	$180	$160	$150	$135

Last Mfr.'s Sug. Retail was $450.

Tulsa Series

TU5 — grand concert style, round soundhole, black pickguard, bound body, 3 stripe rosette, nato back/sides, mahogany neck, 14/20 fret rosewood fingerboard with pearl dot inlay, rosewood bridge with black white dot pins, 3 per side chrome tuners. Available in Natural finish. New 1994.

Mfr.'s Sug. Retail	$250	$200	$150	$125	$100	$90	$80	$75

ACOUSTIC ELECTRIC

ATL10 — single cutaway hollow style, spruce top, oval soundhole, bound body, 3 stripe rosette, maple back/sides/neck, 22 fret rosewood fingerboard with pearl dot inlays, rosewood bridge with white pearl dot pins, 6 per side black diecast tuners, piezo pickup, 3 band equalizer. Available in Black and Blue Night finishes. Mfd. 1992 to date.

Mfr.'s Sug. Retail	$550	$412	$275	$250	$200	$180	$165	$150

ELECTRIC

Artstar Series

AF80 — double cutaway semi hollow style, bound maple top, bound f-holes, raised black pickguard, maple back/sides/neck, 22 fret bound rosewood fingerboard with pearl dot inlay, tunomatic bridge/stop tailpiece, bound blackface peghead with screened flower/logo, 3 per side tuners, chrome hardware, 2 covered humbucker pickups, 2 volume/2 tone controls, 3 position switch. Available in Vintage Sunburst finish. New 1994.

Mfr.'s Sug. Retail	$800	$640	$480	$400	$320	$290	$265	$240

AF200 — single round cutaway semi hollow style, spruce top with bound body and f-holes, raised pickguard, spruce back/sides, mahogany/maple 3 piece neck, 20 fret bound rosewood fingerboard with pearl/abalone rectangle inlays, ebony bridge with trapeze tailpiece, bound peghead, 3 per side nylon head tuners, gold hardware, 2 Super 58 humbuckers, volume/tone control, 3 position selector switch. Available in Antique Violin finish. Mfd. 1991 to date.

Mfr.'s Sug. Retail	$1,600	$1,200	$800	$745	$590	$505	$460	$420

AM200 — double cutaway semi hollow style, burl mahogany top with bound body and f-holes, raised pickguard, burl mahogany back/sides, mahogany/maple 3 piece neck, 20 fret bound rosewood fingerboard with pearl abalone rectangle inlay, tunomatic bridge stop tailpiece, bound peghead, 3 per side nylon head tuners, gold hardware, 2 Super 58 humbuckers, volume/tone control, 3 position selector switch. Available in Antique Violin finish. Mfd. 1991 to date.

Mfr.'s Sug. Retail	$1,500	$1,125	$750	$700	$560	$505	$460	$420

AS80 — single round cutaway semi hollow style, bound maple top, bound f-holes, raised black pickguard, maple back/sides/neck, 22 fret bound rosewood fingerboard with pearl dot inlay, adjustable rosewood bridge/trapeze tailpiece, bound blackface peghead with screened flower/logo, 3 per side tuners, chrome hardware, 2 covered humbucker pickups, 2 volume/2 tone controls, 3 position switch. Available in Vintage Sunburst finish. New 1994.

Mfr.'s Sug. Retail	$650	$520	$390	$325	$260	$235	$215	$195

Grading	100%	98% MINT	95% EXC+	90% EXC	80% VG+	70% VG	60% G

AS200 — double cutaway semi hollow style, flame maple top with bound body and f-holes, raised pickguard, flame maple back/sides, mahogany/maple 3 piece neck, 20 fret bound rosewood fingerboard with pearl abalone rectangle inlay, tunomatic bridge stop tailpiece, bound peghead, 3 per side nylon head tuners, gold hardware, 2 Super 58 humbuckers, volume/tone control, 3 position selector switch. Available in Antique Violin finish. Mfd. 1991 to date.

Mfr.'s Sug. Retail $1,500 $1,125 $750 $700 $560 $505 $460 $420

EX Series

EX160 — offset double cutaway maple body, bolt-on maple neck, 22 fret rosewood fingerboard with pearl dot inlay, standard vibrato, 6 on one side tuners, chrome hardware, 2 single coil/1 humbucker pickups, volume/tone control, 5 position switch. Available in Black and Matte Stain finishes. Disc. 1994.

$230 $195 $165 $130 $120 $110 $100
Last Mfr.'s Sug. Retail was $330.

EX170 — offset double cutaway maple body, bolt-on maple neck, 22 fret maple fingerboard with black dot inlay, standard vibrato, 6 on one side tuners, chrome hardware, humbucker/single coil/humbucker pickups, volume/tone control, 5 position switch. Available in Black, Blue Night and Matte Violin finishes. Disc. 1994.

$245 $210 $175 $140 $125 $115 $105
Last Mfr.'s Sug. Retail was $350.

EX270 — similar to EX170, except has single locking vibrato and black hardware. Available in Black, Blue Night and Candy Apple finishes. Disc. 1994.

$330 $280 $235 $190 $170 $155 $140
Last Mfr.'s Sug. Retail was $470.

EX350 — offset double cutaway basswood body, bolt-on maple neck, 22 fret bound rosewood fingerboard with triangle inlay, double locking vibrato, 6 on one side tuners, chrome hardware, humbucker/single coil/humbucker Ibanez pickups, volume/tone control, 5 position switch. Available in Black, Burgundy Red, Desert Yellow and Laser Blue finishes. Disc. 1994.

$400 $340 $285 $230 $205 $190 $170
Last Mfr.'s Sug. Retail was $570.

EX360 — similar to EX350, except has 2 single coil/1 humbucker Ibanez pickups. Available in Black, Dark Grey, Jewel Blue and Purple Pearl finishes. Disc. 1992.

$350 $300 $250 $200 $180 $165 $150
Last Mfr.'s Sug. Retail was $500.

EX365 — similar to EX350, except has reverse headstock, single coil/humbucker Ibanez pickups. Available in Black, Laser Blue and Ultra Violet finishes. Disc. 1992.

$335 $290 $240 $190 $170 $155 $145
Last Mfr.'s Sug. Retail was $480.

EX370 — offset double cutaway basswood body, bolt-on maple neck, 22 fret bound rosewood fingerboard with triangle inlay, double locking vibrato, 6 on one side tuners, chrome hardware, humbucker/single coil/humbucker Ibanez pickups, volume/tone control, 5 position switch. Available in Black, Burgundy Red, Jewel Blue and Ultra Violet finishes. Disc. 1994.

$400 $340 $285 $230 $205 $190 $170
Last Mfr.'s Sug. Retail was $570.

EX370FM — similar to EX370, except has flame maple top, gold hardware. Available in Antique Violin, Cherry Sunburst and Wine Burst finishes. Disc. 1994.

$455 $390 $325 $260 $235 $215 $195
Last Mfr.'s Sug. Retail was $650.

EX1500 — offset double cutaway maple body, tortoise pickguard, bolt-on maple neck, 22 fret maple fingerboard with black dot inlay, standard vibrato, 6 on one side tuners, gold hardware, humbucker/single coil/humbucker pickups, volume/tone control, 5 position switch. Available in Antique Violin and Black finishes. Mfd. 1993 to 1994.

$300 $260 $215 $175 $155 $140 $130
Last Mfr.'s Sug. Retail was $430.

EX1700 — similar to EX1500, except has bound body, no pickguard, chrome hardware. Available in Cherry Sunburst and Transparent Turquoise finishes. Mfd. 1993 to 1994.

$300 $260 $215 $175 $155 $140 $130
Last Mfr.'s Sug. Retail was $430.

EX3700 — offset double cutaway basswood body, bound flame maple top, bolt-on maple neck, 24 fret maple fingerboard with black dot inlay, double locking vibrato, 6 on one side tuners, gold hardware, humbucker/single coil/humbucker Ibanez pickups, volume/tone control, 5 position switch. Available in Transparent Purple, Transparent Red and Transparent Turquoise finishes. Mfd. 1993 to 1994.

$455 $390 $325 $260 $235 $215 $195
Last Mfr.'s Sug. Retail was $650.

FGM Series

The FGM Series was co-designed by Frank Gambale.

Ibanez AS-200 Artist
courtesy James Browning

Grading	100%	98% MINT	95% EXC+	90% EXC	80% VG+	70% VG	60% G

FGM100 — sculpted thin offset double cutaway mahogany body, one piece maple neck, 22 fret bound rosewood fingerboard with body matching color sharktooth inlay, double locking vibrato, 6 on one side tuners, black hardware, humbucker DiMarzio/single coil DiMarzio/humbucker Ibanez pickups, volume/tone control, 5 position selector switch. Available in Black, Desert Sun Yellow, Pink Salmon and Sky Blue finishes. Mfd. 1991 to 1994.

	$910	$780	$650	$520	$470	$430	$390

Last Mfr.'s Sug. Retail was $1,300.

FGM200 — sculpted thin offset double cutaway mahogany body, one piece maple neck, 22 fret rosewood fingerboard with clay dot inlay, strings thru Gotoh fixed bridge, 6 on one side tuners, black hardware, humbucker/single coil/humbucker DiMarzio pickups, volume/tone control, 5 position selector switch. Available in Black and White finishes. New 1994.

Mfr.'s Sug. Retail	$1,500	$1,200	$900	$750	$600	$540	$495	$450

FGM300 — sculpted thin offset double cutaway mahogany body, one piece maple neck, 22 fret bound rosewood fingerboard with pearl sharktooth inlay, double locking vibrato, 6 on one side tuners, black hardware, humbucker/single coil/humbucker DiMarzio pickups, volume/tone control, 5 position selector switch. Available in Desert Yellow Sun and Metallic Green finishes. New 1994.

Mfr.'s Sug. Retail	$1,700	$1,360	$1,020	$850	$680	$610	$560	$510

GB Series

The GB Series was co-designed by George Benson.

GB5 — single round cutaway hollow style, arched spruce top, bound f-holes, raised bound maple pickguard, bound body, maple back/sides, maple/mahogany 3 piece neck, 20 fret bound ebony fingerboard with pearl split block inlay, ebony bridge with pearl curlicue inlay, ebony tailpiece, bound blackface peghead with pearl flower/logo, 3 per side tuners with pearloid buttons, gold hardware, 2 humbucker Ibanez pickups, 2 volume/2 tone controls, 3 position switch. Available in Brown Sunburst finish. New 1994.

Mfr.'s Sug. Retail	$2,900	$2,320	$1,740	$1,450	$1,160	$1,040	$955	$870

GB10 — single round cutaway hollow style, arched spruce top, bound f-holes, raised bound black pickguard, bound body, maple back/sides, 3 piece maple/mahogany neck, 22 fret bound ebony fingerboard with pearl/abalone split block inlay, ebony bridge with pearl arrow inlays, ebony/metal tailpiece, bound peghead with abalone torch/logo inlay, 3 per side tuners with pearloid buttons, gold hardware, 2 humbucker Ibanez pickups, 2 volume/2 tone controls, 3 position switch. Available in Brown Sunburst and Natural finishes. Mfd. 1978 to date.

Mfr.'s Sug. Retail	$2,000	$1,500	$1,000	$890	$700	$575	$530	$480

The 21st fret has a George Benson signature block inlay.

GB12 — single round cutaway hollow style, arched flame maple top/back/sides, abalone and plastic bound body and f-holes, raised matched pickguard, 22 fret ebony fingerboard with special GB12 inlay, ebony bridge with flower inlay, gold and ebony tailpiece with vine inlay, bound peghead with abalone logo and George Benson 12th Anniversary Ibanez inlays, 3 per side nylon head tuners, gold hardware, 2 humbucker Ibanez pickups, two volume/tone controls, 3 position switch. Available in Brown Sunburst finish. Mfd. 1990 to 1992.

	$1,400	$1,200	$1,000	$800	$720	$660	$600

Last Mfr.'s Sug. Retail was $2,000.

The 21st fret had a George Benson signature scroll inlay.

This was a limited edition 12th Anniversary George Benson model guitar.

GB30 — single round cutaway hollow style, arched maple top/back/sides, bound body and f-holes, raised black pickguard, mahogany neck, 22 fret bound ebony fingerboard with offset pearl dot inlay, tunomatic bridge/stop tailpiece, bound peghead with abalone logo and George Benson standard Ibanez inlay, 3 per side nylon head tuners, black hardware, 2 humbucker pickups, 2 volume/tone controls, 3 position switch. Available in Black and Transparent Red finishes. Mfd. 1991 to 1992.

	$910	$780	$650	$520	$470	$430	$390

Last Mfr.'s Sug. Retail was $1,300.

The 21st fret had a George Benson signature block inlay.

GB100 — single round cutaway hollow style, arched flame maple top/back/sides, bound f-holes, abalone bound body, raised maple pickguard, 22 fret bound ebony fingerboard with special pearl GB12 inlay, ebony bridge with flower inlay, metal/ebony tailpiece with pearl vine inlay, bound blackface peghead with abalone torch/logo inlay, 3 per side tuners with pearloid buttons, gold hardware, 2 humbucker Ibanez pickups, 2 volume/2 tone controls, 3 position switch. Available in Brown Sunburst finish. Mfd. 1993 to date.

Mfr.'s Sug. Retail	$2,500	$1,875	$1,250	$1,195	$920	$830	$760	$690

Ghostrider Series

GR320 — double cutaway bound alder body, mahogany neck, 22 fret bound rosewood fingerboard with pearl dot inlay, strings thru fixed bridge, 3 per side tuners, black hardware, 2 humbucker Ibanez pickups, volume/tone control, 3 position switch. Available in Black and Cherry finishes. New 1994.

Mfr.'s Sug. Retail	$700	$560	$420	$350	$280	$250	$230	$210

Grading		100%	98% MINT	95% EXC+	90% EXC	80% VG+	70% VG	60% G

GR520 — double cutaway alder body, bound carved maple top, mahogany neck, 22 fret bound rosewood fingerboard with abalone/pearl split block inlay, tunomatic bridge/stop tailpiece, bound blackface peghead with screened logo, 3 per side tuners with pearloid buttons, gold hardware, 2 humbucker Ibanez pickups, volume/tone control, 3 position switch. Available in Orange Sunburst and Vintage Sunburst finishes. New 1994.

Mfr.'s Sug. Retail	$800	$640	$480	$400	$320	$290	$265	$240

Iceman Series

IC300 — single horn cutaway asymmetrical bound mahogany body with pointed bottom bout, raised cream pickguard, bolt-on maple neck, 22 fret bound rosewood fingerboard with pearl dot inlay, tunomatic bridge/stop tailpiece, 3 per side tuners, chrome hardware, 2 humbucker Ibanez pickups, volume/tone controls, 3 position switch. Available in Black and Blue finishes. New 1994.

Mfr.'s Sug. Retail	$580	$464	$348	$290	$230	$205	$190	$175

IC500 — single horn cutaway asymmetrical pearloid bound mahogany body with pointed bottom bout, raised pearloid pickguard, maple neck, 22 fret bound rosewood fingerboard with abalone dot inlay, tunomatic bridge/stop tailpiece, bound blackface peghead with pearl logo inlay, 3 per side tuners with pearloid buttons, cosmo black hardware, 2 humbucker Ibanez pickups, volume/tone controls, 3 position switch. Available in Black finish. New 1994.

Mfr.'s Sug. Retail	$1,300	$1,040	$780	$650	$520	$470	$430	$390

JEM Series

The JEM Series was co-designed by Steve Vai. All models in this series have a hand slot routed into the bodies.

JEM555 — offset double cutaway basswood body, body matching pickguard, bolt-on maple neck, 24 fret rosewood fingerboard with pearl inlay, double locking vibrato, 6 on one side tuners, charcoal hardware, humbucker/single coil/humbucker DiMarzio pickups, volume/tone control, 5 position switch. Available in Black and White finishes. New 1994.

Mfr.'s Sug. Retail	$1,000	$800	$600	$500	$400	$360	$330	$300

This instrument's fingerboard has vine inlay to the 12th fret, pearl dot inlay from 15th to 21st, Steve Vai block inlay at 24th fret.

JEM7V — offset double cutaway alder body, pearloid pickguard, bolt-on maple neck, 24 fret ebony fingerboard with pearl vine inlay, double locking vibrato, 6 on one side tuners, gold hardware, humbucker/single coil/humbucker Ibanez pickups, volume/tone control, 5 position switch. Available in White finish. Mfd. 1993 to date.

Mfr.'s Sug. Retail	$2,100	$1,575	$1,050	$1,000	$800	$720	$660	$600

JEM77GMC — offset double cutaway basswood body, transparent pickguard, bolt-on maple neck, 24 fret rosewood fingerboard with fluorescent vine inlay, double locking vibrato, 6 on one side tuners, charcoal hardware, humbucker/single coil/humbucker DiMarzio pickups, volume/tone control, 5 position switch. Available in Green Multi Color finish. Mfd. 1992 to 1994.

		$1,475	$1,260	$1,050	$840	$755	$690	$630

Last Mfr.'s Sug. Retail was $2,100.

JEM77BFP — similar to JEM77GMC, except has maple fingerboard with Blue vine inlay, body matching peghead. Available in Blue Floral Pattern finish. Mfd. 1992 to date.

Mfr.'s Sug. Retail	$2,000	$1,500	$1,000	$945	$750	$650	$595	$540

JEM77FP — similar to JEM77GMC, except has green/red vine fingerboard inlay, body matching peghead. Available in Floral Pattern finish. Mfd. 1992 to date.

Mfr.'s Sug. Retail	$2,000	$1,500	$1,000	$945	$750	$650	$595	$540

JEM77PMC — similar to JEM77GMC, except has a maple fingerboard with 3 color pyramid inlay. Available in Purple Multi Color finish. Mfd. 1991 to 1992.

		$1,475	$1,260	$1,050	$840	$755	$690	$630

Last Mfr.'s Sug. Retail was $2,100.

JEM777 — offset double cutaway basswood body, black pickguard, bolt-on maple neck, 24 fret maple fingerboard with 3 color vanishing pyramid inlay, double locking vibrato, 6 on one side tuners, charcoal hardware, humbucker/single coil/humbucker DiMarzio pickups, volume/tone control, 5 position switch. Available in Desert Sun Yellow finish. Mfd. 1992 to date.

Mfr.'s Sug. Retail	$1,800	$1,350	$900	$845	$670	$575	$530	$480

JEM777V — similar to JEM77GMC, except has Black finish. Disc. 1994.

		$1,190	$1,020	$850	$680	$610	$560	$510

Last Mfr.'s Sug. Retail was $1,700.

JS Series

The JS Series was co-designed by Joe Satriani.

JS1 — offset double cutaway contoured basswood body, bolt-on maple neck, 22 fret rosewood fingerboard with pearl dot inlay, double locking vibrato, 6 on one side tuners, chrome hardware, humbucker/single coil/humbucker DiMarzio pickups, volume/tone control, 5 position switch. Available in Black, Inferno Red and White finishes. Mfd. 1991 to 1994.

		$840	$720	$600	$480	$430	$395	$360

Last Mfr.'s Sug. Retail was $1,200.

Ibanez 10th Anniversary JEM
courtesy Hoshino/Ibanez USA

Grading	100%	98% MINT	95% EXC+	90% EXC	80% VG+	70% VG	60% G

Ibanez Artist
courtesy James Browning

JS3 — similar to JS1, except has 2 humbucker DiMarzio pickups, 3 position switch. Available in Custom Graphic finish. Mfd. 1993 only.

| | | $1,610 | $1,380 | $1,150 | $920 | $830 | $760 | $690 |

Last Mfr.'s Sug. Retail was $2,300.

JS4 — similar to JS1, except has 2 humbucker DiMarzio pickups, 3 position switch. Available in Electric Rainbow finish. Mfd. 1993 only.

| | | $1,610 | $1,380 | $1,150 | $920 | $830 | $760 | $690 |

Last Mfr.'s Sug. Retail was $2,300.

JS5 — similar to JS1, except has 2 humbucker DiMarzio pickups, 3 position switch. Available in Rainforest finish. Mfd. 1993 only.

| | | $1,610 | $1,380 | $1,150 | $920 | $830 | $760 | $690 |

Last Mfr.'s Sug. Retail was $2,300.

JS6 — similar to JS1, except has mahogany body, fixed bridge, 2 humbucker DiMarzio pickups, 3 position switch. Available in Oil finish. Mfd. 1993 only.

| | | $1,610 | $1,380 | $1,150 | $920 | $830 | $760 | $690 |

Last Mfr.'s Sug. Retail was $2,300.

JS100 — offset double cutaway contoured basswood body, bolt-on maple neck, 22 fret rosewood fingerboard with pearl dot inlay, Joe Satriani block inlay at 21st fret, double locking vibrato, 6 on one side tuners, chrome hardware, 2 humbucker Ibanez pickups, volume/tone control, 3 position switch. Available in Black and Transparent Red finishes. New 1994.

| Mfr.'s Sug. Retail | $800 | $640 | $480 | $400 | $320 | $290 | $265 | $240 |

JS600 — similar to JS100, except has strings thru fixed bridge. Available in Black and White finishes. New 1994.

| Mfr.'s Sug. Retail | $700 | $560 | $420 | $350 | $280 | $250 | $230 | $210 |

JS1000 — offset double cutaway contoured mahogany body, bolt-on maple neck, 22 fret rosewood fingerboard with abalone dot inlay, Joe Satriani block inlay at 21st fret, double locking vibrato, 6 on one side tuners, charcoal hardware, 2 humbucker DiMarzio pickups, volume/tone control, 3 position switch, hi-pass filter push/pull switch in volume control, coil tap push/pull switch in tone control. Available in Black Pearl and Transparent Blue finishes. New 1994.

| Mfr.'s Sug. Retail | $1,700 | $1,360 | $1,020 | $850 | $680 | $610 | $560 | $510 |

JS6000 — offset double cutaway contoured mahogany body, bolt-on maple neck, 22 fret rosewood fingerboard with abalone dot inlay, Joe Satriani block inlay at 21st fret, strings thru fixed bridge, 6 on one side tuners, charcoal hardware, 2 humbucker DiMarzio pickups, volume/tone control, 3 position switch, hi-pass filter push/pull switch in volume control, coil tap push/pull switch in tone control. Available in Oil and Transparent Red finishes. New 1994.

| Mfr.'s Sug. Retail | $1,400 | $1,120 | $840 | $700 | $560 | $505 | $460 | $420 |

PG Series

PGM500 — offset double cutaway basswood body, painted f-holes, bolt-on maple neck, 24 fret rosewood fingerboard with clay dot inlay, strings thru fixed bridge, reverse peghead with screened logo, 6 on one side tuners, gold hardware, humbucker/single coil/humbucker DiMarzio pickups, volume control, 5 position switch. Available in Candy Apple finish. New 1994.

| Mfr.'s Sug. Retail | $1,300 | $1,040 | $780 | $650 | $520 | $470 | $430 | $390 |

R Series

R442 — offset double cutaway alder body, bolt-on maple neck, 22 fret maple fingerboard with black dot inlay, locking vibrato, 6 on one side locking tuners, black hardware, 2 single coil/1 humbucker Ibanez pickups, volume/tone control, 5 position switch. Available in Transparent Blue, Transparent Cherry and Transparent Sunburst finishes. Mfd. 1992 only.

| | | $490 | $420 | $350 | $280 | $250 | $230 | $210 |

Last Mfr.'s Sug. Retail was $700.

R540LTD — offset double cutaway basswood body, bolt-on maple neck, 22 fret bound rosewood fingerboard with sharktooth inlay, double locking vibrato, 6 on one side tuners, black hardware, humbucker/single coil/humbucker Ibanez pickups, volume/tone control, 5 position switch. Available in Black, Candy Apple and Jewel Blue finishes. Mfd. 1992 to date.

| Mfr.'s Sug. Retail | $1,000 | $800 | $600 | $500 | $400 | $360 | $330 | $300 |

R540 — similar to R540LTD, except has pearl dot inlay, 2 single coil/1 humbucker Ibanez pickups. Available in Blue Burst finish. Mfd. 1992 only.

| | | $665 | $570 | $475 | $380 | $345 | $315 | $285 |

Last Mfr.'s Sug. Retail was $950.

R540HH — similar to R540, except has 2 humbucker Ibanez pickups. Available in White finish.

| | | $650 | $555 | $465 | $370 | $335 | $305 | $280 |

Last Mfr.'s Sug. Retail was $930.

Grading		100%	98% MINT	95% EXC+	90% EXC	80% VG+	70% VG	60% G

R542 — offset double cutaway stand body, bolt-on maple neck, 22 fret rosewood fingerboard with abalone oval inlay, locking vibrato, 6 on one side locking tuners, black hardware, 3 single coil Ibanez pickups, volume/tone control, 5 position switch. Available in Blue, Candy Apple and White finishes. Mfd. 1992 only.

		$560	$480	$400	$320	$290	$265	$240

Last Mfr.'s Sug. Retail was $800.

RT150 — offset double cutaway alder body, white pickguard, bolt-on maple neck, 24 fret rosewood fingerboard with pearl dot inlay, standard vibrato, 6 on one side tuners, chrome hardware, humbucker/single coil/humbucker pickups, volume/tone control, 5 position switch. Available in Black and Deep Red finishes. Mfd. 1993 only.

		$280	$240	$200	$160	$145	$130	$120

Last Mfr.'s Sug. Retail was $400.

RT450 — similar to RT150, except has tortoise pickguard, locking tuners, Ibanez pickups. Available in Amber, Black and Tobacco Sunburst finishes.

		$385	$330	$275	$220	$200	$180	$165

Last Mfr.'s Sug. Retail was $550.

RT452 — similar to RT450, except has 12 strings, fixed bridge, 6 per side tuners. Available in Amber finish.

		$455	$390	$325	$260	$235	$215	$195

Last Mfr.'s Sug. Retail was $650.

RT650 — offset double cutaway alder body, bound gravure top, pearloid pickguard, bolt-on maple neck, 24 fret bound rosewood fingerboard with pearl dot inlay, standard vibrato, 6 on one side locking tuners, chrome hardware, humbucker/single coil/humbucker Ibanez pickups, volume/tone control, 5 position switch. Available in Transparent Blue and Transparent Red finishes. Mfd. 1993 only.

		$525	$450	$375	$300	$270	$245	$225

Last Mfr.'s Sug. Retail was $750.

RV470 — offset double cutaway alder body, gravure top, transparent pickguard, bolt-on maple neck, 22 fret rosewood fingerboard with pearl dot inlay, standard vibrato, 6 on one side locking tuners, gold hardware, volume/tone control, 5 position switch. Available in Purpleburst and Tobaccoburst finishes. Mfd. 1993 only.

		$595	$510	$425	$340	$305	$280	$255

Last Mfr.'s Sug. Retail was $850.

RG Series

RG270 — offset double cutaway basswood body, bolt-on maple neck, 24 fret maple fingerboard with black dot inlay, double locking vibrato, 6 on one side tuners, chrome hardware, humbucker/single coil/humbucker pickups, volume/tone control, 5 position switch. Available in Black, Crimson Metallic and Emerald Green finishes. New 1994.

Mfr.'s Sug. Retail	$470	$376	$282	$235	$190	$170	$155	$140

RG450 — offset double cutaway basswood body, transparent pickguard, bolt-on maple neck, 24 fret maple fingerboard with black dot inlay, double locking vibrato, 6 on one side tuners, black hardware, humbucker/single coil/humbucker Ibanez pickups, volume/tone control, 5 position switch. Available in Black, Emerald Green and Purple Neon finishes. New 1994.

Mfr.'s Sug. Retail	$585	$468	$351	$295	$235	$210	$195	$175

RG450DX — similar to RG450, except has bound rosewood fingerboard with pearl triangle inlay, cosmo black hardware. Available in Laser Blue and White finishes. New 1994.

Mfr.'s Sug. Retail	$700	$560	$420	$350	$280	$250	$230	$210

RG470 — offset double cutaway basswood body, bolt-on maple neck, 24 fret rosewood fingerboard with pearl dot inlay, double locking vibrato, 6 on one side tuners, black hardware, humbucker/single coil/humbucker Ibanez pickups, volume/tone control, 5 position switch. Available in Black, Crimson Metallic, Emerald Green and Jewel Blue finishes. Mfd. 1993 to date.

Mfr.'s Sug. Retail	$585	$468	$351	$335	$300	$270	$245	$225

Add $50 for left handed version (RG470L).

In 1994, Crimson Metallic finish was introduced, Emerald Green finish was discontinued.

RG470FM — similar to RG470, except has bound figured maple top, maple fingerboard with black dot inlay. Available in Transparent Black and Transparent Purple finishes. New 1994.

Mfr.'s Sug. Retail	$700	$560	$420	$350	$280	$250	$230	$210

RG470FX — similar to RG470, except has strings thru fixed bridge. Available in Black and Laser Blue finishes. New 1994.

Mfr.'s Sug. Retail	$480	$384	$288	$240	$190	$170	$155	$145

RG550 — offset double cutaway basswood body, black pickguard, bolt-on maple neck, 24 fret maple fingerboard with black dot inlay, double locking vibrato, 6 on one side tuners, black hardware, humbucker/single coil/humbucker Ibanez pickups, volume/tone control, 5 position switch. Available in Black, Candy Apple, Electric Blue and Desert Sun Yellow finishes. Mfd. 1991 to date.

Mfr.'s Sug. Retail	$900	$675	$450	$400	$320	$290	$265	$240

In 1994, Electric Blue finish was introduced, Candy Apple and Desert Sun Yellow finishes were discontinued.

RG550DX — similar to RG550, except has body-color-matched mirror pickguard. Available in Laser Blue and Purple Neon finishes. Disc. 1994.

		$595	$510	$425	$340	$305	$280	$255

Last Mfr.'s Sug. Retail was $850.

Grading	100%	98% MINT	95% EXC+	90% EXC	80% VG+	70% VG	60% G

1970s Ibanez Custom Agent
courtesy World Wide Guitars

RG550LTD — similar to RG550, except has body-color-matched mirror pickguard, bound rosewood fingerboard with pearl sharktooth inlay, cosmo black hardware. Available in Black and Purple Neon finishes. New 1994.

Mfr.'s Sug. Retail	$1,000	$800	$600	$500	$400	$360	$330	$300

RG560 — similar to RG550, except has rosewood fingerboard with pearl dot inlay, 2 single coil/1 humbucker Ibanez pickups. Available in Black, Candy Apple and Jewel Blue finishes. Mfd. 1992 only.

		$525	$450	$375	$300	$270	$245	$225

Last Mfr.'s Sug. Retail was $750.

RG565 — similar to RG550, except has body-color matched fingerboard inlay, reverse headstock, single coil/humbucker Ibanez pickups. Available in Candy Apple, Emerald Green and Laser Blue finishes. Mfd. 1992 only.

		$560	$480	$400	$320	$290	$265	$240

Last Mfr.'s Sug. Retail was $800.

RG570 — offset double cutaway basswood body, bolt-on maple neck, 24 fret rosewood fingerboard with pearl dot inlay, double locking vibrato, 6 on one side tuners, black hardware, humbucker/single coil/humbucker Ibanez pickups, volume/tone control, 5 position switch. Available in Black, Candy Apple, Emerald Green, Jewel Blue and Purple Neon finishes. Mfd. 1992 only.

		$525	$450	$375	$300	$270	$245	$225

Last Mfr.'s Sug. Retail was $750.

Add $150 for left handed version (RG570L). Available in Jewel Blue finish.

RG570FM — similar to RG570, except has flame maple top. Available in Amber, Transparent Blue and Transparent Cherry finishes. Mfd. 1992 only.

		$595	$510	$425	$340	$305	$280	$255

Last Mfr.'s Sug. Retail was $850.

RG750 — offset double cutaway basswood body, bolt-on maple neck, 24 fret bound maple fingerboard with sharktooth inlay, double locking vibrato, bound peghead, 6 on one side tuners, black hardware, humbucker/single coil/humbucker Ibanez pickups, volume/tone control, 5 position switch. Available in Black and Candy Apple finishes. Mfd. 1992 only.

		$700	$600	$500	$400	$360	$330	$300

Last Mfr.'s Sug. Retail was $1,000.

RG760 — similar to RG750, except has rosewood fingerboard, 2 single coil/1 humbucker Ibanez pickups. Available in Black, Jewel Blue and Emerald Green finishes.

		$700	$600	$500	$400	$360	$330	$300

Last Mfr.'s Sug. Retail was $1,000.

RG770 — offset double cutaway basswood body, bolt-on maple neck, 24 fret bound rosewood fingerboard with pearl sharktooth inlay, double locking vibrato, bound peghead, 6 on one side tuners, black hardware, humbucker/single coil/humbucker Ibanez pickups, volume/tone control. Available in Black, Emerald Green finishes. Mfd. 1991 to 1994.

		$700	$600	$500	$400	$360	$330	$300

Last Mfr.'s Sug. Retail was $1,000.

Model was available with transparent pickguard, maple fingerboard with body-color-matched sharktooth inlay (RG770DX). Available in Laser Blue and Violet Metallic finishes.

RG1200 — offset double cutaway basswood flame maple top body, pearloid pickguard, bolt-on maple neck, 24 fret bound rosewood fingerboard with abalone oval inlay, double locking vibrato, bound peghead, 6 on one side tuners, humbucker/Ibanez single coil/DiMarzio humbucker pickups, volume/tone control, 5 position switch. Available in Transparent Red and Transparent Blue finishes. Mfd. 1992 only.

		$945	$810	$675	$540	$485	$445	$405

Last Mfr.'s Sug. Retail was $1,350.

RX Series

RX20 — offset double cutaway maple body, white pickguard, bolt-on maple neck, 22 fret maple fingerboard with black dot inlay, standard vibrato, 6 on one side tuners, chrome hardware, 2 humbucker pickups, volume/tone control, 5 position switch. Available in Black and Red finishes. New 1994.

Mfr.'s Sug. Retail	$290	$232	$174	$145	$115	$105	$95	$85

RX160 — offset double cutaway maple body, bolt-on maple neck, 22 fret rosewood fingerboard with pearl dot inlay, standard vibrato, 6 on one side tuners, chrome hardware, humbucker/single coil/humbucker pickups, volume/tone control, 5 position switch. Available in Black, Blue Night and Red finishes. New 1994.

Mfr.'s Sug. Retail	$340	$272	$204	$170	$135	$125	$115	$105

RX170 — similar to RX160, except has maple fingerboard with black dot inlay. Available in Emerald Green, Transparent Blue and Transparent Red finishes. New 1994.

Mfr.'s Sug. Retail	$360	$288	$216	$180	$145	$130	$120	$110

RX270 — similar to RX160, except has bound body, maple fingerboard with black dot inlay. Available in Black, Cherry Sunburst and Transparent Green finishes. New 1994.

Mfr.'s Sug. Retail	$430	$344	$258	$215	$175	$155	$140	$130

Grading	100%	98% MINT	95% EXC+	90% EXC	80% VG+	70% VG	60% G

RX350 — offset double cutaway maple body, pearloid pickguard, bolt-on maple neck, 22 fret maple fingerboard with black dot inlay, standard vibrato, 6 on one side tuners, cosmo black hardware, humbucker/single coil/humbucker Ibanez pickups, volume/tone control, 5 position switch. Available in Black, Emerald Green, Transparent Red and Transparent Turquoise finishes. New 1994.

Mfr.'s Sug. Retail	$480	$384	$288	$240	$190	$170	$155	$145

RX352 — similar to RX350, except has 12 strings, fixed bridge, 6 on one side tuners. Available in Black finish. New 1994.

Mfr.'s Sug. Retail	$580	$464	$348	$290	$230	$205	$190	$175

RX650 — offset double cutaway maple body, bound figured maple top, pearloid pickguard, bolt-on maple neck, 22 fret bound rosewood fingerboard with pearl dot inlay, standard vibrato, 6 on one side tuners, cosmo black hardware, humbucker/single coil/humbucker Ibanez pickups, volume/tone control, 5 position switch. Available in Transparent Green, Transparent Purple and Transparent Red finishes. New 1994.

Mfr.'s Sug. Retail	$570	$456	$342	$285	$230	$205	$190	$170

RX750 — offset double cutaway padauk/mahogany/padauk body, pearloid pickguard, bolt-on maple neck, 22 fret rosewood fingerboard with pearl dot inlay, standard vibrato, 6 on one side locking tuners, gold hardware, humbucker/single coil/humbucker Ibanez pickups, volume/tone control, 5 position switch. Available in Natural finish. New 1994.

Mfr.'s Sug. Retail	$1,000	$800	$600	$500	$400	$360	$330	$300

S Series

S470 — sculpted thin offset double cutaway mahogany body, bolt-on maple neck, 22 fret rosewood fingerboard with pearl dot inlay, double locking vibrato, 6 on one side tuners, black hardware, humbucker/single coil/humbucker Ibanez pickups, volume/tone control, 5 position switch. Available in Black, Jewel Blue, Oil, Transparent Blue and Transparent Red finishes. Mfd. 1991 to date.

Mfr.'s Sug. Retail	$1,000	$750	$500	$450	$360	$325	$300	$275

In 1994, Jewel Blue and Oil finishes were introduced, Transparent Blue was discontinued.

SF470 — similar to S470, except has tunomatic bridge/stop tailpiece. Available in Black and Transparent Red finishes. Mfd. 1991 to date.

Mfr.'s Sug. Retail	$850	$637	$425	$375	$300	$270	$245	$225

SV470 — similar to S470, except has standard vibrato, locking tuners, gold hardware. Available in Black, Oil and Transparent Red finishes. New 1994.

Mfr.'s Sug. Retail	$900	$720	$540	$450	$360	$325	$300	$275

S540 — offset double cutaway mahogany body, bolt-on maple neck, 22 fret maple fingerboard with abalone oval inlay, pearl "Custom Made" inlay at 21st fret, double locking vibrato, 6 on one side tuners, cosmo black hardware, humbucker/single coil/humbucker Ibanez pickups, volume/tone control, 5 position switch. Available in Cayman Green, Jade Metallic and Oil finishes. Mfd. 1991 to date.

Mfr.'s Sug. Retail	$1,200	$900	$600	$555	$420	$380	$345	$315

In 1994, Cayman Green finish was introduced, Jade Metallic was discontinued.

S540BM — similar to S540, except has burl mahogany top, bound rosewood fingerboard, gold hardware. Available in Antique Violin finish.

Mfr.'s Sug. Retail	$1,300	$975	$650	$605	$460	$415	$380	$345

S540FM — similar to S540, except has flame maple top, bound rosewood fingerboard, gold hardware. Available in Cherry Wine, Transparent Black and Transparent Turquoise finishes.

Mfr.'s Sug. Retail	$1,300	$975	$650	$605	$460	$415	$380	$345

S540LTD — similar to S540, except has bound rosewood fingerboard with sharktooth inlay, bound peghead, cosmo black hardware. Available in Black, Emerald Green, Jewel Blue, Lipstick Red and Purple Neon finishes. Mfd. 1991 to date.

Mfr.'s Sug. Retail	$1,250	$937	$625	$555	$435	$360	$330	$300

In 1994, Lipstick Red and Purple Neon finishes were discontinued.

540S7 — sculpted thin offset double cutaway mahogany body, bolt-on maple neck, 22 fret rosewood fingerboard with pearl dot inlay, double locking vibrato, 7 on one side tuners, black hardware, 2 single coil/1 humbucker DiMarzio pickups, volume/tone control, 5 position switch. Available in Black finish. Mfd. 1992 only.

		$910	$780	$650	$520	$470	$430	$390

Last Mfr.'s Sug. Retail was $1,300.

This model was a 7 string, similar to the Universe series.

Talman Series

This series has bodies made out of Resoncast, a composite wood material.

Grading	100%	98% MINT	95% EXC+	90% EXC	80% VG+	70% VG	60% G

Ibanez Universe UV-77MC
courtesy Matt Meridan

TC530 — offset double cutaway body, cream pickguard, bolt-on figured maple neck, 22 fret rosewood fingerboard with pearl dot inlay, standard vibrato, 3 per side tuners, chrome hardware, 3 single coil "lipstick" pickups, volume/tone control, 5 position switch. Mfd. 1994 to date.

Available in Azure Blue Burst and Royal Orangeburst finishes.

Mfr.'s Sug. Retail	$600	$480	$360	$300	$240	$215	$195	$180

Available in Black and Pale Blue finishes.

Mfr.'s Sug. Retail	$550	$440	$330	$275	$220	$200	$180	$165

Available in Gravure Flame Amber finish.

Mfr.'s Sug. Retail	$660	$528	$396	$330	$265	$240	$220	$200

TV650 — single cutaway bound body, white trilam pickguard, bolt-on figured maple neck, 22 fret rosewood fingerboard with pearl dot inlay, standard vibrato, 3 per side tuners, gold hardware, humbucker/single coil/humbucker pickups, volume/tone control, 5 position switch. Available in White finish. New 1994.

Mfr.'s Sug. Retail	$700	$560	$420	$350	$280	$250	$230	$210

TV750 — similar to TV650, except has unbound body. Available in Gravure Quilted Brown Sunburst finish. New 1994.

Mfr.'s Sug. Retail	$700	$560	$420	$350	$280	$250	$230	$210

USA Custom Exotic Wood Series

UCEWFM/UCEWQM — offset double cutaway mahogany body, figured maple top, bolt-on birdseye maple neck, 24 fret rosewood fingerboard with pearl dot inlay, double locking vibrato, 6 on one side tuners, black hardware, humbucker/Ibanez single coil/DiMarzio humbucker pickups, volume/tone control, 5 position switch. Available in Natural, Transparent Blue, Transparent Ebony and Transparent Purple finishes. Mfd. 1992 only.

	$1,190	$1,020	$850	$680	$610	$560	$510

Last Mfr.'s Sug. Retail was $1,700.

Universe Series

This series was co-designed by Steve Vai. All are seven string guitars.

UV7 — offset double cutaway basswood body, transparent pickguard, bolt-on maple neck, 24 fret rosewood fingerboard with green dot inlay, double locking vibrato, 7 on one side tuners, black hardware, humbucker/single coil/humbucker DiMarzio pickups, volume/tone control, 5 position switch. Available in Black finish. Mfd. 1991 to date.

Mfr.'s Sug. Retail	$1,800	$1,350	$900	$845	$670	$575	$530	$480

UV7P — similar to UV7, except has white pickguard and pearl abalone pyramid inlay. Available in White finish. Disc. 1994.

	$1,190	$1,020	$850	$680	$610	$560	$510

Last Mfr.'s Sug. Retail was $1,700.

UV777 — similar to UV7, except has black pickguard, maple fingerboard with 3 color pyramid inlay. Available in Green finish. Disc. 1994.

	$1,260	$1,080	$900	$720	$650	$595	$540

Last Mfr.'s Sug. Retail was $1,800.

UV77 — similar to UV7, except has 3 color pyramid inlay. Available in Multi-colored finish. Disc. 1994.

	$1,540	$1,320	$1,100	$880	$790	$725	$660

Last Mfr.'s Sug. Retail was $2,200.

USA Custom Graphic Series

This series was produced in 1992 only.

92UCGR1 — offset double cutaway basswood body, bolt-on maple neck, 24 fret bound rosewood fingerboard with sharktooth inlay, double locking vibrato, 6 on one side tuners, bound peghead, black hardware, DiMarzio single coil/Ibanez humbucker pickups, volume/tone control. Available in Ice World finish.

	$1,085	$930	$775	$620	$560	$515	$465

Last Mfr.'s Sug. Retail was $1,550.

92UCGR2 — similar to 92UCGR1, except has reverse headstock, DiMarzio humbucker/Ibanez single coil/DiMarzio humbucker pickups. Available in No Bones About It finish.

	$1,120	$960	$800	$640	$575	$530	$480

Last Mfr.'s Sug. Retail was $1,600.

92UCGR3 — similar to 92UCGR1, except has reverse headstock, 2 Ibanez humbucker pickups. Available in Grim Reaper finish.

	$1,085	$930	$775	$620	$560	$515	$465

Last Mfr.'s Sug. Retail was $1,550.

92UCGR4 — similar to 92UCGR1, except has unbound fingerboard with pearl dot inlay, DiMarzio humbucker/Ibanez single coil/DiMarzio humbucker pickups. Available in Angel Depart finish.

	$1,085	$930	$775	$620	$560	$515	$465

Last Mfr.'s Sug. Retail was $1,550.

Grading	100%	98% MINT	95% EXC+	90% EXC	80% VG+	70% VG	60% G

92UCGR5 — similar to 92UCGR1, except has unbound maple fingerboard with black dot inlay, DiMarzio single coil/humbucker pickups. Available in Unzipped finish.

| | $1,050 | $900 | $750 | $600 | $540 | $495 | $450 |

Last Mfr.'s Sug. Retail was $1,500.

92UCGR6 — similar to 92UCGR1, except has unbound rosewood fingerboard with pearl dot inlay, DiMarzio humbucker/Ibanez single coil/DiMarzio humbucker pickups. Available in Sea Monster finish.

| | $1,085 | $930 | $775 | $620 | $560 | $515 | $465 |

Last Mfr.'s Sug. Retail was $1,550.

92UCGR7 — similar to 92UCGR1, except has reverse headstock, DiMarzio humbucker/Ibanez single coil/DiMarzio humbucker pickups. Available in Alien's Revenge finish.

| | $1,120 | $960 | $800 | $640 | $575 | $530 | $480 |

Last Mfr.'s Sug. Retail was $1,600.

92UCGR8 — similar to 92UCGR1, except has unbound maple fingerboard with black dot inlay, 2 DiMarzio humbucker pickups. Available in Cosmic Swirl II finish.

| | $1,050 | $900 | $750 | $600 | $540 | $495 | $450 |

Last Mfr.'s Sug. Retail was $1,500.

VOYAGER Series

The VOYAGER Series was co-designed by Reb Beach.

RBM1 — offset double cutaway mahogany body with vibrato wedge cutaway, metal pickguard, bolt-on maple neck, 22 fret rosewood fingerboard with pearl dot inlay, double locking vibrato, 6 on one side tuners, gold hardware, 2 single coil/1 humbucker pickups, volume control, 5 position switch. Available in Black, Blue or Candy Apple finishes. Mfd. 1991 to 1994.

| | $840 | $720 | $600 | $480 | $430 | $395 | $360 |

Last Mfr.'s Sug. Retail was $1,200.

RBM2 — similar to RBM1, except has koa top, Bolivian rosewood neck/fingerboard. Available in Natural finish. Disc. 1994.

| | $1,475 | $1,260 | $1,050 | $840 | $755 | $690 | $630 |

Last Mfr.'s Sug. Retail was $2,100.

RBM10 — offset double cutaway mahogany body with lower wedge cutaway, metal control plate, bolt-on maple neck, 22 fret rosewood fingerboard with pearl dot inlay, double locking vibrato, 6 on one side tuners, gold hardware, 2 single coil/1 humbucker pickups, volume control, 5 position switch. Available in Black and Emerald Green finishes. Mfd. 1994 to date.

| Mfr.'s Sug. Retail | $800 | $640 | $480 | $400 | $320 | $290 | $265 | $240 |

RBM400 — similar to RBM10, except has Bolivian rosewood neck/fingerboard, clay dot fingerboard inlay, Ibanez pickups. Available in Oil finish. Mfd. 1994 to date.

| Mfr.'s Sug. Retail | $1,500 | $1,200 | $900 | $750 | $600 | $540 | $495 | $450 |

ELECTRIC BASS

Affirma Series

This series was designed by Swiss luthier, Rolf Spuler. His design incorporates a neck that extends half-way through the body with individual bridges for each string. There is a thumb slot, a pearl/abalone "AFR" insignia, and a pearl block with Ibanez and the serial number inscriptions inlaid into the body, located between the single coil pickup and the bridge system. All models are available in a fretless configuration at no additional charge.

A104 — offset double cutaway asymmetrical saman body, maple neck, 24 fret ebony fingerboard with offset pearl inlay at 12th fret, 4 "Mono Rail" bridges, tuning lever on low string bridge, body matching peghead veneer, 2 per side tuners, black hardware, single coil/4 bridge piezo pickups, volume/concentric treble/bass/mix controls, active electronics. Available in Natural finish. Mfg. 1992 to 1993.

| | $1,330 | $1,140 | $950 | $760 | $685 | $625 | $570 |

Last Mfr.'s Sug. Retail was $1,900.

This model is also available with kralo walnut or flame maple body.

A105 — similar to A104, except has 5 strings, 5 Mono Rail bridges, 3/2 per side tuners.

| | $1,400 | $1,200 | $1,000 | $800 | $720 | $660 | $600 |

Last Mfr.'s Sug. Retail was $2,000.

CT Bass Series

CTB1 — offset double cutaway maple body, bolt-on maple 3 piece neck, 22 fret rosewood fingerboard with pearl dot inlay, diecast fixed bridge, 2 per side tuners, chrome hardware, P-style/J-style Ibanez pickups, 2 volume/1 tone controls. Available in Black, Blue Night, Red and White finishes. Mfd. 1992 only.

| | $315 | $270 | $225 | $180 | $160 | $150 | $135 |

Last Mfr.'s Sug. Retail was $450.

Add $50 for left handed version (CTB1L).

Ibanez USRG-10 Custom
courtesy Hoshino/Ibanez USA

Grading	100%	98% MINT	95% EXC+	90% EXC	80% VG+	70% VG	60% G

CTB3 — similar to CTB1, except has CT Custom inlay, black hardware, two volume/tone controls. Available in Black, Blue Night, Natural and Transparent Red finishes.

	$420	$360	$300	$240	$215	$195	$180

Last Mfr.'s Sug. Retail was $600.

CTB5 — offset double cutaway maple body, bolt-on 3 piece maple neck, 22 fret rosewood fingerboard with CT Custom inlay, 5 string diecast fixed bridge, 3/2 per side tuners, black hardware, 2 J-style EMG pickups, 2 volume/tone controls. Available in Black, Natural and Transparent Red finishes. Mfd. 1992 only.

	$490	$420	$350	$280	$250	$230	$210

Last Mfr.'s Sug. Retail was $700.

EX Bass Series

EXB404 — offset double cutaway maple body, maple 3 piece neck, 22 fret rosewood fingerboard with pearl dot inlay, diecast fixed bridge, 4 on one side tuners, chrome hardware, P-style/J-style pickups, 2 volume/1 tone controls. Available in Black, Burgundy Red, Crimson Metallic and Jewel Blue finishes. Curr. mfr.

Mfr.'s Sug. Retail	$450	$337	$225	$215	$175	$155	$140	$130

Add $50 for left handed version (EXB404L). Available in Black finish.

In 1994, Crimson Metallic finish was introduced, Burgundy Red finish was discontinued.

EXB445 — offset double cutaway maple body, bolt-on maple 3 piece neck, 22 fret rosewood fingerboard with pearl dot inlays, 5 string diecast fixed bridge, 4/1 per side tuners, black hardware, 2 J-style EMG pickups, 2 volume/1 tone controls. Available in Black, Burgundy Red and Jewel Blue finishes. Curr. mfr.

Mfr.'s Sug. Retail	$550	$412	$275	$265	$210	$190	$175	$160

In 1994, Jewel Blue finish was introduced, Burgundy Red finish was discontinued.

Iceman Series

ICB300 — single horn cutaway asymmetrical mahogany body with pointed bottom bout, raised cream pickguard, bolt-on maple neck, 22 fret bound rosewood fingerboard with pearl dot inlay, fixed diecast bridge, 2 per side tuners, chrome hardware, 2 Ibanez pickups, 2 volume/1 tone controls, 3 position switch. Available in Black and Blue finishes. New 1994.

Mfr.'s Sug. Retail	$580	$464	$348	$290	$230	$205	$190	$175

ICB500 — single horn cutaway asymmetrical pearloid bound mahogany body with pointed bottom bout, raised pearloid pickguard, maple neck, 22 fret bound rosewood fingerboard with abalone dot inlay, fixed bridge, bound blackface peghead with pearl logo inlay, 3 per side tuners, cosmo black hardware, 2 Ibanez pickups, 2 volume/1 tone controls, 3 position switch. Available in Black finish. New 1994.

Mfr.'s Sug. Retail	$1,300	$1,040	$780	$650	$520	$470	$430	$390

S Bass Series

SB1500 — offset double cutaway bubinga body, bolt-on bubinga/wenge 5 piece neck, 22 fret ebony fingerboard with abalone oval inlays, AccuCast-B bridge, 4 on one side tuners, chrome hardware, P-style/J-style EMG pickups, 2 volume/tone controls. Available in Natural finish. Mfd. 1992 only.

	$910	$780	$650	$520	$470	$430	$390

Last Mfr.'s Sug. Retail was $1,300.

Soundgear Bass Series

SR400 — offset double cutaway maple body, bolt-on 3 piece maple neck, 24 fret rosewood fingerboard with pearl dot inlay, fixed bridge, 2 per side tuners, black hardware, P-style/J-style Ibanez pickup, 2 volume/1 tone controls. Available in Black, Candy Apple, Crimson Metallic and Jewel Blue finishes. Mfd. 1993 to date.

Mfr.'s Sug. Retail	$530	$397	$265	$250	$200	$180	$165	$150

Add $50 for left hand version (SR400L) or fretless fingerboard (SR400FL). Available in Black finish.

In 1994, Crimson Metallic finish was introduced, Candy Apple finish was discontinued.

SR405 — similar to SR400, except has 5 strings, 3/2 per side tuners, 2 humbucker pickups. Available in Black and Jewel Blue finishes. New 1994.

Mfr.'s Sug. Retail	$630	$504	$378	$315	$250	$225	$205	$190

SR500 — offset double cutaway maple body, bolt-on 3 piece maple neck, 24 fret rosewood fingerboard with pearl dot inlay, fixed bridge, 2 per side tuners, black hardware, P-style/J-style active Ibanez pickups, volume/treble/bass/mix controls, active electronics. Available in Black, Emerald Green, Jewel Blue, Natural and Transparent Turquoise finishes. Mfd. 1993 to date.

Mfr.'s Sug. Retail	$700	$525	$350	$325	$260	$235	$215	$195

Add $50 for left hand version (SR500L). Available in Black finish.

In 1994, Emerald Green and Jewel Blue finishes were introduced, Natural and Transparent Turquoise finishes were discontinued.

SR505 — similar to SR500, except has 5 strings, 3/2 per side tuners, 2 J-style EMG pickups. Available in Black, Natural, Transparent Red and Transparent Turquoise finishes. Mfd. 1993 to date.

Mfr.'s Sug. Retail	$800	$600	$400	$375	$300	$270	$245	$225

In 1994, Natural finish was introduced, Transparent Turquoise finish was discontinued.

Grading	100%	98% MINT	95% EXC+	90% EXC	80% VG+	70% VG	60% G

SR506 — similar to SR500, except has 6 strings, wenge fingerboard, 3 per side tuners, 2 humbucker active Ibanez pickups. Available in Black and Transparent Turquoise finishes. New 1994.

Mfr.'s Sug. Retail	$900	$720	$540	$450	$360	$325	$300	$275

SR590 — similar to SR500, except has gold hardware. Available in Natural and Transparent Turquoise finishes. New 1994.

Mfr.'s Sug. Retail	$750	$600	$450	$375	$300	$270	$245	$225

SR800 — offset double cutaway basswood body, bolt-on maple 5 piece neck, 24 fret rosewood fingerboard with pearl dot inlay, AccuCast-B bridge, 2 per side tuners, black hardware, P-style/J-style Ibanez pickups, volume/treble/2 mid/bass/mix controls. Available in Black, Candy Apple, Cayman Green, Jewel Blue and Royal Blue finishes. Curr. mfr.

Mfr.'s Sug. Retail	$850	$637	$425	$380	$280	$250	$230	$210

   Add $150 for left handed version (SR800L). Disc. 1994.

   Add $100 for fretless fingerboard version (SR800F). Mfd. 1992 only.

   In 1994, Cayman Green and Royal Blue finishes were introduced, 3 piece maple neck replaced original item, Candy Apple and Jewel Blue finishes were discontinued.

SR885 — similar to SR800, except has 5 strings, 3/2 per side tuners. Available in Black, Candy Apple, Laser Blue and Royal Blue finishes. Mfd. 1991 to date.

Mfr.'s Sug. Retail	$1,100	$825	$550	$490	$385	$305	$280	$255

   In 1994, Royal Blue finish was introduced, Candy Apple and Laser Blue finishes were discontinued.

SR886 — similar to SR885, except has 6 strings. Available in Black and Candy Apple finishes. Mfd. 1992 only.

		$980	$840	$700	$560	$505	$460	$420

Last Mfr.'s Sug. Retail was $1,400.

SR890 — offset double cutaway ash body, bolt-on 3 piece maple neck, 24 fret rosewood fingerboard with pearl dot inlay, fixed bridge, 2 per side tuners, gold hardware, P-style/J-style active Ibanez pickup, volume/treble/2 mid/bass/mix controls. Available in Transparent Cherry and Transparent Turquoise finishes. Mfd. 1993 only.

		$700	$600	$500	$400	$360	$330	$300

Last Mfr.'s Sug. Retail was $1,000.

SR895 — similar to SR890, except has 5 strings, 3/2 per side tuners. Mfd. 1993 only.

		$840	$720	$600	$480	$430	$395	$360

Last Mfr.'s Sug. Retail was $1,200.

SR900 — offset double cutaway ash body, bolt-on maple 3 piece neck, 24 fret rosewood fingerboard with pearl dot inlay, AccuCast-B bridge, 2 per side tuners, black hardware, P-style/J-style Ibanez pickups, 2 volume/tone controls. Available in Emerald Green and Purple Neon finishes. Mfd. 1992 only.

		$630	$540	$450	$360	$325	$300	$275

Last Mfr.'s Sug. Retail was $900.

SR950 — similar to SR900, except has ebony fingerboard with abalone oval inlay, gold hardware. Available in Transparent Cherry and Transparent Turquoise finishes.

		$700	$600	$500	$400	$360	$330	$300

Last Mfr.'s Sug. Retail was $1,000.

SR1200 — offset double cutaway maple body, figured maple top, thru body 5 piece maple/walnut neck, 24 fret rosewood fingerboard with pearl dot inlay, fixed bridge, 2 per side tuners, gold hardware, P-style/J-style Ibanez pickups, volume/treble/2 mid/bass/mix controls. Available in Natural and Transparent Turquoise finishes. New 1994.

Mfr.'s Sug. Retail	$1,100	$880	$660	$550	$440	$395	$365	$330

SR1205 — similar to SR1200, except has 5 strings, 3/2 per side tuners, 2 humbucker active Ibanez pickups. Available in Natural finish. New 1994.

Mfr.'s Sug. Retail	$1,200	$960	$720	$600	$480	$430	$395	$360

SR1300 — offset double cutaway padauk body, bolt-on 5 piece bubinga/wenge neck, 24 fret wenge fingerboard with pearl dot inlay, fixed bridge, 2 per side tuners, cosmo black hardware, P-style/J-style Ibanez pickup, volume/treble/2 mid/bass/mix controls. Available in Oil finish. Curr. mfr.

Mfr.'s Sug. Retail	$1,400	$1,050	$700	$650	$520	$470	$430	$390

   In 1994, padauk/mahogany/padauk body replaced original item.

SR1305 — similar to SR1300, except has 5 strings, 3/2 per side tuners, black hardware, 2 humbucker active Ibanez pickups.

Mfr.'s Sug. Retail	$1,600	$1,200	$800	$750	$600	$540	$495	$450

SR1306 — similar to SR1300, except has 6 strings, 3 per side tuners, black hardware, 2 humbucker active Ibanez pickups.

Mfr.'s Sug. Retail	$1,800	$1,350	$900	$850	$680	$610	$560	$510

SR1500 — offset double cutaway bubinga or padauk body, bubinga/wenge 5 piece neck, 22 fret ebony fingerboard with pearl dot inlay, fixed bridge, 2 per side tuners, black hardware, P-style/J-style EMG pickups, 2 volume/tone controls. Available in Natural finish. Mfd. 1991 to 1992.

		$980	$840	$700	$560	$505	$460	$420

Last Mfr.'s Sug. Retail was $1,400.

"I feel that there is as much of a demand, if not even more now because the acoustic body guitars are not being produced any where in the world now with quality, except in the U.S., as far as I know."

—Fred Popovich on Johnny Smith

TCG, Sept/Oct 1990

Grading	100%	98% MINT	95% EXC+	90% EXC	80% VG+	70% VG	60% G

SR2000 — offset double cutaway maple body, thru body 5 piece maple/walnut neck, 24 fret wenge fingerboard with abalone oval inlay, fixed bridge, 2 per side tuners, gold hardware, P-style/J-style Ibanez pickups, volume/treble/2 mid/bass/mix controls. Available in Oil and Transparent Purple finishes. Mfd. 1993 only.

	$1,120	$960	$800	$640	$575	$530	$480

Last Mfr.'s Sug. Retail was $1,600.

SR2005 — similar to SR2000, except has 5 strings, 3/2 per side tuners, 2 J-style pickups.

	$1,330	$1,140	$950	$760	$685	$625	$570

Last Mfr.'s Sug. Retail was $1,900.

TR Bass Series

TRB1 — offset double cutaway alder body, bolt-on maple neck, 22 fret rosewood fingerboard with pearl dot inlay, diecast fixed bridge, 4 on one side tuners, black hardware, P-style/J-style pickups, 2 volume/1 tone controls. Available in Black, Candy Apple, Jewel Blue and Transparent Blue finishes. Mfd. 1991 to 1993.

	$300	$260	$215	$175	$155	$140	$130

Last Mfr.'s Sug. Retail was $430.

Add $50 for left handed version (TRB1L). Available in Black finish only.

TRB2 — similar to TRB1, except has ash body, gold hardware. Available in Lavender Stain and Walnut Stain finishes. Mfd. 1993 only.

	$370	$320	$265	$210	$190	$175	$160

Last Mfr.'s Sug. Retail was $530.

TRB3 — similar to TRB1, except has basswood body, P-style/J-style Ibanez pickups, 2 volume/tone controls. Available in Black, Blue and Lipstick Red finishes. Mfd. 1992 only.

	$455	$390	$325	$260	$235	$215	$195

Last Mfr.'s Sug. Retail was $650.

TRB15 — similar to TRB1, except has 5 strings, 4/1 per side tuners, 2 J-style pickups. Available in Black and Transparent Red finishes. Mfd. 1993 only.

	$370	$320	$265	$210	$190	$175	$160

Last Mfr.'s Sug. Retail was $530.

TRB50 — offset double cutaway maple body, bolt-on maple neck, 22 fret maple fingerboard with black dot inlay, fixed bridge, 4 on one side tuners, chrome hardware, P-style pickup, volume/tone control. Available in Black, Red and White finishes. New 1994.

Mfr.'s Sug. Retail	$360	$288	$216	$180	$145	$130	$120	$110

TRB100 — offset double cutaway alder body, bolt-on maple neck, 22 fret rosewood fingerboard with pearl dot inlay, fixed bridge, 4 on one side tuners, black hardware, P-style/J-style pickups, volume/tone/mix control. Available in Black, Candy Apple, Jewel Blue and Transparent Blue finishes. New 1994.

Mfr.'s Sug. Retail	$450	$360	$270	$225	$180	$160	$150	$135

TRB105 — similar to TRB100, except has 5 strings, 4/1 per side tuners, 2 J-style pickups. Available in Black and Transparent Red finishes. New 1994.

Mfr.'s Sug. Retail	$550	$440	$330	$275	$220	$200	$180	$165

TRB200 — offset double cutaway ash body, bolt-on maple neck, 22 fret rosewood fingerboard with pearl dot inlay, fixed bridge, 4 on one side tuners, gold hardware, P-style/J-style pickups, volume/tone/mix control. Available in Lavender Stain and Walnut Stain finishes. New 1994.

Mfr.'s Sug. Retail	$550	$440	$330	$275	$220	$200	$180	$165

USA Custom American Master Bass Series

MAB4FM — offset double cutaway mahogany body, figured maple top, maple/purple heart 3 piece thru body neck, 24 fret rosewood fingerboard with pearl dot inlay, Wilkinson fixed bridge, 2 per side tuners, black hardware, P-style/J-style EMG pickups, 2 volume/tone controls. Available in Natural finish. Disc. 1992.

	$1,820	$1,560	$1,300	$1,040	$935	$860	$780

Last Mfr.'s Sug. Retail was $2,600.

MAB5BE — similar to MAB4FM, except has birdseye maple top and 5 strings.

	$1,960	$1,680	$1,400	$1,120	$1,010	$925	$840

Last Mfr.'s Sug. Retail was $2,800.

IMMAGE

Instruments built in Taiwan in the mid 1980s.

The Immage line consisted of entry level to mid quality designs based on classic American models.

(Source: Tony Bacon and Paul Day, The Guru's Guitar Guide)

IMPERIAL

Instruments produced in Japan.

The Imperial trademark is a brandname used by U.S. importer Imperial Accordian Company of Chicago, Illinois.

(Source: Michael Wright, Guitar Stories Volume One, pg. 76)

ITHACA GUITAR WORKS

Instruments currently built in Ithaca, New York.

The Ithaca Guitar Works consists of both a retail music store and a custom guitar shop. Luthiers Eric Aceto and Dan Hoffman in the Stringed Intrument Division of Ithaca Guitar Works design and build quality Acoustic/Electric guitar models, while Chris Brodwell runs the retail side of the shop. The crew at the Ithaca Guitar Works began playing, fixing, customizing, and building instruments over twenty years ago. The **Oneida** acoustic/electric ($2,850) is constructed with a spruce or cedar top, mahogany or walnut back and sides, and an ebony fingerboard and bridge. The company also offers several other stringed instruments. For further information, please contact Ithaca Guitar Works through the Index of Current Manufacturers located in the back of this book.

J

JACKSON

The Jackson USA and Jackson Custom Shop series guitars are built in Ontario, California. Jackson Professional series guitars are built in Japan, and fully inspected to Jackson standards prior to distribution. Jackson guitars are distributed in the U.S. by their parent company International Music Corporation, who also distributes Ross Electronics and Akai Electronics through their headquarters in Fort Worth, Texas.

The company was founded in 1978 as a joint project between Grover Jackson and Wayne R. Charvel. After building custom guitars for the up-and-coming West Coast rock musicians, Jackson/Charvel was acquired by the International Music Company (IMC) of Fort Worth, Texas. As these guitars gained popularity, it became a necessity that standardized models were established. In about 1992, upper end Charvels began to be incorporated into the Jackson line, becoming the Jackson Professional Series, which were, and still are, manufactured overseas.

ELECTRIC

Grading		100%	98% MINT	95% EXC+	90% EXC	80% VG+	70% VG	60% G

Jackson USA in crackle finish
19th Annual Dallas Show

In 1996, the models in the product line were renamed from their usual name plus designation (ex.: a Rhoads Standard) to a simpler 3 or 4 digit abbreviation (Rhoads Standard = RR2). Older models discontinued prior to 1996 will retain their original designation. New models and continuing models will follow the new designation, and every attempt will be made to clue in readers to the change.

Concept Series

The Concept series was available briefly from 1993 through late 1994. Continuing popularity led to introduction of the Performer Series in 1995, which combined the best design aspects of the Concept series models with new innovations.

JDR-94 — offset double cutaway poplar body, bolt-on maple neck, 24 fret rosewood fingerboard with pearl offset dot inlay, double locking vibrato, reverse blackface peghead with screened logo, 6 on one side tuners, black hardware, humbucker/single coil/humbucker pickups, volume/tone control, 5 position switch. Available in Black, Brite Red and Dark Metallic Blue finishes. Mfd. 1993 to 1994.

	$415	$360	$300	$240	$215	$195	$180

Last Mfr.'s Sug. Retail was $595.

JDX-94 — similar to JDR-94, except has standard fingerboard dot inlay, fixed bridge, standard peghead design, 2 single coil/1 humbucker pickups configuration. Available in Black, Brite Red and Dark Metallic Blue finishes. Mfd. 1993 to 1994.

	$385	$330	$275	$220	$200	$180	$165

Last Mfr.'s Sug. Retail was $550.

JRR-94 — sharkfin poplar body, black pickguard, bolt-on maple neck, 24 fret rosewood fingerboard with pearl dot inlay, tunomatic bridge/strings thru body tailpiece, blackface peghead with screened logo, 6 on one side tuners, black hardware, 2 humbucker pickups, 2 volume/1 tone controls, 3 position switch. Available in Black, Brite Red and Dark Metallic Blue finishes. Mfd. 1993 to 1994.

	$415	$360	$300	$240	$215	$195	$180

Last Mfr.'s Sug. Retail was $595.

JSX-94 — offset double cutaway poplar body, bolt-on maple neck, 24 fret rosewood fingerboard with pearl offset dot inlay, double locking vibrato, blackface peghead with screened logo, 6 on one side tuners, black hardware, 2 single coil/1 humbucker pickups, volume/tone control, 5 position switch. Available in Black, Brite Red and Dark Metallic Blue finishes. Mfd. 1993 to 1994.

	$415	$360	$300	$240	$215	$195	$180

Last Mfr.'s Sug. Retail was $595.

Performer Series

Continuing popularity of the Concept series led to introduction of the Performer Series in 1995, which combined the best design aspects of the Concept series models with new innovations.

PS-1 — offset double cutaway alder body, bolt-on maple neck, 24 fret rosewood fingerboard with pearl dot inlay, JT490 fulcrum vibrato, blackface peghead with screened logo, 6 on one side tuners, black hardware, black pickguard, 2 single coils/1 humbucker pickups, volume/tone control, 5 position switch. Available in Black, Red Violet Metallic, Blue Green Metallic, Black Cherry, and Deep Metallic Blue finishes. Mfd. 1995 to date.

Mfr.'s Sug. Retail	$549	$439	$329	$300	$240	$215	$195	$180

PS-2 — similar to PS-1, except has double locking JT590 tremolo and no pickguard.

Mfr.'s Sug. Retail	$545	$436	$327	$290	$230	$200	$180	$160

Grading	100%	98% MINT	95% EXC+	90% EXC	80% VG+	70% VG	60% G

PS-3 — sharkfin poplar body, black pickguard, bolt-on maple neck, 24 fret rosewood fingerboard with pearl dot inlay, tunomatic bridge/strings thru body tailpiece, blackface peghead with screened logo, 6 on one side tuners, black hardware, 2 humbucker pickups, 2 volume/1 tone controls, 3 position switch. Available in Black, Red Violet Metallic, Blue Green Metallic, Black Cherry, and Deep Metallic Blue finishes. Mfd. 1995 to date.

Mfr.'s Sug. Retail	$545	$436	$327	$290	$230	$200	$180	$160

PS-3T — similar to PS-3, except has double locking JT500 tremolo.

Mfr.'s Sug. Retail	$595	$446	$297	$290	$230	$200	$180	$160

PS-4 — offset double cutaway alder body, bolt-on maple neck, 24 fret rosewood fingerboard with pearl offset dot inlay, double locking vibrato, reverse blackface peghead with screened logo, 6 on the other side tuners, black hardware, 1 middle single coil/2 humbucker pickups, volume/tone control, 5 position switch. Available in Black, Red Violet Metallic, Blue Green Metallic, Black Cherry, and Deep Metallic Blue finishes. Mfd. 1995 to date.

Mfr.'s Sug. Retail	$595	$476	$357	$300	$250	$210	$180	$165

Player's Choice Series

The Player's Choice series was released from 1993 to 1995 and incorporated many of the most requested options from the Jackson Custom Shop. Standardization of designs yielded lower prices.

EXOTIC DINKY — offset double cutaway koa body, bound quilted maple top, bolt-on maple neck, 24 fret bound pau ferro fingerboard with offset pearl dot inlay, double locking vibrato, bound peghead with pearl logo inlay, 6 on one side tuners, gold hardware, 2 stacked coil/1 humbucker Seymour Duncan pickups, volume/tone control, 5 position switch. Available in Tobacco Sunburst, Transparent Blue, Transparent Purple and Transparent Red finishes. Mfd. 1993 to 1995.

	$1,680	$1,440	$1,200	$960	$860	$790	$720

Last Mfr.'s Sug. Retail was $2,400.

FLAMED DINKY — similar to Exotic Dinky, except has flame maple body, bound ebony fingerboard with pearl sharkfin inlay, black hardware, Jackson pickups. Available in Transparent Black, Transparent Blue and Transparent Purple finishes. Mfd. 1993 to 1995.

	$1,540	$1,320	$1,100	$880	$790	$725	$660

Last Mfr.'s Sug. Retail was $2,200.

KING V — V style poplar body, thru body maple neck, 22 fret bound ebony fingerboard with pearl sharkfin inlay, fixed locking bridge, bound peghead with pearl logo inlay, 6 on one side tuners, black hardware, 2 volume/1 tone controls, 5 position switch with opposite switching. Available in Black finish. Mfd. 1993 to 1995.

	$1,540	$1,320	$1,100	$880	$790	$725	$660

Last Mfr.'s Sug. Retail was $2,200.

ORIGINAL RHOADS — sharkfin style poplar body, gold pickguard, thru body maple neck, 22 fret bound ebony fingerboard with pearl sharkfin inlay, tunomatic bridge, strings thru tailpiece with V plate, 6 on one side tuners, gold hardware, 2 humbucker Seymour Duncan pickups, 2 volume/1 tone controls, 3 position switch. Available in Black finish. Mfd. 1993 to 1995.

	$1,600	$1,400	$1,180	$955	$900	$825	$750

Last Mfr.'s Sug. Retail was $2,200.

PHIL COLLEN — offset double cutaway maple body, thru body maple neck, 24 fret bound ebony fingerboard with pearl sharkfin inlay, double locking vibrato, bound peghead with pearl Jackson logo inlay, 6 on one side Gotoh tuners, black hardware, single coil/ humbucker Jackson pickups, volume control, 3 position switch. Available in Metallic Black and Pearl White finishes. Mfd. 1993 to 1995.

	$1,610	$1,380	$1,150	$920	$830	$760	$690

Last Mfr.'s Sug. Retail was $2,300.

RHOADS 10 STRING — sharkfin style quilted maple body, thru body maple, 22 fret bound ebony fingerboard with pearl sharkfin inlay, double locking vibrato, bound peghead with pearl Jackson inlay, double R truss rod cover, 6 on one side tuners, 4 tuners located on bridge end of instrument, gold hardware, volume control, 3 position switch. Available in Transparent Black finish. Mfd. 1993 to 1995.

	$1,750	$1,500	$1,250	$1,000	$900	$825	$750

Last Mfr.'s Sug. Retail was $2,500.

Co-designed by Dan Spitz.

Professional Series

DINKY STANDARD — offset double cutaway basswood body, transparent pickguard, bolt-on maple neck, 24 fret rosewood fingerboard with colored dot inlay, double locking vibrato, 6 on one side tuners, black hardware, 2 stacked coil/1 humbucker Jackson pickups, volume/tone control, 5 position switch. Available in Black, Candy Blue, Dark Metallic Red and Snow White finishes. Mfd. 1991 to 1993.

	$625	$535	$445	$360	$325	$300	$275

Last Mfr.'s Sug. Retail was $895.

DINKY XL (Trans) — similar to Dinky XL, except has flame maple top. Available in Cherry Sunburst, Transparent Blue, Transparent Red and Transparent Violet finishes. Mfd. 1993 to 1995.

Mfr.'s Sug. Retail	$1,095	$821	$547	$545	$435	$395	$360	$330

"The dealer's mark-up depends on a number of factors such as his overhead, the demand for the particular instrument and how fast he wants to move it."

—Lawrence Acunto
TCG, Nov/Dec 1990

Grading	100%	98% MINT	95% EXC+	90% EXC	80% VG+	70% VG	60% G

DX1 (Formerly DINKY XL) — offset double cutaway basswood body, bolt-on maple neck, 24 fret bound rosewood fingerboard with pearl sharkfin inlay, double locking vibrato, 6 on one side tuners, black hardware, 2 stacked coil/1 humbucker Jackson pickups, volume/tone control, 5 position switch. Available in Deep Metallic Blue, Metallic Black and Pearl White finishes. Mfd. 1992 to date.

Mfr.'s Sug. Retail	$995	$796	$597	$500	$400	$360	$330	$300

DX2 (Formerly DINKY EX) — offset double cutaway basswood body, black pickguard, bolt-on maple neck, 22 fret rosewood fingerboard with pearl dot inlay, double locking vibrato, 6 on one side tuners, black hardware, humbucker/single coil/humbucker Jackson pickups, volume/tone control, 5 position switch. Available in Black, Deep Metallic Blue, Deep Metallic Red and Snow White finishes. Mfd. 1993 to date.

Mfr.'s Sug. Retail	$745	$596	$447	$395	$315	$280	$260	$235

DR5 (Fomerly DINKY REVERSE) — offset double cutaway basswood body, bolt-on maple neck, 24 fret maple fingerboard with offset black dot inlay, reverse headstock, double locking vibrato, 6 on one side tuners, black hardware, 2 humbucker Jackson pickups, volume/tone control, 3 position switch. Available in Black, Candy Blue, Dark Metallic Violet and Stone finishes. Mfd. 1992 to date.

Mfr.'s Sug. Retail	$745	$596	$447	$395	$315	$280	$260	$235

This model also available with rosewood fingerboard with pearl dot inlay.

In 1994, the Stone finish was discontinued.

DR3 (Formerly DINKY REVERSE - Trans) — similar to Dinky Reverse, except has flame maple top. Available in Natural Green Sunburst, Natural Purple Sunburst and Natural Red Sunburst finishes. Mfd. 1994 to date.

Mfr.'s Sug. Retail	$895	$671	$447	$445	$360	$325	$300	$275

FB Series

FB2 — offset asymmetrical hourglass shaped poplar body, bolt-on maple neck, 24 fret rosewood fingerboard with dot inlays, chrome hardware, JT500 locking tremolo, 2 exposed humbuckers, 1 volume knob, 3-way selector switch. Available in Black, Mint Green, and Vinatge White finishes. Mfd. 1996 to date.

Mfr.'s Sug. Retail	$795	$636	$477	$470	$420	$365	$315	$285

FB2 (Trans) — similar to the FB2, except has JT390 tunamatic/stop tailpiece. Mfd. 1996 to date.

Mfr.'s Sug. Retail	$725	$616	$507	$440	$380	$315	$280	$255

FUSION EX — offset double cutaway basswood body, black pickguard, bolt-on maple neck, 24 fret rosewood fingerboard with offset white dot inlay, double locking vibrato, 6 on one side tuners, black hardware, 2 single coil/1 humbucker Jackson pickups, volume/tone control, 5 position switch. Available in Black, Deep Metallic Blue, Dark Metallic Red and Snow White finishes. Mfd. 1992 to 1995.

			$485	$415	$350	$280	$250	$230	$210

Last Mfr.'s Sug. Retail was $695.

FUSION HH — offset double cutaway mahogany body, bolt-on maple neck, 24 fret bound rosewood fingerboard with offset pearl dot inlay, double locking vibrato, 6 on one side tuners, black hardware, 2 humbucker Jackson pickups, 3 position switch. Available in Black and Transparent Red finishes. Mfd. 1992 to 1995.

			$625	$535	$445	$360	$325	$300	$275

Last Mfr.'s Sug. Retail was $895.

In 1992, basswood body with Black finish optionally available.

In 1994, basswood body was discontinued.

FUSION PRO — offset double cutaway basswood body, bolt-on maple neck, 24 fret bound ebony fingerboard with pearl sharkfin inlay, double locking vibrato, bound peghead with pearl Jackson logo inlay, 6 on one side tuners, black hardware, 2 stacked coil/1 humbucker Jackson pickups, volume/tone control, 5 position and bypass switches, active electronics. Available in Bright Red, Candy Blue, Metallic Black and Pearl White finishes. Mfd. 1992 to 1994.

			$905	$775	$645	$515	$465	$425	$385

Last Mfr.'s Sug. Retail was $1,295.

FUSION PRO (Trans) — similar to Fusion Pro, except has flame maple top. Available in Cherry Sunburst, Transparent Amber, Transparent Blue and Transparent Red finishes. Disc. 1994.

			$975	$835	$700	$560	$505	$460	$420

Last Mfr.'s Sug. Retail was $1,395.

FUSION XL — offset double cutaway basswood body, bolt-on maple neck, 24 fret bound ebony fingerboard with pearl sharkfin inlay, double locking vibrato, bound peghead with pearl Jackson logo inlay, 6 on one side tuners, black hardware, 2 stacked coil/1 humbucker Jackson pickups, volume/tone control, 5 position switch. Available in Deep Metallic Blue, Dark Metallic Red, Metallic Black and Snow White finishes. Mfd. 1992 to 1994.

			$695	$595	$500	$400	$360	$330	$300

Last Mfr.'s Sug. Retail was $995.

Fusion XL (Trans) — similar to Fusion XL, except has flame maple top. Available in Cherry Sunburst, Transparent Blue, Transparent Red and Transparent Violet finishes. Mfd. 1992 to 1994.

			$765	$655	$545	$435	$395	$360	$330

Last Mfr.'s Sug. Retail was $1,095.

J

Grading	100%	98% MINT	95% EXC+	90% EXC	80% VG+	70% VG	60% G

FX1 (Formerly FUSION STANDARD) — offset double cutaway basswood body, bolt-on maple neck, 24 fret rosewood fingerboard with pearl offset dot inlay, double locking vibrato, bound peghead with pearl Jackson logo inlay, 6 on one side tuners, black hardware, 2 stacked coil/1 humbucker Jackson pickups, volume/tone control, 5 position switch. Available in Black, Candy Blue, Dark Metallic Red and Snow White finishes. Mfd. 1992 to date.

Mfr.'s Sug. Retail	$895	$716	$537	$495	$385	$290	$260	$235

INFINITY PRO — double cutaway asymmetrical mahogany body, bound figured maple top, set in mahogany neck, 22 fret bound rosewood fingerboard with pearl diamond/abalone dot inlay, double locking vibrato, bound peghead with pearl Jackson logo inlay, 6 on one side tuners, chrome hardware, 2 humbucker Jackson pickups, volume/tone control, 3 position switch. Available in Cherry Sunburst, Star Glo, Transparent Blue, Transparent Red and Transparent Violet finishes. Mfd. 1992 to 1994.

	$1,045	$895	$750	$600	$540	$495	$450

Last Mfr.'s Sug. Retail was $1,495.

INFINITY XL — double cutaway asymmetrical bound basswood body, bolt on maple neck, 22 fret rosewood fingerboard with abalone dot inlay, double locking vibrato, 6 on one side tuners, black hardware, 2 humbucker Jackson pickups, volume/tone control, 3 position switch. Available in Black, Deep Metallic Blue, Dark Metallic Red and Magenta finishes. Mfd. 1992 to 1994.

	$695	$595	$500	$400	$360	$330	$300

Last Mfr.'s Sug. Retail was $995.

JTX STD — single cutaway basswood body, pearloid pickguard, bolt-on maple neck, 24 fret maple fingerboard with black dot inlay, double locking Floyd Rose vibrato, 6 on one side tuners, chrome hardware, single coil/humbucker Jackson pickup, volume control, 3 position/mini switches. Available in Black, Deep Metallic Blue, Deep Metallic Red, Magenta, Transparent Pearl Purple and Snow White finishes. Mfd. 1993 to 1995.

	$465	$390	$300	$240	$215	$195	$180

Last Mfr.'s Sug. Retail was $695.

In 1994, Transparent Pearl Purple and Snow White finishes were introduced, Deep Metallic Blue and Magenta were discontinued.

JTX (Trans) — similar to JTX, except has ash body. Available in Transparent Black, Transparent Blue, Transparent Pearl Purple and Transparent Red finishes. Mfd. 1993 only.

	$450	$385	$320	$260	$235	$215	$195

Last Mfr.'s Sug. Retail was $645.

KV2 (Formerly KING V STD.) — V style poplar body, bolt-on maple neck, 22 fret rosewood fingerboard with pearl dot inlay, double locking Floyd Rose vibrato, 6 on one side tuners, black hardware, 2 humbucker Jackson pickups, volume control, 3 position switch. Available in Black, Brite Red, Candy Blue and Snow White finishes. Mfd. 1993 to date.

Mfr.'s Sug. Retail	$795	$596	$397	$370	$300	$270	$245	$225

KE4 (Formerly KELLY STD) — single sharp cutaway radical hourglass style poplar body, bolt on maple neck, 24 fret rosewood fingerboard with pearl dot inlay, double locking Floyd Rose vibrato, 6 on one side tuners, black hardware, 2 humbucker Jackson pickups, volume control, 3 position switch. Available in Black, Deep Metallic Blue, Deep Metallic Red and Deep Metallic Violet finishes. Mfd. 1993 to date.

Mfr.'s Sug. Retail	$795	$596	$397	$395	$315	$280	$260	$235

KE3 (Formerly KELLY XL) — similar to Kelly STD, except has pearl sharkfin fingerboard inlay. Available in Black, Dark Metallic Blue and Dark Metallic Violet finishes. Mfd. 1994 to current.

Mfr.'s Sug. Retail	$945	$756	$567	$500	$400	$360	$330	$300

OC1 — similar to the Surfcaster Standard, except has solid basswood body, squared off 3+3 headstock, bolt-on maple neck, 1 Chandler LST lipstick tube single coil/1 humbucker, stop tailpiece. Available in Gun Metal Gray, Metallic Violet, and Vintage White finishes. Mfd. 1996 to date.

Mfr.'s Sug. Retail	$725	$616	$507	$440	$380	$325	$290	$250

PHIL COLLEN MODEL — unbalanced double cutaway poplar body, thru body maple neck, 24 fret bound ebony fingerboard with pearl sharkfin inlay, double locking vibrato, bound peghead with pearl Jackson logo inlay, 6 on one side Gotoh tuners, black hardware, single coil/humbucker Jackson pickups, volume control, 3 position switch. Available in Metallic Black, Pearl White and Radiant Red Pearl finishes. Mfd. 1991 only.

	$1,185	$1,015	$845	$675	$605	$555	$505

Last Mfr.'s Sug. Retail was $1,695.

RR4 (Formerly RHOADS EX) — sharkfin style poplar body, thru body maple neck, 22 fret rosewood fingerboard with pearl dot inlay, double locking vibrato, 6 on one side tuners, black hardware, 2 humbucker Jackson pickups, volume control, 3 position switch. Available in Black, Bright Red, Candy Blue, Snow White and Stone finishes. Mfd. 1992 to date.

Mfr.'s Sug. Retail	$795	$596	$397	$350	$280	$250	$230	$210

In 1994, Snow White finish was introduced.

RR3 — similar to RR4, except has a maple gravure top and sharkfin inlay. Available in Black, Deep Metallic Blue, Dark Metallic Red and Snow White finishes. Mfd. 1996 to date.

Mfr.'s Sug. Retail	$895	$716	$537	$470	$400	$360	$330	$300

Grading	100%	98% MINT	95% EXC+	90% EXC	80% VG+	70% VG	60% G

SC1 (Formerly SURF HT) — offset double round cutaway asymmetrical semi-hollow basswood body, bound wedge soundhole, bound body, pearloid pickguard, bolt-on maple neck, 24 fret bound rosewood fingerboard with pearl sharkfin inlay, tunomatic bridge/trapeze tailpiece with stylized C, bound peghead with screened logo, roller nut, 3 per side tuners, chrome hardware, 2 single coil lipstick pickups, volume/tone control, 3 position switch, phase reversal in tone control. Available in Black, Metallic Violet and Turquoise finishes. Mfd. 1992 to date.

Mfr.'s Sug. Retail	$895	$716	$537	$480	$400	$360	$330	$300

In 1994, single coil/humbucker pickups configuration replaced original item.

SURFCASTER STANDARD — offset double rounded cutaway asymmetrical semi-hollow basswood body, offset wedge soundhole, bound body and soundhole, pearloid pickguard, bolt-on maple neck, 24 fret bound rosewood fingerboard with pearl sharkfin inlay, standard vibrato, bound peghead, roller nut, 3 per side tuners, chrome hardware, 2 single coil lipstick pickups, volume/tone control, 3 position switch, phase reversal in tone control. Available in Black, Magenta and Turquoise finishes. Mfd. 1992 to 1994.

		$695	$595	$500	$400	$360	$330	$300

Last Mfr.'s Sug. Retail was $995.

SDK2 — similar to the DX1, except has smaller ("Super Dinky") and lighter poplar or ash body, rosewood or maple fingerboard, and 1 single coil/2 humbucking pickups. Available in Black, Cobalt Blue, Red Pearl Satin, Cobalt Blue Satin, and Graphite finishes. Mfd. 1996 to date.

Mfr.'s Sug. Retail	$725	$616	$507	$445	$380	$330	$275	$235

SOLOIST ARCHTOP — offset double cutaway mahogany body, arched flame maple top, thru body maple neck, 24 fret bound ebony fingerboard with pearl sharkfin inlay, tunomatic bridge with thru body string holders, bound peghead with pearl Jackson logo inlay, 6 on one side Gotoh tuners, black hardware, 2 humbucker Jackson pickups, volume/tone control, 3 position switch. Available in Cherry Sunburst, Transparent Amber, Transparent Blue and Transparent Red finishes. Mfd. 1991 only.

	$1,045	$895	$750	$600	$540	$495	$450

Last Mfr.'s Sug. Retail was $1,495.

Add $200 for double locking vibrato.

SOLOIST STANDARD — offset double cutaway poplar body, bolt-on maple neck, 24 fret rosewood fingerboard with dot inlay, double locking vibrato, 6 on one side tuners, black hardware, 2 stacked coil/1 humbucker Jackson pickups, 1 volume/1 tone control, 5 position switch. Available in Bright Red, Deep Metallic Blue, Metallic Blue and Pearl White finishes. Mfd. 1991 to 1995.

		$695	$595	$500	$400	$360	$330	$300

Last Mfr.'s Sug. Retail was $995.

SS Series

Jackson offered the Short Scale series guitars with a scale length of 24 3/4", instead of the usual 25 1/2" scale normally employed. This shorter scale length was an option on the Fusion series for a number of years.

SS1 — offset shallow double cutaway arched basswood or ash body, bolt-on maple neck, 22 fret rosewood fingerboard with dot inlay, 3+3 headstock, chrome hardware, 2 humbuckers, Wilkinson VS-100 tremolo, 1 volume/1 tone control, 3-way switch. Available in Black, Cobalt Blue, Blue Green Pearl, and Red Pearl Satin finishes. Mfd. 1996 to date.

Mfr.'s Sug. Retail	$795	$636	$477	$410	$370	$280	$200	$165

SS2 — similar to the SS1, except has polar body, no arched top, and tunamatic stop tailpiece. Mfd. 1996 to date.

Mfr.'s Sug. Retail	$695	$521	$347	$320	$270	$180	$150	$110

TH Series

The TH series continues to expand on the original **Stealth** series by offering a thinline version and satin finishes.

TH1 (Formerly STEALTH EX) — offset double cutaway basswood or ash body, bolt on maple neck, 22 fret rosewood fingerboard with offset pearl dot inlay, double locking vibrato, 6 on one side tuners, black hardware, 2 single coil/1 humbucker Jackson pickups, volume/tone control, 5 position switch. Available in Black, Metallic Violet, Graphite, Cobalt Blue Satin, and Red Pearl Satin finishes. Mfd. 1991 to date.

Mfr.'s Sug. Retail	$795	$596	$397	$350	$280	$250	$230	$210

Add $100 for left version of this model.

In 1994, Deep Metallic Blue, Dark Metallic Red and Stone finishes were discontinued.

TH2 — similar to the TH1, except has Jackson Custom Fulcrum non-locking tremolo and pointy profile "straight pull" 3+3 headstock. Mfd. 1996 to date.

Mfr.'s Sug. Retail	$725	$543	$362	$325	$265	$235	$210	$190

STEALTH HX — similar to Stealth EX, except has tunomatic bridge, strings thru body tailpiece, 3 humbucker Jackson pickups. Available in Black, Deep Metallic Blue, Deep Metallic Red and Deep Metallic Violet finishes. Mfd. 1991 to 1995.

		$415	$360	$300	$240	$215	$195	$180

Last Mfr.'s Sug. Retail was $595.

STEALTH PRO — offset double cutaway basswood body, bolt-on maple neck, 22 fret ebony fingerboard with offset pearl dot inlay, double locking vibrato, blackface peghead with pearl logo inlay, 6 on one side tuners, black hardware, 2 single coil/1 humbucker Jackson pickups, volume/tone control, 5 position switch. Available in Metallic Blue finish. Mfd. 1991 to 1993.

	$835	$715	$600	$480	$430	$395	$360

Last Mfr.'s Sug. Retail was $1,195.

"It's gotten to the point where you can't buy a good guitar cheap anymore; everybody knows the value of everything with all the information out now about vintage guitars. Everybody's an expert."

—*Fifth Avenue Fred*
TCG, Nov/Dec 1992

J

Grading	100%	98% MINT	95% EXC+	90% EXC	80% VG+	70% VG	60% G

STEALTH PRO (Trans) — similar to Stealth Pro, except has ash body, body matching peghead without pearl inlay. Available in Transparent Amber finish. Mfd. 1991 to 1993.

	$905	$775	$645	$515	$465	$425	$385

Last Mfr.'s Sug. Retail was $1,295.

This model was available with figured maple top in Transparent Blue and Transparent Violet finishes.

STEALTH XL — similar to Stealth Pro, except has ash body, rosewood fingerboard. Available in Transparent Amber, Transparent Blue, Transparent Red and Transparent Violet finishes. Mfd. 1991 to 1993.

	$625	$535	$445	$360	$325	$300	$275

Last Mfr.'s Sug. Retail was $895.

WARRIOR PRO — radically offset X-shaped poplar body, thru body maple neck, 24 fret bound ebony fingerboard with pearl sharkfin inlay, double locking vibrato, bound peghead with pearl Jackson logo inlay, 6 on one side Gotoh tuners, black hardware, 3 single coil Jackson pickups, volume/tone control, 5 position and midrange sweep switches. Available in Candy Blue, Ferrari Red, Midnight Black, Pearl Yellow and Snow White Pearl finishes. Mfd. 1991 only.

	$1,185	$1,015	$845	$675	$605	$555	$505

Last Mfr.'s Sug. Retail was $1,695.

Jackson Student Series

JS 20 — offset double cutaway alder body, bolt-on maple neck, 22 fret rosewood fingerboard with dot inlay, SG 23 non-locking vibrato, blackface peghead with logo, 6 on one side tuners, chrome hardware, 2 single coil/1 humbucker pickups, volume/tone control, 5 position switch. Available in Black, Metallic Blue, and Metallic Red finishes. Mfd. 1996 to date.

Mfr.'s Sug. Retail	$325	$260	$195	$175	$145	$135	$115	$100

Jackson U.S.A. Series

The standard features on these models are the same as those in the Professional Series, with the addition of custom graphic finishes. Jackson USA models are built in Ontario, California in the same facility as the Jackson Custom Shop. The models in this series are the Dinky, Fusion, Rhoads, Soloist and Warrior, and prices usually are an additional $300-$500 over those listed on the corresponding models in the Professional Series.

AT1 — offset double cutaway mahogany (with quilt maple top) or poplar body, bolt-on maple neck, 22 fret rosewood fingerboard, chrome hardware, Wilkinson VS-100 tremolo, 2 exposed humbuckers, 1 volume/1 tone controls, 3-way selector switch. Available in Black, Deep Candy Red, Blue Green Pearl, Transparent Blue, Transparent Green, Cherry Sunburst, and Transparent Black finishes. Mfd. 1996 to date.

Mfr.'s Sug. Retail	$1,495	$1,270	$1,046	$940	$850	$760	$660	$545

AT1 (Trans) — similar to the AT1, except features a Wilkinson GB-100 stop tailpiece and chrome humbucker covers.

Mfr.'s Sug. Retail	$1,445	$1,156	$867	$865	$750	$670	$580	$500

DK1 (Formerly DINKY USA) — offset double cutaway koa body, bound quilted maple top, bolt-on maple neck, 24 fret bound pao ferro fingerboard with offset pearl dot inlay, double locking vibrato, bound peghead with pearl logo inlay, 6 on one side tuners, gold hardware, 2 stacked coil/1 humbucker Seymour Duncan pickups, volume/tone control, 5 position switch. Available in Tobacco Sunburst, Transparent Blue, Transparent Purple and Transparent Red finishes. Mfd. 1993 to date.

Mfr.'s Sug. Retail	$1,595	$1,276	$957	$940	$860	$770	$675	$600

DR2 — similar to the DR5 (Dinky Reverse), except has a poplar or ash body, JT580 locking tremolo, 2 Duncan humbuckers, and ebony fingerboard. Available in Black, Ultra Violet Burst, Deep Candy Red, Graphite, and Cobalt Blue Satin finishes. Mfd. 1996 to date.

Mfr.'s Sug. Retail	$1,445	$1,228	$1,011	$965	$885	$795	$700	$625

FUSION USA — offset double cutaway basswood body, bolt-on maple neck, 24 fret bound ebony fingerboard with pearl sharkfin inlay, double locking vibrato, bound peghead with pearl Jackson logo inlay, 6 on one side tuners, black hardware, 2 stacked coil/1 humbucker Jackson pickups, volume/tone control, 5 position and bypass switches, active electronics. Available in Bright Red, Candy Blue, Metallic Black and Pearl White finishes. Mfd. 1992 to 1994.

	$1,895	$1,475	$1,150	$945	$825	$695	$585

JJ1 — offset dual cutaway poplar or korina body (bass horn slightly extended), bolt-on maple neck, 22 fret rosewood fingerboard with dice inlay 12th fret markers, 3+3 headstock, chrome hardware, 2 exposed humbuckers, Wilkinson GTB 100 stop tailpiece, 1 volume/1 tone control, 3-way selector. Available in Black, Silver Sparkle, and Natural finishes. Mfd. 1996 to date.

Mfr.'s Sug. Retail	$1,295	$1,036	$777	$765	$670	$575	$490	$400

Designed in conjunction with Scott Ian (Anthrax).

KE1 (Formerly KELLY PRO) — single sharp cutaway radical hourglass style poplar body, thru body maple neck, 24 fret bound ebony fingerboard with pearl sharkfin inlay, double locking Floyd Rose vibrato, 6 on one side tuners, black hardware, 2 humbucker Jackson pickups, volume control, 3 position switch. Available in Black, Black Cherry Metallic and Sparkle Green Metallic finishes. Mfd. 1994 to date.

Mfr.'s Sug. Retail	$1,645	$1,233	$822	$795	$635	$575	$525	$475

Grading	100%	98% MINT	95% EXC+	90% EXC	80% VG+	70% VG	60% G

KV1 (Formerly KING V PRO-MUSTAINE) — V style poplar body, thru body maple neck, 24 fret bound ebony fingerboard with pearl sharkfin inlay, fixed locking Kahler bridge, bound peghead, 6 on one side tuners, black hardware, 2 humbucker pickups, 2 volume/1 tone controls, 3 position switch. Available in Black, Cherry Sunburst and Sparkle Silver Metallic finishes. Mfd. 1993 to date.

Mfr.'s Sug. Retail	$1,795	$1,436	$1,077	$950	$800	$740	$670	$550

In 1994, Cherry Sunburst finish was introduced.

PC1 — offset double cutaway koa body with quilted maple top, maple neck, 24 fret quilted maple fingerboard, Original Floyd Rose locking tremolo, gold hardware, Floyd Rose Sustainer pickup/1 DiMarzio HS-2 single coil/1 DiMarzio Super 3 humbucker, 1 volume/1 tone control, 5-way position switch. Available in Amber Sunburst and Natural finishes. Mfd. 1996 to date.

Mfr.'s Sug. Retail	$2,195	$1,756	$1,317	$1,190	$1,075

Designed and built for Phil Collen (Def Leppard).

RANDY RHOADS LIMITED EDITION — sharkfin style maple body, thru body maple neck, 22 fret bound ebony fingerboard with pearl block inlay, standard vibrato, bound peghead, truss rod cover with overlapping RR stamped into it, 6 on one side tuners, gold hardware, 2 humbucker Jackson pickups, 2 volume/tone controls, 3 position switch located on top side of body. Available in White finish with Black pinstriping around body edge. Mfd. 1992 only.

		$1,745	$1,495	$1,250	$1,000	$900	$825	$750

Last Mfr.'s Sug. Retail was $2,495.

This was a reproduction of the original series that was co-designed by Randy Rhoads and luthier Grover Jackson. Only 200 reproductions were built.

RR1 (Formerly RHOADS PRO) — similar to Rhoads EX except has black pickguard, bound ebony fingerboard with pearl sharkfin inlay, bound peghead with pearl logo inlay volume/tone/mid controls, active electronics. Available in Black, Black Cherry, Deep Metallic Blue and Snow White finishes. Mfd. 1987 to date.

Mfr.'s Sug. Retail	$1,795	$1,436	$1,077	$950	$800	$740	$690	$550

In 1994, Snow White finish was discontinued.

RR2 (Formerly RHOADS STD) — similar to RR1, except has maple gravure top, bolt-on neck, and dot fingerboard inlay. Available in Black, Deep Metallic Blue, Dark Metallic Red and Snow White finishes. Mfd. 1993 to date.

Mfr.'s Sug. Retail	$1,295	$1,036	$777	$700	$600	$560	$430	$350

RHOADS USA — similar to RR1 except has black pickguard, bound ebony fingerboard with pearl sharkfin inlay, bound peghead with pearl logo inlay volume/tone/mid controls, active electronics. Available in Black, Black Cherry, Deep Metallic Blue and Snow White finishes. Mfd. 1987 to 1995.

Mfr.'s Sug. Retail	$2,295	$1,721	$1,147	$875	$600	$540	$495	$450

SDK1 — similar to the DK1, except has smaller ("Super Dinky") and lighter poplar or ash body, rosewood or maple fingerboard, and 1 single coil/2 humbucking pickups. Available in Black, Cobalt Blue, Orange/Gold Pearl, Gun Metal Grey, Deep Candy Red, and Graphite finishes. Mfd. 1996 to date.

Mfr.'s Sug. Retail	$1,295	$1,036	$777	$760	$680	$590	$500	$465

SOLOIST USA — offset double cutaway poplar body, thru body maple neck, 24 fret bound ebony fingerboard with pearl sharkfin inlay, double locking vibrato, bound peghead with pearl Jackson logo inlay, 6 on one side tuners, black hardware, 2 stacked coil/1 humbucker Jackson pickups, volume/tone/mid boost controls, 5 position switch, active electronics. Available in Bright Red, Deep Metallic Blue, Metallic Blue and Pearl White finishes. Mfd. 1991 to 1995.

Mfr.'s Sug. Retail	$2,295	$1,721	$1,147	$850	$700	$540	$495	$450

SL1 (Formerly SOLOIST PRO) — offset double cutaway poplar body, thru body maple neck, 24 fret bound ebony fingerboard with pearl sharkfin inlay, double locking vibrato, bound peghead with pearl Jackson logo inlay, 6 on one side tuners, black hardware, 2 stacked coil/1 humbucker Jackson pickups, volume/tone/mid boost controls, 5 position switch, active electronics. Available in Bright Red, Deep Metallic Blue, Metallic Blue and Pearl White finishes. Mfd. 1991 to date.

Mfr.'s Sug. Retail	$1,795	$1,346	$897	$850	$700	$640	$595	$450

SL2 (Formerly SOLOIST XL) — similar to SL1, except has rosewood fingerboard, 2 exposed humbuckers, and no active electronics. Available in Deep Metallic Blue, Dark Metallic Red, Metallic Black and Pearl White finishes. Mfd. 1996 to date.

Mfr.'s Sug. Retail	$1,395	$1,116	$837	$740	$625	$565	$425	$385

Add $100 for neck inlay.

WARRIOR USA — radically offset X-shaped poplar body, thru body maple neck, 24 fret bound ebony fingerboard with pearl sharkfin inlay, double locking vibrato, bound peghead with pearl Jackson logo inlay, 6 on one side Gotoh tuners, black hardware, 3 single coil Jackson pickups, volume/tone control, 5 position and midrange sweep switches. Available in Candy Blue, Ferrari Red, Midnight Black, Pearl Yellow and Snow White Pearl finishes. Available as a custom order only.

		$1,995	$1,385	$1,060	$875	$605	$555	$505

Call the Custom Shop for availability.

Jackson Custom Shop Instruments

The Jackson Custom Shop offers a wide range of woods, custom or airbrushed finishes, and innovative body designs. A current example would be the **Roswell Rhoads**, an advanced sharkfin design machined out of 6061-TS aircraft grade aluminum that features LSR tuners, "crop circle" neck inlays, and a Tom Holmes humbucking pickup. The Jackson

Grading		100%	98% MINT	95% EXC+	90% EXC	80% VG+	70% VG	60% G

Custom Shop also features pyrography, a woodburning technique by artist Dino Muradian that offers a high degree of drawing and shading on the guitar's wood body.

ELECTRIC BASS

Professional Series

CONCERT EX — offset double cutaway poplar body, bolt-on maple neck, 22 fret rosewood fingerboard with white dot inlay, fixed bridge, 4 on one side tuners, black hardware, Jackson P-style/J-style pickups, volume/tone/mix control. Available in Black, Bright Red, Candy Blue, Snow White and Stone finishes. Mfd. 1992 to 1995.

	$415	$360	$300	$240	$215	$195	$180

Last Mfr.'s Sug. Retail was $595.

In 1994, Bright Red and Snow White finishes were discontinued.

CONCERT XL — similar to Concert EX, except has bound fingerboard with pearl sharkfin inlay. Available in Black Cherry, Deep Metallic Blue, Dark Metallic Red, Metallic Black and Pearl White finishes. Mfd. 1992 to 1995.

	$625	$535	$445	$360	$325	$300	$275

Last Mfr.'s Sug. Retail was $895.

In 1994, Pearl White finish was discontinued.

CONCERT V — similar to Concert EX, except has 5 strings, bound fingerboard with sharkfin inlay, Kramer fixed bridge, volume/treble/bass/mix controls, active electronics. Available in Black Cherry, Dark Metallic Blue and Metallic Black finishes. Mfd. 1992 to 1995.

	$695	$595	$500	$400	$360	$330	$300

Last Mfr.'s Sug. Retail was $995.

EL1 — sleek offset double cutaway basswood body, maple neck, 21 fret rosewood fingerboard, black hardware, fixed bridge, P/J Jackson pickups, 1 volume/1 blend/1 tone controls. Available in Black, cobalt Blue, and Red Pearl finishes. Mfd. 1996 to date.

Mfr.'s Sug. Retail	$795	$675	$556	$480	$425	$370	$330	$290

FUTURA EX (formerly the WINGER BASS) — double cutaway asymmetrical offset poplar body, bolt on maple neck, 22 fret rosewood fingerboard with pearl dot inlay, fixed bridge, 4 on one side tuners, black hardware, P-style/J-style Jackson pickups, volume/tone/mix control. Available in Black, Deep Metallic Blue, Magenta and Snow White finishes. Mfd. 1992 to 1995.

	$555	$475	$395	$315	$280	$260	$235

Last Mfr.'s Sug. Retail was $795.

Add $100 for left handed version.
The Winger Bass was co-designed by Kip Winger.

FUTURA PRO (formerly the WINGER BASS) — double cutaway asymmetrical offset maple body, thru body maple neck, 21 fret ebony fingerboard with pearl dot inlay, Kahler fixed bridge, 4 on one side tuners, black hardware, 2 EMG pickups, volume/treble/bass/mix control, active electronics. Available in Candy Red, Metallic Black and Pearl White finishes. Mfd. 1992 to 1993.

	$1,255	$1,075	$895	$715	$645	$590	$540

Last Mfr.'s Sug. Retail was $1,795.

FUTURA PRO (Trans) — similar to Futura Pro, except has lacewood body/neck and has body color matching bound peghead. Available in Carmel Lace, Cinnabar and Natural finishes. Disc. 1993.

	$1,325	$1,135	$950	$760	$685	$625	$570

Last Mfr.'s Sug. Retail was $1,895.

FUTURA XL — similar to Futura Pro, except has Jackson fixed bridge and P-style/J-style pickups. Available in Dark Metallic Red, Metallic Black and Pearl White finishes. Disc. 1993.

	$905	$775	$645	$515	$465	$425	$385

Last Mfr.'s Sug. Retail was $1,295.

FUTURA XL (Trans) — similar to Futura Pro (Trans), except has Jackson fixed bridge and P-style/J-style pickups. Disc. 1993.

	$975	$835	$700	$560	$505	$460	$420

Last Mfr.'s Sug. Retail was $1,395.

TBX — single cutaway asymmetrical hourglass poplar body, thru body maple neck, 21 fret bound rosewood fingerboard with pearl sharkfin inlay, fixed bridge, bound blackface peghead with screened logo, 4 on one side tuners, black hardware, 2 humbucker EMG pickups, 2 volume/tone controls. Available in Black, Dark Metallic Violet and Scarlet Green Metallic finishes. Mfd. 1994 to 1995.

	$1,185	$1,015	$845	$675	$605	$555	$505

Last Mfr.'s Sug. Retail was $1,695.

KB1 (Formerly KELLY BASS) — similar in body design to the KE1, except has poplar body, 22 fret rosewood fingerboard with dot inlay, black hardware, fixed bridge, Jackson P/J pickups, 1 volume/1 blend/1 tone controls. Available in Black and Cobalt Blue. Mfd. 1994 to date.

Mfr.'s Sug. Retail	$795	$596	$397	$300	$240	$215	$195	$180

JAMBOREE

Instruments produced in Japan.

The Jamboree trademark was a brandname used by U.S. importers Elger/Hoshino of Ardmore, Pennsylvania. Jamboree, along with others like Goldentone, King's Stone, and Elger were all used on Japanese guitars imported to the U.S. Elger/Hoshino evolved into Hoshino USA, distributor of Ibanez guitars.

(Source: Michael Wright, Guitar Stories Volume One, pg 76)

JAROCK

Instruments built in Japan during the early 1980s.

These guitars are medium quality Stratocaster-styled solid body guitars.

(Source: Tony Bacon and Paul Day, The Guru's Guitar Guide)

JAROS CUSTOM GUITARS

Instruments built in Rochester, Pennsylvania since 1992. Distribution is handled directly at Jaros Custom Guitars, or through Amanda's Texas Underground of Annapolis, Maryland; and Guitar Gallery of Pittsburgh, Pennsylvania.

Combining years of cabinetmaking and guitar playing, Harry Jaros and his son James decided to build a couple of guitars as a father-and-son project. The original models turned out to be beautifully crafted guitars that had great tone and playability. What started out as a family hobby became a business venture as they decided to produce more of these handcrafted instruments and make them available "for everyone to enjoy". For further information, contact Jaros Custom Guitars through the Index of Current Manufacturers located in the back of this book.

Jaros handcrafted guitars feature a slightly offset double cutaway mahogany body, bookmatched AAA figured maple top and back, eastern hard rock neck-through construction, 25" scale, rosewood fretboard with 12" neck radius, gold Schaller hardware, two Seymour Duncan humbucking pickups, volume/tone controls (coil tap wiring with push/pull pots), and a 3-way selector switch. Jaros finishes his guitars in nitrocellulose clear coat finish.

JASMINE

This trademark is a division of Takamine. Guitars are produced in Japan and distributed by the Kaman Music Corporation of Bloomfield, Connecticut.

Jasmine guitars can be viewed as an "entry-level" step into the Takamine product line. Jasmine guitars may not be as ornate, and may feature different construction methods than Takamine.

ACOUSTIC

Grading		100%	98% MINT	95% EXC+	90% EXC	80% VG+	70% VG	60% G

23-C — classic style, spruce top, round soundhole, bound body, wood inlay rosette, mahogany back/sides, nato neck, 12/19 fret rosewood fingerboard, rosewood tied bridge, 3 per side chrome tuners with pearloid buttons. Available in Natural finish. New 1994.

Mfr.'s Sug. Retail	$270	$216	$162	$135	$110	$100	$90	$80

26-C — classic style, spruce top, round soundhole, 3 stripe bound body, wood inlay rosette, mahogany back/sides, nato neck, 12/19 fret rosewood fingerboard/bridge, 3 per side gold tuners with pearloid buttons. Available in Natural finish. Disc. 1994.

			$195	$165	$140	$110	$100	$90	$80

Last Mfr.'s Sug. Retail was $280.

27-C — classic style, cedar top, round soundhole, bound body, wood inlay rosette, mahogany back/sides, nato neck, 12/19 fret rosewood fingerboard, rosewood tied bridge, 3 per side chrome tuners with pearloid buttons. Available in Natural finish. New 1994.

Mfr.'s Sug. Retail	$200	$160	$120	$100	$80	$70	$65	$60

28-C — classic style, spruce top, round soundhole, 3 stripe bound body, wood inlay rosette, rosewood back/sides, nato neck, 12/19 fret rosewood fingerboard, tied rosewood bridge, 3 per side gold tuners with pearloid buttons. Available in Natural finish. Disc. 1992.

			$245	$210	$175	$140	$125	$115	$105

Last Mfr.'s Sug. Retail was $350.

28C-TC — similar to 28-C, except has single round cutaway, piezo bridge pickup, 4 band EQ. Curr. mfr.

Mfr.'s Sug. Retail	$550	$440	$330	$275	$220	$200	$180	$165

28-RQ — requinto style, spruce top, round soundhole, bound body, wood inlay rosette, rosewood back/sides, nato neck, 12/19 fret extended rosewood fingerboard, tied rosewood bridge with marquetry inlay, 3 per side gold tuners with pearloid buttons. Available in Natural finish. New 1994.

Mfr.'s Sug. Retail	$370	$296	$222	$185	$150	$135	$120	$110

31-S — dreadnought style, spruce top, round soundhole, black pickguard, 3 stripe bound body/rosette, nato back/sides/neck, 14/20 fret rosewood fingerboard with pearl dot inlay, rosewood bridge with white pins, 3 per side chrome tuners. Available in Black finish. New 1994.

Mfr.'s Sug. Retail	$290	$232	$174	$145	$115	$105	$95	$85

J

Grading	100%	98% MINT	95% EXC+	90% EXC	80% VG+	70% VG	60% G

31C-ES — similar to 31-S, except has single round cutaway, piezo bridge pickup, 2 band EQ. Available in Black finish. New 1994.

Mfr.'s Sug. Retail	$400	$320	$240	$200	$160	$145	$130	$120

33-S — dreadnought style, spruce top, round soundhole, black pickguard, stripe bound body/rosette, mahogany back/sides, nato neck, 14/20 fret rosewood fingerboard with pearl dot inlay, rosewood bridge with white black dot pins, 3 per side chrome diecast tuners. Available in Natural finish. Curr. mfr.

Mfr.'s Sug. Retail	$280	$210	$140	$130	$100	$90	$80	$75

33C-ES — similar to 33-S, except has single round cutaway, piezo bridge pickup, 3 band EQ control. Available in Natural finish. Curr. Mfr.

Mfr.'s Sug. Retail	$390	$312	$234	$195	$155	$140	$125	$115

33C-ES-TOB — similar to 33-S, except has single round cutaway, 6 crystal bridge pickups, 2 band EQ control. Available in Transparent Orangeburst finish. Curr. Mfr.

Mfr.'s Sug. Retail	$430	$344	$258	$215	$175	$155	$140	$130

36S-C — classic style, solid spruce top, round soundhole, 3 stripe bound body, wood inlay rosette, rosewood back/sides, nato neck, 12/19 fret rosewood fingerboard, tied rosewood bridge with marquetry inlay, 3 per side gold tuners with pearloid buttons. Available in Natural finish. New 1994.

Mfr.'s Sug. Retail	$450	$360	$270	$225	$180	$160	$150	$135

37-S — dreadnought style, spruce top, round soundhole, black pickguard, bound body, 3 stripe rosette, nato back/sides/neck, 14/20 fret rosewood fingerboard with pearl dot inlay, rosewood bridge with white pins, 3 per side diecast tuners. Available in Natural finish. New 1994.

Mfr.'s Sug. Retail	$250	$200	$150	$125	$100	$90	$80	$75

312-S — 12 string dreadnought style, spruce top, round soundhole, black pickguard, 5 stripe bound body/rosette, mahogany back/sides, nato neck, 14/20 fret rosewood fingerboard with pearl dot inlay, rosewood bridge with white black dot pins, 6 per side chrome tuners. Available in Natural finish. Curr. mfr.

Mfr.'s Sug. Retail	$330	$264	$198	$165	$130	$120	$110	$100

312-ES — similar to 312-S, except has piezo bridge pickup, 2 band EQ. New 1994.

Mfr.'s Sug. Retail	$400	$320	$240	$200	$160	$145	$130	$120

40-S — dreadnought style, round soundhole, black pickguard, 3 stripe bound body/rosette, nato neck, 14/20 fret bound rosewood fingerboard with pearl dot inlay, rosewood bridge with white black dot pins, bound peghead, 3 per side chrome diecast tuners. Available in Natural finish. Disc. 1992.

			$245	$210	$175	$140	$125	$115	$105

Last Mfr.'s Sug. Retail was $350.

40C-ES — similar to 40-S, except has single round cutaway, piezo bridge pickup, 2 band EQ control. Disc. 1994.

			$275	$235	$195	$155	$140	$125	$115

Last Mfr.'s Sug. Retail was $390.

41-S — dreadnought style, spruce top, round soundhole, black pickguard with white outline, 3 stripe bound body/rosette, daowood back/sides, nato neck, 14/20 fret bound rosewood fingerboard with pearl dot inlay, rosewood bridge with white black dot pins, 3 per side chrome diecast tuners. Available in Black finish. Disc. 1994.

			$250	$215	$180	$145	$130	$120	$110

Last Mfr.'s Sug. Retail was $360.

41C-TS — similar to 41-S, except has single round cutaway, crystal bridge pickups, 4 band EQ control. Disc 1994.

			$315	$270	$225	$180	$160	$150	$135

Last Mfr.'s Sug. Retail was $450.

46-S — dreadnought style, spruce top, round soundhole, black pickguard with white outline, 3 stripe bound body/rosette, daowood back/sides, nato neck, 14/20 fret bound rosewood fingerboard with pearl dot inlay, rosewood bridge with white black dot pins, 3 per side chrome diecast tuners. Available in White finish. Disc. 1992.

			$250	$215	$180	$145	$130	$120	$110

Last Mfr.'s Sug. Retail was $360.

46C-TS — similar to 46-S, except has single round cutaway, crystal bridge pickup, 4 band EQ control. Disc. 1992.

			$315	$270	$225	$180	$160	$150	$135

Last Mfr.'s Sug. Retail was $450.

48M-C — single round cutaway classic style, figured maple top, round soundhole, 3 stripe bound body, wood inlay rosette, figured maple back/sides, nato neck, 12/19 fret rosewood fingerboard, tied rosewood bridge, figured maple veneered peghead, 3 per side gold tuners with pearloid buttons. Available in Natural finish. New 1994.

Mfr.'s Sug. Retail	$430	$344	$258	$215	$175	$155	$140	$130

48MC-TC — similar to 48M-C, except has piezo bridge pickup, 4 band EQ.

Mfr.'s Sug. Retail	$590	$472	$354	$295	$235	$210	$195	$180

49-S — dreadnought style, mahogany top, round soundhole, black pickguard, 3 stripe bound body/rosette, mahogany back/sides, nato neck, 14/20 fret bound rosewood fingerboard with pearl dot inlay, rosewood bridge with white black dot pins, bound peghead, 3 per side chrome diecast tuners. Available in Natural finish. Disc. 1992.

			$250	$215	$180	$145	$130	$120	$110

Last Mfr.'s Sug. Retail was $360.

Grading	100%	98% MINT	95% EXC+	90% EXC	80% VG+	70% VG	60% G

49C-TS — similar to 49-S, except has single round cutaway, crystal bridge pickup, 4 band EQ control. Disc. 1992.

| | | $315 | $270 | $225 | $180 | $160 | $150 | $135 |

Last Mfr.'s Sug. Retail was $450.

50C-TS — rounded cutaway dreadnought style, spruce top, round soundhole, black pickguard, 3 stripe bound body/rosette, flame maple back/sides, maple neck, 20 fret bound rosewood fingerboard with pearl dot inlay, rosewood bridge with white black dot pins, body matching peghead, 3 per side chrome diecast tuners, crystal bridge pickups, 4 band volume/EQ control. Available in Blue Stain, Ebony Stain and Red Stain finishes. Disc. 1994.

| | | $420 | $360 | $300 | $240 | $215 | $195 | $180 |

Last Mfr.'s Sug. Retail was $600.

52C-TS — single round cutaway dreadnought style, ash top, round soundhole, black trilam pickguard, ash back/sides, nato neck, 20 fret bound rosewood fingerboard with pearl dot inlay, rosewood bridge with white black dot pins, body matching bound peghead with screened logo, 3 per side chrome die cast tuners, piezo bridge pickup, 4 band EQ. Available in Ebony and Red Stain finishes. New 1994.

| Mfr.'s Sug. Retail | $620 | $496 | $372 | $310 | $250 | $225 | $205 | $190 |

58-TS — jumbo style, cedar top, round soundhole, tortoise pickguard, 3 stripe bound body, wood inlay rosette, daowood back/sides, nato neck, 14/20 fret bound rosewood fingerboard with pearl diamond dot inlay, rosewood bridge with white black dot pins, bound peghead, 3 per side gold diecast tuners, piezo bridge pickup, 4 band EQ control. Available in Natural finish. Curr. mfr.

| Mfr.'s Sug. Retail | $650 | $520 | $390 | $325 | $260 | $235 | $215 | $195 |

60-S — dreadnought style, spruce top, round soundhole, black pickguard, 3 stripe bound body/rosette, rosewood back/sides, nato neck, 14/20 fret fingerboard with pearl dot inlay, rosewood bridge with white black dot pins, 3 per side chrome diecast tuners. Available in Natural finish. Disc. 1992.

| | | $275 | $235 | $195 | $155 | $140 | $125 | $115 |

Last Mfr.'s Sug. Retail was $390.

60-TS — similar to 60-S, except has piezo bridge pickup, 4 band EQ. Disc. 1994.

| | | $350 | $300 | $250 | $200 | $180 | $165 | $150 |

Last Mfr.'s Sug. Retail was $500.

60C-TS — similar to 60-S, except has single round cutaway, piezo bridge pickup, 4 band EQ. Disc. 1994.

| | | $385 | $330 | $275 | $220 | $200 | $180 | $165 |

Last Mfr.'s Sug. Retail was $550.

612-TS — dreadnought style, spruce top, round soundhole, black pickguard, 3 stripe bound body/rosette, rosewood back/sides, nato neck, 14/20 fret bound rosewood fingerboard with pearl dot inlay, rosewood bridge with white black dot pins, 6 per side chrome diecast tuners, piezo bridge pickup, 4 band EQ. Available in Natural finish. Disc. 1994.

| | | $390 | $335 | $280 | $225 | $205 | $190 | $170 |

Last Mfr.'s Sug. Retail was $560.

612C-TS — similar to 612-TS, except has single round cutaway. New 1994.

| Mfr.'s Sug. Retail | $640 | $512 | $384 | $320 | $255 | $230 | $210 | $195 |

70-S — dreadnought style, spruce top, round soundhole, black pickguard, 3 stripe bound body/rosette, Hawaiian koa back/sides, nato neck, 14/20 fret rosewood fingerboard with pearl dot inlay, rosewood bridge with white black dot pins, 3 per side chrome diecast tuners. Available in Natural finish. Disc. 1994.

| | | $280 | $240 | $200 | $160 | $145 | $130 | $120 |

Last Mfr.'s Sug. Retail was $400.

74C-TS — single round cutaway dreadnought style, cedar top, round soundhole, tortoise pickguard, 5 stripe bound body, wood inlay rosette, daowood back/sides, nato neck, 20 fret bound rosewood fingerboard with pearl diamond inlay, rosewood bridge with white black dot pins, bound blackface peghead with screened logo, 3 per side gold diecast tuners, piezo bridge pickup, 4 band EQ. Available in Natural finish. New 1994.

| Mfr.'s Sug. Retail | $630 | $504 | $378 | $315 | $250 | $225 | $205 | $190 |

80S-S — dreadnought style, solid spruce top, round soundhole, black pickguard, 3 stripe bound body/rosette, jacaranda back/sides, nato neck, 14/20 fret bound rosewood fingerboard with pearl dot inlay, rosewood bridge with white black dot pins, bound peghead, 3 per side gold diecast tuners. Available in Natural finish. Curr. mfr.

| Mfr.'s Sug. Retail | $560 | $420 | $280 | $270 | $215 | $195 | $180 | $165 |

ACOUSTIC ELECTRIC

All models in this series have the following features: single round cutaway folk style, round soundhole, 3 stripe bound body/rosette, 21 fret bound rosewood fingerboard with pearl dot inlay, rosewood bridge with white black dot pins, body matching bound peghead, 3 per side chrome die cast tuners, crystal bridge pickups, 3 band EQ, unless otherwise listed. Curr. mfr.

26C-TS — mahogany top/back/sides, abalone body purfling, nato neck, pearl diamond fingerboard inlay, black white dot bridge pins, gold diecast tuners. Available in White/Black finish. New 1994.

| Mfr.'s Sug. Retail | $650 | $520 | $390 | $325 | $260 | $235 | $215 | $195 |

29C-TC — single round cutaway classic style, cedar top, round soundhole, 3 stripe bound body, wood inlay rosette, rosewood back/sides, nato neck, 19 fret rosewood fingerboard, tied rosewood bridge with wood marquetry inlay, 3 per side gold tuners with pearloid tuners, piezo bridge pickup, 3 band EQ. Available in Natural finish. New 1994.

| Mfr.'s Sug. Retail | $570 | $456 | $342 | $285 | $230 | $205 | $190 | $170 |

"Well, it doesn't hurt! But the real key is delivering when the tape goes on. Things really took off after 'Addicted to Love' came out...After that, the work kept coming."

—Lawrence Acunto on
Eddie Martinez
TCG, Nov/Dec 1992

J

Grading	100%	98% MINT	95% EXC+	90% EXC	80% VG+	70% VG	60% G

90C-TS — burled mahogany top/back/sides, nato neck. Available in Light Walnut Stain and Dark Walnut Stain finishes. New 1994.

Mfr.'s Sug. Retail	$650	$520	$390	$325	$260	$235	$215	$195

91C-TS — daowood top/back/sides, nato neck. Available in Black finish.

Mfr.'s Sug. Retail	$570	$427	$285	$240	$190	$170	$155	$145

92C-TS — flame maple top/back/sides, maple neck. Available in Red Stain finish. Disc. 1994.

		$365	$310	$260	$210	$190	$170	$160

Last Mfr.'s Sug. Retail was $520.

93C-TS — silky oak top/back/sides, maple neck. Available in Amber finish. New 1994.

Mfr.'s Sug. Retail	$600	$480	$360	$300	$240	$215	$195	$180

95C-TS — flame maple top/back/sides, maple neck. Available in Ebony Stain finish. Disc. 1994.

		$365	$310	$260	$210	$190	$170	$160

Last Mfr.'s Sug. Retail was $520.

96C-TS — daowood top/back/sides, nato neck, black white dot bridge pins. Available in White finish. Disc. 1994.

		$335	$290	$240	$190	$170	$155	$145

Last Mfr.'s Sug. Retail was $480.

97C-TS — cedar top, daowood back/sides, nato neck, pearl diamond fingerboard inlay, gold diecast tuners. Available in Natural finish.

Mfr.'s Sug. Retail	$600	$480	$360	$300	$240	$215	$195	$180

98C-TS — flame maple top/back/sides, maple neck. Available in Blue Stain finish.

Mfr.'s Sug. Retail	$600	$450	$300	$260	$210	$190	$170	$160

99C-TS — daowood top/back/sides, nato neck. Available in Walnut Sunburst finish. Disc. 1994.

		$335	$290	$240	$190	$170	$155	$145

Last Mfr.'s Sug. Retail was $480.

JAX

Instruments produced in Taiwan during the early 1980s.

These solid body guitars consist of entry level designs based on classic American models.

(Source: Tony Bacon and Paul Day, The Guru's Guitar Guide)

JAY DEE

Instruments built in Birmingham, England from 1977 to date.

The Jay Dee trademark sometimes appears as J D on the headstock of these high quality original design guitars. Luthier John Diggins has been quite successful in building a quality instrument through the years, and has produced some models based on classic American designs as well.

Jay Dee 'Supernatural' basses was distributed in the U.S. for a length of time by Aspen & Associates starting in 1985. Aspen & Associates are the non-tube side of Aspen Pittman's Groove Tubes company.

(Source: Tony Bacon and Paul Day, The Guru's Guitar Guide)

JAY G

See chapter on House Brands.

This trademark has been identified as a "sub-brand" from the budget line of CHRIS guitars by the Jackson-Guldan company of Columbus, Ohio.

(Source: Willie G. Moseley, Stellas & Stratocasters)

J.B. PLAYER

Instruments are produced in Asia, although certain classical guitar models are built in Spain. J. B. Player is a division of MBT International of Charleston, South Carolina.

MBT International is parent company to a number of solid business endeavors such as Musicorp, Engl, USA, MBT Lighting and Sound, and recently acquired Hondo Guitar Company. President and CEO Eddie Toporek was elected president of the Music Distributors Association last January 1996.

J.B. Player offers a wide range of entry to student level instruments in acoustic or electric solid body guitars and basses. Many higher quality models that are currently offered may appeal to working musicians, and feature such such parts as Schaller hardware, Wilkinson bridges, and APC pickups. The

Grading			100%	98% MINT	95% EXC+	90% EXC	80% VG+	70% VG	60% G

1996 catalog illustrates the four different levels offered: the JBP Artist, Standard, Professional, and Sledgehammer series.

ACOUSTIC

JB-300E — single round cutaway dreadnought style, spruce top, black pickguard, round soundhole, 3 stripe bound body/rosette, nato back/sides, mahogany neck, 20 fret bound rosewood fingerboard with pearl dot inlay, rosewood bridge with white black dot pins, bound blackface peghead with screened logo, 3 per side chrome tuners, acoustic pickup, volume/tone control. Available in Brownburst, Cherryburst, Natural and White finishes. New 1994.

Mfr.'s Sug. Retail	$410	$328	$246	$205	$165	$145	$135	$125

JB-402 — dreadnought style, spruce top, round soundhole, black pickguard, bound body, 5 stripe rosette, nato back/sides/neck, 14/20 fret bound rosewood fingerboard with pearl dot inlay, rosewood bridge with white black dot pins, 3 per side chrome diecast tuners. Available in Natural finish. Curr. mfr.

Mfr.'s Sug. Retail	$225	$180	$135	$115	$90	$80	$70	$65

JB-403 — similar to JB-402, except has different binding color. Disc. 1994.

	$175	$150	$125	$100	$90	$80	$75

Last Mfr.'s Sug. Retail was $250.

JB-405-12 — dreadnought style 12 string, spruce top, round soundhole, black pickguard, stripe bound body/rosette, ash back/sides, bound mahogany neck, 14/20 fret bound rosewood fingerboard with pearl dot inlay, rosewood bridge with white black dot pins, 6 per side chrome diecast tuners. Available in Natural finish. Curr. mfr.

Mfr.'s Sug. Retail	$255	$204	$153	$130	$100	$90	$80	$75

JB-407 — dreadnought style, ash top, round soundhole, black pickguard, bound body, 5 stripe rosette, ash back/sides, mahogany neck, 14/20 fret bound fingerboard with pearl dot inlay, rosewood bridge with white black dot pins, 3 per side chrome diecast tuners. Available in Tobacco Sunburst finish. Curr. mfr.

Mfr.'s Sug. Retail	$290	$232	$174	$145	$115	$105	$95	$85

Add $55 for acoustic pickup, active volume/3 band EQ (JB-407E).

JB-450 — dreadnought style, spruce top, round soundhole, black pickguard, imitation abalone bound body/rosette, ash back/sides, mahogany neck, 14/20 fret bound rosewood fingerboard with hexagon imitation abalone inlay, rosewood bridge with white black dot pins, 3 per side chrome diecast tuners. Available in Natural finish. Curr. mfr.

Mfr.'s Sug. Retail	$295	$221	$147	$145	$115	$105	$95	$85

JB-505 — classical style, spruce top, round soundhole, herringbone bound body, wooden inlay rosette, ash back/sides, mahogany neck, 12/18 fret rosewood fingerboard, rosewood bridge, 3 per side chrome tuners with nylon buttons. Available in Natural finish. Disc. 1994.

	$180	$155	$130	$100	$90	$80	$75

Last Mfr.'s Sug. Retail was $260.

Artist Series

JB-1000 — dreadnought style, spruce top, oval soundhole, black pickguard, 3 stripe bound body/rosette, mahogany back/sides/neck, 14/20 fret bound rosewood fingerboard with pearl dot inlay, rosewood bridge with white black dot pins, 3 per side chrome tuners. Available in Black and White finishes. Curr. mfr.

Mfr.'s Sug. Retail	$325	$243	$162	$160	$130	$115	$105	$95

Add $70 for flame maple top and jacaranda back/sides. Available in Natural finish.

The White finish model has black chrome tuners.

JB-5000 — classical style, spruce top, round soundhole, bound body, wooden inlay rosette, mahogany back/sides/neck, 12/18 fret rosewood fingerboard, rosewood bridge, 3 per side gold tuners with pearloid buttons. Available in Natural finish. Disc. 1994.

	$245	$210	$175	$140	$125	$115	$105

Last Mfr.'s Sug. Retail was $350.

JB-8000 — dreadnought style, spruce top, round soundhole, black pickguard, bound body, 5 stripe rosette, rosewood back/sides, mahogany neck, 14/20 fret rosewood fingerboard with pearl dot inlay, rosewood bridge with white black dot pins, 3 per side chrome tuners. Available in Natural finish. Disc. 1994.

	$295	$250	$210	$170	$150	$135	$125

Last Mfr.'s Sug. Retail was $425.

JB-9000 — dreadnought style, spruce top, round soundhole, black pickguard, bound body, 5 stripe rosette, mahogany back/sides/neck, 14/20 fret rosewood fingerboard with pearl dot inlay, rosewood bridge with white black dot pins, 3 per side chrome tuners. Available in Tobacco Sunburst finish. Curr. mfr.

Mfr.'s Sug. Retail	$395	$296	$197	$195	$155	$140	$125	$115

JB-9000-12 — similar to JB-9000, except has 12 strings, black white dot pins, 6 per side tuners. Available in Natural finish.

Mfr.'s Sug. Retail	$410	$328	$246	$205	$165	$145	$135	$125

JBA-2000 — dreadnought style, solid spruce top, tortoise pickguard, round soundhole, 4 stripe bound body, abalone rosette, rosewood back/sides, mahogany neck, 14/20 fret bound rosewood fingerboard with abalone block inlay, rosewood bridge with white black dot pins, 3 per side gold tuners. Available in Natural finish. New 1994.

Mfr.'s Sug. Retail	$540	$432	$324	$270	$215	$195	$180	$165

Grading	100%	98% MINT	95% EXC+	90% EXC	80% VG+	70% VG	60% G

J.B.Player PG Series
courtesy Larry Kellnen

J

KJ-330PU — single round cutaway folk style, figured maple top, oval soundhole, abalone bound body/rosette, maple back/sides, mahogany neck, 20 fret bound rosewood fingerboard with pearl split block inlay, rosewood bridge with white black dot pins, 3 per side gold tuners with amber buttons, acoustic pickup, 4 band EQ, active electronics. Available in Brownburst and Natural finishes. New 1994.

Mfr.'s Sug. Retail	$640	$512	$384	$320	$255	$230	$210	$195

KJ-609WPU — single round cutaway folk style, spruce top, round soundhole, 3 stripe bound body, abalone rosette, maple back/sides, mahogany neck, 20 fret rosewood fingerboard with pearl dot inlay, 12th fret pearl horns inlay, rosewood bridge with white black dot pins, 3 per side chrome tuners, acoustic pickup, active 4 band EQ, active electronics. Available in Natural finish. New 1994.

Mfr.'s Sug. Retail	$615	$492	$369	$310	$245	$220	$205	$185

KMD-905PU — single round cutaway dreadnought style, spruce top, round soundhole, 3 stripe bound body/rosette, mahogany back/sides/neck, 20 fret rosewood fingerboard with pearl dot inlay, rosewood bridge with white black dot pins, 3 per side chrome tuners, acoustic pickup, active volume/3 band EQ. Available in Tobacco Sunburst finish. Curr. mfr.

Mfr.'s Sug. Retail	$530	$397	$265	$245	$195	$175	$160	$150

ACOUSTIC BASS

JBA-3000EAB — single round cutaway folk style, spruce top, round soundhole, 3 stripe bound body/rosette, mahogany back/sides/neck, 22 fret bound rosewood fingerboard with pearl dot inlay, rosewood strings thru bridge, 2 per side chrome tuners, acoustic pickup, active 3 band EQ. Available in Natural finish. New 1994.

Mfr.'s Sug. Retail	$675	$540	$405	$340	$270	$245	$225	$205

ACOUSTIC ELECTRIC

KJ-609WPU — single round cutaway jumbo style, spruce top, round soundhole, bound body, pearl inlay rosette, birdseye maple back/sides/neck, 21 fret rosewood fingerboard with pearl dot inlay, stylized pearl inlay at 12th fret, rosewood bridge with white black dot pins, 3 per side chrome tuners, acoustic pickup, volume/3 band EQ, active electronics. Available in Natural and Transparent Antique Brown finishes. Curr. mfr.

Mfr.'s Sug. Retail	$615	$461	$307	$280	$225	$205	$190	$170

KJ-705WPU — similar to KJ-609WPU, except has mahogany back/sides/neck, 6 on one side tuners. Available in Black and White finishes.

Mfr.'s Sug. Retail	$670	$502	$335	$290	$210	$190	$170	$160

ELECTRIC

PG-111B3 — offset double cutaway hardwood body, black pickguard, bolt-on maple neck, 22 fret rosewood fingerboard with pearl dot inlay, double locking vibrato, 6 on one side tuners, black hardware, 3 single coil pickups, volume/2 tone controls, 5 position switch. Available in Black Pearl, Red Pearl and White Pearl finishes. New 1994.

Mfr.'s Sug. Retail	$485	$363	$242	$240	$190	$170	$155	$145

PG-111HS — similar to PG-111B3, except has 2 single coil/1 humbucker pickups. Curr. mfr.

Mfr.'s Sug. Retail	$500	$400	$300	$250	$200	$180	$165	$150

PG-121 — similar to PG111, except has no pickguard, volume/tone control, 3 mini switches in place of 5 position switch, coil split in tone control. Available in Black Pearl, Black/White Crackle, Fluorescent Pink, Fluorescent Yellow, Red/White Crackle and White Pearl finishes. Curr. mfr.

Mfr.'s Sug. Retail	$600	$480	$360	$300	$240	$215	$195	$180

PGP-111 — similar to PG111, except has neck-through construction, maple body/neck, EMG pickups. Available in Black, Black/White Crackle, Fluorescent Yellow, Red, Red/White Crackle, Red/Yellow Crackle, White and White Pearl finishes. Disc. 1994.

		$385	$330	$275	$220	$200	$180	$165

Last Mfr.'s Sug. Retail was $550.

PGP-120 — sharkfin style maple body, maple neck, 22 fret rosewood fingerboard with pearl triangle inlay, double locking vibrato, 6 on one side tuners, black hardware, 2 single coil/1 humbucker EMG pickups, volume/tone control, 5 position switch. Available in Black, Black Pearl and Black/White Crackle finishes. Disc. 1994.

		$560	$480	$400	$320	$290	$265	$240

Last Mfr.'s Sug. Retail was $800.

PGP-121 — similar to PG121, except has neck thru construct, maple body/neck, EMG pickups. Available in Black, Black Pearl, Fluorescent Pink, Fluorescent Pink/Blue Crackle, Fluorescent Yellow Crackle, Ultra Violet and White Pearl finishes. Disc. 1994.

		$455	$390	$325	$260	$235	$215	$195

Last Mfr.'s Sug. Retail was $650.

Grading		100%	98% MINT	95% EXC+	90% EXC	80% VG+	70% VG	60% G

PGP-150A — offset double cutaway hardwood body, bolt-on maple neck, 24 fret rosewood fingerboard with offset pearl dot inlay, standard vibrato, 6 on one side tuners, black hardware, 2 single coil/1 humbucker pickups, volume/tone controls, 5 position switch. Available in Amber and Cherryburst finishes. New 1994.

Mfr.'s Sug. Retail	$595	$476	$357	$300	$240	$215	$195	$180

Artist Series

JB-400AM — single cutaway semi hollow style, bound flame maple top, bound fang style soundhole, mahogany back/sides/neck, 22 fret bound ebonized rosewood fingerboard with pearl dot inlay, tunomatic bridge/stop tailpiece, bound peghead, 3 per side tuners, gold hardware, 2 humbucker pickups, volume/tone control, 3 position switch. Available in Natural finish. Curr. mfr.

Mfr.'s Sug. Retail	$1,900	$1,520	$1,140	$950	$760	$685	$625	$570

JBA-500 — offset double cutaway alder body, carved ash top, maple neck, 22 fret rosewood fingerboard with pearl wedge inlay, standard vibrato, 6 on one side tuners, black hardware, humbucker/single coil/humbucker covered APC pickups, volume/tone control, 5 position switch. Available in Amber and Walnut finishes. New 1994.

Mfr.'s Sug. Retail	$735	$551	$367	$360	$295	$265	$245	$220

JBA-600 — offset double cutaway hardwood body, mahogany neck, 24 fret rosewood fingerboard with pearl dot inlay, standard vibrato, 3 per side tuners, gold hardware, 2 humbucker covered APC pickups, volume/tone control, 3 position switch. Available in Black and Cherryburst finishes. New 1994.

Mfr.'s Sug. Retail	$850	$680	$510	$425	$340	$305	$280	$255

JB-AL — offset double cutaway semi hollow body, black bound maple top, fang style soundhole, basswood back/sides, bolt-on maple neck, 24 fret rosewood fingerboard with pearl dot inlay, tunomatic bridge/stop tailpiece, 3 per side tuners, gold hardware, single coil/humbucker pickup, volume/tone control, 3 position switch. Available in White finish. Curr. mfr.

Mfr.'s Sug. Retail	$1,475	$1,106	$737	$735	$590	$525	$480	$440

JBA-LTD — offset double cutaway alder body, maple neck, 22 fret rosewood fingerboard with pearl dot inlay, standard vibrato, 6 on one side tuners, chrome hardware, 2 humbucker covered APC pickups, volume/tone control, 3 position switch. Available in Natural finish. New 1994.

Mfr.'s Sug. Retail	$600	$480	$360	$300	$240	$215	$195	$180

Sledgehammer Series

SHG-111 — offset double cutaway hardwood body, white pickguard, bolt-on maple neck, 22 fret maple fingerboard with black dot inlay, standard vibrato, 6 on one side tuners, chrome hardware, 3 single coil pickups, volume/2 tone controls, 5 position switch. Available in Black, Gun Metal Grey, Pink, Phantom Blue, Red, Red/White Crackle, Terminator Red, Ultra Violet, White, 2 Tone Sunburst and 3 Tone Sunburst finishes. Curr. mfr.

Mfr.'s Sug. Retail	$350	$280	$210	$180	$145	$130	$120	$110

This model also available with rosewood fingerboard with pearl dot inlay.

SHG-112-2S — single cutaway hardwood body, black pickguard, bolt on maple neck, 22 fret maple fingerboard with black dot inlay, fixed bridge, 6 on one side tuners, chrome hardware, 2 single coil pickups, 3 position switch. Available in Aged Blonde and Black finishes. Curr. mfr.

Mfr.'s Sug. Retail	$525	$393	$262	$230	$160	$145	$130	$120

In 1994, Cherry Sunburst and Natural finishes replaced original item.

SHG-112-HSS — similar to SHG-112-2S, except has 2 single coil/1 humbucker pickups. Disc. 1994.

			$300	$260	$215	$175	$155	$140	$130

Last Mfr.'s Sug. Retail was $430.

ELECTRIC BASS

JBAB-1N — offset double cutaway hardwood body, maple neck, 24 fret rosewood fingerboard with pearl offset dot inlay, fixed bridge, 3/2 per side tuners, chrome tuners, 2 J-style pickups, 2 volume/2 tone controls. Available in Black and Natural finishes. New 1994.

Mfr.'s Sug. Retail	$825	$660	$495	$415	$330	$300	$275	$250

PGP-113 — offset double cutaway maple body, black pickguard, bolt on maple neck, 20 fret rosewood fingerboard with pearl dot inlay, fixed bridge, 4 on one side tuners, black hardware, P-style/J-style EMG pickups, volume/tone control, 3 position switch. Available in Black, Black Pearl, Red, Red Pearl and White Pearl finishes. Disc. 1994.

			$295	$250	$210	$170	$150	$135	$125

Last Mfr.'s Sug. Retail was $425.

PGP-114 — offset double cutaway hardwood body, bolt-on maple neck, 24 fret rosewood fingerboard with pearl dot inlay, fixed bridge, 2 per side tuners, chrome hardware, P-style/J-style pickups, 1 volume/2 tone controls, 3 position switch. Available in Black Pearl finish. New 1994.

Mfr.'s Sug. Retail	$495	$371	$247	$245	$195	$175	$160	$150

SHB-113 — offset double cutaway hardwood body, black pickguard, bolt-on maple neck, 20 fret rosewood fingerboard with pearl dot inlay, fixed bridge, black hardware, P-style pickup, volume/tone control. Available in Black, Red and White finishes. Curr. mfr.

Mfr.'s Sug. Retail	$400	$320	$240	$200	$160	$145	$130	$120

J D

See JAY DEE.

Instruments built in England.

J D S

Instruments currently built in Asia. Exclusively distributed by Wolf Imports of St. Louis, Missouri.

J D S Limited Edition instruments are medium quality acoustic and solid body electric guitars that feature designs based on popular American classics. For further information contact Wolf Imports through the Index of Current Manufacturers located in the back of this book.

JEDSON

Instruments produced in Japan from the late 1960s through the late 1970s.

The Jedson trademark appears on entry to student level solid body and semi-hollow body guitars; some models with original design and some models based on classic American designs.

(Source: Tony Bacon and Paul Day, The Guru's Guitar Book)

JENNINGS

While some of the instruments were built in Japan, others were 'built' (or shall we say assembled) in England using Japanese and English parts during the early 1970s.

Interestingly enough, the idea of assembling parts produced in other countries in a factory at the final destination and then labeling the finished product "a product of the final destination's country" is still occuring. This production practice is used by many outside the realm of guitar manufacture, so it shouldn't come as a surprise that guitar companies do it too.

Enough asides, back to the guitars! When you reach the Jennings guitars, you come to a proverbial fork in the road. On one hand, there's the entry level solid body guitars based on classic American designs; but on the the other are some higher quality "tiny-bodied" solid body guitars. Instruments should be examined on an individual basis, and then priced accordingly.

(Source: Tony Bacon and Paul Day, The Guru's Guitar Guide)

DAVE JENNINGS

Instruments built in England during the late 1980s.

Luthier David Jennings produced some very respectable original design solid body guitars. Jennings primarily worked as a custom builder, so the overall instruments available might perhaps be a small number. Anyone with a photo of their favorite guitar is encouraged to contact the **Blue Book of Guitars**.

(Source: Tony Bacon and Paul Day, The Guru's Guitar Guide)

JENNINGS-THOMPSON

Instruments currently built in Austin, Texas.

Jennings-Thompson is a high quality, limited production company located in Austin. Ross Jennings personally builds all his instruments along with one other luthier. They limit production to about 30 basses and guitars a year, and work with the customer to ensure that their instrument will be exactly tailored to their playing style.

Pendulum and **Spectrum** basses have a new retail price beginning at $3,699 (4-string) up to $4,099 (6-string). Their guitars carry a list price of $2,599. For further information contact Jennings-Thompson through the Index of Current Manufacturers located in the back of this book.

JERRY BIX

Instruments were built in England during the early 1980s.

While the Musician and Exotic series had some vestiges of Fender-ish styling to them, the Ptera guitars featured original designs. This company also produced some high quality custom models as well.

(Source: Tony Bacon and Paul Day, The Guru's Guitar Guide)

JERRY JONES

Instruments built in Nashville, Tennessee since 1981. Distributed by Jerry Jones Guitars of Nashville, Tennessee.

Luthier Jerry Jones began repair and guitar building at Nashville's Old Time Pickin' Parlour in 1978. By 1980, he had opened his own shop and was building custom guitars as well as designing his own original models. Jones' company has been specializing in reproducing Danelectro models and parts; however,

Jerry Jones Doubleneck
courtesy Dave Rodgers

J

Grading		100%	98% MINT	95% EXC+	90% EXC	80% VG+	70% VG	60% G

the designs have been updated to improve upon original design flaws and to provide a more stable playing instrument.

ELECTRIC

All instruments in this series are available in: Almond, Black, Copper, Red and Turquoise finishes.
Add $50 for below models if with a Neptune bridge (fixed bridge with metal saddles).

BARITONE — single cutaway poplar body, transparent pickguard, bolt-on poplar neck, 23 fret rosewood fingerboard with pearl dot inlay, fixed bridge with rosewood saddle, 3 per side tuners, chrome hardware, 2 lipstick pickups, volume/tone control, 3 position switch. Curr. mfr.

Mfr.'s Sug. Retail	$795	$596	$397	$395	$315	$280	$260	$235

ELECTRIC SITAR — single cutaway poplar body, transparent pickguard, 13 sympathetic strings with own nut/bridge/lipstick pickup, bolt-on poplar neck, 21 fret rosewood fingerboard with white dot inlay, fixed buzz bridge/thru body tailpiece, 6 on one side tuners, chrome hardware, 2 lipstick pickups, 3 volume/tone controls. Curr. mfr.

Mfr.'s Sug. Retail	$1,195	$956	$717	$600	$480	$430	$395	$360

GUITARLIN — deep double cutaway poplar body with hollow sound channels, masonite top/back, transparent pickguard, bolt-on poplar neck, 31 fret rosewood fingerboard with white dot inlay, fixed bridge with rosewood saddle, 3 per side tuners, chrome hardware, 2 lipstick pickups, volume/tone control, 3 position switch. Curr. mfr.

Mfr.'s Sug. Retail	$795	$596	$397	$395	$315	$280	$260	$235

LONGHORN DOUBLENECK — similar to Guitarlin, except has 2 necks, 4 pickups and any combination of guitar/bass necks.

Mfr.'s Sug. Retail	$1,270	$1,016	$762	$635	$510	$460	$420	$380

SHORTHORN — double cutaway poplar body, white pickguard, bolt-on poplar neck, 21 fret rosewood fingerboard with pearl dot inlay, fixed bridge with rosewood saddle, 3 per side tuners, chrome hardware, 3 lipstick pickups, volume/tone control, 5 position switch. Curr. mfr.

Mfr.'s Sug. Retail	$870	$696	$522	$435	$350	$315	$290	$265

SINGLE CUTAWAY — similar to Shorthorn, except has single round cutaway style body.

Mfr.'s Sug. Retail	$870	$696	$522	$435	$350	$315	$290	$265

TWELVE STRING — similar to Single Cutaway, except has 12 strings, fixed bridge with metal saddles, 6 per side tuners, 2 pickups. Curr. mfr.

Mfr.'s Sug. Retail	$895	$671	$447	$445	$360	$325	$300	$275

ELECTRIC BASS

LONGHORN 4 — double deep cutaway bound poplar body with hollow sound chambers, transparent pickguard, bolt on poplar neck, 24 fret rosewood fingerboard with white dot inlay, fixed bridge with rosewood saddle, 2 per side tuners, chrome hardware, 2 lipstick pickups, volume/tone control, 3 position switch. Curr. mfr.

Mfr.'s Sug. Retail	$795	$596	$397	$395	$315	$280	$260	$235

Longhorn 6 — similar to Longhorn 4, except has 6 strings.

Mfr.'s Sug. Retail	$795	$596	$397	$395	$315	$280	$260	$235

SINGLE CUTAWAY 4 — similar to Longhorn 4, except has single cutaway style body. Disc. 1992.

		$415	$360	$300	$240	$215	$195	$180

Last Mfr.'s Sug. Retail was $595.

Single Cutaway 6 — similar to Longhorn 4, except has single cutaway style body, 6 strings. Disc. 1992.

		$415	$360	$300	$240	$215	$195	$180

Last Mfr.'s Sug. Retail was $595.

J G

Instruments produced in Italy during the late 1960s.

The SA series featured four models of medium quality but original designs. Readers are encouraged to write and share whether or not they also share similarities to other Italian-produced guitars of this era to the **Blue Book of Guitars**.

(Source: Tony Bacon and Paul Day, The Guru's Guitar Guide)

J H S

Instruments built in Japan during the late 1970s.

The J H S trademark was the initials of the UK importer **John Hornby Skewes**, who founded his import company in 1965 (See listing under ENCORE). The generally good quality instruments featured both original designs and those based on classic American designs. The line focused primarily on solid body guitars, much like the Encore line today.

(Source: Tony Bacon and Paul Day, The Guru's Guitar Guide)

Jonathan Rose Custom
courtesy Rick Kindrel

JOHN BIRCH

Instruments built in England from early to late 1970s.

While luthier John Birch did build some high quality solid body guitars based on Fender/Gibson designs, he is more renown for his custom guitar building. In the 1980s he teamed up with Barry Kirby to build the Cobra models, including the highly imaginitive Cobra "Rook" for Rook Music.

(Source: Tony Bacon, The Ultimate Guitar Book)

JOLANA

Instruments produced in Czechoslovakia (date unknown).

Entry level production solid bodies, but the two examples viewed have been original designs with headstocks that seem to echo the Fender "Swinger". If they play as cool as they are pointy, then these designs rule!

(Source: Tony Bacon, The Ultimate Guitar Book)

JONATHAN ROSE GUITARS

Instruments built in Nashville, Tennessee since 1981.

These high quality handcrafted guitars feature American made hardware and pickups, as well as highly figured tops. Rose's custom guitars have been played by a number of Nashville's better-known guitar players and session players. Rose, originally an Oregon native, moved to Nashville in the late 1970s. In 1981 he launched both the Rose Guitar Center in Henderson (right outside Nashville) and Jonathan Rose custom guitars. The Rose Guitar Center has been in the same location for the past fifteen years, and features both new and used instrument sales as well as repair and custom work. Jonathan is ably assisted by his wife Angela, and both can be found either at the shop, or at vintage shows displaying their guitars.

(Biography courtesy Jonathan and Angela Rose, June 1996)

Since 1981, Rose has built 200 custom guitars. Of the 200, 25 were basses. The serialization began in 1981 with #1, and Rose maintains a list of the original specifications, colors, woods, and original owners for each and every one.

ELECTRIC

The following models are all available in Translucent, Emerald Green, Amber, Burgundy, Deep Water Blue, Two-tone Heritage Cherry Burst, and Two-tone Tobacco Burst finishes. Additional custom options include:

Add $595 for a Parsons-White String Bender.
Add $200 for a marbelized finish.
Add $700 for a Tree of Life neck inlay.
Add $375 for a mini Tree of Life inlay.
Add $400 for a Horse and Horshoe inlay.
Add $100 for top binding.
Add $250 for top binding with Abalone.
Add $250 for a Floyd Rose Tremolo.
Add $200 for a Wilkerson Convertible Bridge.

CUSTOM — Single cutaway hollow swamp ash body, flamed maple top, two Van Zantz humbucking pickups, one single coil pickup, birdseye maple neck with birdseye fingerboard, and gold hardware. Current mfg.
Mfr.'s Sug. Retail **$1,695**

ELITE — double cutaway alder or mahogany body, quilted or flamed maple top, two Seymour Duncan pickups, and chrome or gold hardware. Current mfg.
Mfr.'s Sug. Retail **$2,495**

F-HOLE HOLLOWBODY — hollow swamp ash body, two Van Zantz single coil pickups, birdseye maple neck with Brazilian rosewood fingerboard, and chrome hardware. Current mfg.
Mfr.'s Sug. Retail **$1,295**

STANDARD — single cutaway alder body, flame or quilted maple top, contoured back, three Seymour Duncan Anico pro II single coil pickups, birdseye maple neck with ebony fingerboard, and gold hardware. Current mfg.
Mfr.'s Sug. Retail **$1,595**

7/8 STRAT STYLE — offset double cutaway swamp ash body, birdseye maple neck, ebony fingerboard, three Seymour Duncan single coil pickups, and chrome hardware. Current mfg.
Mfr.'s Sug. Retail **$1,295**

JOODEE

See DAION.

Instruments produced in Japan from the late 1970 through the 1980s.

Jonathan Rose Custom
courtesy Jonathan & Angela Rose

JORDAN GUITARS

Formerly JVE Guitars.

Instruments built in Rankin, Illinois.

Luthier Patrick Jordan custom builds guitars, sitars, basses, and "bassitars", as well as sitars equipped with a tremolo bar. Unlike the Coral/Danelectro design, Jordan places the 12 sympathetic strings to the rear of the instrument. The model for the acoustic sitar came directly from Calcutta.

Jordan features the usual North American hardwoods such as Ash, Alder, Basswood, Cherry, Maple, and Walnut; but others such as Birch, Butternut, Hickory, Poplar, Sycamore, and Sassafras are optionally available. Jordan's custom template/order sheet gives the player making the commission some control over aspects of the construction, while Jordan maintains control over pickup placement and hardware placement.

For further information, contact Patrick Jordan through his listing in the Index of Current Manufacturers located in the back of this book.

JOSE RAMIREZ

Instruments built in Spain for three generations.

The Ramirez family has been building guitars since Jose' (1858-1923) and brother Manuel began. The family business then passed to Jose' II (1885-1957), and then to Jose' III (born 1922). In the early 1980s, the family workshop employed 17 workers and was producing 1,000 guitars a year.

(Source: Tony Bacon, The Ultimate Guitar Book)

J T G OF NASHVILLE

Instruments built in Japan. Distributed by JTG of Nashville located in Nashville, Tennessee.

While JTG of Nashville currently imports quality Japanese and Mexican acoustic guitars, they offered a solid body electric during the mid-1980s. The **Infinity** guitar was designed by Dave Petschulat, and had a body profile similar to a "sharpened" Gibson Explorer.

The **Infinity** had a highly angular ash body, curly maple neck, six-on-a-side headstock, one humbucking pickup, a custom tremolo, and was offered with either charcoal gray or white with red accents, and red with a light gray accent. Suggested retail price in the 1980s was $595.

JUNIOR

See chapter on House Brands.

This trademark has been identified as a Gibson built budget line available from 1919 through 1926. The pegheads carry no logo, and essentially are 'no-frills' versions of low end Gibsons. They will have a label different from the standard Gibson label of the time, but still credit Gibson as the manufacturer. As a budget line Gibson these guitars possess no adjustable truss rod in the neck.

(Source: Walter Carter, Gibson Guitars: 100 Years of an American Icon)

J

K & S

Instruments built in Berkeley, California.

George Katechis and Marc Silber (K & S), two noted guitar experts, are re-introducing the Acoustic Hawaiian Slide Guitar. Born in the 1920s, these guitars enjoyed moderate success before being overtaken by the louder resonator-driven National guitars of the early 1930s. The new instruments are modeled after designs by Weissenborn, Hilo, and Knutsen.

Prices start at $700 for these solid wood contruction guitars. Wood options include Canadian Cedar top and Spanish Cedar body; Sitka Spruce top and Spanish Cedar, Honduras Mahogany, Maple, or California Koa (Acacia) body; or all California Koa. Instruments are bound and feature Van Gent tuners.

For further information, contact K & S through the Index of Current Manufacturers located in the rear of this book.

STEPHEN KAKOS

Instruments built in Mound, Minnesota since 1975.

Luthier Stephen Kakos began building classical guitars in 1972, and turned to full time building in 1975. Kakos concentrates specifically on classical acoustics, although he has built a few flamenco guitars on request. In addition to guitar building, Kakos also performs some repairs. For further information on models and pricing, please contact luthier Kakos via the Index of Current Manufacturers located in the back of this book.

KALAMAZOO

See chapter on House Brands.

In the late 1930s, the Gibson guitar company decided to offer their own entry level guitars. While similar to models built for other distributors (Cromwell, Fascinator, or Capital) in construction, the Kalamazoo line was originally only offered for about five years. Models included flattop and archtop acoustics, lap steels (and amps), and mandolins.

Kalamazoo instruments, like other Gibson budget instruments, do not have an adjustable truss rod (a key difference), different construction techniques, and no identifying Gibson logo.

In the mid 1960s, Gibson again released an entry level series of guitars under the Kalamazoo trademark, except all models were electric solid body guitars (except a flattop acoustic) that had a double offset cutaway body, bolt-on necks, six on a side headstock, and 1 or 2 pickups. The body profile of late 1960s models then switched to even dual cutaways. The second run of Kalamazoo models came to an end in the early 1970s.

Kalamazoo serial numbers are impressed into the back of the headstock, and feature six digits like the regular Gibson line. However, the Kalamazoo numbers do not match or correspond with the Gibson serialization (in the back of this book). Further information regarding Kalamazoo serialization will appear in future editions of the **Blue Book of Guitars**.

(Source: Walter Carter, Gibson Guitars: 100 Years of an American Icon)

KAMICO

See chapter on House Brands.

This trademark has been identified as the "House Brand" of the Kay Guitar company. As one of the leading suppliers of "House Brand" guitars, Kay apparently felt the need to have an entry-level budget line (!?) of guitars produced in-house.

(Source: Willie G. Moseley, Stellas & Stratocasters)

KAPA

Instruments built in Hyattsville, Maryland between 1962 and 1970.

Kapa guitars were designed and built by Kope Veneman and company, during a successful eight year production. Veneman, a Dutch immigrant, was running a music store during the early 1960s that imported German and Italian guitars. In 1962, Veneman founded his own production facility, and named the company based on initials from his family member's first names: **K**ope, his son **A**lbert, his daughter **P**atricia, and his wife **A**deline. During the eight year run, the Kapa company produced nearly 120,000 decent quality, fair priced instruments.

Kapa guitars were available in four basic body styles, and in three variants thereof (six string, twelve string, and bass guitar). These models include a "mini-Strat" (**Challenger**), a "mini-Jazzmaster" (**Continental**), a teardrop shape (**Minstrel**), and a thinline hollowbody (also a **Challenger**, with different model designations). However, the names are not always consistent with the body styles, and can lead to some confusion. Kapa also produced an unofficial model named the **Cobra**, which is a single pickup model assembled with leftovers from regular production runs.

Kapa guitars were offered with bolt-on necks, six-on-a-side headstocks (or four, if a bass), and many sported a Jazzmaster-ish tremolo system. Early Challenger solid bodies had 2 pickups and a 3-way toggle switch (new retail list $229); "Deluxe" or "Wildcat" models had three (new list $275). The Continental model debuted around 1966 with a slightly slimmer body and differently cut horns, and sliding on/off pickup switches (new list $199). The tear-drop/Minstrel model (new $269) had three single coil pickups, on/off sliders, master volume, and three tone knobs. Keep in mind, however, that the preceding was a rough approximations - it is possible to find models that have different parts than the standards.

(Source: Michael Wright, Guitar Stories Volume One, pgs. 25-29)

KARERA

See TEXARKANA.

Instruments produced in Asia. Distributed by the V.J. Rendano Wholesale Corp.

Karera offers a range of student quality guitars. For further information contact V.J. Rendano Wholesale Corp. through the Index of Current Manufacturers located in the back of this book.

KASUGA

Instruments produced in Japan from the late 1960s through the early 1980s.

Kasuga produced guitars of both original designs and designs based on classic American models. While the quality is medium to good on both solid body or semi-hollowbody guitars, it is generally the "reproduction" models that are found in the music stores. Readers with photos or information concerning original design Kasuga guitars are invited to write the **Blue Book of Guitars**.

KAWAI

Instruments built in Japan during the late 1970s to early 1980s; also additional series offered during the mid 1980s. Distributed in the U.S. market by Kawai America Corporation of Compton, California.

While Kawai continues to be a dominant company in keyboards (notably their high quality pianos and synthesizers) they have been and continue to produce good quality guitars and basses. Although their entire product line is not available in the U.S. market, Kawai does feature a number of startling original designs to augment a number of models based on classic American design.

The Kawai company began producing their own guitars back in 1956, and had participated in importing to the American market. In 1967, the Kawai corporation purchased the Teisco company (of "Teisco Del Rey" guitar fame). Kawai continued distributing the Teisco line in the U.S. through 1973, but then concentrated on domestic distribution of Kawai products thereafter. Kawai returned to the American marketplace in the mid 1980s with a line of quality bass guitar models.

KAY

See chapter on House Brands.

Between the 1930s and the late 1960s, Kay stringed instruments were manufactured and distributed by the Kay Musical Instrument Company of Chicago, Illinois. Kay, along with Harmony, were the two larger suppliers of "House Brand" instruments for distributors and retailers.

The Kay trademark returned in the 1970s. Currently the instruments are produced in Asia, and are distributed by A.R. Musical Enterprises, Inc. of Fishers, Indiana.

The roots of the Kay Musical Instruments company begin back in 1890, when the Groeschel Company of Chicago, Illinois first began building bowl-back (or "potato bug") mandolins. In 1918 Groeschel was changed to the Stromberg-Voisenet Company, and incorporated in 1921. Vice-president C. G. Stromberg directed production of guitars and banjos under the **Mayflower** trademark (See MAYFLOWER). This Stromberg is not to be confused with luthier Charles Stromberg (and son Elmer) of Boston, Massachusetts. Stromberg-Voisenet introduced the process of laminating wood tops and backs in 1924, and also began arching instruments tops and backs. Henry Kay Kuhrmeyer, who later became company president, offered use of his middle name on the more popular "Kay-Kraft" series of Stromberg-Voisenet's guitars, mandolins and banjos.

The Kay era began when Henry Kay Kuhrmeyer bought the Stromberg-Voisenet company in 1928. Kuhrmeyer renamed the company Kay Musical Instruments in 1931, and began mass-producing stringed instruments in large volume. Kay, like Washburn at the turn of the century, claimed production of almost 100,000 instruments a year by the mid 1930s. Kay instruments were both marketed by the company themselves, or produced for "jobbers" (distributors) and retail houses under various names. Rather than produce a list here, the **Blue Book of Guitars** has attempted to identify Kay-produced "House Brands" throughout the alphabetical listing in this text. Many of these instruments were entry level or students instruments then, and should be considered entry level even now. But as Jay Scott (author of **50's Cool: Kay Guitars**) points out, "True, the vast majority of Kay's student-grade and intermediate guitars were awful. But the top of each line - banjo, guitar and mandolin (especially the acoustic and electric jazz guitars and flattop acoustics) - were meritorious pieces of postwar musical art".

Kay introduced upright basses in 1937, and marketed them under both the Kay trademark and K. Meyer (a clever abbreviation of Kuhrmeyer?). After Leo Fender debuted his Precision electric bass at the 1951 NAMM trade show, Kay was the first company to join Fender in the electric bass market as they introduced their K-162 model in 1952. Kay also went on to produce some of the coolest mixtures of classic archtop design and '50s 'modern' acrylic headstocks on the "Gold K" line that debuted in 1957.

Kay Deluxe Dobro
courtesy Hyatt W. Finley

K

1958 Kay Barney Kessel
courtesy Rick King

The Kay Musical Instrument company was sold to an investment group headed by Sydney Katz in 1955. Katz, a former manager of Harmony's service department, was more aggressive and competitive in the guitar market. Kay's production facilities expanded to try to meet the demand of the guitar market in the late 1950s and early 1960s. A large number of guitars were produced for Sears under their **Silvertone** trademark. At the peak of the guitar boom in 1964, Kay moved into a new million dollar facility located near Chicago's O'Hare Airport.

Unfortunately, by 1965 the guitar market was oversaturated as retail demand fell off. While Kay was still financially sound, Katz sold the company to Seeburg. Seeburg, a large jukebox manufacturer based in Chicago, owned Kay for a period of two years. At this time, the whole guitar industry was feeling the pinch of economics. Seeburg wanted to maintain their niche in the industry by acquiring Valco Guitars, Inc. (See NATIONAL or DOBRO) and producing their own amplifiers to go with the electric Kay guitars. Bob Keyworth, the executive vice-president in charge of Kay, suggested the opposite: Seeburg should sell Kay to Valco.

Robert Engelhardt, who succeeded Louis Dopyera in Valco's ownership in 1962, bought Kay from Seeburg in June 1967. Valco moved into the Kay facilities, but Engelhardt's company was underfinanced from the beginning. Engelhardt did make some deal with an investment group or financial company, but after two years the bills couldn't be paid. The investment group just showed up one day, and changed the plant locks. By 1969 or 1970, both Valco Guitars Inc., and the Kay trademark were out of business. Some time later, the rights to the Kay trademark were sold, and began showing up on a series of entry level imported guitars.

(Source: Jay Scott, 50's Cool: Kay Guitars)

1960 Kay bass
courtesy Rick King

KAY KRAFT

Sometimes hyphenated as KAY-KRAFT.

See KAY.

Instruments produced in Chicago, Illinois from the mid 1920s to the mid 1950s.

Henry Kay Kuhrmeyer, who worked his was up from company secretary, treasurer, and later president of Stromberg-Voisenet, lent his middle name to a popular selling line of guitars, mandolins, and banjos. When Kuhrmeyer gained control of Stromberg-Voisenet and changed the name to Kay Musical Instruments, he continued to use the Kay Kaft trademark. Instruments using this trademark could thus be either Stromberg-Voisenet or Kay (depending on the label) but was still produced by the "same" company in the "same" facilities.

KEL KROYDEN

See chapter on House Brands.

Faced with the severe American Depression of the 1930s, Gibson general manager Guy Hart converted most of company production to toy manufacturing as a means to keep his workforce employed. Kalamazoo Playthings produced wood blocks and wooden pull-toys from 1931 to 1933, while the Kel Kroyden offshoot built toy sailboats. Wood bodies, strings...and masts!

Kel Kroyden brand guitars seem to appear at the same time period that Kel Kroyden Toys were introduced. The "Kel" lettering is horizontal on the headstock, while "Kroyden" is lettered vertically.

(Source: Walter Carter, Gibson Guitars: 100 Years of an American Icon)

KEN BEBENSEE

Instruments currently built in San Luis Obispo, California.

Luthier Ken Bebensee's instruments are custom built from the highest grade of sustained yield, exotic woods. Bebensee offers Bartolini pickups, quality hardware, and a lifetime guarantee (to the original purchaser). For further information contact Ken Bebensee Guitars and Basses through the Index of Current Manufacturers located in the back of this book.

ELECTRIC

Stealth Series

Stealth Series instruments feature AAA grade maple top with lightweight ash, cherry or alder body. Hard rock maple and purple heart neck, 24 fret Pau Ferro fingerboard, and laminated neck-through body design. Retail prices begin at $2,000 (4-string fretless bass) up to $2,300 (6-string fretted bass). The Bebensee Standard Guitar has a retail price beginning at $2,000. Bebensee also features a list of additional cost options on any of his models.

Gerald Weber
19th Annual Dallas Show

KENDRICK

Instruments built in Pflugerville, Texas since 1994.

In 1989, Gerald Weber started Kendrick Amplifiers in Pflugerville, Texas. Originally dedicated to reproducing the classic Fender tweeds in exact detail, Kendrick has grown to include their own unique designs. Weber was the first designer to build vintage style amp complete with hand-wiring. Weber also joined a network of hand-built amplifier designers that shared an interest in helping musicians gain a knowledge of the workings of their favorite guitar amps. He began writing his monthly column for **Vintage Guitar Magazine** over four years ago, which was the first technical article that the magazine had ever printed. Weber is also the author of **A Desktop Reference of Hip Vintage Guitar Amps**, which gathers numerous technical tips all in one volume.

Beginning in 1994, Weber offered two guitar models in addition to his amplifier line. The **Kendrick Town House** was briefly produced, and then the design was taken off the marketplace in response to a patent dispute. However, Weber still produces the **Kendrick Continental** ($1,800 factory direct), a solid body electric with an offset, angular feel that features three Lindy Fralin single coil "vintage repro" pickups, swamp ash body, brazilian rosewood fingerboard, and a sunburst finish (custom colors are also available). The **Continental** guitar was inspired as a tribute to Stevie Ray Vaughan and the Austin blues scene.

KENNETH LAWERENCE

Instruments built in Arcata, California since 1986.

Luthier Kenneth Lawerence had a six year backround in European style furniture and cabinet building before he began working at Moonstone Guitars. Lawerence worked with owner/luthier Steve Helgeson for five years constructing guitars and basses at Moonstone before starting his own Lawerence Instruments in 1986. Lawerence also draws upon his twenty-six year musical backround for his designs, which mostly emphasize the electric bass.

Lawerence crafts high quality instruments from responsively harvested rainforest hardwoods from southern Mexico and Central America. The exotic woods featured in Lawerence's instruments share similar sonic characteristics to traditional hardwood choices. Retail prices range from $2,250 (4-string Essential bass) up to $5,100 (6-string Chamberbass). Lawrence offers six different models, in 4-, 5-, or 6-string versions. For further information contact luthier Kenneth Lawerence through the Index of Current Manufacturers located in the back of this book.

KENT

Instruments were produced in Japan during the mid 1960s, and distributed in the U.S. in part by Buegeleisen & Jacobson of New York, New York.

As part of the pre-"copy" wave of Japanese guitars, Kent guitars have an original body design. Some of the Kent guitars were built in Japan by the Teisco company, but the quality level at the time is down at the entry or student level, leaving much to be desired.

(Source: Michael Wright, Guitar Stories Volume One)

KEYSTONE STATE

See WEYMANN & SONS.

K I C S (USA)

See R A J GUITAR CRAFTS.

KIMAXE

Instruments produced in Korea. Distributed by Kenny & Michael's Co., Inc. of Los Angeles, California.

Kimaxe offers a range of student level to intermediate quality guitars based on classic American favorites. For further information contact Kenny & Michael's Co., Inc. through the Index of Current Manufacturers located in the rear of this book.

KIMBARA

Instruments produced in Japan during the mid to late 1970s.

The Kimbara trademark is the brandname used by a UK importer on these mid to good quality original designs. Kimbara also produced a number of solid body guitars based on classic American designs as well.

(Source: Tony Bacon and Paul Day, The Guru's Guitar Guide)

KIMBERLY

Instruments originally produced in Japan. Current production is located in Seoul, Korea. Information and distribution contact in the U.S. is Lindert Guitars of Chelan, Washington.

According to initial research by Michael Wright in his book **Guitar Stories Volume One**, Kimberly-branded guitars that were produced in Japan were sold through the Lafayette company catalog. The exact U.S. importer during this time period has yet to be pinpointed.

Current production of guitars under the Kimberly trademark is the Kimex Trading Co., Ltd. of Seoul, Korea. Kimex produces a number of guitar and bass models that favor classic American designs. While some models feature solid alder, the majority of bodies are ply-constructed. Retail prices for the KS-100 strat-styled model begin at $219, while a KT-200 'tele' lists for $329. Kimberly instruments are designed with the entry level guitarist and student in mind.

Kendrick Continental
courtesy Gerald Weber

K

"I understand that for a lot of the NAMM shows, they would build 3 or 4 of a model to show there and if they didn't get enough orders, they didn't produce the guitar. The White Penguin was made for a NAMM show."

—*Randy Bachman*

TCG, Jan/Feb 1991

KINAL

Instruments currently produced in Vancouver, British Columbia (Canada).

Mike Kinal has been building and designing guitars since the early '70s. Mike began building 6-string electrics and produced the Kinal Standard in 1972. In 1974, Mike produced the Kinal Custom, which was his trademark throughout the '70s and '80s. In 1976, Mike began to build bass guitars — with emphasis on balance and comfort. In 1988, Mike turned his attention to the production of the Voyager Archtop jazz guitar. For further information contact luthier Mike Kinal through the Index of Current Manufacturers located in the back of this book.

KINGSTON

Instruments produced in Japan.

The Kingston trademark is a brandname used by U.S. importer Westheimer Importing Corporation of Chicago, Illinois. Jack Westheimer, who was one of the original guitar importers and distributors, is currently president of Cort Musical Instruments of Northbrook, Illinois.

(Source: Michael Wright, Guitar Stories Volume One, pg 76)

KING'S STONE

Instruments produced in Japan.

The King's Stone trademark was a brandname used by U.S. importers Elger/Hoshino of Ardmore, Pennsylvania. King's Stone, along with others like Goldentone, Jamboree, and Elger were all used on Japanese guitars imported to the U.S. Elger/Hoshino evolved into Hoshino USA, distributor of Ibanez guitars.

(Source: Michael Wright, Guitar Stories Volume One, pg 76)

STEVE KLEIN

Klein Acoustic Guitar Division

Klein Electric Guitar Division

Instruments produced in Sonoma, California since 1976.

Steve Klein first began building electric guitars in Berkeley, California in 1967. A year later, Klein's grandmother introduced him to Dr. Michael Kasha at the University of California in Berkeley. Klein built his first acoustic after that meeting. He briefly attended the California College of Arts and Crafts in 1969, but left to continue building guitars.

In 1970, Klein built his second acoustic guitar. He moved to Colorado in the winter of 1970-1971, but later that summer accepted a job at "The American Dream" guitar shop back in San Diego. This shop was later bought by Bob Taylor and Kurt Listug, and grew into Taylor Guitars.

The third guitar Steve Klein built also had Kasha-inspired designs. Klein travelled to Detroit via Colorado, and met Richard Schneider. Schneider was building Kasha-style classical guitars at the time, and Klein thought that he was going to stay and apprentice with Schneider. Schneider looked at Klein's current guitar and said "Congratulations, You're a guitar builder", and sent Klein back home.

In the Fall of 1972 Klein received his business license. He designed the current acoustic body shape and flying brace, and started work on the Electric Bird guitar. Later the next summer, Klein had finished the first L-457 acoustic; and by 1974 had finished three more acoustics, his first 12 string guitar, and the first small (39.6) body. Klein made a deal with Clayton Johnson (staff member of 'Bill Gramm Presents') to be able to get into concerts to show guitars to professional musicians. Klein got to meet such notables as Stills, Crosby, Young, David Lindly, Doc Watson, Roy Buchanan, John Sebastion (Loving Spoonful), and others. In the summer of 1975, Klein went to Los Angeles with guitars to meet J.D. Souther; he recieved a commission from Joni Mitchell, and set up shop in Oakland.

In 1976, Klein finally settled into his current shop space in Sonoma. He continued building and designing guitars while doing some repair work. Two years later he finished Joni Mitchell's guitar, and the Electric Bird as well. In 1979, Klein met Steve Kauffman at a G.A.L. convention in Boston. That same year, Klein and Carl Margolis began developing a small electric model that was nicknamed "Lumpy" by David Lindly. Klein also did a side project of antique repair, furniture, and chairs for George Lucas at the Skywalker Ranch. On a more personal note, Klein married Lin Marie DeVincent in the spring of 1985, and Michael Hedges played at their wedding.

The MK Electric model was designed in conjunction with Ronnie Montrose in 1986. By 1988 the small Klein electric design was finished, and was debuted at a trade show in 1989. Klein Electric Division was later started that same year, and Steve Klein began designing an acoustic Harp guitar for Michael Hedges. A year later the acoustic Harp project was dropped in favor of an electrical Harp design instead. Hedges and guitar appeared on the cover of the October 1990 issue of **Guitar Player magazine**.

In the early 1990s, Klein began designing an acoustic bass guitar "for and with" Bob Taylor of Taylor Guitars. The first prototypes were assembled by Steve Kauffman in 1993. A large acoustic guitar order came in from Japan a year later, and the shipment was sent in 1995. In order to concentrate on the acoustic guitar production, Klein sold his Electric Division to Lorenzo German that same year, and the

Electric Division still operates out of the original Klein Sonoma facilities. The Taylor/Klein acoustic bass went into production in 1996, and currently there is a waiting period on acoustic models.

ACOUSTIC

Klein currently focuses his attention on acoustic guitar building. His **Basic Klein Acoustic Guitar** features Walnut back and sides, a Spruce top, Rosewood neck, Ebony bridge and fretboard, and gold plated tuners with Ebony buttons. The model S-39.6 carries a list price of $10,850; and the L-45.7 is $11,150. Klein offers a fairly fancy ornamentaion package including mother-of-pearl snowflake inlays on the guitars. Optional custom features included a 12 string variant, Florentine cutaway with hidden heel, and use of Brazilian Rosewood. Contact Luthier Klein in regards to pricing and current availability.

ELECTRIC

Steve Klein began producing electric guitars in 1989, and production continues at the Klein facility today. In 1995, Lorenzo German bought the Electric Division, and continues to produce high quality electrics. The Basic setup of the **BF-96** offers a Swamp Ash or Spruce body, headless one piece bolt-on Rosewood neck, a Steinberger S-Trem bridge, Seymour Duncan pickups, and tone/volume controls plus a five-way pickup selector switch. The list prce is $2,574. The **DT-96** ($2,336) shares many same features, except has a Basswood or Alder body, and differing Seymour Duncan pickups. Both Models feature a number of optional custom features such as a Steinberger Trans-Trem bridge, a chambered body, Novax fingerboards, or Joe Barden pickups. Contact Luthier Lorenzo German in regards to pricing and current availability via the Index of Current Manufacturers located in the rear of this book.

KLIRA

Instruments produced in Germany from late 1950s to current.

The Klira trademark originated in 1887 by builder Johannes Klier (another text gives "Otto" as his first name). The first company electrics appeared in 1958, and solid body guitars followed in 1960. Throughout the 1960s, Klira produced Fender-ish original designs; but as the 1970s started the emphasis was put on versions of Fender and Gibson designs. Instruments are generally good quality functional guitars, and many have multi-laminate necks (akin to a wood 'butcher block').

(Source: Tony Bacon, The Ultimate Guitar Book)

KNIGHT

Instruments made in England during the 1980s.

Luthier Dick Knight produced a number of attractive semi-hollowbody electric guitars, notably the Imperial model. Research continues on this trademark for the next edition of the **Blue Book of Guitars**.

KNOWBUDGE

Instruments built in Santa Barbara, California.

Knowbudge Productions introduces the "**Pinaka T.C. 1-441**" for the 1996-1997 season. With a retail price of $18,369.27, this six-string hollowbody features a sculptured Brunzchelle design, 22 fret ebony neck and graphite nut, and fixed bridge. The passive electronics consist of a volume control, and on/off switch, and a volume bypass switch. While the initial listing appeared in the 1996-97 Guitar Buyer's Guide (produced by Guitar World), no photo was forthcoming. The **Blue Book of Guitars** suggests contacting the company directly for further information via the Index of Current Manufacturers located in the rear of this book.

KNUTSON

Instruments currently built in Forrestville, California.

Knutson Luthiery currently offers high quality, handcrafted instruments. For further information regarding models, pricing, and availability, contact Knutson Luthiery through the Index of Current Manufacturers located in the rear of this book.

KOHNO

Instruments built in Japan from the mid 1960s to current.

Luthier Masaru Kohno was noted as being the leading Japanese "classical" guitarmaker in author Tony Bacon's **Ultimate Guitar Book** (1991). Kohno studied under luthier Arcangel Fernandez in his Madrid workshop, and later opened his own operation in Tokyo during the late 1960s.

KOLL

Instruments currently built in Portland, Oregon.

Luthier Saul Koll combines his background in art (sculpture) and his ten-year experience with instrument repair to design and construct his quality guitars. Most Koll instruments are custom ordered, although he does offer four basic models based on, but not replicas of, vintage style instruments. Koll's guitars are constructed with fine quality tone woods and a neck-through design. Prices run from $1,275 (Jr. Glide) to $1,375 (Thunder Glide Ali) and $1,475 (Duo Glide), up to $2,750 (Super Glide Almighty). For further information contact luthier Koll through the Index of Current Manufacturers located in the back of this book.

KOONTZ

See also STANDEL and HARPTONE.

Instruments built in Linden, New Jersey.

Luthier Stan Koontz designed several different models of acoustic and electric guitars and basses for Bob Crooks' Standel company. The instruments were built in Harptone's New Jersey facilities, and have the 'Standel' logo on the peghead. Koontz also built his own custom guitars that featured striking innovations as side-mounted electronics and a hinged internal f-hole cover.

(Source: Tom Wheeler, American Guitars)

KRAMER

Kramer Musical Industries, the current manufacturer, is located in Eatontown, New Jersey. Kramer (originally BKL) was located in Neptune, New Jersey since its original inception in 1975 to the late 1980s. Current production of Kramer (KMI) instruments is in the new facilities in Eatontown, New Jersey.

All high end and original aluminum-necked models were produced in America. The Focus series of guitars (1985 through 1989) were built in Japan, and the Striker series (also 1985 through 1989) were built in Korea.

Gary Kramer and Dennis Berardi founded the firm in October of 1975 to produce guitars. Kramer, one of the ex-partners of Travis Bean, brought in his guitar building know-how to Berardi's previous retail experience. In the following April, Peter J. LaPlaca joined the two. LaPlaca had worked his way up through Norlin to vice presidency before joining Kramer and Berardi. The original company is named after their three initials: B, K, L.

BKL opened the Neptune factory on July 1, 1976. The first Kramer guitar was co-designed by luthier Phil Petillo, Berardi, and Kramer. Once the prototypes were completed and the factory tooled up, the first production run was completed on November 15, 1976. The first solid body guitars featured an original body design, and a bolt-on aluminum neck with rear wood inlays.

One month after the first production run was finished, Gary Kramer left the BKL company. Guitar production under the Kramer trademark continued. By the early 1980s, the company line consists of 14 different guitar and bass designs with a price range of $649 to $1,418.

In 1985, Berardi bought the Spector company; production and distribution of Spector basses then originated from Kramer's facilities in New Jersey. Throughout the late 1980s, Kramer was one of the guitar companies favored by the hard rock/heavy metal bands (along with Charvel/Jackson). However, the company went into bankruptcy in 1989, attempted refinancing several times, and was purchased at auction by a group that incorporated the holdings under the company name of Kramer Musical Instruments in 1995. Kramer (KMI) recently re-introduced several new models in 1995, again sporting the aluminum neck that is the company's original trademark design. The newly-reformed Kramer (KMI) company also acquired, and owns, the rights to the Spector trademark and Spector instruments designs.

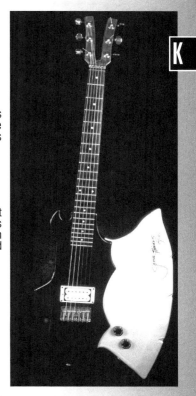

K

ACOUSTIC ELECTRIC

In the mid to late 1980s, Kramer offered several models designed by luthier Danny Ferrington. The Kramer Ferringtons were thin, hollow body acoustics with bridge mounted piezo pickup systems, volume and tone controls. The six on a side headstocks and slimmer profile necks felt more like an electric guitar, and the instruments could be used in performances with minimal feedback problems.

Kramer Ferrington models generally command $250 to $375 in the used market.

ELECTRIC

The first solid body guitars offered in 1975 featured aluminum necks with the open or "prong" v-shape. This is the first identifying clue in comparing a **Travis Bean** versus a **Kramer**, as all Travis Bean models have a "closed top" (which forms a enclosed 'T'). All featured original body designs and two Kramer pickups (they have KRAMER on the pickup covers). In 1978 the DMZ Custom series offered DiMarzio pickups. In the mid 1980s, Kramer began producing conventional wood neck/wood body guitars.

Aluminum neck BKL Kramers have a used price range of $200 to $450, depending on options, colors, and configurations.

The 1980s Kramer 'superstrat' models have different prices that are primarily based on the series/country of origin. While the American models are clearly high quality, the used market is leaning towards more traditional and vintage designs. Models should be priced in relation to demand (i.e. if the local musicians use them, then prices will be stronger than the national average).

MIDI

In the mid 1980s Kramer retailed a MIDI interface unit designed by IVL Technologies called the Pitchrider 7000. Ideally, any guitar could be hooked up to the Pitchrider 7000, have guitar information converted to a MIDI signal, and send that signal to any MIDI compatible synthesizer. Although not a guitar per se, this tool can add an extra dimension to an existing guitar.

Kramer (Gene Simmons) Axe guitar
courtesy Thoroughbred Music

KRUNDAAL

Instruments built in Italy during the 1960s.

There is still a mystery hanging over the Krundaal guitars, as far as the nature of the relationship between Krundaal, Wandre, and Davoli. The Krundaal 'Bikini' model (the guitar features an attached portable amplifier), features two single coil "Davoli" pickups, and under the logo it has stamped "A. Davoli, Made in Italy". Furthermore, the bridge features a stylized "W" design. Consensus currently is that the Davoli factory is the manufacturer, while the 'Wandre' and 'Krundaal' trademarks are either distributors or designers. Further information will be contained in future edition of the **Blue Book of Guitars**.

(Source: Tony Bacon, The Ultimate Guitar Book)

KUSTOM

Instruments built in Chanute, Kansas during the late 1960s.

The Kustom Amplifier company, builders of the famous "tuck-and-roll" covered amps, produced 4 different guitar models in their Kansas factory from 1967 to late 1969. Bud Ross, the founder/designer of Kustom, was a bassist turned second guitarist in the late 1950s who had a knack for electronics and wiring. Along with Fred Berry, Kustom amps debuted at the summer 1965 NAMM show, and eventually the line ranged from small combos to huge P.A.s and bass cabinets.

In 1967, Doyle Reeding approached Ross about building guitars. Along with Wesley Valorie, the three began designing electric guitars. Guitar wizard Roy Clark, who later became a Kustom amp endorser, also had input on the Kustom design. These semi-hollowbody guitars had DeArmond pickups and Bigsby vibratos. Ross estimates that between 2,000 and 3,000 were produced during the two years, all in the Kansas facility.

All models featured similar body designs, and differed on the equipment installed. The **K200A** featured two DeArmond humbuckers, a bound rosewood fingerboard, chrome-plated nut, and a factory Bigsby. The **K200B** had 2 DeArmond single coils, and a trapeze tailpiece. While the **K200C** was similar in pickups and hardware, it featured a smaller headstock design and less fancy tuning machines. The **K200D** was a bass guitar with two DeArmond bass single coils, and an unbound fingerboard.

(Source: Michael Wright, Guitar Stories Volume One, pgs. 155-164)

KYDD

Instruments currently built in Upper Darby, Pennsylvania.

Luthier Bruce Kaminsky custom builds quality electric upright basses. For further information contact luthier Bruce Kaminsky through the Index of Current Manufacturers located in the rear of this book.

K

La BAYE

Instruments built in Neodesha, Kansas in 1967. Designed and distributed by The La Baye company in Green Bay, Wisconsin. Current information can be obtained through Henri's Music of Green Bay (and Appleton), Wisconsin.

Inventor Dan Helland conceived the notion of a minimal-bodied guitar while working at Henri's Music Shop in Green Bay, Wisconsin during the mid 1960s. After receiving some support from owner Henri Czachor and others, Helland had the Holman-Woodell company of Neodesha, Kansas build the first (and only) run of 45 instruments. La Baye guitars share similar stock hardware pieces and pickups installed on Wurlitzer guitars of the same era, as Holman-Woodell were building a number of different trademarked instruments during the mid to late 1960s.

After receiving the first shipment, Helland attended the 1967 Chicago NAMM show (the same show where Ovation first debuted). Unfortunately, the minimal body concept was so far advanced that the market didn't catch up until Steinberger released his first bass in the 1980s! La Baye instruments were produced in 1967, and a total of 45 were shipped to Helland.

Identification is pretty straight forward, given that the 3+3 headstock will say 'La Baye' and '2 x 4'. The 22 fret neck bolts to the rectangular body, and controls are mounted on top and bottom of the body. There were four models: the six string and twelve string guitars, and the short-scale (single pickup) bass as well as the long-scale (2 pickup) bass. However, keep in mind that there are only 45 official La Baye instruments (others were later offered by Holman and 21st Century, from the same factory that built the initial models).

(Source: Michael Wright, Guitar Stories Volume One, pgs. 161-164)

La MANCHA

Instruments currently built in Mexico. Distributed by La Mancha Guitars of Nashville, Tennessee.

Jerry Roberts has been providing fine classical guitars for over a quarter century. In 1996, Roberts debuted the La Mancha line, which offers handcrafted guitars inspired by Fleta, Friederick, Gilbert, Hauser, Ramierez, Romanillos, Ruck, and other legendary makers. The current **Madrid** model (new list $1995), fashioned after Ramirez, is from noted California luthier Kenny Hill. For further information on models and availablility, please contact Jerry Roberts via the Index of Current Manufacturers located in the back of this book.

La PATRIE

Instruments built in La Patrie, Quebec, Canada since 1982. Distributed by LA SI DO, Inc. of St. Laurent, Quebec.

The village of La Patrie, Quebec has long been associated with Robert Godin as far back as the introduction of the Norman Guitar Company in 1972. Other Godin trademark instruments have been built there for years, so it was fitting that the line of classical guitars introduced in 1982 should bear the name of the La Patrie village.

For full overall company history, see GODIN.

ACOUSTIC

La Patrie Series

Grading	100%	98% MINT	95% EXC+	90% EXC	80% VG+	70% VG	60% G

All instruments in this series have the following features, unless otherwise listed: classic style, round soundhole, bound body, wood marquetry rosette, Honduras mahogany neck, 12/19 fret rosewood fingerboard, slotted peghead, 3 per side gold tuners with pearloid buttons. Available in a Natural finish of special alcohol lacquer. Mfg. 1982 to date.

All models are available in left handed versions.

All models may be optionally equipped with L.R. Baggs electronics.

All models may be optionally equipped with EPM electronics.

All models may be optionally equipped in a hardshell case.

COLLECTION — solid spruce top, solid rosewood back/sides, ebony tied bridge, high gloss lacquer finish.

	100%	98%	95%	90%	80%	70%	60%
Mfr.'s Sug. Retail	$625	$468	$312	$310	$250	$225	$205	$190

CONCERT — solid cedar top, mahogany back/sides, rosewood tied bridge, high gloss lacquer finish.

	100%	98%	95%	90%	80%	70%	60%
Mfr.'s Sug. Retail	$392	$313	$235	$235	$190	$170	$155	$140

Grading	100%	98% MINT	95% EXC+	90% EXC	80% VG+	70% VG	60% G

ETUDE — solid cedar top, mahogany back/sides, rosewood tied bridge, lacquer satin finish.

Mfr.'s Sug. Retail	$325	$243	$162	$160	$130	$115	$105	$95

PRESENTATION — solid spruce top, rosewood back/sides, rosewood tied bridge, semi-gloss lacquer finish.

Mfr.'s Sug. Retail	$475	$356	$237	$160	$130	$115	$105	$95

LaCOTE

Instruments built in Paris, France during the early to mid 1800s.

Luthier Rene Lacote was hand building acoustic guitars during the first half of the nineteenth century. According to author Tony Bacon, Lacote is sometimes credited with the invention of the scalloped fingerboard. Many of Lacote's guitars featured relatively small bodies braced with "transverse" strutting inside the top.

During the late 18th century, the European guitar was moving away from earlier designs containing 5 or 6 "courses" (a "course" was a pair of strings) to the simple six single string design. This design is closer to what the modern "classical" guitar looks like today. Lacote's designs in the 1830s followed the six string models.

(Source: Tony Bacon, The Ultimate Guitar Book)

LACEY

Instruments currently built in Nashville, Tennessee.

Luthier Mark Lacey studied formal training in musical instrument technology at the London School of Design. Lacey has been repairing and building fine instruments since 1976, and spent two years affiliated at Gruhn Guitars in Nashville, Tennesee where he gained insight from noted vintage guitar expert George Gruhn. For further information regarding model specifications, availability, and pricing, please contact luthier Mark Lacey through the Index of Current Manufacturers located in the back of this book.

LADO

Instruments built in Scarborough, Ontario (Canada) since early 1970s.

Lado founder and company president Joe Kovacic initially learned the guitar-building craft in Zagreb, Croatia. Kovacic gained luthier experience in Austria, Germany before leaving Europe to move to North America in 1971. Every handcrafted bass and guitar is backed by over thirty years experience.

ELECTRIC

Pro Series

CLASSIC — offset double cutaway curly maple body, thru body maple neck, 24 fret maple fingerboard with black pearl dot inlay, double locking vibrato, 6 on one side Schaller tuners, black hardware, rail/humbucker Seymour Duncan pickups, volume/tone control, 3 position switch. Available in Cobalt Blue, Deep Purple, Oriental Blue, Red and Transparent Black finishes. Curr. mfr.

Mfr.'s Sug. Retail	$1,995	$1,496	$997	$995	$795	$720	$660	$600

This model is also available with Bartolini, DiMarzio, EMG and LADO pickups.

GOLDEN WING — offset double cutaway curly maple body, maple body outline inlay, thru body maple neck, 24 fret ebony fingerboard with brass sharktooth inlay, double locking vibrato, bound reverse headstock, 6 on one side tuners, gold hardware, 2 humbucker Seymour Duncan pickups, volume/tone control, 3 position switch. Available in Cobalt Blue, Deep Purple, Oriental Blue, Red and Transparent Black finishes. Curr. mfr.

Mfr.'s Sug. Retail	$2,595	$1,946	$1,297	$1,295	$1,035	$930	$855	$780

This model is also available with Bartolini, DiMarzio, EMG and LADO pickups.

ROCKER — similar to Classic, except has 7 piece maple/mahogany body/neck construct, 24 fret ebony fingerboard with pearl sharktooth inlay, 2 single coil/1 humbucker pickup.

Mfr.'s Sug. Retail	$2,495	$1,996	$1,497	$1,250	$1,000	$900	$825	$750

This model is also available with Bartolini, DiMarzio, EMG and LADO pickups.

ELECTRIC BASS

Custom Series

STUDIO 604-P — offset double cutaway maple body, carved padauk top, thru body maple/padauk laminated neck, 24 fret ebony fingerboard with pearl dot inlay, fixed bridge, bone nut, padauk veneer on peghead, 2 per side Schaller tuners, black hardware, 2 Bartolini pickups, volume/balance/3 band EQ controls, active electronics. Available in Natural finish. Curr. mfr.

Mfr.'s Sug. Retail	$2,195	$1,756	$1,317	$1,100	$880	$790	$725	$660

Lacey Virtuoso
courtesy Scott Chinery

L

Grading	100%	98% MINT	95% EXC+	90% EXC	80% VG+	70% VG	60% G

STUDIO 605-B — similar to Studio 604-P, except has 5 strings, bubinga wood instead of padauk wood, abalone hexagon fingerboard inlay.

Mfr.'s Sug. Retail	$2,395	$1,796	$1,197	$1,195	$955	$855	$785	$715

STUDIO 606-Z — similar to Studio 604-P, except has 6 strings, zebra wood top, 7 piece maple/zebra/ebony neck, abalone hexagon fingerboard inlay.

Mfr.'s Sug. Retail	$2,595	$1,946	$1,297	$1,295	$1,035	$930	$855	$780

Legend Series

LEGEND 304 — offset double cutaway maple body, thru body maple/wenge neck, 24 fret ebony fingerboard with pearl dot inlay, fixed bridge, 2 per side Schaller tuners, black hardware, 2 EMG pickups, volume/treble/bass/balance controls. Available in Cobalt Blue, Deep Purple, Oriental Blue, Red and Transparent Black finishes. Curr. mfr.

Mfr.'s Sug. Retail	$1,895	$1,516	$1,137	$950	$760	$685	$625	$570

This model is also available with Gotoh tuners and Bartolini pickups.

LEGEND 305 — similar to Legend 304, except has 5 strings.

Mfr.'s Sug. Retail	$2,195	$1,756	$1,317	$1,100	$880	$790	$725	$660

LEGEND 306 — similar to Legend 304, except has 6 strings.

Mfr.'s Sug. Retail	$2,395	$1,796	$1,197	$1,195	$955	$855	$785	$715

Medallion Series

MEDALLION 404 — offset double cutaway maple body, thru body maple neck, 22 fret ebony fingerboard with pearl dot inlay, fixed bridge, 2 per side Schaller or Gotoh tuners, chrome hardware, P-style/J-style EMG pickups, volume/tone/balance controls. Available in Cobalt Blue, Deep Purple, Oriental Blue, Red and Transparent Black finishes. Curr. mfr.

Mfr.'s Sug. Retail	$1,895	$1,516	$1,137	$950	$760	$685	$625	$570

Add $300 for black hardware.

MEDALLION 405 — similar to Medallion 404, except has 5 strings, brass diamond fingerboard inlay and 2 J-style pickups.

Mfr.'s Sug. Retail	$2,395	$1,796	$1,197	$1,195	$955	$855	$785	$715

Add $100 for gold hardware.

Signature Series

504 — offset double cutaway asymmetrical maple body, thru body 5 piece rosewood/maple neck, 24 fret ebony fingerboard with pearl dot inlay, fixed bridge, rosewood veneered peghead with pearl dove/logo inlay, 2 per side Schaller tuners, chrome hardware, P-style/J-style Bartolini pickups, volume/treble/bass/balance controls. Available in Cobalt Blue, Deep Purple, Oriental Blue, Red and Transparent Black finishes. Curr. mfr.

Mfr.'s Sug. Retail	$2,095	$1,571	$1,047	$1,045	$840	$755	$685	$625

Add $400 for stylized pearl fingerboard inlay and black hardware.
Add $500 for stylized abalone fingerboard inlay and gold hardware.

Standard Series

204 — offset double cutaway ash body, thru body maple/ash neck, 22 fret maple fingerboard with black pearl inlay, fixed bridge, 4 on one side Schaller tuners, chrome hardware, P-style/J-style LADO pickups, volume/tone/balance controls. Available in Natural finish. Curr. mfr.

Mfr.'s Sug. Retail	$1,495	$1,196	$897	$750	$600	$540	$495	$450

Add $100 for ebony fingerboard with brass dot inlay.
Add $200 for ebony fingerboard with brass dot inlay and Transparent Black finish.
This model has Bartolini pickups optionally available.

LADY LUCK

Instruments produced in Korea following USA designs and specifications since 1986. Distribution in U.S., Europe, and South America by Lady Luck Industries, Inc. of Cary, Illinois.

In addition to the Lady Luck and Nouveau brands, Lady Luck Industries also distributes Neo Products guitars, Adder Plus pickups and EV Star Cables.

President Teresa Miller has been offering a wide range of imported, affordable guitars that are designed for beginning students up to working professionals. Acoustic electrics have a retail price that ranges from $310 to $378, and a line of electric guitars that start from $210 (LLS1) to $250 (LLS2). The new **Nouveau** series offers an original design, solid ash body with prices beginning at $375. The **Retrospect** series offers guitars with designs based on popular American favorites, and prices begin at $280 (LLT1). **La Femme** ($995) guitars feature a female-figure sculpted, styrene body and Bill Lawrence Keystone pickups.

"STYLE LEADER (a particular Kay model) is not just a great instrument to play, it's a great instrument to be seen playing!!!"
—Ron DeMarino
TCG, July/Aug 1990

L

LAG GUITARS

Instruments currently built in Bedarieux, France. LAG has been building guitars in France since 1980. The Hotline series is designed in France and built to their specifications in Korea.

LAG guitars traditionally are high quality superstrat designed solid bodies, although the company has developed some original designs through the years. Led by Michael Chavarria, the Bedarieux facility currently has eleven workers. LAG has currently cut back on custom models in favor of offering more options on the four series in the new line.

In 1994, Lag introduced the new **Hotline** Series. Hotline guitar designs are conceived in France and built to LAG specifications in Korea. All models come equipped with the new DUNCAN DESIGNED pickups, and are available in one of three colors: Black see-through, Green see-through, or Red see-through.

Current models include the dual cutaway **Roxanne**, the 'superstrat' **Beast**, the traditional styles **Blues** model, and the **Rockline** (the Metalmaster model has been in production for over ten years). Interested individuals can contact the company through the Index of Current Manufacturers located in the back of this book.

ELECTRIC

Grading	100%	98% MINT	95% EXC+	90% EXC	80% VG+	70% VG	60% G

90 COLLECTION — offset double cutaway semi hollow mahogany body, arched curly maple top, bolt-on maple neck, 24 fret ebony fingerboard with offset abalone dot inlay, standard vibrato, roller nut, 3 per side locking Sperzel tuners, gold hardware, 2 humbucker Seymour Duncan pickups, volume/tone/EQ control, 3 position switch, coil split in controls, active electronics. Available in Classic, DeLuxe, and Standard finishes. Curr. mfr.

Mfr.'s Sug. Retail	$1,885	$1,508	$1,131	$945	$755	$680	$620	$565

Soundholes and body binding are optional.

CUSTOM — offset double cutaway alder body, curly maple top, transparent pickguard, bolt-on maple neck, 24 fret maple fingerboard with offset abalone inlay, double locking vibrato, reverse headstock, 6 on one side tuners, black hardware, 2 single coil/1 humbucker Seymour Duncan pickups, volume/tone/EQ control, 5 position switch, coil split in volume control, active electronics. Available in Classic, DeLuxe, Heavy Metal and Standard finishes. Curr. mfr.

Mfr.'s Sug. Retail	$1,800	$1,440	$1,080	$900	$720	$650	$595	$540

This model is also available with birdseye neck, strat style peghead and humbucker/single coil/humbucker pickups.

Rockline Series

This series is available with reverse headstock.

RME — offset double cutaway alder body, bolt-on maple neck, 24 fret rosewood fingerboard with offset abalone dot inlay, double locking vibrato, 6 on one side tuners, black hardware, single coil/trembucker Seymour Duncan pickups, volume control, 3 position switch. Available in Classic, DeLuxe, Heavy Metal and Standard finishes. Curr. mfr.

Mfr.'s Sug. Retail	$1,605	$1,284	$963	$805	$645	$575	$530	$480

RMV — similar to RME, except has 2 single coil/1 trembucker pickups, tone control, 5 position switch.

Mfr.'s Sug. Retail	$1,715	$1,372	$1,029	$860	$685	$615	$565	$515

VRL — sharkfin style alder body, bolt-on maple neck, 24 fret rosewood fingerboard with offset abalone dot inlay, double locking vibrato, 6 on one side tuners, black hardware, humbucker Seymour Duncan pickup, volume control. Available in Heavy Metal and Standard finishes. Curr. mfr.

Mfr.'s Sug. Retail	$1,800	$1,440	$1,080	$900	$720	$650	$595	$540

This model also available with trembucker pickup.

ELECTRIC BASS

The Natural finish models have a walnut, wenge or bubinga body.
Add $390 for 5 string version.
Add $510 for 6 string version.

90 Bass Collection

BC90 — offset double cutaway walnut body, bolt-on maple neck, 24 fret rosewood fingerboard with offset abalone dot inlay, tunomatic bridge/stop tailpiece, 2 per side tuners, black hardware, 2 J-style Bartolini pickups, 2 volume/tone/EQ controls, active electronics. Available in DeLuxe, Natural and Standard finishes. Curr. mfr.

Mfr.'s Sug. Retail	$1,650	$1,320	$990	$825	$660	$595	$545	$495

BC90 THL — offset double cutaway semi hollow alder body, figured maple top, bolt-on maple neck, 24 fret ebony fingerboard with offset abalone dot inlay, tunomatic bridge/stop tailpiece, 2 per side tuners, gold hardware, 2 J-style Bartolini pickups, 2 volume/tone/EQ controls, active electronics. Available in DeLuxe, Natural and Standard finishes. Curr. mfr.

Mfr.'s Sug. Retail	$1,750	$1,400	$1,050	$875	$700	$630	$575	$525

This model is also available with soundholes and binding as options.

LAKEWOOD

Instruments built in Germany. Distributed in the U.S. by Dana B. Goods of Santa Barbara, California.

Luthier Martin Seeliger's Lakewood instruments feature spruce tops, Brazilian or Indian rosewood, walnut, koa, or ovankol backs and sides, mahogany necks, ebony or rosewood fingerboards with abalone inlays, and all wood bindings. For further information contact Dana B. Goods through the Index of Current Manufacturers located in the back of this book.

LAKLAND

Instruments built in Chicago, Illinois since 1994.

Luthier Dan Lakin has been playing and buying/selling bass guitars for a number of years. In 1994, he began offering a high quality, custom built electric bass with a design based on Leo Fender's latter models. The Lakland Bass is offered in either 4-string ($1,895) and 5-string ($2,095) versions and features a swamp ash body, maple neck, maple, rosewood, or ebony fingerboard, and Bartolini pickups. Total production for 1996 for all models is not to exceed 200. For further information contact Lakland Musical Instruments through the Index of Current Manufacturers located in the back of this book.

LANDOLA

Instruments built in Finland. Distributed by Quality First Products of Forest City, North Carolina.

Landola offers several models of quality acoustic guitars. For further information contact Quality First Products through the Index of Current Manufacturers located in the rear of this book.

LANGE

See PARAMOUNT.

See also ORPHEUM.

In the late 1890s, William L. Lange was a partner in Rettberg & Lange, a major East coast banjo producer and distributor. Lange expanded the company into the William L. Lange Company in the early 1920s, and supplied the C. Bruno & Son distributor with both **Paramount** and **Orpheum** banjo lines. In 1934, Lange debuted the Paramount guitar series - and some of the models were built by the C.F. Martin guitar company. Lange was quick to add Orpheum-branded guitars, and some of those models were built by Chicago's Kay company.

Lange's company went out of business in the early 1940s, but New York distributor Maurice Lipsky resumed distribution of Orpheum guitars in 1944. By the late 1940s, the Paramount guitar line was distributed by Gretsch & Brenner. Future model designations/indentifications will appear in updated editons of the **Blue Book of Guitars**.

(Source: Tom Wheeler, American Guitars)

Lakland Deluxe
courtesy Dan Lakin

LARKIN

Instruments currently built in Ireland.

Larkin offers three models of handcrafted acoustic electric guitars. Prices range from $2,250 (ASAP) to $3,600 (ASAS Jazz archtop). For further information contact Larkin through the Index of Current Manufacturers located in the rear of this book.

LARRIVEE

Instruments built in Vancouver, British Columbia (Canada) since 1968.

Luthier Jean Larrivee founded his company back in the late 1960s, and his attention to detail not only in building but special inlay work soon made a Larrivee acoustic the sought after guitar to find.

ACOUSTIC

Unless otherwise noted, all Larrivee models are constructed with the same standard materials: spruce top, round soundhole, wood body binding, wooden inlay rosette, transparent pickguard, rosewood or figured maple back/sides, mahogany neck, bound ebony fingerboard, ebony bridge with black pearl dot pins, and 3 per side chrome tuners. All instruments are available in left handed versions at no additional charge.

In addition, the instruments are available in standard body styles with their own distinct features. Again, variances will be listed.

Numerical suffixes listed below indicate individualized features per model suffix.

05 Mahogany Standard (mahogany back/sides).

09 Standard (pearl logo peghead inlay).

10 Deluxe (abalone purfling on top, abalone/pearl fingerboard inlay, peghead bordered by inlaid silver, hand-engraved Eagle, Gryphon, Pelican or Seahorse on headstock).

19 Special (abalone/pearl fingerboard inlay, hand-engraved Eagle, Gryphon, Pelican or Seahorse on headstock).

50 Standard (ebony fingerboard [pearl dot inlay available on request], pearl logo peghead inlay).

60 Special (Eagle [with feather fingerboard inlay], Stallion and Tiger peghead inlay).

70 DeLuxe (abalone purfled body/rosette, Eagle [with feather fingerboard inlay], Stallion and Tiger peghead inlay).

Grading	100%	98% MINT	95% EXC+	90% EXC	80% VG+	70% VG	60% G

72 Presentation (abalone purfling on all bound edges, abalone rosette, abalone/pearl fingerboard inlay, peghead bordered by inlaid silver, hand-engraved Dancing Ladies, Genies, Jester, Mermaid on Seahorse or Tamborine Lady inlay on headstock, bridge wing inlays).

All instruments are also available with following options:
A 12 string variation is available in the following models for an additional $190: Cutaway, Cutaway Jumbo, Dreadnought, Jumbo, Larrivee and Larrivee Jumbo Series.
Add $140 for Fishman Matrix pickup.
Add $280 for Fishman pickup with preamp.
Add $1,000 for Brazilian rosewood (when available).

Classic Series

L-35 — classic style, unbound fingerboard, tied bridge, 3 per side gold tuners with pearl buttons. Curr. mfr.

	100%	98%	95%	90%	80%	70%	60%
Mfr.'s Sug. Retail	$2,580	$1,935	$1,290	$1,215	$965	$825	$755	$690

L-38 — single sharp cutaway classic style, unbound fingerboard, tied bridge, 3 per side gold tuners with pearl buttons. Curr. mfr.

Mfr.'s Sug. Retail	$2,895	$2,171	$1,447	$1,360	$1,080	$930	$855	$780

Cutaway Series

The instruments in this series have the Larrivee body style with a single sharp cutaway. Curr. mfr.

C-05 — Mahogany Standard

Mfr.'s Sug. Retail	$1,795	$1,346	$897	$810	$640	$535	$490	$445

C-09 — Standard

Mfr.'s Sug. Retail	$2,090	$1,567	$1,045	$975	$770	$660	$605	$550

C-10 — DeLuxe

Mfr.'s Sug. Retail	$2,720	$2,040	$1,360	$1,280	$1,015	$870	$800	$730

C-19 — Special

Mfr.'s Sug. Retail	$2,385	$1,788	$1,192	$1,120	$890	$760	$690	$635

C-50 — Standard. New 1994.

Mfr.'s Sug. Retail	$2,270	$1,702	$1,135	$1,130	$900	$810	$740	$680

C-60 — Special. New 1994.

Mfr.'s Sug. Retail	$2,690	$2,152	$1,614	$1,345	$1,075	$965	$885	$805

C-70 — DeLuxe. New 1994.

Mfr.'s Sug. Retail	$3,200	$2,560	$1,920	$1,600	$1,280	$1,150	$1,055	$960

C-72 — Presentation

Mfr.'s Sug. Retail	$5,390	$4,042	$2,695	$2,575	$2,035	$1,785	$1,640	$1,490

Cutaway Jumbo Series

All the instruments in this series have jumbo Larrivee body styles with a single sharp cutaway. Curr. mfr.

LCJ-05 — Mahogany Standard

Mfr.'s Sug. Retail	$1,840	$1,380	$920	$850	$670	$575	$525	$475

LCJ-09 — Standard

Mfr.'s Sug. Retail	$2,195	$1,646	$1,097	$1,025	$810	$690	$630	$575

LCJ-10 — DeLuxe

Mfr.'s Sug. Retail	$2,825	$2,118	$1,412	$1,330	$1,055	$910	$835	$760

LCJ-19 — Special

Mfr.'s Sug. Retail	$2,490	$1,867	$1,245	$1,160	$920	$795	$730	$665

LCJ-72 — Presentation

Mfr.'s Sug. Retail	$5,595	$4,196	$2,797	$2,680	$2,130	$1,860	$1,700	$1,545

Cutaway Small Body Series

Fashioned after the Larrivee small body style, these instruments have a single sharp cutaway. Curr. mfr.

CS-05 — Mahogany Standard

Mfr.'s Sug. Retail	$1,735	$1,301	$867	$800	$630	$535	$490	$445

CS-09 — Standard

Mfr.'s Sug. Retail	$2,090	$1,567	$1,045	$970	$765	$660	$605	$550

CS-10 — Deluxe

Mfr.'s Sug. Retail	$2,720	$2,040	$1,360	$1,280	$1,015	$870	$800	$730

"At that time, around 1955, solid body guitars had come into vogue, so Gretsch added the Penguin to their solid body line of Duo Jets, Silver Jets, etc., but it was costly to produce and the retail market could not handle such an expensive item."

—*Gordon Dow*
TCG, Sept/Oct 1990

Grading	100%	98% MINT	95% EXC+	90% EXC	80% VG+	70% VG	60% G

CS-19 — Special
Mfr.'s Sug. Retail $2,385 $1,788 $1,192 $1,115 $885 $760 $690 $635

CS-72 — Presentation
Mfr.'s Sug. Retail $5,390 $4,042 $2,695 $2,575 $2,050 $1,785 $1,640 $1,490

Dreadnought Series

All instruments in this series have dreadnought style bodies. Curr. mfr.

D-05 — Mahogany Standard
Mfr.'s Sug. Retail $1,420 $1,065 $710 $650 $510 $430 $390 $360

D-09 — Standard
Mfr.'s Sug. Retail $1,785 $1,338 $892 $825 $650 $555 $510 $460

D-10 — DeLuxe
Mfr.'s Sug. Retail $2,385 $1,788 $1,192 $1,110 $880 $760 $690 $635

D-19 — Special
Mfr.'s Sug. Retail $2,085 $1,563 $1,042 $970 $765 $660 $605 $550

D-50 — Standard. New 1994.
Mfr.'s Sug. Retail $1,970 $1,576 $1,182 $985 $790 $710 $650 $590

D-60 — Special. New 1994.
Mfr.'s Sug. Retail $2,390 $1,912 $1,434 $1,195 $955 $855 $785 $715

D-70 — DeLuxe. New 1994.
Mfr.'s Sug. Retail $2,870 $2,152 $1,435 $1,430 $1,145 $1,030 $945 $860

D-72 — Presentation
Mfr.'s Sug. Retail $4,875 $3,656 $2,437 $2,330 $1,850 $1,610 $1,480 $1,345

Koa Series

All instruments in this series have single sharp cutaway style bodies, koa top/back/sides, seashell fingerboard/bridge wing inlay, dolphin peghead inlay. Disc. 1994.

C-20 — Larrivee style body.
   $1,475 $1,265 $1,055 $845 $760 $690 $635
Last Mfr.'s Sug. Retail was $2,110.

CJ-20 — Larrivee jumbo style body.
   $1,545 $1,325 $1,105 $885 $795 $730 $665
Last Mfr.'s Sug. Retail was $2,210.

CS-20 — Larrivee small style body.
   $1,475 $1,265 $1,055 $845 $760 $690 $635
Last Mfr.'s Sug. Retail was $2,110.

Larrivee Series

All instruments in this series have Larrivee style bodies. Curr. mfr.

L-05 — Mahogany Standard
Mfr.'s Sug. Retail $1,420 $1,065 $710 $650 $510 $430 $390 $360

L-09 — Standard
Mfr.'s Sug. Retail $1,785 $1,338 $892 $825 $650 $555 $510 $460

L-10 — Deluxe
Mfr.'s Sug. Retail $2,385 $1,788 $1,192 $1,120 $890 $760 $690 $635

L-19 — Special
Mfr.'s Sug. Retail $2,085 $1,563 $1,042 $975 $770 $660 $605 $550

L-50 — Standard. New 1994.
Mfr.'s Sug. Retail $1,970 $1,576 $1,182 $985 $790 $710 $650 $590

L-60 — Special. New 1994.
Mfr.'s Sug. Retail $2,390 $1,912 $1,434 $1,195 $955 $855 $785 $715

L-70 — DeLuxe. New 1994.
Mfr.'s Sug. Retail $2,870 $2,152 $1,435 $1,430 $1,145 $1,030 $945 $860

Grading	100%	98% MINT	95% EXC+	90% EXC	80% VG+	70% VG	60% G

L-72 — Presentation
| Mfr.'s Sug. Retail | $4,875 | $3,900 | $2,925 | $2,730 | $1,855 | $1,610 | $1,480 | $1,345 |

Larrivee Jumbo Series

All instruments in this series have Larrivee Jumbo style bodies. Curr. mfr.

LJ-05 — Mahogany Standard
| Mfr.'s Sug. Retail | $1,530 | $1,147 | $765 | $710 | $560 | $465 | $425 | $385 |

LJ-09 — Standard
| Mfr.'s Sug. Retail | $1,895 | $1,421 | $947 | $880 | $695 | $590 | $545 | $495 |

LJ-10 — Deluxe
| Mfr.'s Sug. Retail | $2,500 | $1,875 | $1,250 | $1,170 | $930 | $795 | $730 | $665 |

LJ-19 — Special
| Mfr.'s Sug. Retail | $2,195 | $1,646 | $1,097 | $1,025 | $810 | $690 | $630 | $575 |

LJ-72 — Presentation
| Mfr.'s Sug. Retail | $4,990 | $3,742 | $2,495 | $2,410 | $1,910 | $1,650 | $1,515 | $1,375 |

Larrivee OM Series

All instruments in this series have Larrivee OM style bodies. Curr. mfr.

OM-05 — Mahogany Standard
| Mfr.'s Sug. Retail | $1,420 | $1,065 | $710 | $645 | $510 | $430 | $390 | $360 |

OM-09 — Standard
| Mfr.'s Sug. Retail | $1,785 | $1,338 | $892 | $825 | $650 | $555 | $510 | $460 |

OM-10 — Deluxe
| Mfr.'s Sug. Retail | $2,385 | $1,788 | $1,192 | $1,120 | $890 | $760 | $690 | $635 |

OM-19 — Special
| Mfr.'s Sug. Retail | $2,085 | $1,563 | $1,042 | $970 | $765 | $660 | $605 | $550 |

OM-72 — Presentation
| Mfr.'s Sug. Retail | $4,875 | $3,656 | $2,437 | $2,330 | $1,850 | $1,610 | $1,480 | $1,345 |

Larrivee Small Series

All instruments in this series have Larrivee Small style bodies. Curr. mfr.

LS-05 — Mahogany Standard
| Mfr.'s Sug. Retail | $1,420 | $1,065 | $710 | $645 | $510 | $430 | $390 | $360 |

LS-09 — Standard
| Mfr.'s Sug. Retail | $1,785 | $1,338 | $892 | $825 | $650 | $555 | $510 | $460 |

LS-10 — Deluxe
| Mfr.'s Sug. Retail | $2,385 | $1,788 | $1,192 | $1,120 | $890 | $760 | $690 | $635 |

LS-19 — Special
| Mfr.'s Sug. Retail | $2,085 | $1,563 | $1,042 | $970 | $765 | $660 | $605 | $550 |

LS-72 — Presentation
| Mfr.'s Sug. Retail | $4,875 | $3,656 | $2,437 | $2,330 | $1,850 | $1,610 | $1,480 | $1,345 |

Larrivee 00 Series

All instruments in this series have Larrivee 00 style bodies. Curr. mfr.

00-05 — Mahogany Standard
| Mfr.'s Sug. Retail | $1,420 | $1,065 | $710 | $645 | $510 | $430 | $390 | $360 |

00-09 — Standard
| Mfr.'s Sug. Retail | $1,785 | $1,338 | $892 | $825 | $650 | $555 | $510 | $460 |

00-10 — Deluxe
| Mfr.'s Sug. Retail | $2,385 | $1,788 | $1,192 | $1,120 | $890 | $760 | $690 | $635 |

00-19 — Special
| Mfr.'s Sug. Retail | $2,085 | $1,563 | $1,042 | $970 | $765 | $660 | $605 | $550 |

L

Grading	100%	98% MINT	95% EXC+	90% EXC	80% VG+	70% VG	60% G

00-72 — Presentation
Mfr.'s Sug. Retail $4,875 $3,656 $2,437 $2,330 $1,850 $1,610 $1,480 $1,345

Traditional Jumbo Series

All instruments in this series have Jumbo style bodies. Curr. mfr.

J-05 — Mahogany Standard
Mfr.'s Sug. Retail $1,530 $1,147 $765 $700 $550 $465 $425 $385

J-09 — Standard
Mfr.'s Sug. Retail $1,895 $1,421 $947 $880 $695 $590 $545 $495

J-10 — Deluxe
Mfr.'s Sug. Retail $2,500 $1,875 $1,250 $1,170 $930 $795 $730 $665

J-19 — Special
Mfr.'s Sug. Retail $2,195 $1,646 $1,097 $1,025 $810 $690 $630 $575

J-72 — Presentation
Mfr.'s Sug. Retail $4,990 $3,742 $2,495 $2,385 $1,895 $1,650 $1,515 $1,375

LARSON BROTHERS

1917 photograph

August Larson
courtesy Robert Carl Hartman

Larson Brothers of Maurer & Co. (1900-1944).

Carl Larson immigrated from Sweden during the 1880s and began working in the musical instrument trade in the Chicago area. He soon sent for younger brother August who also had a great aptitude for woodworking. In 1900 August and other investors bought out Robert Maurer's Chicago-based business of manufacturing guitars and mandolins. August and Carl ran the business and maintained the Maurer & Co. name throughout their careers which ended with the death of August in 1944. During that period they produced a vast array of stringed instruments including guitars, harp guitars, mandolin orchestra pieces and harp mandolin orchestra pieces, and a few ukes, taro-patches, tiples, and mandolinettos. Through the years the styles changed and also the basic sizes of guitars and mandolins. They were built larger starting in the mid-1930s to accommodate the demand from players for more volume.

The Larson brothers "house" brand was the Maurer up to the transition period of the larger body instruments when the Euphonon brand was initiated for guitars and mandolins. The Maurer brand was used on guitars and mandolin orchestra pieces of many designs during that approximate 35-year period. The guitars ranged from oak body small guitars to pearl and abalone trimmed guitars and mandolins having tree-of-life inlays on the fingerboards. These are beautifully made instruments of the highest quality, but even the less fancy models are well made in the tradition of the Larson brothers' craftsmanship. The guitars with the 12-fret-to-the-body neck sizes came in widths of 12¾", 13½", 14" and 15".

The Larson brothers also built guitars, harp guitars, and mandolin orchestra pieces for Wm. C. Stahl of Milwaukee and W.J. Dyer of St. Paul, as well as other assorted suppliers who put their own name on the Larsons' products. Stahl and Dyer claimed to be the makers - a common practice during those "progressive years."

1939 photograph

Carl Larson
courtesy Robert Carl Hartman

The Prairie State brand was added in the mid-1920s for guitars only. These followed the styles of the better and best grade Maurer models but incorporated one of three main systems of steel rods running the length of the guitar body. August was awarded three patents for these ideas which included side items such as adjustable bridges, fingerboards and necks.

The Prairie State guitars and the better and best grade Maurers and Stahls had a system of laminated top braces. August patented this idea in 1904 making the Larsons pioneers in designing the first guitars made for steel strings which are the only kind they ever made. The laminated braces were continued in the larger Prairie States and the better and best grade models of the Euphonon brand. An occasional Maurer brand instrument may be found in the larger size bodies which I attribute to those sold by Wack Sales Co. of Milwaukee during this later period. This outlet was not offered the Euphonon brand, so they sold them under the Maurer name.

The Larson brothers sold their wares to many prominent players from the radio stations in Chicago, mainly WLS and WJJD. These stations put on country music shows with live performances and became very popular. The Larsons also built three guitars for Les Paul, one of which was a step in developing the solid body guitar. A Larson fingerboard can be seen on what Les called "The Log" which he submitted to Gibson to sell his solid body idea. Gene Autry and Patsy Montana bought Euphonon guitars from the Larsons' shop in 1937.

The main brands produced by the Larsons were Maurer, Prairie State, Euphonon, W.J. Dyer, and Wm. C. Stahl. J.F. Stetson was Dyer's brand for their regular flat-top guitar, while the Dyer label was used for the "Symphony" series of harp-guitars and harp-mandolin family instruments.

The Larson brands were burned into the center inside back strip below the sound-hole. Typically, if an instrument was altered from standard, it was not branded. This led to many not having any markings. All of the instruments built by the Larsons were handmade. Their degree of craftsmanship has rendered them to be wonderful instruments to play and have become highly collectible. Many people believe that the Larsons' products are as good as Martins and Gibsons, and some believe that they are better. The Larson-built guitars are considered the best harp guitars ever made!

More information regarding the individual brands can be found under their brand names: Maurer, Prairie State, Euphonon, Wm. C. Stahl and W.J. Dyer.

For more information regarding Maurer & Co. and the Larson Brothers, a Maurer/Prairie State catalog, Wm. C. Stahl catalog, the Larson patents, and a CD by Muriel Anderson which demonstrates the different sounds built into many styles of Larson-made guitars, see The Larsons' Creations, Guitars and Mandolins, *by Robert Carl Hartman, Centerstream Publishing, P.O. Box 5450, Fullerton, CA 92635, phone/fax (714) 779-9390.*

LAUNAY KING

Instruments built in England during the mid 1970s.

These high quality solid body guitars featured original design stylings and "ultra-comprehensive" active circuitry. The entire line consisted of two different series of guitars, the Swayback series and the Prototype series.

(Source: Tony Bacon and Paul Day, The Guru's Guitar Guide)

LEA ELECTRIC GUITARS

Instruments built in East Islip, New York since 1995.

Luthier Bob Lea has been building guitars for a number of years, but decided to offer his custom creations to the public in late 1995.

Lea Custom guitars are offered in two models: The Century has a single cutaway body design, while the Robbie is a double cutaway available in two distinct body shapes. All feature a through-body neck design and 24 fret rosewood fingerboard, and two humbuckers. Custom features are offered "in almost limitless combinations", says Lea.

For further information, contact Bob Lea through the Index of Current Manufacturers located in the rear of this book.

LEDUC

Instruments are built in Japan, and distributed by Leduc Instruments of Sun Valley, California. They are also available through World Arts of East Northport, New York.

Leduc electric bass guitars are offered in 4-, 5-, or 6-string variations, and are built of high quality tone woods. The **PAD** series starts at $2,150 up to $2,895; the **U** series ranges from $3,295 to $4,195; and the semi-acoustic **U.Bass** series ranges from $2,995 to $3,895. For further information contact Leduc Instruments through the Index of Current Manufacturers located in the back of this book.

LEVIN

Instruments were built in Sweden during the mid 1960s to the late 1970s. In the early 1970s, The American company Martin bought Levin, and models thereafter bear Martin design influence.

The Levin company of Sweden built good quality flat-top guitars, as well as single cutaway one (or two) pickup archtops. Levin was active from the early 1960s, and was purchased in the early 1970s by the Martin Guitar company (U.S.). While early Levins had some Martin qualities prior to the sale, they definitely showed Martin influence afterwards. However, most acoustic guitars do owe something to the "direct simplicity" of C.F. Martin's original designs from the 1800's. There is very little room for innovations on production guitars due to the nature of Martin's "X-bracing" pattern. Production focused on flat-tops after the company sale.

(Source: Tony Bacon, The Ultimate Guitar Book)

LEW CHASE

Instruments were built in Japan during the late 1970s.

Guitars for the Lew Chase trademark were built by Azumi prior to introduction of their own trademark in the early 1980s. Azumi instruments were generally medium quality solid bodies; expect the same of Lew Chase branded guitars.

(Source: Tony Bacon and Paul Day, The Guru's Guitar Guide)

LEWIS

Instruments currently built in Grass Valley, California.

Luthier Michael A. Lewis has been offering handcrafted guitars for a number of years. For further information contact luthier Michael A. Lewis through the Index of Current Manufacturers located in the back of this book.

LINC LUTHIER

Instruments currently built in Upland, California.

Designer Linc Luthier offers handcrafted instruments that feature exotic hardwoods. All bodies are semi-acoustic, and are designed to create an instrument that is lighter in weight as well as possessing greater audio character. For further information regarding models, available woods, and specifications, please contact Linc Luthier through the Index of Current Manufacturers located in the back of this book.

LINCOLN

Instruments produced in Japan between the late 1970s and the early 1980s.

Lincoln instruments featured both original designs and designs based on classic American favorites; most guitars considered good quality.

(Source: Tony Bacon and Paul Day, The Guru's Guitar Guide)

LINDERT

Instruments currently produced in Chelan, Washington.

All instruments are easily recognizable by Lindert's eye-catching "Thumbs Up" headstock. Lindert offers a series of models with original designs and solid body construction. Prices range from $1,099 to $1,399. For further information contact Lindert through the Index of Current Manufacturers located in the back of this book.

LION

See EGMOND.

Instruments built in Holland during the late 1960s.

Guitars carrying the Lion trademark were built by the Egmond guitar company during the late 1960s. These low quality to entry level instruments featured both original and designs based on classic American favorites in both solid and semi-hollowbody configurations.

(Source: Tony Bacon and Paul Day, The Guru's Guitar Guide)

Lindert Victor model courtesy Lindert Guitars

LOGABASS

Instruments are built in Japan, and distributed by Leduc Instruments of Sun Valley, California. Instruments are also available through World Arts of East Northport, New York.

Instruments are built by Sanox (S S S Sound Company, Ltd.) in Kanie Aichi (Japan) and are high quality basses.

LONE STAR

Instruments currently made in Mexico. Distributed by M&M Merchandisers, Inc. of Fort Worth, Texas.

Lone Star guitars are available with laminate, solid cedar, or solid spruce tops and are designed for the beginner to intermediate student. For further information contact M&M Merchandisers, Inc. through the Index of Current Manufacturers located in the back of this book.

LOPER

Instruments built in Hawthorne, Florida since 1995. Distributed by Guitar Works of Hawthorne, Florida.

Luthier Joe Loper is currently building high quality custom bass guitars that feature a neck-through design. His original designs contain a number of stylish innovations that indicate fine attention to detail. For further information, contact Loper at the Guitar Works via the Index of Current Manufacturers located in the back of this book.

LoPRINZI

Instruments built in Rosemont, Hopeville, and Plainsboro, New Jersey from 1972 to 1980.

Thomas R. LoPrinzi, along with his brother Augustino, originally founded LoPrinzi guitars in New Jersey in early 1972. The business grew from a two- and three-man operation into a staff of 18 employees. Modern production techniques enabled the LoPrinzi brothers to pare the number of employees back to 7 while still producing 60 to 80 guitars a month in the late 1970s. Augustino LoPrinzi, tired of overseeing production, sold the business to Maark Corporation (a subsidiary of AMF). His brother Thomas was then named president of LoPrinzi Guitars. The AMF-owned company continued producing guitars for a number of years, and finally closed the doors in 1980. Years later, Augustino called AMF to request his old trademark back. Working with vice president Dick Hargraves, Augustino officially had the trademark transferred back, and has combined it to form the current **Augustino LoPrinzi** line of classical guitars.

(Source: Hal Hammer)

LoPrinzi guitars were available in three sizes: Standard, folk, and 12-string. Early designs featured German silver Spruce tops and Brazilian Rosewood; later models had tops built out of Canadian and Alaskan Spruce, and bodies constructed with Indian Rosewood, Flamed Maple, and Honduran Mahogany. All models have an adjustable truss rod, Ebony fingerboard, pearl or abalone inlays, and a Rosewood bridge.

LORD

Instruments built in Japan.

Guitars with the Lord trademark originated in Japan, and were distributed in the U.S. by the Halifax company.

(Source: Michael Wright, Guitar Stories Volume One, pg. 76)

LOTUS

See ARBOR.

Instruments produced in Korea, and distributed by Midco International of Effingham, Illinois.

Lotus guitars are designed for the novice/entry level guitarist.

LOWDEN

Instruments built by hand in Ireland since 1973, and distributed in the U.S. by Quality First Products of Forest City, North Carolina. Some models produced between 1981 and 1985 were built by Japanese luthiers. Full production returned to Ireland in 1985.

In 1973, luthier George Lowden began designing and manufacturing hand built guitars in Ireland. Demand outgrew the one-person effort and the production of some models were farmed out to luthiers in Japan in 1981. However, full production was returned to Ireland in 1985.

ACOUSTIC

Grading	100%	98% MINT	95% EXC+	90% EXC	80% VG+	70% VG	60% G

Dreadnought Series

D-22 — dreadnought style, cedar top, round soundhole, wood bound body, abalone rosette, mahogany back/sides, mahogany/sycamore 5 piece neck, 14/20 fret ebony fingerboard with pearl dot inlay, rosewood bridge, rosewood veneered peghead with pearl logo inlay, 3 per side gold tuners with amber buttons. Available in Natural finish. Mfd. 1993 to date.

| Mfr.'s Sug. Retail | $2,390 | $1,912 | $1,434 | $1,195 | $955 | $855 | $785 | $715 |

D-32 — dreadnought style, spruce top, round soundhole, wood bound body, abalone rosette, mahogany back/sides, mahogany/sycamore 5 piece neck, 14/20 fret ebony fingerboard with pearl dot inlay, rosewood bridge, rosewood veneered peghead with pearl logo inlay, 3 per side gold tuners with amber buttons. Available in Natural finish. Mfd. 1993 to date.

| Mfr.'s Sug. Retail | $2,790 | $2,232 | $1,674 | $1,395 | $1,115 | $1,005 | $920 | $835 |

D-45 — dreadnought style, cedar top, round soundhole, wood bound body, abalone rosette, Brazilian rosewood back/sides, mahogany/sycamore 5 piece neck, 14/20 fret ebony fingerboard with pearl dot inlay, rosewood bridge, rosewood veneered peghead with pearl logo inlay, 3 per side gold tuners with amber buttons. Available in Natural finish. New 1994.

| Mfr.'s Sug. Retail | $7,390 | $5,912 | $4,434 | $3,695 | $2,955 | $2,660 | $2,435 | $2,215 |

F Series

F-22 — folk style, cedar top, round soundhole, wood bound body, wood inlay rosette, mahogany back/sides, mahogany/rosewood 5 piece neck, 14/20 fret ebony fingerboard with pearl dot inlay, rosewood bridge, pearl logo inlay and rosewood veneer on peghead, 3 per side gold tuners with pearl buttons. Available in Natural finish. Disc. 1994.

| | $1,500 | $1,290 | $1,075 | $860 | $775 | $710 | $645 |

Last Mfr.'s Sug. Retail was $2,145.

F-24 — similar to F-22, except has spruce top, maple back/sides. New 1994.

| Mfr.'s Sug. Retail | $2,790 | $2,232 | $1,674 | $1,395 | $1,115 | $1,005 | $920 | $835 |

F-32 — similar to F-22, except has spruce top, rosewood back/sides. Curr. mfr.

| Mfr.'s Sug. Retail | $2,790 | $2,092 | $1,395 | $1,375 | $1,100 | $990 | $905 | $825 |

F-34 — similar to F-22, except has spruce top, koa back/sides. New 1994.

| Mfr.'s Sug. Retail | $3,190 | $2,552 | $1,914 | $1,595 | $1,275 | $1,145 | $1,050 | $950 |

Grading	100%	98% MINT	95% EXC+	90% EXC	80% VG+	70% VG	60% G

F-38 — similar to F-22, except has abalone/wood bound body/rosette, Brazilian rosewood back/sides, abalone leaf fingerboard inlay. Curr. mfr.

Mfr.'s Sug. Retail	$5,590	$4,192	$2,795	$2,510	$1,975	$1,645	$1,505	$1,370

LSE Series

LSE-I — venetian cutaway folk style, spruce top, round soundhole, wood bound body, wood inlay rosette, mahogany 2 piece neck, 20 fret ebony fingerboard, rosewood bridge, pearl logo inlay and rosewood veneer on peghead, 3 per side gold tuners with pearl buttons, transducer bridge pickup. Available in Natural finish. Curr. mfr.

Mfr.'s Sug. Retail	$2,590	$1,942	$1,295	$1,190	$940	$790	$725	$660

LSE-II — similar to LSE-I, except has Indian rosewood back/sides.

Mfr.'s Sug. Retail	$2,990	$2,242	$1,495	$1,365	$1,075	$900	$825	$750

O Series

O-10 — jumbo style, cedar top, round soundhole, wood bound body, wood inlay rosette, mahogany back/sides, mahogany 2 piece neck, 14/20 fret ebony fingerboard, rosewood bridge, rosewood veneered peghead with pearl logo inlay, 3 per side gold tuners with amber buttons. Available in Natural finish. Curr. mfr.

Mfr.'s Sug. Retail	$1,990	$1,492	$995	$940	$745	$645	$590	$540

O-12 — similar to O-10, except has spruce top.

Mfr.'s Sug. Retail	$1,990	$1,492	$995	$965	$750	$675	$615	$560

O-12/12 — similar to O-10, except has 12 strings, spruce top, 6 per side tuners. Curr. mfr.

Mfr.'s Sug. Retail	$2,590	$2,072	$1,554	$1,295	$1,035	$930	$855	$775

O-22 — jumbo style, cedar top, round soundhole, wood bound body, wood inlay rosette, mahogany back/sides, mahogany/sycamore 5 piece neck, 14/20 fret ebony fingerboard, rosewood bridge, rosewood veneered peghead with pearl logo inlay, 3 per side gold tuners with amber buttons. Available in Natural finish. Disc. 1994.

		$1,500	$1,290	$1,075	$860	$775	$710	$645

Last Mfr.'s Sug. Retail was $2,145.

O-22/12 — similar to O-22, except has 12 strings, 6 per side tuners.

		$1,715	$1,470	$1,220	$975	$875	$805	$730

Last Mfr.'s Sug. Retail was $2,445.

O-23 — jumbo style, cedar top, round soundhole, wood bound body, abalone/wood inlay rosette, walnut back/sides, mahogany/sycamore 5 piece neck, 14/20 fret ebony fingerboard, rosewood bridge, rosewood veneered peghead with pearl logo inlay, 3 per side gold tuners with amber buttons. Available in Natural finish. Curr. mfr.

Mfr.'s Sug. Retail	$2,390	$1,792	$1,195	$1,190	$945	$790	$725	$660

O-25 — jumbo style, cedar top, round soundhole, wood bound body, wood inlay rosette, Indian rosewood back/sides, mahogany/rosewood 5 piece neck, 14/20 fret ebony fingerboard, rosewood bridge, pearl logo inlay and rosewood veneer on peghead, 3 per side gold tuners with amber buttons. Available in Natural finish. Curr. mfr.

Mfr.'s Sug. Retail	$2,790	$2,092	$1,395	$1,300	$1,030	$880	$805	$735

O-25/12 — similar to O-25, except has 12 strings, 6 per side tuners. Disc. 1994.

		$1,930	$1,650	$1,370	$1,095	$985	$900	$820

Last Mfr.'s Sug. Retail was $2,750.

O-32 — similar to O-25, except has spruce top, pearl tuner buttons.

Mfr.'s Sug. Retail	$2,790	$2,092	$1,395	$1,375	$1,100	$990	$905	$825

O-32/12 — similar to O-25, except has 12 strings, spruce top, 6 per side tuners with pearl buttons. New 1993.

Mfr.'s Sug. Retail	$3,190	$2,552	$1,914	$1,595	$1,275	$1,145	$1,050	$950

O-35 — jumbo style, cedar top, round soundhole, wood bound body, wood inlay rosette, Indian rosewood back/sides, mahogany/rosewood 5 piece neck, 14/20 fret ebony fingerboard, rosewood bridge, pearl logo inlay and rosewood veneer on peghead, 3 per side gold tuners with amber buttons. Available in Natural finish. New 1994.

Mfr.'s Sug. Retail	$3,990	$3,192	$2,394	$1,995	$1,595	$1,435	$1,315	$1,195

O-37 — jumbo style, spruce top, round soundhole, wood bound body, wood inlay rosette, Brazilian rosewood back/sides, mahogany/rosewood 5 piece neck, 14/20 fret ebony fingerboard, rosewood bridge, pearl logo inlay and rosewood veneer on peghead, 3 per side gold tuners with amber buttons. Available in Natural finish. New 1994.

Mfr.'s Sug. Retail	$5,790	$4,632	$3,474	$2,895	$2,315	$2,085	$1,910	$1,735

O-38 — jumbo style, black cedar top, round soundhole, abalone/wood bound body/rosette, Brazilian rosewood back/sides, mahogany/rosewood 5 piece neck, 14/20 fret ebony fingerboard with abalone leaf inlay, rosewood bridge, pearl logo inlay and rosewood veneer on peghead, 3 per side gold tuners with amber buttons. Available in Natural finish. Curr. mfr.

Mfr.'s Sug. Retail	$5,790	$4,342	$2,895	$2,635	$2,080	$1,745	$1,600	$1,455

Grading	100%	98% MINT	95% EXC+	90% EXC	80% VG+	70% VG	60% G

O-45 — jumbo style, spruce top, round soundhole, abalone bound body/rosette, Brazilian rosewood back/sides, mahogany/rosewood 5 piece neck, 14/20 fret ebony fingerboard, rosewood bridge, rosewood veneered peghead with abalone logo inlay, 3 per side gold tuners with amber buttons. Available in Natural finish. New 1994.

Mfr.'s Sug. Retail	$7,390	$5,912	$4,434	$3,695	$2,955	$2,660	$2,435	$2,215

S Series

S-23 — folk style, cedar top, round soundhole, wood bound body, abalone/wood inlay rosette, walnut back/sides, mahogany/sycamore 5 piece neck, 14/20 fret ebony fingerboard, rosewood bridge, rosewood veneered peghead with pearl logo inlay, 3 per side gold tuners with ebony buttons. Available in Natural finish. Mfd. 1993 to date.

Mfr.'s Sug. Retail	$2,390	$1,912	$1,434	$1,195	$955	$855	$785	$715

S-23S — similar to S-23, except has German spruce top. New 1994.

Mfr.'s Sug. Retail	$2,790	$2,232	$1,674	$1,395	$1,115	$1,005	$920	$835

S-25 — folk style, cedar top, round soundhole, wood bound body, abalone/wood inlay rosette, rosewood back/sides, mahogany/sycamore 5 piece neck, 14/20 fret ebony fingerboard, rosewood bridge, rosewood veneered peghead with pearl logo inlay, 3 per side gold tuners with ebony buttons. Available in Natural finish. Mfd. 1993 to date.

Mfr.'s Sug. Retail	$2,790	$2,232	$1,674	$1,395	$1,115	$1,005	$920	$835

S-25J — similar to S-25, except has single round cutaway, slotted peghead, 3 per side tuners with pearloid buttons, bridge transducer pickup. Mfd. 1993 to date.

Mfr.'s Sug. Retail	$2,990	$2,392	$1,794	$1,495	$1,195	$1,075	$985	$895

LOWRY

Instruments built in Concord, California from 1975 to 1990s.

Lowry guitars offered custom built, reverse string, no headstock guitar models. The **Modaire** model was offered in several design variations and was priced from $1,250 up to $3,000. For further information contact Lowry through the Index of Current Manufacturers located in the rear of this book.

LTD

Instruments currently built in Korea. Distributed by the E S P Guitar Company, Inc., of Hollywood, Calfornia.

LTD instruments are designed and distributed by the ESP Guitar Company. LTD instruments feature ESP pickups, and standard finishes include Black, Candy Apple Red, Metallic Purple, and Metallic Blue. Translucent finishes are an additional $100.

ELECTRIC

The LTD **Horizon** ($795) features a offset double cutaway body and 2 humbuckers. The **Mirage** ($895) model has a reverse headstock, 2 single coils, and 1 humbucker, and the **M-2** ($1,095) is based on a popular ESP M-II model. The LTD **Ultra Tone** ($895) is based on the ESP/George Lynch model, and the **Eclipse** ($795) is a single cutaway model with 2 humbuckers.

LYLE

Instruments were built in Japan.

While guitars with the Lyle trademark originated in Japan, the U.S. distributor is still unknown. Further research continues for upcoming editions of the **Blue Book of Guitars**.

(Source: Michael Wright, Guitar Stories Volume One)

LYNX

Instruments produced in Japan during the mid 1970s.

The Lynx trademark is the brandname used by a UK importer, and can be found on very low budget/low quality solid body guitars.

(Source: Tony Bacon and Paul Day, The Guru's Guitar Guide)

G.W. LYON

See WASHBURN.

Instruments built in Korea since the early 1990s. Distributed in the U.S. by Washburn International of Vernon Hills, Illinois.

G.W. Lyon offers a range of instruments designed for the student or beginner guitarist at affordable prices and decent entry level quality. For further information, contact Washburn International through the Index of Current Manufacturers located in the rear of this book.

RIC McCURDY

Instruments currently built in New York, New York.

Luthier Ric McCurdy has been producing handcrafted archtop guitars since the early '80s. Originally based in Santa Barbara, California, he moved to New York City in 1991. McCurdy studied archtop guitar building, and took classes from Robert Benedetto in 1993. McCurdy has been building archtops full time for the past three years, and estimates he has built about 250 guitars total since 1983. Current models such as the **Moderna** and **Monaco** retail at $3,750 and are constructed of Sitka spruce and flamed maple. McCurdy offers a number of standard options, and will discuss custom features with individual clients. For further information contact luthier Ric McCurdy through the Index of Current Manufacturers located in the back of this book.

(Source: Hal Hammer)

MCINTURFF

Instruments built in Fuquay, North Carolina since 1996. Distributed by Terry C. McInturff Guitars of Fuquay Varina, North Carolina.

Luthier Terry C. McInturff has been building and servicing guitars full-time since 1977. Through the years McInturff has owned three custom guitar shops; contributed to the production of several hundred custom basses for a nationally known firm; and worked as a luthier for Hamer guitars. McInturff credits builder/designer Michael Dressner for the formation of certain attitudes and opinions.

McInturff's varied luthiery and musical experiences has resulted in the rare opportunities to experiment with guitar designs and to test those designs on stage and in the recording studio. The results were unveiled in 1996 at the Summer N.A.M.M. show where McInturff, his wife Tracy, and Paddy Shetley displayed numerous high quality guitars for the first time.

McCurdy Archtop
courtesy Ric McCurdy

ELECTRIC

All instruments feature pickups exclusively designed by Steve Blucher of DiMarzio for McInturff guitars.

TCM MONARCH — offset double cutaway Honduran Mahogany body, graphite-reinforced Honduran mahogany set-neck design, 22 fret Indian rosewood fingerboard with brass bound abalone dot inlays, nickel plated hardware, stop tailpiece or TCM Vibe Bridge non-locking tremolo system, 3+3 headstock design and Schaller M-6 tuning machines, TCM Narrowfield single coil pickups in neck and mid position, TCM Midfield mini humbucker in bridge position, 1 volume and 1 tone control, five way selector switch. Nitro cellulose finish available in Faded Cherry or Old Gold Transparent. Current production.

    Mfr.'s Sug. Retail   **$2,650**

        Price includes a deluxe hardshell case.
        Optional Solo Switch sends bridge pickup full-bore to the output jack.

TCM EMPRESS — offset double cutaway Honduran Mahogany body, AAA grade flamed or quilted bigleaf maple hand carved top, graphite-reinforced Honduran mahogany set-neck design, 22 fret Indian rosewood fingerboard with brass bound abalone dot inlays, nickel plated hardware, TCM Vibe Bridge non-locking tremolo system, graphite/teflon composite nut, 3+3 headstock design and custom built locking tuning machines, TCM Narrowfield single coil pickups in neck and mid position, TCM Midfield mini humbucker in bridge position, 1 volume and 1 tone control, five way selector switch. Nitro cellulose finish available in Faded Amberburst, Old Gold Transparent, or Tangerine Transparent. Current production.

    Mfr.'s Sug. Retail   **$3,150**

        Price includes a deluxe hardshell case.
        Adjustable fixed bridge, stop tailpiece, and Schaller M-6 tuners available at no extra cost.
        Optional Solo Switch sends bridge pickup full-bore to the output jack.
        Optional TCM Wide Field pickup in bridge position.

TCM GLORY — offset double cutaway Honduran Mahogany body, world class flamed or quilted maple hand carved top, graphite-reinforced Honduran mahogany set-neck design, 22 fret ivoroid bound Indian rosewood or Pau Ferro fingerboard with abalone parallelogram inlays, gold hardware, TCM Vibe Bridge non-locking tremolo system, graphite/teflon composite nut, 3+3 headstock design and TCM Zebra Nut custom built locking tuning machines, DiMarzio custom built pickups, 1 volume and 1 tone control, five way selector switch. Nitro cellulose finish available in Faded Amberburst, Old Gold Transparent, Shetley Blue, or Tangerine Transparent. Current production.

    Mfr.'s Sug. Retail   **$3,850**

        Price includes a deluxe hardshell case.
        Adjustable fixed bridge, stop tailpiece, and Schaller M-6 tuners available at no extra cost.
        Optional tuned semi-hollow body is available.
        Optional Seymour Duncan Antiquity pickups are offered.
        Optional Solo Switch sends bridge pickup full-bore to the output jack.

TCM Glory Custom — same as the TCM Glory, except features neck and body constructed out of African Limba wood. Current production.

Mfr.'s Sug. Retail $4,100

   Price includes a deluxe hardshell case.

TCM ZODIAC — similar in production to the TCM Glory model, except features a 150 piece neck inlay of abalone, mother-of-pearl, awabi shell, brass, and ivoroid depicting the constellations of the Zodiac, and AAAAA grade flamed or quilted hand carved maple top. Finished in transparent, wood enhancing colors. Current production.

Mfr.'s Sug. Retail $4,650

   Price includes a deluxe hardshell case.

TCM Zodiac Custom — similar to the TCM Zodiac as featured above, except neck and body are African Limba wood. Current production.

Mfr.'s Sug. Retail $4,900

   Price includes a deluxe hardshell case.

McLAREN

Instruments currently built in San Diego, California.

Luthier Bruce McLaren has been handcrafting "butcher block" laminate body, neck-through designed guitars for a number of years. For further information contact luthier Bruce McLaren through the Index of Current Manufacturers located in the rear of this book.

MCSWAIN GUITARS

Instruments currently built in Charlotte, North Carolina.

Luthier Stephen McSwain produces elaborate handcarved guitar bodies that are later built into full guitars. His high degree of relief turns the bodies into playable works of art. For further information regarding one-of-a-kind designs, pricing and availability, please contact luthier Stephen McSwain through the Index of Current Manufacturers located in the back of this book.

MACCAFERRI

Instruments produced by the atelier of Henri Selmer and Co. of Paris, France between 1931 to 1932 as Selmer "modele Concert".

Maccaferri instruments produced in America during the early 1950s; others later as he stayed active in luthiery. Instruments designed for the Selmer company in France date to the 1930s; however, due to a dispute, less than 300 were made.

Italian-born luthier Mario Maccaferri (1900-1993) was a former classical guitarist turned guitar designer and builder. Born in Bologna, Italy in 1900, Maccaferri began his apprenticeship to luthier/guitarist Luigi Mozzani in 1911. At age 16 Maccaferri began classical guitar studies at the Academy in Siena, and graduated with highest possible honors in 1926. Between 1931 and 1932, Maccaferri designed and built a series of instruments for the French Selmer company. Although they were used by such notables as Django Reinhardt, a dispute between the company and Maccaferri led to a short production run. In the two years (1931-1932) that Maccaferri was with Selmer, he estimated that perhaps 200 guitars were built.

In 1936 Maccaferri moved to New York. He founded Mastro Industries, which became a leading producer of plastic products such as clothespins, acoustical tiles, and eventually Arthur Godfrey ukuleles. In 1953, Maccaferri introduced another innovative guitar made out of plastic. This archtop guitar featured a through-neck design, 3+3 headstock tuners, and two f-holes. Despite the material involved, Maccaferri did not consider them to be a toy. Along with the archtop model Maccaferri produced a flattop version. But the 1953 market was not quite prepared for this new design, and Maccaferri took the product off the market and stored them until around 1980 (then released them again). In the mid 1950s Maccaferri was on friendly terms with Nat Daniels of Danelectro fame. As contemporaries, they would gather to discuss amplification in regards to guitar design, but nothing came of their talks. Maccaferri stayed busy with his plastics company and was approached by Ibanez in the early 1980s to endorse a guitar model. As part of the endorsement, Maccaferri was personally signing all the labels for the production run.

   (Source: George Gruhn and Dan Forte, Guitar Player magazine, February 1986; and Paul Hostetter, Guitares Maurice Dupont)

S. B. MACDONALD

Instruments currently built in Huntington, New York.

Luthier MacDonald specializes in custom built instruments, repair and restoration. His instruments are made strictly by special order and are designed for the individual customer. MacDonald offers both acoustic and electric solid body guitars. For further information contact luthier S.B. MacDonald through the Index of Current Manufacturers located in the back of this book.

MAC YASUDA

Instruments currently built in Newport Beach, California.

Mac Yasuda is internationally recognized as a vintage guitar authority and collector, as well as a first-rate musician. In the late 1980s, Yasuda met Greg Rich, who was then acquiring a reputation as a builder of

S.B. MacDonald acoustic
courtesy S.B. MacDonald

collectible, musical instruments for a major guitar producer. In 1992, Rich collaborated with Mark Taylor (see TUT TAYLOR) to create a company to produce his latest custom designs. Mac Yasuda currently contracts Rich and Taylor to produce his namesake high quality, custom guitars.

MADEIRA

See GUILD.

Instruments were built in Japan during the early 1970s to late 1980s.

The Madeira line was imported in to augment Guild sales in the U.S. during the early 1970s. The first run of solid body electrics consisted of entry level reproductions of classic Fender, Gibson, and even Guild designs (such as the S-100). The electric models were phased out in a year (1973 to 1974), but the acoustics were continued.

The solid body electrics were reintroduced briefly in the early 1980s, and then introduced again in 1990. The line consisted of three guitar models (ME-200, ME-300, ME-500) and one bass model (MBE-100). All shared similar design acoutrements such as bolt-on necks and various pickup configurations.

(Source: Michael Wright, Vintage Guitar Magazine, December 1995)

MAGNATONE

Instruments built in California circa 1960s.

Magnatone is more recognized for their series of brown and gold amplifiers produced during the early 1960s than the company's guitars. Like Standel (and the early years at Fender), Magnatone wanted a guitar line to offer retailers. In 1962, Paul Barth (of National/Rickenbacker/Bartell fame) designed four models that consisted of a 1- or 2-pickup solid body, a 3/4 scale beginner's electric guitar, and an electric acoustic (retail prices ranged from $99 to $299). The guitar line was renamed in 1965 to the **Starstream** series, and all models were redesigned with a double cutaway body. There were three electric acoustics models (that ranged from $350 to $420), and three solid body electrics (one a 3/4 size) and a bass guitar (ranging from $170 to $290). Magnatone debuted the **Mark** series in 1966, which consisted of single cutaway/one pickup 'Mark III Standard'; the single cutaway/two pickup 'Mark III Deluxe'; the double cutaway 'Mark IV'; and and the double cutaway equipped with a Bigsby tremolo called the 'Mark V'. Both the Mark IV and the Mark V models were designed by Paul Bigsby.

Magnatone ownership has been identified to Estey Electronics, Estey Musicial Instrument Corporation, and Magna Electronics. Magnatone maintained showrooms on both coasts, with one in West Hempstead, New York, and the other in Torrance, California.

(Source: Tom Wheeler, American Guitars)

Magnatone Mark III
courtesy Kevin Macy

MANEA

Instruments currently built in Goodlettsville, Tennessee.

Luthier Dumitru Manea handcrafts both a steel string model (M-2000) and a classical model (AV-1) that feature hand-carved spruce or cedar tops, mahogany or cedar necks and Indian rosewood back and sides. Both models feature ebony fingerboards and bridges, and a number of additionally priced design options. The **M-2000** has a retail price of $2,795 and the **AV-1** lists at $2,995. For further information contact luthier Dumitru Manea through the Index of Current Manufacturers located in the back of this book.

MANSON

Instruments built in Devon, England from the late 1970s to date.

Stringed instruments bearing the Manson name come from two separate operations. Acoustic guitars, mandolins, bouzoukis (and even triplenecks!) are built by Andrew Manson at A.B. Manson & Company. Electric guitars and electric basses are built by Hugh Manson at Manson Handmade Instruments. Andrew and Hugh Manson have been plying their luthier skills for over twenty five years. Hugh, like Andrew, draw on a wealth of luthier knowledge as they tailor the instrument directly to the player commissioning the work. Hand sizing (for neck dimensions), custom wiring, or custom choice of wood - it's all done in house. Both facilities are located in Devon, and both Mansons build high quality instruments respective of their particular genre. For further information regarding model specifications, pricing, and availablility, please contact either Andrew or Hugh Manson via the Index of Current Manufacturers located in the back of this book.

According to authors Tony Bacon and Paul Day (The Guru's Guitar Guide), Manson instruments can be dated by the first two digits of the respective instrument's serial number.

MANTRA

Instruments currently produced in Italy.

The Mantra **MG** series is constructed of lightweight magnesium alloy, with a bolt-on wood neck. Casting of the innovative body is handled in Italy, while the necks are built in the U.S. by Warmoth Guitars. For further information contact Mantra Guitars through the Index of Current Manufacturers located in the rear of this book.

Magnatone
courtesy Kevin Macy

Manzer Blue Absynthe
courtesy Scott Chinery

MANZER

Instruments built in Toronto, Canada since 1978 to date.

Luthier Linda Manzer was first inspired to build stringed instruments after seeing Joni Mitchell perform on a dulcimer in 1969. Manzer began building full time in 1974, and apprenticed under Jean Claude Larrivee until 1978. In 1983, Manzer spent several months with James D'Aquisto while learning the art of archtop guitar building. Manzer gained some industry attention after she completed Pat Metheny's 'Pikasso' multi-necked guitar (the model has four necks sharing one common body and 42 strings). In 1990, Manzer was comissioned by the Canadian Museum of Civilization to create a guitar for one of their displays. In addition to building the high quality guitar that she is known for, Manzer included inlay designs in the shape of one of Canada's endangered species on the neck. The extra ornamentation served as a reminder for enviromental concerns. Noted players using Manzer guitars include Pat Metheny, Bruce Cockburn, and Heather Bishop.

ACOUSTIC

Archtop Series

All three archtop models are built of the highest grade aged German Spruce tops. The **Studio** ($9,500) and the **Au Naturel** ($12,500) are offered in either 16 1/2" or 17 1/4" wide bodies. The Studio has an Ivoroid bound body, and bound Ebony fingerboard with dot inlays. The Au Naturel features wood binding, high grade woods, and an Orchid inlay. The **Concert Deluxe** ($14,500) possesses a larger body at 18", Deluxe binding, a bound fingerboard with a split block inlay, and an engraved scroll in peghead.

Flattop Series

There are several Manzer flattop models, each with their own 'personality'. Again, construction features aged German Spruce or Western Cedar, Indian Rosewood, and Ebony. Manzer's most popular model, the **Manzer Steel String** ($5,000) has a 25 1/2" scale, Rosewood back and sides, and an Ebony fingerboard. The **Baritone** ($5,500) was designed in conjunction with Craig Snyder, and features a longer 29" scale. The longer scale supports the lower tuning (either low B to B, or low A to A) thus giving guitars access to a fuller voice. Back and sides are contructed of Curly Koa, and the fingerboard and bridge are Ebony. The **Cowpoke** ($5,000) shares construction similarities with the standard Manzer, but features a larger and deeper body. Original inspiration was derived from a "tall guy who wanted a Manzer, only bigger!" The **Classical** ($6,000) offers a design that accomodates both traditional classical playing and modern jazz styles. All flattop models, with the exception of the Little Manzer Steel ($3,000) and the Little Manzer classical ($3,400), are available in a single cutaway design for an additional $300. For further information, pricing, and availability contact luthier Manzer through the Index of Current Manufacturers located in the back of this book.

MARATHON

See chapter on House Brands.

This trademark had been identified as a "House Brand" previously used by Abercrombie & Fitch during the 1960s by author/researcher Willie G. Moseley. However, a number of newer guitars sporting the same trademark have been recently spotted. These guitars are built in Korea by the Samick company, and serve as an entry level instrument for the novice guitarist.

MARCHIONE

Instruments currently built in New York, New York.

Marchione currently produces high quality, handcrafted electric guitars that range in price from $2,200 to $4,500. For further information contact Marchione Guitars through the Index of Current Manufacturers located in the rear of this book.

MARINA

Instruments produced in Korea from the late 1980s to date.

These medium quality solid body guitars sported both original and designs based on classic Fender styles.

(Source: Tony Bacon and Paul Day, The Guru's Guitar Guide)

MARLIN

Instruments originally produced in East Germany, then production moved to Korea. Since 1989, the trademark "Marlin by Hohner" has been produced in Korea.

The Marlin trademark originally was the brandname of a UK importer. The first "Sidewinder" and "Slammer" series were medium quality strat-styled solid body guitars from East Germany. When production moved to Korea, the models changed to "Blue Fin", "Master Class", "State of the Art", "Loner", and "Nastie" designations.

In 1989, a variation of the trademark appeared. Headstocks now bore a "Marlin by Hohner" description. Still Korean produced, but whether this is a new entry level series for the Hohner company or a Marlin variant is still being researched. Further updates will appear in the next edition of the **Blue Book of Guitars**.

(Source: Tony Bacon and Paul Day, The Guru's Guitar Guide)

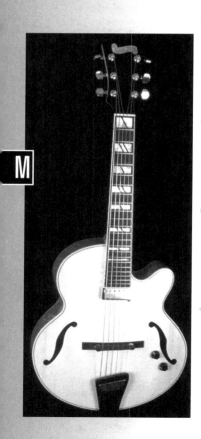

Manzer Archtop
courtesy Linda Manzer

MARLING

Instruments produced in Japan during the 1970s.

As the Italian-based EKO guitar company was winding down, they were marketing an EKO guitar copy built in Japan. These guitars were poor quality compared to the 1960s Italian EKOs.

(Source: Michael Wright, Guitar Stories Volume One)

MARTELLE

See chapter on House Brands.

The distributor of this Gibson-built budget line of guitars has not yet been identified. Built to the same standards as other Gibson guitars, they lack the one true 'Gibson' touch: an adjustable truss rod. "House Brand" Gibsons were available to musical instrument distributors in the late 1930s and early 1940s.

(Source: Walter Carter, Gibson Guitars: 100 Years of an American Icon)

MARTIN

Instruments produced in Nazareth, Pennsylvania since 1839. C.F. Martin & Company was originally founded in New York in 1833, but the Martin family moved to Pennsylvania six years later.

Although C.F. Martin moved Martin guitars to Nazareth, Pennsylvania in 1839 (company started in 1833), the guitars retained the New York labels until 1898. C.A. Zoebich & Sons, the New York sales agency, retained the exclusive rights to sell Martins during that time period. The Martin guitar company has always been helmed by a Martin family member. Though the company has had its share of trials and tribulations, they have been producing quality guitars during their 160 years of operation.

Martin did build guitars for other retailers, teachers, and musical instrument distributors; unlike Harmony's or Kay's house brands, though, 'retitled' Martins were the exception and not the rule. If any of these trademarks are spotted, here's a partial hint to origin: the Bacon Banjo Company (circa 1924), Bitting Special (Bethlehem), Oliver Ditson (certain models only), Carl Fischer (New York, 1929), William Foden (Foden Specials), J.A. Handley (instructor in Lowell, Massachusetts), Montgomery Ward (circa 1932), Paramount (certain guitars), Rolando (J.J. Milligan Music), Rudick's (Akron, Ohio circa 1935), Southern California Music Company (hawaiian guitar models circa 1917-1920), S.S. Stewart (certin models circa 1923-1925), John Wanamaker (Philadelphia, circa 1909), H.A. Weymann & Son (ukuleles and 'taropatch' ukes, circa 1925), Wurlitzer (circa 1922-1924), and Wolverine (Grinnell Brothers, Detroit).

(Source: Mike Longworth, Martin Guitars: A History, and Tom Wheeler, American Guitars)

Martin has been in the same location for 160 years and serialization has remained intact and consistent since their first instrument. When trying to determine the year of an instrument's construction, some quick notes about features can be helpful. The few notes contained herein are for readily identifying the instrument upon sight and are by no means meant to be used for truly accurate dating of an instrument. All items discussed are for flat-top steel string guitars and involve instruments that are standard production models.

The earliest dreadnoughts, and indeed just about all instruments produced with a neck that joins the body at the 12th fret, have bodies that are bell shaped on the top, as opposed to the more square shouldered styles of most dreadnoughts. Between 1929 to 1934, Martin began placing 14 fret necks on most of their instruments and this brought about the square shouldered body style. A few models maintained 12 fret necks into the late 1940s and one model had a 12 fret neck until the late 1980s.

Turn of the century instruments have square slotted pegheads with the higher end models (Models 42 and 45) displaying an intricate pearl fern inlay that runs vertically up the peghead. This was replaced by a vertical inlay known as the "flowerpot" or the "torch" inlay, in approximately 1905. In 1932, the "C.F. Martin & Co. Est. 1833" scroll logo began appearing on certain models' pegheads. By approximately 1934, a solid peghead with a vertical pearl "C.F. Martin" inlay had replaced the former peghead design.

Bridges from the 1900s are rectangular with "pyramid" wings. In approximately 1929, the "belly" bridge replaced the rectangle bridge. This bridge has a straight slot cut across the entire length of the center section of the bridge. In 1965, the straight cut saddle slot was changed to a routed slot. It was in approximately 1936, that Martin began using the "tied" bridge on their instruments.

Pickguards were not standard features on instruments until approximately 1933 when tortoise pickguards were introduced. In 1966, black pickguards became standard. In 1969, Martin stopped using Brazilian rosewood for its regular production instruments, ending with serial number #254498. As a result, premiums are being asked for instruments manufactured from this exotic wood. Martin began to use East Indian rosewood for standard production instruments after 1969.

ACOUSTIC

PRE-1900 MODELS — instruments in this group have the following features: parlour style bodies, solid spruce tops, round soundholes, Brazilian rosewood back/sides, mahogany neck, 12/18 fret ebony fingerboard, slotted pegheads, 3 per side tuners with plastic buttons. Available in Natural finish. Mfd. 1833 to 1898.

Prior to 1898, Martin instruments were not serialized, though a date may be found inside the body on the instrument's top.

Grading	100% MINT	98% EXC+	95% EXC+	90% EXC	80% VG+	70% VG	60% G

Standard Models — bound body/rosette, ebony pyramid bridge with black pearl dot pins.

	$2,750	$2,500	$2,000	$1,750	$1,500	$1,250	$950

Body binding/purfling and rosette styles vary between instruments.

Deluxe Models — pearl bound bodies/rosettes, ivory bridge with pins.

	$7,500	$6,750	$6,000	$5,000	$4,250	$3,250	$2,000

Body binding/purfling and rosette styles vary between instruments.

BACKPACKER — paddle style body, solid spruce top, round soundhole, one-piece mahogany body/neck with hollowed out sound cavity, 15 fret hardwood fingerboard with white dot inlay, hardwood bridge with white black dot pins, 3 per side chrome mini tuners. Available in Natural finish. Mfd. 1993 to date.

Mfr.'s Sug. Retail	$225	$168	$112	$100	$80	$70	$65	$60

Backpacker Electric — similar to Backpacker, except has acoustic bridge pickup.

Mfr.'s Sug. Retail	$350	$262	$175	$160	$130	$115	$105	$95

CUSTOM 15 — flat-top body, solid spruce top, round soundhole, tortoise pickguard, herringbone bound body, 5 stripe rosette, rosewood back/sides, 14/20 fret ebony fingerboard with pearl diamond inlay, ebony bridge with white black dot pins, rosewood peghead veneer, 3 per side chrome tuners. Available in Natural finish. Curr. mfr.

Mfr.'s Sug. Retail	$3,070	$2,302	$1,535	$1,480	$1,150	$1,035	$950	$865

STYLE 15 — flat-top body, mahogany top, round soundhole, 2 stripe bound body/rosette, mahogany back/sides/neck, 14/20 fret rosewood fingerboard with white dot inlay, rosewood bridge with white pins, black face peghead with logo decal, 3 per side nickel tuners with plastic buttons. Available in Natural finish. Mfd. 1935 to 1944, reintroduced 1948 to 1961.

1935-1944		$1,200	$1,030	$860	$685	$615	$565	$515
1948-1961		$875	$750	$625	$500	$450	$415	$375

Early models were produced with birch or maple bodies.

Production of this model was suspended during WWII.

STYLE 17 — bellshape flat-top body, spruce top, round soundhole, rosewood bound body, mahogany back/sides, cedar neck, 12/19 fret ebony fingerboard with pearl dot inlay, ebony bridge with black pins, slotted peghead with 3 per side diecast tuners with plastic buttons. Available in Natural finish. Mfd. 1909 to 1937.

1909-1913		$1,025	$880	$735	$585	$525	$485	$440
1914-1921		$1,250	$1,070	$895	$715	$645	$590	$535
1922-1928		$850	$730	$610	$485	$435	$400	$365
1929-1937		$750	$640	$535	$430	$390	$355	$325

In 1914, 3 stripe rosette was added.

In 1922, mahogany top, 1 stripe rosette, ebony nut, pointed bridge replaced respective items.

In 1927, rosewood fingerboard/bridge replaced respective items.

Between 1929 and 1930, this instrument was also referred to as the Style 25 on the production tables.

In 1931, a pickguard became optional.

In 1934, a 14 fret model was introduced in sizes 0-17 and 00-17.

In 1935, Dark finish replaced Natural finish.

In 1936, this model was made with nickel plated tuner buttons.

Available in sizes 2-17, 0-17 and 00-17.

STYLE 18 — bellshape flat-top body, spruce top, round soundhole, wood bound body, rope patterned wood inlay rosette, rosewood back/sides, cedar neck, 12 fret ebony fingerboard, pointed ebony bridge with ebony pearl dot pins, 3 per side brass tuners with ivory buttons. Mfd. 1898 to 1935.

1898-1928		$1,200	$1,030	$860	$685	$615	$565	$515
1929-1935		$5,500	$4,715	$3,930	$3,145	$2,830	$2,595	$2,360

In 1901, 3 stripe rosette replaced original item.

In 1909, fingerboard inlay was added.

In 1917, this model became available in a 19 fret version, with mahogany back/sides/neck.

In 1919, rosewood bound body became available.

In 1920, 20 fret fingerboard became standard.

In 1923, this model became available with steel strings, gut strings optional, with a dark top at extra charge, and a regular pointed bridge.

In 1930, a belly bridge with a slanted saddle became available.

Grading	100%	98% MINT	95% EXC+	90% EXC	80% VG+	70% VG	60% G

STYLE 21 — bellshape flat-top body, round soundhole, rosewood bound body, herringbone rosette, rosewood back/sides, cedar neck, 12/19 fret ebony fingerboard, ebony pyramid bridge, slotted peghead, 3 per side brass tuners with ivory buttons. Available in Natural finish. Mfd. 1898 to 1955.

	100%	98%	95%	90%	80%	70%	60%
1898-1926	$2,500	$2,140	$1,785	$1,430	$1,285	$1,180	$1,070
1927-1938	$3,200	$2,750	$2,290	$1,835	$1,650	$1,515	$1,375
1939-1955	$1,700	$1,460	$1,215	$970	$870	$800	$730

In 1901, pearl diamond fingerboard inlay was added.

By 1917, ebony pearl dot bridge pins were added.

By 1923, mahogany neck replaced original item.

In 1923, 12/20 fret fingerboard replaced original item.

In 1930, belly bridge and slanted saddle were added.

In 1932, a pickguard became optional, black plastic body binding replaced original item.

By 1936, tortoise body binding became standard.

In 1944, dot fingerboard inlay became standard.

In 1947, rosewood fingerboard/bridge became standard.

STYLE 28 — bellshape flat-top body, spruce top, round soundhole, ivory/herringbone bound body, pearl rosette, rosewood back/sides, cedar neck, 12/19 fret ebony fingerboard, ebony bridge, 3 per side tuners. Available in Natural finish. Mfd. 1898 to 1934.

	100%	98%	95%	90%	80%	70%	60%
1898-1922	$2,025	$1,740	$1,450	$1,160	$1,040	$955	$870
1923-1934	$10,500	$9,000	$7,500	$6,000	$5,400	$4,950	$4,500

In 1901, pearl diamond fingerboard inlay was added.

In 1917, 12/20 fret fingerboard became standard.

In 1919, plastic body binding became standard.

By 1923, mahogany neck became standard.

In 1927, white black dot bridge pins were added.

In 1928, gut strings were replaced with steel.

In 1932, pickguard became optional.

STYLE 30 — bellshape flat-top body, spruce top, round soundhole, ivory/herringbone bound body, pearl rosette, rosewood back/sides, cedar neck, 12/19 fret ivory bound ebony fingerboard with pearl diamond inlay, ebony bridge, 3 per side silver tuners with ivory buttons. Available in Natural finish. Mfd. 1901 to 1917.

	100%	98%	95%	90%	80%	70%	60%
	$1,800	$1,540	$1,285	$1,025	$925	$845	$770

STYLE 42 — bellshape flat-top body, solid spruce top, round soundhole, ivory/pearl bound body, pearl rosette, rosewood back/sides, cedar neck, 12/19 fret ivory bound ebony fingerboard with pearl snowflake inlay, ivory bridge, 3 per side silver tuners with pearl buttons. Available in Natural finish. Mfd. 1875 to 1942.

	100%	98%	95%	90%	80%	70%	60%
	$3,675	$3,150	$2,625	$2,100	$1,890	$1,730	$1,575

Archtop Series

Tailpiece variations were common on all arch and carved top instruments.

C-1 — auditorium style, carved spruce top, round soundhole, raised black pickguard, bound top/rosette, mahogany back/sides/neck, 14/20 fret rosewood fingerboard with white dot inlay, rosewood bridge/trapeze tailpiece, vertical pearl logo inlay on headstock, 3 per side nickel tuners. Available in Sunburst finish. Mfd. 1931 to 1942.

	100%	98%	95%	90%	80%	70%	60%
	$1,250	$1,000	$850	$750	$650	$550	$450

In 1934, f-holes replaced original item.

C-2 — similar to C-1, except has stripe bound body/rosette, rosewood back/sides, ebony fingerboard with pearl snowflake inlay, ebony bridge. Available in Dark Lacquer finish. Mfd. 1931 to 1942.

	100%	98%	95%	90%	80%	70%	60%
	$1,750	$1,500	$1,250	$1,000	$900	$775	$650

In 1934, f-holes replaced original item, Golden Brown top finish became standard.

In 1935, bound fingerboard, pickguard were introduced.

In 1939, hexagon fingerboard inlay was introduced.

C-3 — similar to C-1, except has 2 stripe bound body/rosette, pearl bound pickguard, rosewood back/sides, bound ebony fingerboard with pearl snowflake inlay, ebony bridge, gold tailpiece, bound peghead, gold single unit tuners. Available in Lacquer finish. Mfd. 1932 to 1935.

	100%	98%	95%	90%	80%	70%	60%
	$2,750	$2,250	$1,750	$1,500	$1,250	$1,000	$900

In 1934, Stained top finish was introduced, bound pickguard, f-holes replaced original items.

F-1 — concert style body, carved spruce top, f-holes, raised black pickguard, stripe bound top, mahogany back/sides/neck, 14/20 fret ebony fingerboard with white dot inlay, adjustable ebony bridge/trapeze tailpiece, logo decal on headstock, 3 per side nickel tuners. Available in Sunburst finish. Mfd. 1940 to 1942.

	100%	98%	95%	90%	80%	70%	60%
	$1,525	$1,300	$1,090	$870	$785	$720	$650

F-2 — similar to F-1, except has rosewood back/sides.

	100%	98%	95%	90%	80%	70%	60%
	$1,725	$1,480	$1,235	$985	$890	$815	$740

1934 Martin Archtop
courtesy Lloyd Bennett

M

Grading	100%	98% MINT	95% EXC+	90% EXC	80% VG+	70% VG	60% G

F-7 — similar to F-1, except has bound pickguard, rosewood back/sides, bound fingerboard with ivoroid hexagon inlay, bound peghead with pearl vertical logo inlay, chrome hardware. Available in Sunburst finish. Mfd. 1935 to 1942.

	$2,750	$2,500	$2,250	$2,000	$1,850	$1,750	$1,650

In 1937, pearloid fingerboard inlay replaced original item.

F-9 — similar to F-1, except has stripe bound pickguard, rosewood back/sides, bound fingerboard with pearl hexagon inlay, bound peghead with pearl vertical logo inlay, gold hardware. Available in Golden Brown Sunburst finish. Mfd. 1935 to 1942.

	$3,750	$3,500	$3,000	$2,500	$2,000	$1,500	$1,250

R-17 — grand concert style body, arched mahogany top, f-holes, raised black pickguard, bound body, mahogany back/sides/neck, 14/20 fret rosewood fingerboard, rosewood bridge/trapeze tailpiece, logo decal on peghead, 3 per side nickel single unit tuners. Available in Sunburst finish. Mfd. 1934 to 1942.

	$675	$580	$485	$385	$350	$320	$290

R-18 — similar to R-17, except has arched spruce top, 3 stripe bound body/rosette, white dot fingerboard inlay. Mfd. 1932 to 1941.

	$875	$750	$625	$500	$450	$415	$375

In 1933, f-holes replaced original item.

Classical Series

The following features are common to all instruments in this series: Body Length - 19 1/8 inches, Upper Bout Width - 10 3/4 inches, Lower Bout Width - 14 7/16 inches.

Unless indicated otherwise, all instruments in this series have classic style bodies, solid spruce top, bound body, mahogany neck, 12/19 fret fingerboard, tied bridge, slotted peghead, 3 per side gold pearl button tuners. Available in Natural finishes.

N-10 — wooden inlay rosette, mahogany back/sides, rosewood fingerboard/bridge. Mfd. 1969 to 1985.

	$450	$315	$270	$225	$180	$160	$150

N-10, Current Manufacture — this model is a special order instrument.

Mfr.'s Sug. Retail	$2,620	$2,096	$1,572	$1,310	$1,045	$940	$865	$785

N-20 — wooden inlay rosette, rosewood back/sides, ebony fingerboard/bridge. Mfd. 1968 to date.

Mfr.'s Sug. Retail	$3,190	$2,392	$1,595	$1,535	$1,215	$1,040	$955	$870

D Series

The following features are common to all instruments in this series: Body Length - 20 15/16 inches, Upper Bout Width - 11 1/2 inches, Lower Bout Width - 15 5/8 inches.

D-1 — spruce top, round soundhole, black pickguard, bound body, 3 stripe rosette, mahogany back/sides/neck, 14/20 fret rosewood fingerboard with pearl dot inlay, rosewood bridge with brown white dot pins, mahogany peghead veneer, 3 per side chrome tuners. Available in Natural finish. Mfd. 1993 to date.

Mfr.'s Sug. Retail	$1,099	$879	$659	$600	$500	$460	$380	$330

D-1R — similar to D-1, except has rosewood back/sides. New 1994.

Mfr.'s Sug. Retail	$1,300	$975	$650	$625	$500	$450	$415	$375

D-16T — spruce top, round soundhole, black pickguard, 3 stripe bound body/rosette, mahogany back/sides/neck, 14/20 fret rosewood fingerboard with pearl dot inlay, rosewood bridge with black pins, rosewood peghead veneer, 3 per side chrome tuners. Available in Natural finish. Mfd. 1986 to date.

Mfr.'s Sug. Retail	$1,650	$1,237	$825	$775	$620	$560	$515	$465

Koa back/sides offered in limited quantities (D-16K).

In 1987, ash or walnut back/sides were offered in limited quantities (D-16A/D-16W).

D-16TR — similar to the D-16T, except has rosewood back and sides. New 1996.

Mfr.'s Sug. Retail	$1,850	$1,480	$1,110	$975	$820	$760	$615	$565

D-18 — solid spruce top, round soundhole, tortoise bound body, 3 stripe purfling/rosette, mahogany back/sides/neck, 14/20 fret ebony fingerboard with pearl dot inlay, ebony bridge with black white dot pins, 3 per side chrome tuners. Available in Natural finish. Mfd. 1931 to date.

		100%	98%	95%	90%	80%	70%	60%
1931-1939		$10,500	$9,500	$8,750	$8,000	$7,250	$6,000	$4,750
1940-1944		$7,500	$6,500	$5,750	$5,000	$4,250	$3,250	$2,500
1945-1949		$3,250	$3,000	$2,650	$2,000	$1,750	$1,500	$1,200
1950-1959		$2,000	$1,750	$1,500	$1,250	$1,000	$850	$750
1960-1969		$1,500	$1,250	$1,000	$800	$700	$600	$500
1970-1985		$1,250	$1,000	$800	$700	$600	$500	$400
Curr. Mfr.'s Sug. Retail	$2,030	$1,624	$1,218	$1,040	$820	$650	$595	$540

In 1932, pickguard was optionally available.

By 1956, rosewood fingerboard/bridges replaced original items.

Grading	100%	98% MINT	95% EXC+	90% EXC	80% VG+	70% VG	60% G

D-18S — similar to D-18, except has prewar dreadnought style body, 12/20 fret fingerboard. Mfd. 1968 to 1994.

		$1,630	$1,400	$1,165	$930	$840	$770	$700

Last Mfr.'s Sug. Retail was $2,330.

D12-18 — similar to D-18, except has 12 strings, 6 per side tuners. Mfd. 1973 to date.

1973-1985		$1,250	$1,000	$900	$800	$700	$550	$400
Curr. Mfr.'s Sug. Retail	$2,350	$1,762	$1,175	$1,115	$885	$765	$700	$635

This is a special order instrument.

D-19 — spruce top, round soundhole, black pickguard, 3 stripe bound body/rosette, mahogany back/sides/neck, 14/20 fret rosewood fingerboard with pearl dot inlay, rosewood bridge with white black dot pins, rosewood peghead veneer with logo decal, 3 per side chrome tuners. Available in Dark Brown finish. Mfd. 1976 to 1988.

		$1,250	$1,00	$800	$700	$600	$500	$400

D12-20 — solid spruce top, round soundhole, black pickguard, 3 stripe bound body/rosette, mahogany back/sides/neck, 12/20 fret rosewood fingerboard with pearl dot inlay, rosewood bridge with black white dot pins, 6 per side chrome tuners. Available in Natural finish. Mfd. 1964 to 1994.

		$1,000	$750	$650	$550	$450	$350	$300

Last Mfr.'s Sug. Retail was $2,480.

D-21 — spruce top, round soundhole, tortoise bound body, herringbone rosette, Brazilian rosewood back/sides, mahogany neck, 14/20 fret Brazilian rosewood fingerboard with pearl dot inlay, Brazilian rosewood bridge with black pins, 3 per side chrome tuners. Mfd. 1956 to 1969.

		$3,500	$3,250	$2,750	$2,250	$1,750	$1,500	$1,250

D-25K — spruce top, round soundhole, black pickguard, bound body, 4 stripe purfling, 5 stripe rosette, koa back/sides, mahogany neck, 14/20 fret rosewood fingerboard with pearl dot inlay, rosewood bridge with black white pins, rosewood veneered peghead with screened logo, 3 per side chrome tuners. Available in Natural finish. Mfd. 1980 to 1987.

		$1,050	$900	$750	$600	$540	$495	$450

Last Mfr.'s Sug. Retail was $1,610.

D-25K2 — similar to D-25K, except has koa top. Available in Natural finish. Mfd. 1980 to 1987.

		$1,050	$900	$750	$600	$540	$495	$450

Last Mfr.'s Sug. Retail was $1,735.

D-28 — solid spruce top, round soundhole, black pickguard, bound body, herringbone purfling, 5 stripe rosette, rosewood 2 piece back/sides, 14/20 fret ebony fingerboard with pearl diamond inlay, ebony bridge with white black dot pins, 3 per side chrome tuners. Available in Natural finish. Mfd. 1931 to date.

Martin produced a number of D-28 Herringbone guitars between 1931 to 1933. Depending on the condition, a D-28 from these three years may be worth $48,000 (or more). The **Blue Book of Guitars** highly recommends that several professional appraisals be secured before buying/selling/trading any 1931-1933 D-28 guitars with herringbone trim.

1934-1935		$38,500	$35,000	$30,000	$25,000	$20,000	$17,500	$15,000
1936-1939		$30,000	$27,000	$22,500	$18,000	$14,000	$11,000	$9,200
1940-1942		$25,000	$22,000	$17,000	$14,000	$10,000	$8,000	$6,500
1943-1944		$18,000	$15,000	$10,000	$8,500	$6,000	$4,500	$3,000
1945-1946		$9,500	$7,500	$6,500	$5,600	$4,900	$3,700	$2,900
1947-1949		$6,750	$6,200	$6,000	$5,250	$4,500	$3,250	$2,500
1950-1959		$4,750	$4,500	$4,000	$3,500	$3,000	$2,250	$1,750
1960-1969		$3,750	$3,500	$3,000	$2,750	$2,250	$1,750	$1,350
1970-1985		$1,250	$1,000	$900	$800	$725	$650	$550
1986-1995		$1,250	$1,000	$900	$800	$725	$650	$550
Curr. Mfr.'s Sug. Retail	$2,330	$1,747	$1,165	$1,060	$825	$740	$680	$620

In 1935, Shaded top finish was optionally available.

1936 was the last year for the 12 fret model. These models may command a higher premium.

In 1944, pearl dot fingerboard inlay replaced the split diamond inlays, and was last year for scalloped bracing.

In 1945, the new bracing was introduced.

1946 was the last year that the herringbone trim around the top was offered (although the last batch was in early 1947).

D12-28 — similar to D-28, except has 12 strings. Mfd. 1970 to date.

1970-1985		$1,750	$1,500	$1,250	$1,000	$750	$650	$550
Curr. Mfr.'s Sug. Retail	$2,530	$1,897	$1,265	$1,130	$900	$780	$715	$650

D-28S — similar to D-28, except has a bell shape dreadnought style body, 12/20 fret fingerboard, slotted headstock. Mfd. 1968 to 1994.

		$1,830	$1,570	$1,310	$1,045	$940	$865	$785

Last Mfr.'s Sug. Retail was $2,620.

Martin D-28
courtesy Blue Chip Guitars

Grading		100%	98% MINT	95% EXC+	90% EXC	80% VG+	70% VG	60% G

1968 Martin D-35 12 String
courtesy Kenneth Little

D-28V — similar to D-28, fashioned after the original dreadnought design, herringbone bound body, square headstock. Available in Antique Top finish. Mfd. 1983 to 1985.

		100%	98%	95%	90%	80%	70%	60%
		$5,000	$4,500	$4,000	$3,500	$3,000	$2,500	$2,000

Last Mfr.'s Sug. Retail was $2,600.

Brazilian rosewood was used in place of Indian rosewood.
This was a Vintage Series instrument. 260 instruments were produced.

DC-28 — similar to D-28, except has single round cutaway, 14/22 fret fingerboard. Mfd. 1981 to date.

	100%	98%	95%	90%	80%	70%	60%
Mfr.'s Sug. Retail $2,810	$2,107	$1,405	$1,330	$1,055	$920	$840	$765

D-35 — solid spruce top, round soundhole, tortoise pickguard, 5 stripe bound body/rosette, rosewood 3 piece back/sides, mahogany neck, 14/20 fret bound ebony fingerboard with pearl dot inlay, ebony bridge with white black dot pins, 3 per side chrome tuners. Available in Natural finish. Mfd. 1965 to date.

	100%	98%	95%	90%	80%	70%	60%
1965-1969		$3,750	$3,500	$3,000	$2,750	$2,250	$1,750	$1,350
1970-1985		$1,250	$1,000	$900	$800	$725	$650	$550
Curr. Mfr.'s Sug. Retail $2,430	$1,822	$1,215	$1,110	$865	$780	$715	$650

In 1968, black pickguard replaced original item.

D-35S — similar to D-35, except has a bell shape dreadnought style body, 12/20 fret fingerboard, slotted headstock. Mfd. 1968 to 1994.

	100%	98%	95%	90%	80%	70%	60%
	$1,930	$1,655	$1,380	$1,105	$995	$910	$825

Last Mfr.'s Sug. Retail was $2,760.

D12-35 — similar to D-35S, except has 12 strings. Mfd. 1965 to 1994.

	100%	98%	95%	90%	80%	70%	60%
1965-1969	$3,750	$3,500	$3,250	$3,000	$2,500	$1,750	$1,250
1970-1994	$1,750	$1,500	$1,250	$1,000	$750	$650	$550

Last Mfr.'s Sug. Retail was $2,760.

D-37K — spruce top, round soundhole, tortoise pickguard, 5 stripe bound body, abalone rosette, figured koa 2 piece back/sides, mahogany neck, 14/20 fret ebony fingerboard with pearl inlay, ebony bridge with white black dot pins, koa peghead veneer with logo decal, 3 per side chrome tuners. Available in Amber Stain finish. Mfd. 1980 to date.

	100%	98%	95%	90%	80%	70%	60%
Mfr.'s Sug. Retail $2,740	$2,055	$1,370	$1,300	$1,030	$890	$820	$745

This is a special order instrument.

D-37K2 — similar to D-37K, except has figured koa top, black pickguard.

	100%	98%	95%	90%	80%	70%	60%
Mfr.'s Sug. Retail $2,920	$2,190	$1,460	$1,380	$1,095	$955	$875	$795

This is a special order instrument.

D-41 — solid spruce top, round soundhole, black pickguard, bound body, abalone purfling/rosette, rosewood back/sides, mahogany neck, 14/20 fret bound ebony fingerboard with abalone hexagon inlay, ebony bridge with white abalone dot pins, rosewood veneer on bound peghead with white pearl vertical logo inlay, 3 per side gold tuners. Available in Natural finish. Mfd. 1969 to date.

	100%	98%	95%	90%	80%	70%	60%
1969		$12,500	$11,000	$9,750	$9,000	$8,500	$7,750	$6,500
1970-1985		$2,250	$2,000	$1,750	$1,250	$1,000	$900	$800
Curr. Mfr.'s Sug. Retail $3,960	$2,970	$1,980	$1,870	$1,400	$1,215	$1,115	$1,015

In 1987, tortoise pickguard, smaller abalone hexagon fingerboard inlay, abalone logo peghead inlay replaced original items.

D12-41 — similar to D-41, except has 12 strings, 12/20 fret fingerboard, 6 per side tuners. Disc. 1994.

	100%	98%	95%	90%	80%	70%	60%
	$2,700	$2,315	$1,930	$1,540	$1,390	$1,270	$1,155

Last Mfr.'s Sug. Retail was $3,860.

D-41S — similar to D-41, except has a prewar dreadnought style body, 12/20 fret fingerboard, slotted headstock. Mfd. 1969 to 1994.

	100%	98%	95%	90%	80%	70%
	$2,595	$2,230	$1,860	$1,485	$1,335	$1,225	$1,115

Last Mfr.'s Sug. Retail was $3,720.

D-45, PREWAR — solid spruce top, round soundhole, bound body, abalone purfling back/top, abalone rosette, rosewood back/sides, mahogany neck, 14/20 fret bound ebony fingerboard with snowflake inlay, ebony bridge with white abalone dot pins, rosewood veneer on bound peghead with abalone vertical logo inlay, 3 per side chrome tuners. Available in Natural finish. Mfd. 1933 to 1942.

The price of Prewar D-45s is constantly increasing. According to Mike Longworth at Martin, only 91 instruments were produced between 1933 and 1942. Currently, the market has only accounted for 72 of the 91. Furthermore, 25 of the 72 have been refinished or oversprayed. Depending on the condition, a Prewar D-45 may be worth $125,000 (or more). The **Blue Book of Guitars** highly recommends that several professional appraisals be secured before buying/selling/trading any Prewar Martin D-45.

D-45 — Production resumed in 1968, and continues to date.

	100%	98%	95%	90%	80%	70%	60%
1968-1969		$19,000	$16,500	$13,500	$11,500	$10,000	$9,250	$7,000
1970-1972		$7,000	$5,750	$5,250	$4,750	$4,200	$3,600	$2,950
1973-1985		$5,800	$3,750	$3,240	$2,750	$2,500	$2,000	$1,750
1986-1995		$4,500	$3,250	$2,750	$2,250	$2,050	$1,530	$1,240
Curr. Mfr.'s Sug. Retail $7,480	$6,358	$5,236	$4,640	$4,150	$3,700	$3,100	$2,400

1968 and 1969 were the last full production models to be constructed with Brazilian Rosewood back and sides. The 1968 models command a slightly higher premium over the 1969 models.

"Another big surprise is the re-kindled love affair we British are having with the good old reliable plain Jane of the guitar market SG. This time two years ago they were about as popular as a fart in a spacesuit."

—*Ian Farrell*

TCG, Sept/Oct 1990

M

D-45S — similar to D-45, except has a prewar dreadnought style body, 12/20 fret fingerboard, slotted headstock. Mfd. 1969 to 1994.

$4,800 $4,115 $3,430 $2,740 $2,475 $2,260 $2,055

Last Mfr.'s Sug. Retail was $6,860.

D12-45 — similar to D-45S, except has 12 strings, 6 per side tuners with pearl buttons. Mfd. 1969 to 1994.

$4,500 $4,000 $3,750 $3,250 $2,500 $2,000 $1,500

Last Mfr.'s Sug. Retail was $7,020.

D-60 — solid spruce top, round soundhole, tortoise pickguard, 3 stripe bound body/rosette, birdseye maple back/sides, maple neck, 14/20 fret ebony fingerboard with pearl snowflake inlay, ebony bridge with white red dot pins, birdseye maple veneer on ebony bound peghead, 3 per side gold tuners with ebony buttons. Available in Natural finish. Mfd. 1990 to 1995.

$2,115 $1,790 $1,480 $1,175 $1,035 $950 $860

Last Mfr.'s Sug. Retail was $3,060.

D-62 — similar to D-60, except has figured maple back/sides, mahogany neck, figured maple peghead veneer, gold tuners with pearl buttons. Mfd. 1988 to 1995.

$1,665 $1,415 $1,170 $910 $820 $750 $685

Last Mfr.'s Sug. Retail was $2,420.

D-76 (BICENTENNIAL LIMITED EDITION) — solid spruce top, round soundhole, black pickguard, herringbone bound body/rosette, rosewood 3 piece back/sides, mahogany neck, 14/20 fret ebony fingerboard with 13 pearl star inlays, ebony bridge with white black dot pins, rosewood peghead veneer with pearl eagle/logo inlay, 3 per side gold tuners. Available in Natural finish. Mfd. 1976 only.

$1,750 $1,500 $1,250 $1,000 $850 $750 $650

There were 1,976 models mfd., with an additional 98 (D-45E) exclusively for employees.

HD-28 — solid spruce top, round soundhole, black pickguard, herringbone bound body/rosette, rosewood 2 piece back/sides, 14/20 fret ebony fingerboard with pearl dot inlay, ebony bridge with white black dot pins, 3 per side chrome tuners. Available in Natural finish. Mfd. 1976 to date.

1976-1985 $1,750 $1,500 $1,350 $1,250 $1,000 $850 $700
Curr. Mfr.'s Sug. Retail $2,770 $2,077 $1,385 $1,260 $980 $875 $805 $735

Also available with solid red cedar top (CHD-28) and larch top (LHD-28).

In 1994, larch top was discontinued.

HD-28LE — similar to HD-28, except has tortoise pickguard, pearl diamond/square fingerboard inlay.

$2,400 $1,920 $1,560 $1,320 $1,080 $820 $720

This was a Special Edition guitar with a Limited Edition label. This model was Guitar-of-the-Month for December, 1985.

HD-282R — similar to HD-28, except has larger soundhole, 2 rows of herringbone purfling.
Mfr.'s Sug. Retail $2,900 $2,175 $1,450 $1,310 $1,025 $925 $845 $770

HD-35 — solid spruce top, round soundhole, black pickguard, herringbone bound body/rosette, rosewood 3 piece back/sides, 14/20 fret bound ebony fingerboard with pearl dot inlay, ebony bridge with white black dot pins, 3 per side chrome tuners. Available in Natural finish. Mfd. 1978 to date.

1978-1985 $1,750 $1,500 $1,350 $1,250 $1,000 $850 $700
Curr. Mfr.'s Sug. Retail $3,140 $2,355 $1,570 $1,430 $1,115 $1,005 $920 $835

Also available with solid red cedar top (CHD-35).

J Series

The following features are common to all instruments in this series: Body Length - 20 1/8 inches, Upper Bout Width - 11 11/16 inches, Lower Bout Width - 16 inches.

J-18 — solid spruce top, round soundhole, tortoise pickguard, 5 stripe bound body/rosette, mahogany back/sides/neck, 14/20 fret rosewood fingerboard with pearl dot inlay, rosewood bridge with black white dot pins, rosewood peghead veneer, 3 per side chrome tuners with ebony buttons. Available in Natural finish. Mfd. 1988 to date.
Mfr.'s Sug. Retail $2,300 $1,725 $1,150 $1,030 $790 $710 $650 $590

J-21 — spruce top, round soundhole, tortoise pickguard, 5 stripe bound body/rosette, rosewood back/sides, mahogany neck, 14/20 fret rosewood fingerboard with pearl dot inlay, rosewood bridge with black white dot pins, rosewood veneer peghead, 3 per side chrome tuners. Available in Natural finish. Mfd. 1985 to date.
Mfr.'s Sug. Retail $2,520 $1,890 $1,260 $1,190 $945 $820 $750 $685

This model is a special order instrument.

J-40 — solid spruce top, round soundhole, black pickguard, 5 stripe bound body/rosette, rosewood back/sides, mahogany neck, 14/20 fret bound ebony fingerboard with abalone hexagon inlay, ebony bridge with white abalone dot pins, rosewood peghead veneer, 3 per side chrome tuners. Available in Natural finish. Mfd. 1985 to date.
Mfr.'s Sug. Retail $3,250 $2,437 $1,625 $1,155 $1,075 $875 $805 $730

J-40BK — similar to J-40, except has Black Finish. Curr. mfr.
Mfr.'s Sug. Retail $3,470 $2,602 $1,735 $1,355 $1,055 $950 $870 $790

JC-40 — similar to J-40, except has single round cutaway. Mfd. 1987 to date.
Mfr.'s Sug. Retail $3,390 $2,542 $1,695 $1,315 $1,025 $920 $840 $765

M

Grading	100%	98% MINT	95% EXC+	90% EXC	80% VG+	70% VG	60% G

J12-40 — similar to J-40, except has 12 strings, 6 per side gold tuners with ebony buttons. Curr. mfr.

Mfr.'s Sug. Retail	$3,350	$2,512	$1,675	$1,295	$1,000	$900	$825	$750

J-65 — solid spruce top, round soundhole, tortoise pickguard, tortoise bound body, 3 stripe rosette, figured maple back/sides, maple neck, 14/20 fret bound ebony fingerboard with pearl dot inlay, ebony bridge with white red dot pins, rosewood peghead veneer with logo decal, 3 per side gold tuners with pearl buttons. Available in Natural finish. Mfd. 1985 to 1995.

	$1,730	$1,470	$1,215	$945	$850	$780	$710

Last Mfr.'s Sug. Retail was $2,520.

J12-65 — similar to J-65, except has 12 strings, 6 per side tuners. Disc. 1995.

	$1,795	$1,525	$1,260	$980	$875	$805	$735

Last Mfr.'s Sug. Retail was $2,610.

Custom J-65 — solid spruce top, round soundhole, tortoise pickguard, white body binding, herringbone purfling, 3 stripe rosette, figured maple back/sides, maple neck, 14/20 fret bound ebony fingerboard with pearl dot inlay, ebony bridge with white red dot pins, rosewood peghead veneer with logo decal, 3 per side gold tuners with pearl buttons. Available in Natural finish. New 1994.

Mfr.'s Sug. Retail	$2,900	$2,320	$1,740	$1,450	$1,160	$1,040	$955	$870

Custom J-65 Electric — similar to Custom J-65, except has MEQ-932 acoustic amplification system. New 1994.

Mfr.'s Sug. Retail	$3,070	$2,456	$1,842	$1,535	$1,225	$1,100	$1,010	$920

M Series

The following features are common to all instruments in this series: Body Length - 20 1/8 inches, Upper Bout Width - 11 11/16 inches, Lower Bout Width - 16 inches.

CM-0089 — grand auditorium style, spruce top, round soundhole, tortoise pickguard, bound body, herringbone purfling, pearl rosette, rosewood back/sides, mahogany neck, 14/20 fret ebony fingerboard with pearl dot inlay, rosewood bridge with white black dot pins, 3 per side chrome tuners. Available in Natural finish. Mfd. 1979 only.

25 of these instruments were produced.

There has not been sufficient quanity traded to quote prices.

J-21M — flat-top body, spruce top, round soundhole, tortoise pickguard, tortoise bound body, herringbone rosette, rosewood back/sides, mahogany neck, 14/20 fret rosewood fingerboard with pearl dot inlay, rosewood bridge with black white pins, 3 per side chrome tuners. Available in Natural finish. Mfd. 1985 to 1987.

	$1,165	$1,000	$835	$665	$600	$550	$500

Last Mfr.'s Sug. Retail was $1,665.

J-21MC — similar to J-21M, except has single round cutaway, oval soundhole, 5 stripe rosette, ebony buttoned tuners. Mfd. 1987.

	$1,225	$1,050	$875	$700	$630	$575	$525

Last Mfr.'s Sug. Retail was $1,750.

This was a limited edition instrument, 57 were produced.

J-40M — flat-top body, spruce top, round soundhole, black pickguard bound body, 5 stripe purfling/rosette, Indian rosewood back/sides, mahogany neck, 14/20 fret bound ebony fingerboard with abalone hexagon inlay, ebony bridge with white black dot pins, rosewood veneered peghead with logo decal, 3 per side gold tuners. Available in Natural finish. Mfd. 1985 to 1987.

	$1,300	$1,115	$930	$740	$670	$610	$555

Last Mfr.'s Sug. Retail was $1,860.

J-40M BLE — similar to J-40M, except has Brazilian rosewood back/sides, pearl snowflake/diamond fingerboard inlay, pearloid buttoned tuners. Mfd. 1987.

	$2,095	$1,800	$1,500	$1,200	$1,080	$990	$900

Last Mfr.'s Sug. Retail was $3,000.

This was a limited edition instrument, 17 were produced.

J12-40M — similar to J-40M, except has 12 strings, 6 per side tuners. Mfd. 1985 to 1987.

	$1,345	$1,150	$960	$770	$690	$630	$575

Last Mfr.'s Sug. Retail was $1,920.

J-45M DELUXE — flat-top body, spruce top, round soundhole, tortoise pickguard, tortoise bound body, abalone purfling/rosette, Indian rosewood back/sides, mahogany neck, 14/20 fret abalone bound fingerboard with abalone hexagon inlay, abalone bound peghead with rosewood veneer, abalone vertical logo peghead inlay, 3 per side gold tuners with ebony buttons. Available in Natural finish. Mfd. 1987.

	$4,830	$4,140	$3,450	$2,760	$2,485	$2,275	$2,070

Last Mfr.'s Sug. Retail was $6,900.

This was a limited edition instrument, 17 were produced.

J-65M — flat-top body, spruce top, round soundhole, tortoise pickguard, tortoise bound body, 5 stripe purfling/rosette, flamed maple back/sides, mahogany neck, 14/20 fret bound ebony fingerboard with pearl dot inlay, ebony bridge with white tortoise dot pins, rosewood veneered peghead with logo decal, 3 per side gold tuners. Available in Natural finish. Mfd. 1985 to 1987.

	$1,265	$1,085	$905	$720	$650	$595	$540

Last Mfr.'s Sug. Retail was $1,805.

M

Grading	100%	98% MINT	95% EXC+	90% EXC	80% VG+	70% VG	60% G

J12-65M — similar to J-65M, except has 12 strings, 6 per side tuners. Mfd. 1985 to 1994.

| | $1,310 | $1,120 | $935 | $745 | $675 | $615 | $560 |

Last Mfr.'s Sug. Retail was $1,870.

M-18 — flat-top body, spruce top, round soundhole, black pickguard, bound body, 3 stripe purfling/rosette, mahogany back/sides/neck, 14/20 fret rosewood fingerboard with pearl dot inlay, rosewood bridge with black white dot pins, 3 per side chrome tuners. Available in Natural finish. Mfd. 1984 to 1987.

| | $1,085 | $930 | $775 | $620 | $560 | $515 | $465 |

Last Mfr.'s Sug. Retail was $1,550.

The first instruments of this line had ebony fingerboards/bridges. Three have a Blue/Red/White finish.

M-21 — flat-top body, spruce top, round soundhole, tortoise bound body, pearl rosette, rosewood back/sides, mahogany neck, 14/20 fret rosewood fingerboard with pearl snowflake inlay, rosewood bridge with black white dot pins, 3 per side chrome tuners. Mfd. 1984.

| | $1,120 | $960 | $800 | $640 | $575 | $530 | $480 |

Last Mfr.'s Sug. Retail was $1,600.

This was a limited edition instrument, 16 instruments were manufactured.

M-36 — flat-top body, solid spruce top, round soundhole, tortoise pickguard, 5 stripe bound body/rosette, rosewood back/sides, mahogany neck, 14/20 fret bound ebony fingerboard with pearl dot inlay, rosewood bridge with white black dot pins, rosewood veneer on bound peghead, 3 per side chrome tuners. Available in Natural finish. Mfd. 1978 to date.

| Mfr.'s Sug. Retail | $2,540 | $1,905 | $1,270 | $1,135 | $900 | $780 | $715 | $650 |

Early production models came with an unbound peghead.

This instrument began production as the M-35. After 26 were manufactured, the model was renamed the M-36.

M-38 — similar to M-36, except has abalone rosette. Mfd. 1977 to date.

| Mfr.'s Sug. Retail | $3,150 | $2,362 | $1,575 | $1,410 | $1,115 | $970 | $890 | $810 |

M-64 — similar to M-36, except has figured maple back/sides/neck, unbound fingerboard/peghead. Mfd. 1985 to 1995.

| | $1,715 | $1,445 | $1,190 | $945 | $820 | $750 | $685 |

Last Mfr.'s Sug. Retail was $2,520.

MC-28 — single round cutaway flat-top body, solid spruce top, oval soundhole, black pickguard, 3 stripe bound body/rosette, rosewood back/sides, mahogany neck, 22 fret ebony fingerboard with pearl dot inlay, ebony bridge with white black dot pins, rosewood peghead veneer, 3 per side chrome tuners. Available in Natural finish. Mfd. 1981 to date.

| Mfr.'s Sug. Retail | $2,810 | $2,107 | $1,405 | $1,285 | $1,000 | $900 | $825 | $750 |

MC-37K — single round cutaway flat-top body, spruce top, oval soundhole, tortoise pickguard, bound body, pearl rosette, figured koa back/sides, mahogany neck, 22 fret ebony fingerboard with abalone flake inlay, ebony bridge with white black dot pins, 3 per side chrome tuners. Available in Amber Stain finish. Mfd. 1981 to 1987.

| | $1,400 | $1,200 | $1,000 | $800 | $720 | $660 | $600 |

Last Mfr.'s Sug. Retail was $2,000.

18 of these instruments were produced.

MC-68 — single round cutaway flat-top body, solid spruce top, oval soundhole, tortoise pickguard, 5 stripe bound body/rosette, figured maple back/sides, maple neck, 22 fret bound ebony fingerboard with abalone dot inlay, ebony bridge with white abalone dot pins, rosewood veneer on bound peghead with abalone inlay, 3 per side gold tuners. Available in Natural and Sunburst finishes. Mfd. 1985 to 1995.

| | $2,015 | $1,710 | $1,415 | $1,105 | $995 | $910 | $825 |

Last Mfr.'s Sug. Retail was $2,930.

OM Series

The following features are common to all instruments in this series: Body Length - 19 3/8 inches, Upper Bout Width - 11 1/4 inches, Lower Bout Width - 15 5/8 inches.

OM-18 — spruce top, tortoise pickguard, round soundhole, wooden bound body, rope pattern rosette, mahogany back/sides/neck, 14/20 fret ebony fingerboard with pearl dot inlay, ebony bridge with black pearl dot pins, 3 per side tuners with ivoroid buttons. Available in Natural finish. Mfd. 1930 to 1933.

| | $4,500 | $3,855 | $3,215 | $2,570 | $2,315 | $2,120 | $1,930 |

This model had banjo style tuners.

OM-21 — solid spruce top, round soundhole, tortoise pickguard, bound body, herringbone rosette, rosewood back/sides, mahogany neck, 14/20 fret rosewood fingerboard with pearl dot inlay, rosewood bridge with black dot pins, 3 per side chrome tuners. Available in Natural finish. New 1994.

| Mfr.'s Sug. Retail | $2,110 | $1,582 | $1,055 | $990 | $790 | $715 | $655 | $595 |

OM-28 — spruce top, round soundhole, black pickguard, 5 stripe bound body/rosette, rosewood back/sides, mahogany neck, 14/20 fret ebony fingerboard with pearl dot inlay, ebony bridge with white black dot pins, rosewood peghead veneer, 3 per side chrome tuners. Available in Natural finish. Mfd. 1929 to 1933.

| | $15,000 | $12,500 | $10,500 | $9,250 | $8,500 | $7,500 | $6,000 |

OM-28, Current Manufacture — these instruments were reintroduced as special order items.

| Mfr.'s Sug. Retail | $2,750 | $2,200 | $1,650 | $1,385 | $1,095 | $955 | $875 | $795 |

"This is where my friend's comment comes in…guitar dealers as musical instrument grave robbers…Dig up the tools of the music of the past - AND SELL THEM! Hey, I admit it - it gives me a kick."

—Skip Henderson
TCG, Sept/Oct 1990

M

Grading	100%	98%	95%	90%	80%	70%	60%
		MINT	EXC+	EXC	VG+	VG	G

OM-45 — solid spruce top, round soundhole, black pickguard, abalone bound body/rosette, rosewood back/sides, mahogany neck, 14/20 fret bound ebony fingerboard with abalone snowflake inlay, ebony bridge with white abalone dot pins, bound rosewood veneered peghead with abalone logo inlay, 3 per side gold banjo style tuners with ivoroid buttons. Available in Natural finish. Mfd. 1930 to 1933.

$60,000 $55,000 $47,500 $40,000 $32,500 $27,500 $20,000

OM-45 Deluxe — similar to OM-45, except has abalone vine pickguard inlay, abalone snowflake bridge wings inlay. Mfd. 1930.

$75,000 $70,000 $65,000 $57,500 $50,000 $42,500 $35,000

OM-45 Reissue — similar to OM-45, except has abalone hexagon fingerboard inlay, gold enclosed tuners. Mfd. 1977 to 1994.

$4,570 $3,920 $3,265 $2,610 $2,350 $2,155 $1,960
Last Mfr.'s Sug. Retail was $6,530.

This model was reintroduced as a special order instrument.

O Series

The following features are common to all instruments in this series: Body Length - 19 1/8 inches, Upper Bout Width - 9 1/2 inches, Lower Bout Width - 13 1/2 inches.

O-15 — mahogany top, round soundhole, 2 stripe bound body/rosette, black pickguard, mahogany back/sides/neck, 14/20 fret rosewood fingerboard with white dot inlay, rosewood bridge with white pins, black face peghead with logo decal, 3 per side nickel tuners with plastic buttons. Available in Natural finish. Mfd. 1935 to 1961.

$900 $850 $800 $700 $600 $475 $350

O-16NY — spruce top, round soundhole, 3 stripe bound body/rosette, mahogany back/sides/neck, 12/19 fret rosewood fingerboard, rosewood bridge with black white dot pins, slotted peghead 3 per side tuners with plastic buttons. Available in Natural finish. Mfd. 1961 to date.

1961-1969		$950	$900	$850	$750	$650	$500	$375
1970-1992		$850	$800	$750	$650	$600	$550	$425
Curr. Mfr.'s Sug. Retail	$2,400	$1,800	$1,200	$1,140	$905	$785	$720	$655

This instrument is currently a special order instrument.

The current production of this instrument features a solid peghead with tuners running parallel to the peghead.

O-17 — mahogany top, round soundhole, mahogany back/sides, cedar neck, 12/20 fret ebony fingerboard with pearl dot inlay, ebony bridge with black pins, slotted peghead, 3 per side nickel tuners with plastic buttons. Available in Natural finish. Mfd. 1906 to 1968.

$950 $900 $850 $750 $650 $500 $375

In 1914, rosewood bound body, 3 stripe rosette was introduced.

In 1927, rosewood fingerboard/bridge replaced original items.

In 1929, rosewood bound body was discontinued.

In 1931, pickguard became optionally available.

In 1934, 14/20 fret fingerboard replaced original item.

In 1936, solid peghead, all metal tuners replaced original items.

O-18 — solid spruce top, round soundhole, wood bound body, rope rosette, rosewood back/sides, cedar neck, 12/19 fret ebony fingerboard, pyramid ebony bridge with black pearl dot pins, 3 per side brass tuners with ivory buttons. Available in Natural finish. Mfd. 1898 to date.

	100%	98%	95%	90%	80%	70%	60%
1898-1944	$2,000	$1,750	$1,500	$1,250	$1,000	$800	$600
1945-present	$1,250	$1,000	$900	$800	$650	$500	$375

In 1909, pearl dot fingerboard inlay was introduced.

In 1917, mahogany back/sides/neck replaced original items.

In 1919, rosewood bound body was introduced.

In 1920, 12/20 fret fingerboard became standard.

In 1921, straight bridge replaced original item.

In 1923, belly bridge replaced respective item.

In 1932, pickguard became optionally available.

In 1934, black body binding replaced original item.

By 1935, 14/20 fret fingerboard became standard item.

By 1956, rosewood fingerboard/bridge replaced original item.

O-21 — solid spruce top, round soundhole, wood bound body, herringbone rosette, rosewood back/sides, cedar neck, 12/19 fret ebony fingerboard with pearl dot inlay, pyramid ebony bridge with ebony pearl dot pins, 3 per side brass tuners with ivory buttons. Available in Natural finish. Mfd. 1898 to 1948.

$2,750 $2,500 $2,250 $2,000 $1,500 $1,250 $950

In 1917, mahogany neck replaced original item.

In 1923, 12/20 fret fingerboard became standard item.

In 1927, belly bridge replaced original item.

In 1932, pickguard became optionally available.

M

Grading	100%	98% MINT	95% EXC+	90% EXC	80% VG+	70% VG	60% G

O-28 — solid spruce top, round soundhole, ivory bound body, herringbone rosette, rosewood back/sides, cedar neck, 12/19 fret ebony fingerboard, pyramid ebony bridge with ebony pearl dot pins, 3 per side brass tuners with ivory buttons. Available in Natural finish. Mfd. 1898 to 1937.

| | $3,750 | $3,500 | $3,000 | $2,500 | $2,000 | $1,500 | $1,250 |

In 1901, pearl dot fingerboard inlay was introduced.
In 1917, 12/20 fret fingerboard replaced original item, mahogany neck replaced original item.
In 1929, belly bridge replaced original item.
In 1934, pickguard became standard item, 14/20 fret fingerboard replaced respective item.

O-30 — solid spruce top, round soundhole, ivory bound body/colored purfling, pearl rosette, rosewood back/sides, cedar neck, 12/19 fret ivory bound ebony fingerboard with pearl dot inlay, pyramid ebony bridge with ebony pearl dot pins, 3 per side silver brass tuners. Available in Natural finish. Mfd. 1899 to 1921.

| | $4,250 | $4,000 | $3,500 | $3,000 | $2,500 | $1,750 | $1,500 |

O-42 — solid spruce top, round soundhole, ivory bound body, pearl purfling/rosette, rosewood back/sides, cedar neck, 12/19 fret ivory bound ebony fingerboard with pearl diamond/snowflake inlay, pyramid ivory bridge with ebony pearl dot pins, 3 per side silver tuners with pearl buttons. Available in Natural finish. Mfd. 1898 to 1930.

| | $5,500 | $5,000 | $4,500 | $3,750 | $3,250 | $2,500 | $1,750 |

In 1914, ivory peghead pegs were optionally available.
In 1919, plastic binding, ebony bridge replaced original items.
In 1923, mahogany neck, 12/20 fret fingerboard, nickel tuners replaced original items.
In 1929, belly bridge replaced original item.

O-45 — solid spruce top, round soundhole, ivory bound body, pearl purfling/rosette, Brazilian rosewood back/sides, cedar neck, 12/19 fret ivory bound ebony fingerboard with pearl snowflake/diamond inlay, pyramid ivory bridge with ebony pearl dot pins, ivory/pearl bound peghead with pearl torch inlay, 3 per side brass tuners with ivory buttons. Available in Natural finish. Mfd. 1904 to 1930.

| | $10,000 | $9,500 | $8,750 | $7,750 | $6,750 | $6,000 | $4,750 |

In 1917, 12/20 fret fingerboard replaced original item.
In 1919, plastic binding, ebony bridge replaced original items.
In 1929, belly bridge replaced original item.

OO Series

The following features are common to all instruments in this series: Body Length - 19 5/8 inches, Upper Bout Width - 9 3/4 inches, Lower Bout Width - 14 1/8 inches.

Unless indicated otherwise, all instruments in this series have classic style bodies, solid spruce top, round soundhole, bound body, mahogany neck, 12/19 fret fingerboard, tied bridge, slotted peghead, 3 per side gold pearl button tuners. Available in Natural finishes.

OO-16C — solid spruce top, round soundhole, bound body, 3 stripe rosette, mahogany back/sides/neck, 12/19 fret rosewood fingerboard, tied rosewood bridge, slotted peghead, 3 per side tuners with pearl buttons. Available in Natural finish. Disc. 1994.

| | $1,630 | $1,400 | $1,165 | $930 | $840 | $770 | $700 |

Last Mfr.'s Sug. Retail was $2,330.

OO-16NY — solid spruce top, bound body, mahogany back/sides/neck, 12/19 fret rosewood fingerboard, tied rosewood bridge, slotted peghead, 3 per side tuners with plastic buttons. Available in Natural finish. Mfd. 1961 to 1975.

| | $1,250 | $1,000 | $900 | $825 | $700 | $550 | $450 |

OO-17 — mahogany top, round soundhole, 3 stripe bound body/rosette, mahogany back/sides/neck, 14/20 fret rosewood fingerboard, rosewood bridge with black pins, 3 per side tuners. Available in Dark Natural finish. Mfd. 1908 to 1987.

| | $1,250 | $1,000 | $900 | $825 | $700 | $550 | $450 |

This instrument was a special order item.

OO-18 — 3 stripe rosette, mahogany back/sides, rosewood fingerboard/bridge. Mfd. 1898 to 1994.

| 1898-1945 | $2,250 | $2,000 | $1,750 | $1,500 | $1,250 | $950 | $750 |
| 1946-1994 | $1,500 | $1,250 | $1,000 | $850 | $700 | $600 | $550 |

Last Mfr.'s Sug. Retail was $2,480.

OO-18C — similar to the OO-18. Mfd. 1962 to 1978.

| | $1,500 | $1,250 | $1,000 | $850 | $700 | $600 | $550 |

OO-18G — mahogany back/sides, ebony fingerboard/bridge. Available in polished Lacquer finish. Mfd. 1936 to 1962.

| | $1,100 | $770 | $660 | $550 | $440 | $395 | $365 |

After the 1940s, these models came with a rosewood fingerboard/bridge.

OO-21 — spruce top, round soundhole, black pickguard, multibound body, 3 stripe rosette, rosewood back/sides, mahogany neck, 12/19 fret rosewood fingerboard with pearl dot inlay, rosewood bridge with black white dot pins, rosewood veneered solid peghead with screened logo, 3 per side chrome tuners. Available in Natural finish. New 1994.

| Mfr.'s Sug. Retail | $2,730 | $2,184 | $1,638 | $1,365 | $1,090 | $980 | $900 | $820 |

Grading	100%	98% MINT	95% EXC+	90% EXC	80% VG+	70% VG	60% G

OO-21NY — spruce top, round soundhole, tortoise bound body, herringbone rosette, rosewood back/sides, mahogany neck, 12/19 fret ebony fingerboard, ebony bridge with black white dot pins, slotted peghead with logo decal, 3 per side tuners. Available in Natural finish. Mfd. 1898 to 1987.

	$3,250	$3,000	$2,750	$2,250	$1,750	$1,500	$1,000

OO-28 — herringbone bound body, 3 stripe rosette, rosewood back/sides ebony fingerboard/bridge. Mfd. 1898 to 1940.

	$4,000	$3,750	$3,250	$2,750	$2,250	$1,750	$1,375

OO-28C — 3 stripe rosette, rosewood back/sides, ebony fingerboard/bridge. Mfd. 1966 to 1994.

	$1,930	$1,655	$1,380	$1,105	$995	$910	$825

Last Mfr.'s Sug. Retail was $2,760.

OO-28G — rosewood back/sides, 12/20 fret ebony fingerboard. Mfd. 1936 to 1962.

	$1,100	$940	$785	$630	$565	$515	$470

OO-30 — rosewood back/sides/fingerboard/bridge. Mfd. 1899 to 1921.

	$4,750	$4,500	$4,000	$3,500	$2,750	$2,250	$1,750

OO-42 — pearl bound body/rosette, rosewood back/sides/fingerboard/bridge. Mfd. 1898 to 1942.

	$7,500	$7,000	$6,500	$5,750	$5,000	$4,000	$2,750

OO-45 — pearl bound body/rosette/fingerboard/peghead, rosewood back/sides/fingerboard/bridge. Mfd. 1904 to 1942.

	$15,000	$12,500	$10,500	$9,500	$7,750	$6,500	$5,250

OOO Series

The following features are common to all instruments in this series: Body Length - 10 3/4 inches, Upper Bout Width - 10 3/4 inches, Lower Bout Width - 15 inches.

OOO-16 — solid spruce top, round soundhole, tortoise pickguard, bound body, 3 stripe rosette, mahogany back/sides/neck, 14/20 fret rosewood fingerboard with pearl snowflake inlay, rosewood bridge with black white dot pins, rosewood peghead veneer, 3 per side chrome tuners. Available in Natural finish. Mfd. 1990 to date.

Mfr.'s Sug. Retail	$1,680	$1,260	$840	$795	$635	$550	$505	$455

OOO-16C — similar to OOO-16, except has single round cutaway, oval soundhole, 22 fret fingerboard.

Mfr.'s Sug. Retail	$1,860	$1,395	$930	$880	$675	$605	$555	$505

OOO-18 — solid spruce top, round soundhole, black pickguard, wood bound body, rope rosette, rosewood back/sides, cedar neck, 12/19 fret ebony fingerboard, ebony pyramid bridge with black pearl dot pins, 3 per side brass tuners with ivory buttons. Available in Natural finish. Mfd. 1911 to date.

1911-1944		$3,500	$3,000	$2,750	$2,250	$1,750	$1,500	$1,250
1945-1985		$1,750	$1,500	$1,250	$1,000	$850	$750	$600
Curr. Mfr.'s Sug. Retail	$2,130	$1,704	$1,278	$1,145	$880	$790	$725	$660

This is a special order instrument.

In 1909, pearl dot inlay fingerboard was introduced.

In 1917, mahogany back/sides/neck replaced original items.

In 1920, 12/20 fret fingerboard became standard.

In 1929, straight bridge replaced original item.

In 1930, belly bridge replaced respective item.

In 1932, pickguard became optionally available.

In 1934, black body binding, 14/20 fret fingerboard, all metal tuners replaced original items.

By 1956, rosewood fingerboard/bridge replaced original item.

OOO-21 — solid spruce top, round soundhole, wood bound body, herringbone rosette, rosewood back/sides, cedar neck, 12/19 fret ebony fingerboard with pearl dot inlay, ebony pyramid bridge with black pearl dot pins, 3 per side brass tuners with ivory buttons. Available in Natural finish. Mfd. 1902 to 1965.

1902-1944	$5,000	$4,500	$4,000	$3,250	$2,500	$2,000	$1,750
1945-1965	$3,500	$3,000	$2,750	$2,250	$1,750	$1,500	$1,000

In 1923, mahogany neck, 12/20 fret fingerboard replaced original items.

In 1930, belly bridge replaced original item.

In 1932, pickguard became optionally available.

In 1939, 14/20 fret fingerboard replaced respective item.

By 1956, rosewood fingerboard/bridge replaced original item.

M

"'Hmmm…What'd you pay for this?' (My standard reply - 'That?' 'Oh, nothing, I found it on the trash about two blocks from your house.')"

—Skip Henderson

TCG, Sept/Oct 1990

Grading		100%	98% MINT	95% EXC+	90% EXC	80% VG+	70% VG	60% G

OOO-28 — solid spruce top, round soundhole, ivory bound body, herringbone purfling, 5 stripe rosette, rosewood back/sides, cedar neck, 12/19 fret ebony fingerboard, ebony pyramid bridge with black pearl dot pins, 3 per side brass tuners with ivory buttons. Available in Natural finish. Mfd. 1902 to date.

		100%	98%	95%	90%	80%	70%	60%
1902-1944		$10,000	$9,500	$9,000	$8,250	$7,500	$6,000	$4,750
1945-1969		$6,000	$5,500	$5,000	$4,250	$3,500	$2,750	$1,750
1970-1985		$1,500	$1,250	$1,000	$850	$700	$600	$500
Curr. Mfr.'s Sug. Retail	$2,430	$1,944	$1,458	$1,300	$1,030	$890	$820	$745

In 1901, pearl diamond fingerboard inlay was introduced.

In 1917, 12/20 fret fingerboard replaced original item, mahogany neck replaced original item.

In 1929, belly bridge replaced original item.

In 1932, pickguard became optionally available.

In 1934, pickguard became standard item, 14/20 fret fingerboard replaced respective item.

In 1944, pearl dot fingerboard inlay replaced original item.

In 1947, 5 stripe purfling replaced original item.

OOO-28C — similar to OOO-28, except has classical style body. Mfd. 1962 to 1966.

			$725	$505	$435	$360	$290	$260	$240

OOO-42 — solid spruce top, round soundhole, ivory bound body, pearl purfling/rosette, rosewood back/sides, cedar neck, 12/19 fret ivory bound ebony fingerboard with pearl diamond/snowflakes inlay, ivory bridge with black pearl dot pins, 3 per side silver tuners with pearl buttons. Available in Natural finish. Mfd. 1918 to 1943.

		$19,500	$13,650	$11,700	$9,750	$7,800	$7,020	$6,435

In 1919, plastic body binding, ebony bridge replaced original items.

In 1923, mahogany neck, 12/20 fret fingerboard, nickel tuners replaced original items.

In 1929, belly bridge replaced original item.

In 1932, pickguard became optionally available.

In 1938, 14/20 fret fingerboard replaced respective item.

OOO-45 — solid spruce top, round soundhole, ivory bound body, pearl purfling top/back/sides, pearl rosette, rosewood back/sides, cedar neck, 12/19 fret ivory bound ebony fingerboard with pearl diamond/snowflakes inlay, ivory bridge with black pearl dot pins, pearl bound slotted peghead with pearl torch inlay, 3 per side silver tuners with pearl buttons. Available in Natural finish. Mfd. 1906 to 1994.

		100%	98%	95%	90%	80%	70%	60%
1906-1930		$25,000	$20,500	$17,500	$15,000	$12,500	$10,000	$8,500
1939-1942		$40,000	$35,000	$30,500	$25,000	$20,500	$15,000	$12,000
1970-1994		$4,000	$3,750	$3,500	$3,000	$2,500	$2,000	$1,500

Last Mfr.'s Sug. Retail was $6,530.

In 1917, 12/20 fret fingerboard replaced original item.

In 1919, ebony bridge replaced original item.

In 1923, plastic binding replaced original item.

In 1929, belly bridge replaced original item.

In 1932, pickguard became optionally available.

In 1934, pearl peghead logo inlay was introduced, 14/20 fret fingerboard replaced respective item.

In 1936, chrome tuners replaced original item.

In 1939, gold tuners replaced respective item.

5 Series

The following features are common to all instruments in this series: Body Length - 16 inches, Upper Bout Width - 8 1/4 inches, Lower Bout Width - 11 1/4 inches.

5-16 — spruce top, round soundhole, 3 stripe bound body/rosette, mahogany back/sides/neck, 12/19 fret rosewood fingerboard, rosewood bridge with black white dot pins, 3 per side chrome tuners. Available in Natural finish. Mfd. 1962 to 1963.

			$925	$790	$660	$530	$475	$435	$395

5-17 — mahogany top, round soundhole, mahogany back/sides/neck, 12/19 fret rosewood fingerboard, rosewood bridge with black pins, 3 per side die cast tuners with nickel buttons. Available in Dark finish. Mfd. 1938 to 1945.

			$550	$470	$395	$315	$285	$260	$235

ACOUSTIC BASS

Unless otherwise listed, all models have jumbo style bodies, and are available with fretless fingerboard at no additional charge.

Add $325 to all models for acoustic bridge pickup with active preamp, volume/tone control.

B-40 — jumbo style, solid spruce top, round soundhole, black pickguard, 5 stripe bound body/rosette, rosewood back/sides, mahogany neck, 17/23 fret ebony fingerboard, ebony bridge with white black dot pins, rosewood peghead veneer, 2 per side chrome tuners. Available in Natural finish. Mfd. 1988 to date.

Mfr.'s Sug. Retail		$2,900	$2,175	$1,450	$1,320	$1,025	$925	$845	$770

BC-40 — similar to B-40, except has single round cutaway, oval soundhole. Mfd. 1990 to date.

Mfr.'s Sug. Retail		$3,120	$2,340	$1,560	$1,420	$1,110	$1,000	$915	$830

Refinished Martin 000-45
courtesy Donald Colden

M

Grading	100%	98% MINT	95% EXC+	90% EXC	80% VG+	70% VG	60% G

B-540 — similar to B-40, except has 5 strings, striped ebony fingerboard/bridge, 5/2 per side tuners. Mfd. 1992 to 1995.

| | $1,920 | $1,635 | $1,355 | $1,055 | $950 | $870 | $790 |

Last Mfr.'s Sug. Retail was $2,790.

B-65 — similar to B-40, except has tortoise pickguard, figured maple back/sides. Mfd. 1987 to 1995.

| | $1,795 | $1,525 | $1,260 | $980 | $875 | $805 | $735 |

Last Mfr.'s Sug. Retail was $2,610.

ELECTRIC

D-28E — dreadnought style, spruce top, round soundhole, black pickguard, 3 stripe bound body/rosette, rosewood back/sides, 14/20 fret ebony fingerboard with pearl dot inlay, ebony bridge with white black dot pins, 3 per side tuners, gold hardware, 2 single coil exposed DeArmond pickups, 2 volume/2 tone controls, 3 position switch. Available in Natural finish. Mfd. 1959 to 1965.

| | $1,830 | $1,280 | $1,095 | $915 | $730 | $660 | $605 |

E Series

These models have offset round double cutaway body, mahogany neck, round wave cresting style peghead, 3 per side tuners.

E-18 — 9 piece maple/rosewood/walnut body, 22 fret rosewood fingerboard with pearl dot inlay, Leo Quan wrapped bridge, brass nut, rosewood peghead veneer with CFM logo decal, Sperzel tuners, chrome hardware, 2 humbucker covered DiMarzio pickups, 2 volume/2 tone controls, 3 position/phase switches. Available in Natural finish. Mfd. 1979 to 1982.

| | $400 | $280 | $240 | $200 | $160 | $145 | $130 |

Brass control knobs found on earlier models, replaced by black plastic on later models.

Approximately 5,307 of these instruments were made.

EM-18 — 9 piece maple/rosewood/walnut body, 22 fret rosewood fingerboard with pearl dot inlay, Leo Quan wrapped bridge, brass nut, rosewood peghead veneer with CFM logo decal, Sperzel tuners, chrome hardware, 2 humbucker exposed DiMarzio pickups, 2 volume/2 tone controls, 3 position/phase/coil tap switches. Available in Natural finish. Mfd. 1979 to 1982.

| | $450 | $315 | $270 | $225 | $180 | $160 | $150 |

A few models found with Mighty Mite pickups, brass control knobs found on earlier models, replaced by black plastic on later models.

Approximately 5,629 of these instruments were made.

E-28 — mahogany body, thru body neck, 24 fret ebony fingerboard with pearl dot inlay, Schaller tunomatic tailpiece, ebony peghead veneer with CFM logo decal, Schaller tuners, chrome hardware, 2 humbucker exposed Seymour Duncan pickups, 2 volume/treble/bass controls, 3 position/phase/bypass switches, active electronics. Available in Sunburst finish. Mfd. 1981 to 1982.

| | $650 | $455 | $390 | $325 | $260 | $235 | $215 |

Approximately 4,854 of these instruments were made.

F Series

These guitars have a traditional style Martin headstock.

F-50 — single round cutaway semi hollow bound plywood body, f-holes, raised black pickguard, mahogany neck, 20 fret rosewood fingerboard with white dot inlay, adjustable plexiglass bridge/trapeze tailpiece, 3 per side tuners, chrome hardware, adjustable exposed pickup, volume/tone control. Available in Sunburst finish. Mfd. 1961 to 1965.

| | $625 | $440 | $375 | $310 | $250 | $225 | $205 |

F-55 — similar to F-50, except has 2 pickups, 2 volume/2 tone controls, 3 position switch.

| | $750 | $525 | $450 | $375 | $300 | $270 | $245 |

F-65 — similar to F-50, except has double cutaway, Bigsby style vibrato, 2 pickups, 2 volume/2 tone controls, 3 position switch.

| | $550 | $385 | $330 | $275 | $220 | $200 | $180 |

GT Series

These guitars have a non-traditional large headstock, with 2 sharp upper corners scooping down to the center.

GT-70 — single round cutaway semi hollow bound plywood body, arch top, f-holes, raised white pickguard, mahogany neck, 22 fret bound rosewood fingerboard with white dot inlay, adjustable bridge/Bigsby style vibrato, bound peghead with logo decal, 3 per side tuners, chrome hardware, 2 exposed pickups, 2 volume/2 tone controls, 3 position switch. Available in Black and Burgundy finishes. Mfd. 1965 to 1968.

| | $750 | $525 | $450 | $375 | $300 | $270 | $245 |

GT-75 — similar to GT-70, except has double round cutaways.

| | $775 | $540 | $460 | $385 | $310 | $280 | $255 |

Martin F-65
courtesy Robert Hauener

M

Grading	100%	98% MINT	95% EXC+	90% EXC	80% VG+	70% VG	60% G

GT-75-12 — similar to GT-70, except has twelve strings, double round cutaways.

	$600	$420	$360	$300	$240	$215	$195

This model had a traditional style headstock.

ELECTRIC BASS

These models have offset round double cutaway body, mahogany neck, round wave cresting style peghead, 2 per side tuners.

EB-18 — 9 piece maple/rosewood/walnut body, 22 fret rosewood fingerboard with pearl dot inlay, Leo Quan fixed bridge, brass nut, rosewood peghead veneer with CFM logo decal, Grover tuners, chrome hardware, exposed DiMarzio pickup, volume/tone control, 2 position switch. Available in Natural finish. Mfd. 1979 to 1982.

	$425	$295	$250	$210	$170	$150	$135

Approximately 5,226 of these instruments were made.

EB-28 — mahogany body, thru body mahogany neck, 22 fret ebony fingerboard with pearl dot inlay, Schaller tunomatic bridge/stop tailpiece, rosewood peghead veneer with CFM logo decal, Schaller tuners, chrome hardware, P-style/J-style exposed DiMarzio pickups, 2 volume/treble/bass controls, 3 position/phase/bypass switches, active electronics. Available in Sunburst finish. Mfd. 1981 to 1982.

	$650	$455	$390	$325	$260	$235	$215

Approximately 4,854 of these instruments were made.

MARVEL

See also Premier.

Instruments built in Japan.

The Peter Sorkin Music Company of New York, New York was an importer/distributor of Premier guitars and amplifiers. Many Premier guitars were built in New York using Italian or other foriegn parts, and sometimes the instruments would be rebranded (Marvel, Royce, Bell-Tone, or Strad-O-Lin). Marvel guitars have been identified as the budget line distributed by Sorkin. Marvel guitars may be completely imported or have parts that are imported (which would make the guitar partially U.S. built: a helpful tip for all you American xenophobes).

(Source: Michael Wright, Guitar Stories Volume One, pg. 76)

MASTER

Instruments currently built in Los Angeles, California.

Luthier George Gorodnitski has been building fine handcrafted acoustic and semi-hollowbody electric guitars for a number of years. For further information contact luthier George Gorodnitski through the Index of Current Manufacturers located in the rear of this book.

MASTER'S BASS

Instruments currently built in Waco, Texas.

Luthier Duane P. Greene currently offers three models of high quality, exotic wood, neck-through design, bass guitars. The **Reality** bass has a retail price of $1,995 to $2,250; the **Dream Bass** ranges between $3,899 and $4,299; and the top-of-the-line **Fantasy** bass lists from $4,599 to $4,999. All basses are offered in 4-, 5-, and 6-string configuration, although 7-string models are an option. For further information contact luthier Duane P. Greene through the Index of Current Manufacturers located in the back of this book.

MASTERTONE

See chapter on House Brands.

While the Mastertone designation was applied to high end Gibson banjos in the 1920s, the MASTERTONE trademark was used on a Gibson-produced budget line of electric guitars beginning in 1941. Some acoustic "Hawaiian" guitars from the 1930s by Gibson also carried the Mastertone label.

While built to the same standards as other Gibson guitars, they lack the one 'true' Gibson touch: an adjustable truss rod. "House Brand" Gibsons were available to musical instrument distributors in the late 1930s and early 1940s.

(Source: Walter Carter, Gibson Guitars: 100 Years of an American Icon)

TOM MATES

Instruments built in England.

Luthier Tom Mates produces handcrafted acoustic guitars. One notable player using a rather ornately inlaid version is Dave Pegg (of Jethro Tull).

(Source: Tony Bacon, The Ultimate Guitar Book)

M. Mazzella 10 String
courtesy Mario Mazzella

M

14 1/2" Maurer
courtesy Robert Carl Hartman

M

Megas Custom
courtesy Scott Chinery

MATON

Instruments produced in Australia during the 1960s.

The Maton trademark was established in 1946 by British emigre Bill May. The Maton company is still the largest guitar producer in Australia. A brief listing of their medium quality electric solid body guitars include such models as the Wedgtail, Flamingo, Fyr Byrd, and Ibis; semi-hollowbodies include the Slender Line, Starline, and Supreme models. Any Australian guitar players/readers are invited to send information for future updates in upcoming editions to the **Blue Book of Guitars**.

(Source: Tony Bacon and Paul Day, The Guru's Guitar Guide)

MAURER & CO.

See LARSON BROTHERS (1900-1944).

The Maurer brand was used by Robert Maurer prior to 1900 and by the Larson brothers, Carl and August, starting in 1900. The Larsons produced guitars, ukes, and mandolin family instruments under this brand until the mid-1930s when they, and the rest of the industry, changed designs from the small body guitars with slot pegheads and 12-frets-to-the-body necks to larger bodies with necks becoming narrower but extending the fingerboard to now have 14 frets-to-the-body.

The most commonly found Maurer instrument is the flat-top guitar having either X-bracing or was patented by August in 1904. The Maurers were offered in student grade, intermediate grade and best mandola, octave mandolin, mando-cello and mando-bass.

The style of the Maurers was carried through in the instruments sold to Wm. C. Stahl and the Prairie State brand. They ranged from the very plain to the pearl and abalone trimmed with the fanciest having a beautiful tree-of-life fingerboard. The Maurers are high quality instruments and are more commonly found than the other Larson brands.

For more detailed information regarding all the Larson brands, the Larson patents, and a Maurer/Prairie State catalog reprint, see The Larsons' Creations, Guitars and Mandolins, *by Robert Carl Hartman, Centerstream Publishing, P.O. Box 5450, Fullerton, CA 92635, phone/fax (714) 779-9390.*

MAXTONE

Instruments produced in Taiwan, and distributed by the Ta Feng Long Enterprises Company, Ltd. of Tai Chung, Taiwan.

Maxtone instruments are generally entry level to intermediate quality guitars.

MAYA

See also EL MAYA.

Instruments produced in Japan from the mid 1970s through the mid 1980s.

Maya guitars span the range of entry level to medium quality solid body, semi-hollowbody, and archtops that feature both original designs and other designs based on classic American favorites. The Maya company also produced a secondary trademark called "El Maya" that featured good quality Fender-based designs as well as some originals.

(Source: Tony Bacon and Paul Day, The Guru's Guitar Guide)

MAYFLOWER

Instruments built in Chicago, Illinois from 1918 to 1928.

The Groeschel Company of Chicago, Illinois first began building bowl-back (or "potato bug") mandolins in 1890. In 1918 Groeschel was changed to the Stromberg-Voisenet Company, who produced guitars and banjos under the Mayflower trademark. This Stromberg company is not to be confused with luthier Charles Stromberg (and son Elmer) of Boston, Massachusetts.

Henry Kay Kuhrmeyer bought the Stromberg-Voisenet company in 1928, and renamed it Kay Musical Instruments in 1931 (See KAY).

MDX

Instruments built in West Point, Massachusetts. Distributed by MDX Sound Lab of West Point, Massachusetts.

Dann Maddox and partners have combined custom guitar and bass building and a computer website to introduce the concept of a "virtual custom shop". Orders can be received at their address (http://www.mdxguitars.com), and guitars can be designed wholly through the internet. Maddox can be reached at his email site (dann@mdxguitars.com).

MEGAS

Instruments built in San Francisco, California since 1989.

Luthier Ted Megas was born in Bethlehem, Pennsylvania and raised in Hamburg, New York. He was drawn toward music at an early age and played in rock bands in his early teens. Megas began to learn his craft by modifying the guitars he played. After high school, Megas attended the Ohio State University as an engineering student, but left to pursue his musical interests in blues and jazz. In 1973 Megas moved to San Francisco, where he established a woodworking business. Luthier Megas made his first guitars in the mid 1970s, and in 1989 he decided to work full time at what he felt was the best combination of his skills and interests - building archtop guitars.

For further information regarding models, pricing, and options, please contact luthier Ted Megas via the Index of Current Manufacturers located in the back of this book.

(Biography courtesy Ted and Bonnie Megas, June 1996)

MEISEL

Instruments produced in Asia. Distributed by Meisel Stringed Instruments of Springfield, New Jersey.

Meisel has a wide range of stringed instruments such as violins, violas, and upright double basses. For further information contact Meisel Stringed Instruments through the Index of Current Manufacturers located in the rear of this book.

MELOBAR

Instruments built in Sweet, Idaho since the mid 1960s.

Melobar was founded by designer Walt Smith to provide steel guitarists the opportunity to stand up and also be able to play chord voicings without the traditional pedals or knee levers. Smith, a teacher/performer (and cattle rancher), passed away at age 70 in 1990. His son, Ted Smith continues to operate the family-run business, and continues to provide these high quality instruments to steel guitarist.

> Walt Smith continued to make improvements on his initial design through the years, and the refinement produced the Powerslide '88 model in the late 1980s. The model can be operated with 10 strings or six, and features a Bill Lawrence pickup. Other model variations featured body designs based on Strat, Explorer, or Flying V shapes; the same designs were offered in a comfortable foam body as well.
>
> Some of the original metal acoustic Melobars were built by Dobro, while the first electric solid body models were produced by Semie Moseley (of Mosrite fame).

(Source: Teisco Del Rey, Guitar Player magazine, September 1991)

MELODY

Instruments produced in Italy from the late 1970s through to the mid 1980s.

Here's a company with the proper perspective: though their designs that were based on classic American favorites were of medium quality, Melody original design guitars were of better quality. The Blue Sage series was introduced in 1982, and included a model called the "Nomad" that featured a built-in amp and speaker.

(Source: Tony Bacon, The Ultimate Guitar Book)

MENKEVICH GUITAR

Instruments currently built in Philadelphia, Pennsylvania.

Luthier Menkevich has been handcrafting quality guitars for a number of years. For further information contact luthier Menkevich through the Index of Current Manufacturers located in the back of this book.

MERCHANT

Instruments currently built in New York, New York.

Luthier/designer Steve Merchant has been offering quality, electric, upright basses for a number of years. For further information contact luthier/designer Steve Merchant through the Index of Current Manufacturers located in the back of this book.

MERCURY GUITARS

Instruments built in Berkeley, California since 1994.

Mercury Guitars currently consists of three people: Linda Delgado, partner Doug Pelton, and employee Norm Devalier. Mercury Guitars has been doing business in the San Francisco Bay area for approximately 1 and 1/2 years. The first six months of this time focused on the design of the current **Artemis**, **El Grande**, and **Vintage** models. Mercury Guitars wanted to provide the player with a point of reference from which to begin (hence the reference to the vintage instrument). The company is currently able to produce about a dozen instruments per month, and expects to expand their operation in the next year.

The staff at Mercury Guitars hand selects all woods, seeking to use renewable sources while insuring good resonant qualities. Their finish choice also affirms their commitment to the enviroment as they utilize a water based product which has been specifically engineered for the guitar industry.

Megas Archtop
courtesy Ted Megas

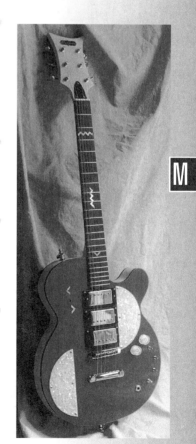

Mercury El Grande
courtesy Linda Delgado and Doug Pelton

M

Mesrobian Archtop
courtesy Carl Mesrobian

MERLIN

Instruments produced in Korea during the late 1970s.

The Merlin trademark was a brandname of a UK importer. The Merlin guitar was an extremely entry level, single pickup solid body guitar. As we like to say up north in the winter time, I prefer to buy my wood by the truckload, not piece by piece.

(Company information courtesy Tony Bacon and Paul Day, The Guru's Guitar Guide).

MERRILL

Instruments produced in New York, New York circa late 1880s.

Company president Neil Merrill began experimenting with aluminum in the mid-1880s. He debuted his aluminum bodied guitars in 1894 and offered a wide range of stringed instruments based on this design.

(Source: Tom Wheeler, American Guitars)

MESROBIAN

Instruments currently built in Salem, Massachusetts.

Luthier Carl Mesrobian offers a high quality, 17 inch archtop model that features a hand-graduated Sitka spruce top and figured maple back and sides. For further information contact luthier Carl Mesrobian through the Index of Current Manufacturers located in the rear of this book.

MESSENGER

Instruments built in San Francisco, California between 1968 and 1971. Distributed by Musicraft of San Francisco, California.

Messenger guitars and basses featured a single piece metal alloy neck in a design that pre-dated Travis Bean and Kramer instruments. Messenger instruments also feature distinctive f-holes, a thin body, and stereo output.

(Source: Tom Wheeler, American Guitars)

METROPOLITAN

Instruments are built in Houston, Texas since 1995 and are distributed by Alamo Music Products of Houston, Texas.

Metropolitan Guitars was concieved by David Wintz, based on the idea that others (hopefully, many others) would find the retro styling of the old National Glenwood as appealing as he did. The original National "Glenwood" models had a formed plastic body and a bolt-on metal neck; Wintz' **Tanglewood** model features a body of either Swamp Ash or Basswood, a mahogany set-neck, and both a LR Baggs transducer and a pair of Rio Grande humbuckers. Retail list for the Tanglewood Deluxe is $1,695; the Custom is $2,495; and the Custom Deluxe w/piezo bridge is $2,795. Wintz debuted the Metropolitan in March of 1996.

(Source: Hal Hammer)

MIAMI

Instruments produced in Japan during the mid 1970s.

The Miami trademark is the brandname used by a British importer. Instruments tended to be entry level solid body guitars.

(Source: Tony Bacon and Paul Day, The Guru's Guitar Guide)

MICHAEL

Instruments built in Japan during the mid 1980s.

The Michael trademark was a brandname used by a UK importer. The 'Metro' model was a medium quality strat design solid body.

(Source: Tony Bacon and Paul Day, The Guru's Guitar Guide)

MICHAEL DOLAN

Instruments currently built in Santa Rosa, California.

Luthier Michael Dolan has been handcrafting quality guitars for a number of years. For further information contact luthier Michael Dolan through the Index of Current Manufacturers located in the back of this book.

1996 Metropolitan
courtesy David Wintz

MICHIGAN

Instruments produced in East Germany from the late 1950s through the early 1960s.

The Michigan trademark was a brandname utilized by a British importer. Quality ranged from entry level to intermediate on models that were either solid body, semi-hollow, or archtop.

(Source: Tony Bacon and Paul Day, The Guru's Guitar Guide)

BOB MICK

Instruments currently built in New Mexico. Distributed by Martin Distributing of Las Cruces, New Mexico.

Luthier Bob Mick has a JM-1 ($1,299) short scale bass "built like our top-of-the-line basses, only smaller!" as well as the M-4 ($3,150) neck-through design that features maple and exotic woods in its contruction. There are also five and six string versions as well. Furthermore, luthier Mick can custom build any basses from "simple designs to the exotic" in bolt-on or neck-through. Contact Bob Mick via the Index of Current Manufacturers located in the rear of this book.

MICRO-FRETS

Instruments built in Frederick, Maryland between 1967 and 1974.

Micro-frets Signature
courtesy Rick King

During the expansion of the "pop" music market in the 1960s, many smaller guitar producers entered the electric instrument market to supply the growing public demand for guitars. One such visionary was Ralph J. Jones, who founded the Micro-Frets organization in 1967. Jones, who primarily handled design concepts, electronics, and hardware innovations, received financial backing from his former employer (a successful Maryland real estate magnate). It is estimated that Jones began building his prototypes in 1965, at his Wheaten, Maryland workshop. By 1967 production began at the company factory located at 100 Grove Road in Frederick, Maryland. Ralph J. Jones was the company president and treasurer, and was assisted by F. M. Huggins (vice-president and general manager) and A. R. Hubbard (company secretary) as well as the working staff.

Micro-Frets guitars were shown at the 1968 NAMM show. The company did the greatest amount of production between 1969 and 1971, when 1,700 of the less than 3,000 total guitars were made. Jones passed away sometime in 1973, and was succeeded by Huggins as president. When Micro-Frets closed operations in Maryland in either 1974 or 1975, the company assets were purchased by David Sturgill. Sturgill, who served as the company president of Grammer Guitars for three years, let his sons John and Danny gain access to leftover Micro-Frets parts. In addition to those parts, they had also purchased the remains of New Jersey's Harptone guitar company. The two assembled a number of solid body guitars which were then sold under the 'Diamond-S' trademark. Unfortunately, that business venture did not catch on, and dissipated sometime in 1976.

The entire production of the Micro-Frets company is less than 3,000 guitars and basses produced. As in the case of production guitars, neck plates with stamped serial numbers were pre-purchased in lots, and then bolted to the guitars during the neck attachment. The serial numbers were utitlized by Micro-Frets for warranty work, and the four digit numbers do fall roughly in a useable list. Jim Danz, a Micro-Frets enthusiast, began detailing a listing of serial numbers through the years, and the results showed up in a company history by Michael Wright in **Vintage Guitar Magazine**. This list should be used for **rough approximations** only. Between the company start-up in 1967 and 1969, serial numbers 1000 to 1300 (around 300 instruments produced). During the transition period, a couple of dozen instruments were produced. From 1969 to 1971, serial numbers 1323 to 3000 (around 1700 instruments produced). Finally, in the company's home stretch between 1971 and 1974, serial numbers 3000 to 3670 (roughly 700 instruments produced).

Furthermore, a survey of company production indicates three predominant styles or similarities shared by various production models through the years. Again, this information is a rough approximation based on viewed models, and any errors in it are the fault of this author (so don't blame Jim Danz!).

Style I (1967 to 1969): Most of the Micro-Fret guitars are actually hollow bodied guitars built by joining two separate top and bottom slabs of routed-out solid wood. As a result, earlier models will feature a side "gasket" on the two body halves. The early vibrato design looks similar to a Bigsby. The pickguard will have two levels, and the thumbwheel controls are set into a scalloped edge on the top half. Pickups will be DeArmond, Micro-Frets "Hi-Fi"s, or german-made Schallers or possibly Hofners. Tuning pegs will be Grovers (some with pearl grips) or Schallers (on the high end models).

Style II (1969 to 1971): The side gaskets are gone, but side seams should be noticable. The bi-level pickguard is white, the top half is shorter than the lower, and now conventional knobs are utilized. Guitars now sport only Micro-Fret pickups, but there are a number of different designs.

Style III (1971 or 1972 until 1974): No side seams are visible, but then a number of solid body guitars are being introduced as well. The bi-level pickguard now has a clear plastic short top half. Micro-Fret pickups are again used, although some were built with extra booster coils and three switches for tonal options. There are still some unsubstantiated reports of possible 12 string versions, or even a resonator model!

Micro-Fret guitars have a range from $350 to $800 depending on condition

MIGHTY MITE

Parts and instruments were built in U.S. during the 1970s and early 1980s. Parts are currently distributed by Westheimer Corporation of Northbrook, Illinois.

The Mighty Mite company was probably better known for its high quality replacement parts it produced rather than the guitars they made available. Mighty Mite parts are still currently offered. For further

Micro-frets Spacetone
courtesy Rick King

information contact Westheimer Corporation through the Index of Current Manufacturers located in the back of this book.

(Source: Tony Bacon and Paul Day, The Guru's Guitar Guide)

MIKE CHRISTIAN GUITAR TECHNOLOGY

Guitar pickup parts produced in West Babylon, New York.

Mike Christian does not produce guitars, but does market a bridge mounted piezo pickup that can be utilized on a player's guitar that expands the range of sound produced. A guitar player could have access to both the output of his magnetic pickups, and piezo "acoustic" sound as well; then process them separately for a wide range of sound. A number of luthiers are installing this system as optional equipment on their instruments. For further information, contact Mike Christian via the Index of Current Manufacturers located in the back of this book.

MIKE LULL

Instruments currently built in Bellevue, Washington.

Luthier Mike Lull has been building guitars for several bands in the Seattle area for years. Lull and two partners opened their own repair shop based on Lull's customizing and repair talents in 1978. Lull has been the sole owner of the Guitar Works since 1983 and still offers repair and restoration services in addition to his custom built instruments. For further information contact Mike Lull's Guitar Works through the Index of Current Manufacturers located in the back of this book.

MIRAGE (M J GUITAR)

Instruments currently built in Sebastopol, California.

Luthier Mark Johnson currently offers three models based on his innovative design. Features include a redesigned open headstock, a hollow body, and sleek double cutaway profile. The **Standard** ($1,895) has an alder body and a maple top; the **Classic** ($1,995) features a mahogany back and maple or mahogany top; and the **Custom** ($2,495) has a mahogany back and flame or curly maple top. All models feature a stop tailpiece and two humbuckers, although many options are offered. For further information contact M.J. Guitar Engineering through the Index of Current Manufacturers located in the back of this book.

MIRAGE (TAIWAN)

Instruments produced in Taiwan during the late 1980s.

Entry level to intermediate quality guitars based on classic American designs.

(Source: Tony Bacon and Paul Day, The Guru's Guitar Guide)

MITCHELL

Instruments currently built in Wall, New Jersey.

Mitchell Guitars have been producing fine quality instruments for a number of years. For further information contact Mitchell Guitars through the Index of Current Manufacturers located in the rear of this book.

MODULUS GRAPHITE

Instruments built in San Francisco, California since the early 1980s.

Geoff Gould, an aerospace engineer and bass player, was intrigued by an Alembic-customized bass he saw at a Greatful Dead concert. Assuming that the all wood construction was a heavy proposition, he fashioned some samples of carbon graphite and presented them to Alembic. An experimental model with a graphite neck was displayed in 1977, and a patent issued in 1978. Gould formed the Modulus Graphite company with other ex-aerospace partners to provide necks for Alembic, and also build necks for Music Man's Cutlass bass model as well as their own Modulus Graphite guitars. Modulus Graphite's first products were Fender-style replacement necks, but in the early 1980s five- and six-string bass models were introduced. Since then, the Modulus neck patent has been licensed to several companies, and Modulus has supplied finished necks to Peavey, Ibanez, Moonstone, Aria, and Zon as well.

All necks are made of a graphite/epoxy composite, all fingerboards are made of a phenolic/ebonol mixture, unless otherwise listed.

All models are available with the following standard finishes, unless otherwise listed: Amber, Clear Blue, Clear Green, Clear Red, Deep Black, Monza Red, Pure White, Sea Foam Green, Surf Green and Vintage Pink.

Custom color finishes include: Black Cherry, Blue/Greenburst, Blue/Purpleburst, Blue Velvet, Charcoal Metalflake, Cherryburst, Clear Black, Green Velvet, Honeyburst and Purple Metalflake.
Add $100 for Custom Color finishes.

ELECTRIC

The following options are available on all models in this series:
Add $75 for black or gold hardware.
Add $100 for body matching colored neck.

Grading	100%	98% MINT	95% EXC+	90% EXC	80% VG+	70% VG	60% G

Add $200 for double locking or standard vibrato.

Blackknife Series

BOB WEIR SIGNATURE — offset double cutaway alder body, cocabola top, thru body neck, 24 fret fingerboard with white dot inlay, double locking Floyd Rose vibrato, 6 on one side tuners, black hardware, 2 single coil/1 humbucker EMG pickups, volume/tone/active electronics control, 3 mini switches. Curr. mfr.

Mfr.'s Sug. Retail	$3,200	$2,560	$1,920	$1,600	$1,280	$1,150	$1,055	$960

CLASSIC — offset double cutaway alder body, figured maple top, bolt-on neck, 22 fret fingerboard with white dot inlay, fixed bridge, 6 on one side tuners, gold hardware, humbucker/single coil/humbucker EMG pickups, volume/tone/active electronics control, 3 mini switches. Curr. mfr.

Mfr.'s Sug. Retail	$2,495	$1,996	$1,497	$1,250	$1,000	$900	$825	$750

CUSTOM — offset double cutaway alder body, figured maple top, thru body neck, 24 fret fingerboard with white dot inlay, double locking Floyd Rose vibrato, 6 on one side tuners, gold hardware, humbucker/single coil/humbucker EMG pickups, volume/tone/active electronics control, 3 mini switches. Curr. mfr.

Mfr.'s Sug. Retail	$2,995	$2,246	$1,497	$1,495	$1,195	$1,075	$985	$895

MODEL T — single cutaway alder body, bolt-on neck, 22 fret fingerboard with white dot inlay, strings thru bridge, 6 on one side tuners, chrome hardware, 1 Seymour Duncan/1 Van Zandt single coil pickups, volume/tone control, 3 position switch. Curr. mfr.

Mfr.'s Sug. Retail	$1,695	$1,271	$847	$845	$675	$605	$555	$505

Model T Custom — similar to Model T, except has figured maple top, black hardware, active electronics control.

Mfr.'s Sug. Retail	$2,095	$1,571	$1,047	$1,045	$840	$755	$685	$625

SPECIAL 3H — offset double cutaway alder body, bolt-on neck, 22 fret fingerboard with white dot inlay, double locking Floyd Rose vibrato, 6 on one side tuners, chrome hardware, 2 single coil/1 humbucker EMG pickups, volume/tone control, 3 mini switches. Curr. mfr.

Mfr.'s Sug. Retail	$1,995	$1,496	$997	$995	$795	$720	$660	$600

Special 3H Custom — similar to Special 3H, except has figured maple top, black hardware, active electronics control.

Mfr.'s Sug. Retail	$2,395	$1,796	$1,197	$1,195	$955	$855	$785	$715

VINTAGE — offset double cutaway alder body, white pickguard, bolt-on neck, 22 fret fingerboard with white dot inlay, 3 single coil Van Zandt pickups, volume/2 tone controls, 5 position switch. Curr. mfr.

Mfr.'s Sug. Retail	$1,895	$1,516	$1,137	$950	$760	$685	$625	$570

Vintage Custom — similar to Vintage, except has figured maple top, black hardware.

Mfr.'s Sug. Retail	$2,295	$1,836	$1,377	$1,150	$920	$825	$755	$690

ELECTRIC BASS

The following options are available on all models in this series:
Add 10% for left handed version.
Add $100 for fretless fingerboard.
Add $100 for Kahler bridge upgrade.
Add $100 for black or gold hardware.
Add $100 for body matching colored neck.
Add $600 for piezo bridge pickup (4-string).
Add $700 for piezo bridge pickup (5-string).
Add $800 for piezo bridge pickup (6-string).
Add $200 for fretless fingerboard with lines.
Add $200 for Bartolini pickups with treble/bass controls.
Add $250 for Bartolini pickups with treble/bass/mix controls.

M92 Series

M92-4 — offset double cutaway alder body, black pickguard, bolt-on neck, 24 fret fingerboard with white dot inlay, fixed bridge, 2 per side tuners, chrome hardware, covered humbucker pickup, volume/treble/bass controls, active electronics. Available in Black, Monza Red, Natural, Seafoam Green, Transparent Blue, Transparent Green, Transparent Red, Transparent Yellow, Vintage Pink and White finish. Mfd. 1993 to date.

Mfr.'s Sug. Retail	$1,795	$1,346	$897	$895	$715	$645	$590	$540

This model has poplar body optionally available.

In 1994, pearloid pickguard replaced original item.

Grading	100%	98% MINT	95% EXC+	90% EXC	80% VG+	70% VG	60% G

M92-5 — similar to M92-4, except has 5 strings, Schaller bridge, 3/2 per side tuners.
Mfr.'s Sug. Retail $1,995 $1,496 $997 $995 $795 $720 $660 $600

Prime Series

MODULUS PRIME-4 — offset double cutaway ash body, bolt-on neck, 24 fret cocabola fingerboard, fixed bridge, 2 per side tuners, chrome hardware, humbucker pickup, volume/treble/bass controls, active electronics. Available in Natural finish. Mfd. 1993 to date.
Mfr.'s Sug. Retail $1,995 $1,496 $997 $995 $795 $720 $660 $600
Add $100 for Transparent Color finishes.

Modulus Prime-5 — similar to Modulus Prime-4, except has 5 strings, Schaller bridge, 3/2 per side tuners.
Mfr.'s Sug. Retail $2,195 $1,756 $1,317 $1,100 $880 $790 $725 $660

Modulus Prime-6 — similar to Modulus Prime-4, except has 6 strings, APM bridge, 3 per side tuners.
Mfr.'s Sug. Retail $2,495 $1,996 $1,497 $1,250 $1,000 $900 $825 $750

Quantam Series

4 SPi — offset double cutaway alder body, bolt-on neck, 24 fret fingerboard with white inlay, fixed Modulus/Gotoh bridge, 2 per side tuners, chrome hardware, 2 active EMG pickups, 2 volume/treble/bass controls. Curr. mfr.
Mfr.'s Sug. Retail $2,195 $1,756 $1,317 $1,100 $880 $790 $725 $660
The treble/bass controls are concentric in some models.
This model has poplar body optionally available.

5 SPi — similar to 4 SPi, except has 5 strings, Schaller bridge, 3/2 per side tuners.
Mfr.'s Sug. Retail $2,395 $1,796 $1,197 $1,195 $955 $855 $785 $715

6 SPi — similar to 4 SPi, except has 6 strings, APM bridge, 3 per side tuners.
Mfr.'s Sug. Retail $2,695 $2,156 $1,617 $1,350 $1,080 $970 $890 $810

4 SPi CUSTOM — offset double cutaway alder body, figured maple top, bolt-on neck, 24 fret fingerboard with white inlay, fixed Modulus/Gotoh bridge, 2 per side tuners, black hardware, 2 active EMG pickups, 2 volume/1 treble/1 bass controls. Curr. mfr.
Mfr.'s Sug. Retail $2,495 $1,996 $1,497 $1,250 $1,000 $900 $825 $750
This model has poplar body optionally available.

5 SPi Custom — similar to 4 SPi Custom, except has 5 strings, Schaller bridge, 3/2 per side tuners.
Mfr.'s Sug. Retail $2,695 $2,156 $1,617 $1,350 $1,080 $970 $890 $810

6 SPi Custom — similar to 4 SPi Custom, except has 6 strings, APM bridge, 3 per side tuners.
Mfr.'s Sug. Retail $2,995 $2,246 $1,497 $1,495 $1,195 $1,075 $985 $895

4 SPi SWEET SPOT — offset double cutaway alder body, figured maple top, bolt-on neck, 24 fret fingerboard with white inlay, fixed Modulus/Gotoh bridge, 2 per side tuners, black hardware, 1 active covered EMG pickup, volume/treble/bass controls, active electronics. New 1994.
Mfr.'s Sug. Retail $2,095 $1,571 $1,047 $1,045 $840 $755 $685 $625
This model has gold hardware optionally available.

5 SPi Sweet Spot — similar to 4 SPi Sweet Spot, except has 5 strings, Schaller bridge, 3/2 per side tuners. New 1994.
Mfr.'s Sug. Retail $2,295 $1,836 $1,377 $1,150 $920 $825 $755 $690

6 SPi Sweet Spot — similar to 4 SPi Sweet Spot, except has 6 strings, APM bridge, 3 per side tuners. New 1994.
Mfr.'s Sug. Retail $2,595 $1,946 $1,297 $1,295 $1,035 $930 $855 $780

Thru Body Series

4 TBX — offset double cutaway alder body, figured maple top, thru body neck, 24 fret fingerboard with white dot inlay, fixed Modulus/Gotoh bridge, graphite/epoxy nut, 2 per side Modulus/Gotoh tuners, gold hardware, 2 humbucker EMG pickups, 2 volume/treble/bass controls. Curr. mfr.
Mfr.'s Sug. Retail $3,695 $2,771 $1,847 $1,760 $1,405 $1,225 $1,120 $1,025
The treble/bass controls are concentric in some models.

5 TBX — similar to 4 TBX, except has 5 strings, Schaller bridge, 3/2 per side tuners.
Mfr.'s Sug. Retail $4,095 $3,071 $2,047 $1,935 $1,535 $1,325 $1,215 $1,100
In 1994, ABM bridge replaced original item.

6 TBX — similar to 4 TBX, except has 6 strings, Kahler bridge, 3 per side tuners.
Mfr.'s Sug. Retail $4,495 $3,371 $2,247 $2,110 $1,675 $1,435 $1,315 $1,195
In 1994, ABM bridge replaced original item.

MONROE

Instruments built near El Paso, Texas circa late 1980s on.

Luthier Robert Monroe Turner was a former apprentice to **Guitar Player** columnist and repairer Dan Erlewine. Turner founded Monroe Guitars in 1988 and debuted his line of high quality, solid body electrics

---

"I find it curious then, that [guitar shows] are not better attended by the general public. I hear complaints that the prices are too high and that these shows are becoming a swap meet for dealers..."

—Lawrence Acunto
TCG, Jan/Feb 1991

M

at the 1989 NAMM Show. Further information on Monroe Guitars will be updated in future editions of the **Blue Book of Guitars**.

(Source: Tom Wheeler, American Guitars)

MONTALVO

Instruments built in Mexico and distributed by K & S Guitars of Berkeley, California.

Montalvo guitars are the result of a collaboration between George Katechis-Montalvo (a highly skilled craftsman) and Marc Silber (a noted guitar historian, restorer and designer). Montalvo had already been importing guitars from Mexico since 1987. Silber joined him in 1990 to found the K & S Guitar Company. K & S introduced higher quality woods, glues, finishes and American builders' knowledge to the Mexican luthiers for actual production in Mexico. The resulting K & S guitars are set up and inspected at their Berkeley, California shop.

Montalvo classical and flamenco acoustic guitars are constructed of Engelmann spruce or Canadian red cedar tops, mahogany or Spanish cedar necks, and rosewood or ebony fingerboards. Retail prices range from $900 up to $1,850. For further information contact Montalvo through the Index of Current Manufacturers located in the back of this book.

MONTANA

Instruments are produced in Korea and distributed by the Kaman Music Corporation of Bloomfield, Connecticut.

Montana produces a range of acoustic and acoustic/electric guitars priced for the novice and intermediate players. For further information, contact Kaman Music Corporation through the Index of Current Manufacturers located in the back of this book.

MONTCLAIR

See chapter on House brands.

This trademark has been identified as a "House Brand" of Montgomery Wards.

(Source: Willie G. Moseley, Stellas & Stratocasters)

Monteleone Rocket Convertible
courtesy Scott Chinery

MONTELEONE

Instruments currently built in Islip, New York.

Luthier John Monteleone has been building guitars and mandolins for almost three decades. His archtop guitars feature such unique ideas as a flush-set truss rod cover, recessed tuning machine retainers, and a convex radiused headstock. For further information, contact luthier John Monteleone through the Index of Current Manufacturers located in the rear of this book.

MONZA

Instruments built in Holland, circa unknown.

While Monza guitars sports a "Made in Holland" sticker on the back of the headstock, the electronics and tailpiece/bridge on one identified model are clearly Italian (possibly 1960s?). The instrument features 20 fret neck, six on a side headstock and tuners, two pickups, a tremolo/bridge unit, 3 switches, 3 volume/tone knobs, and a offset double cutaway with a scroll on the bass horn reminiscent of the 1960s Premier guitars.

(Source: Teisco Del Rey, "Off the Wall" column in Guitar Player, February 1984)

MOON

Instruments currently built in Japan.

The Moon Corporation currently offers three different series of high quality bass guitars. The instruments are based on the classic Jazz model, but feature high quality pickups and hardware. For further information, contact Dan Lenard at the Luthiers Access Group through the Index of Current Manufacturers located in the back of this book.

MOONSTONE

Instruments built in Eureka, California. Guitar production has been in various locations in California since 1972. Sales and orders are handled directly at the shop by luthier Steve Helgeson.

In 1972, self-taught luthier Steve Helgeson began building acoustic instruments in an old shingle mill located in Moonstone Heights, California. Three years later, Helgeson moved to Arcata, California, and began producing electric **Earth Axe** guitars. By 1976, Helegeson had moved to a larger shop and increased his model line and production. Helgeson hit boom sales in the early 1980s, but tapered off production after the market shifted in 1985. Rather than shift with the trends, Helgeson preferred to maintain his own designs. In 1988, a major disaster in the form of a deliberately set fire damaged some of his machinery. Steve's highly figured wood supply survived only a minor scorching. Helgeson moved

Monteleone Archtop
courtesy John Monteleone

M

and reopened his workshop in 1990 at the current location in Eureka, California, where he builds his new acoustic design (the J-90), and custom electrics.

All Moonstone instruments are constructed from highly figured woods. Where burl wood was not used in the construction, the wood used is highly figured. Almost all necks are reinforced with veneers, or stringers. Bass necks are reinforced with thru body graphite stringers. Some models can also be found with necks entirely made of graphite composite with phenolic fingerboards. Helgeson commissioned Modulus Graphite to produce these necks, and used them on models like the Eclipse Standard, Deluxe Basses, Vulcan Standard and Deluxe guitars, the M-80, D-81 Eagle 6- and 12-string models, as well as the D-81 Standard and the "Moondolin" (mandolin). In 1981, most wood necks were reinforced with a Graphite Aluminum Honeycomb Composite (G.A.H.C.) beam with stainless steel adjustment rod.

ACOUSTIC

Grading	100%	98% MINT	95% EXC+	90% EXC	80% VG+	70% VG	60% G

D-81 EAGLE 6 — dreadnought style, spruce top, round soundhole, black pickguard, bound body, wood inlay rosette, quilted maple back/sides, graphite neck, 14/20 fret bound phenolic fingerboard with abalone vine inlay, eagle shape ebony bridge with black pins, walnut burl peghead veneer with abalone halfmoon/logo inlay, 3 per side gold tuners. Available in Natural finish. Mfd. 1981 to 1984.

	100%	98%	95%	90%	80%	70%	60%
	$1,450	$1,240	$1,035	$830	$745	$680	$625

This instrument originally sold for $2,075.

D-81 Eagle 12 — similar to D-81 Eagle 6, except has 12 strings, 6 per side tuners.

	100%	98%	95%	90%	80%	70%	60%
	$1,580	$1,355	$1,130	$900	$810	$745	$675

This instrument originally sold for $2,255.

J-90 — auditorium style, sitka spruce top, round soundhole, bound body, wooden inlay rosette, wenge back/sides/neck, 14/20 fret ebony fingerboard with abalone/pearl flower/vine inlay, ebony bridge with pearl flower wing inlay, black pearl dot bridge pins, ebony peghead veneer with abalone halfmoon/logo inlay, 3 per side gold tuners. Available in Natural finish. Mfd. 1992 to date.

		100%	98%	95%	90%	80%	70%	60%
Mfr.'s Sug. Retail	$3,300	$2,640	$1,980	$1,650	$1,320	$1,190	$1,090	$990

This model is a custom order instrument and is hand built by Steve Helgeson.

ELECTRIC

EAGLE — double cutaway hand carved burl maple body, 5 piece maple/padauk neck, 24 fret padauk bound ebony fingerboard with pearl bird inlay, LQBA bridge/tailpiece, walnut burl peghead veneer with pearl halfmoon/logo inlay, 3 per side tuners, gold hardware, 2 humbucker Bartolini pickups, 2 volume/1 tone controls, 3 position switch, push/pull preamp switch in volume control, active electronics. Available in Natural finish. Mfg. 1980 to 1984.

	100%	98%	95%	90%	80%	70%	60%
	$1,945	$1,665	$1,390	$1,115	$1,000	$915	$830

This instrument originally sold for $2,780.

A licensed falconer, Helgeson's inspiration for this model came from the training and hunting with his raptors. Only 11 of these guitars were built.

EXPLODER — radical offset hour glass burl wood body, thru body 2 piece maple neck, 24 fret rosewood fingerboard with pearl dot inlay, LQBA bridge/tailpiece, figured wood peghead veneer with screened logo, 3 per side tuners, gold hardware, 2 humbucker covered Bartolini pickups, 2 volume/1 tone controls, 3 position/phase switches. Available in Natural finish. Mfd. 1980 to 1983.

	100%	98%	95%	90%	80%	70%	60%
	$675	$580	$485	$385	$350	$320	$290

This instrument originally sold for $965.

This model had DiMarzio pickups optionally available.

FLAMING V — V style burl wood body, thru body 2 piece maple neck, 24 fret rosewood fingerboard with pearl dot inlay, LQBA bridge/tailpiece, figured wood peghead veneer with screened logo, 3 per side tuners, gold hardware, 2 humbucker covered Bartolini pickups, 2 volume/1 tone controls, 3 position/phase switches. Available in Natural finish. Mfd. 1980 to 1984.

	100%	98%	95%	90%	80%	70%	60%
	$675	$580	$485	$385	$350	$320	$290

This instrument originally sold for $965.

DiMarzio pickups were optionally available.

M-80 — double cutaway semi hollow body, carved figured maple top/back/sides, f-holes, raised multilayer black pickguard, bound body, 2 piece figured maple neck, 24 fret bound ebony fingerboard with abalone snowflake inlay, LQBA bridge/tailpiece, figured wood peghead veneer with abalone halfmoon/logo inlay, 3 per side tuners, gold hardware, 2 humbucker covered Bartolini pickups, 2 volume/tone controls, 3 position/phase switches. Available in Natural finish. Mfd. 1980 to 1984.

	100%	98%	95%	90%	80%	70%	60%
	$1,185	$1,015	$845	$675	$605	$555	$505

This instrument originally sold for $1,690.

Burl walnut pickguard, tunable bridge/tailpiece, PAF pickups, Orange-Honey finish and Tobacco Burst finish optionally available.

Grading	100%	98% MINT	95% EXC+	90% EXC	80% VG+	70% VG	60% G

PULSAR — mini radical offset hourglass alder body, black pickguard, maple neck, 24 fret rosewood fingerboard with pearl dot inlay, LQBA bridge/tailpiece, blackface peghead with screened logo, 3 per side tuners, gold hardware, humbucker exposed DiMarzio pickup, volume/tone control. Available in Black finish. Mfd. 1980 to 1983.

| | $565 | $485 | $405 | $325 | $295 | $270 | $245 |

This instrument originally sold for $810.

This instrument also found with Lawrence pickup.

Eclipse Series

DELUXE — offset double cutaway padauk core body, bookmatch burl top/back, thru body 2 piece maple neck, 24 fret bound ebony fingerboard with pearl diamond/star inlay, LQBA bridge/tailpiece, burl walnut peghead veneer with pearl halfmoon/logo inlay, 3 per side tuners, gold hardware, 2 humbucker covered Bartolini pickups, 2 volume/2 tone controls, 3 position/phase switches. Available in Natural finish. Mfd. 1979 to 1983.

| | $1,005 | $860 | $720 | $575 | $515 | $475 | $430 |

This instrument originally sold for $1,435.

STANDARD — offset double cutaway mahogany core body, bookmatch burl top/back, thru body 2 piece maple neck, 24 fret rosewood fingerboard with pearl dot inlay, LQBA bridge/tailpiece, burl wood peghead veneer with screened logo, 3 per side tuners, gold hardware, 2 humbucker covered Bartolini pickups, 2 volume/tone controls, 3 position/phase switches. Available in Natural finish. Mfd. 1979 to 1983.

| | $850 | $730 | $610 | $485 | $435 | $400 | $365 |

This instrument originally sold for $1,215.

Standard 12 — similar to Standard except has 12 strings, Quan tunable bridge, 6 per side tuners.

| | $930 | $795 | $660 | $530 | $475 | $435 | $395 |

This instrument originally sold for $1,325.

Standard Doubleneck — this instrument has same specs as Standard and the Standard 12 (two necks sharing the same body) with each neck having separate electronics and a 3 position neck selector.

| | $1,440 | $1,235 | $1,025 | $820 | $740 | $680 | $615 |

This instrument originally sold for $2,055.

Vulcan Series

DELUXE — double cutaway carved burl maple body, 5 piece maple/padauk neck, 24 fret bound ebony fingerboard with pearl diamond/star inlay, LQBA bridge/tailpiece, burl walnut peghead veneer with pearl halfmoon/logo inlay, 3 per side tuners, gold hardware, 2 humbucker covered Bartolini pickups, master volume/2 volume/2 tone controls, 5 position tone control, 3 position/boost switches, active electronics. Available in Natural finish. Mfd. 1977 to 1984.

| | $1,175 | $1,005 | $840 | $675 | $605 | $555 | $505 |

This instrument originally sold for $1,680.

STANDARD — double cutaway mahogany body, bound carved bookmatch burl maple top, 2 piece maple neck, 24 fret rosewood fingerboard with pearl dot inlay, LQBA bridge/tailpiece, burl maple peghead veneer with screened logo, 3 per side tuners, gold hardware, 2 humbucker covered Bartolini pickups, 2 volume/tone controls, 3 position/phase switches. Available in Natural finish. Mfd. 1977 to 1984.

| | $850 | $730 | $610 | $485 | $435 | $400 | $365 |

This instrument originally sold for $1,215.

ELECTRIC BASS

ECLIPSE DELUXE — offset double cutaway padauk core body, bookmatch burl top/back, thru body 3 piece maple/padauk neck with graphite stringers, 24 fret bound ebony fingerboard with pearl diamond/star inlay, fixed bridge, burl walnut peghead veneer with pearl halfmoon/logo inlay, 2 per side tuners, gold hardware, 2 J-style Bartolini pickups, 2 volume/tone controls, 3 position/phase switches. Available in Natural finish. Mfd. 1980 to 1984.

| | $1,045 | $895 | $750 | $600 | $540 | $495 | $450 |

This instrument originally sold for $1,495.

Eclipse Standard — offset double cutaway mahogany core body, bookmatch burl top/back, thru body 3 piece maple/padauk neck with graphite stringers, 24 fret rosewood fingerboard with pearl dot inlay, fixed bridge, burl maple peghead veneer with screened logo, 2 per side tuners, gold hardware, 2 J-style Bartolini pickups, 2 volume/tone controls, phase switch. Available in Natural finish. Mfd. 1980 to 1984.

| | $905 | $775 | $645 | $515 | $465 | $425 | $385 |

This instrument originally sold for $1,295.

EXPLODER — radical offset hour glass burl wood body, thru body 3 piece maple/padauk neck with graphite stringers, 24 fret rosewood fingerboard with pearl dot inlay, fixed bridge, burl maple peghead veneer with screened logo, 2 per side tuners, gold hardware, 2 J-style Bartolini pickups, 2 volume/1 tone controls, 3 position/phase switches. Available in Natural finish. Mfd. 1980 to 1983.

| | $885 | $760 | $635 | $505 | $455 | $415 | $380 |

This instrument originally sold for $1,265.

M

Grading	100%	98% MINT	95% EXC+	90% EXC	80% VG+	70% VG	60% G

Morse Archtop
courtesy John David Morse

FLAMING V — V style burl wood body, thru body 3 piece maple/padauk neck with graphite stringers, 24 fret rosewood fingerboard with pearl dot inlay, fixed bridge, maple burl peghead veneer with screened logo, 2 per side tuners, gold hardware, 2 J-style Bartolini pickups, 2 volume/1 tone controls, 3 position/phase switches. Available in Natural finish. Mfd. 1981.

$885	$760	$635	$505	$455	$415	$380

This instrument originally sold for $1,265.

VULCAN — double cutaway burl maple body, 3 piece maple/padauk neck, 24 fret bound ebony fingerboard with pearl diamond/star inlay, fixed bridge, burl walnut peghead veneer with pearl halfmoon/logo inlay, 2 per side tuners, gold hardware, humbucker covered Bartolini "P" pickup, 2 volume/tone controls, active tone circuit. Available in Natural finish. Mfd. 1982 to 1984.

$740	$635	$530	$420	$380	$350	$315

This instrument originally sold for $1,055.

Vulcan II — similar to Vulcan, except has carved top.

$810	$695	$580	$460	$415	$380	$345

This instrument originally sold for $1,155.

MORCH

Instruments built in Denmark from 1970 to the mid 1980s.

These high quality guitars feature original designs in both solid body and semi-hollow body construction. Importation to Britain began in 1976.

(Source: Tony Bacon and Paul Day, The Guru's Guitar Guide)

MORELLI

Instruments currently built in Port Chester, New York.

Morelli guitars are offered in custom models that feature various wood, hardware and pickup options. Retail prices start at $1,899, and Morelli does offer both 12-string and double-neck models. For further information, contact Morelli through the Index of Current Manufacturers located in the back of this book.

MORRELL

Instruments built in Tennessee. Distributed by the Joe Morrell Music Distributing Company of Bristol, Tennessee.

The Morrell company offers a wide range of stringed instruments all built in the U.S., such as resonator guitars, lap steel guitars, dulcimers, and flaptop mandolins. The Resonator guitars are offered in both round- and square-necked models (in natural or tobacco sunburst finishes), as well as replacement parts for performing repairs on other resonator models. The Resonator guitars carry a list price of $995. For further information, contact the Joe Morrell Music Distributing Company through the Index of Current Manufacturers located in the back of this book.

MORRIS

Instruments produced in Korea by the Samick factory. Some instruments have been produced in Japan by the Morris company.

Morris company offers a wide range of acoustic and solid body electric guitars designed for the beginning student up to the intermediate player.

JOHN DAVID MORSE

Instruments built in Santa Cruz, California since 1978. Luthier Morse is currently concentrating on violin making.

Luthier John David Morse combined his artistic backrounds in music, sculpture, and woodcarving with the practical scientific knowledge of stress points and construction techniques to produce a superior modern archtop guitar. Morse, a descendent of Samuel Morse (the telegraph and Morse code), studied under fine violin makers Henry Lannini and Arthur Conner to learn the wood carving craft. Morse still combines scientific processes in his building, and has identified means to recreate his hand graduated tops.

Past Morse apprentices include Richard Hoover (Santa Cruz Guitar Company) and luthier Jeff Traugott. Morse is currently making fine quality violins. A number of his violins are currently in use with the San Francisco Symphony, and he is building models currently for concertmaster Ramond Kobler and conductor Herbert Blomstedt. Possible commissions for archtop models should be discussed with luthier Morse.

Mortoro 8 String Custom Archtop
courtesy Gary Mortoro

MORTORO

Instruments built in Miami, Florida since 1992.

M

Gary Mortoro has been building fine handcrafted instruments under the guidance and direction of Master Luthier Robert Benedetto since 1991. Mortoro combines his skilled craftsmanship with his musical sensitivity to produce a fine archtop guitar. For further information, contact luthier Gary Mortoro through the Index of Current Manufacturers located in the back of this book.

MOSES UPRIGHT BASSES

Instruments currently produced in Eugene, Oregon.

Stephen Mosher has been offering replacement graphite necks for several years. Moses, Inc. lists 115 models available in 4-, 5-, and 6-string bass and 6-string guitar. Moses also produces the **KB** series graphite upright basses, available in 4- or 5-string configurations and a 42 inch scale. For further information regarding pricing, models, and availability, contact Moses, Inc. through the Index of Current Manufacturers located in the back of this book.

MOSRITE GUITARS

Instruments produced in Bakersfield, California during the 1960s; earlier models built in Los Angeles, California during the mid to late 1950s. There were other factory sites around the U.S. during the 1970s and 1980s: other notable locations include Carson City, Nevada; Jonas Ridge, North Carolina; and Booneville, Arkansas (previous home of Baldwin-operated Gretsch production during the 1970s). Distribution in the 1990s was handled by Unified Sound Association, Inc. Production of Mosrite guitars ceased in 1994.

Luthier/designer Semie Moseley (1935-1992) was born in Durant, Oklahoma. The family moved to Bakersfield, California when Moseley was 9 years old, and Semie left school in the seventh grade to travel with an evangelistic group playing guitar.

Moseley, 18, was hired by Paul Barth to work at Rickenbacker in 1953. While at Rickenbacker, Moseley worked with Roger Rossmeisl. Rossmeisl's "German carve" technique was later featured on Moseley's guitar models as well. Moseley was later fired from Rickenbacker in 1955 for building his own guitar at their facilities. With the help of Reverend Ray Boatright, who cosigned for guitar building tools at Sears, Moseley began building his original designs. The Mosrite trademark is named after Mo<u>se</u>ley and Boat<u>rite</u> ("-rite"). After leaving Rickenbacker, Moseley built custom instruments for various people around southern California, most notably Joe Maphis (of "Town Hall Party" fame). Moseley freelanced some work with Paul Barth's 'Barth' guitars, as well as some neck work for Paul Bigsby. After traveling for several months with another gospel group, Moseley returned to Bakersfield and again set up shop. Moseley built around 20 guitars for Bob Crooks (STANDEL). When Crooks asked for a Fender-styled guitar model, Moseley flipped a Stratocaster over, traced the rough outline, and built the forerunner to the 'Ventures' model.

Mosrite Joe Maphis 12/6
19th Annual Dallas Show

After Nokie Edwards (Ventures) borrowed a guitar for a recording session, Stan Wagner (Ventures Manager) called Moseley to propose a business collaboration. Mosrite would produce the instruments, and use the Venture's organization as the main distributor. The heyday of the Mosrite company was the years between 1963 and 1969. When the demand set in, the company went from producing 35 guitars a month to 50 and later 300. The Mosrite facility had 105 employees at one point, and offered several different models in addition to the Ventures model (such as the semi-hollowbody Celebrity series, the Combo, and the Joe Maphis series). In 1963, investors sold the Dobro trademark to Moseley, who built the first 100 or 150 out of parts left over from the Dobro plant in Gardenia. Later Bakersfield Dobros can be identified by the serial number imprinted on the end of the fingerboard. Another facility built the Mosrite amplifiers and fuzz pedals, and paid for the rights to use the name.

The amplifier line proved to be the undoing of Mosrite. While some of the larger amplifers are fine, one entry level model featured a poor design and a high failure rate. While covering for returns, the Ventures organization used up their line of credit at their bank, and the bank shut down the organization. In doing so, the Mosrite distribution was shut down as well. Moseley tried a deal with Vox (Thomas Organ) but the company was shut down in 1969. Moseley returned to the Gospel music circuit, and transfered the Dobro name to OMI in a series of negotiations. Between the mid 1970s and the late 1980s, Moseley continued to find backers and sporadically build guitars. His final guitar production was located in Booneville, Arkansas. The Unified Sound Association was located in a converted Walmart building, and 90% of production was earmarked for the Japanese market.

Moseley passed away in 1992. His two biggest loves were Gospel music, and building quality guitars. Throughout his nearly forty year career, he continued to persevere in his guitar building. Unified Sound Association stayed open through 1994 under the direction of Loretta Moseley, and then later closed its doors as well.

(Information courtesy of Andy Moseley and Hal Hammer [1996]; additional information courtesy Willie G. Moseley, Stellas and Stratocasters, and Tom Wheeler, American Guitars).

Semie's designs offered numerous innovations, most notable being the Vibra-Mute vibrato. This item was designed for the Ventures models and can be used to help identify early Mosrite instruments. The early vibratos (pre-1977) have Vibra-Mute and Mosrite on them, while later vibratos have Mosrite alone on them. More distinction can be made among the earliest instruments with Vibra-Mutes by observing the casting technique used. While the early vibratos were sandcast, later units were diecast (once funding was available).

MOSSMAN

Instruments built in Winfield, Kansas from 1969 to 1977. Some models were available from Mossman's private shop after 1977.

Mosrite Gospel Encounters
courtesy Ed Roth

Current production of Mossman guitars has been centered in Sulphur Springs, Texas since 1989.

Luthier Stuart Mossman originally built acoustic guitars in his garage in 1969. Mossman then founded the S. L. Mossman Company, and set up a factory to produce guitars. Around 1,400 guitars had been built between 1970 and 1975, when a fire struck the factory in February. With the support of local businessmen, Mossman returned to production. However, due to a disagreement with his distributors, the Mossman company closed shop in August of 1977. Stuart Mossman then opened a private shop, and offered a number of instruments privately.

In 1989, Bob Casey and partners resurrected the Mossman trademark in Sulpher Springs, Texas. With a factory located on Main street, the company is currently concentrating on high quality acoustic guitars. For futher information, please contact Mossman Guitars through the index of Current Manufacturers located in the back of this book.

MTD

Instruments built in Kingston, New York since 1994.

Luthier Michael Tobias has been handcrafting guitars and basses since 1977. The forerunner of MTD, Tobias Guitars was started in Orlando, Florida in April 1977. Tobias' first shop name was the Guitar Shop, and he sold that business in 1980 and moved to San Francisco to be partners in a short lived manufacturing business called Sierra Guitars. The business made about 50 instruments and then Tobias left San Francisco in May of 1981 to start a repair shop in Costa Mesa, California.

Several months later, Tobias left Costa Mesa and moved to Hollywood. Tobias Guitars continued to repair instruments and build custom basses for the next several years with the help of Bob Lee, and Kevin Almieda (Kevin went on to work for Music Man). The company moved into 1623 Cahuenga Boulevard in Hollywood and after a year quit the repair business. Tobias Guitars added Bob McDonald, lost Kevin to Music Man, and then got Makoto Onishi. The business grew in leaps and bounds. In June of 1988 the company had so many back orders, it did not accept any new orders until the January NAMM show in 1990.

After several attempts to move the business to larger, better equipped facilities, Michael Tobias sold Tobias Guitars to Gibson on 1/1/90. Late in 1992, it was decided that in the best corporate interests, Tobias Guitars would move to Nashville. Michael Tobias left the company in December 1992, and was a consultant for Gibson as they set up operations in Nashville.

By contractual agreement, after Tobias' consulting agreement with Gibson was up, he had a 1 year non competition term. That ended in December 1993. During that time, Tobias moved to The Catskills in upstate New York and set up a small custom shop. Tobias started designing new instruments and building prototypes in preparation for his new venture. The first instruments were named Eclipse. There are 50 of them and most all of them are 35" bolt ons. There are three neck-thrus. Tobias finally settled on MTD as the company name and trademark. As of this writing (2-22-96) he has delivered 120 MTD basses.

Tobias is currently building between 4 and 6 instruments per month. Along with the MTD electric basses, he is building acoustic bass guitars. Tobias has one helper who works 2 days per week. He apprenticed to Rick Turner for 1 year. Tobias is also doing design and development work for other companies.

(Source: Michael Tobias, MTD fine hand made guitars and basses)

All MTD instruments are delivered with a wenge neck/wenge fingerboard, or maple neck/pau ferro fingerboard. 21 Frets plus a 'Zero' fret, 35" and scale length. Prices include plush hard shell cases.

The standard finish for body and neck is a tung oil base with a urethane top coat. Wood choices for bodies: swamp ash, poplar, and alder. Other woods, upon request, may require up charges. Exotic tops are subject to availability.

Add $500 for a "10 Top" of burl, flamed, or quilted maple, myrtle, or mahogany.

Add $300 for lacquer finish: sunburst (amber or brown), c-thru's (transparency) of red, coral blue, or honey gold.

Add $150 for a hand rubbed oil stain.

Add $100 for a lined fretless neck.

Add $350 for a left handed model.

Add $300 for a korina body.

ACOUSTIC BASS

ABG 4 — 4 string Acoustic bass, flamed myrtle back and sides, spruce top. Mfg. 1994 to date.

    Mfr.'s Sug. Retail   **$2,750**

        Acoutic Basses are only available as a direct purchase from MTD.

        Model can be ordered in 34" or 35" scale.

        Add $175 for Fishman Transducer.

        Add $150 for Highlander system.

ABG 5 — 5 string Acoustic bass, flamed myrtle back and sides, spruce top. Mfg. 1994 to date.

    Mfr.'s Sug. Retail   **$2,900**

        Acoutic Basses are only available as a direct purchase from MTD.

        Model can be ordered in 34" or 35" scale.

        Add $175 for Fishman Transducer.

        Add $150 for Highlander system.

ELECTRIC BASS

435 — Mfg. 1994 to date.
   Mfr.'s Sug. Retail $3,300

535 — 2+3 headstock, Mfg. 1994 to date.
   Mfr.'s Sug. Retail $3,500

635 — Mfg. 1994 to date.
   Mfr.'s Sug. Retail $3,700

MULTI-STAR

See MUSIMA.

Instruments produced in East Germany during the 1970s and 1980s.

The Multi-Star trademark was a brandname used by the Musima company on a series of solid body guitars featuring designs based on popular American classics.

(Source: Tony Bacon and Paul Day, The Guru's Guitar Guide)

MULTIVOX

Instruments produced in New York City, New York during the 1950s and 1960s; later models had imported hardware but were still 'built' in New York.

Multivox was the manufacturing subsidary of the Peter Sorkin Music Company, which built products under the Premier trademark. Sorkin began the Multivox company in the mid 1940s. Multivox eventually established a separate corporate identity, and continued in extistence for fourteen or so years after the Sorkin company closed down in the 1970s.

(Source: Michael Wright, Guitar Stories Volume One, pg. 7)

MUNCY

Instruments are built in Kingston, Tennessee.

Luthier Gary Muncy designed the solid body 'Bout Time model that features a new innovative neck design. Constructed from CNC machined aluminum, the neck's fretboard is made from bloodwood which is then shaped between the sunken frets similar to scalloping. Fingering notes occurs in the in-between areas so the string makes contact at the raised area. For further information, contact Gary Muncy through the Index of Current Manufacturers located in the back of this book.

MURPH

Instruments built in San Fernando, California between 1965 and 1966.

Designer/inventor Pat Murphy was responding to his children's musical interests when he began manufacturing Murph guitars in the mid 1960s. Murphy put the family run shop together with equipment picked up at auctions, and contracted a violin maker named Rick Geiger to help with production. After a falling out with Geiger, Murphy began manufacturing guitars in midsummer of 1965.

The company originally was to be called York, but a brass instrument manufacturer of the same name caused them to use the Murph trademark. Pat Murphy estimated that perhaps 1,200 to 1,500 guitars were built in the one year production span. Models were built in lots of 50, and a total of nearly 100 guitars were built a week.

Models included the semi-hollow **Gemini**, and the solid body **Squire**. Some of the Squire "seconds" were finished with vinyl upholstery and snap buttons and were designated the "**Westerner**" model. The Gemini had a retail price of $279, the Squire I (one pickup) at $159.50, and the Squire II (two pickups) listed at $189.50. One model called the **Continental IV** was a single pickup semi-hollowbody design that was priced around $239. Murphy also produced a full-size kit guitar called the **Tempo**, correponding bass guitar models for the line, and heart-shaped bodied guitars in six or twelve string version. Bridges and tremolos were from the Gotz company in Germany, and the tuning machines were Klusons. Pickups were hand wound in the guitar production facility. Pat Murphy was also contracted to make a small number of guitars for Sears under the Silvertone label.

(Source: Teisco Del Rey, Guitar Player magazine, June 1986)

MUSIC MAN

See ERNIE BALL/MUSIC MAN.

Instruments originally produced in Fullerton, California between 1976 and 1979.

The original Music Man company was put together in March of 1972 by two ex-Fender executives. Tom Walker (a chief salesman) and Forrest White (ex-vice president and general manager of Fender) made their mark early, with a successful line of guitar amplifiers. In 1976, Music Man introduced new solid body guitar models designed and built by Leo Fender. After abiding by a ten year "no compete" clause

Murph 12 String
courtesy Teisco Del Rey

in the sale of Fender Electrical Instrument Company (1965-1975), Fender's CLF Research factory provided Music Man with numerous guitar and bass models through an exclusive agreement.

Leo Fender and George Fullerton (another ex-Fender employee) began building facilities for CLF Research in December of 1974. Fullerton was made vice president of CLF in March 1976, and the first shipment of instruments from CLF to Music Man was in June of the same year. Some of the notable designs in early Music Man history are the Sabre and Stingray series of guitars and basses.

In 1978, the controlling interest at Music Man expressed a desire to buy the CLF factory and produce instruments directly. Fender and Fullerton turned down repeated offers, and Music Man began cutting production orders. The controversy settled as CLF Research stopped manufacturing instruments for Music Man in late 1979. Fender then began working on new designs for his final company, G & L.

Music Man's trademark and designs were purchased in 1984 by Ernie Ball. The Ernie Ball company, known for its string sets and Earthwood basses, set up production in its San Luis Obispo factory. Ernie Ball/Music Man has retained the high level of quality from original Fender/CLF designs, and has introduced some innovative designs to their current line.

For model designations and prices, see ERNIE BALL/MUSIC MAN.

MUSIMA

See also OTWIN & RELLOG.

Instruments produced in East Germany from the late 1950s to date.

The Musima company produced a number of guitars under other trademarks. In the late 1950s, solid body and semi-hollowbody guitars with original designs were exported to Britian under the **Otwin & Rellog** trademark. These guitars were available through the early 1960s, then the company issued their own medium quality solid body guitars such as the 707 and 708 during the mid 1960s.

In the 1970s and 1980s, Musima released numerous solid body guitars based on classic American designs under such trademarks as **Marlin**, **Multi-Star**, and even **Kay**!

NADINE

Instruments produced in Japan during the late 1980s.

The Nadine trademark is a brandname used by a British importer. Nadine guitars are good quality Fender-derived and 'superstrat' models.

(Source: Tony Bacon and Paul Day, The Guru's Guitar Guide).

NADY

Instruments point of origin is still unknown, but were available in the mid 1980s. Distributed by Nady Systems, Inc. of Emeryville, California.

The Nady company is best know for its wireless guitar and microphone systems that were introduced in 1977. In 1985 Nady introduced a guitar model ("Lightning") and a bass model ("Thunder") that featured a built-in wireless unit in a production guitar. A similar idea was attempted by the Micro-Frets company in the late 1960s, as both the Voyager and Orbiters models can be found with the wireless transmitter protruding from the upper horn. Nady instruments came with the 501 VHF reciever, although they could be upgraded to the 601 or 701 receivers as well.

The instruments featured a maple through-neck design, offset double cutaway alder bodies (or wings), six on a side (four for the bass) tuning machines, 24 fret ebony fingerboard with mother-of-pearl lightning bolt inlays, black hardware, and a black finish. The Lightning had two humbucking pickups and a locking tremolo system; the Thunder had a P/J pickup combination.

Nady also offered a 300 watt MOSFET bass amp that was rack mountable, as well as a 100 watt MOSFET rack mountable guitar head. The guitars are equipped with 1/4" jacks so they can still be used conventionally; however, the full package would be the instrument <u>and</u> the 501 VHF receiver. Pricing for these instruments would depend on condition, playablility, working electronics, and receiver. The 501 system was okay for the time; Nady builds a much better wireless system now.

NASH

Instruments built in Markneukirchen, Germany since 1996. Distributed in the U.S. by Musima North America of Tampa, Florida.

Nash acoustics guitars debuted in the United States, Canada, and South American markets in 1996. The guitars are built by Musima, Germany's largest acoustic guitar manufacturer. The company headquarters in Markneukirchen, Germany are near the Czech border.

In 1991, Musima was purchased by industry veteran Helmet Stumpf following the German re-unification. The Musima facilities currently employs 130 workers, and continue to produce Musima stringed instruments as well as the Nash acoustic guitars.

NASHVILLE GUITAR COMPANY

Instruments currently built in Nashville, Tennessee.

Nashville guitars custom steel string acoustic guitars ($2,800 to $5,000) feature German or Sitka Spruce tops, Mahogany, Koa, Indian Rosewood, or Brazilian Rosewood back and sides, a mahogany neck, and an Ebony or Rosewood fingerboard. For further information, please contact the Nashville Guitar Company via the Index of Current Manufacturers located in the rear of this book.

NATIONAL

Instruments produced in Los Angeles, California during the mid 1920s to the mid 1930s. Company moves to Chicago, Illinois in mid 1930s and formally changes name to VALCO (but still produces National guitars).

When Valco went out of business in 1969, the National trademark was acquired by Strum 'n Drum of Chicago, Illinois. The National trademark was then applied to a series of Japanese built guitars.

The Dopyera family emigrated from the Austro-Hungary area to Southern Califonia in 1908. In the early 1920s, John and Rudy Dopyera began producing banjos in Southern California. They were approached by guitarist George Beauchamp to help solve his 'volume' (or lack thereof) problem with other instruments in the vaudeville orchestra. In the course of their conversation, the idea of placing aluminum resonators in a guitar body for amplification purposes was developed. John Dopyera and his four brothers (plus some associates like George Beauchamp) formed National in 1925. The initial partnership between Dopyera and Beauchamp lasted for about two years, and then John Dopyera left National to form the Dobro company. National's corporate officers in 1929 consisted of Ted E. Kleinmeyer (pres.), George Beauchamp (sec./gen. mngr.), Adolph Rickenbacker (engineer), and Paul Barth (vice pres.). In

National Duolian
courtesy Bluesland Amplifiers

National Resonator guitar
courtesy Thoroughbred Music

late 1929, Beauchamp leaves National, and joins up with Adolph Rickenbacker to form Ro-Pat-In (later Electro String/Rickenbacker).

At the onset of the American Depression, National was having financial difficulties. Louis Dopyera bought out the National company; and as he owned more than 50% of the stock in Dobro, "merged" the two companies back together (as National Dobro). In 1936, the decision was made to move the company to Chicago, Illinois. Chicago was a veritable hotbed of mass produced musical instruments during the early to pre-World War II 1900s. Manufacturers like Washburn and Regal had facilities, and major wholesalers and retailers like the Tonk Bros. and Lyon & Healy were based there. Victor Smith, Al Frost, and Louis Dopyera moved their operation to Chicago, and in 1943 formally announced the change to VALCO (The initials of their three first names: V-A-L company). Valco worked on war materials during World War II, and returned to instrument production afterwards. Valco produced the National/Supro/Airline fiberglass body guitars in the 1950s and 1960s, as well as wood-bodied models.

In 1969 or 1970, Valco Guitars, Inc. went out of business. The assets of Valco/Kay were auctioned off, and the rights to the National trademark were bought by the Chicago, Illinois-based importers Strum 'n Drum. Strum 'n Drum, which had been importing Japanese guitars under the **Norma** trademark, were quick to introduce National on a line of Japanese produced guitars that were distributed in the U.S. market. Author/researcher Michael Wright points out that the National "Big Daddy" bolt-neck black LP copy was one of the first models that launched the Japanese "Copy Era" of the 1970s.

(Early company history courtesy Bob Brozman, The History and Artistry of National Resonator Instruments)

NATIONAL RESO-PHONIC GUITARS

Instruments built in San Luis Obispo, California since 1988.

Founders Don Young and McGregor Gaines met in 1981. Young had been employed on and off at OMI (building Dobro-style guitars) since the early 1970s. After their first meeting, Young got McGregor a job at OMI, and was exposed to guitar production techniques. In the mid to late 1980s, both Young and McGregor had disagreements with the management at OMI over production and quality, and the two soon left to form the National Reso-Phonic Guitars company in 1988. The company has been producing several models of resonator acoustic guitars in the last eight years, and recently announced their plan to release a single cutaway resonator model later this fall. Contact National Reso-Phonic through the Index of Current Manufacturers located in the rear of this book.

(Early company history courtesy Bob Brozman, The History and Artistry of National Resonator Instruments)

NED CALLAN

See also C M I, SHAFTESBURY, P C, and SIMMS-WATTS.

Instruments built in England from the early to late 1970s.

The Ned Callan trademark is a pseudonym for custom luthier Peter Cook. Cook successfully mass-produced enough decent quality solid body guitars to warrant other trademarks: Shaftesbury and Simms-Watts were the brandnames of British importers; P C (Cook's initials) and C M I (guessing Cook Musical Instruments - ?) perhaps other marketing devices? Outside of the headstock moniker, the guitars themselves seemed the same.

ELECTRIC GUITARS

First Series

The two models in the First Series were produced between 1970 and 1975. Both had 2 single coil pickups, 4 controls, and a selector switch. The **Custom** model featured offset dual cutaways, while the **Salisbury** only had a single cutaway body design.

Second Series

The two models in the Second Series were even more similar: both shared the same rounded body design with two forward horns that earned them the nicknames of "Nobbly Neds"; 2 pickups, and two control switches plus a selector switch. The **Hombre** had chrome pickups, while the **Cody** had black pickups. Both models produced from 1973 to 1975.

(Source: Tony Bacon and Paul Day, The Guru's Guitar Guide)

NEO

Instruments produced in Buckingham, Pennsylvania since 1991. Distributed by Lady Luck Industries, Inc. of Cary, Illinois.

Neo custom guitars and basses feature a body of tough, clear acrylic and a Neon tube (plus power supply) that lights up as the instrument is played. The **Neo** guitars were developed to provide extra visual effects that neon lighting can provide to a musician in the course of a performance. The **Basic** model has a retail price of $1,995, and features a 22 fret ebony fingerboard and 2 EMG humbuckers with active preamp. Additionally, the company has expanded this concept to include electric bass guitars and violins. For further information, contact Lady Luck Industries via the Index of Current Manufacturers located in the back of this book.

N

NEUSER BASS GUITARS

Instruments built in Finland by the Neuser Co., Ltd. Distributed by Armadillo Enterprises of Clearwater, Florida.

Neuser builds two models of high quality custom basses, and both are available in 4-, 5-, and 6-string configurations. Both models feature an offset double cutaway profile, although the **Courage** model has more pronounced horns. Models are contructed from Maple, Walnut, Mahogany, Ash, Alder, Bubinga, and Ebony woods, and finished in Nitrocellulose or wax. The **Courage** has a retail list price ranging from $1,860 up to $2,090; the **Cloudburst** ranges from $2,330 to $2,560.

Nickerson Equinox Custom
courtesy Scott Chinery

NERVE

Instruments built in England during the mid 1980s.

There were three different high quality models produced by Nerve. The original design solid body guitars were "headless", meaning no headstocks at the end of the neck. Model designations were the Energy, Reaction, and the System. Anyone wishing to share knowledge for upcoming editions of the **Blue Book of Guitars** is invited to write, and hopefully send photos.

(Source: Tony Bacon and Paul Day, The Guru's Guitar Guide)

N.I.C.E.

Instruments currently built in Basel, Switzerland.

N.I.C.E. produces several high quality guitars. For further information regarding model specifications and pricing, please contact N.I.C.E. via the Index of Current Manufacturers located in the back of this book.

NICKERSON

Instruments built in Northampton, Massachusetts since the early 1980s.

Luthier Brad Nickerson, born and raised on Cape Cod, Massachusetts, has been building archtop guitars since 1982. Nickerson attended the Berklee College of Music, and worked in the graphic arts field for a number of years. While continuing his interest in music, Nickerson received valuable advice from New York luthier Carlo Greco, as well as Cape Cod violin builder Donald MacKenzie. Nickerson also gained experience doing repair work for Bay State Vintage Guitars (Boston), and The Fretted Instrument Workshop (Amherst, Massachusetts).

With his partner Lyn Hardy, Nickerson builds archtop, flattop, and electric guitars on a custom order basis. Nickerson is also available for restorations and repair work. Instruments are constructed out of Sitka or European Spruce tops, European cello or figured Maple back and sides, and Ebony tailpiece, bridge, and fingerboard. Prices range from $2,200 (Skylark) up to $8,000 (the 18" body Equinox). For further information regarding specifications and availability, please contact Nickerson Guitars via the Index of Current Manufacturers located in the back of this book.

KARI NIEMINEN

See VERSOUL.

Prior to the introduction of the Versoul trademark, luthier Kari Nieminen of Finland used his name on his hand-built guitars. Nieminen, an industrial designer, teaches at the University of Art and Design in Helsinki.

NIGHTINGALE

Instruments built in England since the late 1980s.

Luthier Bernie Goodfellow features original designs on his high quality solid body guitars.

(Source: Tony Bacon and Paul Day, The Guru's Guitar Guide)

NINJA

Instruments produced in Korea since the late 1980s.

The Ninja trademark is a brandname used by a British importer on these entry level to intermediate quality guitars. The Instrument designs are based on classic American favorites.

(Source: Tony Bacon and Paul Day, The Guru's Guitar Guide)

ROY NOBLE

Instruments currently built in California. Distributed by the Stringed Instument Division of Missoula, Montana.

Luthier Roy Noble has been handcrafting acoustic guitars for over 37 years. Noble has been plying his guitar building skills since the 1950s, when he first began building classical instruments after studying the construction of Jose Ramirez' Concert models. Noble later moved to a dreadnaut steel string acoustic design in the late 1950s and early 1960s as he practiced his craft repairing vintage instruments, and has produced anywhere from two to twenty guitars a year since then. Noble constantly experimented with

Nickerson Archtop
courtesy Brad Nickerson

the traditional uses of tonewoods, and his designs reflect the innovative use of coco bolo in bridges, and western red cedar for tops.

In 1964/1965, Noble replaced the top and neck on Clarence White's pre-war Martin D-28 when it came in for repairs (this instruments is currently owned by Tony Rice). White so enjoyed the sound that he later recorded with two Noble acoustics in many of his studio recordings.

(Source: Michael R. Stanger and Greg Boyd, Stringed Instrument Division)

Noble currently offers two models: an orchestra-sized acoustic or a dreadnought-sized acoustic. Models are built in one of three configurations. The **Standard** features mahogany and Indian rosewood construction, while the **Deluxe** features mahogany, Indian rosewood, koa, pau ferro, or coco bolo. The **Custom** offers construction with koa, pau ferro, coco bolo or CITES certified Brazilian rosewood. For further information regarding models, specifications, and pricing please contact the Stringed Instrument Division through the Index of Current Manufacturers located in the back of this book

TONY NOBLES

Instruments currently built in Austin, Texas.

Shellacious! Luthier Tony Noble builds high quality guitars and also writes a column in **Vintage Guitar Magazine**. For further information, contact Precision Guitarworks via the Index of Current Manufacturers located in the rear of this book.

NORMA

Instruments were built in Japan during the 1960s by the Tombo company.

These Japanese built guitars were distributed in the U.S. market by Strum and Drum, Inc. of Chicago, Illinois.

(Source: Michael Wright, Guitar Stories Volume One)

NORMAN

Instruments built in La Patrie, Quebec, Canada since 1972. Norman Guitars are distributed by La Si Do, Inc., of St. Laurent, Canada.

In 1968, Robert Godin set up a custom guitar shop in Montreal called Harmonilab. Harmonilab quickly became known for it's excellent work and musicians were coming from as far away as Quebec City to have their guitars adjusted. Harmonilab was the first guitar shop in Quebec to use professional strobe tuners for intonating guitars.

Although Harmonilab's business was flourishing, Robert was full of ideas for the design and construction of acoustic guitars. So, in 1972 the **Norman Guitar Company** was born. From the beginning the Norman guitars showed signs of the innovations that Godin would eventually bring to the guitar market. By 1978 Norman guitars had become quite successful in Canada and France, and continued expansion into the U.S. market. Today, Norman guitars and other members of the La Si Do guitar family are available all over the world.

For full company history, see GODIN.

ACOUSTIC

Grading	100% MINT	98% EXC+	95% EXC	90% EXC	80% VG+	70% VG	60% G

All models are available in left handed versions.
All models may be optionally equipped with L.R. Baggs electronics.

B-15 — dreadnought style, wild cherry top, round soundhole, black pickguard, bound body, black ring rosette, wild cherry back/sides, mahogany neck, 14/21 fret rosewood fingerboard with pearl dot inlay, rosewood bridge with white black dot pins, 3 per side chrome tuners. Available in Natural finish. Current model.

Mfr.'s Sug. Retail	$350	$280	$210	$175	$140	$125	$115	$105

B-15 (12) — similar to B-15, except has 12 strings, 6 per side tuners.

Mfr.'s Sug. Retail	$436	$348	$261	$235	$190	$170	$155	$140

B-20 — dreadnought style, solid spruce top, round soundhole, black pickguard, bound body, one ring rosette, cherry back/sides, mahogany neck, 14/21 fret rosewood fingerboard with pearl dot inlay, rosewood bridge with white black dot pins, 3 per side chrome tuners. Available in Natural finish. Current model.

Mfr.'s Sug. Retail	$399	$319	$239	$200	$160	$145	$130	$120

Add $67 for high Gloss finish.

B-20 (12) — similar to B-20, except has 12 strings, 6 per side tuners.

Mfr.'s Sug. Retail	$515	$386	$257	$235	$190	$170	$155	$140

B-20 CW — similar to B-20, except has round cutaway.

Mfr.'s Sug. Retail	$525	$393	$262	$260	$210	$190	$170	$160

Add $60 for high Gloss finish.

B-20 Folk — similar to B-20, except has folk style body. Curr. mfr.

Mfr.'s Sug. Retail	$460	$368	$276	$230	$185	$165	$150	$140

Grading	100%	98% MINT	95% EXC+	90% EXC	80% VG+	70% VG	60% G

B-20 (12) — similar to B-20, except has 12 strings, 6 per side tuners.

Mfr.'s Sug. Retail	$515	$412	$309	$260	$205	$185	$170	$155

B-50 — dreadnought style, solid spruce top, round soundhole, black pickguard, bound body, 3 ring wooden inlay rosette, maple back/sides, mahogany neck, 14/21 fret rosewood fingerboard with pearl dot inlay, rosewood bridge with white black dot pins, 3 per side chrome tuners. Available in Natural finish. Curr. mfr.

Mfr.'s Sug. Retail	$745	$596	$447	$375	$300	$270	$245	$225

B-50 (12) — similar to B-50, except has 12 strings, 6 per side tuners.

Mfr.'s Sug. Retail	$850	$680	$510	$425	$340	$305	$280	$255

ST-40 — dreadnought style, solid cedar top, round soundhole, black pickguard, bound body, 3 stripe rosette, mahogany back/sides/neck, 14/21 fret rosewood fingerboard with pearl dot inlay, rosewood bridge with white black dot pins, 3 per side chrome tuners. Available in Natural finish. Curr. mfr.

Mfr.'s Sug. Retail	$485	$363	$242	$240	$190	$170	$155	$145

ST-68 — dreadnought style, solid spruce top, round soundhole, black pickguard, bound body, 3 ring wooden inlay rosette, rosewood back/sides, mahogany neck, 14/21 fret ebony fingerboard with pearl dot inlay, ebony bridge with white black dot pins, 3 per side chrome tuners. Available in Natural finish. Curr. mfr.

Mfr.'s Sug. Retail	$1,035	$828	$621	$520	$415	$375	$340	$310

NORTHWORTHY

Instruments built in England since 1987.

These original design solid body guitars are generally of very good quality, and feature such model designations as the Dovedale, Edale, and the Milldale. Futher research continues for the next edition of the **Blue Book of Guitars**.

(Source: Tony Bacon and Paul Day, The Guru's Guitar Guide)

NOUVEAU GUITARS

See LADY LUCK.

NOVA GUITARS

See BUSCARINO.

Instruments built in Florida since 1981.

Luthier John Buscarino trained under such Master Luthiers as August Lo Prinzi and John Benedetto before starting his own business. Buscarino founded the Nova Guitar Company in 1981, and produced a number of high quality guitars under that logo before changing to the current trademark of his last name.

NOVAX

Instruments built in San Leandro, California since 1985. Novak has built custom guitars since 1970, in locations from New York to California.

Luthier Ralph Novak began playing guitar at age 14 in 1965, and also began experimenting with guitar design, modifying guitars, and making (crude) custom parts.

By age 16, Novak was repairing and customizing guitars for friends, and doing some freelance repair for local music stores. Novak continued part-time repairwork through high school at Stuyvesant in New York; and through college at Brooklyn College, where he studied music as a major. By age 19 Novak was working with Charles LoBue at GuitarLab in Greenwich Village in New York. Later, he quit college to work full-time at GuitarLab, where he worked with some of New York City's finest guitarists and built cutom guitars. In his spare time Novak began working on innovative designs with LoBue.

Around 1975, LoBue and GuitarLab moved uptown to Alex's Music on west 48th street. Novak stayed at Alex's for about a year, and then began free lance repair work for several stores on west 48th as well as seeing private clients in his repair shop in a downtown loft.

In 1978, Novak and LoBue moved to the San Francisco Bay area, and worked together until LoBue moved back to New York City. Novak stayed in the Bay area and worked at Subway Guitars in Berkeley, later becoming a partner and helping to build it into the viable repair shop it is today. In 1985 Novak left the partnership to open his own repair shop in Oakland, where he also built several custom instruments a year. In 1989 Novak received a U.S. patent for his "Fanned Fret" system, and began working on prototypes to find the optimum scale length combination for guitar and bass. In 1992 the Novax fretboard was mentioned in **Business Week** magazine's "1992 Idea Winners", and received the Industrial Design Society Award for Excellence in 1993 (the last music-related award was Ned Steinberger's headless bass in 1982).

The first official Novax guitar was completed in 1993, as the result of several years of researching and developing, gathering opinions and suggestions from players of all styles of music. Novak eventually obtained custom hardware for his system, and since then has concentrated on building Expression series

Novax Expression
courtesy Ralph Novak

N

and Tribute model guitars and basses. Due to the labor-intensive nature of the work, Novak has "retired" from the daily repair business to focus directly on his guitars.

(Biography courtesy Ralph Novak, 3-18-96)

The patented Novax "Fanned Fretboard" has been licensed out to such notables as Dingwall Designer Guitars, Klein Custom Guitars, Acacia Instruments, and in late 1995 Moses Graphite announced retrofit epoxy-graphite necks for Precision and Jazz basses.

ELECTRIC

Expression Series

The Expression Guitars are set-neck models with ergonomic body shapes that are highly carved for comfort and beauty.

EXPRESSION CLASSIC — offset double cutaway body features choices of Walnut, Maple, Lacewood, Zebrano, Swamp Ash, or Birch; vertical-grain Eastern Rock Maple neck, patented 22 fret "Fanned Fret" design, choice of fingerboard materials such as Wenge, Purpleheart, Paduak, Rosewood, Ebony, or Bird's Eye Maple; choice of three nut widths, Bartolini pickups, volume knob, rotary switching tone knob, pickup blend knob, 3+3 headstock design and chrome tuners. Available in Natural finish. Produced from 1993 to current.

Mfr.'s Sug. Retail $2,650
> List price includes case.
> Add $120 for Active circuitry with gain boost and active/passive switching.
> Add $175 for Active circuitry with treble and bass boost (16 Db cut/boost).

EXPRESSION CUSTOM — offset double cutaway body features a laminate design of highly figured book-matched maple over a body core of Paduak, Lacewood, or Purpleheart; vertical-grain Eastern Rock Maple neck, patented 22 fret "Fanned Fret" design, choice of wood-bound fingerboard materials such as Wenge, Purpleheart, Paduak, Rosewood, Ebony, or Bird's Eye Maple; choice of three nut widths, Bartolini pickups, active circuitry (4 different choices), volume knob, rotary switching tone knob, pickup blend knob, gold or black chrome hardware, 3+3 headstock design. Available in Natural finish. Current production.

Mfr.'s Sug. Retail $3,150
> List price includes case.
> Add $200 for vertical-grain Paduak neck.

EXPRESSION BARITONE — offset double cutaway body features choice of Walnut, Birch, or Lacewood; vertical-grain Eastern Rock Maple neck, patented 22 fret "Fanned Fret" design, choice of fingerboard materials such as Wenge, Purpleheart, Paduak, Rosewood, or Ebony; Bartolini "Soapbar" pickups, extra bass-cut circuitry, volume knob, rotary switching tone knob, pickup blend knob, gold or black chrome hardware, 3+3 headstock design. Available in Natural finish. Current production.

Mfr.'s Sug. Retail $2,850
> List price includes gig bag.
> The Baritone model is a specially designed long-scale guitar in "B" tuning.

Tribute Series

The Tribute models are built in tribute to the pioneering work of Leo Fender, and feature bolt-on necks as well as body designs that recall the classic lines of Fender's work.

TRIBUTE GUITAR — Tribute body designs are either single cutaway ("Tele") or double cutaway ("Strat") based solids available in Alder, Ash, or Swamp Ash; body styles are also available in non-traditional laminated exotic woods. Patended "Fanned Fret" fingboard, Bartolini pickups mounted to the pickguard, Bartolini circuitry, traditional hardware and styling. Current production.

Mfr.'s Sug. Retail $1,950
> Add $500 for laminated body and rear routed electronics (eliminates pickguard).

ELECTRIC BASS

EXPRESSION BASS 4 STRING — offset double cutaway body features choice of Walnut, Birch, Maple, or Lacewood; vertical-grain Eastern Rock Maple neck, patented "Fanned Fret" design, choice of fingerboard materials such as Wenge, Purpleheart, Paduak, Rosewood, or Ebony; Bartolini "Soapbar" pickups, Bartolini circuitry, volume knob, tone knob, pickup blend knob, 2+2 headstock design. Available in Natural finish. Current production.

Mfr.'s Sug. Retail $2,650

EXPRESSION BASS 5 STRING — similar to Expression Bass, except has five strings. Current production.

Mfr.'s Sug. Retail $2,750

EXPRESSION BASS 6 STRING — similar to Expression Bass, except has six strings. Current production.

Mfr.'s Sug. Retail $2,850

EXPRESSION CUSTOM BASS — offset double cutaway body features a laminate design of highly figured bookmatched maple over a body core of Paduak, Lacewood, or Purpleheart; vertical-grain Eastern Rock Maple neck, patented "Fanned Fret" design, choice of wood-bound fingerboard materials such as Wenge, Purpleheart, Paduak, Rosewood, Ebony, or Bird's Eye Maple; Bartolini pickups, Bartolini circuitry, volume knob, tone knob, pickup blend knob, gold or black chrome hardware, 2+2 headstock design. Available in Natural finish. Current production.

Mfr.'s Sug. Retail $3,150
> List price includes case.

EXPRESSION CUSTOM BASS 5 STRING — similar to Expression Custom Bass, except has five strings. Current production.

Mfr.'s Sug. Retail $3,250

"One day the son of a sax player in Jim Marshall's dance band came in with a request for the 'biggest and loudest' amp Jim could make...The sax player's son was Pete Townsend and what he got was the first 100 watt head atop an 8X12 cabinet."

—Richie Fliegler
TCG, Nov/Dec 1990

N

EXPRESSION CUSTOM BASS 6 STRING — similar to Expression Custom Bass, except has six strings. Current production.

Mfr.'s Sug. Retail $3,350

TRIBUTE BASS — Tribute body designs are a double cutaway ("Precison") or ("Jazz") based solids available in Alder, Ash, or Swamp Ash; body styles are also available in non-traditional laminated exotic woods. Patended "Fanned Fret" fingerboard, Bartolini pickups mounted to the pickguard, Bartolini circuitry, traditional hardware and styling. Current production.

Mfr.'s Sug. Retail $1,950

Add $500 for laminated body and rear routed electronics (eliminates pickguard).

Add $175 for active tone shaping electronics.

NYC MUSIC PRODUCTS

Instruments built in Brooklyn, New York. Distributed by Matthews & Ryan Musical Products of Brooklyn, New York.

NYC bass guitars are built by the luthiers at Fodera with a more traditional design.

ELECTRIC BASS

Empire Series

Both four string models have a 34" scale, 21 fret rosewood fingerboard with mother-of-pearl inlay dots, either EMG or Bartolini J/J pickup combinations, black hardware, and a clear Natural satin finish. The **Model 1** (list $2,400) features an Alder body and a Northern Rock Maple bolt-on neck. The **Model 2** (list $2,400) has a Swamp Ash body and a Northern Rock Maple bolt-on neck, but substitutes a maple fingerboard. The addition of an optional high grade Curly Maple or Quilted Maple top is an extra $500.

The Empire 5 string models are similar to the 4 strings, except the scale length is 35". Both the **Model 1 5 String** and **Model 2 5 String** carry a list price of $3,195 respectively. The addition of an optional high grade Curly Maple or Quilted Maple top is an extra $500.

N

OAKLAND

Instruments produced in Japan from the late 1970s through the early 1980s.

These good quality solid body guitars featured both original designs and designs based on classic American favorites.

(Source: Tony Bacon and Paul Day, The Guru's Guitar Guide)

ODELL

Circa unknown.

David Pavlick is the current owner of this "mystery guitar". The 3+3 headstock features a decal which reads "Odell - Vega Co., - Boston", and features a 16 1/2" archtop body, one Duo-Tron pickup, 20 fret neck, volume/tone controls mounted on the trapeze tailpiece. Inside one f-hole there is "828H1325" stamped into the back wood. Any readers with further information are invited to write to the **Blue Book of Guitars**.

(Source: David J. Pavlick, Woodbury, Connecticut)

ODYSSEY

Instruments built in Canada during the 1980s.

Luthier Attila Balogh crafted these high quality solid body guitars beginning as early as 1980s. The original designs featured series such as the Hawk, 100, 400, and Attila models.

In March 1983, Balogh was commissioned by Paul Dean (Loverboy) to produce a limited run of 50 "Paul Dean" models. These models were similar to the custom handcrafted guitar the Dean himself built.

The **Blue Book of Guitars** did track down a description of the Carved Ash Series 200. Offered beginning in 1980, the double cutaway unbound ash body featured 2 humbuckers, a stop tailpiece, 4 knobs and other switches, 24 fret neck-thru design with ebony fingerboard and abalone inlay dots, and a 3+3 peghead. A companion bass was offered in the same advertisement in Frets magazine (February 1980), and it mentioned that the parts and switching were similar to the ones in the Series 100 instruments.

The last given company address is 115 Bowser Avenue, North Vancouver, British Columbia (Canada), V7P 3H1. Anyone with information is invited to write the **Blue Book of Guitars** for future updates.

(Some information courtesy Pat and the staff at Value - Plus Co. Ltd., of Winnipeg, Manitoba)

O F B GUITARS

See PAT WILKINS.

Instruments built in Virginia Beach, Virginia during the early 1990s.

O'HAGAN

Instruments built in St. Louis Park (a suburb of Minneapolis), Minnesota from 1979 to 1983. Distributed by the Jemar Corporation of St. Louis Park, Minnesota.

O'Hagan guitars were developed by Jerry O'Hagan. O'Hagan, a former clarinetist and music teacher, began importing the Grande brand acoustic guitars from Japan in 1975. In 1979, the O'Hagan guitar company was formed to build quality, affordable solid body guitars.

The most eye-catching model was the Shark (basic retail list $529), which was introduced in 1979. The body design recalls a rounded off Explorer, and features maple and walnut in a neck-through design. The vaguely offset headstock features 3+3 tuning machine alignment, and the guitar has two humbuckers, a 3-way pickup selector switch, two volume knobs and a master tone knob. Other models may feature push/pull coil tap potentiometers (this option cost an extra $90), and a phase switch. O'Hagan also developed the NightWatch model, initially a single cutaway LP-style guitar (new list $479), and then joined by a dual cutaway model (same retail list price) of the same name.

In 1980, O'Hagan introduced his most popular model, the Twenty Two (retail list $529). This model, again built of Maple and Walnut, is based on the popular Flying V design. The Laser model, a sort of Strat-based design, featured a six-on-a-side headstock and either three single coils or a humbucker. All guitar models had a bass counterpart (prices ran an additional $10 to $50 extra, depending on the model). As O'Hagans were basically handbuilt custom instruments, various options can be found on existing models.

In 1983, both a nationwide recession and a resurgence in traditional guitar design (the beginning of 'Strat-mania') took a toll on the four year old company. When a bank note became due, the company

ODell-Vega Co.,-Boston
courtesy David J. Pavlik

Old Kraftman
courtesy John Beeson

was unable to pay. The I.R.S. had an outstanding bill due as well, and seized company holdings to auction off. The O'Hagan company, which tried to provide quality guitars at an affordable price, closed its door for good. Over ten years after the fact, Jerry O'Hagan is still involved with music as he performs with Jerry O'Hagan and His Orchestra, a 16 to 20 piece big band that performs swing jazz.

O'Hagan instruments can be identified by the "O'Hagan" decal, or a glued on "OH" logo which also featured a cloverleaf. Instruments may also sport a "Jemar Corporation" decal back by the serial number. It is estimated that only 3,000 instruments were produced during the company's four year production. One dating method to use is based on the instrument's pickup (if the original pickups are still installed). Instruments built between 1979 and 1980 had pickups by Mighty Mite; in 1981 they were switched to DiMarzio; and finally O'Hagan settled on Schaller pickups in 1982 to 1983.

(Source: Michael Wright, Guitar Stories Volume One, pgs. 277-281)

OLD KRAFTSMAN

See chapter on House Brands.

This trademark has been identified as a "House Brand" of Speigel. Author/researcher Willie G. Moseley reports one source seeing the trademark in a 1937 Speigel catalog.

(Source: Willie G. Moseley, Stellas & Stratocasters)

OLSON

Instruments currently built in Circle Pines, Minnesota.

Luthier Jim Olson began building acoustic guitars full time in 1977. Olson had previous backgrounds in woodworking and guitar playing, and combined his past favorites into his current occupation. Olson's creations have been used by James Taylor (since 1989), Phil Keaggy, Sting, and Kathy Matthea. Olson handcrafts 60 guitars a year, and currently has a waiting list. For further information regarding models, availability, and pricing please contact luthier Olson via the Index of Current Manufacturers located in the back of this book.

ONYX

Instruments built in Korea during the 1980s.

The Onyx trademark was the brandname of an Australian importer. These solid body guitars were generally entry level to intermediate quality; however, the late '80s model 1030 bears a passing resemblance to a Mosrite Mark I with modern hardware.

(Source: Tony Bacon, The Ultimate Guitar Book)

OPTEK

Instruments produced in Korea. Distributed in the U.S. market by Optek Music Systems of Raleigh, North Carolina.

Optek Music Systems was formed by Rusty Schaffer in 1989, as a means to help and educate new and existing guitarists through the use of the **Fretlight** learning aid. The Fretlight is an integration of a student level guitar and LED display (built into the neck). The guitar student has the option of choosing one of the twelve musical keys and either chords, scales, or notes for the display. The corresponding LEDs on the neck light up and help the beginning player visualize fingering patterns. In 1997, the company plans to offer the **Smartlight** guitar line, which connects to the home personal computer.

(Source: Hal Hammer)

The **Fretlight** models were offered at three different levels. The entry level **Original** (retail list $599) model had a solid finish, while the intermediate **Artist** ($799) had a translucent finish and Seymour Duncan pickups. The top-of-the-line **Pro** ($1,099) had a flamed maple top, Seymour Duncan Alnico II pickups, and gold hardware. Guitars are produced in the same Korean factory as Gibson/Epiphone, Ibanez, and Washburn; the U.S. Optek facility checks quality control, assembly, and setups prior to shipping.

OPUS

Instruments produced in Japan.

The Opus trademark is a brandname of U.S. importers Ampeg/Selmer.

(Source: Michael Wright, Guitar Stories Volume One, pg. 76)

ORANGE

Instruments produced in Korea during the mid 1970s.

While this solid body guitar did feature an original body design and two humbucking pickups, the finish was painted black!

(Source: Tony Bacon and Paul Day, The Guru's Guitar Guide)

Optek FG-200 Artist
courtesy Hal Hammer

ORBIT

See TEISCO DEL REY.

Instruments built in Japan during the mid to late 1960s.

The Orbit trademark is the brandname of an UK importer. Orbit guitars were produced by the same folks who built Teisco guitars in Japan; so while there is the relative coolness of the original Teisco design, the entry level quality is the drawback.

(Source: Tony Bacon and Paul Day, The Guru's Guitar Guide)

ORIGINAL MUSIC INSTRUMENT
COMPANY, INC.

Instruments currently built in Long Beach, California. O M I is now a division of the Gibson Guitar Corporation, and distribution is handled through the Gibson corporation of Nashville, Tennessee.

In 1960, Emil Dopyera and brothers Rudy and John founded the Original Music Instrument company to build resonator guitars. They soon resumed production on models based on their wood-body Dobros. In the late 1960s, OMI also began production of metal-bodied resonators roughly similar to their old National designs. Ron Lazar, a Dopyera nephew, took over the business in the early 1970s. In 1993, OMI was sold to the Gibson Guitar Corporation, although production is still centered in California. For further information on OMI/Dobro, see current model listings under DOBRO.

(Early company history courtesy Bob Brozman, The History and Artistry of National Resonator Instruments)

ORPHEUM

See LANGE.

Orpheum guitars were introduced by distributor William L. Lange Company (New York) in the mid 1930s, and also distributed by C. Bruno & Son. Some Orpheum models were built in Chicago, Illinois by the Kay company. Lange's company went out of business in the early 1940s, but New York distributor Maurice Lipsky resumed distribution of Orpheum guitars in 1944. Future model designations/indentifications will appear in updated editons of the **Blue Book of Guitars**.

(Source: Tom Wheeler, American Guitars)

1950s Orpheum fiberglass
courtesy Thoroughbred Music

OSCAR SCHMIDT

Instruments currently built in Korea, and distributed by Oscar Schmidt International of Vernon Hills, Illinois.

The original Oscar Schmidt company was based in Jersey City, New Jersey, and was established in the late 1800s by Oscar Schmidt and his son, Walter. The Oscar Schmidt company produced a wide range of stringed instruments and some of the tradenames utilized were Stella, Sovereign, and LaScala among others. The company later changed its name to Oscar Schmidt International, and in 1935 or 1936 followed with the Fretted Instrument Manufacturers. After the company went bankrupt, the Harmony Company of Chicago, Illinois purchased rights to use Oscar Schmidt's trademarks in 1939.

In the late 1900s, the Oscar Schmidt trademark was revived by the Washburn International Company of Illinois. Oscar Schmidt currently offers both acoustic guitars and other stringed instruments for the beginning student up to the intermediate player.

(Source: Tom Wheeler, American Guitars)

OTHON

Instruments currently built in Ovale, California.

Luthier Robert Othon currently offers high quality, solid body, 'super strat' style guitars that feature a lightweight top of solid rock. Othon's patented process produces a layer of stone so thin that it adds only 6 to 8 ounces to the total weight. For further information, contact luthier Robert Othon through the Index of Current Manufacturers located in the back of this book.

OTWIN

See MUSIMA.

Instruments built in East Germany in the late 1950s to early 1960s.

Instruments with the Otwin brandname were built by the Musima company in Germany during the late 1950s on. Earlier models were available in original designs of both solid body and semi-hollow body configurations through the early 1960s.

(Source: Tony Bacon and Paul Day, The Guru's Guitar Guide)

OVATION

Instruments built in New Hartford, Connecticut since 1967. Distribution is handled by the Kaman Music Corporation of Bloomfield, Connecticut.

Othon Viking
courtesy Robert Othon

O

The Ovation guitar company, and the nature of the Ovation guitar's synthetic back are directly attributed to founder Charles H. Kaman's experiments in helicopter aviation. Kaman, who began playing guitar back in high school, trained in the field of aeronautics and graduated from the Catholic University in Washington, D.C. His first job in 1940 was with a division of United Aircraft, home of aircraft inventor Igor Sikorsky. In 1945, Kaman formed the Kaman Aircraft Corporation to pursue his helicopter-related inventions.

As the company began grow, the decision was made around 1957 to diversify into manufacturing products in different fields. Kaman initially made overtures to the Martin company, as well as exploring both Harmony and Ludwig drums. Finally, the decision was made to start fresh. Due to research in vibrations and resonances in the materials used to build helicopter blades, guitar development began in 1964 with employees John Ringso and Jim Rickard. In fact, it was Rickard's pre-war Martin D-45 that was used as the 'test standard'. In 1967, the Ovation company name was chosen, incorporated, and settled into its 'new facilities' in New Hartford, Connecticut. The first model named that year was the Balladeer.

Ovation guitars were debuted at the 1967 NAMM show. Early players and endorsers included Josh White, Charlie Byrd, and Glen Campbell. Piezo pickup equipped models were introduced in 1972, as well as other models. During the early 1970s, Kaman Music (Ovation's parent company) acquired the well-known music distributors Coast, and also part of the Takamine guitar company. By 1975, Ovation decided to release an entry level instrument, and the original Applause/Medallion/Matrix designs were first built in the U.S. before production moved into Korea.

In 1986, Kaman's oldest son became president of Kaman Music. Charles William "Bill" Kaman II had begun working in the Ovation factory at age 14. After graduating college in 1974, Bill was made Director of Development at the Moosup Connecticut plant. A noted Travis Bean guitar collector (see Kaman's Travis Bean history later in this book), Bill Kaman remained active in the research and development aspect of model design. Kaman helped design the Viper III, and the UK II solidbodies.

In 1986, Bill Kaman gathered all branches of the company "under one roof" as the Kaman Music Corporation (KMC). As the Ovation branch was now concentrating on acoustic and acoustic/electric models, the corporation bought the independent Hamer company in 1988 as the means to re-enter the solid body guitar market. Furthermore, KMC began distributing Trace-Elliot amplifiers the same year, and bought them in 1992. The Kaman Music Corporation acts as the parent company, and has expanded to cover just about all areas of the music business. As a result, the Ovation branch now concentrates specifically on producing the best acoustic guitars, with the same attention to detail that the company was founded on.

(Source: Walter Carter, The History of the Ovation Guitar)

(Information collected in Mr. Carter's Ovation Appendices was researched and compiled by Paul Bechtoldt)

ACOUSTIC

Grading	100%	98% MINT	95% EXC+	90% EXC	80% VG+	70% VG	60% G

All Ovation acoustic and acoustic/electric instruments have a synthetic rounded back/sides construction. The model number in parenthesis following the name is the current assigned model number.

Adamas Series

All Adamas models have a composite top consisting of 2 carbon-graphite layers around a birch core, and carved fiberglass body binding. There are also 11 various sized soundholes with leaf pattern maple veneer around them, situated around the upper bouts on both sides of the fingerboard. All models have 6 piezo bridge pickups, volume/3 band EQ controls, and an active OP-24 preamp. The Adamas model was introduced in 1976.

ADAMAS 6 (Model 1687) — folk style, composite top, mahogany neck, 14/24 fret walnut extended fingerboard with maple/ebony inlay, walnut bridge with carved flower designs, carved flower design on peghead, 3 per side gold tuners. Available in Beige, Black, Blue, Brown and Red finishes. Current production.

Mfr.'s Sug. Retail	$3,099	$2,634	$2,169	$1,940	$1,790	$1,375	$1,150	$825

Adamas Cutaway (Model 1587) — similar to Adamas 6, except has venetian cutaway, no soundholes on cutaway side.

Mfr.'s Sug. Retail	$3,199	$2,719	$2,239	$2,000	$1,790	$1,400	$1,100	$875

Adamas 12 (Model 1688) — similar to Adamas 6, except has 12 strings.

Mfr.'s Sug. Retail	$3,299	$2,804	$2,309	$2,050	$1,800	$1,450	$1,250	$950

Adamas II Series

Similar to the original Adamas series, the Adamas II featured the standard Ovation headstock and bridge instead of the carved Walnut, and a five piece mahogany and maple laminate neck instead of the solid walnut neck. The Adamas II model was introduced in early 1982.

ADAMAS II (Model 1681) — folk style, composite top, mahogany/maple 5 piece neck, 14/24 fret walnut extended fingerboard with maple/ebony triangle inlay, walnut bridge, walnut veneer on peghead, 3 per side gold tuners. Available in Beige, Black, Blue, Brown and Red finishes. Current production.

Mfr.'s Sug. Retail	$2,100	$1,680	$1,260	$1,050	$840	$755	$690	$630

Grading	100%	98% MINT	95% EXC+	90% EXC	80% VG+	70% VG	60% G

Adamas II Cutaway (Model 1581) — similar to Adamas II, except has venetian cutaway, no soundholes on cutaway side.

| Mfr.'s Sug. Retail | $2,200 | $1,760 | $1,320 | $1,100 | $880 | $790 | $725 | $660 |

In 1994, soundholes on cutaway side were introduced.

Adamas II 12 (Model 1685) — similar to Adamas II, except has 12 strings, 6 per side tuners.

| Mfr.'s Sug. Retail | $2,300 | $1,840 | $1,380 | $1,150 | $920 | $830 | $760 | $690 |

Adamas II Cutaway Shallow (Model 1881) — similar to Adamas II, except has shallow bowl body, venetian cutaway. Mfg. 1994 to current.

| Mfr.'s Sug. Retail | $2,200 | $1,760 | $1,320 | $1,100 | $880 | $790 | $725 | $660 |

Adamas II 12 Shallow (Model 1885) — similar to Adamas II, except has shallow bowl body, 12 strings, 6 per side tuners. Mfg. 1994 to current.

| Mfr.'s Sug. Retail | $2,400 | $1,920 | $1,440 | $1,200 | $960 | $860 | $790 | $720 |

Balladeer Series

The Balladeer was the first model introduced by the Ovation company in 1967.

CUSTOM BALLADEER (Model 1712) — folk style, spruce top, round soundhole, 5 stripe bound body, leaf pattern rosette, 5 piece mahogany/maple neck, 14/20 fret ebony fingerboard, 12th fret pearl diamond/dot inlay, walnut strings thru bridge with pearl dot inlay, 3 per side nickel tuners, 6 piezo bridge pickups, volume control, 3 band EQ, FET preamp. Available in Black, Natural, Sunburst and White finishes. Current production.

| Mfr.'s Sug. Retail | $995 | $746 | $497 | $490 | $420 | $380 | $345 | $315 |

This model has cedar top optionally available.

In 1994, the Vintage finish was introduced.

In 1994, the White finish was discontinued.

In 1994, The pearl dot bridge inlay was discontinued.

Custom Balladeer Cutaway (Model 1860) — similar to Custom Balladeer, except has single round cutaway, shallow bowl body.

| Mfr.'s Sug. Retail | $1,095 | $876 | $657 | $575 | $460 | $415 | $380 | $345 |

Custom Balladeer 12 — similar to Custom Balladeer, except has 12 strings, 6 per side chrome tuners with pearloid buttons. Disc. 1994.

| | | $875 | $750 | $625 | $500 | $450 | $415 | $375 |

Last Mfr.'s Sug. Retail was $1,250.

CUSTOM BALLADEER CLASSIC — single round cutaway classic style, cedar top, round soundhole, 5 stripe bound body, leaf pattern rosette, 5 piece mahogany/maple neck, 19 fret extended ebony fingerboard, rosewood tied bridge, 3 per side gold tuners with pearloid buttons, 6 piezo bridge pickups, volume/3 band EQ control, FET preamp. Available in Natural finish. New 1994.

| Mfr.'s Sug. Retail | $1,495 | $1,196 | $897 | $750 | $600 | $540 | $495 | $450 |

This model has shallow bowl body optionally available.

STANDARD BALLADEER (Model 1111) — folk style, spruce top, round soundhole, 5 stripe bound body, leaf pattern rosette, cedro neck, 14/20 fret rosewood fingerboard with pearl dot inlay, rosewood strings thru bridge with pearl dot inlay, 3 per side chrome tuners. Available in Amber Cadillac Green and Tobacco Sunburst finishes. Mfd. 1993 to date.

| Mfr.'s Sug. Retail | $695 | $556 | $417 | $350 | $280 | $250 | $230 | $210 |

Standard Balladeer Electric (Model 1711) — similar to Standard Balladeer, except has piezo bridge pickups, 4 band EQ.

| Mfr.'s Sug. Retail | $795 | $596 | $397 | $395 | $315 | $280 | $260 | $235 |

Standard Balladeer Cutaway (Model 1761) — similar to Standard Balladeer, except has single round cutaway, deep bowl, piezo bridge pickups, 4 band EQ.

| Mfr.'s Sug. Retail | $895 | $671 | $447 | $445 | $360 | $325 | $300 | $275 |

Standard Balladeer Cutaway (Model 1861) — similar to Standard Balladeer, except has single round cutaway, super shallow bowl, piezo bridge pickups, 4 band EQ.

| Mfr.'s Sug. Retail | $895 | $671 | $447 | $445 | $360 | $325 | $300 | $275 |

Celebrity Series

The Celebrity series is Ovation's entry level introduction to the porduct line. This series features the largest number of models, features, and finishes - as well as the same commitment to quality as found on the higher priced models.

CELEBRITY (Model CC-11) — folk style, spruce top, round soundhole, 5 stripe bound body, leaf pattern rosette, mahogany neck, 14/20 fret bound rosewood fingerboard with pearl dot inlay, walnut bridge with pearloid dot inlays, rosewood veneer on peghead, 3 per side chrome tuners. Available in Barnboard, Brownburst, Natural and Sunburst finishes. Curr. mfr.

| Mfr.'s Sug. Retail | $400 | $300 | $200 | $190 | $150 | $135 | $120 | $110 |

In 1994, Sunburst finish was discontinued.

Celebrity Electric (CC-67) — similar to Celebrity, except has piezo bridge pickups, 4 band EQ. Available in Barnboard, Brownburst and Natural finishes. New 1994.

| Mfr.'s Sug. Retail | $500 | $400 | $300 | $250 | $200 | $180 | $165 | $150 |

Grading		100%	98% MINT	95% EXC+	90% EXC	80% VG+	70% VG	60% G

Celebrity 12 (Model CC-15) — similar to Celebrity, except has 12 strings, 6 per side tuners. Available in Natural and Sunburst finishes. Curr. mfr.

Mfr.'s Sug. Retail	$500	$375	$250	$235	$190	$170	$155	$140

Celebrity 12 Electric (Model CC-65) — similar to Celebrity, except has 12 strings, 6 per side tuners, piezo bridge pickups, 4 band EQ. Available in Natural finish. New 1994.

Mfr.'s Sug. Retail	$600	$480	$360	$300	$240	$215	$195	$180

CELEBRITY CLASSIC — classic style, spruce top, round soundhole, 5 stripe bound body, leaf pattern rosette, mahogany neck, 12/19 fret bound rosewood fingerboard, walnut bridge, 3 per side gold tuners with pearloid buttons. Available in Natural finish. Curr. mfr.

Mfr.'s Sug. Retail	$400	$300	$200	$190	$150	$135	$120	$110

Celebrity Classic E — similar to Celebrity Classic, except has piezo bridge pickups, 4 band EQ. Available in Natural finish. New 1994.

Mfr.'s Sug. Retail	$500	$400	$300	$250	$200	$180	$165	$150

Celebrity Classic Cutaway — similar to Celebrity Classic, except has venetian cutaway, piezo bridge pickups, volume/tone control. Curr. mfr.

Mfr.'s Sug. Retail	$600	$450	$300	$265	$210	$190	$175	$160

CELEBRITY CUTAWAY — single round cutaway folk style, spruce top, round soundhole, 5 stripe bound body, leaf pattern rosette, mahogany neck, 20 fret bound rosewood fingerboard with pearloid diamond/dot inlay, walnut bridge with pearloid dot inlay, walnut veneer on peghead, 3 per side chrome tuners, 6 piezo bridge pickups, volume/tone control. Available in Barnboard, Brownburst, Natural and Sunburst finishes. Mfd. 1991 to date.

Mfr.'s Sug. Retail	$550	$412	$275	$250	$200	$180	$165	$150

In 1994, Barnboard finish was discontinued.

Celebrity Cutaway Shallow — similar to Celebrity Cutaway, except has shallow bowl body.

Mfr.'s Sug. Retail	$600	$450	$300	$265	$210	$190	$175	$160

Celebrity Deluxe Series

The Celebrity Deluxe series features the same multiple soundholes of the Adamas and Elite designs on a laminated spruce or cedar top.

CELEBRITY DELUXE (Model CC-267) — folk style, cedar top, multi-sized soundholes with leaf pattern maple veneer, 5 stripe bound body, mahogany neck, 14/23 fret bound rosewood extended fingerboard with pearl diamond/dot inlay, rosewood strings thru bridge, rosewood veneered peghead with logo decal, 3 per side gold tuners, piezo bridge pickups, 4 band EQ. Available in Antique Sunburst and Natural finishes. Current production.

Mfr.'s Sug. Retail	$650	$520	$390	$325	$260	$235	$215	$195

This model has spruce and sycamore tops optionally available.

Celebrity Deluxe Cutaway (Model CC-268) — similar to Celebrity Deluxe, except has single round cutaway. Available in Black, Natural and Wineburst finishes.

Mfr.'s Sug. Retail	$700	$560	$420	$350	$280	$250	$230	$210

Celebrity Deluxe Cutaway Shallow (Model CC-257) — similar to Celebrity Deluxe, except has single round cutaway, and shallow bowl body. Available in Black, Natural, Sycamoreburst, Sunburst and Wineburst finishes.

Mfr.'s Sug. Retail	$750	$600	$450	$375	$300	$270	$245	$225

Classic Series

CLASSIC — classic style, cedar top, round soundhole, 5 stripe bound body, leaf pattern rosette, 5 piece mahogany/maple neck, 12/19 fret extended ebony fingerboard, walnut bridge, walnut veneer on peghead, 3 per side gold tuners, piezo bridge pickup, volume/3 band EQ control, active preamp. Available in Natural finish. Disc. 1994.

				$995	$850	$710	$570	$510	$465	$425

Last Mfr.'s Sug. Retail was $1,420.

Classic Cutaway — similar to Classic, except has venetian cutaway. Available in Natural and White finishes. Disc. 1994.

				$1,065	$910	$760	$610	$550	$505	$455

Last Mfr.'s Sug. Retail was $1,520.

This model had shallow bowl optionally available.

Collector's Series

The Collector's Series offers limited edition guitars. Beginning in 1982, a different model is featured each year, and production of that model is limited to that year only.

(Information compiled by Paul Bechtoldt, and is featured in Walter Carter's "The History of the Ovation Guitar" book.)

Not enough of these limited edition models have traded to be able to record market prices. The following descriptions will list the number of instruments built per model, and the listed retail price as a guideline for interested collectors and players.

1982 COLLECTOR'S (Model 1982-8) — Bowl back acoustic guitar, round soundhole. Mfd. 1982 only.

Mfr.'s Sug. retail was $995.

A total of 1,908 guitars were produced.

"A number of well-known collectors and exhibitors said, 'What kind of fool would buy a guitar for $150,000?' These same folks sell numerous big dollar pieces to the Japanese contingent yearly."

—TCG, May/June 1993

1983 COLLECTOR'S (Model 1983-B) — Super shallow bowl, single cutaway, round soundhole. Available in Barnboard (exaggerated grain) finish. Mfd. 1983 only.

> Mfr.'s Sug. retail was $995.
> A total of 2,754 guitars were produced.

1984 COLLECTOR'S (Model 1984-5) — Elite model design, Super shallow bowl, single cutaway. Available in Ebony stain finish. Mfd. 1984 only.

> Mfr.'s Sug. retail was $995.
> A total of 2,637 guitars were produced.

1985 COLLECTOR'S (Model 1985-1) — Elite model design, Super shallow bowl, single cutaway. Available in Autumnburst finish. Mfd. 1985 only.

> Mfr.'s Sug. retail was $1,095.
> A total of 2,198 guitars were produced.

1985 COLLECTOR'S (Model 2985-1) — similar to the 1985 Collector's model, except offered in limited quanities as a 12 string model. Available in Autumnburst finish. Mfd. 1985 only.

> Mfr.'s Sug. retail was $1,195.
> A total of 715 guitars were produced.

1986 COLLECTOR'S (Model 1986-6) — Super shallow bowl, single cutaway, round soundhole. Available in Pearl White finish. Mfd. 1986 only.

> Mfr.'s Sug. retail was $1,095.
> A total of 1,858 guitars were produced.

1986 COLLECTOR'S (Model 2986-6) — similar to the 1986 Collector's model, except offered in limited quantities as a 12 string model. Available in Pearl White finish. Mfd. 1986 only.

> Mfr.'s Sug. retail was $1,195.
> A total of 392 guitars were produced.

1987 COLLECTOR'S (Model 1987-7) — Elite model design, deep bowl, single cutaway. Available in Nutmeg stain finish. Mfd. 1987 only.

> Mfr.'s Sug. retail was $1,800.
> A total of 820 guitars were produced.

1987 COLLECTOR'S (Model 1987-5) — similar to the 1987 Collector's model, except offered in limited quantities in a Black finish. Mfd. 1987 only.

> Mfr.'s Sug. retail was $1,800.
> A total of 108 guitars were produced.

1988 COLLECTOR'S (Model 1988-P) — Elite model design, Super shallow bowl, single cutaway. Available in a Pewter finish. Mfd. 1988 only.

> Mfr.'s Sug. retail was $1,195.
> A total of 1,177 guitars were produced.

1989 COLLECTOR'S (Model 1989-8) — Super shallow bowl, single cutaway, round soundhole. Available in Blue Pearl finish. Mfd. 1989 only.

> Mfr.'s Sug. retail was $1,299.
> A total of 981 guitars were produced.

1990 COLLECTOR'S (Model 1990-7) — Elite model design, bird's eye maple top, deep bowl, single cutaway. Available in Nutmeg finish. Mfd. 1990 only.

> Mfr.'s Sug. retail was $1,599.
> A total of 500 guitars were produced.

1990 COLLECTOR'S (Model 1990-1) — similar to the 1990 Collector's model (1990-7), except offered in extremely limited quantities in a Sunburst finish. Mfd. 1990 only.

> Mfr.'s Sug. retail was $1,599.
> A total of 50 guitars were produced.

1990 COLLECTOR'S (Model 199S-7) — similar to the 1990 Collector's model (1990-7), except offered in limited quantities with a Super shallow bowl and Nutmeg finish. Mfd. 1990 only.

> Mfr.'s Sug. retail was $1,599.
> A total of 750 guitars were produced.

1990 COLLECTOR'S (Model 199S-1) — similar to the 1990 Collector's model (1990-7), except offered in limited quantities with a Super shallow bowl and a Sunburst finish. Mfd. 1990 only.

> Mfr.'s Sug. retail was $1,599.
> A total of 100 guitars were produced.

1991 COLLECTOR'S (Model 1991-4) — Deep bowl, single cutaway, round soundhole. Available in Natural finish. Mfd. 1991 only.

> Mfr.'s Sug. retail was $1,159.
> A total of 1,464 guitars were produced.

1991 COLLECTOR'S (Model 1991-5) — Deep bowl, single cutaway, round soundhole. Available in Black Metallic finish. Mfd. 1991 only.

> Mfr.'s Sug. retail was $1,159.
>
> A total of 292 guitars were produced.

1992 COLLECTOR'S (Model 1992-H) — Elite model design, quilted ash top, Super shallow bowl, single cutaway. Available in Honeyburst finish. Mfd. 1992 only.

> Mfr.'s Sug. retail was $1,699.
>
> A total of 1,995 guitars were produced.

1993 COLLECTOR'S (Model 1993-4) — single round cutaway folk style, solid spruce top, multi upper bout soundholes, 5 stripe bound body, multiple woods veneer around soundholes, medium bowl body, mahogany/padauk/ebony 5 piece neck, 22 fret ebony fingerboard with 12th fret banner inlay, strings thru walnut bridge, maple logo inlay on peghead, 3 per side gold Schaller tuners with ebony buttons, piezo bridge pickup, volume/3 band EQ control, active preamp. Available in Natural finish. Mfd. 1993 only.

> Mfr.'s Sug. retail was $1,499.
>
> A total of 1,537 guitars were produced.

1994 COLLECTOR'S (Model 1994-7) — single round cutaway folk style, solid spruce top, round soundhole, bound body, multi wood purfling, ash/ebony/pearl rosette, medium bowl body, mahogany/ebony/purpleheart 5 piece neck, 21 fret ebony extended fingerboard with 12th fret banner inlay, strings thru ebony bridge, ebony veneered peghead with screened logo, 3 per side gold tuners with ebony buttons, piezo bridge pickup, Optima EQ system. Available in Nutmeg finish. Mfd. 1994 only.

> Mfr.'s Sug. retail was $1,695.
>
> A total of 1,763 guitars were produced.

1995 COLLECTOR'S (Model 1995-7) — New mid-depth bowl, single cutaway, round soundhole. Available in Nutmeg finish. Mfd. 1995 only.

> Mfr.'s Sug. retail was $1,899.
>
> A total of 1,502 guitars were produced.

1996 COLLECTOR'S (Model 1996-TPB) — Solid Sitka Spruce top, Mid-depth bowl, single cutaway, five piece Mahogany/maple/ebony neck, bound ebony fingerboard with mother of pearl inlay, Stereo HexFX piezo pickup system, 3+3 headstock, round soundhole. Available in a Transparent Burgundy finish. Mfd. 1996 only.

> Mfr.'s Sug. retail was $2,199.
>
> A total of 1,280 guitars were produced.

Elite Series

Grading	100%	98% MINT	95% EXC+	90% EXC	80% VG+	70% VG	60% G

The Elite Series design is similar to the Adamas models, but substitutes a solid Spruce or solid Cedar top in place of the composite materials. Standard models feature 22 soundholes of varying sizes, while the cutaway models only have 15 soundholes.

ELITE (Model 1718) — folk style, spruce top, 5 stripe bound body, 5 piece mahogany/maple neck, 14/22 fret extended rosewood fingerboard with maple triangle inlay, walnut bridge, 3 per side gold tuners, 6 piezo bridge pickups, volume control, 3 band EQ, active OP-24 preamp. Available in Black, Natural, Natural Cedar, Sunburst and White finishes. Current production.

	100%	98%	95%	90%	80%	70%	60%
Mfr.'s Sug. Retail	$1,395	$1,046	$697	$685	$550	$495	$450	$410

> In 1994, White finish was discontinued.

Elite Cutaway (Model 1768) — similar to Elite, except has cutaway in treble bout.

Mfr.'s Sug. Retail	$1,495	$1,121	$747	$735	$590	$525	$480	$440

> This model has cedar top optionally available.
>
> This model has shallow bowl body optionally available.

Elite 12 (Model 1868) — similar to Elite, except has 12 strings, 6 per side tuners. Disc. 1994.

	$1,100	$945	$785	$630	$565	$515	$470

> Last Mfr.'s Sug. Retail was $1,575.

Elite Cutaway 12 (Model 1858) — similar to Elite, except has 12 strings, single round cutaway, 6 per side tuners. Mfg. 1994 to current.

Mfr.'s Sug. Retail	$1,695	$1,271	$847	$845	$675	$605	$555	$505

ELITE STANDARD (Model 6718) — folk style, spruce top, 5 stripe bound body, mahogany neck, 14/22 fret extended rosewood fingerboard, strings thru rosewood bridge with pearl dot inlay, rosewood veneered peghead with ebony/maple logo inlay, 3 per side chrome tuners, piezo bridge pickups, volume control, 3 band EQ, active preamp. Available in Cherry Sunburst, Root Beer and Vintage finishes. Mfd. 1993 to date.

Mfr.'s Sug. Retail	$1,095	$821	$547	$545	$435	$395	$360	$330

Elite Standard Cutaway (Model 6768) — similar to Elite Standard, except has single round cutaway.

Mfr.'s Sug. Retail	$1,195	$956	$717	$600	$480	$430	$395	$360

Grading	100%	98% MINT	95% EXC+	90% EXC	80% VG+	70% VG	60% G

Elite Standard Cutaway Shallow (Model 6868) — similar to Elite Standard Cutaway, except has a Super shallow bowl back.

Mfr.'s Sug. Retail	$1,195	$956	$717	$600	$480	$430	$395	$360

Folklore Series

The Folklore series was introduced in 1979. Current listings feature the new updated versions that have been re-introduced to the Ovation line.

FOLKLORE (Model 6774) — single cutaway solid Sitka spruce top, round soundhole, mid-depth bowl back, inlaid rosette, 5 piece mahogany/maple neck, 21 fret ebony fingerboard, walnut bridge, 3 per side slotted headstock, OP-X preamp. Available in a Natural finish. Current production.

Mfr.'s Sug. Retail	$1,549	$1,161	$774

Country Artist (Model 6773) — similar to Folklore model, except is designed for nylon string use. Available in Natural finish.

Mfr.'s Sug. Retail	$1,549	$1,161	$774

LEGEND SERIES

The Legend series shares similar design patterns with the Custom Legend models, except a less ornate rosette and a standard Ovation bridge instead of the custom carved Walnut version. Outside of the all acoustic Model 1117, Legend series models feature the active OP-24 preamp electronics.

LEGEND (Model 1117) — folk style, spruce top, round soundhole, 5 stripe bound body, leaf pattern rosette, 5 piece mahogany/maple neck, 14/20 fret bound rosewood fingerboard with pearl diamond/dot inlay, walnut bridge, walnut veneer on peghead, 3 per side gold tuners. Available in Black, Natural, Sunburst and White finishes. Current production.

Mfr.'s Sug. Retail	$995	$796	$597	$520	$415	$375	$340	$310

In 1994, Cherry Cherryburst and Tobacco sunburst finishes were introduced, bound ebony fingerboard replaced original item, Sunburst and White finishes were discontinued.

Legend Electric (Model 1717) — similar to Legend, except has piezo bridge pickups, volume control, 3 band EQ, active preamp. Mfg. 1994 to current.

Mfr.'s Sug. Retail	$1,195	$956	$717	$600	$480	$430	$395	$360

Legend Cutaway Electric (Model 1767) — similar to Legend, except has single round cutaway, volume control, 3 band EQ, active preamp. Current production.

Mfr.'s Sug. Retail	$1,295	$1,036	$777	$680	$545	$490	$445	$405

Legend Cutaway Electric Shallow (Model 1867) — similar to Legend Cutaway Electric, except has a Super shallow bowl back. Current production.

Mfr.'s Sug. Retail	$1,295	$1,036	$777	$680	$545	$490	$445	$405

Legend 12 Electric — similar to Legend, except has 12 strings, 6 per side tuners, volume/3 band EQ controls, active preamp. Disc. 1994.

	$1,020	$875	$730	$585	$525	$480	$440

Last Mfr.'s Sug. retail was $1,450.

Legend 12 Cutaway Electric (Model 1866) — similar to Legend, except has 12 strings, single round cutaway, 6 per side tuners, volume control, 3 band EQ, active preamp. Available in Black, Cherry Cherryburst and Natural finishes. Current production.

Mfr.'s Sug. Retail	$1,395	$1,116	$837	$745	$630	$565	$515	$470

Custom Legend Series

Custom Legend models have an AAA grade Solid Sitka Spruce top, spruce struts, custom bracing, and the active OP-24 piezo electronics package.

CUSTOM LEGEND (Model 1719) — folk style, spruce top, round soundhole, abalone bound body, abalone leaf pattern rosette, 5 piece mahogany/maple neck, 14/20 fret bound ebony fingerboard with abalone diamond/dot inlay, strings thru walnut bridge with carved flower design/pearl dot inlay, walnut veneered peghead with abalone logo inlay, 3 per side gold tuners with pearloid buttons, piezo bridge pickups, volume control, 3 band EQ, active preamp. Available in Black, Natural, Sunburst and White finishes. Current production.

Mfr.'s Sug. Retail	$1,595	$1,276	$957	$800	$640	$575	$530	$480

In 1994, Cherry Cherryburst finish was introduced, White finish was discontinued.

Custom Legend Cutaway (Model 1869) — similar to Custom Legend, except has single round cutaway.

Mfr.'s Sug. Retail	$1,700	$1,360	$1,020	$850	$680	$610	$560	$510

This model is also available with shallow bowl body.

Custom Legend 12 (Model 1759) — similar to Custom Legend, except has 12 strings, 6 per side tuners.

Mfr.'s Sug. Retail	$1,795	$1,436	$1,077	$900	$720	$650	$595	$540

"The guitars today are absolutely the best since I've been involved with [Gibson]. They're the best I've seen. The guys building them now are as much vintage freaks as you and I."

—Lawrence Acunto on Elliot Easton
TCG, May/June 1993

O

Grading	100%	98% MINT	95% EXC+	90% EXC	80% VG+	70% VG	60% G

LONGNECK (Model DS 768) — similar to the Elite model six string, except has a scale length of 28.35" and is tuned one full step lower than a standard guitar. Five piece maple and mahogany neck, gold-plated hardware, and OP-X preamp. Available in Natural and Cherry Cherryburst. New 1995.

Mfr.'s Sug. Retail	$1,699	$1,274	$849

Pinnacle Series

PINNACLE — folk style, spruce top, 5 stripe bound body, leaf pattern rosette, mahogany neck, 14/20 fret rosewood fingerboard with white dot inlay, rosewood bridge with white dot inlay, rosewood veneer on peghead, 3 per side chrome tuners, 6 piezo bridge pickups, volume control, 3 band EQ, FET preamp. Available in Barnboard, Black, Ebony Stain, Natural, Opaque Blue, Sunburst, Transparent Blue Stain and White finishes. Mfd. 1991 to 1992.

$630	$540	$450	$360	$325	$300	$275

Last Mfr.'s Sug. Retail was $900.

Pinnacle Shallow Cutaway — similar to Pinnacle, except has single round cutaway, shallow bowl body. Mfd. 1991 to 1994.

$700	$600	$500	$400	$360	$330	$300

Last Mfr.'s Sug. Retail was $1,000.

Ultra Deluxe Series

The Ultra Deluxe models feature a solid spruce top, two piece mahogany neck, on-board OP-24Plus electronics, and a 20 fret bound rosewood fingerboard.

ULTRA DELUXE (Model 1312-D) — folk style, spruce top, round soundhole, 5 stripe bound body, leaf pattern rosette, 14/20 fret bound rosewood fingerboard with abalone diamond/dot inlay, walnut bridge with white dot inlay, rosewood veneer on peghead, 3 per side gold tuners. Available in Barnboard, Black, Brownburst, Natural and Sunburst finishes. Current production.

Mfr.'s Sug. Retail	$500	$375	$250	$240	$190	$170	$155	$145

This model has flame maple top with Brownburst finish optionally available.

In 1994, Barnboard, Black and Sunburst finishes were discontinued.

Ultra Deluxe Electric (Model 1517-D) — similar to Ultra Deluxe, except has piezo bridge pickups, 4 band EQ, FET preamp. Available in Black and Natural finishes. New 1994.

Mfr.'s Sug. Retail	$600	$480	$360	$300	$240	$215	$195	$180

This model has flame maple top with Brownburst finish optionally available.

Ultra Deluxe 12 (Model 1515-D) — similar to Ultra Deluxe, except has 12 strings, 6 per side tuners. Disc. 1994.

$370	$320	$265	$210	$190	$175	$160

Last Mfr.'s Sug. Retail was $530.

Ultra Deluxe 12 Electric — similar to Ultra Deluxe, except has 12 strings, 6 per side tuners, piezo bridge pickups, 4 band EQ, preamp. Available in Black and Natural finishes. New 1994.

Mfr.'s Sug. Retail	$700	$560	$420	$350	$280	$250	$230	$210

Ultra Deluxe Cutaway (Model 1528-D) — similar to Ultra Deluxe, except has single round cutaway, piezo bridge pickups, volume/tone control, FET preamp. Available in Barnboard, Brownburst and Sunburst finishes. Disc. 1994.

$510	$440	$365	$290	$260	$240	$220

Last Mfr.'s Sug. Retail was $730.

Ultra Deluxe Shallow Cutaway — similar to Ultra Deluxe, except has single round cutaway, shallow bowl body, piezo bridge pickups, volume/tone control, FET preamp. Available in Barnboard, Black, Brownburst, Natural, Redburst, Sunburst and White finishes. Disc. 1994.

Mfr.'s Sug. Retail	$700	$560	$420	$390	$315	$280	$260	$235

This model has flame maple top with Brownburst finish optionally available.

In 1994, Orangeburst finish was introduced, Barnboard, Redburst, Sunburst and White finishes were discontinued.

ACOUSTIC BASS

CELEBRITY (Model CC-74) — single round cutaway folk style, spruce top, round soundhole, 5 stripe bound body, leaf pattern rosette, mahogany neck, 20 fret bound rosewood fingerboard with pearloid diamond/dot inlay, walnut bridge with pearloid dot inlay, walnut veneer on peghead, 2 per side chrome tuners, piezo bridge pickups, volume/tone control, FET preamp. Available in Ebony Stain, Natural and Sunburst finishes. Mfd. 1993 to date.

Mfr.'s Sug. Retail	$600	$480	$360	$300	$240	$215	$195	$180

In 1994, Black finish was introduced, Ebony Stain and Sunburst finish were discontinued.

CELEBRITY DELUXE (Model CC-274) — single round cutaway folk style, cedar top, multi-sized soundholes with leaf pattern maple veneers, 5 stripe bound body, mahogany neck, 23 fret rosewood extended fingerboard with pearl dot inlay, rosewood strings thru bridge, rosewood veneered peghead with logo decal, 2 per side gold tuner, piezo bridge pickups, 4 band EQ. Available in Antique Sunburst, Black, Natural and Sunburst finishes. New 1994.

Mfr.'s Sug. Retail	$800	$640	$480	$400	$320	$290	$265	$240

This model has spruce and sycamore tops optionally available.

Celebrity Deluxe 5 (Model CC-275) — similar to Celebrity Deluxe, except has 5 strings, 19 fret fingerboard, 3/2 per side chrome tuners. Available in Black finish. New 1994.

Mfr.'s Sug. Retail	$850	$680	$510	$425	$340	$305	$280	$255

Grading	100%	98% MINT	95% EXC+	90% EXC	80% VG+	70% VG	60% G

ELITE (Model B-768) — single round cutaway folk style, spruce top, 5 stripe bound body, multiple soundholes around the top bouts with leaf pattern veneer, 5 piece mahogany/maple neck, 22 fret extended rosewood fingerboard with maple triangle inlay, walnut bridge, 2 per side gold tuners, piezo bridge pickup, volume/3 band EQ control, active preamp. Available in Black, Natural and Sunburst finishes. Mfd. 1992 to date.

Mfr.'s Sug. Retail $1,999 $1,599 $1,199 $1,050

> In 1994, bound fingerboard was introduced, Sunburst finish was discontinued.

ELITE 5 (Model B-5768) — similar to the Elite bass, except has five strings and a 2+3 headstock design. Available in Black and Natural finishes. Mfd. 1995 to current.

Mfr.'s Sug. Retail $2,099 $1,574 $1,049

ACOUSTIC/ELECTRIC

Viper Series

The Viper name is back! Originally a solid body guitar from the mid 1970s to the early 1980s, the Viper name has now been affixed to a new, 1990s acoustic/electric slim body design. The Viper model has a solid Spruce top, and a mahogany body with acoustic chambers. An on-board active electronics package (volume and three band EQ) allows control over feedback.

VIPER (Model EA 68) — single cutaway mahogany body with routed sound chamber, bound spruce top, 14 multi-size soundholes with various leaf wood overlay, 5 piece mahogany/maple neck, 24 fret bound ebony fingerboard, strings thru rosewood bridge, rosewood veneered peghead with screened logo, 3 per side gold tuners, 6 piezo bridge pickups, volume/3 band EQ controls. Available in Black and Natural finishes. New 1994.

Mfr.'s Sug. Retail $1,899 $1,424 $949

VIPER 12 (Model EA 58) — similar to the Viper, except in 12 string variation. Available in Black and Natural finishes.

Mfr.'s Sug. Retail $1,999 $1,499 $999

VIPER NYLON (Model EA 63) — similar to the Viper, except in 6 string nylon variation. Available in Black finish only.

Mfr.'s Sug. Retail $1,899 $1,424 $949

ACOUSTIC/ELECTRIC BASS

Arguably, all of the Ovation acoustic basses are "Acoustic/Electric" by the nature of the on-board piezo pickups and electronics packages. However, their design nature is acoustic, and the company has reinforced the sound with a pickup system. On the other hand, just as the new Viper model is a hybrid of technologies, so then is Viper bass that follows.

VIPER BASS (Model EAB 68) — single cutaway mahogany body with routed sound chamber, bound spruce top, 14 multi-size soundholes with various leaf wood overlay, 5 piece mahogany/maple neck, 24 fret bound ebony fingerboard, strings thru rosewood bridge, rosewood veneered peghead with screened logo, 2 per side gold tuners, 4 piezo bridge pickups, volume/3 band EQ controls. Available in Black, Cherry Cherryburst, and Natural finishes. New 1994.

Mfr.'s Sug. Retail $2,199 $1,649 $1,099

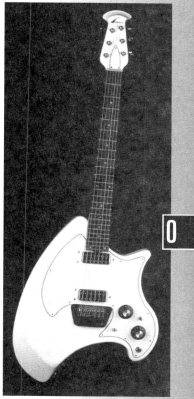

ELECTRIC

Although Ovation's solid body guitars are generally overshadowed by the fine acoustic models, they still are good playable instruments that offer a change of pace from the traditional market favorites. Ovation introduced the **Electric Storm** semi-hollowbody guitars in 1968, and they were available through 1973. The Electric Storm models featured bodies built in Germany, and hardware by Schaller. American-built solidbodies were presented beginning 1972, and various models survived through to 1983. Early models featured an on-board FET preamp, and are probably the first production guitars with 'active electronics'.

In 1984, Ovation produced the **Hard Body** series, which featured Korean-built necks and bodies, DiMarzio pickups and Schaller hardware. The Hard Body series was only briefly offered for a year, and can be identified by the natural wood strip bearing the Ovation name on the lower section of the four- or six-on-a-side headstocks. The 3+3 headstock looks similar to other Ovation headstocks. Model names range from GP (Guitar Paul) to GS (Guitar Strat) which are pretty self explanatory in regards to the model they resembled. Both solid body guitars and basses were offered. In 1988, Kaman bought the independent Hamer company, a move which brought the company back into the solid body guitar field in a competitive way.

> The solid body Ovation market currently is in a flux, as models in the 80 to 90% condition range in price from $250 to $700.

BREADWINNER (Model 1251) — mahogany back and neck, dot inlay position markers, two large single coil pickups, Master volume knob, master tone knob, midrange filter switch, three way pickup selector switch. Available in a textured Black, White, Tan, or Blue finish. Mfg. 1972 to 1979.

> Original list price was $349.
>
> In 1975, single coil pickups were replaced by humbuckers.
>
> In 1976, blue finish was deleted.

Ovation Breadwinner
courtesy William Kaman II

DEACON (Model 1252) — single cutaway "kidney shaped" body, diamond shaped position markers, Master volume knob, master tone knob, midrange filter switch, three way pickup selector switch. Available in sunburst finish. Mfg. 1973 to 1980.

> Original list price was $449.
>
> In 1975, single coil pickups were replaced by humbuckers.
>
> In 1976, colors were expanded to Red, Black, and Natural finishes.

DEACON DELUXE — similar to the Deacon, except featured different hardware and pickups. Mfg. 1972 to 1980.

DEACON TWELVE STRING (Model 1253) — similar to the Deacon, except in 12-string configuration. Mfg. 1976 to 1980.

ECLIPSE (Model K-1235) — economy model of the ELectric Storm series. Available in Black finish only. Mfg. 1970 to 1973.

HURRICANE (Model K-1120) — similar to the Thunderhead model, except in a twelve string variation. Mfg. late 1968 to 1969.

PREACHER (Model 1281) — double cutaway mahogany body, 24 1/2" scale, two humbucking pickups. Mfg. 1975 to 1978.

PREACHER DELUXE (Model 1282) — similar to the Preacher, except features a series/parallel pickup switch and a midrange control. Mfg. late 1975 to 1978.

PREACHER DELUXE TWELVE STRING (Model 1283) — similar to the Preacher Deluxe, except in a twelve string configuration. Mfg. late 1975 to 1978.

THUNDERHEAD (Model K-1360) — double cutaway semi-hollow body, gold-plated hardware, two DeArmond humbucking pickups, master volume knob, two separate tone control knobs, phase switch on bass bout, pickup balance/blend switch on treble bout. Available in Natural, Nutmeg, or Walnut Green finishes. Mfg. 1968 to 1972.

> Thunderhead (Model K-1460) with vibrato was introduced in 1968.
>
> In 1970, the Thunderhead changed designation to K-1213; the Thunderhead with vibrato was designated K-1212.
>
> In 1971, Electric Storm models were offered in Red, Nutmeg, and Black.
>
> In spring of 1971, the Thunderhead changed designation to K-1233; the Thunderhead with vibrato was designated K-1234.

TORNADO (Model K-1160) — similar to the Thunderhead model, except features separate volume knobs for each pickup, chrome hardware, and no phase switch. Available in Red or Sunburst. Mfg. late 1968 to 1973.

> Tornado (Model K-1260) with vibrato was introduced in 1968.
>
> In 1970, the Tornado changed designation to K-1211; the Tornado with vibrato was designated K-1212.
>
> In spring of 1971, the Tornado changed designation to K-1231; the Tornado with vibrato was designated K-1232.

UK II (Model 1291) — double cutaway Urelite (Urethane) material on an aluminum frame, set-neck design, two humbucking pickups, two volume knobs, two tone knobs, series/parallel pickup switching, three way pickup selector switch on upper bass bout. Mfg. 1980 to 1983.

> The UK II designation was short for Ultra Kaman II.

VIPER (Model 1271) — single cutaway ash body, bolt-on one piece maple neck, maple or ebony fingerboard, two single coil pickups, 25" scale, Master Volume knob, Master tone knob, three way pickup selector switch. Mfg. 1975 to 1983.

> While most bodies were built of ash, some were built using maple or Mahogany.

VIPER III (Model 1273) — similar to the Viper, except has three single coil pickups with different individual windings, and three on/off pickup selector switches. Mfg. 1975 to 1983.

ELECTRIC BASS

MAGNUM I (Model 1261) — double offset cutaway mahogany body, graphite reinforced neck, humbucking pickup (neck position) and double coil pickup (bridge position), stereo output, string mute. Mfg. 1974 to 1978.

MAGNUM II (Model 1262) — similar to the Magnum I, except featured a three band active EQ. Mfg. 1974 to 1978.

MAGNUM III (Model 1263) — similar to the Magnum I, except features less radical body styling (deeper bass bout cutaway), two split-coil humbuckers. Mfg. 1978 to 1983.

MAGNUM IV (Model 1264) — similar to the Magnum II, except features less radical body styling (deeper bass bout cutaway), two split-coil humbuckers. Mfg. 1978 to 1983.

TYPHOON I (Model K-1140) — similar to the Thunderhead guitar model, except in four string bass version. Mfg. late 1968 to 1972.

TYPHOON II (Model K-1240) — similar to the Typhoon I model, except initial models have a smaller body and shorter cutaway horns. Mfg. late 1968 to 1969.

> Originally catalogued as the "Williwaw", which means 'Mountain Wind' (in keeping with the Electric Storm motif).
>
> In mid 1969, the body design was changed to resemble other Electric Storm models.
>
> In 1970, the Typhoon II changed designation to K-1222.

TYPHOON III (Model K-1340) — similar to the Typhoon I, except fretless. Mfg. 1969 to 1970.

TYPHOON IV (Model K-1216) — similar to the Typhoon III. Mfg. 1970 to 1972.

TYPHOON V (Model K-1217) — Mfg. 1971 to 1972.

OVERWATER BASS

Instruments built in the United Kingdom from the late 1970s to current.

Luthier Chris May has been building high quality guitars and basses since 1978. May has built a number of custom basses with innovative design, such as the C Bass (1985) which features a lower-than-standard tuning of C-F-Bb-Eb. This 36" scale bass was tuned 2 full steps below conventional 4 string tuning.

In 1995, The Overwater Guitar Company moved to their new headquarters in Carlisle, Cumbria (the last town on A69 before Scotland). The new Overwater Jam Factory, Ltd. features two rehearsal studios, a 24 track recording facility, and a retail outlet for musical equipment sales in addition to May's workshops. May also helped develop the Delta line of bass amplification for Carlsboro.

ELECTRIC

May offers the **Advance** custom guitar and the **'S'** and **'T' Traditional** series models in one of three configurations: The **Standard** has a one-piece neck-through design, and solid wings. The **Deluxe** features a one- or two-piece neck-through design, and an overlaid flat top. The **Pro** configuration is a one- or two-piece neck-through with a carved top. Bolt-on necks are also offered.

Advance necks can be walnut, mahogany, or maple, and the bodies constructed of solid mahogany or walnut (with the option of a flat or carved maple top). Traditional series guitars are generally built with maple necks and either sycamore, light ash, or alder bodies. Fingerboards can be rosewood, ebony, or maple. Customers can specify pickup and electronics, and choice of finish.

ELECTRIC BASS

Chris May is featuring three bass models: the original styles of the **Progress** and **Fusion**, as well as the traditional styled **'J'** model. Basses are offered in 4-, 5-, 6-, 7-, 8-string configurations (only 4- and 5-string on the 'J' series). Again, there are three different variants in the bass model offering: the **Classic** has a two- or three-piece neck-through design and solid wings. The **Deluxe** features a three-piece neck-through design with laminated wings, and the **Pro** has similar construction with multi-laminated wings. While the 'J' series features a bolt-on neck, the body can still be upgraded to a Deluxe or a Pro.

Bass necks can be laminated of maple/walnut or maple/sycamore, and the bodies constructed of sycamore, maple or walnut. The traditional 'J' basses are generally built with maple necks and either sycamore, light ash, walnut, or alder bodies. Fingerboards can be rosewood, ebony, or maple. Customers can specify pickup and electronics, and choice of finish.

"My brother Dave got me a 3/4 size electric guitar. It had no name on it. It was custom made by someone and based upon a Les Paul. I got some flat-sound strings and got into Dick Dale big time."

—*Greg Martin on Phil Keaggy*

TCG, May/June 1993

O

PACK LEADER

Instruments built in England during the late 1970s.

This high quality solid body guitar was built by luthier Roger Bucknall (Fylde Guitars), and its original design was available in either a Rosewood or Walnut version.

> For further information on Roger Bucknall, see FYLDE.

(Source: Tony Bacon and Paul Day, The Guru's Guitar Guide)

PALMER

Instruments produced in Korea from the late 1980s to date.

Palmer instruments are entry level solid body guitars that feature designs based on popular market leaders. Models encountered are the Biscayne, Growler, Baby, and Six.

(Source: Tony Bacon and Paul Day, The Guru's Guitar Guide)

PANGBORN

Instruments built in England from the late 1970s to the late 1980s.

Luthier Ashley Pangborn has specialized in high quality custom order solid body guitars, as well as standard models such as the Warrior and the Warlord.

(Source: Tony Bacon and Paul Day, The Guru's Guitar Guide)

PANORMO

Instruments built in London, England during the early nineteenth century.

During the early 1800s, luthier Louis Panormo ran a productive workshop in London. Panormo, the son of an Italian violin-maker, was one of the few outside of Spain that braced the tops of his acoustics with 'fan-strutting', and advertised himself as the "only maker of guitars in the Spanish style".

(Source: Tony Bacon, The Ultimate Guitar Book)

PARAMOUNT

See LANGE.

Instruments produced in America during the 1930s and 1940s.

In 1934, the William L. Lange Company (New York) debuted the Paramount guitar series - and some of the models were built by the C.F. Martin guitar company. However, Lange's company went out of business in the early 1940s. In the late 1940s, the Paramount guitar line was re-introduced and distributed by Gretsch & Brenner. Future model designations/indentifications will appear in updated editons of the **Blue Book of Guitars**.

(Source: Tom Wheeler, American Guitars)

PARKER GUITARS

Instruments currently produced in New York. Distributed by Korg USA of Westbury, New York.

Designer Ken Parker began building unconventional archtop guitars in the 1970s. He then took a job with (now defunct) Stuyvesant Music in New York City, working both in the repair shop as well as building **Guitar Man** instruments. Parker's backround in repairing and customizing guitars became the groundwork for the innovative design of the **Fly** guitar.

ELECTRIC

Fly Series

All instruments in this series have the following specs: offset double cutaway carved poplar one piece body/neck, 24 fret carbon/fiber epoxy fingerboard, blackface peghead with screened logo, 6 on one side locking Sperzel tuners, and black hardware.

The fingerboard and peghead veneer on these instruments are made from the same synthetic composite material. Parker guitars are carved from solid wood, and then have a thin layer of carbon/glass/epoxy composite material applied as a strengthening measure. Instruments are then finished in a gloss urethane paint.

"All rosewood models under discussion were made of Brazilian rosewood which imparts a dark, full sound with greater bass response than the mahogany, adding distinct higher partials to the notes as well."

—Stan Jay & Larry Wexer

TCG, Nov/Dec 1990

Grading	100%	98% MINT	95% EXC+	90% EXC	80% VG+	70% VG	60% G

F — fixed Parker bridge, 2 exposed humbucker pickups, master volume/volume/tone controls, 3 position switch. Mfg. 1994 only.

	$1,140	$975	$815	$650	$580	$535	$485

Last Mfr.'s Sug. Retail was $1,625.

FV — standard Parker vibrato, vibrato tension wheel, 2 exposed humbucker pickups, master volume/volume/tone controls, 3 position switch. Mfg. 1994 only.

	$1,335	$1,145	$955	$765	$690	$630	$575

Last Mfr.'s Sug. Retail was $1,910.

FD — fixed Parker bridge, 2 exposed humbucker/6 piezo bridge pickups, master volume/humbucker volume/tone controls, stacked volume/tone piezo control, two 3-position switches. Mfg. 1994 only.

	$1,375	$1,180	$985	$785	$710	$650	$590

Last Mfr.'s Sug. Retail was $1,960.

FLY DELUXE (FDV) — standard Parker vibrato, vibrato tension wheel, 2 exposed humbucker/6 piezo bridge pickups, master volume/humbucker volume/tone controls, stacked volume/tone piezo control, two 3-position switches. Available in Black, Majik Blue, Galaxie Gray, Euro Red, White, Ruby Red, Italian Plum, Emerald green, Antique Gold, and Dusty Black. Mfg. 1994 to current.

Mfr.'s Sug. Retail	$2,340	$1,872	$1,404	$1,225

Fly Classic (FCV) — similar to the Fly Deluxe, except features a solid mahogany body, and finished top. Available in Transparent Cherry and Rootbeer Metallic finishes. New 1996.

Mfr.'s Sug. Retail	$2,540	$2,032	$1,524	$1,325

Fly Supreme (FSV) — similar to the Fly Deluxe, except features a solid maple body, and finished top. Available in Transparent Honey finish. New 1996.

Mfr.'s Sug. Retail	$2,540	$2,032	$1,524	$1,325

NIGHTFLY (NFV1) — solid maple body, 22 fret neck composed of modulus carbon and glass fiber, bolt-on design, six on a side locking Sperzel tuners, pickguard, free-floating vibrato, 3 single coil Dimarzio pickups plus a Fishman passive piezo-transducer bridge pickup. Controls include Volume and Tone knobs plus a five way selector switch for the magnetic system, a Volume knob for the piezo system, and an overall selector switch for magnetic/piezo/both systems. Available in Black Pearl, White Pearl, Sunburst, Transparent Red and Transparent Blue New 1996.

Mfr.'s Sug. Retail	$1,199	$899	$599

Nightfly (NFV2) — similar to the NiteFly, except features 2 single coil DiMarzio pickups (neck/mid) and 1 DiMarzio humbucker (bridge). New 1996.

Mfr.'s Sug. Retail	$1,249	$936	$624

PATRICK EGGLE GUITARS

Instruments currently manufactured in Coventry, England. Distributed in the U.S. market by Quality First Products, Inc. of Forest City, North Carolina.

In 1993-1994, two models (New York-USA and Los Angeles-USA) were assembled with Patrick Eggle components in Santa Barbara, California. Full production is again maintained in England.

Patrick Eggle Guitars were introduced in 1991. This British company produces several high quality solid body guitar models, and their **Berlin** was voted the Making Music "British Guitar of the Year" award.

ELECTRIC

All models listed below are available in left handed versions free of charge. There is a $25 charge for Maple Leaf inlays.

BERLIN SERIES

DELUXE — offset double cutaway maple body, carved figured maple top, mahogany neck, 24 fret ebony fingerboard with abalone dot inlay, abalone maple leaf inlay on 12th fret, locking Wilkinson vibrato, 3 per side locking Sperzel tuners, gold hardware, 2 humbucker Eggle pickups, volume/coil tap control, 3 position switch. Available in Antique Gold, Bahamian Blue, Burny Amber, Burgundy Burst, Chardonnay Rouge, Chardonnay Rouge Burst, Cherry, Cherry Burst, Citrus Green, Citrus Green Burst, Deep Sea Blue, Emerald Isle Blue, Pink Glow, Pink Glow Burst, Purple Haze, Shamu Blue, Shamu Blue Burst, Tobacco Burst, Vintage Gold Burst, and Walnut finishes. Disc. 1994.

	$980	$840	$700	$560	$505	$460	$420

Last Mfr.'s Sug. Retail was $1,400.

PLUS — offset double cutaway mahogany body, carved figured maple top, mahogany neck, 24 fret ebony fingerboard with abalone dot inlay, tunomatic bridge/stop tailpiece, body matching peghead, 3 per side locking Sperzel tuners, chrome hardware, 2 humbucker Eggle pickups, volume/tone control, 3 position switch, coil tap in tone control. Available in Antique Gold, Bahamian Blue, Chardonnay Rouge, Cherry, Pink Glow, and Walnut finishes. Disc. 1994.

	$560	$480	$400	$320	$290	$265	$240

Add 10% for gold hardware.

Last Mfr.'s Sug. Retail was $800.

Grading	100%	98% MINT	95% EXC+	90% EXC	80% VG+	70% VG	60% G

PRO — offset double cutaway mahogany body, carved figured maple top, mahogany neck, 22 fret ebony fingerboard with abalone dot inlay, tunomatic bridge/stop tailpiece, body matching tailpiece, 3 position locking Sperzel tuners, chrome hardware, 2 humbucker Eggle pickups, volume/tone control, 3 position switch. Available in Antique Gold, Bahamian Blue, Burgundy Burst, Chardonnay Rouge, Chardonnay Rouge Burst, Cherry, Cherry Burst, Deep Sea Blue, Emerald Isle Blue, Pink Glow, Pink Glow Burst, Purple Haze, Tobacco Burst, Vintage Gold Burst, and Walnut finishes. Current production.

| Mfr.'s Sug. Retail | $2,400 | $2,112 | $1,848 | $1,775 | $1,600 | $1,400 | $1,150 | $975 |

The Berlin Pro is also offered with a 24 fret fingerboard, gold hardware, or Wilkinson VS 100 tremolo.

STAGE — offset double cutaway mahogany body, carved figured maple top, mahogany neck, 24 fret ebony fingerboard with abalone dot inlay, tunomatic bridge/stop tailpiece, body matching tailpiece, 3 per side locking Sperzel tuners, chrome hardware, 2 humbucker Eggle pickups, volume/tone control, 3 position switch. Available in Antique Gold, Bahamian Blue, Burgundy Burst, Chardonnay Rouge, Chardonnay Rouge Burst, Cherry, Cherry Burst, Deep Sea Blue, Emerald Isle Blue, Pink Glow, Pink Glow Burst, Purple Haze, Tobacco Burst, Vintage Gold Burst, and Walnut finishes. Current production.

| Mfr.'s Sug. Retail | $1,400 | $1,232 | $1,078 | $1,050 | $970 | $890 | $750 | $600 |

STANDARD — offset double cutaway mahogany body, carved figured maple top, mahogany neck, 24 fret ebony fingerboard with abalone dot inlay, tunomatic bridge/stop tailpiece, body matching tailpiece, 3 per side locking Sperzel tuners, chrome hardware, 2 humbucker Eggle pickups, volume/tone control, 3 position switch. Available in Black, Natural and White finishes. Disc. 1994.

| | $420 | $360 | $300 | $240 | $215 | $195 | $180 |

Add 10% for gold hardware.

Last Mfr.'s Sug. Retail was $600.

UK DLX-4HT — offset double cutaway mahogany body, highest quality (AAAA) carved figured maple top, mahogany neck, 22 fret ebony fingerboard with abalone maple leaf inlay, tunomatic bridge/stop tailpiece, 3 per side Sperzel tuners, chrome hardware, 2 humbucker Eggle pickups, volume/tone control, 3 position switch. Available in Natural finish. Disc. 1994.

| | $1,995 | $1,710 | $1,425 | $1,140 | $1,025 | $940 | $855 |

Last Mfr.'s Sug. Retail was $2,850.

UK DLS-4A — similar to UK DLX-4HT, except has Wilkinson vibrato, locking Sperzel tuners. Disc. 1994.

| | $2,170 | $1,860 | $1,550 | $1,240 | $1,115 | $1,025 | $930 |

Last Mfr.'s Sug. Retail was $3,100.

UK PLUS ULTRA — offset double cutaway mahogany body, carved figured maple top, mahogany neck, 22 fret ebony fingerboard with abalone dot inlay, tunomatic bridge/stop tailpiece, 3 per side Sperzel tuners, chrome hardware, 2 humbucker Eggle pickups, volume/tone control, 3 position switch. Available in Antique Gold, Cherry, Cherry Burst and Tobacco Burst finishes. Disc. 1994.

| | $1,330 | $1,140 | $950 | $760 | $685 | $625 | $570 |

Last Mfr.'s Sug. Retail was $1,900.

UK Plus-1A — offset double cutaway mahogany body, carved figured maple top, mahogany neck, 22 fret ebony fingerboard with abalone dot inlay, tunomatic bridge/stop tailpiece, 3 per side Sperzel tuners, chrome hardware, 2 humbucker Eggle pickups, volume/tone control, 3 position switch. Available in Natural finish. Disc. 1994.

| | $910 | $780 | $650 | $520 | $470 | $430 | $390 |

Last Mfr.'s Sug. Retail was $1,300.

UK Plus-2A — similar to Plus-1A, except has higher quality (AA) carved maple top. Disc. 1994.

| | $1,050 | $900 | $750 | $600 | $540 | $495 | $450 |

Last Mfr.'s Sug. Retail was $1,500.

UK Plus-3A — similar to Plus-1A, except has higher quality (AAA) carved maple top, abalone maple leaf fingerboard inlay. Disc. 1994.

| | $1,360 | $1,165 | $970 | $775 | $695 | $635 | $580 |

Last Mfr.'s Sug. Retail was $1,940.

UK PRO ULTRA — offset double cutaway mahogany body, carved figured AAA maple top, mahogany neck, 24 fret ebony fingerboard with abalone dot inlay, locking Wilkinson vibrato, 3 per side locking Sperzel tuners, chrome hardware, 2 humbucker Eggle pickups, volume/tone control, 3 position switch. Available in Antique Gold, Cherry, Cherry Burst and Tobacco Burst finishes. Disc. 1994.

| | $1,715 | $1,470 | $1,225 | $980 | $875 | $805 | $735 |

Last Mfr.'s Sug. Retail was $2,450.

Grading	100%	98% MINT	95% EXC+	90% EXC	80% VG+	70% VG	60% G

UK Pro-3A — offset double cutaway mahogany body, carved figured AAA maple top, mahogany neck, 24 fret ebony fingerboard with abalone dot inlay, locking Wilkinson vibrato, 3 per side locking Sperzel tuners, chrome hardware, 2 humbucker Eggle pickups, volume/tone control, 3 position switch. Available in Natural finish. Disc. 1994.

	$1,540	$1,320	$1,100	$880	$790	$725	$660

Last Mfr.'s Sug. Retail was $2,200.

LEGEND SERIES

JS — offset double cutaway, maple body, carved figured maple top, figured maple neck, 24 fret ebony fingerboard with pearl maple leaf inlay, locking Wilkinson vibrato, ebony veneer on peghead, 3 per side locking Sperzel tuners, 2 active humbucker Reflex pickups, volume/tone control, 3 position switch, coil tap in volume control, active electronics. Available in Antique Gold, Bahamian Blue, Burny Amber, Burgundy Burst, Chardonnay Rouge, Chardonnay Rouge Burst, Cherry, Cherry Burst, Citrus Green, Citrus Green Burst, Deep Sea Blue, Emerald Isle Blue, Natural, Pink Glow, Pink Glow Burst, Purple Haze, Shamu Blue, Shamu Blue Burst, Tobacco Burst, Vintage Gold Burst, and Walnut finishes. Disc. 1994.

	$1,225	$1,050	$875	$700	$630	$575	$525

Last Mfr.'s Sug. Retail was $1,750.

This instrument was designed for Big Jim Sullivan.
This model had black hardware optionally available.

LOS ANGELES SERIES

PLUS — offset double cutaway maple body, bolt-on maple neck, 24 fret maple fingerboard with black pearl dot inlay, locking Wilkinson vibrato, 3 per side locking Sperzel tuners, chrome hardware, 3 dual rail pickups, volume/tone control, 5 position rotary switch, mini switch, active electronics. Available in Antique Gold, Cherry, Cherry Burst, Citrus Green, Pink Glow, Purple Haze, Shamu Blue and Shamu Blue Burst finishes. Disc. 1994.

	$595	$510	$425	$340	$305	$280	$255

Last Mfr.'s Sug. Retail was $850.

PRO — offset double cutaway maple body, bolt-on maple neck, 24 fret maple fingerboard with black pearl dot inlay, locking Wilkinson vibrato, ebony peghead veneer, 3 per side locking Sperzel tuners, gold hardware, 3 stacked coil Reflex pickups, volume/tone control, 5 position rotary switch, active electronics. Available in Antique Gold, Burgundy Burst, Chardonnay Rouge, Chardonnay Rouge Burst, Cherry, Cherry Burst, Citrus Green, Citrus Green Burst, Pink Glow, Pink Glow Burst, Purple Haze, Shamu Blue, Shamu Blue Burst and Vintage Gold Burst finishes. Disc. 1994.

	$770	$660	$550	$440	$395	$365	$330

Last Mfr.'s Sug. Retail was $1,100.

STANDARD — offset double cutaway maple body, bolt-on maple neck, 24 fret maple fingerboard with black pearl dot inlay, locking Wilkinson vibrato, 3 per side locking Sperzel tuners, chrome hardware, 3 dual rail pickups, volume/tone control, 5 position rotary switch, mini switch, active electronics. Available in Black, Natural, USA Blue, USA Pink, USA Red and USA Yellow finishes. Disc. 1994.

	$455	$390	$325	$260	$235	$215	$195

Last Mfr.'s Sug. Retail was $650.

USA-HT — offset double cutaway alder body, pearloid pickguard, bolt-on maple neck, 22 fret rosewood fingerboard with pearl dot inlay, fixed Wilkinson bridge, 3 per side Sperzel tuners, 2 single coil/1 humbucker Seymour Duncan pickups, volume/tone control, 5 position rotary switch, mini switch, active electronics. Available in Calypso Green, Creme, Iris Red, Mauve and Silver Metallic finishes. Disc. 1994.

	$770	$660	$550	$440	$395	$365	$330

Last Mfr.'s Sug. Retail was $1,100.

Creme finish available with tortoise pickguard only.

USA-T — similar to USA-HT, except has locking Sperzel tuners, Wilkinson vibrato. Disc. 1994.

	$840	$720	$600	$480	$430	$395	$360

Last Mfr.'s Sug. Retail was $1,200.

NEW YORK SERIES

DELUXE — offset double cutaway semi hollow mahogany body, carved bound figured maple top, maple/rosewood neck, 22 fret ebony fingerboard with pearl NY inlay at 12th fret, tunomatic bridge, string thru body tailpiece, 3 per side Sperzel tuners, gold hardware, 2 humbucker pickups, volume/tone control, 3 position switch, coil tap in tone control. Available in Antique Gold, Bahamian Blue, Burny Amber, Burgundy Burst, Chardonnay Rouge, Chardonnay Rouge Burst, Cherry, Cherry Burst, Citrus Green, Citrus Green Burst, Deep Sea Blue, Emerald Isle Blue, Pink Glow, Pink Glow Burst, Purple Haze, Shamu Blue, Shamu Blue Burst, Tobacco Burst, Vintage Gold Burst, and Walnut finishes. Disc. 1994.

	$420	$360	$300	$240	$215	$195	$180

Last Mfr.'s Sug. Retail was $600.

PLUS — offset double cutaway mahogany body, pearloid pickguard, bolt-on maple neck, 22 fret rosewood fingerboard with offset pearl dot inlay, tunomatic bridge, string thru body tailpiece, 3 per side Sperzel tuners, chrome hardware, single coil/humbucker pickups, volume/tone control, mini switch, coil tap in tone control. Available in Antique Gold, Burny Amber, Cherry, Citrus Green and Deep Sea Blue. Disc. 1994.

	$475	$405	$340	$270	$245	$225	$205

Last Mfr.'s Sug. Retail was $675.

Add 10% for gold hardware.

P

Grading	100%	98% MINT	95% EXC+	90% EXC	80% VG+	70% VG	60% G

STANDARD — offset double cutaway mahogany body, pearloid pickguard, bolt-on maple neck, 22 fret rosewood fingerboard with offset pearl dot inlay, tunomatic bridge, string thru body tailpiece, 3 per side Sperzel tuners, chrome hardware, single coil/humbucker pickups, volume/tone control, mini switch, coil tap in tone control. Available in Black, Natural, USA Blue, USA Pink, USA Red and USA Yellow finishes. Disc. 1994.

	$350	$300	$250	$200	$180	$165	$150

Last Mfr.'s Sug. Retail was $500.

UK PLUS — offset double cutaway mahogany body, AA figured maple top, bolt-on maple neck, 22 fret rosewood fingerboard with offset pearl dot inlay, tunomatic Wilkinson bridge, string thru body tailpiece, 3 per side Sperzel tuners, chrome hardware, 2 humbucker Seymour Duncan pickups, volume/tone control, 3 position switch. Available in Cherry Burst, Deep Sea Blue and Vintage Gold finishes. Disc. 1994.

	$1,050	$900	$750	$600	$540	$495	$450

Last Mfr.'s Sug. Retail was $1,500.

USA MODEL R — offset double cutaway mahogany body, bolt-on maple neck, 22 fret rosewood fingerboard with offset pearl dot inlay, tunomatic Wilkinson bridge/stop tailpiece, 3 per side Sperzel tuners, chrome hardware, 2 single coil Seymour Duncan pickups, volume/tone control, 3 position switch. Available in Amber, Natural Oil, Red and Red Oil finishes. Disc. 1994.

	$700	$600	$500	$400	$360	$330	$300

Last Mfr.'s Sug. Retail was $1,000.

Add $100 for strings thru body tailpiece.

USA MODEL T — similar to USA Model R, except has single coil/humbucker Seymour Duncan pickups. Disc. 1994.

	$700	$600	$500	$400	$360	$330	$300

Last Mfr.'s Sug. Retail was $1,000.

Add $100 for strings thru body tailpiece.

PATTERSON

Instruments currently built in Falcon Heights, Minnesota.

Patterson series custom basses are offered in a neck-through design, and 4-, 5-, and 6-string configurations. These high quality basses have a multi-laminated body, two Kent Armstrong soapbar pickups, a Patterson active 4-band EQ, and a 26 fret fingerboard constructed out of ebony, wenge, or maple. Prices range from $2,800 to $3,200. For further information, please contact Patterson Guitars via the Index of Current Manufacturers located in the rear of this book.

PAUL REED SMITH

Instruments produced in Stevensville, Maryland. PRS Guitars was originally located in Annapolis, Maryland since 1985, and as of 1996 completed the move to newer and larger facilities.

Combining the best aspects of vintage design traditions in modern instruments, luthier Paul Reed Smith devised a guitar that became very influential during the late 1980s. With meticulous attention to detail, design, and production combined with the concept of "graded" figured wood tops, PRS guitars became touchstone to today's high end guitar market.

Originally working out of his home in the mid 1970s, Smith began learning the guitar repair trade. He continued to work out of a small repair shop for the better part of eight years. By 1982 he had finished designing and building a guitar that combined his original ideas with traditional ones. His original facility in Annapolis was opened in 1985, and through the years continues to experiment with pickup design, body and neck variations, and even amplification and speaker systems.

ACOUSTIC

This series of instruments was designed and built by Dana Bourgeois and Paul Reed Smith.

CUSTOM CUTAWAY — single flat cutaway dreadnought style, spruce top, round soundhole, abalone bound body and rosette, figured maple back/sides, mahogany neck, 20 fret Brazilian rosewood fingerboard with abalone bird inlay, Brazilian rosewood bridge with ebony pearl dot pins, 3 per side chrome locking PRS tuners, volume/tone control, preamp system. Available in Amber Sunburst, Antique Natural, Black Cherry, Grayblack and Walnut Sunburst finishes. Disc. 1992.

	$1,810	$1,550	$1,295	$1,035	$930	$855	$775

Last Mfr.'s Sug. Retail was $2,590.

MAHOGANY CUTAWAY — single flat cutaway dreadnought style, spruce top, round soundhole, wood bound body and rosette, mahogany back/sides/neck, 20 fret rosewood fingerboard, rosewood bridge with ebony pearl dot pins, rosewood veneer on peghead, 3 per side chrome locking PRS tuners, volume/tone control, preamp system. Available in Antique Natural, Black and Natural finishes. Disc. 1992.

	$1,380	$1,180	$985	$790	$710	$650	$590

Last Mfr.'s Sug. Retail was $1,970.

ROSEWOOD SIGNATURE — dreadnought style, spruce top, round soundhole, abalone bound body and rosette, rosewood back/sides, mahogany neck, 20 fret Brazilian rosewood fingerboard with abalone bird inlay, Brazilian rosewood bridge with ebony pearl dot pins, 3 per side gold locking PRS tuners, gold endpin, volume/tone control, preamp system. Available in Antique Natural and Rosewood Sunburst finishes. Disc. 1992.

	$2,225	$1,915	$1,595	$1,275	$1,145	$1,050	$950

Last Mfr.'s Sug. Retail was $3,190.

PRS 10th Anniversary
courtesy Gary Canady

P

Grading	100% MINT	98% EXC+	95% EXC	90% VG+	80% VG	70% G	60%

'92 PRS Custom 22
courtesy Gary Canady

ELECTRIC

CE BOLT-ON — offset double cutaway carved alder body, bolt-on maple neck, 24 fret rosewood fingerboard with abalone dot inlay, standard PRS vibrato, 3 per side PRS locking tuners, chrome hardware, 2 humbucker PRS pickups, volume/tone control, 5 position rotary switch. Available in Black and Classic Red finishes. Curr. mfr.

Mfr.'s Sug. Retail	$1,560	$1,170	$780	$705	$555	$465	$425	$385

Also available with 22 fret fingerboard (CE 22 Bolt-On).

CE Bolt-On Maple Top — similar to CE Bolt-On, except has figured maple top. Available in Black Cherry, Black Sunburst, Cherry Sunburst, Dark Blue, Emerald Green, Greyblack, Orange, Purple, Royal Blue, Scarlet Red, Scarlet Sunburst, Tobacco Sunburst, Tortoise Shell, Vintage Sunburst and Vintage Yellow finishes. Curr. mfr.

Mfr.'s Sug. Retail	$1,860	$1,395	$930	$855	$675	$575	$525	$475

Also available with 22 fret fingerboard (CE 22 Bolt-On Maple Top).

In 1994, Black Cherry, Emerald Green and Orange finishes were introduced.

CUSTOM — offset double cutaway mahogany body, flame maple top, mahogany neck, 24 fret rosewood fingerboard with abalone/pearl moon inlay, standard PRS vibrato, 6 per side locking PRS tuners, chrome hardware, 2 humbucker PRS pickups, volume/tone control, 5 position rotary switch. Available in Black Cherry, Black Sunburst, Emerald Green, Greyblack, Purple, Royal Blue, Scarlet Red, Scarlet Sunburst, Tortoise Shell and Whale Blue finishes. Curr. mfr.

Mfr.'s Sug. Retail	$2,180	$1,635	$1,090	$1,010	$800	$680	$620	$565

Also available with 22 fret fingerboard (Custom 22).

This model has PRS wrapover bridge/tailpiece optionally available.

In 1994, Purple finish was introduced.

EG BOLT-ON (EG1) — offset double cutaway alder body, white pickguard, bolt-on maple neck, 22 fret rosewood fingerboard with pearl dot inlay, standard PRS vibrato, 3 per side locking PRS tuners, chrome hardware, humbucker/single coil/humbucker pickups, volume control, push-pull tone control, 5 position switch, coil tap in tone control. Available in Black, Black Sunburst, Classic Red and Seafoam Green finishes. Curr. mfr.

Mfr.'s Sug. Retail	$1,280	$960	$640	$600	$475	$390	$355	$325

This model also available with 2 single coil/1 humbucker pickups with coil tap in tone control (EG2), and 3 single coil pickups with dual tone in tone control (EG3).

In 1994, Seafoam Green finish was introduced.

EG Bolt-On Maple Top — similar to EG Bolt-On, except has 3 piece maple top. Available in Black Cherry Burst, Black Sunburst, Emerald Green Burst, Grey Black Burst, Purple Burst, Royal Blue Burst, Scarlet Burst, Tri-Color Sunburst and Whale Blue Burst finishes. Curr. mfr.

Mfr.'s Sug. Retail	$1,580	$1,185	$790	$715	$565	$475	$435	$395

In 1994, Black Cherry Burst, Emerald Green Burst, Purple Burst, Royal Blue Burst, Scarlet Burst, Tri-Color Sunburst and Whale Blue Burst finish were introduced.

EG Bolt-On LH — similar to EG Bolt-On, except is left handed version. Mfd. 1993 only.

		$890	$770	$640	$510	$460	$420	$380

Last Mfr.'s Sug. Retail was $1,285.

EG Bolt-On LH Maple Top — similar to EG Bolt-On, except is left handed version, has 3 piece maple top. Available in Black Sunburst and Greyblack Sunburst finishes.

		$1,110	$955	$795	$630	$570	$520	$475

Last Mfr.'s Sug. Retail was $1,585.

McCARTY MODEL — offset double cutaway mahogany body, carved figured maple top, mahogany neck, 22 fret rosewood fingerboard with abalone/pearl moon inlay, PRS wrapover bridge/tailpiece, blackface peghead with screened logo, 3 per side tuners with plastic buttons, 2 covered humbucker pickups, volume/tone control, 3 position switch. Available in McCarty Sunburst and McCarty Tobacco Sunburst finishes. New 1994.

Mfr.'s Sug. Retail	$2,900	$2,320	$1,740	$1,450	$1,160	$1,040	$955	$870

This instrument was built as a tribute to Ted McCarty.

McCarty Standard — similar to McCarty Model, except has Custom Black and Gold Top finishes. New 1994.

Mfr.'s Sug. Retail	$2,760	$2,208	$1,656	$1,380	$1,105	$995	$910	$825

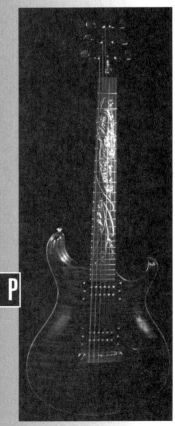

PRS Dragon III
courtesy Gary Canady

P

Grading	100%	98% MINT	95% EXC+	90% EXC	80% VG+	70% VG	60% G

STANDARD — offset double cutaway carved mahogany body/neck, 24 fret rosewood fingerboard with abalone/pearl moon inlay, standard vibrato, 3 per side locking PRS tuners, chrome hardware, 2 humbucker PRS pickups, volume/tone control, 5 position rotary switch. Available in Black, Natural and Vintage Cherry finishes. Curr. mfr.

Mfr.'s Sug. Retail	$2,040	$1,530	$1,020	$945	$750	$635	$580	$530

This model has PRS wrapover bridge/tailpiece optionally available.

Also available with 22 fret fingerboard (Standard 22).

Artist Series

ARTIST — offset double cutaway mahogany body, carved flame maple top, mahogany neck, 24 fret rosewood fingerboard with abalone bird inlay, standard PRS vibrato, abalone signature peghead inlay, 3 per side locking PRS tuners, chrome hardware, 2 humbucker PRS pickups, volume/tone/5 position control, certificate of authenticity. Available in Amber, Dark Cherry Sunburst, Indigo and Teal Black finishes. Mfd. 1990 to 1994.

	$2,645	$2,270	$1,890	$1,510	$1,360	$1,245	$1,135

Last Mfr.'s Sug. Retail was $3,780.

In 1993, curly maple top was introduced, 22 fret maple bound fingerboard replaced original item, semi hollow body, stop tailpiece became optionally available.

ARTIST II — offset double cutaway mahogany body, carved figured maple top, mahogany neck, 22 fret maple purfled rosewood fingerboard with abalone bird inlay, PRS wrapover bridge/tailpiece, maple purfled peghead with abalone signature inlay, 3 per side locking PRS tuners, gold hardware, 2 humbucker PRS pickups, volume/tone control, 5 position rotary switch, certificate of authenticity. Available in Amber, Dark Cherry Sunburst, Indigo and Teal Black finishes. New 1994.

Mfr.'s Sug. Retail	$4,400	$3,520	$2,640	$2,200	$1,760	$1,585	$1,450	$1,320

This model has semi hollow body, standard PRS vibrato optionally available.

Artist Ltd — similar to Artist II, except has abalone purfled fingerboard with 14K gold bird inlay, abalone purfled peghead with pearl eagle inlay. New 1994.

Mfr.'s Sug. Retail	$7,000	$5,600	$4,200	$3,500	$2,800	$2,520	$2,310	$2,100

Limited quantity of 200 instruments mfd.

Dragon Series

DRAGON — offset double cutaway mahogany body, arched bound flame maple top, mahogany neck, 22 fret ebony fingerboard with intricate dragon inlay, PRS wrapover bridge/tailpiece, abalone signature inlay on peghead, 3 per side locking PRS tuners, gold hardware, 2 humbucker PRS pickups, volume/tone control, 5 position rotary control. Available in Amber, Dark Cherry Sunburst, Indigo and Teal Black finishes. Mfd. yearly.

The fingerboard dragon inlays on these instruments are made of various seashell, precious metals and stones, each year the inlay becomes more elaborate.

Dragon I - 1992 Series — 50 mfd.

	$17,500	$15,000	$12,500	N/A	N/A	N/A	N/A

Last Mfr.'s Sug. Retail was $8,000.

Dragon II - 1993 Series — 218 piece fingerboard inlay, 100 mfd.

	$13,500	$11,570	$9,640	N/A	N/A	N/A	N/A

Last Mfr.'s Sug. Retail was $11,000.

Dragon III - 1994 Series — 438 piece fingerboard inlay, 100 mfd.

Mfr.'s Sug. Retail	$16,000	$12,800	$9,600	$8,000	$6,400	$5,760	$5,280	$4,800

ELECTRIC BASS

Paul Reed Smith briefly introduced two bass guitar models. Built with the same high quality and attention to detail, the **Basic Four** (four string) and **Basic Five** (five string) models featured 34" scale, volume/tone/pickup selector controls, 2+2 (or 3+2) headstock configuration, set neck design, three pickups, as well as the figured wood tops and translucent finishes.

Prices on **Basic Four** models in 80% to 90% range from $800 to $1,100; **Basic Five** models range from $1,000 to $1,300.

PRS Basic Five
courtesy Jimmy Gravity

PBC

Instruments currently built in Coopersburg, Pennsylvania.

Luthier/designer David Bunker built numerous radically designed guitars during the mid 1960s and 1970s. Rather than be different for different's sake, Bunker's creations were designed to solve certain inherent solid body design flaws. Later designs began to follow more traditional forms, but still included some advanced design concepts. Bunker is currently involved with PBC Guitar Technology, Inc., which is having success with the "Tension-Free" neck design and the Wishbone hollowbody series.

PC

See also NED CALLAN.

Instruments built in England from the early 1970s through the mid 1980s.

PBC Wishbone AC-300
courtesy Jay Wolfe

The P C brand is the trademark of custom luthier Peter Cook, who produced the original design **Axis** solid body guitar for a number of years.

(Source: Tony Bacon and Paul Day, The Guru's Guitar Guide)

PEAR CUSTOM

Instruments currently built in Pleasanton, California.

Luthier Tom Palecki offers custom body designs and a wide range of colors in solids, metallics, clears, and pearls. Palecki also offers customizing, repair, and graphics services at his workshop. For further information, please contact Pear Custom Guitars via the Index of Current Manufacturers located in the rear of this book.

PEARL

Instruments produced in Italy starting in the late 1970s, and then production moved to Japan. Production ended sometime in the early 1980s.

The Pearl trademark appeared on a number of instruments manufactured (at first) by the Gherson company of Italy. These medium quality guitars featured both original designs on some models, and copies of classic American designs on others. Production of Pearl guitars moved to Japan (circa 1978-1979) and continued on for another couple of years. Although Italy had a tradition of guitar manufacture throughout the years, the cheaper labor costs that Japan was featuring at the time eventually won out in production considerations.

(Source: Tony Bacon and Paul Day, The Guru's Guitar Guide)

PEAVEY

Instruments built in Meridian and Leaksville, Mississippi. Distributed by Peavey Electronics Corporation, who have been located in Meridian, Mississippi since 1965.

Peavey also has a factory and distribution center in Corby, England to help serve and service the overseas market. All Peavey guitars and basses are built in America.

Peavey Electronics is one of the very few major American musical instrument manufacturers still run by the original founding member and owner. Hartley Peavey took his inital skills of building 'handmade' guitar amplifiers and built a company that was ranked **third** out of one hundred in estimated 1995 Sales by MMR magazine.

Hartley Peavey grew up in Meridian, Mississippi and spent some time working in his father's music store repairing record players. He gained some recognition locally for the guitar amplifiers he built by hand while he was still in school, and decided months prior to college graduation to go into business for himself. In 1965 Peavey Electronics was started out of the basement of Peavey's parents; and the saturated guitar amp market propelled Peavey towards building P.A. systems. By 1968 the product demand was great enough to warrant building a small cement block factory on rented land and hire another staff member.

The demand for Peavey products continued to grow, and by the early 1970s the company's roster had expanded to 150 employees. Emphasis was still placed on P.A. construction, although both guitar and bass amps were doing well. The Peavey company continued to diversify and produce all the components needed to build the finished product. After twelve years of manufacturing, the first series of Peavey guitars was begun in 1977, and introduced at the 1978 NAMM show. An advertising circular used by Peavey in the late '70s compared the price of an American built T-60 (plus case) for $350 versus the Fender Stratocaster's list price of $790 or a Gibson Les Paul for $998.50 (list). In light of those list prices, it's also easy to see where the Japanese guitarmakers had plenty of manuevering room during their "copy" era.

The "T-Series" guitars were introduced in 1978, and the line expanded from three models up to a total of seven in five years. In 1983, the product line changed, and introduced both the mildly wacky Mystic and Razer original designs (the Mantis was added in 1984) and the more conservative Patriot, Horizon, and Milestone guitars. The Fury and Foundation basses were also added at this time. After five years of stop tailpieces, the first Peavey "Octave Plus" vibratos were offered (later superceeded by the Power bend model). Pickup designs also shifted from the humbuckers to single or double 'blade' pickups.

Models that debuted in 1985 included the vaguely stratish Predator, and the first doubleneck (!), the Hydra. In response to the guitar industry shifting to 'superstrat' models, the Impact was introduced in 1986. Guitars also had the option of a Kahler locking tremolo, and two offsprings of the '84 Mantis were released: The Vortex I or Vortex II. The Nitro series of guitars were available in 1987, as well as the Falcon, Unity, and Dyna-Bass. Finally, to answer companies like Kramer or Charvel, the Tracer series and the Vandenberg model(s) debuted in 1988.

As the U.S. guitar market grew more conservative, models like the Generation S-1 and Destiny guitars showed up in guitar shops. Peavey basses continued to evolve into sleeker and more solid instruments like the Palaedium, TL series or B Ninety. 1994 saw the release of the MIDIBASE (later the Cyberbass) that combined magnetic pickups with a MIDI-controller section. Rather than stay stuck in a design "holding pattern", Peavey continues to change and revise guitar and bass designs, and they continue the almost twenty year tradition of American built electric guitars and basses.

(Model History, nomenclature, and description courtesy Grant Brown, head of the Peavey Repair section)

Information on virtually any Peavey product, or a product's schematic is availble through Peavey Repair. Grant Brown, the head of the Repair section, has been with Peavey Electronics for over seventeen years.

ACOUSTIC

IN 1994, a series of Peavey acoustic guitars was announced. Although some models were shipped in quanity, the acoustic line was not as wide spread as other guitar models that were introduced. Peavey acoustics have a solid Alpine Spruce top, and either laminated or solid rosewood sides, and a mahogany neck. So, if some Peavey acoustics are encountered, the following list will at least indicate the range envisioned.

Dreadnought Series

The **SD-9P** ($499) was the only model to feature a solid cedar top in the dreadnought design. The **SD-11P** ($599) featured the same body design with a Spruce top and laminated mahogany sides and back, and the **DD-21P** ($699) substitutes laminated rosewood in place of the mahogany. The **SD-11PCE** ($759) featured a single cutaway and piezo under-the-bridge pickup system with 3 band EQ and volume control.

Jumbo Series

The **CJ-33PE** ($1,049) featured the Jumbo body design and a piezo system; the **CJ-3312PE** ($1,099) was the accompanying 12 string model.

Compact Cutaway Series

Two models comprise the Compact body design that featured a single cutaway: the **CC-37PE** ($1,099) had a five piece mahogany/rosewood neck, piezo pickup system, and Schaller hardware; the **CC-3712PE** ($1,149) was the accompanying 12 string model.

ACOUSTIC ELECTRIC

Grading			100%	98% MINT	95% EXC+	90% EXC	80% VG+	70% VG	60% G

ECOUSTIC — single rounded cutaway dreadnought style, cedar top, oval soundhole, bound body, 5 stripe rosette, mahogany back/sides, maple neck, 22 fret rosewood fingerboard with white dot inlay, rosewood bridge with white pins, 3 per side gold tuners, piezo bridge pickup, 3 band EQ. Available in Black, Natural and Transparent Red finishes. Current production.

Mfr.'s Sug. Retail	$959	$719	$479

ECOUSTIC ATS — single rounded cutaway dreadnought style, Maple top, oval soundhole, bound body, 5 stripe rosette, Poplar back/sides, Rock Maple neck, 22 fret rosewood fingerboard with white dot inlay, rosewood ATS Tremolo bridge with white pins, 3 per side chrome tuners, piezo bridge pickup, 3 band EQ. Available in Black, Natural and Transparent Red finishes. New 1995.

Mfr.'s Sug. Retail	$999	$749	$499

ELECTRIC

AXCELERATOR — offset double cutaway poplar body, pearloid pickguard, bolt-on maple neck, 22 fret rosewood fingerboard with pearl dot inlay, Peavey Power Bend III non-locking tremolo, 6 on one side locking tuners, chrome hardware, 3 Db2 dual blade humbucking pickups, volume/tone control, 5 position switch. Available in Black, Candy Apple Red, Transparent Blue, Transparent Red, and Metallic Gold finishes. Mfg. 1994 to date.

Mfr.'s Sug. Retail	$799	$599	$399	$350	$280	$250	$230	$210

This model has a Swamp Ash body optionally available.

Axcelerator AX — similar to Axcelerator, except has swamp ash body, Floyd Rose double locking vibrato, non locking tuners, gold hardware 2 Db2 dual blade/1 Db4 quad blade humbucker pickups, three way "turbo" (allows bridge pickup to be tapped as single coil, dual coil, and full humbucking modes) switch. Available in Blonde, Transparent Blue, Transparent Green and Transparent Red finishes. Mfg. 1995 to date.

Mfr.'s Sug. Retail	$799	$639	$479	$400	$320	$290	$265	$240

This model has maple fingerboard with black dot inlay optionally available.

Axcelerator F — similar to Axcelerator, except has swamp ash body, Floyd Rose double locking vibrato, non locking tuners, gold hardware 2 dual blade/1 quad blade humbucker pickups. Available in Blonde, Transparent Blue, Transparent Green and Transparent Red finishes. Offered 1994 only.

	$560	$480	$400	$320	$290	$265	$240

Last Mfr.'s Sug. Retail was $799.

Options such as Swamp Ash body and AX pickup assembly (2 Db2 dual blade and 1 Db4 quad blade humbuckers) were offered on the regular Axcelerator. The Axcelerator F model evolved into the current Axcelerator AX model.

CROPPER CLASSIC — single cutaway mahogany body with figured maple top, bolt-on hard rock maple neck, 22 fret rosewood fingerboard, Db2 dual blade humbucker, Db4 quad blade humbucker, gold hardware, master volume and tone controls, three way pickup selector switch, two position coil-tap switch. Available in Onion Green, Black, Rhythm Blue, Memphis Sun. Current production.

Mfr.'s Sug. Retail	$949	$806	$664	$625

This model was designed in conjunction with guitarist Steve Cropper.

"Elmer [Stromberg] could actually finish a Master 400 in one month during the late '40s and early '50s. The Master 400 was his ultimate expression and his proudest achievement...It rivaled the Gibson Super 400 introduced in 1934 and the D'Angelico New Yorker and Epiphone Emperor introduced in 1936."
—Jim Speros
TCG, Jan/Feb 1993

P

DEFENDER — offset double cutaway poplar body, white laminated pickguard, bolt-on maple neck, 24 fret rosewood fingerboard with pearl dot inlay, double locking Floyd Rose vibrato, 6 on one side tuners, chrome hardware, exposed humbucker/single coil/humbucker pickups, volume/tone control, 5 position switch. Available in Black, Candy Apple Red, Cobalt Blue and White finishes. Mfg. 1994 to 1995.

	100%	98%	95%	90%	80%	70%	60%
	$410	$355	$295	$235	$210	$195	$180

Last Mfr.'s Sug. Retail was $590.

Defender F — similar to Defender, except has alder body, black pearloid lam pickguard, humbucker/single coil rail/humbucker pickups. Available in Metallic Purple, Metallic Silver, Pearl Black and Pearl White finishes. Mfg. 1994 to 1995.

	100%	98%	95%	90%	80%	70%	60%
	$560	$480	$400	$320	$290	$265	$240

Last Mfr.'s Sug. Retail was $799.

DESTINY — offset double cutaway poplar body, thru body rock maple neck, 24 fret bound rosewood fingerboard, pearl dot inlays, Kahler double locking vibrato, 6 on one side tuners, black hardware, 2 high output single coil/1 Alnico humbucker pickups, volume/tone control, 5 position pickup selector and coil tap switch. Available in Black, Blue, White, and Red finishes. Mfd. 1989 to 1994.

	100%	98%	95%	90%	80%	70%	60%
	$560	$515	$470	$360	$310	$270	$220

Last Mfr.'s Sug. Retail was 699.95

Destiny Custom — offset double cutaway mahogany body, quilted maple top, thru body flamed maple neck, 24 fret bound rosewood fingerboard, pearl oval inlay at 12th fret, double locking vibrato, 6 on one side tuners, gold hardware, 2 high output single coil/1 Alnico humbucker pickups, volume/tone control, 5 position pickup selector and a coil tap switch. Available in Honey Burst, Transparent Black, Transparent Blue, Transparent Honey Burst and Transparent Red finishes. Mfd. 1989 to 1994.

	100%	98%	95%	90%	80%	70%	60%
	$700	$660	$560	$470	$360	$330	$300

Last Mfr.'s Sug. Retail was $1,000.

DETONATOR — offset double cutaway poplar body, bolt-on hard rock maple neck, 24 fret rosewood fingerboard with pearl dot inlay, Peavey Floyd Rose double locking tremolo, 6 on one side tuners, chrome hardware, ceramic Humbucker/single coil/humbucker configuration, volume/tone control, 5 position switch, white laminated pickguard. Available in Gloss Black, Cobalt Blue, Gloss White, and Candy Apple Red finishes. Current production.

Mfr.'s Sug. Retail	$589	$471	$353	$325

Detonator AX — similar to the Detonator, except has alder body, Alnico humbucker/Db2 dual blade single coil/Alnico humbucker configuration, Power Bend III tremolo system, locking tuning machines, pearloid pickguard. Available in Pearl Black, Metallic Purple, Pearl White, and Metallic Silver finishes. Current production.

Mfr.'s Sug. Retail	$779	$623	$467	$400

Detonator JX — similar to the Detonator, except has poplar body, 2 ceramic single coil and 1 ceramic humbucker pickups, Power Bend II tremolo system, non-locking tuning machines, white laminated pickguard. Available in Gloss Black, Gloss Dark Blue, Gloss White, and Gloss Red finishes. Current production.

Mfr.'s Sug. Retail	$419	$335	$251	$240

EVH Wolfgang Series

The EVH Wolfgang series was designed in conjunction with Edward Van Halen. Van Halen, who had great success with the Peavey 5150 amplifiers he also helped develop, named the guitar model after his son.

EVH WOLFGANG (Stop Tailpiece/Solid Colors) — bound offset double cutaway basswood body, arched top, bolt-on graphite-reinforced bird's eye maple neck, 22 fret bird's eye maple fingerboard with black dot inlays, 25 1/2" scale, stop tailpiece, non-tremolo bridge, 3+3 headstock, chrome tuners, chrome hardware, 2 ceramic humbuckers, volume/tone controls, 3 position pickup selector. Available in Gloss Black and Gloss Ivory finishes. New 1996.

Mfr.'s Sug. Retail	$1,498

EVH Wolfgang (Floyd Rose/Solid Colors) — similar to the EVH Wolfgang, except has a Peavey Floyd Rose double locking tremolo system.

Mfr.'s Sug. Retail	$1,598

EVH Wolfgang (Stop Tailpiece/Transparent Colors) — similar to the EVH Wolfgang, except features a stop tailpiece/non-tremolo bridge and an arched top of figured maple. Available in Transparent Amber, Transparent Purple, Transparent Red, and Sunburst finishes.

Mfr.'s Sug. Retail	$1,778

EVH Wolfgang (Floyd Rose/Transparent Colors) — similar to the EVH Wolfgang, except has a Peavey Floyd Rose double locking tremolo system and an arched top of figured maple. Available in Transparent Amber, Transparent Purple, Transparent Red, and Sunburst finishes.

Mfr.'s Sug. Retail	$1,798

Falcon Series

FALCON — double offset cutaway poplar body, bolt-on bi-laminated maple neck, 22 fret maple fingerboard, 25 1/2" scale, six on a side tuners, three single coil pickups, Kahler locking tremolo system, volume/tone controls, five way pickup selector, white pickguard. Mfd. 1986 to 1988.

	100%	98%	95%	90%	80%	70%	60%
	$300	$280	$220	$170	$140	$110	$85

Last Mfr.'s Sug. Retail was $399.50.

Grading	100%	98% MINT	95% EXC+	90% EXC	80% VG+	70% VG	60% G

Falcon Custom — similar to the Falcon, except featured a rosewood fingerboard and different fingerboard radius. Mfd. 1986 to 1990.

| | $325 | $285 | $245 | $190 | $160 | $140 | $120 |

Last Mfr.'s Sug. Retail was $449.50.

In 1988, the Falcon Custom's body design was restyled into a sleeker profile similar to the Falcon Classic and Falcon Active that were offered that same year.

In 1988, a Flame Maple neck with Rosewood or Maple fingerboards replaced the standard rock maple neck.

In 1989, changes involved a Figured Maple neck with a Rosewood fingerboard, pickups were upgraded to the HRS (Hum Reducing System) models, carved maple top over poplar body, gold hardware, Power Bend II tremolo and locking tuning machines, and a graphite nut.

FALCON ACTIVE — similar to the Falcon, except body was restyled to sleeker design lines, Flame Maple bi-laminated neck with Rosewood or Flame Maple fingerboard, and active Bi-FET pickups replaced the original passive system. Active electronics powered by an on-board 9 volt battery. Mfd. 1988 to 1989.

| | $450 | $410 | $350 | $305 | $240 | $190 | $160 |

Last Mfr.'s Sug. Retail was $549.

Falcon Classic — similar to the Falcon Active, except has Flame Maple bi-laminated neck and Flame Maple fingerboard, 3 passive single coil pickups, Power Bend non-locking tremolo system. Mfd. 1988 to 1989.

| | $300 | $275 | $245 | $190 | $160 | $140 | $120 |

Last Mfr.'s Sug. Retail was $349.50.

Falcon Standard — similar to the Falcon Classic, except has a Figured Maple bi-laminated neck and rosewood fingerboard, 3 HRS (Hum Reducing System) passive single coil pickups, Power Bend II non-locking tremolo and graphite saddles, locking tuning machines. Mfd. 1989 to 1990.

| | $300 | $275 | $245 | $190 | $160 | $140 | $120 |

Last Mfr.'s Sug. Retail was $349.50.

G-90 — offset double cutaway poplar body, bolt-on rock maple neck, 24 fret bound rosewood fingerboard with pearl dot inlay, Floyd Rose double locking tremolo, reverse headstock, 6 on one side tuners, black hardware, 2 HRS single coil/1 Alnico tapped humbucker pickups, volume/tone control, 5 position pickup selector, coil tap switch. Available in Black, Blue, Eerie Dess Black, Eerie Dess Blue, Eerie Dess Multi, Eerie Dess Red, Pearl White, Raspberry Pearl, and Sunfire Red finishes. Disc. 1994.

| | $420 | $360 | $300 | $240 | $215 | $195 | $180 |

Last Mfr.'s Sug. Retail was $600.

Generation Series

GENERATION S-1 — single cutaway mahogany body, Flame Maple top, bolt-on laminated maple neck, 22 fret rosewood fingerboard with pearl dot inlay, fixed brass bridge, graphlon nut, 6 on one side tuners, gold hardware, active single coil/humbucker pickup, volume/tone control, 3 position pickup selector, coil tap switch. Available in Transparent Amber, Transparent Black, Transparent Blue and Transparent Red finishes. Mfg. 1988 to 1994.

| | $560 | $480 | $400 | $320 | $290 | $265 | $240 |

Last Mfr.'s Sug. Retail was $800.

Generation S-2 — similar to Generation S-1, except has Kahler double locking tremolo system. Mfg. 1990 to 1994.

| | $560 | $480 | $400 | $320 | $290 | $265 | $240 |

Last Mfr.'s Sug. Retail was $800.

Generation S-3 — similar to Generation S-1, except has hollow sound chambers, maple fingerboard with black dot inlay, 3 stacked coil pickups, coil tap in tone control. Available in Transparent Black, Transparent Blue, Transparent Honey Sunburst and Transparent Red finishes. Mfg. 1991 to 1994.

| | $350 | $300 | $250 | $200 | $180 | $165 | $150 |

Last Mfr.'s Sug. Retail was $500.

Generation Custom — similar to Generation S-1, except has solid Poplar body, Flame Maple neck, Ebony fingerboard, black hardware, Black Chrome Kahler double locking tremolo, Active electronics, Peavey single coil/humbucker pickups, volume/tone controls, three way pickup selector, coil tap switch. Mfg. 1989 to 1994.

| | $560 | $480 | $400 | $320 | $290 | $265 | $240 |

Last Mfr.'s Sug. Retail was $799.

Generation Standard — similar to Generation S-1, except has solid Poplar body, Flame Maple bi-laminated neck, 22 fret Flame Maple fingerboard, chrome hardware, six on a side headstock, 2 single coil pickups, master volume/master tone controls, and three way pickup selector. Mfg. 1989 to 1994.

| | $330 | $300 | $240 | $200 | $160 | $110 | $85 |

Last Mfr.'s Sug. Retail was $429.

HORIZON — offset double cutaway hardwood body, bi-laminated hard rock maple neck, 23 fret rosewood neck, 24 3/4" scale, chrome hardware, six on a side tuners, 2 dual blade humbucking pickups, stop tailpiece, master volume control, two tone controls (one per pickup), three way pickup selector. Available in Natural, White, Black, and Sunburst finishes. Mfg. 1983 to 1986.

| | $250 | $200 | $170 | $160 | $130 | $105 | $85 |

Last Mfr.'s Sug. Retail was $379.

The tone control for the humbucking pickups allows the capability of single or dual coil output. Fully opening the pot to "10" achieves single coil mode. Turning counterclockwise to "7" brings the second coil into operation. Tone circuitry is standard in function between "7" and "0".

P

Grading	100%	98% MINT	95% EXC+	90% EXC	80% VG+	70% VG	60% G

Horizon II — similar to the Horizon, except features an extra 'single blade' single coil pickup in the middle position. Extra three way switch controls the middle pickup only: off/in phase with the other pickups/out-of-phase with the other pickups. Mfg. 1983 to 1986.

| | $560 | $480 | $400 | $320 | $290 | $265 | $240 |

Last Mfr.'s Sug. Retail ranged from $349 to $499.

This model had the option of a Peavey Octave Plus tremolo system.

Horizon II Custom — similar to the Horizon II, except features a black phenolic fingerboard and pearl or metallic finishes. Mfd. 1984 to 1985.

| | $350 | $275 | $250 | $200 | $125 | $90 | $75 |

Last Mfr.'s Sug. Retail ranged from $475 to $525.

HYDRA — offset double cutaway hardwood body, bi-laminated hard rock maple necks in a 12/6 configuration, 24 fret maple fingerboards, both necks in 24 3/4" scale, 2 dual blade humbuckers per neck, master volume knob, two tone knobs (one per pickup), 3 way pickup selector (6 string), 3 way pickup selector (12 string), 3 way neck selector switch. Mfd. 1984 to 1986.

| | $750 | $580 | $490 | $380 | $290 | $250 | $230 |

Last Mfr.'s Sug. Retail was $1,099.

The tone control for the humbucking pickups allows the capability of single or dual coil output. Fully opening the pot to "10" achieves single coil mode. Turning counterclockwise to "7" brings the second coil into operation. Tone circuitry is standard in function between "7" and "0".

Jeff Cook Hydra — similar to Hydra, except has Kahler double locking tremolo system on six string neck, as well as "Jeff Cook" on headstock. Mfg. 1985 to 1986.

| | $790 | $600 | $500 | $420 | $320 | $260 | $240 |

Last Mfr.'s Sug. Retail was $1,299.50.

This model had design input and was used by Jeff Cook (Alabama).

Impact Series

The Impact Series, introduced in 1985, featured 'superstrat' styling and a sleek body profile. The later Impact series (Firenza, Milano, and Torino) further explored the Impact body design with other pickup configurations such as dual humbuckers.

IMPACT 1 — offset double cutaway Poplar body, hard rock neck, 22 fret "Polyglide" polymer fingerboard with pearl dot inlay, Kahler locking tremolo system, 6 on one side tuners, Black chrome or gold-on-brass hardware, 2 P-6 single coils/1 P-12 humbucker pickups, master volume control, master tone control, three pickup selector mini-switches. Available in Pearl Black and Pearl White finishes. Mfd. 1985 to 1987.

| | $490 | $420 | $350 | $280 | $250 | $230 | $210 |

Last Mfr.'s Sug. retail was $749.50.

Impact 2 — similar to Impact 1, except has a rosewood fingerboard in place of the synthetic fingerboard. Available in Pearl Black and Pearl White finishes.

| | $460 | $410 | $350 | $305 | $270 | $215 | $170 |

Last Mfr.'s Sug. retail was $519.

Impact 1 Unity — similar to Impact 1, except has an ebony fingerboard, neck-through design, Black chrome hardware, 2 single coil/1 Alnico humbucker pickups. Available in Pearl Black and Pearl White finishes. Mfd. 1987 to 1989.

| | $560 | $480 | $400 | $320 | $290 | $265 | $240 |

Last Mfr.'s Sug. retail was $799.

IMPACT FIRENZA — offset double cutaway poplar body, white laminated pickguard, bolt-on maple neck, 22 fret rosewood fingerboard with pearl dot inlay, 25" scale, Power Bend III standard tremolo, 6 on one side tuners, chrome hardware, 2 exposed single coil/1 humbucker pickups, volume/tone control, 5 position selector switch. Available in Powder Blue, Red, Seafoam Green and White finishes. Current production.

| Mfr.'s Sug. Retail | $600 | $480 | $360 | $300 | $240 | $215 | $195 | $180 |

Impact Firenza AX — similar to the Impact Firenza, except has an alder body. Available in Metallic Silver or Pearl Black finishes with a pearloid pickguard.

| Mfr.'s Sug. Retail | $729 | $583 | $437 | $400 | $320 | $290 | $265 | $240 |

This model has an ash body optionally available, and finished in Transparent Grape with pearloid pickguard or Sunburst with tortoiseshell pickguard.

Impact Milano — offset double cutaway maple body, figured maple top, 25" scale, bolt-on rock maple neck, 24 fret rosewood fingerboard with pearl dot inlay, Power Bend III standard vibrato, 6 on one side locking tuners, chrome hardware, 2 Alnico exposed humbucker pickups, volume/tone control, 5 position switch. Available in Antique Amber, Metallic Green, Transparent Blue and Transparent Red finishes. Mfd. 1994 to 1995.

| | $560 | $480 | $400 | $320 | $290 | $265 | $240 |

Last Mfr.'s Sug. retail price was $799.

Impact Torino I — offset double cutaway mahogany body, figured maple top, 25" scale, set-in mahogany neck, 24 rosewood fingerboard with pearl/abalone 3-D block inlay, tunomatic bridge/stop tailpiece, 6 on one side tuners, chrome hardware, 2 Alnico exposed humbucker pickups, volume/tone control, 5 position switch. Available in Cherry Sunburst, Honey Sunburst, Metallic Gold and Transparent Red finishes. Mfd. 1994 to 1995.

| | $700 | $600 | $500 | $400 | $360 | $330 | $300 |

Last Mfr.'s Sug. retail price was $999.

"At the age of twelve, Gene [Autry] got his first guitar. He ordered it from a Sears, Roebuck catalog for $7.95 plus 74 cents shipping, money he had earned by diligently bailing hay on his uncle's farm."

—Steve Evans

TCG, May/June 1993

Grading	100%	98% MINT	95% EXC+	90% EXC	80% VG+	70% VG	60% G

Impact Torino II — similar to Impact Torino I, except had a Power Bend III standard vibrato and locking tuners.

| | $700 | $600 | $500 | $400 | $360 | $330 | $300 |

Last Mfr.'s Sug. Retail was $999.

MANTIS — single cutaway "flying V" ('pointy V'?) hardwood body, bi-laminated hard rock maple neck, 23 fret rosewood neck, 24 3/4" scale, chrome hardware, six on a side tuners, 1 dual blade humbucking pickup, fixed bridge, master volume control, master tone control. Mfg. 1984 to 1986.

| | N/A | $275 | $250 | $200 | $125 | $90 | $75 |

Last Mfr.'s Sug. Retail was $269.50.

This model had the Octave Plus tremolo system optionally available.

In 1985, a Kahler 'Flyer' locking tremolo was optionally available (Mantis LT).

MILESTONE — offset double cutaway hardwood body, bi-laminated hard rock maple neck, 24 fret rosewood neck, 24 3/4" scale, chrome hardware, six on a side tuners, 2 dual blade humbucking pickups, fixed bridge, master volume control, two tone controls (one per pickup), three way pickup selector, pickup phase switch (either in or out-of-phase). Mfg. 1983 to 1986.

| | N/A | $275 | $250 | $200 | $125 | $90 | $75 |

Last Mfr.'s Sug. Retail ranged from $324 to $449.1

This model had the Octave Plus tremolo system optionally available.

The tone control for the humbucking pickups allows the capability of single or dual coil output. Fully opening the pot to "10" achieves single coil mode. Turning counterclockwise to "7" brings the second coil into operation. Tone circuitry is standard in function between "7" and "0".

Milestone Custom — similar to the Milestone, except features a phenolic fingerboard and pearl or metallic finishes. Mfd. 1985 to 1986.

| | N/A | $275 | $250 | $200 | $125 | $90 | $75 |

Last Mfr.'s Sug. Retail was $499.

Milestone 12 — similar to the Milestone, except features a 12 string configuration. Mfd. 1985 to 1986.

| | $375 | $350 | $300 | $225 | $190 | $175 | $125 |

Last Mfr.'s Sug. Retail was $519.50.

MYSTIC — offset double cutaway-dual "rounded wings" hardwood body, bi-laminated hard rock maple neck, 23 fret rosewood neck, 24 3/4" scale, chrome hardware, six on a side tuners, 2 dual blade humbucking pickups, fixed bridge, master volume control, two tone controls (one per pickup), three way pickup selector. Available in Blood Red, White, Frost Blue, Inca Gold, Silver, Sunfire Red, and Black finishes. Mfd. 1983 to 1986.

| | N/A | $275 | $250 | $200 | $125 | $90 | $75 |

Last Mfr.'s Sug. Retail was $399.

This model had the Octave Plus tremolo system optionally available.

The tone control for the humbucking pickups allows the capability of single or dual coil output. Fully opening the pot to "10" achieves single coil mode. Turning counterclockwise to "7" brings the second coil into operation. Tone circuitry is standard in function between "7" and "0".

Nitro Series

The Nitro Series debuted in 1986, and featured a number of models designed towards Hard Rock players.

NITRO I — dual offset cutaway hardwood body, bi-laminated maple neck, 22 fret rosewood fingerboard, 25 1/2" scale, six on a side "pointy" headstock, black hardware, Peavey Precision tuners, Kahler locking tremolo system, exposed polepiece humbucker, master volume knob. Mfd. 1986 to 1989.

| | $300 | $275 | $225 | $170 | $140 | $120 | $95 |

Last Mfr.'s Sug. Retail price was $399.50.

Nitro I Active — similar to the Nitro I, except features active circuitry and an extra tone control knob. System requires a 9 volt battery. Mfd. 1988 to 1990.

| | $450 | $400 | $340 | $290 | $245 | $180 | $160 |

Last Mfr.'s Sug. Retail price was $549.

Nitro I Custom — similar to the Nitro I, except features recessed Floyd Rose/Kahler locking tremolo. Mfd. 1987 to 1989.

| | $350 | $305 | $275 | $205 | $160 | $140 | $120 |

Last Mfr.'s Sug. Retail price was $499.50.

NITRO II — dual offset cutaway hardwood body, bi-laminated maple neck, 22 fret rosewood fingerboard, 25 1/2" scale, six on a side "pointy" headstock, black hardware, Peavey Precision tuners, Kahler locking tremolo system, two exposed polepiece humbuckers, master volume knob, master tone knob, three way pickup selector switch. Mfd. 1987 to 1989.

| | $350 | $300 | $250 | $190 | $175 | $150 | $125 |

Last Mfr.'s Sug. Retail price was $449.50.

NITRO III — dual offset cutaway hardwood body, bi-laminated maple neck, 22 fret rosewood fingerboard, 25 1/2" scale, six on a side "pointy" headstock, black hardware, Peavey Precision tuners, Kahler locking tremolo system, 2 exposed polepiece single coil pickups, 1 exposed polepiece humbuckers, master volume knob, master tone knob, 3 individual pickup selector mini switches. Mfd. 1987 to 1989.

| | $380 | $320 | $275 | $215 | $190 | $170 | $135 |

Last Mfr.'s Sug. Retail price was $499.50.

P

Grading		100%	98% MINT	95% EXC+	90% EXC	80% VG+	70% VG	60% G

Nitro III Custom — similar to the Nitro III, except features Alnico pickups and recessed Floyd Rose/Kahler locking tremolo system. Mfd. 1987 to 1989.

	$475	$445	$385	$325	$260	$210	$170

Last Mfr.'s Sug. Retail price was $599.50.

Nitro Limited — similar to the Nitro III, except features 22 fret Ebony fingerboard, gold hardware, neck-through body design, Alnico pickups and recessed Floyd Rose/Kahler locking tremolo system. Mfd. 1987 to 1989.

	$700	$600	$500	$400	$360	$330	$300

Last Mfr.'s Sug. Retail price was $1,000.

NITRO C-2 — dual offset cutaway hardwood body, bi-laminated maple neck, 22 fret rosewood fingerboard, 25 1/2" scale, six on a side "pointy" headstock, black hardware, Peavey Precision tuners, Floyd Rose locking tremolo system, 1 HRS single coil pickup (middle position), 2 Alnico humbuckers, master volume knob, master tone knob, 3 individual pickup selector mini switches. Mfd. 1990 to 1992.

	$490	$460	$350	$280	$225	$180	$140

Last Mfr.'s Sug. Retail price was $599.

Nitro C-3 — similar to the Nitro C-2, except features 2 Alnico single coil pickups and 1 Alnico humbucker. Mfd. 1990 to 1992.

	$490	$460	$350	$280	$225	$180	$140

Last Mfr.'s Sug. Retail price was $599.

ODYSSEY — single cutaway mahogany body, carved flame maple top, set mahogany neck, 24 fret bound ebony fingerboard with white arrow inlay, 24 3/4" scale, tunomatic bridge/stop tailpiece, graphlon nut, bound peghead, 3 per side tuners, gold hardware, 2 humbucking Alnico pickups, 2 volume/2 tone controls, 3 position and coil split switches, straplocks. Available in '59 Vintage Sunburst, Tobacco Sunburst, Transparent Black, Transparent Blue and Transparent Red finishes. Mfd. 1990 to 1994.

	$700	$600	$500	$400	$360	$330	$300

Last Mfr.'s Sug. Retail price was $1,000.

Odyssey 25th Anniversary — similar to Odyssey, except has bound Quilted Maple top, 2 color pearl 3D block fingerboard inlay, black hardware, black pearl tuning machines, straplocks. Available in Transparent Black finish.

	$950	$790	$650	$520	$470	$430	$390

Last Mfr.'s Sug. Retail was $1,300.

PATRIOT — double cutaway hardwood body, bi-laminated hard rock maple neck, 23 fret fingerboard, 23 3/4" scale, chrome hardware, six on a side headstock, graphlon top nut, black laminated pickguard, 2 single coil blade pickups, volume/tone controls, three way pickup selector switch. Mfd. 1983 to 1986.

	$200	$185	$145	$115	$95	$85	$65

Last Mfr.'s Sug. Retail ranged from $229 to $299.

Patriot Plus — similar to the Patriot model, except features dual blade humbucker in the bridge position instead of a single coil, and a 24 3/4" scale. Mfd. 1983 to 1986.

	$200	$185	$145	$115	$95	$85	$65

Last Mfr.'s Sug. Retail was $249.

The tone control for the humbucking pickup allows the capability of single or dual coil output. Fully opening the pot to "10" achieves single coil mode. Turning counterclockwise to "7" brings the second coil into operation. Tone circuitry is standard in function between "7" and "0".

Patriot With Tremolo — similar to the Patriot model, except features a 24 3/4" scale, a Power Bend standard tremolo, 1 humbucker in the bridge position, and a volume control. Mfd. 1986 to 1990.

	$200	$185	$145	$115	$95	$85	$65

Last Mfr.'s Sug. Retail was $259.50.

Predator Series

The Predator models were introduced in the mid 1980s, and the first model featured a dual humbucker, locking tremolo design. After several years, the design was modified to three single coils pickups instead, and later to the popular single/single/humbucker variant.

PREDATOR (Original Model) — double cutaway hardwood body, bi-laminated hard rock maple neck, 23 fret fingerboard, 24 3/4" scale, chrome hardware, six on a side headstock, black laminated pickguard, Kahler 'Flyer' locking tremolo system, 2 exposed polepiece humbucking pickups, volume control, tone controls, three way pickup selector switch. Mfd. 1985 to 1988.

	$275	$225	$175	$115	$95	$85	$65

Last Mfr.'s Sug. Retail was $399.50.

PREDATOR (Contemporary Model) — offset double cutaway poplar body, white pickguard, bolt-on maple neck, 22 fret maple fingerboard with black dot inlay, 25 1/2" scale, Power Bend standard vibrato, 6 on one side tuners, chrome hardware, 3 single coil pickups, volume/2 tone controls, 5 position switch. Available in Black, Red and White finishes. Mfg. 1990 to current.

Mfr.'s Sug. Retail	$299	$239	$179	$150	$110	$95	$80	$70

In 1996, when the Predator AX was discontinued, the Predator model was upgraded with the rosewood fingerboard, 2 single coil/1 humbucker pickups, and Power Bend III tremolo system.

The Predator model is currently offered in Metallic Red, Metallic Dark Blue, Sunburst, and Gloss Black.

P

Grading	100%	98% MINT	95% EXC+	90% EXC	80% VG+	70% VG	60% G

Predator AX — similar to Predator, except has rosewood fingerboard with pearl dot inlay, 2 single coil/1 humbucker pickups, volume/tone control, 3 position mini switch. Available in Black, Powder Blue, Red and White finishes. Mfd. 1994 to 1995.

	$245	$210	$175	$140	$125	$115	$105

Last Mfr.'s Sug. retail price was $349.

Predator DX — similar to Predator AX, except has maple fingerboard. Mfd. 1994 to 1995.

	$245	$210	$175	$140	$125	$115	$105

Last Mfr.'s Sug. retail price was $349.

RAPTOR I — offset double cutaway body, white pickguard, bolt-on maple neck, 21 fret rosewood fingerboard with white dot inlay, 25 1/2" scale, Power Bend standard vibrato, 6 on one side tuners, chrome hardware, 3 single coil pickups, volume/2 tone controls, 5 position switch. Available in Gloss Black, Gloss Red and Gloss White finishes. Current Production.

Mfr.'s Sug. Retail	$219	$175	$131	$120	$100	$90	$80	$70

Raptor I Sunburst — similar to the Raptor I, except in Sunburst finish. Current production.

Mfr.'s Sug. Retail	$229	$183	$137	$125	$100	$90	$80	$70

RAZER — offset double cutaway-angular hardwood body, bi-laminated hard rock maple neck, 23 fret maple neck with black dot inlays, 24 3/4" scale, chrome hardware, six on a side tuners, 2 dual blade humbucking pickups, fixed bridge, master volume control, two tone controls (one per pickup), three way pickup selector. Available in Blood Red, White, Frost Blue, Silver, Inca Gold, Sunfire Red, and Black finishes. Mfg. 1983 to 1986.

	$275	$250	$200	$150	$100	$90	$75

Last Mfr.'s Sug. Retail was $399.50.

This model had the Octave Plus tremolo system optionally available.

The tone control for the humbucking pickups allows the capability of single or dual coil output. Fully opening the pot to "10" achieves single coil mode. Turning counterclockwise to "7" brings the second coil into operation. Tone circuitry is standard in function between "7" and "0".

REACTOR — single cutaway poplar body, white pickguard, metal controls mounted plate, bolt-on maple neck, 22 fret maple fingerboard with black dot inlay, 25 1/2" scale, strings thru fixed bridge, 6 on one side tuners, chrome hardware, 2 single coil pickups, volume/tone control, 3 position switch. Available in Gloss Black, Gloss Red and Gloss White finishes. Current production.

Mfr.'s Sug. Retail	$409	$327	$245	$210	$150	$100	$90	$80

Reactor AX — similar to Reactor, except has Alder or Swamp Ash body, and 2 Db2-T dual blade humbucking pickups. Available in Gloss Black, Powder Blue, Sea Green (Alder body: pearloid pickguard); Blonde or Sunburst (Swamp Ash: tortoiseshell pickguard). Current Production.

Mfr.'s Sug. Retail	$559	$447	$335	$300	$240	$180	$130	$110

T SERIES

The T series guitars and basses were originally designed by Chip Todd in 1977, and debuted at the 1978 NAMM show. The three prototypes shown were T-60 and T-30 guitars, and a T-40 bass.

Chip Todd was primarily an engineer who repaired guitars on the side. Todd was hired out of his Houston guitar repair shop, and initially handled the drafting and design by himself. Hartley Peavey had a great deal of input on the initial designs, and the tone circuit was invented by noted steel guitarist Orville "Red" Rhodes. Todd was eventually assisted by Gerald Pew, Bobby Low, and Charley Gressett. According to researcher Michael Wright, Chip Todd left Peavey in 1981 and currently works in the TV satellite electronics - although he does have a new patent on guitar design that he is considering applying for.

Peavey's inital concept was to use machinery to control efficiency and quality control. Borrowing an idea from gun manufacturing, Peavey bought a controlled carving machine to maintain strict tolerances in design. In a seeming parallel to the Fender debut of "plank guitars" and other derisive comment in 1951 leading to other manufacturers building solid body electrics in 1952, the guitar industry first insisted that "you can't build guitars on a computer". A year later, everybody was investigating numerical controllers (and later the CAD/CAM devices). If Leo Fender is the father of the mass produced solid body guitar (among other honors), then Hartley Peavey is the father of the modern solid body production technique.

(Source material courtesy Michael Wright, Guitar Stories Volume One)

T-15 — double offset cutaway body, bolt-on bi-laminated rock maple neck, 20 fret fingerboard, 23 1/2" scale, chrome hardware, six on a side tuners, cream and black laminated pickguard, two oversized 'blade' style single coil pickups, master volume knob, master tone knob, three way pickup selector switch. Available in Natural finish. Mfg. 1981 to 1983.

	$135	$125	$100	$90	$80	$70	$60

Last Mfr.'s Sug. Retail was $199.50.

The T-15 was offered with the optional "Electric Case". The molded plastic case's center area contained a 10 watt amp and 5" speaker, and had a pre- and post-gain controls, and an EQ control. The "Electric Case" can be viewed as Peavey's solid state version of Danelectro's tube "Amp-in-Case" concept. The T-15 Guitar with Electric Case retailed as a package for $259.50.

"The Sears, Roebuck Company introduced the Gene Autry "Roundup" guitar in the fall of 1931; it cost $9.75. The "Roundup" had a natural finished spruce top, mahogany back and sides and a mahogany neck."
—Steve Evans
TCG, May/June 1993

Grading	100%	98% MINT	95% EXC+	90% EXC	80% VG+	70% VG	60% G

T-25 — double offset cutaway body, bolt-on bi-laminated rock maple neck, 23 fret fingerboard, 24 3/4" scale, chrome hardware, six on a side tuners, two 'double blade' style humbucking pickups, master volume control, two tone controls (first for the neck pickup and the other for the bridge pickup), three way pickup selector switch. Available in Natural, Sunburst, Sunfire Red, and Frost Blue finishes. Mfg. 1982 to 1983.

	$210	$190	$160	$130	$120	$110	$100

Last Mfr.'s Sug. Retail ranged from $299.50 to $374.50.

The tone control for the humbucking pickup allows the capability of single or dual coil output. Fully opening the pot to "10" achieves single coil mode. Turning counterclockwise to "7" brings the second coil into operation. Bridge pickup is full humbucking at the "0" setting.

T-25 Special — similar to the T-25, except features a black phenolic fingerboard, Gloss Black finish, and a black laminated pickguard. Mfd. 1982 to 1983.

	$250	$210	$180	$160	$130	$110	$100

Last Mfr.'s Sug. Retail was $399.50.

T-26 — double offset cutaway body, bolt-on bi-laminated rock maple neck, 23 fret fingerboard, 24 3/4" scale, chrome hardware, six on a side tuners, three 'blade' style single coil pickups, master volume control, two tone controls (first for the neck pickup and the other for the bridge pickup), five way pickup selector switch. Available in Natural, Sunburst, Sunfire Red, and Frost Blue finishes. Mfg. 1982 to 1983.

	$250	$210	$180	$160	$140	$115	$105

Last Mfr.'s Sug. Retail ranged from $324 to $419.

Both the neck and the bridge single coil pickup have their own tone control. **The center pickup does not have a tone control, but functions thru either of the two tone controls when employed in the humbucking modes.**

T-27 — double offset cutaway body, bolt-on bi-laminated rock maple neck, 23 fret fingerboard, 24 3/4" scale, chrome hardware, six on a side tuners, two 'blade' style single coil pickups and one 'double blade' style humbucker, master volume control, two tone controls (first for neck and middle pickups and the other for the bridge pickup), five way pickup selector switch. Available in Natural, Sunburst, Sunfire Red, and Frost Blue finishes. Mfg. 1982 to 1983.

	$230	$205	$180	$160	$140	$115	$105

Last Mfr.'s Sug. Retail ranged from $344 to $419.

The tone control for the humbucking pickup allows the capability of single or dual coil output. Fully opening the pot to "10" achieves single coil mode. Turning counterclockwise to "7" brings the second coil into operation. Bridge pickup is full humbucking at the "0" setting.

T-27 Limited — similar to the T-27, except features upgraded electronics and a rosewood neck. Mfd. 1982 to 1983.

	$260	$235	$190	$165	$145	$120	$110

Last Mfr.'s Sug. Retail was $374.50.

T-30 — double offset cutaway body, bolt-on bi-laminated rock maple neck, 20 fret fingerboard, 23 1/2" scale, six on a side tuners, three 'blade' style single coil pickups, master volume knob, master tone knob, five way pickup selector switch. Available in Natural finish. Mfg. 1981 to 1983.

	$200	$180	$160	$130	$110	$95	$85

Last Mfr.'s Sug. Retail was $259.50.

The T-30 Guitar w/Electric Case package retailed at $319.50.

T-60 — double offset cutaway body, bolt-on bi-laminated rock maple neck, 23 fret maple fingerboard, 25 1/2" scale, chrome hardware, six on a side tuners, two 'double blade' style humbucking pickups, two volume controls, two tone controls (one per pickup), pickup phase switch, three way pickup selector switch. Available in Natural, Black, White, and Sunburst finish. Mfd. 1978 to 1988.

	$250	$225	$190	$160	$135	$115	$95

First Mfr.'s Sug. Retail was $350 (with case).
Last Mfr.'s Sug. Retail ranged from $399.50 to $459.50.

Finishes other than Natural command a higher premium.

The T-60 was the first Peavey production guitar.

The T-60 had an optional rosewood fingerboard.

Blood Red and Burgundy finishes were offered in 1982.

The original "Red" Rhodes-designed pickups allows the capability of single or dual coil output. Fully opening the pot to "10" achieves single coil mode. Turning counterclockwise to "7" brings the second coil into operation, and achieving full range humbucking tone. Rotation of the control from "7" to "0" further contours the tone circuit.

The Phase switch is a two position switch which reverses the coil relationship in the bridge pickup when the **pickup switch is in the middle position.** Up is in phase, and down is out-of-phase.

T-JR (JUNIOR) — similar to the T-60 guitar, except featured an "octave" neck and smaller body dimensions (like a mandolin). Mfg. 1982 to 1983.

	$150	$140	$120	$100	$90	$80	$75

Last Mfr.'s Sug. Retail was $199.95

T-1000 LT — double offset Western Poplar body, rock maple neck, 24 fret rosewood fingerboard, Recessed Floyd Rose licensed Double locking tremolo system, 2 single coil and 1 coil-tapped humbucker pickups, master volume control, master tone control, 5 way pickup selector switch. Mfd. 1992 to 1994.

	100%	98%	95%	90%	80%	70%	60%
	$525	$475	$400	$340	$280	$225	$185

Last Mfr.'s Sug. Retail was $699.

Tracer Series

The original Tracer model was introduced in 1988. Subsequent models were styled to compete with Charvel/Jackson, Ibanez, and Kramer instruments in the Hard Rock music genre.

TRACER — offset double cutaway poplar body, bolt-on bi-laminated maple neck, 22 fret maple fingerboard with black dot inlay, 25 1/2" scale, Power Bend standard tremolo, graphlon nut, 6 on one side tuners, chrome hardware, 1 humbucker pickup, volume/tone control. Available in Black, Red and White finishes. Mfg. 1988 to 1994.

	$215	$195	$165	$130	$120	$110	$100

Last Mfr.'s Sug. Retail was $299.

In 1991, after numerous Tracer models had been offered, the original Tracer was "turbo charged" from its basic model with the addition of 2 single coil pickups, 24 fret maple fingerboard, a new 24 3/4" scale, and a five way pickup selector switch. The "new, updated" Tracer was similar to the Tracer Custom without the Kahler locking tremolo.

Tracer LT — similar to updated and revised Tracer ("Tracer '91"?), except has rosewood fingerboard with white dot inlay, a Floyd Rose double locking vibrato, and black hardware. Available in Black, Metallic Blue, Metallic Red and White finishes. Mfg. 1991 to 1994.

	$300	$260	$215	$175	$155	$140	$130

Last Mfr.'s Sug. Retail was $424.

TRACER II — similar to the original Tracer ("Tracer '88"?), except features a single coil pickup (neck position) and humbucker (bridge position), and three way pickup selector switch. Available in Black, Metallic Blue, Metallic Red and White finishes. Mfg. 1989 to 1990.

	$300	$260	$215	$175	$155	$140	$130

Last Mfr.'s Sug. Retail was $359.

Tracer II '89 — similar to updated and revised Tracer ("Tracer '91"?), with the 24 3/4" scale, yet shares all the same hardware and configuration of the previous Tracer II. Thus, the only verifiable difference is the scale length. Whip out the measuring stick. Mfg. 1989 to 1991.

	$300	$260	$215	$175	$155	$140	$130

Last Mfr.'s Sug. Retail was $359.

TRACER CUSTOM — similar to the updated and revised Tracer ("Tracer '91"?) with the 2 single coil/1 humbucker pickups, but maintains the original 25 1/2" scale. New additions include a five way pickup selector switch, a coil tap, black hardware, and a Kahler/Floyd Rose double locking tremolo. Mfg. 1989 to 1990.

	$425	$400	$340	$275	$215	$170	$130

Last Mfr.'s Sug. Retail was $529.

Tracer Custom '89 — similar to the Tracer Custom, except has shorter 24 3/4" scale length. Also similar to the revised Tracer ("Tracer '91"), except the Custom '89 has a locking Kahler tremolo and the Tracer doesn't. Mfg. 1989 to 1991.

	$325	$290	$235	$195	$165	$145	$130

Last Mfr.'s Sug. Retail was $459.

TRACER DELUXE — similar to the Tracer II, except has a Kahler/Floyd Rose locking tremolo and black hardware; the Deluxe model maintains the original 25 1/2" scale and 22 fret fingerboard. Mfg. 1988 to 1990.

	$320	$280	$225	$175	$155	$140	$130

Last Mfr.'s Sug. Retail was $429.

Tracer Deluxe '89 — similar to the Tracer Deluxe, except has shorter 24 3/4" scale, and a 24 fret maple fingerboard. Mfg. 1989 to 1991.

	$325	$290	$235	$195	$165	$145	$130

Last Mfr.'s Sug. Retail was $459.

This model has a reverse headstock optionally available.

Vandenburg Series

The Vandenburg series of the late 1980s was designed in conjunction with guitarist Adrian Vandenburg.

VANDENBERG SIGNATURE — offset double cutaway poplar body with side slot cuts, bolt-on bi-laminated maple neck, 24 fret ebony fingerboard with pearl dot inlay, 24 3/4" scale, Kahler/Floyd Rose double locking vibrato, reverse headstock, 6 on the other side tuners, black hardware, single coil/Alnico humbucker pickups, volume/tone control, 3 position switch. Available in '62 Blue, Black, Pearl White, Raspberry Pearl, Rock-It Pink and Sunfire Red finishes. Mfg. 1988 to 1994.

	$425	$390	$305	$250	$180	$160	$125

Last Mfr.'s Sug. Retail was $850.

This model came new with a certificate signed by Adrian Vandenberg.

P

Grading	100%	98% MINT	95% EXC+	90% EXC	80% VG+	70% VG	60% G

Vandenburg Custom — offset double cutaway mahogany body with side slot cuts, set maple neck, 24 fret rosewood fingerboard with white stripes and arrows inlay, 24 3/4" scale, Kahler/Floyd Rose double locking vibrato, reverse headstock, 6 on the other side tuners, black hardware, 1 HCS single coil/1 Alnico humbucker pickups, 2 master volume controls, 3 position pickup selector knob. Available in Transparent Honey Sunburst, Transparent Pink and Transparent Violet finishes. Mfg. 1989 to 1994.

	$880	$740	$600	$460	$405	$360	$300

Last Mfr.'s Sug. Retail was $1,299.

The neck pickup volume control has a push-pull coil-tap built in. The coil tap directly affects the **bridge** humbucker, and converts it from single coil to humbucker mode.

Vandenburg Quilt Top — offset double cutaway mahogany body with side slot cuts, carved Quilted Maple top, set mahogany neck, 24 fret bound rosewood fingerboard with white stripes and arrows inlay, Floyd Rose double locking vibrato, reverse headstock, 6 on the other side tuners, gold hardware, 2 humbucker pickups, volume/tone control, 3 position pickup selector switch, coil tap mini switch. Available in Transparent Honey Sunburst, Transparent Pink and Transparent Violet finishes. Mfg. 1990 to 1994.

	$980	$840	$700	$560	$505	$460	$420

Last Mfr.'s Sug. Retail was $1,399.

Vandenberg Puzzle — similar to the Vandenberg Quilt Top, except features a one piece mahogany body with carved top, and black finish with white puzzle graphics. Mfd. 1989 to 1992.

	$1,080	$940	$800	$760	$605	$560	$450

Last Mfr.'s Sug. Retail was $1,599.

VORTEX 1 — single cutaway flared hardwood body, bi-laminated maple neck, 22 fret "Polyglide" polymer fingerboard, 25 1/2" scale, black hardware, six on a side tuners, Kahler locking tremolo system, two P-12 adjustable polepiece humbucking pickups, master volume knob, master tone knob, three way selector switch. Available in Jet Black, Flourescent Red, Flourescent Pink, and Pearl White finishes. Mfd. 1985 to 1986.

	$450	$840	$700	$560	$505	$460	$420

Last Mfr.'s Sug. Retail was $699.50.

VORTEX 2 — similar specifications as the Vortex 1, except features a tapered "sharkfin/Flying V" body design. All other pickup and hardware descriptions as previously described. Available in Jet Black, Flourescent Red, Flourescent Pink, and Pearl White finishes. Mfd. 1985 to 1986.

	$450	$840	$700	$560	$505	$460	$420

Last Mfr.'s Sug. Retail was $699.50.

ELECTRIC BASS

Axcelerator Series

AXCELERATOR — offset double cutaway poplar body, pearloid pickguard, bolt-on maple neck, 21 rosewood fingerboard with pearl dot inlay, fixed bridge, 4 on one side tuners, chrome hardware, 2 VFL active covered humbucker pickups, volume/stacked tone/mix controls. Available in Candy Apple Red, Cobalt Blue, Metallic Gold, Metallic Green and Pearl Black finishes. System requires a 9 volt battery. Mfd. 1994 to date.

Mfr.'s Sug. Retail	$600	$480	$360	$300	$240	$215	$195	$180

AXCELERATOR 2-T — offset double cutaway poplar body, pearloid pickguard, bolt-on maple neck, 21 rosewood fingerboard with pearl dot inlay, 2-Tek bridge, 4 on one side tuners, chrome hardware, 2 VFL active covered humbucker pickups, volume/stacked tone/mix controls. Available in Candy Apple Red, Cobalt Blue, Metallic Gold, Metallic Green and Pearl Black finishes. System requires a 9 volt battery. New 1996.

Mfr.'s Sug. Retail	$899	$719	$539	$500

In 1996, the standard Axcelerator model was offered with a 2-Tek bridge. While physically the same specifications as the original, the addition of the 2-Tek technology opens up the sonic qualities by a perceptible amount.

Axcelerator 5 — similar to Axcelerator, except has 5 strings, 4/1 per side tuners, 35" scale, Wilkinson WBB5 bridge. Available in Candy Apple Red, Metallic Purple, Metallic Silver and Pearl Black finishes. Current production.

Mfr.'s Sug. Retail	$769	$615	$461	$390	$310	$260	$240	$220

The revised design Axcelerator is optionally available with a fretless neck.

Axcelerator Fretless — similar to Axcelerator, except has fretless pau ferro fingerboard. Available in Candy Apple Red, Cobalt Blue, Metallic Gold and Pearl Black finishes. Mfd. 1994 to 1995.

	$455	$390	$325	$260	$235	$215	$195

Last Mfr.'s Sug. Retail was $650.

Axcelerator Plus — similar to Axcelerator, except has swamp ash body and pau ferro fingerboard. Available in Blonde or Sunburst finish with a tortoiseshell pickguard, or Transparent Grape or Transparent Red finish with pearloid pickguard. Current production.

Mfr.'s Sug. Retail	$799	$639	$479	$450	$375

B-NINETY — offset double cutaway poplar body with 'access scoops', bolt-on bi-laminated maple neck, 21 fret rosewood fingerboard with white dot inlay, 34" scale, fixed bridge, graphlon nut, 4 on one side "mini" bass tuners, black hardware, P/J-style pickups, 2 volume/1 master tone controls. Available in '62 Blue, Black, Charcoal Gray, Pearl White, Raspberry Pearl and Sunfire Red finishes. Mfd. 1990 to 1994.

	$350	$300	$250	$200	$180	$165	$150

Last Mfr.'s Sug. Retail was $499.

This model was also available in a left handed version.

Grading	100%	98% MINT	95% EXC+	90% EXC	80% VG+	70% VG	60% G

B-Ninety Active — similar to B-Ninety, except has active electronics. Mfd. 1990 to 1994.

		$385	$330	$275	$220	$200	$180	$165

Last Mfr.'s Sug. Retail was $549.

B-QUAD-4 — deep offset double cutaway Flame Maple body, bolt-on Modulus Graphite neck, 24 fret phenolic fingerboard with pearl "B" inlay at 12th fret, fixed bridge, 4 on one side tuners, gold hardware, 2 covered active humbucker/4 piezo bridge pickups, master volume, 2 stacked volume/tone controls, piezo volume/tone controls, stereo/mono switch, Dual mono/stereo 1/4" outputs. Available in Transparent Teal and Transparent Violet finishes. Mfg. 1994 to date.

Mfr.'s Sug. Retail $2,118 $1,588 $1,059

The B-Quad-4 was designed in conjunction with jazz bassist Brian Bromberg, and the design is based in part on Bromberg's prior custom-built model.

This model has black hardware with Natural and White finishes optionally available.

Instrument contains on-board 4 x 2 stereo mixing controls for the piezo pickup system. There are four pairs of volume/stereo panning controls on the back plate for adjustment of the stereo field from the dual output jacks.

B-QUAD-5 — similar to the B-Quad-4, except has five strings and a 5-on-a-side headstock. Introduced in 1995.

Mfr.'s Sug. Retail $2,418 $1,813 $1,209

CYBERBASS (Formerly MIDIBASS) — offset double cutaway poplar body, black pearloid lam pickguard, bolt-on maple neck, 22 fret rosewood fingerboard with pearl dot inlay, fixed bridge, 4 on one side tuners, chrome hardware, 2 covered active humbucker pickups, 2 stacked controls, mini switch. Available in Candy Apple Red, Montana Green and Pearl Black finishes. Mfg. 1994 to date.

Mfr.'s Sug. Retail $1,799 $1,349 $899

This model has volume/volume/MIDI volume/master tone controls and can be used to trigger a synthesized sound module, sound bass notes through the conventional magnetic pickups, or combine the two.

Cyberbass 5 — similar to the Cyberbass, except has five strings and a 5-on-a-side headstock. Introduced in 1995.

Mfr.'s Sug. Retail $1,999 $1,499 $999

Dyna-Bass Series

DYNA-BASS — offset double cutaway poplar body, bolt-on bi-laminated maple neck, 21 fret rosewood fingerboard with white dot inlay, 34" scale, Schaller fixed bridge, graphlon nut, 4 on one side "mini" tuners, gold hardware, 2 active humbucker pickups, volume control, 2 stacked tone controls, pickup blend control, active/passive bypass mini switch. System requires a 9 volt battery. Available in '62 Blue, Black, Charcoal Gray, Pearl White and Sunfire Red finishes. Mfg. 1985 to 1994.

		$540	$450	$375	$290	$250	$230	$210

Last Mfr.'s Sug. Retail was $729.

A Kahler Bass Tremolo was optionally available.

In 1991, the original Super Ferrite pickups were changed to newer humbucker style.

In 1986, the Dyna-Bass was offered with an optional Kahler Bass Tremolo (retail list $929).

Dyna-Bass 5 — similar to Dyna-Bass, except has 5 strings, 4/1 per side tuners, 5 string Schaller bridge, and 34" scale. Mfd. 1987 to 1994.

		$525	$450	$375	$300	$270	$245	$225

Last Mfr.'s Sug. Retail was $799.50.

Dyna-Bass Unity — similar to Dyna-Bass, except has active P/J pickups, neck through contruction, black chrome hardware, and 21 fret Ebony fingerboard. Mfd. 1987 to 1990.

		$525	$450	$375	$300	$270	$245	$225

Last Mfr.'s Sug. Retail was $799.

Dyna-Bass Unity Ltd. — similar to Dyna-Bass Unity, except has figured maple top, gold hardware. Available in Honey Sunburst finish. Mfd. 1988 to 1990.

		$775	$745	$650	$580	$490	$400	$330

Last Mfr.'s Sug. Retail was $1,100.

Forum Series

FORUM — offset double cutaway poplar body, white laminated pickguard, bolt-on bi-laminated Eastern maple neck, 21 fret rosewood fingerboard with pearl dot inlay, 34" scale fixed bridge, graphlon nut, 4 on one side tuners, chrome hardware, P-style/J-style ceramic humbucker pickups, 2 volume/1 tone control. Available in Black, Red and White finishes. Mfr. 1993 to date.

Mfr.'s Sug. Retail	$499	$374	$249	$240	$160	$145	$130	$120

In 1995, the P/J pickup combination was replaced with an active humbucker in the 'P' position. The three controls then became volume, treble and bass controls. The new configuration is the current model.

Forum Plus — similar to Forum, except has P-style/J-style active pickups. Available in Candy Apple Red, Cobalt Blue, Metallic Green and Pearl Black finishes. Mfd. 1993 to 1995.

		$425	$360	$270	$220	$190	$170	$160

Last Mfr.'s Sug. retail price was $520.

P

Grading	100%	98% MINT	95% EXC+	90% EXC	80% VG+	70% VG	60% G

Forum AX — similar to the revised 1995 Forum, except has either Alder or Swamp Ash bodies, ABM fixed bridge, 2 active VFL humbuckers, and volume/pickup blend/tone controls. Available in Candy Apple Red, Pearl Black (alder bodies); Blonde, Sunburst (Swamp Ash bodies) finishes. Current production.

Mfr.'s Sug. Retail	$729	$583	$437	$425	$315	$240	$190	$160

Forum 5 — similar to the revised 1995 Forum, except has 5 strings, 35" scale, either Alder or Swamp Ash bodies, Peavey fixed bridge, 2 active VFL-Plus humbuckers, and volume/pickup blend/tone controls. Available in Pearl White, Pearl Black (alder bodies); Transparent Grape, Sunburst (Swamp Ash bodies) finishes. Current production.

Mfr.'s Sug. Retail	$789	$631	$473	$455	$335	$270	$205	$180

Foundation Series

FOUNDATION — offset double cutaway poplar body, bolt-on maple neck, 21 fret maple fingerboard with black dot inlay, fixed bridge, 34" scale, graphlon nut, 4 on one side tuners, chrome hardware, 2 single coil pickups, 2 volume/1 tone control. Available in Gloss Black, Gloss Red, Sunburst and Gloss White finishes. Mfg. 1983 to date.

Mfr.'s Sug. Retail	$439	$329	$219	$165	$130	$120	$110	$100

Add $30 for Foundation model with Rosewood fingerboard.

In 1994, Sunburst finish was discontinued.

Foundation 5 — similar to Foundation, except has 5 strings, 4/1 per side tuners.

Mfr.'s Sug. Retail	$470	$352	$235	$225	$180	$160	$150	$135

Foundation Fretless — similar to Foundation, except has fretless rosewood fingerboard with fret lines.

Mfr.'s Sug. Retail	$429	$343	$257	$215	$175	$140	$130	$120

Foundation Custom — similar to the Foundation, except features a black phenolic fingerboard and pearly or metallic finishes. Mfd. 1984 to 1985.

	$310	$275	$250	$200	$125	$90	$75

Last Mfr.'s Sug. Retail ranged from $394.50 to $474.50.

Foundation S — similar to Foundation, except has P/J humbucking pickups, hardwood body, two volume/1 tone control. Mfd. 1986 to 1990.

	$360	$330	$280	$220	$180	$150	$130

Last Mfr.'s Sug. retail price was $419.50.

Foundation S Active — similar to Foundation S, except has active Bi-Fet P/J humbucking pickups. System requires a 9 volt battery. Mfd. 1988 to 1990.

	$400	$380	$310	$250	$190	$150	$130

Last Mfr.'s Sug. retail price was $449.50.

FURY — offset double cutaway poplar body, white pickguard, bolt-on maple neck, 21 fret maple fingerboard with black dot inlay, 34" scale, fixed bridge, graphlon nut, 4 on one side tuners, chrome hardware, P-style pickup, volume/tone control. Available in Gloss Black, Gloss Red, Sunburst and Gloss White finishes. Mfg. 1983 to date.

Mfr.'s Sug. Retail	$399	$319	$239	$230	$180	$160	$140	$110

The original 1983 Fury model was similar in design to the earlier T-20.

In 1994, the Sunburst finish was discontinued.

MIDIBASE — offset double cutaway alder body, maple neck, 21 fret rosewood fingerboard with white dot inlay, fixed bridge, graphlon nut, 4 on one side tuners, black hardware, 2 humbucker pickups, 2 volume/tone/mix controls, bypass switch. Available in Pearl White finish. Mfg. 1992 to 1993.

	$1,400	$1,080	$850	$N/A	$N/A	$N/A	$N/A

Last Mfr.'s Sug. Retail was $1,800.

Basic concept and MIDI controller design by Australian bassist and electrical engineering student Steve Chick. Chick began working on a bass synthesizer in his spare time in 1982, put out his own MB4 'retrofit' system during the mid 1980s, and began working with the Peavey corporation in 1991.

In early 1994, the 'MidiBass' name was changed to 'Cyberbass' after another company proved prior use of the name (See CYBERBASS).

MILESTONE II — offset double cutaway body, single piece maple neck, 20 fret rosewood fingerboard, 34" scale, fixed bridge, one split-coil pickup, 4 on a side tuners, chrome hardware, white laminated pickguard, volume/tone controls. Available in Gloss Black, Gloss Red, Gloss White, and Powder Blue Sunburst finishes. Current production.

Mfr.'s Sug. Retail	$269	$201	$134	$120	$100	$90	$80	$70

Add $10 for Milestone II in Sunburst.

PALAEDIUM — offset double cutaway three piece alder body, bolt-on maple neck, 21 fret ebony fingerboard with pearl dot inlay, 34" scale, Leo Quan Bad Ass II fixed bridge, graphlon nut, 4 on one side tuners, gold hardware, 2 humbucker pickups, volume/tone/mix control. Available in Transparent Amber, Transparent Red and Transparent Violet finishes. Mfd. 1991 to 1994.

	$560	$480	$400	$320	$290	$265	$240

Last Mfr.'s Sug. Retail was $800.

The Palaedium model was developed in part by bassist Jeff Berlin.

Grading	100%	98% MINT	95% EXC+	90% EXC	80% VG+	70% VG	60% G

PATRIOT — offset double cutaway maple or southern ash body, bi-laminated maple neck, 21 fret fingerboard, 34" scale, fixed bridge, four on a side tuners, chrome hardware, graphlon nut, one single coil pickup, black laminated pickguard, volume/tone controls. Available in Gloss or Satin finishes. Mfd. 1984 to 1988.

	$250	$200	$175	$150	$130	$110	$90

Last Mfr.'s Sug. Retail ranged $225 to $332.

Patriot Custom — similar to the Patriot, except features a rosewood fingerboard and color matched peghead. Mfd. 1986 to 1988.

	$250	$200	$175	$150	$130	$110	$90

Last Mfr.'s Sug. Retail was $310.

RJ-IV — offset double cutaway maple body, neck-thru body bi-laminated maple neck, 21 fret Macassar Ebony fingerboard with pearl arrow inlay, fixed bridge, graphlon nut, 4 on one side "mini" tuners, Hipshot Bass Extender Key, black hardware, P-style/J-style active pickups, volume control, 3 band EQ controls, pickup selector toggle switch. Available in Black Pearl Burst, Blue Pearl Burst, Purple Pearl Burst and Red Pearl Burst finishes. Mfd. 1990 to 1994.

	$770	$660	$550	$440	$395	$365	$330

Last Mfr.'s Sug. Retail was $1,049.

Model designed in conjunction with bassist Randy Jackson.

This model had a koa body/neck, rosewood fingerboard, and Hipshot D Tuner optionally available.

RSB — offset double cutaway poplar body, bolt-on rock maple neck, 24 fret maple fingerboard with black dot inlay, 34" scale, fixed brass bridge, 4 on one side "mini" tuners, gold hardware, graphlon nut, 2 VFL active humbucker pickups, volume/tone/mix controls. Available in Black finish. Mfg. 1993 to 1995.

	$560	$480	$410	$330	$250	$230	$210

Last Mfr.'s Sug. retail price was $700.

RSB Koa — similar to RSB, except has koa body, pau ferro fingerboard with pearl dot inlay. Available in Oil finish. Mfd. 1993 to 1995.

	$640	$560	$480	$410	$330	$265	$240

Last Mfr.'s Sug. retail price was $800.

RUDY SARZO SIGNATURE — offset double cutaway ash body, thru body maple/purpleheart 5 piece neck, 24 fret ebony fingerboard with pearl oval inlay, fixed Schaller brass bridge, brass nut, 4 on one side tuners, gold hardware, 2 ceramic humbucker pickups, volume/tone/3 band EQ controls, bypass switch, active electronics. Available in Transparent Black, Transparent Red and Transparent Violet finishes. Mfd. 1989 to 1994.

	$770	$660	$550	$440	$395	$365	$330

Last Mfr.'s Sug. Retail was $1,100.

T SERIES

The T series guitars and basses were originally designed by Chip Todd in 1977, and three models debuted in 1978 (T-60 and T-30 guitars, and a T-40 bass).

T-20 — double offset cutaway maple or southern ash body, bi-laminated hard rock maple neck, 21 fret maple fingerboard, 34" scale, chrome hardware, fixed bridge, four on a side headstock, 'single blade' single coil pickup, volume knob, tone knob, brown laminated pickguard. Available in Natural, Sunfire Red, and Frost Blue finishes. Mfd. 1982 to 1985.

	$200	$175	$150	$125	$115	$100	$90

Last Mfr.'s Sug. Retail ranged from $299 to $374.

This model was also available with a fretless neck.

T-40 — double offset cutaway body, bolt-on bi-laminated rock maple neck, 23 fret fingerboard, 34" scale, chrome hardware, fixed bridge, four on a side tuners, two 'double blade' style humbucking pickups, two volume controls, two tone controls (one per pickup), pickup phase switch, three way pickup selector switch, brown laminated pickguard. Available in Natural, White, Black, and Sunburst finishes. Mfd. 1978 to 1988.

	$250	$200	$150	$125	$115	$100	$90

Last Mfr.'s Sug. Retail ranged from $399 to $484 (with case).

The T-40 was the first Peavey production bass.

This model was also offered with a fretless neck.

In 1982, Blood Red and Burgundy finished were offered.

The original "Red" Rhodes-designed pickups allows the capability of single or dual coil output. Fully opening the tone potentiometer to "10" achieves single coil mode. Turning counterclockwise to "7" brings the second coil into operation, and achieving full range humbucking tone. Rotation of the control from "7" to "0" further contours the tone circuit.

The Phase switch is a two position switch which reverses the coil relationship in the bridge pickup when the **pickup switch is in the middle position**. Up is in phase, and down is out-of-phase.

T-45 — double offset cutaway hardwood body, bi-laminated hard rock maple neck, 21 fret maple fingerboard, 34" scale, chrome hardware, fixed bridge, four on a side tuners, dual blade humbucker, master volume knob, two tone knobs. Available in Black, White, Sunburst, Blood Red, and Burgundy finishes. Mfd. 1982 to 1986.

	$225	$200	$150	$125	$115	$100	$90

Last Mfr.'s Sug. Retail ranged from $434.50 to $459.50.

The humbucking pickup can be used in either single coil or dual coil mode. Fully opening the tone potentiometer to "10" achieves single coil mode. Turning counterclockwise to "7" brings the second coil into operation, and achieving full range humbucking tone. Rotation of the control from "7" to "0" further contours the tone circuit.

"...now you have to devote the whole mortgage to the purchase of some varieties of vintage American guitars..."

—Jay Scott

TCG, Mar/Apr 1991

Grading		100%	98% MINT	95% EXC+	90% EXC	80% VG+	70% VG	60% G

TL-FIVE — offset double cutaway Eastern Flame Maple body, neck-thru body maple/purpleheart 5 piece neck, 24 fret ebony fingerboard with pearl oval inlay, Schaller fixed brass bridge, graphlon nut, 3/2 per side tuners, gold hardware, 2 Super Ferrite humbucker pickups, volume/blend controls, treble/mid/bass controls, bypass mini-toggle, 3-band active electronics. Available in Honey Sunburst, Transparent Black, Transparent Blue, Transparent Emerald, Transparent Red and Transparent Violet finishes. Mfd. 1988 to date.

		100%	98%	95%	90%	80%	70%	60%
Mfr.'s Sug. Retail	$1,699	$1,274	$849	$750	$600	$540	$495	$450

In 1991, the VFL humbuckers were introduced.

In 1994, the Transparent Violet finish was discontinued.

TL-Six — similar to TL-Five, except has 6 strings, pearl arrow fingerboard inlay, 4/2 per side tuners, Kahler 6 string bridge, gold hardware, 2 P-style pickups. Mfd. 1989 to date.

		100%	98%	95%	90%	80%	70%	60%
Mfr.'s Sug. Retail	$1,899	$1,519	$1,139	$950	$760	$685	$625	$570

UNITY — offset double cutaway poplar body with scoop access styling, neck-thru body bi-laminated maple neck, 21 fret rosewood fingerboard with pearl dot inlay, fixed bridge, graphlon nut, 4 on one side tuners, black hardware, P-style/J-style pickups, 2 volume/tone control. Available in '62 Blue, Black, Charcoal Gray, Pearl White and Sunfire Red finishes. Mfg. 1987 to 1994.

			98%	95%	90%	80%	70%	60%
			$490	$420	$350	$280	$250	$230	$210

Last Mfr.'s Sug. Retail was $700.

Unity Koa — similar to Unity, except has solid Koa neck-thru design, Koa body, gold hardware. Available in Natural finish. Mfg. 1988 to 1994.

			98%	95%	90%	80%	70%	60%
			$525	$450	$375	$300	$270	$245	$225

Last Mfr.'s Sug. Retail was $750.

M. V. PEDULLA

Instruments built in Rockland, Massachusetts since 1975.

The M.V. Pedulla company was founded back in the late 1970s by brothers Michael Vincent and Ted Pedulla. They originally produced some acoustic guitars, as well as electrics (one model outfitted with MIDI triggers compatible with the Roland GR-700 series). Once they discovered the unique design that lead to the MVP and Buzz bass models, they began to specialize directly in high quality handcrafted basses.

Stock equipment found on M.V. Pedulla basses include Bartolini pickups and on-board preamps, ABM bridges, and Pedulla/Gotoh tuning machines.

ELECTRIC BASS

All models in this series are available with the following options:

Add $300 for left handed version.

Add $100 for birdseye maple fingerboard.

Add $225 for active tone filter system (TBIBT).

Add $200 for custom tinted colors: Arctic Night, Charcoal, Emerald Green, Vintage Cherry or Violet.

MVP/Buzz Series

This series consists of 2 models, the MVP and the Buzz. The MVP is a fretted instrument, while the Buzz is fretless - all other aspects are identical. Both Mark Egan and Tim Landers helped design and perfect the Buzz Bass. The following are model descriptions and prices in this series:

Add $100 for black or gold hardware; the Deluxe.

Add $200 for flame maple body, black or gold hardware; the Custom (A).

Add $400 for higher quality flame maple body, black or gold hardware; the Custom (AA).

Add $600 for highest quality flame maple body, black or gold hardware; the Signature (AAA).

Add $900 for quilted maple body, black or gold hardware; the Limited Edition.

The Custom (A), Custom (AA), Signature and Limited Edition models are available in Amber Tint, Amber/Cherry Sunburst, Cherry Tint, Gold/Amber Sunburst, Light Gold Tint, Natural and Peacock Blue Tint finishes.

MVP 4/Buzz Series

STANDARD — offset double cutaway flame maple body, thru body maple laminate neck, 24 fret ebony fingerboard with pearl dot inlay, fixed bridge, brass nut, 2 per side tuners, chrome hardware, P-style/J-style Bartolini pickups, volume/tone/mix control, active electronics. Available in Champagne, Black, Lime Green, Metallic Midnight Blue, Red and White finishes. Disc. 1994.

			98%	95%	90%	80%	70%	60%
			$1,440	$1,265	$1085	$N/A	$N/A	$N/A	$N/A

Last Mfr.'s Sug. Retail was $1,775.

This model had 2 J-style or 2 humbucker Bartolini pickups optionally available.

Custom — similar to Standard except has AA figured maple body. New 1994.

		100%	98%	95%	90%	80%	70%	60%
Mfr.'s Sug. Retail	$2,375	$1,900	$1,425	$1,280				

Deluxe — similar to Standard, except it is new! Introduced in 1994.

		100%	98%	95%	90%	80%	70%	60%
Mfr.'s Sug. Retail	$2,175	$1,740	$1,305	$1,190				

Grading	100%	98% MINT	95% EXC+	90% EXC	80% VG+	70% VG	60% G

Signature — similar to Standard except has AAA figured maple body. New 1994.

| Mfr.'s Sug. Retail | $2,675 | $2,273 | $1,872 | $1,635 | | | |

MVP 5/Pentabuzz Series

STANDARD — offset double cutaway flame maple body, thru body maple laminate neck, 24 fret ebony fingerboard with pearl dot inlay, fixed bridge, brass nut, 3/2 per side tuners, chrome hardware, P-style/J-style Bartolini pickups, volume/tone/mix controls, active electronics. Available in Champagne, Black, Lime Green, Metallic Midnight Blue, Red and White finishes. Disc. 1994.

| | $1,550 | $1,340 | $1,135 | $N/A | $N/A | $N/A | $N/A |

Last Mfr.'s Sug. Retail was $2,075.

This model had 2 J-style or 2 humbucker Bartolini pickups optionally available.

Custom — similar to Standard except has AA figured maple body. New 1994.

| Mfr.'s Sug. Retail | $2,675 | $2,140 | $1,605 | $1,435 | | | |

Deluxe — similar to Standard, except has upgraded tonewoods. Introduced in 1994.

| Mfr.'s Sug. Retail | $2,475 | $1,980 | $1,485 | $1,335 | | | |

Signature — similar to Standard except has AAA figured maple body. New 1994.

| Mfr.'s Sug. Retail | $2,975 | $2,528 | $2,082 | $1,880 | | | |

MVP 6/Hexabuzz Series

STANDARD — offset double cutaway flame maple body, thru body maple laminate neck, 24 fret ebony fingerboard with pearl dot inlay, fixed bridge, brass nut, 3 per side tuners, chrome hardware, 2 J-style Bartolini pickups, volume/tone/mix controls, active electronics. Available in Champagne, Black, Lime Green, Metallic Midnight Blue, Red and White finishes. Disc. 1994.

| | $1,790 | $1,460 | $1,180 | $N/A | $N/A | $N/A | $N/A |

Last Mfr.'s Sug. Retail was $2,275.

This model had 2 humbucker Bartolini pickups optionally available.

Custom — similar to Standard except has AA figured maple body. New 1994.

| Mfr.'s Sug. Retail | $2,875 | $2,300 | $1,725 | $1,650 | | | |

Deluxe — similar to Standard, except has upgraded tonewoods. Introduced in 1994.

| Mfr.'s Sug. Retail | $2,675 | $2,140 | $1,605 | $1,535 | | | |

Signature — similar to Standard except has AAA figured maple body. New 1994.

| Mfr.'s Sug. Retail | $3,175 | $2,698 | $2,222 | $1,990 | | | |

MVP 8/Octabuzz Series

STANDARD — offset double cutaway flame maple body, thru body maple laminate neck, 24 fret ebony fingerboard with pearl dot inlay, fixed bridge, brass nut, 4 per side tuners, chrome hardware, P-style/J-style Bartolini pickups, volume/tone/mix controls, active electronics. Available in Champagne, Black, Lime Green, Metallic Midnight Blue, Red and White finishes. Disc. 1994.

| | $1,650 | $1,440 | $1,235 | $980 | $N/A | $N/A | $N/A |

Last Mfr.'s Sug. Retail was $2,075.

This model had 2 J-style or 2 humbucker Bartolini pickups optionally available.

Custom — similar to Standard except has AA figured maple body. Introduced in 1994.

| Mfr.'s Sug. Retail | $2,675 | $2,273 | $1,872 | $1,745 | | | |

Deluxe — similar to Standard, except has upgraded tonewoods. Introduced in 1994.

| Mfr.'s Sug. Retail | $2,475 | $2,103 | $1,732 | $1,635 | | | |

Signature — similar to Standard except has AAA figured maple body. New 1994.

| Mfr.'s Sug. Retail | $2,975 | $2,528 | $2,082 | $1,880 | | | |

Exotic Series

ES 4 CUSTOM — offset double cutaway flame maple body, thru body maple neck, 24 fret ebony fingerboard with pearl dot inlay, fixed bridge, brass nut, 2 per side Gotoh tuners, chrome hardware, 2 humbucker Bartolini pickups, volume/tone/mix controls, active electronics. Available in Amber Sunburst, Amber Tint, Cherry Sunburst, Cherry Tint, Emerald Tint, Green/Emerald Sunburst, Light Gold Tint, Natural and Peacock Blue Tint finishes. Disc. 1994.

| | $1,960 | $1,625 | $1,285 | $1050 | $N/A | $N/A | $N/A |

Last Mfr.'s Sug. Retail was $2,375.

ES 5 — similar to ES4, except has 5 strings, 3/2 per side tuners. Disc. 1994.

| | $2,170 | $1,805 | $1,335 | $1,065 | $N/A | $N/A | $N/A |

Last Mfr.'s Sug. Retail was $2,675.

Grading	100%	98% MINT	95% EXC+	90% EXC	80% VG+	70% VG	60% G

ES 6 — similar to ES4, except has 6 strings, 3 per side tuners. Disc. 1994.

	$2,200	$1,825	$1,430	$1,145	$N/A	$N/A	$N/A

Last Mfr.'s Sug. Retail was $2,875.

Mark Egan Signature Series

This series is co-designed by Mark Egan.

ME 4 — offset double cutaway flame maple body, thru body maple neck, 24 fret ebony fingerboard with pearl dot inlay, ebony thumbrests, fixed bridge, brass nut, 2 per side Gotoh tuners, chrome hardware, 2 J-style pickups, volume/tone/mix controls, active electronics. Available in Amber Sunburst, Amber Tint, Cherry Sunburst, Cherry Tint, Emerald Green Tint, Green/Blue Sunburst, Light Gold Tint, Natural and Peacock Blue Tint finishes. Curr. mfr.

Mfr.'s Sug. Retail	$2,875	$2,156	$1,437	$1,380	$1,095

ME 5 — similar to ME4, except has 5 strings, 3/2 per side tuners.

Mfr.'s Sug. Retail	$3,175	$2,381	$1,587	$1,525	$1,215

ME 6 — similar to ME4, except has 6 strings, 3 per side tuners.

Mfr.'s Sug. Retail	$3,375	$2,531	$1,687	$1,635	$1,280

ME 4F+8 — offset double cutaway flame maple body, double neck construct with all Pedulla neck, bridge, pickup and electronic variations available, one neck is a fretless 4 string, the other is a fretted 8 string. Available in Amber Sunburst, Amber Tint, Cherry Sunburst, Cherry Tint, Emerald Green Tint, Green/Blue Sunburst, Light Gold Tint, Natural and Peacock Blue Tint finishes. Curr. mfr.

Mfr.'s Sug. Retail	$6,150	$4,920	$3,690	$3,225	$2,865

SERIES II Series

S-II 4 — offset double cutaway poplar body, bolt-on maple neck, fretless or 22 fret rosewood fingerboard with pearl dot inlay, fixed bridge, brass nut, 2 per side Gotoh tuners, black hardware, P-style/J-style Bartolini pickups, volume/tone/mix controls. Available in Black, Champagne, Lime Green, Midnight Blue, Red, Yellow and White finishes. Disc. 1994.

	$835	$725	$660	$580	$N/A	$N/A	$N/A

Last Mfr.'s Sug. Retail was $1,195.

S-II 5 — similar to S-II 4, except has 5 strings, maple body, 3/2 per side tuners, humbucker Bartolini pickups, active electronics. Disc. 1994.

	$1,115	$955	$795	$635	$N/A	$N/A	$N/A

Last Mfr.'s Sug. Retail was $1,595.

S-II 6 — similar to S-II 4, except has 6 strings, maple body, 3 per side tuners, humbucker Bartolini pickups, active electronics. Disc. 1994.

	$1,255	$1,075	$895	$715	$N/A	$N/A	$N/A

Last Mfr.'s Sug. Retail was $1,795.

ThunderBass/ThunderBuzz Series

This series has 2 variations - the ThunderBass, which features a 24 fret fingerboard, and the ThunderBuzz, which has a fretless fingerboard.

T 4 — offset double cutaway figured maple body, thru body maple/bubinga 5 piece neck, ebony fingerboard with pearl dot inlay, fixed bridge, 2 per side MVP/Gotoh tuners, black hardware, 2 humbucker Bartolini pickups, volume/tone/pan controls. Available in Natural finish. Mfd. 1993 to date.

AA — higher grade figured maple body.

Mfr.'s Sug. Retail	$2,575	$1,931	$1,287	$1,230	$1,015

AAA — highest grade figured maple body.

Mfr.'s Sug. Retail	$2,875	$2,300	$1,725	$1,680	$1,295

This model has gold hardware optionally available.

T 5 — similar to T4, except has 5 strings, 3/2 per side tuners.

AA — higher grade figured maple body.

Mfr.'s Sug. Retail	$2,875	$2,300	$1,725	$1,660	$1,275

AAA — highest grade figured maple body.

Mfr.'s Sug. Retail	$3,175	$2,540	$1,905	$1,840	$1,525

T 6 — similar to T4, except has 6 strings, 3 per side tuners.

AA — higher grade figured maple body.

Mfr.'s Sug. Retail	$3,075	$2,460	$1,845	$1,675	$1,275

AAA — highest grade figured maple body.

Mfr.'s Sug. Retail	$3,375	$2,700	$2,025	$1,835	$1,495

T 8 — similar to T4, except has 8 strings, 2 per side tuners, 4 tuners on bottom bout. New 1994.

AA — higher grade figured maple body.

Mfr.'s Sug. Retail	$2,875	$2,156	$1,437	$1,430	$1,145

"'Taking offers' and 'what's it worth to you' are not appropriate selling positions for a dealer in fine collectible Americana"

—Jay Scott

TCG, Mar/Apr 1991

Grading		100%	98% MINT	95% EXC+	90% EXC	80% VG+	70% VG	60% G

AAA — highest grade figured maple body.
> Mfr.'s Sug. Retail $3,175 $2,540 $1,905 $1,690 $1,260

ThunderBass/ThunderBuzz Exotic Top Series

This series has 2 variations - the ThunderBass, which features a 24 fret fingerboard, and the ThunderBuzz, which has a fretless fingerboard.

ET 4 — offset double cutaway flame maple body, bubinga top, thru body neck, 24 fret ebony fingerboard with pearl dot inlay, fixed bridge, brass nut, 2 per side Gotoh tuners, chrome hardware, 2 humbucker Bartolini pickups, volume/tone/mix controls, active electronics. Available in Natural finish. Curr. mfr.
> Mfr.'s Sug. Retail $2,975 $2,231 $1,487 $1,400 $1,110
>> This model has AAA grade flamed maple, birdseye maple, quilted maple and zebrawood tops optionally available.

ET 5 — similar to ET4, except has 5 strings, 3/2 per side tuners.
> Mfr.'s Sug. Retail $3,275 $2,456 $1,637 $1,545 $1,230

ET 6 — similar to ET4, except has 6 strings, 3 per side tuners.
> Mfr.'s Sug. Retail $3,475 $2,606 $1,737 $1,655 $1,310

ET 8 — similar to ET4 except has 8 strings, 2 per side tuners on peghead, 4 tuners on bottom bout. New 1994.
> Mfr.'s Sug. Retail $3,275 $2,620 $1,965 $1,640 $1,310

Thunderbolt Series

TB 4 — offset double cutaway maple body, flamed maple top, bolt-on maple neck, 22 fret rosewood fingerboard with pearl dot inlay, fixed bridge, 2 per side tuners, 2 humbucker Bartolini pickups, volume/tone/mix controls, mini switch, active electronics. Available in Black, Cherry, Light Gold and Peacock Blue finishes. New 1994.
> Mfr.'s Sug. Retail $1,895 $1,516 $1,137 $950 $760
>> This model has birdseye maple top optionally available.

TB 5 — similar to TB4, except has 5 strings, 3/2 per side tuners.
> Mfr.'s Sug. Retail $1,995 $1,496 $997 $995 $795

TB 6 — similar to TB4, except has 6 strings, 3 per side tuners.
> Mfr.'s Sug. Retail $2,195 $1,756 $1,317 $1,100 $880

PENNCO

See chapter on House Brands.

This trademark has been identified as a "House Brand" of the Philadelphia Music Company of Philadelphia, Pennsylvania. The trademark has been identified as either PENCO or PENNCO for Philadelphia Music, the U.S. distributor of these Japanese-built instruments during the 1960s.

> *(Source: Michael Wright, Guitar Stories, Vol. 1)*

PENNCREST

See chapter on House Brands.

This trademark has been identified as a "House Brand" of J. C. Penneys.

> *(Source: Willie G. Moseley, Stellas & Stratocasters)*

PENSA CLASSIC

Instruments built in New York, New York since 1995.

Rudy Pensa continues the tradition of producing high quality custom guitars first started in 1985 with his collaboration with John Suhr under the Pensa-Suhr trademark.

PENSA-SUHR

Instruments produced in New York, New York between the mid 1980s to early 1990s.

Rudy Pensa founded Rudy's Music Shop on West 48th street in New York back in 1978. Rudy's Music Shop features both retail instruments, amps, and effects as well as vintage classics. In 1983 John Suhr added a repair section to the shop, and within two years the pair collaborated on custom guitars and basses. Pensa-Suhr instruments feature exotic woods, pickup and wiring options, and other upgrades that the player could order. Pensa-Suhr instruments were high quality, and built along the lines of classic American designs.

John Suhr left a number of years ago to join the Fender custom shop, and has been active in helping modernize the Fender Precision designs as well as his Custom Shop duties. Rudy Pensa maintained Rudy's Music Shop in New York City, and continues producing guitars and basses under the **Pensa Classic** trademark.

P

PERFORMANCE

Instruments built in Hollywood, California.

The Performance guitar shop has been building custom guitars, doing custom work on guitars, and performing quality repair work for a good number of years.

ELECTRIC

The **Corsair 22** model features a double cutaway Ash body, 22 fret Maple neck, 2 humbuckers, Schaller Floyd Rose locking tremolo, volume and tone knobs, pickup selector switch and Performance tuners. The guitar comes complete with an oil finish, and has a retail price beginning at $1,850. Performance also offers the **Corsair 24**, a similar model guitar that features a 24 fret fingerboard (two octaves). Retail price begins at $1,950.

PETE BACK

Instruments built in England during the early 1980s.

While luthier Pete Back is noted for his custom one-of-a-kind guitar designs, he also produced the PB5 model as sort of a standard solid body with an original design.

(Source: Tony Bacon and Payl Daym The Guru's Guitar Guide)

PETILLO

Instruments built in Ocean, New Jersey since the late 1970s or early 1980s.

Luthier Phil Petillo was one of the original co-designers of the Kramer aluminum neck guitar in 1976. Petillo built the four prototypes for Kramer (BKL), although he later severed his connections with the company. Petillo has since concentrated on building both acoustics and electric guitars in his private workshop.

(Source: Tom Wheeler, American Guitars)

Phantom model
courtesy Phantom Guitar Works

PHANTOM GUITAR WORKS

Instruments built in Portland, Oregon since 1995.

Phantom Guitar Works is producing modern versions of Vox classic designs. Models in the current product line include the **Mandoguitar**, the five sided **Phantom** and **Phantom Bass**, the **Teardrop**, **Teardrop B.J.**, and the **Teardrop Bass**. New list prices for the models in standard colors are $995 per instrument, and a tri-color sunburst finish is an additional $100. For further information, please contact Phantom Guitar Works via the Index of Current Manufacturers located in the rear of this book.

PHILIP KUBICKI

Instruments built in Clifton, New Jersey and currently distributed through Philip Kubicki Technology of Clifton, New Jersey.

Luthier Phil Kubicki worked for Fender company for several years, and notably was part of Roger Rossmeisl's staff during production of the LTD model. After leaving Fender, Kubicki gained a reputation for his custom guitar building. He formed his company, Philip Kubicki Technology (PKT) to produce acoustic guitars, components (especially high quality necks), and short scale travel electric guitars.

In 1983, Kubicki formalized design plans for the Ex Factor 4 bass. This revolutionary headless-designed bass debuted in 1985. In 1988, Kubicki entered into a trademark and licensing deal with Fender Musical Instruments Corporation which allowed him time for research while Fender built, distributed, and marketed the concept of the Factor bass. By 1992, the deal was dissolved, and Kubicki gained control back over his bass designs.

Most people are not aware of the custom guitars that luthier Kubicki has built. There are two models of short scale travel guitars, built in quanities of less than 300: The Arrow (a Flying V) and another based roughly on a Les Paul. Both instruments have high quality pickups and hardware, and are generally signed and numbered by Kubicki. Kubicki has also built a number of quality acoustic guitars, again in limited amounts.

ELECTRIC BASS

All instruments are available in Bahama Green, Black, Charcoal Pearl, Midnight Blue Pearl, Red, Tobacco Sunburst, Transparent Blue Burst, Transparent Burgundy, Red, White and Yellow finishes.

Factor Series

EX FACTOR 4 — offset double cutaway wave style maple body with screened logo, laminated maple neck, 24 fret ebony fingerboard, fixed aluminum bridge with fine tuners (reverse tuning design), 4 string anchors on peghead with low E string clasp, black hardware, 2 Kubicki humbucker pickups, stacked volume/mix control, stacked treble/bass control, 5 position rotary switch, active electronics. Mfg. 1985 to date.

Mfr.'s Sug. Retail	$2,500	$2,000	$1,500	$1,250	$1,000	$900	$825	$750

This model has fretless fingerboard optionally available.

The E string clasp allows the player access to the two fret extension (i.e., down to 'D' without retuning) on the headstock.

Grading		100%	98% MINT	95% EXC+	90% EXC	80% VG+	70% VG	60% G

FACTOR — similar to Ex Factor 4, except has no low E string clasp. Curr. mfr.

Mfr.'s Sug. Retail		$2,500	$2,000	$1,500	$1,250	$1,000	$900	$825	$750

Key Factor Series

KEY FACTOR 4 — offset double cutaway wave style maple body with screened logo, bolt-on laminated maple neck, 24 fret maple fingerboard, fixed aluminum bridge, 2 per side tuners, black hardware, 2 Kubicki humbucker pickups, stacked volume/mix control, stacked treble/bass control, 5 position rotary switch, active electronics. New 1994.

Mfr.'s Sug. Retail		$1,500	$1,200	$900	$750	$600	$540	$495	$450

This model has rosewood fingerboard optionally available.

This model has fretless fingerboard optionally available.

Key Factor 5 — similar to Key Factor 4, except has 5 strings, 3/2 per side tuners. New 1994.

Mfr.'s Sug. Retail		$1,500	$1,200	$900	$750	$600	$540	$495	$450

PICKARD

Instruments built in England from the late 1970s through the mid 1980s.

These good quality solid body guitars feature original designs, pickups and hardware by custom builder Steve Pickard.

(Source: Tony Bacon and Paul Day, The Guru's Guitar Guide)

PIMENTEL & SONS

Instruments currently built in Albuquerque, New Mexico.

Luthier Lorenzo Pimentel builds high quality classical and steel string acoustic guitars and requintos. Pimentel, originally born in Durango, Mexico, learned guitar making from his older brothers. Though trained as a baker, Pimentel moved to El Paso, Texas, in 1948 to work for master violin maker Nagoles. A few years later, Pimentel moved to Albuquerque, and began building guitars as his livelihood. Today, Lorenzo Pimentel and his sons produce perhaps 40 to 80 guitars a month, and the entire family is involved in some aspect of the business.

List prices may run from $700 up to $3,000, depending on the model and woods used in the contruction. Only Lorenzo Pimentel builds the top-of-the-line **Grand Concert** model, while his sons professionally build other models in the line. For further information regarding models, specifications, and pricing please contact luthier Lorenzo Pimentel and Sons through the Index of Current Manufacturers located in the rear of this book.

RONALD PINKHAM

Instruments currently built in Glen Cove, Maine. Distributed by Woodsound Studio of Glen Cove, Maine.

Luthier Ronald Pinkham currently offers high quality concert-grade classic and steel-string acoustic guitars, as well as cellos. Pinkham also has one of the largest orchestral and fretted instrument repair facilities in New England. For further information, please contact luthier Pinkham through the Index of Current Manufacturers located in the rear of this book.

PLAYER

Instruments built in Scarsdale, New York during the mid 1980s.

The Player model MDS-1B attempted to give the musician control over his sound by providing pop-in modules that held different pickups. The MDS-1B model was routed for two modules (other models were either routed for one or three). The plastic modules that housed the DiMarzio pickups were inserted from the back of the guitar into mounting rings that had four phospor-bronze self-cleaning contacts. Empty modules were also available if the musician wanted to install his own choice of pickups to the guitar.

The offset double cutaway body was one piece Honduran mahogany, and featured a bolt-on neck with either rosewood or ebony or maple fingerboards. The headstock had six on one side Gotoh mini tuners, and the bridge was a Kahler locking tremolo. The scale length was 25 1/2" and had 22 frets. Controls consisted of a master volume and master tone, individual volume knobs for each pickup, and a three way pickup selector switch. The price of $1,100 included a hardshell case, but the pickups were optional!

The last given address for the Player Instrument Corporation was Box 1398, Scarsdale, New York (10583).

PRAIRIE STATE

See LARSON BROTHERS (1900-1944).

The Larson brothers added the Prairie State brand to Maurer & Co. in the mid-1920s. This brand was used exclusively for guitars. The main difference between the Maurer and the Prairie State was the use of a support rod and an adjustable rod running the length of the guitar body from end block to neck block. These 12-fret-to-the-body guitars have the double rod system, which may vary according to the period it was made because August Larson was awarded three patents for these ideas. The rod closest to the sound-hole is larger than the lower one, and, in some cases, is capable of making adjustments to the fingerboard height. The function of the lower rod is to change the angle of the neck. Most all Prairie States have laminated top braces and laminated necks. They were built in the lower bout widths of 13½", 14" and 15" for the standard models, but special order guitars were built up to 21" wide. In the Mid-1930s, the Prairie State guitars were built in the larger 14-fret-to-the-body sizes, all now sporting the large rod only. The common body widths of these are 15", 16", 17", 19" and a rare 21". The single cutaway style was used on one known 19" f-hole and one 21" guitar. The Prairie State guitar is rarer than the other Larson brands. They are of very high quality and are sought by players and collectors. The rigid body produces great sustain and a somewhat different sound from the Maurers and Euphonon guitars. Almost all the Prairie State guitars were made with beautiful rosewood back and sides except the f-hole models which were commonly made with maple bodies, all having select spruce tops.

For more information regarding other Larson-made brands, see MAURER, EUPHONON, WM. C. STAHL, W.J. DYER, and THE LARSON BROTHERS.

For more detailed information regarding all the Larson brands and a Maurer/Prairie State catalog reprint, see The Larsons' Creations, Guitars and Mandolins, *by Robert Carl Hartman, Centerstream Publishing, P.O. Box 5450, Fullerton, CA 92635, phone/fax (714) 779-9390.*

PRAIRIE VOICE

See chapter on House Brands.

This trademark has been identified as a Harmony-built "Roy Rodgers" style guitar built specifically for the yearly Canadian "Calgary Stampede". **Blue Book of Guitars** is interested in more information on either the guitars produced for this celebration, or the celebration itself!

(Source: Willie G. Moseley, Stellas & Stratocasters)

PREMIER

Instruments produced in New York during the 1950s and 1960s. Later models manufactured in Japan.

Premier was the brandname of the Peter Sorkin Music Company. Premier-branded solid body guitars were built at the Multivox company of New York, and distribution of those and the later Japanese built Premiers was handled by the Sorkin company of New York City, New York. Other guitars built and distributed (possibly as rebrands) were ROYCE, STRAD-O-LIN, BELLTONE, and MARVEL.

Premier solid body guitars featured a double offset cutaway body, and the upper bout had a 'carved scroll' design, bolt-on necks, a bound rosewood fingerboard, 3+3 headstocks (initially; later models featured 6-on-a-side), and single coil pickups. Later models of the mid to late 1960s featured wood bodies covered in sparkly plastic. Towards the end of the production, numerous body/neck/electronics/hardware parts were from overseas manufacturers like Italy and Japan, and the guitars were assembled in the U.S. Some models, like the acoustic line, were completely made in Japan during the early 1970s. By the mid-1970s, both the Sorkin company and Premier guitars had ceased, but Multivox continued importing and distributing Hofner instruments through the early 1980s.

(Source: Michael Wright, Guitar Stories Volume One, pgs. 7-18)

PROFILE

Instruments produced in Japan during the mid to late 1980s.

Profile guitars are generally good quality models based on Fender designs.

(Source: Tony Bacon and Paul Day, The Guru's Guitar Guide)

PULSE

Instruments built in Korea during the mid to late 1980s.

These entry level to intermediate quality guitars feature designs based on classic American favorites. Pulse trademark instruments were solid body guitars.

(Source: Tony Bacon and Paul Day, The Guru's Guitar Guide)

PURE-TONE

See chapter on House Brands.

This trademark has been identified as a "House Brand" of Selmer (UK).

(Source: Willie G. Moseley, Stellas & Stratocasters)

"... seller should accurately describe the guitar for sale. Restorations, area of refinish, changed parts, repaired cracks and any other salient modifications should be noted."

—Jay Scott

TCG, Mar/Apr 1991

P

QUEST

Instruments built in Japan during the mid 1980s. Distribution in the U.S. market was handled by Primo, Inc. of Marlboro, Massachusetts.

Quest solid body guitars featured some original designs as well as designs based on classic American favorites. Overall, the quality of the instruments were medium to good, a solid playable rock club guitar.

Some of the instruments featured in the Quest line while they were briefly imported to the U.S. were an Explorer copy with turned-down point on the treble horn (ATAK-6X), and a Bass model similar to a P-Bass with squared off horns and P/J pickup combination (Manhatten M3-BZ). Other models will be updated in future editions of the **Blue Book of Guitars**.

Quest instruments are generally priced between $250 to $350.

Q

R & L

See ROMAN & LIPMAN

Instruments built in Danbury, Connecticut since the early 1990s.

RAINSONG

Instruments currently produced in Maui, Hawaii since 1994. Distributed by Kuau Technology, Ltd. since 1985. Previous instrument production was a joint effort between facilities in Hawaii and Albuquerque, New Mexico.

Kuau Technology, Ltd. was initally founded in 1982 by Dr. John A. Decker, Jr. to research and provide development on optical instrumentation and marine navigation. Decker, a physicist with degrees in engineering, also enjoys playing classical guitar. Since 1985, the company began concentrating on developing and manufacturing graphite/epoxy Classical and Steel String guitars. Members of the design team included Dr. Decker, as well as noted luthier Lorenzo Pimentel and composite materials expert George M. Clayton. In the company's beginning, the R & D facility was in Maui, Hawaii; and manufacturing was split between Escondido, California and Pimentel and Sons guitar makers of Albuquerque, New Mexico. The California facility handled the work on the composite materials, and the Pimentels in New Mexico supplied the lutherie and finishing work (Pimentel and Son themselves build quality wooden guitars). The Rainsong All-Graphite acoustic guitar has been commerically available since 1992.

In December, 1994 full production facilities were opened in Maui, Hawaii. George Clayton of Bi-Mar Productions assisted in development of the factory and manufacturing processes, then returned to the mainland to continue his own work. The product line has expanded to include classical models, steel string acoustic guitars and basses, acoustic/electric models, and hollowbody electric guitars and basses. Kuau Technologies, Ltd. currently employs ten people on their production staff.

Rainsong guitars and basses feature Rainsong's proprietary graphite/epoxy technology, Schaller tuning machines, optional Fishman transducers, and EMG pickups (on applicable models). Models also available with a single cutaway, in left-handed configurations, a choice of three peghead inlay designs, side-dot fret markers, and wood marquetry rosette. Instruments shipped in a hardshell case.

Rainsong Power Song
courtesy Kuau Technology, Ltd.

ACOUSTIC

CLASSICAL — black unidirectional-graphite soundboard, 650 mm scale, 2" width at nut, slotted (open) peghead with 3+3 configuration, gold Schaller tuners with ebony buttons, and abalone rosette. Current mfg.
Mfr.'s Sug. Retail $3,500
The Classical model is patterned after Pimentel & Sons "Grand Concert" model.

FLAMENCO — similar to the Classical, except has solid headstock. Current mfg.
Mfr.'s Sug. Retail $3,750

DREADNOUGHT — dreadnought size body, choice of 14/20 or 12/20 fret fingerboard, solid peghead, Fishman Axis-M transducer, Schaller black tuning pegs, Dolphin inlay design on the twelfth fret, and side dot markers. Current mfg.
Mfr.'s Sug. Retail $3,500

WINDSONG — similar to the Dreadnought, except has a Jumbo-shaped body with single cutaway. Current mfg.
Mfr.'s Sug. Retail $3,950

ACOUSTIC BASS

ACOUSTIC BASS — body patterned similar to the Windsong guitar, 844 mm scale, 4 strings, 2+2 solid headstock, Fishman Axis-M transducer/preamp, abalone rosette, side dot fret markers, and Dolphin inlay on twelfth fret. Current mfg.
Mfr.'s Sug. Retail $4,000

ACOUSTIC/ELECTRIC

JAZZ GUITAR — single cutaway body, f-holes, 648 mm scale, EMG 91 Custom pickup, Mike CHristian tune-o-matic acoustic piezo bridge, 3+3 headstock, black Schaller tuning machines, 1 volume/1 tone control, and graphite tailpiece. Current mfg.
Mfr.'s Sug. Retail $4,500

WINDSONG ACOUSTIC/ELECTRIC — similar to the Windsong acoustic model, except has thinner body, oval soundhole, Fishman Axis-M transducer/preamp, and oval abalone rosette. Current mfg.
Mfr.'s Sug. Retail $4,000

STAGESONG — similar to the Windsong Acoustic/Electric model, except has no soundhole in the top soundboard. Current mfg.
Mfr.'s Sug. Retail $3,750

Rarebird Stratohawk
courtesy Bruce Clay

STAGESONG CLASSICAL — similar to the Stagesong, except has classical stylings. Current mfg.
Mfr.'s Sug. Retail $3,950

ACOUSTIC/ELECTRIC BASS

STAGESONG BASS — similar to the Acoustic Bass, except has no soundhole in the top soundboard. Current mfg.
Mfr.'s Sug. Retail $4,250

ELECTRIC

STORMSONG — similar to the Jazz Guitar model, except has a 12-string configuration, 2 EMG humbuckers, 1 volume/1 tone control, 3-way selector. Current mfg.
Mfr.'s Sug. Retail $3,750

RAJ GUITAR CRAFTS

Instruments currently built in Asia. Distributed by KICS USA of Adelanto, California.

All RAJ models are constructed from Southsea hardwoods, and feature meticulously inlaid shell that highlights the body designs. The **Hunter Series** features such designs as the **Eagle** ($1,295), which possesses a body design that follows 'superstrat' lines. The **Jag** ($1,395) body design is reminiscent of the Fender Jaguar model, albeit more flowing body curves. The **Shark**'s ($1,195) original design suggests a cross between a Flying V and Bo Diddeley's rectangular guitar of the 1950s (prettier than the description suggests). For further information, contact KICS USA via the Index of Current Manufacturers located in the back of this book.

RALEIGH

Instruments built in Chicago, Illinois. Distributed by the Aloha Publishing and Musical Instrument Company of Chicago, Illinois.

The Aloha company was founded in 1935 by J. M. Raleigh. True to the nature of a "House Brand" distributor, Raleigh's company distributed both Aloha instruments and amplifiers and Raleigh brand instruments through his Chicago office. Acoustic guitars were supplied by Harmony, and initial amplifiers and guitars for the Aloha trademark were supplied by the Alamo company of San Antonio, Texas. By the mid 1950s, Aloha was producing their own amps, but continued using Alamo products.

(Source: Michael Wright, Vintage Guitar Magazine, August 1996, pg. 22)

RAMTRACK

Instruments built in Redford, Michigan.

The innovative people at Ramtrack have attempted to answer the age-old dilemma of the working musician: how many guitars do you need to bring to a show to convincingly recreate famous guitar sounds? Obviously, a single coil pickup does not sound like a humbucker, and different configurations of pickups exist on a multitude of solid body guitar designs. The Ramtrack guitar design consists of a solid body guitar with modules containing different pickup combinations that are removable from the body.

RANGE RIDER

See chapter on House Brands.

This trademark has been identified as a "House Brand" of the Monroe Catalog House.

(Source: Willie G. Moseley, Stellas & Stratocasters)

RANSOM

Instruments currently built in San Francisco.

Ransom custom builds high quality bass guitars in a 4-, 5-, and 6-string configuration. Basses are constructed of alder bodies with quilted or flame maple tops, 24 fret maple, rosewood, or ebony fingerboards, and feature Bartolini, EMG, or Seymour Duncan pickups. Retail prices range from $1,500 to $2,200; however, for further information, contact Ransom through the Index of Current Manufacturers located in the rear of this book.

RAREBIRD

Rarebird Osprey
courtesy Bruce Clay

Instruments currently built in Denver, Colorado.

Luthier Phillip Bruce Clay combined years learning general woodworking from his father, and classical training from the Guitar Research and Design (G.R.D.) School of Vermont to produce high quality handcrafted custom guitars. Clay has over 19 years practical experience in his building, restorations, and repairwork. The instruments feature high quality tonewoods, fine hand carving and shaping, set neck designs that all but eliminate the chunky heelblock of typical production guitars, and solid hardware and pickup configurations. For further information on specifications, pricing, and availability, please contact luthier Bruce Clay via the Index of Current Manufacturers located in the rear of this book.

(Source: Hal Hammer)

RAVER

Instruments produced in Japan during the mid 1970s.

Very entry level solid body guitars that featured 2 pickups; it leads one to ask "why two?" when costs are being cut everywhere else in the design. Oh, the joys of the manufacturing process...

(Source material courtesy Tony Bacon and Paul Day, The Guru's Guitar Guide; disparaging remarks courtesy this author)

R.C. ALLEN

Instruments currently built in Almonte, California.

Luthier R.C. Allen has been building fine quality guitars for a number of years. Allen is currently concentrating on producing archtop models. For further information, contact luthier R.C. Allen through the Index of Current Manufacturers located in the rear of this book.

REBETH

Instruments built in England during the early 1980s.

Luthier Barry Collier built a number of custom guitars during the early 1980s, and has a strong eye for original designs.

(Source: Tony Bacon, The Ultimate Guitar Book)

RECORDING KING

See chapter on House Brands.

Recording King was the House Brand of Montgomery Wards. The high end models were built by Gibson, but the low end models were built by other makers. Recording King also had several endorsers, such as singing cowboy movie star Ray Whitley, country singer/songwriter Carson Robison, and multi-instrumental virtuoso Roy Smeck.

Recording King models built by Gibson will not have an adjustable truss rod (like other budget brands Gibson produced). Chances are that the low end, Chicago-built models do not either. Further research will appear in future editions of the **Blue Book of Guitars**.

(Source: Walter Carter, Gibson Guitars: 100 Years of an American Icon)

REDONDO

See chapter on House Brands.

This trademark has been identified as a "House Brand" of the Tosca Company.

(Source: Willie G. Moseley, Stellas & Stratocasters)

REGAL

Instruments currently produced in Korea and Indonesia. Distributed by Saga Musical Instruments of San Francisco, California.

Original Regal instruments produced beginning 1896 in Indianapolis, Indiana. Regal reappeared in Chicago, Illinois in 1908, possibly tied to Lyon and Healy (WASHBURN). U.S. production was centered in Chicago from 1908 through the late 1960s.

Models from the mid 1950s to the late 1960s produced in Chicago, Illinois by the Harmony company. Some Regal models licensed to Fender, and some appear with Fender logo during the late 1950s to mid 1960s (prior to Fender's own flat-top and Coronado series).

Emil Wulschner was a retailer and wholesaler in Indianapolis, Indiana during the 1880s. In the early 1890s he added his stepson to the company, and changed the name to 'Wulschner and Son'. They opened a factory around 1896 to build guitars and mandolins under three different trademarks: Regal, University, and 20th Century. Though Wulschner passed away in 1900, the factory continued on through 1902 or 1903 under control of a larger corporation. The business end of the company let it go when the economy faltered during those final years. This is the end of the original Regal trademarked instruments.

In 1904 Lyon & Healy (WASHBURN) purchased the rights to the Regal trademark, thousands of completed and works in progress instruments, and the company stockpile of raw materials. A new Regal company debuted in Chicago, Illinois in 1908 (it is not certain what happened during those four years) and it is supposed that they were tied to Lyon & Healy. The new company marketed ukeleles and tenor guitars, but not six string guitars. However, experts have agreed that Regal built guitar models for other labels (Bruno, Weyman, Stahl, and Lyon & Healy) during the 1910-1920 era. Regal eventually announced that their six string models would be distributed through a number of wholesalers.

Rarebird Telehawk
courtesy Bruce Clay

Rarebird Falcon XL
courtesy Bruce Clay

R

Resurrection Guitar
courtesy Pat O'Donnell

In 1930, the Tonk Bros. Company acquired the rights to the Washburn trademark when the then-current holder (J. R. Stewart Co.) went bankrupt. Regal bought the rights to the Stewart and LeDomino names from Tonk Bros., and was making fretted instruments for all three trademarks. Also in the early 1930s, Regal had licensed the use of Dobro resonators in a series of guitars. In 1934 they acquired the rights to manufacture Dobro brand instruments when National-Dobro moved to Chicago from California. Regal then announced that they would be joining the name brand guitar producers that sold direct to dealers in 1938. Regal was, in effect, another producer of 'house brand' guitars prior to World War II.

It has been estimated by one source that Regal-built Dobros stopped in 1940, and were not built from then on. During World War II, guitar production lines were converted to the war effort. After the war, the Regal Musical Instrument company did not do as well as the pre-war production numbers. In 1954 the trademark and company fixtures were sold to Harmony. Harmony, along with Kay, were the other major producers of 'house brand' instruments. Regal guitars were licensed to Fender in the late 1950s, and some of the Harmony built 'Regals' were rebranded with the Fender logo. This agreement continued up until the mid 1960s, when Fender introduced their own flat-top guitars.

In 1987, Saga Musical Instruments reintroduced Regal dobros to the U.S. market. The RD-45 model was available in roundneck or squareneck options.

(Early Regal history courtesy John Teagle, Washburn: Over One Hundred Years of Fine Stringed Instruments. This noteworthy book brilliantly unravels core histories of Washburn, Regal, and Lyon & Healy and is a recommended "must read" to guitar collectors.)

RELLOG

See MUSIMA

Instruments built in East Germany in the late 1950s to early 1960s.

Instruments with the Rellog brandname were built by the Musima company in Germany during the late 1950s on. Earlier models were available in original designs of both solid body and semi-hollow body configurations through the early 1960s.

(Source: Tony Bacon and Paul Day, The Guru's Guitar Guide)

RENAISSANCE

Instruments produced in Malvern, Pennsylvania from 1977 to 1980.

Renaissance guitars was founded by John Marshall, Phil Goldberg, and Dan Lamb in the late 1970s. Marshall, who played guitars in a number of local bands in the 1960s, was friends with local luthier Eric Schulte. Schulte, a former apprentice of Sam Koontz (Harptone and Standel guitars) taught Marshall guitar-building skills. In 1977, Marshall began gathering together information and building jigs, and received some advice from Augustino LoPrinzi on a visit to New Jersey. Goldberg was then a current owner of a northern Delaware music store, and Lamb was a studio guitarist with prior experience from Musitronics (the effects company that built Mu-tron and Dan Armstrong modules). A number of wooden guitar and bass prototypes were built after the decision to use Plexiglass was agreed upon.

In 1979, the then-fledgling company was experiencing financial troubles. Marshall left the company, and a new investor named John Dragonetti became a shareholder. Unfortunately, the company's financial position, combined with the high cost of production, did not provide a stable position. Renaissance guitars closed down during the fall of 1980.

In a related sidenote, one of the Renaissance employees was guitarist/designer Dana Sutcliffe. Sutcliffe went on to form his Dana Guitar Design company, and was involved in guitar designs for St. Louis Music's Alvarez line in 1990. One awarding-winning model was the "Dana Scoop" guitar, which won the Music Retailer's "Most Innovative" award in 1992.

Renaissance instruments were constructed from either greyish "Bronze", clear, or "see through" black Plexiglass. Necks were built of a maple laminate, with ebony fingerboards and brass position markers. The 3+3 (2+2 for bass) headstocks had Schaller tuning machines, and the instruments featured DiMarzio pickups, a brass nut and bridge, and an active circuit designed by Dan Lamb and Hank Zajac. The original 1979 product line consisted of the Model SPG single cutaway guitar (list $725), the Model SPB single cutaway bass with 2 P-Bass DiMarzios (list $750), and the Model DPB double cutaway bass with 1 P-Bass DiMarzio (list $625). A smaller number of pointy horn double cutaway basses and guitars were later developed (S-100G or B, S-200B, T-100B, and T-200G). Production is estimated to be around 300 to 330 instruments built in the three years.

(Source: Michael Wright, Guitar Stories Volume One, pgs. 263-268)

RESURRECTION GUITARS

Instruments built in Jensen Beach, Florida since 1994.

Partners Robin Venturini and Master Luthier Pat O'Donnell have been offering custom guitars and basses on a special order basis for over two years. In addition, they will "resurrect" your old axe to better than new condition by upgrading components and applying a new finish.

Resurrection guitar models feature a 3-piece neck built through the body for better sustain, an Oak or Cypress single cutaway "tapered" body, Grover tuners, Schaller bridges, EMG pickups, and a natural or tinted Nitro-lacquer finish. Workmanship and materials carries a lifetime warranty. For more information or current pricing, contact O'Donnell and Venturini at Resurrection Guitars via the Index of Current Manufacturers located in the rear of this book.

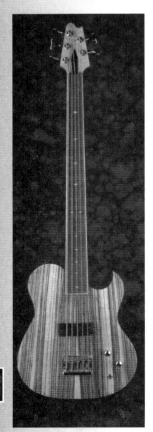

Resurrection 5 String Bass
courtesy Robin Venturini

REVELATION

Instruments built in Korea, based on designs formulated by the Hohner Guitar Research Team. Distributed by HSS, Inc. (a Division of Hohner), located in Richmond, Virginia.

Revelation series guitars featured solid poplar bodies, maple necks, 24 fret rosewood fingerboards, Wilkinson bridges, Schaller tuners, and either 3 single coils or 1 single/1 humbucker pickups. Retail price for either model listed at $899.

REX

See chapter on House Brands.

This trademark has been identified as a "House Brand" of the Great West Music Wholesalers of Canada by author/researcher Willie G. Moseley.

However, in the early 1900s, REX was also a "sub-brand" of the Fred Gretsch Manufacturing Company. Friedrich Gretsch arrived in the U.S. in 1872, and by 1883 had begun his own business in New York City. His son, Fred (often referred to as Fred, Sr. in company histories) had expanded the drum and banjo production with the addition of mandolins in the 1900s. By 1920 the Fred Gretsch Mfg. Co. had settled into its new ten story building in Brooklyn, New York, and was offering music dealers a very large line of instruments that included banjos, mandolins, guitars, violins, drums, and other band instruments. Gretsch used both the 20th Century and Rex trademarks prior to introduction of the GRETSCH trademark in 1933.

REYNOLDS

Instruments currently built in Austin, Texas.

Luthier Ed Reynolds began repairing instruments in 1974 and then building in 1976. While based in Chicago, Illinois, Reynolds gained a reputation for being a quality repairman. In 1991, Reynolds relocated to Austin, Texas and has continued to build electric guitars and basses. For further information, contact luthier Ed Reynolds through the Index of Current Manufacturers located in the rear of this book.

RIBBECKE

Instruments built in San Francisco bay area in California since 1973.

Luthier Tom Ribbecke has been building and repairing guitars and basses for over twenty three years in the San Francsico bay area. Ribbecke's first lutherie business opened in 1975 in San Francisco's Mission District, and remained open and busy for ten years. In 1985 Ribbecke closed down the storefront in order to focus directly on client commissions.

Ribbecke guitars are entirely hand built by the luthier himself, while working directly with the customer. Beyond his signature and serial number of the piece, Ribbecke also offers a history of the origin of all materials involved in construction.

All prices quoted are the base price new, and does not reflect additions to the comissioned piece. For further information, please contact luthier Tom Ribbecke through the Index of Current Manufacturers located in the back of this book.

Ribbecke Archtop
courtesy Scott Chinery

ACOUSTIC

17" ARCH TOP (EITHER MONTEREY or HOMAGE) — Construction material as quoted in the base price is good Quality Domestic Figured Maple back and sides, Sitka Spruce top, Ebony fingerboard, Ebony pickguard, gold hardware, and solid Ebony tailpiece. Available in 25.4", 25", or 24.75" scale length. Current production.
Mfr.'s Sug. Retail $6,000

The **Monterey** features a cascade type peghead design, while the **Homage** features a peghead design reminiscent of a D'Angelico.

This model is also available as a 16" body style at the same base price.

This model is available in an 18" body format. Call for specifics.

ACOUSTIC STEEL STRING — First Quality Spruce top, Indian Rosewood back and sides, Ebony fingerboard, Ebony Bridge, and dot inlays. Current production.
Mfr.'s Sug. Retail $3,000

SOUND BUBBLE STEEL STRING — Solid carved top, First Quality Indian Rosewood back and sides, Ebony fingerboard, Ebony bridge, and dot inlays. Current production.
Mfr.'s Sug. Retail $3,500

The Sound Bubble, a slightly domed area on the bass side of the lower bout, increases the guitar's ability to translate the energy of the strings into sound. Patented in 1981 by artisan Charles Kelly and luthier Tom Ribbecke.

ACOUSTIC BASS

CARVED TOP ACOUSTIC BASS — Solid carved Spruce top with elliptical soundhole, Maple back and sides, Ebony fingerboard, 34" scale, chrome hardware, and dot inlays. Available in Natural finish only. Current production.
Mfr.'s Sug. Retail $3,200

Ribbecke 17" Archtop
courtesy Tom Ribbecke

Ribbecke Testadura
courtesy Tom Ribbecke

ELECTRIC

TESTADURA (THINLINE STYLE) — Instrument constructed of First Grade Domestic Maple or Rosewood back and sides, solid carved top and back, Ebony pickguard, carbon fiber braced, Master volume and tone controls, dot inlays, and chrome hardware. Available in Natural finish. Current production.

Mfr.'s Sug. Retail $4,000

RICKENBACKER

Instruments produced in Santa Ana, California. Distributed by Rickenbacker International Corporation of Santa Ana, California. Rickenbacker instruments have been produced in California since 1934.

In 1925, John Dopyera (and brothers) joined up with George Beauchamp and Adolph Rickenbacker and formed National to build resonator guitars. Beauchamp's attitudes over spending money causes John Dopyera to leave National and start the Dobro company. While at National, Beauchamp, Rickenbacker and Dopyera's nephew, Paul Barth, designed the "Frying Pan" electric lap steel. In 1929 or 1930, Beauchamp got either forced out or fired from National - and so allied himself with Adolph Rickenbacker (National's tool and die man) and Barth to form Ro-Pat-In.

In the summer of 1932, Ro-Pat-In started building aluminum versions of the "Frying Pan" prototype. Early models have "Electro" on the headstock. Two years later, "Rickenbacker" (or sometimes "Rickenbacher") was added to the headstock, and Ro-Pat-In was formally changed to the Electro String Instrument Corporation. Beauchamp left Electro sometime in 1940, and Barth left in 1956 to form his own company.

In December of 1953, F.C. Hall bought out the interests of Rickenbacker and his two partners. The agreement stated that the purchase was complete, and Electro could "continue indefinitely to use the trade name Rickenbacker". Hall, founder of Radio-Tel and an early Fender distributor, had his Fender distributorship bought out by Leo Fender and Don Randall. The Rickenbacker company was formed in 1965 as an organizational change (Electro is still the manufacturer, and Rickenbacker is the sales company). Rickenbacker instruments gained popularity as the Beatles relied on a number of their guitars in the 1960s. One slight area of confusion: the model names and numbers differ from the U.S. market to models imported in to the U.K. market.

In 1984 John Hall (F.C. Hall's son) officially took control by purchasing his father's interests in both the Rickenbacker, Inc. and Electro String companies. Hall formed the Rickenbacker International Corporation (RIC) to combine both interests.

(Source: Tom Wheeler, American Guitar)

ACOUSTIC

Grading	100%	98% MINT	95% EXC+	90% EXC	80% VG+	70% VG	60% G

385 — dreadnought style, maple top, round soundhole, pickguard, checkered body/rosette, maple back/sides/neck, 21 fret rosewood fingerboard with pearl triangle inlay, rosewood bridge with white pins. Available in Burst finishes. Mfd. 1958 to 1972.

1958-1965	$2,000	$2,140	$1,785	$1,430	$1,285	$1,180	$1,070
1966-1972	$1,250	$1,130	$1,070	$960	$900	$850	$800

This model was also available in a classic style body (385-S).

385-J — similar to 385, except has jumbo style body.

	$2,250	$2,060	$1,865	$1,570	$1,415	$1,295	$1,180

390 — while a few prototypes were made circa 1957, this model was never put into production.

ELECTRIC

Rickenbacker pegheads are generally of the same pattern and design. They have 3 per side tuners and plastic, or metal, logo imprinted plates. Twelve string pegheads are the same size as six string pegheads, with 6 tuners (3 per side) running parallel to the peghead face and 6 tuners running perpendicular with routed slots in the peghead face to accommodate string winding. Most necks are maple, however, some are maple/walnut laminates. Pickguards and peghead plates are usually color matched, and controls are usually pickguard mounted. Any differences will be listed where appropriate. Hardware, binding, peghead logo plate and pickguard color is dependent on finish, unless otherwise listed.

In 1964, R style trapeze tailpieces replaced all other trapeze tailpieces.

Grading	90%	80%	70%	60%	50%	40%	20%

ELECTRO SPANISH — folk style, maple top, F holes, bound body, maple back/sides/neck, 14/19 fret rosewood fingerboard with pearl dot inlay, rosewood bridge/trapeze tailpiece, pearl veneer on classic style peghead with metal logo plate, horseshoe pickup. Available in Stained finish. Mfd. 1932 to 1935.

	$1,200	$1,040	$890	$720	$640	$590	$535

In 1934, body binding and volume control were added.

This model was replaced by the Ken Roberts model.

Grading	90%	80%	70%	60%	50%	40%	20%

KEN ROBERTS ELECTRO-SPANISH — concert style, laminated bound mahogany top, F holes, laminated mahogany back/sides, mahogany neck, 17/22 fret bound rosewood fingerboard with white dot inlay, compensating bridge/Kauffman vibrato tailpiece, pearloid peghead veneer with brass logo plate, 3 per side tuners, nickel hardware, horseshoe pickup, volume control. Available in Two Tone Brown finish. Mfd. 1935 to 1940.

	$500	$430	$360	$285	$260	$235	$215

From 1935-1937, the volume control was octagon shaped.

In 1938, round volume control with ridges replaced original item.

Grading	100%	98% MINT	95% EXC+	90% EXC	80% VG+	70% VG	60% G

200 Series

220 HAMBURG — double cutaway maple body, thru body maple neck, 24 fret rosewood fingerboard with pearloid dot inlay, fixed bridge, 3 per side tuners, 2 humbucker pickups, 2 volume/2 tone controls, 3 position switch. Available in Fireglo, Jetglo, Mapleglo, Midnight Blue, Red and White finishes. Mfd. 1987 to date.

Mfr.'s Sug. Retail	$900	$675	$450	$325	$300	$275	$245	$215

260 EL DORADO — similar to 220, except has bound body/fingerboard, gold hardware.

Mfr.'s Sug. Retail	$1,050	$787	$525	$380	$345	$315	$280	$240

300 Series

This series is also called the *Capri Series.*

This series utilizes a hollow body, white binding, inlaid fingerboard and Rick-o-Sound jacks. These are available in Fireglo or Natural Grain finish, unless otherwise indicated.

310 — offset pointed double cutaway semi hollow ¾ size maple body, 21 fret rosewood fingerboard with white dot inlay, tunomatic bridge/trapeze tailpiece, chrome hardware, 2 covered pickups, volume/tone control, 3 position switch. Available in Autumnglo, Fireglo, Mapleglo, Natural or Two-Tone Brown finishes. Mfd. 1958 to 1971. Reintroduced 1981 to 1988.

1958-1964	$3,000	$2,570	$2,140	$1,715	$1,545	$1,415	$1,285
1965-1971	$2,000	$1,670	$1,940	$1,415	$1,245	$1,115	$1,030

In 1963, a mixer control was added.

Instruments were inconsistently produced with and without f-holes.

The 310 model was reintroduced 1981 to 1988.

1981-1988	$500	$470	$430	$400	$360	$310	$280

315 — similar to 310, except has Kauffman vibrato. Mfd. 1958 to 1975.

1958-1964	$3,000	$2,570	$2,140	$1,715	$1,545	$1,415	$1,285
1965-1969	$2,000	$1,670	$1,940	$1,415	$1,245	$1,115	$1,030
1970-1975	$500	$470	$430	$400	$360	$310	$280

320 — offset pointed double cutaway semi hollow ¾ size maple body, bi-level pickguard, thru body maple neck, 21 fret rosewood fingerboard with pearloid dot inlay, tunomatic bridge/R-style trapeze tailpiece, 3 per side tuners, chrome hardware, 3 chrome bar pickups, 2 volume/2 tone/mix controls, 3 position switch. Available in Fireglo, Jetglo, Mapleglo, Midnight Blue, Red and White finishes. Mfd. 1958 to 1994.

1958-1964	$5,000	$4,355	$4,270	$3,715	$3,045	$2,615	$2,485
1965-1971	$3,500	$3,070	$2,640	$2,215	$2,045	$1,915	$1,730
1972-1994	$800	$680	$575	$460	$410	$380	$345

Last Mfr.'s Sug. Retail was $1,000.

325 — similar to 320, except has Kauffman vibrato. Available in Fireglo, Mapleglo, Natural or Two-Tone Brown finishes. Mfd. 1958 to 1975.

1958-1964	$6,000	$5,285	$4,570	$3,860	$3,570	$3,360	$3,145
1965-1971	$4,500	$3,785	$3,070	$2,360	$2,070	$1,860	$1,645
1972-1975	$800	$685	$575	$460	$410	$380	$345

In 1964, "R" style trapeze tailpieces replaced all other trapeze tailpieces.

330 — offset double cutaway semi hollow maple body, wedge shaped soundhole, bi-level pickguard, thru body maple neck, 24 fret rosewood fingerboard with pearl dot inlay, tunomatic bridge/R-style trapeze tailpiece, 3 per side tuners, 2 single coil pickups, 2 volume/2 tone/mix controls, 3 position switch. Available in Fireglo, Jetglo, Mapleglo, Midnight Blue, Red and White finishes. Mfd. 1958 to date.

1958-1964	$2,000	$1,640	$1,285	$1,030	$985	$880	$775
1965-1984	$1,000	$920	$875	$800	$715	$670	$555
Curr. Mfr.'s Sug. Retail	$1,200	$900	$600	$480	$430	$390	$360	$330

In 1963, a mixer control was added.

330/12 — similar to 330, except has 12 strings, 6 per side tuners. Mfd. 1965 to date.

1965-1985	$1,300	$1,100	$915	$720	$640	$580	$525
Curr. Mfr.'s Sug. Retail	$1,300	$975	$650	$500	$370	$320	$280	$240

Late 1950s Rickenbacker electric courtesy Thoroughbred Music

R

Grading	100%	98% MINT	95% EXC+	90% EXC	80% VG+	70% VG	60% G

1970 Rickenbacker "Light Show"
courtesy Gordy & Marcia Lupo

331 — similar to 330, except has Plexiglass top with frequency controlled flashing lights. Mfd. 1970 to 1975.

| | $4,500 | $3,815 | $3,130 | $2,440 | $2,175 | $1,960 | $1,755 |

Originally, this model was released with an external power supply box.

This model was also nicknamed the "Light Show".

340 — offset double cutaway semi hollow maple body, wedge soundhole, bi-level pickguard, thru body maple neck, 24 fret rosewood fingerboard with pearl dot inlay, tunomatic bridge/R-style trapeze tailpiece, 3 per side tuners, 3 single coil pickups, 2 volume/2 tone/mix controls, 3 position switch. Available in Fireglo, Jetglo, Mapleglo, Midnight Blue, Red and White finishes. New 1994.

| Mfr.'s Sug. Retail | $1,325 | $993 | $662 | $480 | $430 | $390 | $360 | $330 |

340/12 — similar to 340, except has 12 strings, 6 per side tuners. New 1994.

| Mfr.'s Sug. Retail | $1,425 | $1,068 | $712 | $415 | $370 | $310 | $265 | $225 |

350 — offset pointed double cutaway semi hollow maple body, bi-level pickguard, thru body maple neck, 24 fret rosewood fingerboard with pearloid dot inlay, tunomatic bridge/R-style trapeze tailpiece, 3 chrome bar pickups, 2 volume/2 tone/mix controls, 3 position switch, stereo output. Available in Fireglo, Jetglo, Mapleglo, Midnight Blue, Red and White finishes. Mfd. 1985 to date.

| Mfr.'s Sug. Retail | $1,270 | $952 | $635 | $480 | $430 | $390 | $360 | $330 |

This model also referred to as the "350 Liverpool".

360 — offset double cutaway semi hollow maple body, wedge shaped soundhole, pickguard, thru body maple neck, 21 fret bound rosewood fingerboard with pearl triangle inlay, tunomatic bridge/R-style trapeze tailpiece, 2 single pickups, 2 volume/2 tone diamond controls, 3 position switch. Available in Autumnglo, Black, Fireglo, Natural and Two Tone Brown finishes. Mfd. 1958 to date.

1958-1964		$3,000	$2,500	$2,000	$1,500	$1,300	$1,150	$1,000
1965-1974		$1,250	$1,235	$820	$610	$520	$480	$390
1975-1990		$750	$730	$580	$525	$485	$445	$400
Curr. Mfr.'s Sug. Retail	$1,320	$990	$660	$530	$475	$435	$395	$335

The above description is referred to as the Old Style which ran from 1958-1968.

In the early 1960s, round control knobs and bi-level pickguards began replacing original items.

In 1960, stereo output became optional.

In 1963, a mixer control was added.

In 1964, the 360 New Style was released and featured an unbound rounded top, bound soundhole and checkered body binding which ran from 1964-1990.

360/12 — similar to 360, except has 12 strings, 6 per side tuners.

| 1965-1974 | | $1,800 | $1,535 | $1,270 | $1,055 | $900 | $820 | $750 |
| 1975-1990 | | $800 | $670 | $540 | $485 | $445 | $400 | $380 |

365/360WB — offset double cutaway semi hollow maple body, wedge shaped soundhole, pickguard, thru body maple neck, 21 fret bound rosewood fingerboard with pearl triangle inlay, tunomatic bridge/vibrato tailpiece, 2 single pickups, 2 volume/2 tone diamond controls, 3 position switch. Available in Autumnglo, Black, Fireglo, Natural and Two Tone Brown finishes. Mfd. 1958 to date.

1958-1964		$3,000	$2,500	$2,000	$1,500	$1,300	$1,150	$1,000
1965-1984		$1,250	$1,235	$820	$610	$520	$480	$390
1985-1990		$700	$680	$600	$520	$465	$400	$385
Curr. Mfr.'s Sug. Retail	$1,320	$990	$660	$590	$465	$425	$390	$340

In 1985, this model was reintroduced as 360VB featuring Old Style body, high gain pickups and R style tailpiece.

In 1991, this model was renamed the 360WB and is still in production.

360/12WB — similar to 360WB, except has 12 strings, 6 per side tuners.

| 1958-1968 | | $5,200 | $4,485 | $3,770 | $2,960 | $2,770 | $2,460 | $2,245 |
| Curr. Mfr.'s Sug. Retail | $1,530 | $1,147 | $765 | $665 | $520 | $450 | $405 | $355 |

See 365 description, above.

Models between 1964 to 1967 command the higher premium (up to $6,500 for Individual clean/original guitars).

370 — offset double cutaway semi hollow maple body, wedge shaped soundhole, pickguard, thru body maple neck, 21 fret bound rosewood fingerboard with pearl triangle inlay, tunomatic bridge/R-style trapeze tailpiece, 3 single pickups, 2 volume/2 tone diamond controls, 3 position switch. Available in Autumnglo, Black, Fireglo, Natural and Two Tone Brown finishes. Mfd. 1958 to date.

1958-1964		$3,000	$2,500	$2,000	$1,500	$1,300	$1,150	$1,000
1965-1984		$1,250	$1,235	$820	$610	$520	$480	$390
1985-1990		$700	$680	$600	$520	$465	$400	$385
Curr. Mfr.'s Sug. Retail	$1,445	$1,083	$722	$575	$515	$470	$430	$390

370WB — similar to 370, except has tunomatic bridge/vibrato tailpiece. New 1994.

| Mfr.'s Sug. Retail | $1,555 | $1,244 | $933 | $780 | $620 | $560 | $515 | $465 |

370/12 — similar to 370, except 12 strings, 6 per side tuners.

| Mfr.'s Sug. Retail | $1,545 | $1,158 | $772 | $665 | $520 | $450 | $405 | $355 |

R

Grading		100%	98% MINT	95% EXC+	90% EXC	80% VG+	70% VG	60% G

370/12WB — similar to 370, except has 12 strings, tunomatic bridge/vibrato tailpiece, 6 per side tuners.

1958-1968		$5,200	$4,485	$3,770	$2,960	$2,770	$2,460	$2,245
Curr. Mfr.'s Sug. Retail	$1,655	$1,241	$827	$665	$520	$450	$405	$355

381 — offset sharp double cutaway semi hollow maple body, carved top, white bi-level pickguard, checkered bound body, bound wedge shaped soundhole, thru body maple neck, 21 fret bound rosewood fingerboard with pearl triangle inlay, tunomatic bridge/trapeze tailpiece, chrome hardware, 2 chrome bar pickups, 2 volume/2 tone/mix controls, 3 position switch. Available in Brownburst and Natural finishes. Mfd. 1958 to 1963. Reintroduced late 1968 to 1974.

1958-1964	$5,000	$4,285	$3,570	$2,860	$2,570	$2,360	$2,145
1965-1969	$4,000	$3,430	$2,860	$2,285	$2,060	$1,885	$1,715
1970-1974	$2,500	$2,000	$1,500	$1,300	$1,150	$1,000	$890

The original run of this series, 1958-early 1960s, had single pickguards, 2 controls. Fingerboard inlay was both dot and triangle. There were also a number of variations that Rickenbacker produced, some with F shaped soundholes and some with vibratos.

400 Series

The tulip style body shape acquired its nickname from the cutaways radiating out at a 45 degree angle, curving outwards to rounded point, then curving back into a standard.

400 COMBO — tulip style maple body, gold pickguard, thru body maple neck, 21 fret rosewood fingerboard with white dot inlay, covered pickup, volume/tone control, 2 position switch. Available in Blue Green, Golden and Jet Black finishes. Mfd. 1956 to 1958.

	$1,200	$1,030	$810	$685	$595	$500	$440

This was the first through-body neck construction that Rickenbacker manufactured.

In 1957, an extra switch was added.

420 — cresting wave style maple body, white pickguard, thru body maple neck, 21 fret rosewood fingerboard with white dot inlay, fixed bridge, chrome hardware, chrome bar pickup, volume/tone control, 2 position switch. Available in Sunburst finish. Mfd. 1965 to 1984.

	$850	$715	$570	$510	$465	$425	$380

425 — similar to 420, except has vibrato. Mfd. 1958 to 1973.

1958-1963	$850	$715	$570	$510	$465	$425	$380
1964-1973	$400	$315	$260	$210	$180	$160	$140

Replaced the 400 Combo.

In 1965, the vibrato was added, at which time the 420 was introduced as the non-vibrato instrument in this style.

450 COMBO — cresting wave style maple body, white pickguard, thru body maple neck, 21 fret rosewood fingerboard with pearl dot inlay, fixed bridge, chrome hardware, 2 chrome bar pickups, 2 volume/2 tone controls, 3 position switch. Available in Black, Fireglo, Natural and Sunburst finishes. Mfd. 1957 to 1984.

1957-1958	$1,250	$1,000	$850	$700	$600	$525	$450
1959-1984	$700	$580	$520	$475	$435	$380	$295

This model was introduced with a tulip style body, metal pickguard, 2 controls and a rotary switch located on the upper treble bout. It was manufactured this way for one year.

In 1958, the cresting wave body style was introduced.

In 1966, the 4 controls were introduced.

From 1962 to 1977, 3 pickups were optional .

450/12 — similar to 450, except has 12 strings, 6 per side tuners. Mfd. 1964 to 1985.

	$600	$540	$505	$465	$400	$370	$330

460 — similar to 450, except has bound body, bound fingerboard with pearl triangle inlay, mixer control. Available in Black, Fireglo and Natural finishes. Mfd. 1961 to 1985.

	$750	$675	$630	$575	$535	$490	$440

In 1962, stereo output became standard.

470 — while a few prototypes were made circa 1971, this model was never put into full production. Some examples have been priced around $400.

480 — cresting wave style maple body, white pickguard, bolt-on maple neck, 24 fret bound rosewood fingerboard with white dot inlay, covered tunomatic bridge/R style trapeze tailpiece, cresting wave style peghead, chrome hardware, 2 single coil exposed pickups, 2 volume/2 tone controls, 3 position switch. Mfd. 1973 to 1984.

	$350	$295	$260	$235	$215	$190	$165

R

Grading	100%	98% MINT	95% EXC+	90% EXC	80% VG+	70% VG	60% G

481 — similar to 480, except has bound body, slanted frets, pearl triangle fingerboard inlay, 2 humbucker exposed pickups, phase switch. Mfd. 1973 to 1984.

	$350	$295	$260	$235	$215	$190	$165

600 Series

600 COMBO — offset double cutaway maple body, carved top, black pickguard, maple neck, 21 fret rosewood fingerboard with white dot inlay, fixed bridge, chrome hardware, single coil horseshoe pickup, volume/tone control, 2 position switch. Available in Blond finish. Mfd. 1954 to 1959.

	$800	$730	$680	$630	$575	$515	$465

These instruments had both set and bolt-on necks.

According to Rickenbacker's own records, there were apparently quite a few variations of this model.

These models were on the price lists as having cresting wave style bodies until 1969, though none were ever produced.

610 — cresting wave style maple body, bi-level pickguard, thru body maple neck, 21 fret rosewood fingerboard with pearl dot inlay, tunomatic bridge/R-style trapeze tailpiece, 3 per side tuners, 2 single coil pickups, 2 volume/2 tone/mix controls, 3 position switch. Available in Fireglo, Jetglo, Mapleglo, Midnight Blue, Red and White finishes. Mfd. 1987 to date.

Mfr.'s Sug. Retail	$1,000	$750	$500	$370	$310	$280	$240	$200

610/12 — similar to 610, except has 12 strings, 6 per side tuners.

Mfr.'s Sug. Retail	$1,100	$825	$550	$420	$360	$330	$290	$250

615/610/VB — similar to 610, except has roller bridge/vibrato tailpiece, chrome hardware, 2 chrome bar pickups, 2 volume/2 tone controls. Available in Black, Fireglo and Natural finishes. Mfd. 1962 to 1977.

	$735	$585	$525	$485	$440	$400	$365

In 1985, this model was reintroduced as the 610VB. Mfd. 1985 to 1990.

620 — similar to 610, except has bound body, bound fingerboard with pearl triangle inlay, 2 single coil exposed pickups. Available in Fireglo, Jetglo, Mapleglo, Midnight Blue, Red and White finishes. Mfd. 1977 to date.

Mfr.'s Sug. Retail	$1,100	$825	$550	$395	$365	$330	$300	$260

620/12 — similar to 620, except has 12 strings, 6 per side tuners. Mfd. 1981 to date.

Mfr.'s Sug. Retail	$1,200	$900	$600	$400	$370	$340	$310	$275

In 1989, the deluxe trim was replaced by standard trim.

625/620VB — similar to 610, except has bound body, bound fingerboard with pearl triangle inlay, roller bridge/vibrato tailpiece, 2 chrome bar pickups. Available in Fireglo, Jetglo, Mapleglo, Midnight Blue, Red and White finishes. Mfd. 1977 to 1994.

	$475	$450	$415	$380	$335	$300	$260

Last Mfr.'s Sug. Retail was $1,450.

In 1985, this model was reintroduced as the 620VB. Mfd.1985 to 1990.

650 Series

All models in this series have a cresting wave style body, pickguard, maple thru body neck, 24 fret maple fingerboard with black dot inlay, fixed bridge, 3 per side tuners, 2 humbucker pickups, 2 volume/2 tone/mix controls, 3 position switch. Available in Natural finish unless otherwise listed. Mfd. 1992 to date.

650 COMBO — offset double sharp cutaway maple body, carved top, pickguard, maple neck, 21 fret rosewood fingerboard with white dot inlay, fixed bridge, single coil horseshoe pickup, volume control. Available in Natural and Turquoise Blue finishes. Mfd. 1957 to 1960.

	$1,070	$895	$715	$645	$590	$535	$485

In late 1957, a chrome bar pickup replaced the horseshoe pickup.

650A (ATLANTIS) — maple body, chrome hardware. Available in Vintage Turquoise finish.

Mfr.'s Sug. Retail	$1,100	$825	$550	$450	$340	$295	$265	$230

650C (Colorado) — walnut body, chrome hardware. Available in Jetglo Black finish. New 1994.

Mfr.'s Sug. Retail	$1,100	$825	$550	$450	$340	$295	$265	$230

650D (Dakota) — walnut body, walnut peghead laminate, chrome hardware.

Mfr.'s Sug. Retail	$1,000	$750	$500	$400	$300	$260	$230	$220

650E (Excalibur) — African vermillion body, African vermillion peghead laminate, gold hardware.

Mfr.'s Sug. Retail	$1,200	$900	$600	$500	$390	$330	$295	$260

"The guitar is a piece of wood and that piece of wood has its own character. It is up to me to match that character to the player for whom I'm building the guitar."

—L. Acunto on James L. D'Aquisto

TCG, Mar/Apr 1991

R

Grading		100%	98% MINT	95% EXC+	90% EXC	80% VG+	70% VG	60% G

650S (Sierra) — walnut body, walnut peghead laminate, gold hardware.

Mfr.'s Sug. Retail $1,100 $825 $550 $450 $340 $295 $265 $230

800 Series

800 (COMBO) — offset double cutaway maple body, carved top, black pickguard, maple neck, 21 fret rosewood fingerboard with white dot inlay, fixed bridge, chrome hardware, double coil horseshoe pickup, 2 volume controls, 2 selector switches. Available in Blond and Turquoise Blue finishes. Mfd. 1954 to 1959.

$985 $825 $660 $590 $545 $495 $425

In 1957, the pickguard was enlarged and the controls were mounted on it, a chrome bar pickup replaced one of the 'horseshoe' pickups, and Turquoise Blue finish became optionally available.

This model was on the price list through 1969, though it was no longer available.

850 COMBO — offset double sharp cutaway maple body, carved top, pickguard, maple neck, 21 fret rosewood fingerboard with white dot inlay, fixed bridge, double coil horseshoe pickup, volume/tone controls, 2 switches. Available in Natural and Turquoise Blue finishes. Mfd. 1957 to 1960.

$1,285 $1,070 $860 $770 $710 $645 $600

In late 1957, the horseshoe pickup was replaced by a single coil horseshoe and chrome bar pickups. This model was on the price lists through 1967.

There were several variations of this model that were made with 3 pickup designs or through-body neck constructions.

900 & 1000 Series

900 — tulip style ¾ size maple body, white pickguard, thru body maple neck, 21 fret rosewood fingerboard with white dot inlay, fixed bridge, chrome hardware, single coil pickup, volume/tone control, 2 position switch. Available in Black, Brown, Fireglo, Gray and Natural finishes. Mfd. 1957 to 1980.

$400 $345 $310 $285 $260 $230 $200

In 1958, a chrome bar pickup replaced the original pickup.

In 1961, Fireglo finish became optionally available.

By 1974, cresting wave body style became standard.

950 — similar to 900, except has 2 pickups.

$450 $400 $360 $335 $310 $280 $245

In 1958, a chrome bar pickup replaced the original pickup.

In 1961, Fireglo finish became optionally available.

By 1974, cresting wave body style became standard.

1000 — similar to 900, except has 18 fret fingerboard. Mfd. 1957 to 1971.

$400 $345 $310 $285 $260 $230 $200

In 1958, a chrome bar pickup replaced the original pickup.

In 1961, Fireglo finish became optionally available.

Export Series

These instruments were offered by Rose, Morris & Co. Ltd., for exclusive distribution in the U.K.

1997 — offset double cutaway semi hollow maple body, F-style soundhole, white bi-level pickguard, thru body maple neck, 21 fret rosewood fingerboard with pearl dot inlay, tunomatic bridge/trapeze tailpiece, 3 per side tuners, chrome hardware, 2 pickups, 2 volume/2 tone/mix controls, 3 position switch. Available in Fireglo finish. 1964 to 1969.

1964-1969 $1,500 $1,285 $1,070 $860 $770 $710 $645

In 1966, Autumnglo finish was introduced.

Limited Edition Series

230GF — double cutaway semi hollow maple body, chrome pickguard with **Glenn Frey** signature, thru body maple neck, 24 fret ebony fingerboard with pearl dot inlay, fixed bridge, chrome peghead logo plate, 3 per side tuners, black hardware, 2 humbucker pickups, chrome volume/tone control, 3 position mini switch. Available in Jetglo finish. Current production.

Mfr.'s Sug. Retail $1,000 $750 $500 $350 $300 $275 $225 $200

325JL — offset double cutaway semi hollow 3/4 size maple body, white bi-level pickguard with **John Lennon** signature and graphic, thru body maple neck, 21 fret rosewood fingerboard with pearl dot inlay, tunomatic bridge/vintage vibrato, white peghead logoplate, 3 per side tuners, chrome hardware, 3 pickups, 2 volume/2 tone/mix controls, 3 position switch. Available in Jetglo finish. Mfd. 1990 to 1994.

$1,250 $965 $770 $690 $630 $575 $500

Last Mfr.'s Sug. Retail was $1,700.

350SH — offset sharp double cutaway semi hollow maple body, bi-level pickguard with **Susanna Hoffs** signature, checkered body binding, thru body maple neck, 24 fret bound rosewood fingerboard with pearl triangle inlay, tunomatic bridge/R-style trapeze tailpiece, 2 chrome bar/1 humbucker pickups, 2 volume/2 tone/mix controls, 3 position switch, stereo output. Available in Jetglo finish. Mfd. 1988 to 1991.

$600 $525 $435 $390 $355 $325 $280

A limited edition of 250 were built.

Rickenbacker 325 JL (John Lennon) courtesy Joe Chambers

Grading	100% MINT	98% EXC+	95% EXC+	90% EXC	80% VG+	70% VG	60% G

355JL — offset double cutaway semi hollow 3/4 size maple body, white bi-level pickguard with **John Lennon** signature and graphic, thru body maple neck, 21 fret rosewood fingerboard with pearl dot inlay, tunomatic bridge/trapeze tailpiece, white peghead logoplate, 3 per side tuners, chrome hardware, 3 pickups, 2 volume/2 tone/mix controls, 3 position switch. Available in Jetglo finish. Mfd. 1990 to 1994.

	$1,200	$1,030	$855	$680	$615	$560	$500

Last Mfr.'s Sug. Retail was $1,730.

355/12JL — similar to 355JL, except has 12 strings, 6 per side tuners. Mfd. 1990 to 1994.

	$1,200	$1,015	$835	$730	$650	$580	$530

Last Mfr.'s Sug. Retail was $1,830.

370/12RM — offset double cutaway semi hollow bound maple body, bound wedge shaped soundhole, bi-level pickguard with **Roger McGuinn** signature, thru body maple neck, 21 fret bound rosewood fingerboard with pearl triangle inlay, tunomatic bridge/R-style trapeze tailpiece, 6 per side tuners, chrome hardware, 3 chrome bar pickups, 2 volume/2 tone/mix controls, 3 position switch. Available in Fireglo and Mapleglo finishes. Mfd. 1988 only.

	$1,250	$1,070	$860	$770	$710	$645	$600

Subtract $150 for no signature.

A total of 1,000 of these instruments were made, the first 250 of which were signed by Roger McGuinn.

The few models in mapleglo command a higher premium ($1,500).

381JK — double cutaway semi hollow maple body, carved top/back, checkered body binding, bound wedge style soundhole, white bi-level pickguard with **John Kay** signature and wolf head logo, thru body maple neck, 21 fret bound rosewood fingerboard with pearl triangle inlay, tunomatic bridge/R-style trapeze tailpiece, black peghead logoplate, 3 per side tuners, chrome hardware, 2 humbucker pickups, 2 volume/2 tone/mix controls, 4 position/phase switches, active electronics. Available in Jetglo finish. Mfd. 1988 to date.

Mfr.'s Sug. Retail	$1,800	$1,350	$900	$595	$540	$500	$470	$420

660/12TP — cresting wave style bound figured maple body, checkered body binding, gold bi-level pickguard with **Tom Petty** signature, thru body maple neck, 21 fret bound rosewood fingerboard with pearl triangle inlay, tunomatic bridge/trapeze tailpiece, gold peghead logoplate, 6 per side tuners, chrome hardware, 2 pickups, 2 volume/2 tone/mix controls, 3 position switch. Available in Fireglo and Jetglo finish. Mfd. 1991 to date.

Mfr.'s Sug. Retail	$1,700	$1,275	$850	$610	$560	$510	$460	$390

Vintage Reissue Series

The instruments in this series are reproductions from the 1960s, using vintage style pickups, authentic hardware and knobs. The Vintage Reissue Series is made in small quantities (25-50 annually).

1997 — offset double cutaway semi hollow maple body, F-style soundhole, white bi-level pickguard, thru body maple neck, 21 fret rosewood fingerboard with pearl dot inlay, tunomatic bridge/trapeze tailpiece, 3 per side tuners, chrome hardware, 2 pickups, 2 volume/2 tone/mix controls, 3 position switch. Available in Fireglo, Jetglo, and Mapleglo finishes. Curr. mfr.

1964-1969		$1,500	$1,285	$1,070	$860	$770	$710	$645
Mfr.'s Sug. Retail	$1,430	$1,072	$715	$510	$465	$425	$380	$325

Originally released in 1964 for exclusive United Kingdom distribution.

1997SPC — similar to 1997, except has 3 pickups. Mfd. 1993 to date.

Mfr.'s Sug. Retail	$1,555	$1,166	$777	$560	$515	$465	$400	$365

1997VB — similar to 1997, except has vibrato tailpiece. Mfd. 1988 to 1994.

	$750	$600	$540	$495	$450	$400	$340

Last Mfr.'s Sug. Retail was $1,500.

325V59 — offset double cutaway semi hollow 3/4 size maple body, gold bi-level pickguard, thru body maple neck, 21 fret rosewood fingerboard with pearl dot inlay, tunomatic bridge/Bigsby vibrato tailpiece, 3 per side tuners, chrome hardware, 3 pickups, 2 volume/2 tone controls, 3 position switch. Available in Jetglo and Mapleglo finishes. Mfd. 1991 to date.

Mfr.'s Sug. Retail	$1,660	$1,245	$830	$595	$545	$495	$400	$360

Reproduction of model released in 1959.

325V63 — similar to 325V59, except has white pickguard, vintage vibrato, 2 volume/2 tone/mix controls. Available in Jetglo finish. Current production.

Mfr.'s Sug. Retail	$1,660	$1,245	$830	$595	$545	$495	$400	$360

Reproduction of model released in 1963.

350V63 — offset sharp double cutaway semi hollow maple body, bi-level pickguard, thru body maple neck, 21 fret rosewood fingerboard with pearloid dot inlay, tunomatic bridge/R-style trapeze tailpiece, 3 chrome bar pickups, 2 volume/2 tone/mix controls, 3 position switch, stereo output. Available in Jetglo finish. Mfd. 1994 to date.

Mfr.'s Sug. Retail	$1,690	$1,267	$845	$605	$555	$505	$465	$400

Reproduction of model released in 1963.

350/12V63 — similar to 350V63, except has 12 strings, 6 per side tuners. Mfd. 1994 to date.

Mfr.'s Sug. Retail	$1,790	$1,342	$895	$640	$585	$535	$490	$420

Grading		100%	98% MINT	95% EXC+	90% EXC	80% VG+	70% VG	60% G

360V64 — offset double cutaway semi hollow bound maple body, wedge soundhole, white bi-level pickguard, thru body maple neck, 21 fret rosewood fingerboard with pearl triangle inlay, tunomatic bridge/trapeze tailpiece, 3 per side tuners, chrome hardware, 2 pickups, 2 volume/2 tone/mix controls, 3 position switch. Available in Fireglo finish. Current production.

Mfr.'s Sug. Retail	$1,560	$1,170	$780	$625	$560	$515	$470	$410

    Reproduction of model released in 1964.

360/12V64 — similar to 360V64, except has 12 strings, 6 per side tuners. Available in Fireglo finish. Mfd. 1985 to date.

Mfr.'s Sug. Retail	$1,660	$1,328	$996	$830	$665	$595	$545	$495

381V68/381V69 — offset double cutaway semi hollow bound maple body, figured maple top/back, bound wedge soundhole, white bi-level pickguard, checkered bound body, thru body maple neck, 21 fret bound rosewood fingerboard with pearl triangle inlay, tunomatic bridge/R-style trapeze tailpiece, 3 per side tuners, chrome hardware, 2 pickups, 2 volume/2 tone/mix controls, 3 position switch. Available in Fireglo, Jetglo and Mapleglo finishes. Mfd. 1987 to date.

Mfr.'s Sug. Retail	$2,190	$1,642	$1,095	$645	$575	$525	$480	$425

    Reproduction of model released in 1968.

    In 1991, model was renamed 381V69.

381/12V69 — similar to 381V69, except has 12 strings, 6 per side tuners. Mfd. 1989 to date.

Mfr.'s Sug. Retail	$2,290	$1,717	$1,145	$760	$695	$615	$570	$515

Double Neck Series

362/12 — offset double cutaway semi hollow checkered bound maple body, bound wedge shaped soundhole, white pickguard, thru body maple/walnut laminate necks, 24 fret bound rosewood fingerboards with pearl triangle inlay, tunomatic bridges/R style tailpieces, 6 per side/3 per side tuners, chrome hardware, 2 single coil exposed pickups per neck, 2 volume/2 tone/mix controls, two 3 position switches, stereo output. Available in Natural finish. Mfd. 1975 to 1985.

	$1,500	$1,285	$1,070	$860	$770	$710	$645

    This was a special order instrument.

4080 — cresting wave style bound maple body, 2 piece black pickguard, maple necks, bound rosewood fingerboards with pearl triangle inlay, fixed bridge for bass neck, tunomatic/R style trapeze tailpiece for guitar neck, cresting wave style pegheads, 2 per side tuners for bass neck, 3 per side tuners for guitar neck, chrome hardware, 2 single coil exposed pickups per neck, 2 volume/2 tone/1 mix controls, two 3 position switches, stereo output. Available in Natural finish. Mfd. 1975 to 1985.

	$800	$685	$575	$460	$410	$380	$345

    Bass neck may be maple/walnut laminate and had 20 frets. The guitar neck had 24 frets.

4080/12 — similar to 4080, except has 12 strings, 6 per side tuners on the guitar neck. Mfd. 1978 to 1985.

	$800	$685	$575	$460	$410	$380	$345

ELECTRIC BASS

2000 Series

2020 HAMBURG — double cutaway maple body, thru body maple neck, 20 fret rosewood fingerboard with pearl dot inlay, fixed bridge, 2 per side tuners, 2 single coil pickups, 2 volume/2 tone controls, toggle switch, active electronics. Available in Fireglo, Jetglo, Mapleglo, Midnight Blue, Red, and White finishes. Mfd. 1984 to date.

Mfr.'s Sug. Retail	$1,000	$750	$500	$330	$300	$270	$240	$200

2060 EL DORADO — similar to 2020, except has double bound body, bound fingerboard, gold hardware.

Mfr.'s Sug. Retail	$1,200	$900	$600	$345	$310	$290	$260	$215

4000 Series

    All models in this series have the following, unless otherwise listed: cresting wave style maple body, pickguard, thru body maple neck, 20 fret rosewood fingerboard, fixed bridge, 2 per side tuners, single coil/horseshoe pickups, 2 volume/2 tone controls, 3 position switch.

4000 — cresting wave style maple body, white pickguard, thru body mahogany neck, 20 fret rosewood fingerboard with white dot inlay, fixed bridge, cresting wave peghead with maple laminate wings, 2 per side tuners, chrome hardware, horseshoe pickup, volume/tone control. Available in Autumnglo, Brownburst, Black, Fireglo, and Natural finishes. Mfd. 1957 to 1987.

1957-1960	$5,000	$4,430	$3,860	$3,285	$2,860	$2,385	$1,915
1961-1965	$3,000	$2,285	$2,070	$1,640	$1,200	$1,060	$945
1966-1969	$2,000	$1,430	$1,080	$985	$815	$765	$615
1970-1987	$750	$600	$500	$400	$360	$330	$300

    This was the first production Rickenbacker Bass guitar.

    In 1958, a walnut neck replaced the mahogany neck.

    In 1960, a maple/walnut laminated neck replaced the walnut neck. Fireglo finish became optionally available.

    In 1963, a bridge string mute was added and Autumnglo and Black finishes became optional.

    In 1964, the horseshoe pickup was replaced by a single coil pickup with a metal cover.

R

Grading	100%	98% MINT	95% EXC+	90% EXC	80% VG+	70% VG	60% G

4001 — cresting wave style checkered bound maple body, white pickguard, thru body maple/walnut neck, 20 fret bound rosewood fingerboard with pearl triangle inlay, fixed bridge, cresting wave peghead, 2 per side tuners, chrome hardware, bar/horseshoe pickups, 2 volume/2 tone controls, 3 position switch. Available in Fireglo and Natural finishes. Mfd. 1961 to 1986.

	100%	98%	95%	90%	80%	70%	60%
1961-1964	$4,000	$3,430	$2,860	$2,285	$2,060	$1,885	$1,715
1965-1969	$3,000	$2,570	$2,140	$1,715	$1,545	$1,415	$1,285
1970-1986	$650	$535	$440	$345	$310	$285	$260

> This model was available fretless on special order (4001FL).
>
> In the early '60s, a few models had ebony fingerboards.
>
> In 1964, the horseshoe pickup was replaced by a single coil pickup with a metal cover.
>
> In 1965, Natural finish became optionally available.
>
> Stereo output was originally a special order item on the 4001 until 1971 when it became optionally available.

4001S — similar to 4001, except has unbound body, dot fingerboard inlay. Mfd. 1964 to 1967. Reintroduced 1980 to 1986.

	100%	98%	95%	90%	80%	70%	60%
1964-1967	$5,000	$4,285	$3,570	$2,860	$2,570	$2,360	$2,145
1980-1986	$850	$760	$640	$515	$465	$425	$385

> This was also known as the export Model 1999. Original release instruments were manufactured in low quantites and are rare finds.
>
> This was the model made famous by Paul McCartney and Chris Squire.

4002 — similar to 4000, except has checkered bound figured maple body, figured maple/walnut 5 piece neck, bound ebony fingerboard with pearl triangle inlay, 2 humbucker exposed pickups, 2 volume/2 tone controls, 3 position switch, stereo and direct outputs. Available in Mapleglo and Walnut finishes. Mfd. 1981 only.

	100%	98%	95%	90%	80%	70%	60%
	$750	$640	$570	$485	$425	$390	$350

> This was a Limited Edition instrument.

4003 — cresting wave style bound maple body, 2 piece white pickguard, thru body maple neck, 20 fret bound rosewood fingerboard with pearl triangle inlay, fixed bridge, cresting wave style peghead, 2 per side tuners, chrome hardware, 2 single coil exposed pickups (metal cover over bridge pickup), 2 volume/2 tone controls, 3 position switch, stereo output. Available in Natural finish. Mfd. 1973 to date.

		98%	95%	90%	80%	70%	60%
Mfr.'s Sug. Retail	$1,300	$975	$650	$480	$430	$390	$355	$310

> This model has fretless fingerboard with pearl dot inlay (4003FL) optionally available.
>
> In 1985, pickguard was replaced with one piece unit.

4003S — similar to 4003, except has no binding, dot fingerboard inlay, mono output. Available in Red finish. Mfd. 1980 to date.

		98%	95%	90%	80%	70%	60%
Mfr.'s Sug. Retail	$1,200	$900	$600	$480	$430	$390	$355	$310

4003S/5 — similar to 4003, except has 5 strings, no binding, dot fingerboard inlay, 3/2 per side tuners, mono output. Mfd. 1987 to date.

		98%	95%	90%	80%	70%	60%
Mfr.'s Sug. Retail	$1,400	$1,050	$700	$480	$430	$390	$355	$310

4003S/8 — similar to 4003, except has 8 strings, no binding, dot fingerboard inlay, 4 per side tuners, mono output. Mfd. 1987 to date.

		98%	95%	90%	80%	70%	60%
Mfr.'s Sug. Retail	$1,630	$1,222	$815	$595	$535	$490	$440	$390

4004C (Cheyenne) — cresting wave style walnut body, thru body maple neck, 20 fret maple fingerboard with black dot inlay, fixed bridge, cresting wave style peghead with walnut laminates, 2 per side tuners, gold hardware, 2 humbucker exposed pickups, volume/tone control, 3 position mini switch. Available in Natural finish. Mfd. 1993 to date.

		98%	95%	90%	80%	70%	60%
Mfr.'s Sug. Retail	$1,430	$1,072	$715	$425	$395	$360	$320	$280

4004L (Laredo) — similar to 4004C, except has hardwood body, chrome hardware. Available in Jetglo finish. New 1994.

		98%	95%	90%	80%	70%	60%
Mfr.'s Sug. Retail	$1,430	$1,072	$715	$425	$395	$360	$320	$280

4005 — offset double cutaway semi hollow maple body, rounded top, bound wedge shaped soundhole, white pickguard, thru body maple/walnut laminate neck, 21 fret bound rosewood fingerboard with pearl triangle inlay, tunomatic bridge/R style trapeze tailpiece, cresting wave style peghead, 2 per side tuners, chrome hardware, 2 single coil exposed pickups, 2 volume/2 tone/mix controls, 3 position switch. Available in Fireglo and Natural finishes. Mfd. 1965 to 1984.

	100%	98%	95%	90%	80%	70%	60%
1965-1969	$2,500	$2,140	$1,785	$1,430	$1,285	$1,180	$1,070
1970-1984	$1,250	$1,070	$895	$715	$645	$590	$535

4005WB — similar to 4005, except has bound body. Mfd. 1966 to 1984.

	100%	98%	95%	90%	80%	70%	60%
	$3,000	$2,570	$2,140	$1,715	$1,545	$1,415	$1,285

4005/6 — similar to 4005, except has 6 strings, 3 per side tuners. Mfd. 1965 to 1978.

	100%	98%	95%	90%	80%	70%	60%
	$3,500	$3,000	$2,500	$2,000	$1,800	$1,650	$1,500

4005/8 — similar to 4005, except has 8 strings, 4 per side tuners. Mfd. 1967 to 1984.

	100%	98%	95%	90%	80%	70%	60%
	$3,000	$2,340	$1,885	$1,430	$1,285	$1,180	$1,070

1981 Rickenbacker 4003 bass
courtesy Michael Gangi

Grading	100%	98% MINT	95% EXC+	90% EXC	80% VG+	70% VG	60% G

4008 — cresting wave style bound maple body, white pickguard, thru body maple neck, 21 fret bound rosewood fingerboard with pearl triangle inlay, fixed bridge, cresting wave style peghead, 4 per side tuners, chrome hardware, 2 single coil exposed pickups (metal cover over bridge pickup), 2 volume/2 tone controls, 3 position switch. Available in Fireglo and Natural finishes. Mfd. 1972 to 1984.

	$400	$345	$310	$285	$260	$225	$200

This model was available on special order only.

Limited Edition Series

2030GF — double cutaway maple body, chrome pickguard with Glenn Frey signature, thru body maple neck, 20 fret ebony fingerboard with pearl dot inlay, fixed bridge, chrome peghead logoplate, 2 per side tuners, black hardware, 2 humbucker pickups, chrome volume/tone control, 3 position mini switch. Available in Jetglo finish. Current production.

Mfr.'s Sug. Retail	$1,050	$787	$525	$380	$345	$315	$280	$250

4001CS — cresting wave maple body, white pickguard with Chris Squire signature, thru body maple neck, 20 fret vermilion fingerboard with pearl dot inlay, fixed bridge, white peghead logoplate, 2 per side tuners, chrome hardware, single coil/horseshoe pickups, 2 volume/2 tone controls, 3 position switch. Available in Cream Lacquer finish. Curr. mfr.

Mfr.'s Sug. Retail	$1,530	$1,147	$765	$630	$550	$505	$455	$410

The fingerboard and peghead on this model are carved from one piece of African vermillion.

Vintage Series

4001V63 — cresting wave style maple body, white pickguard, thru body maple neck, 20 fret rosewood fingerboard with pearl dot inlay, fixed bridge, 2 per side tuners, chrome hardware, single coil/horseshoe pickups, 2 volume/2 tone controls, 3 position switch. Available in Fireglo and Mapleglo finishes. Mfd. 1984 to date.

Mfr.'s Sug. Retail	$1,660	$1,245	$830	$665	$595	$545	$495	$435

Reproduction of model released in 1963.

RICKMANN

Instruments built in Japan during the late 1970s.

The Rickmann trademark is a brandname used by an UK importer. Instruments are generally intermediate quality copies of classic American designs.

(Source: Tony Bacon and Paul Day, The Guru's Guitar Guide)

RICO

See B. C. RICH

STEVE RIPLEY

Instruments built in Tulsa, Oklahoma.

Luthier Steve Ripley had established a reputation as both a guitarist and recording engineer prior to debuting his Stereo Guitar models at the 1983 NAMM show. Ripley's designs were later licensed by Kramer (BKL). In 1986, Ripley moved to Tulsa, Oklahoma and two years later severed his relationship with Kramer. Further updates will be featured in future editions of the **Blue Book of Guitars**.

(Source: Tom Wheeler, American Guitars)

RITZ

See WRC GUITARS

Instruments built in Calimesa, California since 1989; the Ritz trademark was then superceded by the current WRC Guitars trademark.

Ritz guitars were high quality solid body designs by Wayne R. Charvel (of Charvel/Jackson fame). After a year of production, the trademark was changed to WRC.

(Source: Tony Bacon and Paul Day, The Guru's Guitar Guide)

RIVERHEAD

Instruments built in Japan during the mid 1980s.

Riverhead produced the 'Unicorn' model which featured 2 pickups, a smaller original shaped body, and a "headless" neck (no headstock; reverse stringing). Authors Bacon and Day mention a guitar model RUG2090 (**R**iverhead **U**nicorn **G**uitar 2090 perhaps?). Good quality construction and materials are featured on these instruments.

(Source: Tony Bacon and Paul Day, The Guru's Guitar Guide)

R

1995 Robin Avalon Goldtop
courtesy David Wintz

ROBERTS

Instruments built in Brea, California during the early 1990s.

Inventor Curt Roberts and his artist wife, Elizabeth, invented four-sided guitar neck, as a means to supply guitarists with a number of alternative tunings on a single instrument. The **Roto-Caster** is available in 2-, 3-, or 4-neck configurations. For further information, contact Curt Roberts through the Index of Current Manufacturers located in the rear of this book.

ROBIN GUITARS

Instruments are built in Houston, Texas, since 1982 and are distributed by Alamo Music Products of Houston, Texas.

In 1972, David Wintz teamed up with a friend to open a guitar shop in Houston, Texas. After ten years of dealing, repairing, and restoring vintage guitars, Wintz began building quality instruments and offering them for sale. In addition to building guitars, Wintz began offering Rio Grande pickups in 1993. Originated by veteran pickup winder Bart Wittrock, the Rio Grande pickups are offered in a variety of sounds/applications and colors - including sparkle finishes!

(Source: Hal Hammer)

> As a further supplement to the standard models listed below, Robin's Custom Shop can assemble virtually anything on a special order basis. Custom graphics and a variety of finishes are also available.

ELECTRIC

Grading	100%	98% MINT	95% EXC+	90% EXC	80% VG+	70% VG	60% G

Robin guitars feature Rio Grande pickups as standard equipment.

Avalon Series

AVALON CLASSIC — single cutaway mahogany body, figured maple top, mahogany neck, 22 fret rosewood fingerboard with abalone dot inlay, tunomatic bridge/stop tailpiece, blackface peghead with pearl logo inlay, 3 per side tuners with plastic buttons, nickel hardware, 2 exposed humbucker Seymour Duncan pickups, volume/tone control, 3 position switch. Available in Antique Violinburst, Antique Amber, and Antique Tobaccoburst finishes. New 1994.

Mfr.'s Sug. Retail	$2,795	$2,096	$1,397	$995	$795	$720	$660	$600

Add $180 for Bigsby Tailpiece.
Add $400 for abalone dolphin inlay on neck.

Avalon Classic Custom — similar to Avalon Classic, except has excellent grade figured maple top, abalone dolphin fingerboard inlay. New 1994.

Mfr.'s Sug. Retail	$3,195	$2,396	$1,597	$1,250	$1,000	$900	$825	$750

AVALON DELUXE — single cutaway ash body, figured maple top, mahogany neck, 22 fret rosewood fingerboard with pearl dot inlay, tunomatic bridge/stop tailpiece, blackface peghead with pearl logo inlay, 3 per side tuners with plastic buttons, nickel hardware, 2 exposed humbucker Seymour Duncan pickups, volume/tone control, 3 position switch. Available in Metallic Gold and Cherry finishes. New 1994.

Mfr.'s Sug. Retail	$1,795	$1,346	$897	$795	$635	$575	$525	$475

Add $180 for Bigsby Tailpiece.
Add $400 for abalone dolphin inlay on neck.

AVALON FLATTOP — single cutaway ash body, tortoise multilam pickguard, mahogany neck, 22 fret rosewood fingerboard with pearl dot inlay, tunomatic bridge/stop tailpiece, blackface peghead with screened logo, 3 per side tuners with plastic buttons, nickel hardware, 2 exposed humbucker Seymour Duncan pickups, volume/tone control, 3 position switch. Available in Old Blonde and Metallic Gold finishes. New 1994.

Mfr.'s Sug. Retail	$1,595	$1,196	$797	$745	$515	$465	$425	$385

Add $180 for Bigsby Tailpiece.
Add $400 for abalone dolphin inlay on neck.

Machete Series

All models in this series have reverse single cutaway asymmetrical bodies with terraced cuts on front and back. Pegheads are asymmetrically V-shaped.

MACHETE CUSTOM — figured maple body, thru body maple neck, 24 fret ebony fingerboard with pearl dot inlay, double locking vibrato, blackface peghead with screened logo, 4/2 per side Sperzel tuners, black hardware, 2 Seymour Duncan blade humbucker pickups, volume/tone control, 3 position switch. Available in Antique Amber and Ruby Red finishes. Mfd. 1991 to 1995.

			$1,575	$1,380	$1,160	$955	$855	$785	$715

Last Mfr.'s Sug. Retail was $2,195.

In 1994, mahogany body, figured maple top, set mahogany neck, rosewood fingerboard, tunomatic bridge/stop tailpiece, chrome hardware, pole piece humbucker pickups replaced original items.

Grading	100%	98% MINT	95% EXC+	90% EXC	80% VG+	70% VG	60% G

Machete Custom Classic — figured maple body, thru body maple neck, 24 fret ebony fingerboard with pearl dot inlay, double locking vibrato, blackface peghead with screened logo, 4/2 per side tuners, black hardware, 2 Seymour Duncan blade humbucker pickups, volume/tone control, 3 position switch. Available in Antique Amber and Ruby Red finishes. Mfd. 1991 to 1995.

	$1,735	$1,520	$1,295	$1,080	$970	$890	$810

Last Mfr.'s Sug. Retail was $2,395.

In 1994, mahogany body, excellent grade figured maple top, set mahogany neck, tunomatic bridge/stop tailpiece, chrome hardware, pole piece humbucker pickups replaced original items.

MACHETE DELUXE — mahogany body, thru body mahogany neck, 24 fret rosewood fingerboard with pearl dot inlay, double locking vibrato, body matching peghead with screened logo, 4/2 per side tuners, black hardware, 2 Seymour Duncan blade humbucker pickups, volume/tone control, 3 position switch. Available in Cherry finish. Mfd. 1991 to 1995.

	$1,440	$1,255	$1,100	$880	$790	$725	$660

Last Mfr.'s Sug. Retail was $1,995.

In 1994, poplar body, set maple neck, pole piece humbucker pickups replaced original items.

MACHETE SPECIAL — ash body, bolt-on maple neck, 24 fret rosewood fingerboard with pearl dot inlay, double locking vibrato, blackface peghead with screened logo, 4/2 per side tuners, black hardware, 2 humbucker PJ Marx pickups, volume/tone control, 3 position switch. Available in Natural Oil finish. Mfd. 1991 to 1994.

	$695	$595	$500	$400	$360	$330	$300

Last Mfr.'s Sug. Retail was $995.

MACHETE STANDARD — ash body, bolt-on maple neck, 24 fret rosewood fingerboard with pearl dot inlay, double locking vibrato, body matching peghead with screened logo, 4/2 per side tuners, black hardware, 2 Seymour Duncan blade humbucker pickups, volume/tone control, 3 position switch. Available in Blue and Cherry finishes. Current production.

Mfr.'s Sug. Retail	$1,770	$1,327	$885	$825	$660	$595	$545	$495

Add $400 for abalone dolphion inlays on neck.

Medley Series

All models in this series have V-shaped peghead optionally available.

MEDLEY SPECIAL — offset double cutaway ash body, bolt-on maple neck, 24 fret rosewood fingerboard with pearl dot inlay, double locking Floyd Rose vibrato, reverse blade peghead, 6 on one side Sperzel tuners, black hardware, single coil/humbucker exposed pickups, volume control, 3 position switch. Available in Oil finish. Mfd. 1991 to 1995.

	$695	$595	$500	$400	$360	$330	$300

Last Mfr.'s Sug. Retail was $995.

MEDLEY STANDARD II — offset double cutaway Swamp Ash or Basswood body, bolt-on maple neck, 24 fret rosewood fingerboard with pearl dot inlay, double locking Floyd Rose vibrato, reverse blade peghead, 6 on one side Sperzel tuners, black hardware, single 2 exposed Seymour Duncan humbucker pickups, volume/tone control, 3 position switch. Available in Blue, Cherry, Natural, Pearl Black and Purple finishes. Mfd. 1991 to date.

Mfr.'s Sug. Retail	$1,770	$1,327	$885	$725	$580	$520	$475	$435

Add $400 for abalone dolphin inlays on neck.

Medley Standard II-Texas Curly Slabtop — similar to Medley Standard II, except has mahogany body, curly maple top. Available in Natural finish. Disc. 1995.

	$1,270	$1,080	$900	$720	$650	$595	$540

Last Mfr.'s Sug. Retail was $1,820.

Medley Standard II-Texas Quilted Slabtop — similar to Medley Standard II, except has mahogany body, quilted maple top. Available in Natural finish. Disc. 1995.

	$1,300	$1,110	$925	$740	$670	$610	$555

Last Mfr.'s Sug. Retail was $1,870.

MEDLEY STANDARD IV — offset double cutaway hardwood body, bolt-on maple neck, 24 fret rosewood fingerboard with pearl dot inlay, double locking Floyd Rose vibrato, reverse blade peghead, 6 on one side Sperzel tuners, black hardware, 2 stacked coil rail/1 pole piece Seymour Duncan humbucker exposed pickups, volume/tone control, 5 position switch. Available in Blue, Cherry, Green, Pearl White and Purple finishes. Mfd. 1991 to 1995.

	$1,095	$910	$760	$610	$550	$505	$455

Last Mfr.'s Sug. Retail was $1,580.

Medley Standard IV-Curly — similar to Medley Standard IV, except has curly maple body. Mfd. 1991 to 1994.

	$1,345	$1,150	$960	$770	$690	$630	$575

Last Mfr.'s Sug. Retail was $1,920.

MEDLEY VI EXOTIC TOP — offset double cutaway hardwood body, bound figured maple top, bolt-on maple neck, 24 fret rosewood fingerboard with pearl dot inlay, double locking Floyd Rose vibrato, reverse blade peghead, 6 on one side Sperzel tuners, black hardware, single coil rail/exposed pole piece Seymour Duncan humbucker pickups, volume/tone control, 5 position switch. Mfd. 1991 to 1995.

	$1,245	$1,050	$875	$700	$630	$575	$525

Last Mfr.'s Sug. Retail was $1,790.

1995 Robin Machete
courtesy David Wintz

R

Grading	100%	98% MINT	95% EXC+	90% EXC	80% VG+	70% VG	60% G

MEDLEY STUDIO IV — offset double cutaway ash body, bolt-on maple neck, 24 fret maple fingerboard with black dot inlay, standard Wilkinson vibrato, reverse blade peghead, 6 on one side locking Sperzel tuners, chrome hardware, 2 single coil rail/1 exposed pole piece humbucker Seymour Duncan pickups, volume/tone control, 5 position switch. Disc. 1995.

	$1,115	$955	$795	$635	$575	$525	$475

Last Mfr.'s Sug. Retail was $1,595.

Ranger Series

RANGER CUSTOM — offset double cutaway bound ash body, white pickguard, metal controls mounted plate, bolt-on figured maple neck, 22 fret rosewood fingerboard with pearl dot inlay, fixed strings thru bridge, reverse peghead, 6 on one side tuners, chrome hardware, humbucker/2 single coil pickups, volume/tone control, 5 position switch. Available in Cherry, Orange and Three Tone Sunburst finishes. Mfg. 1991 to 1995.

	$980	$840	$700	$560	$505	$460	$420

Last Mfr.'s Sug. Retail was $1,420.

In 1994, standard peghead replaced original item.

Ranger Custom Exotic Top — similar to Ranger Custom, except has bound figured maple top, pearloid pickguard, standard peghead. Disc. 1995.

	$1,135	$970	$810	$645	$575	$530	$480

Last Mfr.'s Sug. Retail was $1,620.

RANGER REVIVAL — offset double cutaway hardwood body, pearloid pickguard, bolt-on maple neck, 22 fret rosewood fingerboard with pearl dot inlay, standard vibrato, 6 on one side Sperzel tuners, 3 single coil pickups, 1 volume/2 tone controls, 5 position switch. Current production.

Mfr.'s Sug. Retail	$1,595	$1,196	$797	$585	$465	$420	$385	$350

Add $100 for ash body.

RANGER SPECIAL — offset double cutaway ash body, controls mounted on a metal plate, bolt-on maple neck, 22 fret rosewood fingerboard with pearl dot inlay, fixed strings thru bridge, reverse peghead, 6 on one side tuners, chrome hardware, humbucker/2 single coil pickups, volume/tone control, 5 position switch. Available in Natural Oil finish. Mfd. 1991 to 1995.

	$695	$595	$500	$400	$360	$330	$300

Last Mfr.'s Sug. Retail was $995.

In 1994, standard peghead replaced original item.

RANGER STANDARD — offset double cutaway poplar body, pearloid pickguard, controls mounted on a metal plate, bolt-on maple neck, 22 fret rosewood fingerboard with pearl dot inlay, fixed strings thru bridge, reverse peghead, 6 on one side tuners, chrome hardware, humbucker/2 single coil pickups, volume/tone control, 5 position switch. Available in Pearl Black, Pearl Red and Pearl White finishes. Mfd. 1991 to 1995.

	$810	$685	$575	$460	$410	$380	$345

Last Mfr.'s Sug. Retail was $1,595.

Add $100 for ash body.

In 1994, standard peghead replaced original item.

WRANGLER — similar to Ranger Standard, except has vintage-style fixed bridge. Available in 3-tone Sunburst, Old Blonde, and Black. Current production.

Mfr.'s Sug. Retail	$1,595	$1,196	$797	$650	$540	$460	$370	$300

Add $750 for optional Parson White B-Bender.

RANGER STUDIO — offset double cutaway ash body, white pickguard, controls mounted on a metal plate, bolt-on maple neck, 22 fret rosewood fingerboard with pearl dot inlay, fixed strings thru bridge, reverse peghead, 6 on one side locking Sperzel tuners, chrome hardware, 3 single coil pickups, volume/tone control, 5 position switch. Available in Cherry Sunburst, Three Tone Sunburst, Tobacco Sunburst, Two Tone Sunburst, Unburst, Violin Sunburst and the following Transparent finishes: Blue, Bone White, Charcoal Black, Cherry, Green, Honey, Lavender, Natural, Old Blonde, Orange, Purple, Rootbeer, Violet and Yellow. Mfd. 1991 to 1995.

	$1,075	$910	$760	$610	$550	$505	$455

Last Mfr.'s Sug. Retail was $1,540.

In 1994, standard peghead replaced original item.

Standard Series

RAIDER STANDARD II — asymmetrical double cutaway reverse hardwood body, bolt-on maple neck, 24 fret rosewood fingerboard with pearl dot inlay, double locking vibrato, reverse headstock, 6 on one side tuners, black hardware, 2 humbucker Seymour Duncan pickups, volume/tone control, 3 position switch. Available in Blue, Cherry, Natural, Pearl Black and Purple finishes. Disc. 1992.

	$1,015	$870	$725	$580	$520	$475	$435

Last Mfr.'s Sug. Retail was $1,450.

Raider Standard IV — similar to Ranger Standard II, except has 2 stacked coil/1 humbucker Seymour Duncan pickups, tone control, 5 position/coil tap switch. Available in Blue, Cherry, Green, Pearl White and Purple finishes. Disc. 1992.

	$1,065	$910	$760	$610	$550	$505	$455

Last Mfr.'s Sug. Retail was $1,520.

Grading	100%	98% MINT	95% EXC+	90% EXC	80% VG+	70% VG	60% G

TEDLEY STANDARD VI — single cutaway hardwood body, bolt-on maple neck, 24 fret rosewood fingerboard with pearl dot inlay, double locking vibrato, reverse headstock, 6 on one side tuners, black hardware, stacked coil/humbucker Seymour Duncan pickups, volume/tone control, 3 position switch. Available in Cherry, Orange, Pearl Black and Purple finishes. Mfd. 1991 to 1994.

		$1,015	$870	$725	$580	$520	$475	$435

Last Mfr.'s Sug. Retail was $1,450.

Savoy Series

SAVOY CLASSIC — single cutaway mahogany semi-hollow body, carved curly maple top, mahogany neck, 22 fret rosewood fingerboard with abalone dot inlay, 24.75" scale, tunomatic bridge/stop tailpiece, 2 f-holes, blackface peghead with pearl logo inlay, 3 per side tuners with plastic buttons, nickel hardware, 2 Rio Grande humbuckers, volume/tone control, 3 position switch on upper bass bout. Available in Antique Violinburst, Antique Amber, and Wine Red. Current production.

Mfr.'s Sug. Retail $2,995 $2,246 $1,497 $1,295 $995

Add $180 for Bigsby Tailpiece.

Add $400 for abalone dolphin inlay on neck.

SAVOY DELUXE — single cutaway Swamp Ash (solid) or Poplar (semi-hollow) body, carved arched top, mahogany neck, 22 fret rosewood fingerboard with pearl dot inlay, 2 f-holes, tunomatic bridge/stop tailpiece, blackface peghead with pearl logo inlay, 3 per side tuners with plastic buttons, nickel hardware, 2 Rio Grande humbucker pickups, volume/tone control, 3 position switch on upper bass bout. Available in Metallic Gold, Cherry, Orange, and Old Blonde finishes. Current production.

Mfr.'s Sug. Retail $1,995 $1,496 $997 $895 $735

Add $180 for Bigsby Tailpiece.

Add $400 for abalone dolphin inlay on neck.

Cherry finish can be supplemented with an optional Bigsby and gold-plated hardware.

ELECTRIC BASS

JAYBIRD (formerly Ranger Jaybird) — offset double cutaway asymmetrical ash body, pearloid pickguard, controls mounted on a metal plate, bolt-on maple neck, 20 fret rosewood fingerboard with pearl dot inlay, fixed bridge, reverse peghead, 4 on one side tuners, chrome hardware, 2 J-style pickups, volume/tone control, 3 position switch. Mfd. 1991 to date.

Mfr.'s Sug. Retail $1,265 $948 $632 $575 $460 $410 $380 $345

In 1994, standard peghead replaced original item.

JAYWALKER (formerly Ranger Jaywalker) — offset double cutaway asymmetrical ash body, figured maple top, bolt-on maple neck, 20 fret ebony fingerboard with pearl dot inlay, fixed bridge, 4 on one side tuners, black hardware, 2 J-style Bartolini pickups, volume/treble/bass/mix controls. Mfd. 1991 to date.

Mfr.'s Sug. Retail $1,865 $1,398 $932 $925 $740 $665 $610 $555

MACHETE 5 STRING — reverse single cutaway asymmetrical body with terraced ash body, bolt-on maple neck, 24 fret rosewood fingerboard with pearl dot inlay, fixed Schaller bridge, V-shaped peghead, 3/2 per side tuners, black hardware, 2 Bartolini pickups, volume/treble/bass/mix controls, active electronics. Available in Transparent Cherry, Transparent Green and Pearl Black finishes. Mfd. 1991 to date.

Mfr.'s Sug. Retail $1,865 $1,398 $932 $925 $740 $665 $610 $555

In 1994, ebony fingerboard replaced original item.

MEDLEY — offset double cutaway ash body, bolt-on maple neck, 24 fret rosewood fingerboard with pearl dot inlay, fixed bridge, V-shaped peghead, 2 per side tuners, black hardware, P-style/J-style pickups, volume/tone control, 3 position switch. Available in Pearl Black, Pearl White, Transparent Blue and Transparent Cherry finishes. Mfd. 1991 to date.

Mfr.'s Sug. Retail $1,265 $948 $632 $575 $460 $410 $380 $345

In 1994, reverse blade peghead replaced original item.

RANGER — offset double cutaway ash body, black pickguard, controls mounted on a metal plate, bolt-on maple neck, 20 fret maple fingerboard with black dot inlay, fixed bridge, reverse peghead, 4 on one side Sperzel tuners, chrome hardware, P-style/J-style pickups, volume/tone control, 3 position switch. Available in Pearl Black, Pearl Red and Transparent Old Blonde finishes. Mfd. 1991 to date.

Mfr.'s Sug. Retail $1,265 $948 $632 $575 $460 $410 $380 $345

In 1994, standard peghead replaced original item.

Ranger Bass VI — similar to Ranger, except has 24 fret rosewood fingerboard with pearl dot inlay, fixed strings thru bridge, 6 on side Sperzel tuners, 3 single coil pickups. New 1994.

Mfr.'s Sug. Retail $1,365 $1,092 $819 $685 $545 $490 $450 $410

Ranger Special — similar to Ranger, except has no pickguard, rosewood fingerboard. Disc. 1994.

			$695	$595	$500	$400	$360	$330	$300

Last Mfr.'s Sug. Retail was $995.

ROBINSON

Instruments currently built in Newburyport, Massachusetts.

1996 Robin Savoy
courtesy David Wintz

Robinson Custom Guitars currently offers two models (SC-1 and SC-2) as well as custom design solid body electrics. Options include choice of woods, figured or exotic tops, hardware, and pickups. For further information, contact Robinson Custom Guitars through the Index of Current Manufacturers located in the rear of this book.

ROCKINGER

Instruments and parts produced in Germany since 1978.

Rockinger has been producing numerous high quality replacement parts for a number of years; it seems only natural for them to produce quality original design guitars as well.

(Source: Tony Bacon, The Ultimate Guitar Book)

ROCKOON

Instruments produced in Japan by Kawai.

Good quality solid body guitars and basses featuring 'superstrat' and original designs. Basses are the sleeker body design prevalent since the mid 1980s (RB series). Superstrats such as the RG, RF, or RGT series feature variations on single/humbucker pickup combinations. Rockoon guitars are equipped with Rockoon/Kawai or Shadow pickups, and Schaller hardware.

ROCKSON

Instruments built in Taiwan during the late 1980s.

Rockson solid body guitars featured designs based on the then-popular 'superstrat' design, and other Fender-derived designs.

(Source: Tony Bacon and Paul Day, The Guru's Guitar Guide)

RODRIQUEZ GUITARS

Instruments currently built in Madrid, Spain. Distributed in the U.S. market by Fender Musical Instruments Corporation of Scottsdale, Arizona.

Luthier Manuel Rodriguez, grandson of noted flamenco guitarist Manuel Rodriguez Marequi, has been building classical style guitars for a number of years. He began learning guitar construction at the age of 13 in Madrid and apprenticed in several shops before opening his own. Rodriguez emigrated to Los Angeles in 1959 and professionally built guitars for nearly 15 years. In 1973, Rodriguez returned to Spain and currently builds high quality instruments.

ROGER

Instruments built in West Germany from the late 1950s to mid 1960s.

Luthier Wenzel Rossmeisl built very good to high quality archtop guitars as well as a semi-solid body guitar called 'Model 54'. Rossmeisl derived the trademark name in honor of his son, Roger Rossmeisl.

Roger Rossmeisl (1927-1979) was raised in Germany and learned luthier skills from his father, Wenzel. One particular feature was the "German Carve", a feature used by Wenzel to carve an indented plane around the body outline on the guitar's top. Roger Rossmeisl then travelled to America, where he briefly worked for Gibson in Kalamazoo, Michigan (in a climate not unlike his native Germany). Rossmeisl shortly moved to California, and was employed at the Rickenbacker company. During his tenure at Rickenbacker, Rossmeisl was responsible for the design of the Capri and Combo guitars, and custom designs. His apprentice was a young Semie Moseley, who later introduced the "German Carve" on his **Mosrite** brand guitars. Rossmeisl left Rickenbacker in 1962 to help Fender develop their own line of acoustic guitars (Fender had been licensing Harmnony-made Regals up till then), and later introduced the Montego and LTD archtop electrics.

ROGERS

See chapter on House Brands.

This trademark has been identified as a "House Brand" of Selmer (UK).

(Source: Willie G. Moseley, Stellas & Stratocasters)

ROLAND

Instruments built in Japan during the late 1970s and mid 1980s. Distributed in the U.S. by Roland Musical Instruments of Los Angeles, California.

Instruments built for Roland by Fugi Gen Gakki (Ibanez, Greco), and feature both a 1/4" phono plug and a 24-pin cable attachment.

One of the first things to check for when encountering a Roland synth-guitar is that 24-pin cable. Even if you aren't going to use the synthesizer, just having the cable brings the value up!

The Roland company was founded in Japan, and his been one of the premier synthesizer builders since its inception in 1974. By 1977, the company began experimenting with guitar synthesis. Traditionally, synthesizers have been linked with keyboards as their key mechanism which is easier to adapt to "trigger" the synthesized "voice". Early keys on keyboards were as simple as the lightswitch in your house: press down for "on", release for "off". As synthesizers continued to evolve (today's model uses microprocessors similar to a home computer), the keys provided more information like "velocity" (how hard the key was struck, held, or released - just like a piano).

In 1977, Roland reasoned that the keyboard provided the controlling information to the synthesizer, or was the "controller". In a similar parallel, then, Roland introduced a guitar "controller" and a separate synthesizer. The first system (1977-1980) featured the GR-500 synth and the GS-500 guitar, a vaguely Gibsonish single cutaway model with 10 plus switches. The GR-500 featured sounds from the current keyboard synths, are fairly large and full of switches.

Roland's second series (1980-1984) was a direct improvement on their initial design. The GR-300 (blue box) and the GR-100 (yellow box) are much more compact and designed to be placed on the floor. Roland introduced four guitar models: two (202, 505) were based on Fender-ish styles, and two (303, 808) were more Gibson-esque. The first bass-driven synth was also introduced with the G-33 "controller" and the GR-33B synth in a floor package. The tracking, or reproduction of note(s) struck and when, was better than the previous unit. The tracking (response time) has always been the biggest hurdle to overcome in guitar systhesis, with many units being rejected by guitarists because they don't respond quick enough, or with the same dynamics as the original part. Fair enough, but when you consider the amount of information provided by striking one note on a guitar string (pitch, note length, bend, vibrato, etc) you can see the innate difficulty Roland struggled with.

The third series (1984-1986) is the most striking system from Roland. The effects pedal look of the blue and yellow boxes was replaced by the sleek looking GR-700 and GR-700B (bass unit). Standard guitar design was replaced by the G-707 and G-77 guitar and bass "controllers" which featured an offset design that made lap placement damn near impossible, and a 'stabilizer bar' that ran from the body to the headstock. The futuristic designs looked exciting, and certainly were high quality, but the unusual appearance led to a quick exit from the market.

One of the key downfalls to the whole Roland system of synthesis was the fact that a guitar player had to buy the full package from Roland. No matter what your favorite guitar was, you could only synthesize through a Roland model guitar. Alternate keyboard controllers had been available to keyboardists for a number of years, and the "controller" just had to be a collection of keys that could trigger a synth. Thanks to the advent of MIDI and formalized MIDI codes beginning in 1982, company A's controller could run Company B and Company C's synthesizers. In 1988 (possibly 1989) Roland made an important breakthrough when they introduced the GK-2 Synthesizer Driver. The GK-2 was a small decoder unit that had a hex designed string pickup that mounted near the bridge of your favorite guitar, as well as a 1/4" phone plug to pick up additional information from the magnetic pickups. The signal ran back to the GR-50, and signal information could be split into MIDI and regular guitar signal for additional sound reinforcement. At this point, Roland got out of the guitar business, and completely into the guitar synthesis business because they finally supplied a "box" that you could slip on your favorite guitar.

Currently, Roland markets an upgraded synth driver (GK-2A), which some companies such as Fender and Godin build directly into production models. The rack mounted GR-50 has been upgraded into the GR-1 floor unit, and even the GR-1's 200 "voices" can be expanded into 400 total as well as driving an external synthesizer. Furthermore, Roland has recently introduced a new unit called the VG-8 (for "virtual guitar") which processes the information sent by a GK-2A driver into different (non-synth) pathways to create a whole new category of 'guitar processing'.

ELECTRIC/SYNTHESIZER CONTROLLER

Grading	100%	98% MINT	95% EXC+	90% EXC	80% VG+	70% VG	60% G

During Roland's second series of guitar synths (1980 to 1984) a number of other guitar builders also produced instruments that could 'drive' the Roland GR-100 and GR-300 synthesizers (and later the GR-700). Roland's dedication to the guitar synth made them the de facto industry standard.

Prices listed after each model reflect the 1986 retail price. If you do find the following instruments, now you know why they have the funny plug and extra knobs on them!
Gibson Les Paul ($1,299) and Explorer ($1,049); Hamer A 7 Phantom ($1,500); Modulus Graphite Blacknife Special Synth Controller ($1,500); M.V. Pedulla MVP-S guitar ($1,745) Steinberger GL2T-GR ($2,250); Zion Turbo Synth ($1,395).

Original list price of the GR-100 was $595; the GR-300 was $995 (!). There was a splitter box called the US-2 that could be used to patch the two units together.

G-202 — offset double cutaway body, six-on-a-side tuners, 2 humbuckers, pickup selector switch on pickguard's treble bout, 2 volume and 2 tone knobs, three synth dedicated switches. Mfg. 1980 to 1984.

	$300	$275	$225	$175	$150	$125	$100

The G-202 guitar controller was designed to be used in conjunction with the GR-100 and GR-300 model synthesizers.

G-303 — slightly offset double cutaway body, 3+3 headstock, 2 humbuckers, pickup selector switch on upper bass bout, 2 volume and 2 tone knobs, chrome hardware, 3 dedicated synth switches, bridge, and stop tailpiece. Mfg. 1980 to 1984.

	$300	$275	$225	$175	$150	$125	$100

The G-303 guitar controller was designed to be used in conjunction with the GR-100 and GR-300 model synthesizers.

G-505 — offset double cutaway body, six-on-a-side tuners, 3 single coils, 5-way pickup selector switch on pickguard's treble bout, 2 volume and 2 tone knobs, tremolo bridge, three synth dedicated switches. Mfg. 1980 to 1984.

	$350	$325	$275	$225	$175	$150	$125

The G-505 guitar controller was designed to be used in conjunction with the GR-100 and GR-300 model synthesizers.

Grading	100% MINT	98% EXC+	95% EXC+	90% EXC	80% VG+	70% VG	60% G

G-707 — asymetrical "sharkfin" body with extra 'stabilizing' graphite arm that connects to headstock, reverse six on a side headstock, 2 covered humbuckers, selector switch. Mfg. 1983 to 1986.

	$300	$275	$225	$175	$150	$125	$100

The G-707 guitar controller was designed to be used in conjunction with the GR-700 model synthesizer. The whole package, when introduced in 1983, had a retail price of $2,995 (Guitar controller, $995; GR-700 floor unit, $1,995).

G-808 — slightly offset double cutaway body, laminated central strip with body "wings", 3+3 headstock, 2 humbuckers, pickup selector switch on upper bass bout, 2 volume and 2 tone knobs, gold hardware, 3 dedicated synth switches, bridge, and stop tailpiece. Mfg. 1980 to 1984.

	$300	$275	$225	$175	$150	$125	$100

The G-808 guitar controller was designed to be used in conjunction with the GR-100 and GR-300 model synthesizers.

GS-500 — single cutaway hardwood body, 2 humbuckers, 3+3 headstock, pickup selector switch, 2 volume and 2 tone knobs, extra synth-dedicated knobs and switches. Mfg. 1977 to 1980.

	$250	$225	$160	$140	$120	$100	$90

The GS-500 guitar controller was designed to be used in conjunction with the GR-500 model synthesizer.

ELECTRIC BASS/SYNTH CONTROLLER

G-33 — offset double cutaway body, four on a side tuners, 1 pickup, fixed bridge, 1 volume and 2 tone knobs, assorted synth-dedicated controls. Mfg. 1980 to 1984.

	$350	$325	$265	$225	$175	$125	$110

The G-33 guitar controller was designed to be used in conjunction with the GR-33B model synthesizer.

B-88 — Similar to the G-33, except featured a center laminated strip and 2 body "wings", and same pickup/synth configuration. Natural finish. Mfd. 1980 to 1984.

	$375	$350	$280	$240	$180	$140	$115

The G-88 guitar controller was designed to be used in conjunction with the GR-33B model synthesizer.

G-77 — asymetrical "sharkfin" body with extra 'stabilizing' graphite arm that connects to headstock, reverse four on a side headstock, 2 pickups, selector switches. Mfg. 1984 to 1985.

	$275	$250	$200	$160	$140	$120	$100

The G-77 guitar controller was designed to be used in conjunction with the G-700B model synthesizer.

ROMAN & LIPMAN

Instruments built in Danbury, Connecticut since 1991. Distributed by Roman & Lipman Guitars of Danbury, Connecticut.

Luthier Ed Roman and his partner Barry Lipman founded R & L in the early 1990s to offer custom built instruments to players who were not satisfied with the usual production guitars. R & L, a successful division of the East Coast Music Mall, began offering custom instruments that featured the "most spectacular" wood available. Ed Roman specifically makes a number of trips yearly to gather wood, and personally selects each piece. Roman also maintains another company called Exotic Tonewoods that makes these pieces of exotic woods available to custom luthiers and guitar builders. Exotic Tonewoods and Ed Roman's World Class Guitars can be reached at 203.746.4995 (Fax: 203.746.0488).

Due to the variances in wood, hardware, and pickups, the following models show no listed "base" price. However, these high quality instruments are still fairly reasonable for the options available to the player. Certain models have been listed for $1,995 up to $2,995 in past publications. For a proper rate quote, contact Roman & Lipman Guitars via the Index of Current Manufacturers located in the back of this book.

ELECTRIC

The following model descriptions are the general parameters for the listing as each instrument is based on a custom order. In other words, there is no "standard" base model - guidelines, body designs, and customer satisfaction are the rules of thumb.

The **Penetrator** guitar was first introduced in 1991, and is Roman & Lipman's neck-through solid body guitar. This model boasts a stright string pull with a 3+3 headstock design; choices of over 15 different body woods, 10 different fingerboard woods, pickups, bridges and electronics. The neck-through design also sports Roman & Lipman's trademarked 'No heel neck joint'.

The **Sceptre** guitar was introduced in 1992, and is Roman & Lipman's only bolt-on neck model. This traditional style guitar boasts high quality tone-wood bodies such as Koa, Quilted Maple and Mahogany combinations, Myrtlewood, Spalted Maple, Burl Maple, and over 10 more choices. Numerous fingerboard materials include Pau Ferro, Brazilian Rosewood, Snakewood, Koa, Macassar Ebony, Flame Maple, Figured Wenge, and others. R & L also offers numerous hardware, pickup, and electronic options.

ELECTRIC BASS

The **Intruder** bass was offered beginning in 1994 as a four, five, or six string hand constructed instrument. Featuring such tone woods as Quilted Maple, Koa, Korina, Congalo Alves, and Bubinga, these basses have a five piece neck-through body construction. Different scale lengths, a variety of electronics, pickups combine with R & L's exclusive "Posi-Phase" bridge systems which helps detract the Low B phase cancellation problems on 5 and 6 string models.

Roman & Lipman Custom 5 String
courtesy Ed Roman

The **Invader** bass was introduced just last year. A slightly different body design differentiates the Invader from its older brother, the Intruder, but both basses share similar woods, contruction, and options. All Roman & Lipman instruments are hand built in the U.S. with American components, with the exception of certain imported exotic woods.

ROSCOE

Instruments built in Greensboro, North Carolina since 1971.

Luthier Keith Roscoe opened a shop in Greensboro, North Carolina in 1971 called 'The Guitar Shop'. From its early origins of four or five guitars a year, the workshop turned into a production facility capable of 20 to 30 guitars a month. Roscoe had produced over 900 custom guitars by 1990, and three quarters of them featured custom airbrush or color finishes. Roscoe Guitars can be contacted via the Index of Current Manufacturers located in the back of this book.

(Source: Tom Wheeler, American Guitars)

ROSETTI

See EGMOND.

See also SHERGOLD.

Instruments produced in Holland during the early 1960s through the mid 1970s; one solid body model built in England by another company in 1969.

The Rosetti trademark was a brand name used by an UK importer. The Rosetti name turned up on Dutch-built Egmond solid and semi-hollowbody guitars during the 1960s. The same British importer also stocked a Shergold-made solid body model 'Triumph' in 1969.

(Source: Tony Bacon and Paul Day, The Guru's Guitar Guide)

ROTOSOUND

Instruments built in England in the mid 1970s.

English custom luthier John Birch both designed and built the Rotosound instruments. This high quality solid body did not have any cut-aways in the overall design, and a modular pickup configuration offered the variety of 10 different plug-ins.

(Source: Tony Bacon and Paul Day, The Guru's Guitar Guide)

ROY CUSTOM GUITARS

Instruments built in Chelmsford, Ontario (Canada).

Roy Custom Guitars offers a completely handcrafted instrument that is available in either left- or right-handed configurations. The **RR Custom Electric Guitar** features a Curly Maple or Cherry wood carved top over a Honduran Mahogany or Alder back. The five piece maple and wenge set-neck has an ebony or rosewood fingerboard, and either gold plated or chromed Gotoh hardware. Retail list price starts at $1,195. For information concerning options and further pricing, please contact Roy Custom Guitars via the Index of Current Manufacturers listed in the rear of this book.

ROYAL

Instruments built in England from 1980 to current.

Some of these high quality solid body guitars feature designs based on previous Fender and Gibson favorites. Other original designs include the Medusa and Electra models.

(Source: Tony Bacon and Paul Day, The Guru's Guitar Guide)

ROYALIST

See chapter on House Brands.

This trademark has been identified as a "House Brand" of the RCA Victor Records Store.

(Source: Willie G. Moseley, Stellas & Stratocasters)

RUBIO

Instruments built in Spain, America, and England throughout this luthier's career.

English Master Luthier David Rubio apprenticed in Madrid, Spain at the workshop of Domingo Esteso (which was maintained by Esteso's nephews). In 1961 Rubio built guitars in New York City, New York. Returning to England in 1967, he set up a workshop and continued his guitar building. One of Rubio's apprentices was Paul Fischer, who has gone on to gain respect for his own creations.

ROBERT RUCK

Instruments built in Washington since 1966.

Luthier Robert Ruck has been building high quality classical guitars since 1966. Ruck hand-crafts between 25-30 guitars a year, and estimates that he has produced around 600 instruments altogether. Ruck's guitars are sought after by classical guitarists, and do not surface too often on the collectible market. For further information as to models, specifications, and availablility, please contact luthier Ruck via the Index of Current Manufacturers located in the back of this book.

RUSTLER

Instruments currently produced in Mason City, Iowa.

Rustler Guitars combine the classic look found in desirable, vintage, single cutaway guitars with the sound, playability, and quality of a custom builder. Instruments are constructed of a curly maple top over alder back and side bodies, and feature gold hardware, 6 on a side tuners, and rosewood, maple, or ebony fingerboards. For further information, contact Rustler Guitars through the Index of Current Manufacturers located in the back of this book.

RWK

Instruments built in Highland Park, Illinois since 1991. Distributed by RWK Guitars of Highland Park, Illiniois.

After achieving some success repairing guitars both for himself and friends in the music business, Bob Karger started hand-making guitars in 1991. He wanted to build something that was not only contemporary but would stand the test of time. That is why the company slogan is "Classic Guitars Built Today". The initial design, which to-date is the only design built, is named "SET". This is an acronym for Solid Electric Through-neck.

His goal is to build a guitar which takes advantage of what has been developed so far in the solid electric guitar world and go that extra step. The body is highly contoured, including the noticeable lack of an upper bout, to provide comfort and ease of play. Its through-neck design, along with having the strings anchored through the back of the body, is directly aimed at generating maximun sustain. Because they are handmade, this provides the flexibility of being able to substitute parts and variation in construction aspects, such as neck feel and radius, to easily suit the musician's preference.

(Biography courtesy Bob Karger, RWK Guitars, July 18, 1996)

ELECTRIC

S.E.T. (Solid Electric Through-neck) — Single cutaway ergonomic shaped maple body, solid maple through-neck design, cream top binding, 24 fret bound ebony fingerboard with dot inlay, string through-body bridge, 3 per side Schaller tuners, gold-plated hardware, 2 humbucker pickups (either Adder Plus Dual Coil/Humbuckers or Schaller "Golden 50" PAF style), 2 volume and 2 tone controls, 3 position switch. Translucent Natural finish. Current production.
   Mfr.'s Sug. Retail $799

RYBSKI

Instruments currently built in Wartrace, Tennessee. Distributed by Dan Lenard located in Chicago, Illinois.

Luthier Slawomir "Rybski" Waclawik brings close to twenty years of research to the development and custom building of each bass. Waclawik, a bassist himself, combines exotic woods with modern designs.

ELECTRIC BASS

Instruments all feature 34" scale, and a 24 fret (two octave) neck design.

Rybski pickups were designed by the luthier and Poland's "sound wiz" Jan Radwanski. Pickups are wood covered to match the body of the instrument.

Information on these custom instruments show both a retail price and a direct price. For further information on pricing and custom orders, please contact luthier Waclawik through the Index of Current Manufacturers in back of book.

BASIC — Padauk neck; Cherry, Mahogany, or Ash body; Two Rybski 'single coil' pickups, active electronics, 4 controls (Treble, Bass, Master Volume, Pickup Blend). Current mfg.
   Mfr.'s Sug. Retail $2,750
      For 5 string version add $200.
      For 6 string version add $350.

PRO — Padauk, Purpleheart or Satinwood neck; Padauk, Zebrawood, Bubinga, or Ash with Top body; Top material could be Padauk, Zebrawood, Purpleheart, or Rosewood; 2 Rybski 'double coil' pickups, active electronics, controls (Treble, Bass, Master Volume, Pickup Blend, Pickup Coil Switches, Parallel Series Switch). Current mfg.
   Mfr.'s Sug. Retail $3,250
      For 5 string version add $250.
      For 6 string version add $500.

Rustler TL (model 4022)
courtesy Rustler Guitars

R

RWK S.E.T.
courtesy Bob Karger

SPECIAL — Purpleheart, Satinwood, Pau Ferro, or Jatoba neck; Zebrawood, Purpleheart, Wenge, Satinwood or Ash with Top body; Top material could be Zebrawood, Purpleheart, Rosewood, Bubinga, or Wenge; 2 Rybski 'double coil' pickups, active electronics (9 or 18 volt system), controls (Treble, Middle, Bass, Master Volume, Pickup Blend, Pickup Coil Switches, Parallel Series Switch). Current mfg.

Mfr.'s Sug. Retail   **$3,650**

For 5 string version add $250.

For 6 string version add $500.

R

R

S

S

Instruments produced in Japan.

The 'S' trademark is the brandname of the Jack Westheimer's WMI Importing Company of Chicago, Illinois. The 'S' designation was used on the mid 1960s Kingston guitars, built by Teisco Co. Ltd. of Japan.

(Source: Michael Wright, Guitar Stories Volume One)

SADOWSKY

Instruments produced in New York, New York since 1979. Distributed by Sadowsky Guitars Ltd. of Manhattan, New York.

Roger Sadowsky, a noted East Coast repairman and luthier, has been providing quality customizing and repairs in his shop since 1979. Sadowsky originally apprenticed with Master Luthier Augie LoPrinzi in New Jersey between 1972 and 1974; he then spent five years as the head of the service department for Medley Music Corporation located outside of Philadelphia, Pennsylvania. Upon opening his own shop, Sadowsky initially concentrated on proper instruments set-ups and repair for studio musicians and touring personnel. This backround of repair work on top-notch personal instruments became the basis for Sadowsky's later designs.

Sadowsky's instruments are based on time-tested Fender designs, with primary difference being the the attention paid to the choice of woods. The better a guitar sounds acoustically translates into a better sound when used electronically. The nature of custom work versus production line assembly insures that a player will get the features specified, and Sadowsky has also introduced his own custom active preamps and circuitry. In 1985, Sadowsky was joined by associate Jay Black, a former apprentice of Dick Boak at Martin. Other current staff members include Norio Imai and Ken Fallon.

Sadowsky builds an outboard version of his bass preamp for players unable (or unwilling, in the case of a vintage instrument) to have a preamp installed in their instruments. This preamp simply consists of a volume, bass, and treble knobs, but the simplicity of the controls belies the sophisticated nature of the circuitry.

ELECTRIC

Sadowsky electrics are avaible in three basic model designs. The "vintage Strat" style features three Sadowsky or Joe Barden single coil pickups mounted to a pickguard and a bolt-on neck. Bodies are Alder ($2,000) maple/alder combination, or Swamp Ash ($2,075). A variation that features a "bent" or slightly arched maple top over an alder body and rear-mounted pickups and controls (no pickguard) has a retail list price of $2,200.

Sadowsky offers a vintage style "Tele" model that consists of a swamp ash body, Joe Barden Tele pickups, and vintage style hardware for $2,100. All three models have numerous options available.

ELECTRIC/ACOUSTIC

A new model introduced in the early 1990s was the Electric Nylon string model, which features a single cutaway solid body, bolt-on maple neck, and a Fishman transducer mounted under the bridge saddle. The 22 fret rosewood fingerboard features dot inlays, and the headstock is a six on a side design with Gotoh tuning machines. Base retail price is $2,200, and a MIDI option model lists at $2,800.

ELECTRIC BASS

The name of the game here is Jazz. Be it a four string or five string model, the Sadowsky bass model has a slightly slimmer, sleeker body design. The vintage model features an Alder body and traditional pickups mounted to a pickguard design. The Swamp Ash or "bent" Maple top over a Swamp Ash body models feature rear mounted pickups and controls, thus eliminating the pickguard and displaying the attractive tops. All models feature custom Sadowsky pickups and onboard preamp (EMG pickups are an option), choice of rosewood or maple fingerboards; and solid, sunburst, or transparent finishes. Retail list prices begin at $1,925 (Alder), $2,000 (Swamp Ash), $2,200 (Maple top over Swamp Ash body) for the four string models. Five string models are offered in Ash ($2,300) and a Maple top over an Ash body ($2,500). All models have numerous options available.

SAEHAN

Instruments currently built in Korea.

The Saehan Int'l Co., Ltd. build entry level to medium quality solid body and acoustic guitars based on Classic American designs.

SAKAI

Instruments produced in Japan during the early 1970s.

The Sakai trademark is a brandname of a United Kingdom importer on these entry level to intermediate instruments. The solid and semi-hollowbody guitars have some original designs and designs based on classic American favorites.

(Source: Tony Bacon and Paul Day, The Guru's Guitar Guide)

SAKURA

Instruments produced in Japan during the mid 1970s. Production moved to Korea during the 1980s.

The Sakura trademark is a brandname of a UK importer. Entry level to intermediate quality instruments with some original design and others favoring classic American designs.

(Source: Tony Bacon and Paul Day, The Guru's Guitar Guide)

SAMICK

Instruments produced in Korea since 1965. Current production of instruments is in Korea and City of Industry, California. Distribution in the U.S. market is handled by the Samick Music Corporation located in City of Industry, California.

For a number of years, the Samick corporation was the "phantom builder" of instruments for a number of other trademarks. When the Samick trademark was finally introduced to the U.S. guitar market, a number of consumers thought that the company was brand new. However, Samick has been producing both upright and grand pianos, as well as stringed instruments for nearly forty years.

The "Samick Piano Co." was established in Korea in 1958. By January of 1960 they had started to produce upright pianos, and within four years became the first Korean piano exporter. One year later in 1965, the company began maufacturing guitars, and by the early 1970s expanded to produce grand pianos and harmonicas as well. In 1973 the company incorporated as the "Samick Musical Instruments Mfg. Co., Ltd" to reflect the diversity it emcompassed.

Samick continued to expand into guitar production. They opened a branch office in Los Angeles in 1978, and a brand new guitar factory in 1979. One month before 1981 Samick also opened up a branch office in West Germany.

Throughout the 1980s Samick continued to grow, prosper, and win awards for quality products and company productivity. The "Samick Products Co." was established in 1986 as an affiliate producer of other products, and the company was listed on the Korean Stock Exchange in September of 1988. With their size of production facilities (the company claims to be "cranking out over a million guitars a year", according to a recent brochure), Samick could be referred to as modern day producer of "House Brand" guitars as well as their own brand. In the past couple of years Samick acquired Valley Arts, a guitar company known for its one-of-a-kind instruments and custom guitars. This merger stabilized Valley Arts as the custom shop "wing" of Samick, as well as supplying Samick with quality American designed guitars. Samick continues to expand through the use of innovative designs, partnerships with high exposure endorsees, and new projects such as the Robert Johnson Commemorative and the D'Leco Charlie Christian Commemorative guitars.

(Samick company history courtesy Rick Clapper)

ACOUSTIC

Grading	100%	98% MINT	95% EXC+	90% EXC	80% VG+	70% VG	60% G

ASPEN — dreadnought style, spruce top, round soundhole, black pickguard, 3 stripe bound body/rosette, sapele back/sides, nato neck, 14/20 fret rosewood fingerboard, rosewood bridge with white black dot pins, rosewood veneer on peghead, 3 per side chrome tuners. Available in Natural finish. Disc. 1994.

	100%	98%	95%	90%	80%	70%	60%
	$175	$150	$125	$100	$90	$80	$75

Last Mfr.'s Sug. Retail was $250.

AUSTIN — single round cutaway dreadnought style, solid cedar top, oval soundhole, 5 stripe bound body/rosette, cedar back/sides, maple neck, 14/20 fret bound rosewood fingerboard with pearl dot inlay, stylized pearl inlay at 12th fret, rosewood bridge with white black dot pins, cedar veneer on bound peghead, 3 per side gold tuners, piezo pickup, volume/tone slider control. Available in Natural finish. Disc. 1994.

	100%	98%	95%	90%	80%	70%	60%
	$315	$270	$225	$180	$160	$150	$135

Last Mfr.'s Sug. Retail was $450.

CHEYENNE — folk style, spruce top, round soundhole, black pickguard, mahogany back/sides, nato neck, 14/20 fret rosewood fingerboard with pearl dot inlay, rosewood bridge with white black dot pins, rosewood veneer on peghead, gold tuners. Available in Natural finish. Disc. 1994.

	100%	98%	95%	90%	80%	70%	60%
	$250	$215	$180	$145	$130	$120	$110

Last Mfr.'s Sug. Retail was $360.

DEL REY — classical style, solid spruce top, round soundhole, bound body, wooden inlay rosette, rosewood back/sides, nato neck, 12/19 fret rosewood fingerboard, rosewood bridge, rosewood peghead veneer, 3 per side chrome tuners. Available in Pumpkin finish. Disc. 1994.

	100%	98%	95%	90%	80%	70%	60%
	$210	$180	$150	$120	$110	$100	$90

Last Mfr.'s Sug. Retail was $300.

Grading	100%	98% MINT	95% EXC+	90% EXC	80% VG+	70% VG	60% G

GALLOWAY — single round cutaway dreadnought style, maple top, round soundhole, black pickguard, 3 stripe bound body/rosette, maple back/sides/neck, 14/20 fret bound rosewood fingerboard with pearl dot inlay, rosewood bridge with white black dot pins, 3 per side chrome tuners, piezo pickup, volume/tone slider control. Available in Natural finish. Disc. 1994.

| | | $280 | $240 | $200 | $160 | $145 | $130 | $120 |

Last Mfr.'s Sug. Retail was $400.

GRANADA — single round cutaway classical style, spruce top, round soundhole, bound body, wooden inlay rosette, rosewood back/sides, nato neck, 12/19 fret rosewood fingerboard, rosewood bridge, rosewood peghead veneer, 3 per side chrome tuners, active piezo pickup, volume/tone slider control. Available in Pumpkin finish. Disc. 1994.

| $230 | $195 | $165 | $130 | $120 | $110 | $100 |

Last Mfr.'s Sug. Retail was $330.

GREENBRIAR — dreadnought style, spruce top, round soundhole, black pickguard, 3 stripe bound body/rosette, mahogany back/sides, nato neck, 14/20 fret rosewood fingerboard with pearl dot inlay, rosewood bridge with black white dot pins, 3 per side chrome tuners. Available in Natural finish. Disc. 1994.

| $175 | $150 | $125 | $100 | $90 | $80 | $75 |

Last Mfr.'s Sug. Retail was $250.

Add $50 for solid spruce top (Bluebird).

Add $80 for single round cutaway, piezo pickup, volume/tone slider control (Laredo).

Subtract $10 for left handed design, acoustic pickup, volume/tone control (Beaumont).

This model was available with 12 strings, nato back/sides (SW21012 Savannah).

JASMINE — dreadnought style, solid cedar top, round soundhole, tortoise pickguard, 3 stripe bound body, herringbone rosette, walnut back/sides, nato neck, 14/20 fret bound rosewood fingerboard with pearl block inlay, rosewood bridge with white pearl dot pins, walnut veneer on bound peghead, 3 per side chrome tuners. Available in Natural finish. Disc. 1994.

| $195 | $165 | $140 | $110 | $100 | $90 | $80 |

Last Mfr.'s Sug. Retail was $280.

LA GRANDE — classical style, cedar top, round soundhole, bound body, wooden inlay rosette, rosewood back/sides, nato neck, 12/19 fret rosewood fingerboard, rosewood bridge, rosewood peghead veneer, 3 per side chrome tuners. Available in Pumpkin finish. Disc. 1994.

| $250 | $215 | $180 | $145 | $130 | $120 | $110 |

Last Mfr.'s Sug. Retail was $360.

LA TOUR — classical style, solid spruce top, round soundhole, bound body, wooden inlay rosette, sapele back/sides, nato neck, 12/19 fret rosewood fingerboard, rosewood bridge, rosewood peghead veneer, 3 per side chrome tuners. Available in Pumpkin finish. Disc. 1994.

| $145 | $125 | $100 | $80 | $70 | $65 | $60 |

Last Mfr.'s Sug. Retail was $280.

LAUREL — dreadnought style, solid spruce top, round soundhole, black pickguard, 3 stripe bound body/rosette, nato neck, 14/20 fret bound rosewood fingerboard with pearl Tree of Life inlay, ebony bridge with white pearl dot pins, bound peghead with pearl logo inlay, 3 per side gold tuners. Available in Natural finish. Disc. 1994.

| | | $280 | $240 | $200 | $160 | $145 | $130 | $120 |

Last Mfr.'s Sug. Retail was $400.

MAGNOLIA — jumbo style, sycamore top, round soundhole, black pickguard, 5 stripe bound body/rosette, nato back/sides/neck, 14/20 fret bound rosewood fingerboard with pearl dot inlay, rosewood bridge with white black dot pins, 3 per side black chrome tuners. Available in Black and White finishes. Disc. 1994.

| $230 | $195 | $165 | $130 | $120 | $110 | $100 |

Last Mfr.'s Sug. Retail was $330.

NIGHTINGALE — dreadnought style, solid spruce top, round soundhole, black pickguard, 3 stripe bound body/rosette, imitation birdseye back/sides, nato neck, 14/20 fret bound rosewood fingerboard with pearl dot inlay, rosewood bridge with white black dot pins, bound headstock, 3 per side chrome tuners. Available in Transparent Black finish. Disc. 1994.

| $245 | $210 | $175 | $140 | $125 | $115 | $105 |

Last Mfr.'s Sug. Retail was $350.

NIGHTINGALE 12 — dreadnought style, maple top, round soundhole, black pickguard, 3 stripe bound body/rosette, maple back/sides, nato neck, 14/20 fret bound rosewood fingerboard with pearl dot inlay, rosewood bridge with white black dot pins, 6 per side chrome tuners. Available in Transparent Black finish. Disc. 1994.

| $210 | $180 | $150 | $120 | $110 | $100 | $90 |

Last Mfr.'s Sug. Retail was $300.

SANTA FE — dreadnought style, nato top, round soundhole, black pickguard, bound body, 5 stripe rosette, nato back/sides/neck, 14/20 fret nato fingerboard with pearl dot inlay, ebonized maple bridge with black pins, 3 per side chrome tuners. Available in Black, Gloss Brown, and White finishes. Disc. 1994.

| $125 | $110 | $90 | $70 | $65 | $60 | $50 |

Last Mfr.'s Sug. Retail was $180.

Add $50 for acoustic pickup, volume/tone control (SW115E1).

"In 1987, D'Aquisto received an order from...Hank Risen who gave D'Aquisto carte blanche to build whatever he wanted to...The result of this order was the Avant Garde, a striking 18-inch guitar, unique not only in appearance but in construction and sound, undoubtedly the finest guitar D'Aquisto had built to date."

—Lawrence Acunto TCG, May/June 1993

Grading	100%	98% MINT	95% EXC+	90% EXC	80% VG+	70% VG	60% G

SEVILLE — classical style, spruce top, round soundhole, bound body, wooden inlay rosette, mahogany back/sides, nato neck, 12/19 fret rosewood fingerboard, rosewood bridge, 3 per side chrome tuners. Available in Pumpkin finish. Disc. 1994.

	$125	$110	$90	$70	$65	$60	$50

Last Mfr.'s Sug. Retail was $180.

SWEETWATER — folk style, spruce top, round soundhole, 3 stripe bound body/rosette, mahogany back/sides, nato neck, 14/20 fret rosewood fingerboard with pearl dot inlay, rosewood bridge with white pins, 3 per side chrome tuners. Available in Natural finish. Disc. 1994.

	$155	$130	$110	$90	$80	$70	$65

Last Mfr.'s Sug. Retail was $220.

VICKSBURG — dreadnought style, solid spruce top, round soundhole, black pickguard, herringbone bound body/rosette, rosewood back/sides, nato neck, 14/20 fret bound rosewood fingerboard with pearl diamond inlays, rosewood bridge with white black dot pins, 6 per side gold tuners. Available in Natural finish. Disc. 1994.

	$315	$270	$225	$180	$160	$150	$135

Last Mfr.'s Sug. Retail was $450.

Handcrafted Series

CHAMBRAY — single round cutaway folk style, solid cedar top, round soundhole, rosewood pickguard, wooden bound body, wooden inlay rosette, rosewood back/sides, nato neck, 14/20 fret ebony fingerboard with pearl dot inlay, ebony bridge with black white dot pins, rosewood veneer on peghead with pearl logo inlay, 3 per side Schaller gold tuners with pearl buttons, acoustic pickup, volume/tone control, preamp. Available in Natural finish. Disc. 1994.

	$770	$660	$550	$440	$395	$365	$330

Last Mfr.'s Sug. Retail was $1,100.

MARSEILLES — folk style, solid spruce top, round soundhole, tortoise shell pickguard, wooden bound body, wooden inlay rosette, ovankol back/sides, nato neck, 14/20 fret bound rosewood fingerboard with pearl dot inlay, ebony bridge with white black dot pins, ovankol veneer on peghead with pearl logo inlay, 3 per side chrome tuners. Available in Natural finish. Disc. 1994.

	$320	$275	$230	$185	$165	$150	$140

Last Mfr.'s Sug. Retail was $460.

VERSAILLES — similar to Marseilles, except has solid cedar top, rosewood back/sides, brown white dot bridge pins. Disc. 1994.

	$490	$420	$350	$280	$250	$230	$210

Last Mfr.'s Sug. Retail was $700.

Classical Series

Instruments in this series have the following features: classic body, round soundhole, bound body, marquetry rosette, 12/19 fret fingerboard, slotted peghead, tied bridge, 3 per side tuners with plastic buttons.

LC015G — mahogany top/back/sides/neck, rosewood fingerboard/bridge, chrome tuners. Available in Natural finish. New 1994.

Mfr.'s Sug. Retail	$140	$112	$84	$70	$55	$50	$45	$40

LC025G — spruce top, mahogany back/sides/neck, rosewood fingerboard/bridge, chrome tuners. Available in Natural finish. New 1994.

Mfr.'s Sug. Retail	$170	$127	$85	$80	$65	$60	$55	$45

SC310 — spruce top, mahogany back/sides/neck, rosewood fingerboard/bridge, chrome tuners. Available in Pumpkin finish. New 1994.

Mfr.'s Sug. Retail	$180	$144	$108	$90	$70	$65	$60	$50

SC330 — spruce top, rosewood back/sides, mahogany neck, rosewood fingerboard/bridge, chrome tuners. Available in Pumpkin finish. New 1994.

Mfr.'s Sug. Retail	$270	$216	$162	$135	$110	$100	$90	$80

SC450 — spruce top, maple back/sides, mahogany neck, rosewood fingerboard/bridge, chrome tuners. Available in Pumpkin finish. New 1994.

Mfr.'s Sug. Retail	$210	$157	$105	$100	$80	$70	$65	$60

Concert Folk Series

SF210 — flat-top body, spruce top, round soundhole, bound body, multistripe purfling/rosette, mahogany back/sides/neck, 14/20 fret rosewood fingerboard with pearl dot inlay, rosewood bridge with black white dot pins, 3 per side chrome tuners. Available in Natural finish. New 1994.

Mfr.'s Sug. Retail	$220	$176	$132	$110	$90	$80	$70	$65

Grading	100%	98% MINT	95% EXC+	90% EXC	80% VG+	70% VG	60% G

SF291 — similar to SF210, except has solid spruce top, rosewood back/sides, gold tuners.

	100%	98% MINT	95% EXC+	90% EXC	80% VG+	70% VG	60% G
Mfr.'s Sug. Retail	$360	$288	$216	$180	$145	$130	$120	$110

Exotic Wood Series

SD50 — dreadnought style, spruce top, round soundhole, black pickguard, bound body, multistripe purfling/rosette, maple back/sides, mahogany neck, 14/20 fret rosewood fingerboard with pearl diamond-dot inlay, maple veneered peghead with pearl split diamond/logo inlay, rosewood bridge with white black dot pins, 3 per side chrome tuners. Available in Natural finish. New 1994.

	100%	98%	95%	90%	80%	70%	60%
Mfr.'s Sug. Retail	$300	$240	$180	$150	$120	$110	$100	$90

SD60 S — dreadnought style, solid spruce top, round soundhole, black pickguard, bound body, multistripe purfling/rosette, bubinga back/sides, mahogany neck, 14/20 fret rosewood fingerboard with abalone diamond-dot inlay, rosewood bridge with white black dot pins, bubinga veneered peghead with abalone split diamond/logo inlay, 3 per side chrome tuners. Available in Natural finish. New 1994.

	100%	98%	95%	90%	80%	70%	60%
Mfr.'s Sug. Retail	$450	$360	$270	$225	$180	$160	$150	$135

SD80 CS — dreadnought style, figured maple top, round soundhole, black pickguard, bound body, multistripe purfling/rosette, maple back/sides, mahogany neck, 14/20 fret bound rosewood fingerboard with abalone pearl diamond-dot inlay, bound peghead with abalone split diamond/logo inlay, rosewood bridge with white black dot pins, 3 per side chrome tuners. Available in Sunburst finish. New 1994.

	100%	98%	95%	90%	80%	70%	60%
Mfr.'s Sug. Retail	$350	$280	$210	$175	$140	$125	$115	$105

SW270 HSNM — dreadnought style, solid cedar top, round soundhole, black pickguard, bound body, herringbone purfling/rosette, walnut back/sides, mahogany neck, 14/20 fret bound rosewood fingerboard with pearl block inlay, bound peghead with pearl logo inlay, rosewood bridge with white black dot pins, 3 per side chrome tuners. Available in Natural finish. New 1994.

	100%	98%	95%	90%	80%	70%	60%
Mfr.'s Sug. Retail	$280	$224	$168	$140	$110	$100	$90	$80

Player Series

LW025G — dreadnought style, spruce top, round soundhole, black pickguard, bound body, multistripe rosette, nato back/sides, mahogany neck, 14/20 fret rosewood fingerboard with pearl dot inlay, rosewood bridge with white black dot pins, 3 per side chrome tuners. Available in Natural finish. New 1994.

	100%	98%	95%	90%	80%	70%	60%
Mfr.'s Sug. Retail	$190	$152	$114	$95	$75	$70	$65	$55

SW015 — dreadnought style, mahogany top, round soundhole, black pickguard, bound body, multistripe rosette, mahogany back/sides/neck, 14/20 fret rosewood fingerboard with pearl dot inlay, rosewood bridge with white black dot pins, 3 per side chrome tuners. Available in Black, Natural and White finishes. New 1994.

	100%	98%	95%	90%	80%	70%	60%
Mfr.'s Sug. Retail	$180	$144	$108	$90	$70	$65	$60	$50

SW115 — similar to SW015, except has neck pickup, volume/tone controls. Available in Black, Natural and White finishes. New 1994.

	100%	98%	95%	90%	80%	70%	60%
Mfr.'s Sug. Retail	$230	$184	$138	$115	$90	$80	$70	$65

SW210 — dreadnought style, spruce top, round soundhole, black pickguard, bound body, multistripe rosette, mahogany back/sides/neck, 14/20 fret rosewood fingerboard with pearl dot inlay, rosewood bridge with white black dot pins, 3 per side chrome tuners. Available in Natural finish. New 1994.

	100%	98%	95%	90%	80%	70%	60%
Mfr.'s Sug. Retail	$250	$200	$150	$125	$100	$90	$80	$75

SW210 CE — similar to SW210, except has single round cutaway, piezo bridge pickup, 4 band EQ. Available in Natural finish. New 1994.

	100%	98%	95%	90%	80%	70%	60%
Mfr.'s Sug. Retail	$330	$264	$198	$165	$130	$120	$110	$100

SW210 12 — similar to SW210, except has 12 strings, 6 per side tuners. Available in Natural finish. New 1994.

	100%	98%	95%	90%	80%	70%	60%
Mfr.'s Sug. Retail	$250	$200	$150	$125	$100	$90	$80	$75

SW230 HS 12 — dreadnought style, solid spruce top, round soundhole, black pickguard, bound body, herringbone purfling/rosette, rosewood back/sides, mahogany neck, 14/20 fret rosewood fingerboard with pearl dot inlay, rosewood bridge with black white dot pins, 6 per side tuners gold tuners. Available in Natural finish. New 1994.

	100%	98%	95%	90%	80%	70%	60%
Mfr.'s Sug. Retail	$450	$360	$270	$225	$180	$160	$150	$135

SW260 12B — dreadnought style, maple top, round soundhole, black pickguard, bound body, multistripe purfling/rosette, mahogany back/sides/neck, 14/20 fret rosewood fingerboard with pearl dot inlay, rosewood bridge with black white dot pins, 6 per side chrome tuners. Available in Black finish. New 1994.

	100%	98%	95%	90%	80%	70%	60%
Mfr.'s Sug. Retail	$300	$240	$180	$150	$120	$110	$100	$90

Pro Series

All instruments in this series are handmade.

S7 — concert style, spruce top, round soundhole, rosewood pickguard, bound body, multistripe wood purfling/rosette, rosewood back/sides, mahogany neck, 14/20 fret bound ebony fingerboard with pearl dot inlay, ebony bridge with black white dot pins, pearl peghead logo inlay, 3 per side chrome tuners. Available in Natural finish. New 1994.

	100%	98%	95%	90%	80%	70%	60%
Mfr.'s Sug. Retail	$700	$560	$420	$350	$280	$250	$230	$210

Grading		100%	98% MINT	95% EXC+	90% EXC	80% VG+	70% VG	60% G

S7EC — similar to S7, except has single round cutaway, piezo bridge pickup, volume/tone controls. Available in Natural finish. New 1994.

Mfr.'s Sug. Retail	$1,100	$880	$660	$550	$440	$395	$365	$330

SDT10CE — single round cutaway dreadnought style, ash top, round soundhole, tortoise pickguard, bound body, multistripe purfling/rosette, ash back/sides, maple neck, 14/20 fret bound rosewood fingerboard with pearl diamond/dot inlay, rosewood bridge with white black dot pins, bound peghead with pearl logo inlay, 3 per side chrome tuners, piezo bridge pickup, 4 band EQ. Available in Natural finish. New 1994.

Mfr.'s Sug. Retail	$450	$360	$270	$225	$180	$160	$150	$135

SW260CE — single round cutaway dreadnought style, maple top, round soundhole, tortoise pickguard, bound body, multistripe purfling/rosette, maple back/sides/neck, 14/20 fret bound rosewood fingerboard with pearl diamond/dot inlay, rosewood bridge with white black dot pins, bound peghead with pearl logo inlay, 3 per side chrome tuners, piezo bridge pickup, 4 band EQ. Available in Natural finish. New 1994.

Mfr.'s Sug. Retail	$400	$320	$240	$200	$160	$145	$130	$120

SW630 HS — dreadnought style, solid spruce top, round soundhole, black pickguard, bound body, herringbone purfling/rosette, rosewood back/sides, mahogany neck, 14/20 fret bound rosewood fingerboard with pearl tree-of-life inlay, rosewood bridge with white black dot pins, bound peghead with pearl logo inlay, 3 per side gold tuners. Available in Natural finish. New 1994.

Mfr.'s Sug. Retail	$400	$320	$240	$200	$160	$145	$130	$120

SW730 SP — dreadnought style, solid spruce top, round soundhole, black pickguard, bound body, multistripe purfling/rosette, rosewood back/sides, mahogany neck, 14/20 fret ebony fingerboard with abalone dot inlay, ebony bridge with black white dot pins, bound peghead with abalone logo inlay, 3 per side chrome tuners. Available in Natural finish. New 1994.

Mfr.'s Sug. Retail	$840	$672	$504	$420	$335	$300	$275	$250

SW790 SP — dreadnought style, solid spruce top, round soundhole, black pickguard, bound body, multistripe purfling/rosette, jacaranda back/sides, mahogany neck, 14/20 fret bound ebony fingerboard with abalone dot inlay, ebony bridge with black white dot pins, bound peghead with abalone logo inlay, 3 per side chrome tuners. Available in Natural finish. New 1994.

Mfr.'s Sug. Retail	$720	$576	$432	$360	$290	$260	$240	$220

Value Series

C41 — dreadnought style, mahogany top, round soundhole, black pickguard, bound body, multistripe rosette, mahogany back/sides/neck, 14/20 fret rosewood fingerboard with pearl dot inlay, rosewood bridge with black pins, 3 per side chrome tuners. Available in Natural finish. New 1994.

Mfr.'s Sug. Retail	$160	$120	$80	$75	$60	$55	$50	$45

LW015 — dreadnought style, mahogany top, round soundhole, black pickguard, bound body, multistripe rosette, mahogany back/sides/neck, 14/20 fret rosewood fingerboard with pearl dot inlay, rosewood bridge with black pins, 3 per side chrome tuners. Available in Natural finish. New 1994.

Mfr.'s Sug. Retail	$150	$120	$90	$75	$60	$55	$50	$45

ACOUSTIC BASS

KINGSTON BASS — single round cutaway hollow style, maple top, bound body, F holes, maple back/sides/neck, 24 fret bound rosewood fingerboard, thru strings rosewood bridge, 2 per side black chrome tuners, piezo pickup, volume/tone slider control. Available in Black, Natural, Pearl White and Tobacco Sunburst finishes. Disc. 1994.

			$490	$420	$350	$280	$250	$230	$210

Last Mfr.'s Sug. Retail was $700.

HF590 — single round cutaway flat-top body, maple top, bound f holes, bound body, maple back/sides/neck, 21 fret bound fingerboard with pearl dot inlay, strings thru rosewood bridge, blackface peghead with pearl logo inlay, 2 per side black tuners, piezo bridge pickup, 4 band EQ. Available in Black, Natural, Pearl White and Tobacco Sunburst finishes. New 1994.

Mfr.'s Sug. Retail	$700	$560	$420	$350	$280	$250	$230	$210

HF5690 — similar to HF590, except has 5 strings, arched figured maple top, 3/2 per side tuners. Available in Transparent Black finish. New 1994.

Mfr.'s Sug. Retail	$950	$760	$570	$475	$380	$345	$315	$285

This model has fretless fingerboard with Natural finish optionally available.

ACOUSTIC ELECTRIC

BLUE RIDGE — single round cutaway folk style, figured maple top, oval soundhole, 5 stripe bound body, wooden rosette cap, maple back/sides, nato neck, 22 fret bound rosewood fingerboard with pearl dot inlay, rosewood strings thru bridge, 6 on one side black chrome tuners, active piezo pickup, volume/tone control. Available in Blue Burst, Natural and Tobacco Sunburst finishes. Disc. 1994.

			$350	$300	$250	$200	$180	$165	$150

Last Mfr.'s Sug. Retail was $500.

"Mere words do not even begin to describe this unique creation of the master builder of the twentieth century. It is unlikely any fretted instrument will come to light in the next 50 years which will equal it in rarity or collectability."

—Stanley M. Jay

TCG, May/June 1993

Grading	100%	98% MINT	95% EXC+	90% EXC	80% VG+	70% VG	60% G	

EAG88 — single round cutaway flat-top body, spruce top, round soundhole, bound body, wood purfling, abalone rosette, maple back/sides, mahogany neck, 24 fret bound extended rosewood fingerboard with pearl dot inlay, strings thru rosewood bridge, bound peghead with screened logo, 6 on one side black tuners, piezo bridge pickup, volume/tone controls. Available in Natural finish. New 1994.

Mfr.'s Sug. Retail	$500	$400	$300	$250	$200	$180	$165	$150

EAG89 — single round cutaway flat-top body, figured maple top, round soundhole, bound body, wood purfling, abalone rosette, rosewood back/sides, mahogany neck, 24 fret bound extended rosewood fingerboard with pearl dot inlay, strings thru rosewood bridge, bound peghead with screened logo, 6 on one side gold tuners, piezo bridge pickup, volume/tone controls. Available in Natural, Red Stain and Sunburst finishes. New 1994.

Mfr.'s Sug. Retail	$600	$480	$360	$300	$240	$215	$195	$180

EAG93 — single round cutaway flat-top body, solid spruce top, round soundhole, bound body, abalone purfling/rosette, rosewood back/sides, mahogany neck, 24 fret bound extended ebony fingerboard with pearl eagle inlay, strings thru rosewood bridge, abalone bound peghead with screened logo, 6 on one side gold tuners, piezo bridge pickup, 4 band EQ. Available in Natural finish. New 1994.

Mfr.'s Sug. Retail	$1,000	$800	$600	$500	$400	$360	$330	$300

ELECTRIC

KR-660 — offset double cutaway acrylic body, bolt-on maple neck, 24 fret bound rosewood fingerboard with pearl "V" inlay, double locking Floyd Rose vibrato, 6 on one side tuners, gold hardware, 2 single coil/1 humbucker pickups, volume/tone controls, 5 position switch. Available in Clear finish. New 1994.

Mfr.'s Sug. Retail	$640	$512	$384	$320	$255	$230	$210	$195

This is a Limited Edition instrument.

Alternative Series

AURORA — offset double cutaway alder body, bolt-on maple neck, 24 fret bound rosewood fingerboard with pearl dot inlay, double locking vibrato, 6 on one side tuners, black hardware, single coil/humbucker pickup, volume/tone control, 3 position switch. Available in Aurora finish. Disc. 1994.

			$345	$295	$245	$195	$175	$160	$150

Last Mfr.'s Sug. Retail was $490.

HAWK, NIGHTBREED, VIPER — offset double cutaway alder body, bolt-on maple neck, 24 fret bound rosewood fingerboard with pearl triangle inlay, double locking vibrato, 6 on one side tuners, black hardware, 2 single coil rail/1 humbucker pickups, volume/2 tone controls, 5 position switch. Disc. 1994.

Hawk — available in Hawk Graphic finish.

			$405	$350	$290	$230	$205	$190	$175

Last Mfr.'s Sug. Retail was $580.

Nightbreed — available in Nightbreed Graphic finish.

			$455	$390	$325	$260	$235	$215	$195

Last Mfr.'s Sug. Retail was $650.

Viper — available in Viper Graphic finish.

			$455	$390	$325	$260	$235	$215	$195

Last Mfr.'s Sug. Retail was $650.

ICE CUBE — offset double cutaway acrylic body, bolt-on maple neck, 24 fret rosewood fingerboard with pearl V inlay, double locking vibrato, 6 on one side tuners, gold hardware, 2 single coil/1 humbucker pickups, volume/tone control, 5 position switch. Available in Clear finish. Disc. 1994.

			$365	$310	$260	$210	$190	$170	$160

Last Mfr.'s Sug. Retail was $520.

Jazz/Blues Series

BLUENOTE — single round cutaway bound hollow body, arched maple top, raised black pickguard, f holes, maple back/sides/neck, 22 fret bound rosewood fingerboard with abalone/pearl block inlay, adjustable rosewood bridge/trapeze tailpiece, bound blackface peghead with pearl vines/logo inlay, 3 per side tuners, gold hardware, 2 covered humbucker pickups, 2 volume/2 tone controls, 3 position switch. Available in Golden Sunburst, Natural and Tobacco Sunburst finishes. Disc. 1994.

			$420	$360	$300	$240	$215	$195	$180

Last Mfr.'s Sug. Retail was $600.

KINGSTON — double rounded cutaway semi hollow style, arched figured maple top, raised black pickguard, bound body, F holes, maple back/sides, nato neck, 22 fret bound rosewood fingerboard with pearl cross inlay, tunomatic bridge/stop tailpiece, bound peghead with pearl vines/logo inlay, 3 per side tuners, chrome hardware, 2 humbucker pickups, 2 volume/2 tone controls, 3 position switch. Available in Black, Cherry Sunburst, Golden Sunburst and Natural finishes. Disc. 1994.

			$370	$320	$265	$210	$190	$175	$160

Last Mfr.'s Sug. Retail was $530.

Kingston Classic — similar to Kingston, except has gold hardware. Available in Cherry Sunburst, Golden Sunburst, Natural and Tobacco Sunburst finishes. Disc. 1994.

			$390	$335	$280	$225	$205	$190	$170

Last Mfr.'s Sug. Retail was $560.

Grading	100%	98% MINT	95% EXC+	90% EXC	80% VG+	70% VG	60% G

WABASH — single round cutaway hollow style, arched maple top, raised bound black pickguard, bound body, F holes, maple back/sides/neck, 20 fret bound rosewood fingerboard with pearl block inlay, adjustable rosewood bridge/trapeze tailpiece, bound peghead with pearl flower inlay, 3 per side tuners, gold hardware, 2 humbucker pickups, 2 volume/2 tone controls, 3 position switch. Available in Cherry Sunburst, Golden Sunburst and Natural finishes. Disc. 1994.

| | $420 | $360 | $300 | $240 | $215 | $195 | $180 |

Last Mfr.'s Sug. Retail was $600.

Performance Series

LEGACY — offset double cutaway alder body, bolt-on maple neck, 24 fret bound rosewood fingerboard with pearl boomerang inlay, double locking vibrato, 6 on one side tuners, gold hardware, 2 single coil rail/1 humbucker pickups, volume/tone control, 5 position/coil tap switches. Available in Natural finish. Disc. 1994.

| | $390 | $335 | $280 | $225 | $205 | $190 | $170 |

Last Mfr.'s Sug. Retail was $560.

PROPHET — similar to Legacy, except has ash body, thru body neck. Available in Transparent Black and Transparent Red finishes. Disc. 1994.

| | $420 | $360 | $300 | $240 | $215 | $195 | $180 |

Last Mfr.'s Sug. Retail was $600.

RENEGADE — offset double cutaway alder body, bolt-on maple neck, 24 fret maple fingerboard with black dot inlay, standard vibrato, 6 on one side tuners, chrome hardware, 3 single coil pickups, volume/tone control, 5 position switch. Available in Cobalt Blue and Metallic Red finishes. Disc. 1994.

| | $265 | $225 | $190 | $150 | $135 | $120 | $110 |

Last Mfr.'s Sug. Retail was $380.

SCANDAL — similar to Renegade, except has bound rosewood fingerboard, 2 humbucker pickups, 2 volume/1 tone control, 3 position switch. Available in Fluorescent Green and Metallic Black finishes. Disc. 1994.

| | $210 | $180 | $150 | $120 | $110 | $100 | $90 |

Last Mfr.'s Sug. Retail was $300.

SCORPION — offset double cutaway alder body, bolt-on maple neck, 24 fret bound rosewood fingerboard with pearl boomerang inlay, double locking vibrato, 6 on one side tuners, gold hardware, 2 single coil/1 humbucker pickups, volume/tone control, 5 position switch, push/pull coil tap in tone control. Available in Black, Metallic Red and Pearl White finishes. Disc. 1994.

| | $365 | $310 | $260 | $210 | $190 | $170 | $160 |

Last Mfr.'s Sug. Retail was $520.

Scorpion Plus — similar to Scorpion, except has sharktooth fingerboard inlay, direct switch. Available in Black, Blue, Metallic Red and Pearl White finishes. Disc. 1994.

| | $315 | $270 | $225 | $180 | $160 | $150 | $135 |

Last Mfr.'s Sug. Retail was $450.

STINGER — offset double cutaway bound alder body, bolt-on maple neck, 24 fret bound rosewood fingerboard with pearl boomerang inlay, double locking vibrato, 6 on one side tuners, gold hardware, 2 single coil rail/1 humbucker pickups, volume/tone control, 5 position/coil tap switches. Available in Antique Red Sunburst and Black finishes. Disc. 1994.

| | $380 | $325 | $270 | $215 | $195 | $180 | $165 |

Last Mfr.'s Sug. Retail was $540.

S Series

Instruments in this series have the following features, unless otherwise listed: offset double cutaway body, bolt-on maple neck, 21 fret fingerboard, standard vibrato, 6 on one side tuners, chrome hardware, 3 single coil pickups, 1 volume/2 tone controls, 5 position switch. Available in Black, Metallic Red and Pearl White finishes.

DS-100 — hardwood body, white pickguard, maple fingerboard with black dot inlay. New 1994.

| Mfr.'s Sug. Retail | $200 | $160 | $120 | $100 | $80 | $70 | $65 | $60 |

SMX-3 — bound carved mahogany body, 22 fret bound ebony fingerboard with pearl dot inlay, double Floyd Rose vibrato, gold hardware, 2 single coil/1 humbucker pickups, volume/tone controls. Available in Cherry Sunburst finish. New 1994.

| Mfr.'s Sug. Retail | $650 | $520 | $390 | $325 | $260 | $235 | $215 | $195 |

SMX-4 — mahogany body, bound figured maple top/back, 22 fret bound ebony fingerboard with pearl dot inlay, tunomatic bridge/stop tailpiece, gold hardware, 2 single coil/1 humbucker pickups, volume/tone controls. Available in Transparent Black, Transparent Blue and Transparent Red finishes. New 1994.

| Mfr.'s Sug. Retail | $540 | $432 | $324 | $270 | $215 | $195 | $180 | $165 |

SSM-1 — alder body, pearloid pickguard, maple fingerboard with black dot inlay. Available in Black, Candy Apple Red, Lake Placid Blue, Pearl White, Sea Foam Green and Tobacco Sunburst finishes. New 1994.

| Mfr.'s Sug. Retail | $320 | $256 | $192 | $160 | $130 | $115 | $105 | $95 |

SSM-2 — alder body, white pickguard, rosewood fingerboard with pearl dot inlay, double locking Floyd Rose vibrato, 2 single coil/1 humbucker pickups. Available in Black, Candy Apple Red, Lake Placid Blue, Pearl White, Tobacco Sunburst and Transparent Black finishes. New 1994.

| Mfr.'s Sug. Retail | $400 | $320 | $240 | $200 | $160 | $145 | $130 | $120 |

Grading	100%	98% MINT	95% EXC+	90% EXC	80% VG+	70% VG	60% G

SSM-3 — alder body, white pickguard, rosewood fingerboard with pearl dot inlay, double locking Floyd Rose vibrato, gold hardware, 2 single coil/1 humbucker pickups, volume/tone controls. Available in Black, Candy Apple Red and Tobacco Sunburst finishes. New 1994.

Mfr.'s Sug. Retail	$450	$360	$270	$225	$180	$160	$150	$135

SV-430 — alder body, rosewood fingerboard with pearl dot inlay. New 1994.

Mfr.'s Sug. Retail	$250	$200	$150	$125	$100	$90	$80	$75

SV-460 — alder body, black pickguard, rosewood fingerboard with pearl dot inlay. New 1994.

Mfr.'s Sug. Retail	$260	$208	$156	$130	$100	$90	$80	$75

SVE-130 — alder body, white pickguard, maple fingerboard with black dot inlay. New 1994.

Mfr.'s Sug. Retail	$220	$176	$132	$110	$90	$80	$70	$65

T Series

Instruments in this series have the following features, unless otherwise listed: single cutaway body, bolt-on maple neck, 21 fret fingerboard, fixed bridge, 6 on one side tuners, chrome hardware, 2 single coil pickups, volume/tone control, 3 position switch.

RANGER 3 — alder body, rosewood fingerboard with pearl dot inlay, strings thru bridge, 3 single coil pickups, 5 position switch. Available in Black and Blue finishes. New 1994.

Mfr.'s Sug. Retail	$500	$400	$300	$250	$200	$180	$165	$150

SMX-1 — bound carved ash body, 24 fret bound ebony fingerboard with pearl dot inlay, double locking Floyd Rose vibrato, gold hardware, 2 single coil/1 humbucker pickups, 5 position switch. Available in Cherry Sunburst and Vintage Sunburst finishes. New 1994.

Mfr.'s Sug. Retail	$650	$520	$390	$325	$260	$235	$215	$195

SMX-2 — bound carved ash body, 22 fret ebony fingerboard with pearl dot inlay, strings thru bridge, bound peghead, gold hardware. Available in Cherry Sunburst and Tobacco sunburst finishes. New 1994.

Mfr.'s Sug. Retail	$500	$400	$300	$250	$200	$180	$165	$150

STM-1 — ash body, 22 fret maple fingerboard with black dot inlay, Gotoh locking tuners. Available in Natural finish. New 1994.

Mfr.'s Sug. Retail	$350	$280	$210	$175	$140	$125	$115	$105

TO-120 — ash body, black pickguard, controls mounted on a metal plate, maple fingerboard with black dot inlay, chrome hardware. Available in Natural finish. New 1994.

Mfr.'s Sug. Retail	$290	$232	$174	$145	$115	$105	$95	$85

TO-320 — ash body, back pickguard, controls mounted on a metal plate, maple fingerboard with black dot inlay, gold hardware. Available in Black finish. New 1994.

Mfr.'s Sug. Retail	$340	$272	$204	$170	$135	$125	$115	$105

TL650 — quilted maple body, 22 fret maple fingerboard with black dot inlay, tunomatic bridge/stop tailpiece, gold hardware. Available in Oyster finish. New 1994.

Mfr.'s Sug. Retail	$500	$400	$300	$250	$200	$180	$165	$150

Trad Jazz Series

HJ650 — single round cutaway arched hollow body, maple top, bound holes, raised black pickguard, bound body, maple back/sides/neck, 20 fret bound rosewood fingerboard with pearl block inlay, adjustable rosewood bridge/trapeze tailpiece, bound peghead with pearl flower/logo inlay, 3 per side tuners, gold hardware, 2 humbucker pickups, 2 volume/2 tone controls, 3 position switch. Available in Natural and Sunburst finishes. New 1994.

Mfr.'s Sug. Retail	$600	$480	$360	$300	$240	$215	$195	$180

SAT450 — double cutaway semi hollow body, arched flame maple top, bound f holes, raised black pickguard, maple back/sides, mahogany neck, 22 fret bound rosewood fingerboard with pearl dot inlay, tunomatic bridge/stop tailpiece, bound peghead with pearl leaf/logo inlay, 3 per side tuners, chrome hardware, 2 humbucker pickups, 2 volume/2 tone controls, 3 position switch. Available in Black finish. New 1994.

Mfr.'s Sug. Retail	$530	$424	$318	$265	$210	$190	$175	$160

SAT650 — similar to SAT450, except has gold hardware. Available in Sunburst finish. New 1994.

Mfr.'s Sug. Retail	$600	$480	$360	$300	$240	$215	$195	$180

Add $100 for bird'seye maple body with Burgundy Stain finish.

Vintage Guitar Series

SOUTHSIDE — offset double cutaway laminated body, white pickguard, bolt-on maple neck, 21 fret maple fingerboard with black dot inlay, standard vibrato, 6 on one side tuners, chrome hardware, 3 single coil pickups, volume/2 tone controls, 5 position switch. Disc. 1994.

			$155	$130	$110	$90	$80	$70	$65

Last Mfr.'s Sug. Retail was $220.

> "I went to the Mayo Clinic and told them that they should start a Les Paul section of the hospital for Les Paul players to fix their backs."
>
> —L. Acunto on Les Paul
>
> TCG, Jan/Feb 1993

Grading	100%	98% MINT	95% EXC+	90% EXC	80% VG+	70% VG	60% G

Southside Classic, Legend — offset double cutaway body, white pickguard, bolt-on maple neck, 22 fret rosewood fingerboard pearl dot inlay, standard vibrato, 6 on one side tuners, chrome hardware, 3 single coil pickups, volume/2 tone controls, 5 position switch. Disc. 1994.

		$235	$200	$170	$135	$125	$115	$105

Last Mfr.'s Sug. Retail was $340.

Classic — alder body. Available in Antique Orange, Pacific Blue, Candy Apple Red, Seamist Green and Tobacco Sunburst finishes. Disc. 1994.

		$225	$195	$160	$130	$115	$105	$95

Last Mfr.'s Sug. Retail was $320.

Legend — ash body. Available in Natural and Transparent Ivory finishes. Disc. 1994.

		$235	$200	$170	$135	$125	$115	$105

Last Mfr.'s Sug. Retail was $340.

Southside Heavy — similar to Southside, except has black pickguard, 22 fret rosewood fingerboard with pearl dot inlay, 2 single coil/1 humbucker pickups. Disc. 1994.

		$195	$165	$140	$110	$100	$90	$80

Last Mfr.'s Sug. Retail was $280.

Southside Special — similar to Southside, except has 22 fret rosewood fingerboard with pearl dot inlay. Disc. 1994.

		$190	$160	$135	$110	$100	$90	$80

Last Mfr.'s Sug. Retail was $270.

UPTOWN — single cutaway laminated body, white pickguard, bolt-on maple neck, 21 fret maple fingerboard with black dot inlay, fixed bridge, 6 on one side tuners, chrome hardware, 2 single coil pickups, volume/tone control, 3 position switch. Available in Butterscotch and Transparent Ivory finishes. Disc. 1994.

		$205	$175	$145	$115	$105	$95	$85

Last Mfr.'s Sug. Retail was $290.

Uptown Classic — similar to Uptown, except has alder body, gold hardware. Available in Black finish. Disc. 1994.

		$235	$200	$170	$135	$125	$115	$105

Last Mfr.'s Sug. Retail was $340.

Uptown Legend — similar to Uptown, except has ash body, black pickguard. Available in Natural and Transparent Ivory finishes. Disc. 1994.

		$235	$200	$170	$135	$125	$115	$105

Last Mfr.'s Sug. Retail was $340.

ELECTRIC BASS

AURORA — offset double cutaway alder body, maple neck, 24 fret rosewood fingerboard, fixed bridge, 4 on one side tuners, black hardware, P-style/J-style pickup, volume/mid/bass/balance controls. Available in Aurora Multi Palette finish. Disc. 1994.

		$365	$310	$260	$210	$190	$170	$160

Last Mfr.'s Sug. Retail was $520.

JAVELIN — offset double cutaway asymmetrical alder body, white pickguard, thumb rest, bolt-on maple neck, 20 fret rosewood fingerboard, fixed bridge, 4 on one side tuners, chrome hardware, 2 J-style pickups, 2 volume/1 tone control. Available in Black, Pearl White, Sunburst finishes. Disc. 1994.

		$245	$210	$175	$140	$125	$115	$105

Last Mfr.'s Sug. Retail was $350.

JB420 — offset double cutaway asymmetrical alder body, white pickguard with thumbrest, controls mounted on a metal plate, bolt-on maple neck, 21 fret rosewood fingerboard with pearl dot inlay, fixed bridge, 4 on one side tuners, 2 J-style pickups, 2 volume/1 tone controls. Available in Black, Pearl White and Sunburst finishes. New 1994.

Mfr.'s Sug. Retail	$350	$280	$210	$175	$140	$125	$115	$105

PB110 — offset double cutaway alder body, black pickguard, bolt-on maple neck, 20 fret maple fingerboard with black dot inlay, fixed bridge, 4 on one side tuners, chrome hardware, P-style pickup, volume/tone controls. Available in Black, Candy Apple Red and Pearl White finishes. New 1994.

Mfr.'s Sug. Retail	$270	$216	$162	$135	$110	$100	$90	$80

PRESTIGE — offset double cutaway laminated body, black pickguard, thumb rest, bolt-on maple neck, 20 fret maple fingerboard with black dot inlay, fixed bridge, 4 on one side tuners, P-style pickup, volume/tone control. Available in Black, Metallic Red and Pearl White finishes. Disc. 1994.

		$190	$160	$135	$110	$100	$90	$80

Last Mfr.'s Sug. Retail was $270.

Prestige GT — similar to Prestige, except has alder body, no pickguard, 24 fret rosewood fingerboard with pearl dot inlay. Available in Black, Pearl White, Tobacco Sunburst and Transparent Blue finishes. Disc. 1994.

		$210	$180	$150	$120	$110	$100	$90

Last Mfr.'s Sug. Retail was $300.

Grading	100%	98% MINT	95% EXC+	90% EXC	80% VG+	70% VG	60% G

PROPHET — offset double cutaway alder body, thru body 3 piece maple neck, 24 fret rosewood fingerboard with pearl dot inlay, fixed bridge, 4 on one side tuners, gold hardware, P-style/J-style pickups, volume/tone control, 3 position switch. Available in Transparent Black, Transparent Blue, and Transparent Red finishes. Disc. 1994.

		$420	$360	$300	$240	$215	$195	$180

Last Mfr.'s Sug. Retail was $600.

SCBM-1 — offset double cutaway ash body, bolt-on maple neck, 20 fret rosewood fingerboard with pearl dot inlay, fixed bridge, 4 on one side tuners, black hardware, J-style/P-style pickups, 2 volume/1 tone controls, active electronics. Available in Transparent Blue, Transparent Black and Transparent Red finishes. New 1994.

Mfr.'s Sug. Retail	$500	$400	$300	$250	$200	$180	$165	$150

Add $80 for gold hardware with Transparent Black finish.

SCBM-2 — similar to SCBM-1, except has 5 strings, 4/1 per side tuners. Available in Transparent Blue finish. New 1994.

Mfr.'s Sug. Retail	$560	$448	$336	$280	$225	$205	$190	$170

Add $20 for gold hardware with Cherry Sunburst, Transparent Black, Transparent Blue and Transparent Red finishes.

SMBX-1 — offset double cutaway mahogany body, bound figured maple top, bolt-on maple neck, 20 fret bound ebony fingerboard with pearl dot inlay, fixed bridge, bound peghead, 4 on one side tuners, gold hardware, J-style/P-style pickups, 2 volume/1 tone controls, active electronics. Available in Cherry Sunburst finish. New 1994.

Mfr.'s Sug. Retail	$580	$464	$348	$290	$230	$205	$190	$175

SMBX — similar to SMBX-1, except has 5 strings, 4/1 per side tuners. Available in Cherry Sunburst and Transparent Black finishes. New 1994.

Mfr.'s Sug. Retail	$660	$528	$396	$330	$265	$240	$220	$200

THUNDER — offset double cutaway alder body, bolt-on maple neck, 24 fret rosewood fingerboard with pearl dot inlay, fixed bridge, 4 on one side tuners, gold hardware, P-style/J-style pickups, volume/tone control, 3 position switch. Available in Black Finishing Net, Granite White Sunburst and Pearl White finishes. Disc. 1994.

		$260	$220	$185	$150	$135	$120	$110

Last Mfr.'s Sug. Retail was $370.

Thunder-5 — similar to Thunder, except has 5 string configuration, 4/1 per side tuners, 2 volume/1 tone controls. Available in Black, Granite Gold, Grayburst, Metallic Red and Pearl White finishes. Disc. 1994.

		$350	$300	$250	$200	$180	$165	$150

Last Mfr.'s Sug. Retail was $500.

This model available with active pickups.

THUNDERBOLT — offset double cutaway alder body, bolt-on maple neck, 24 fret rosewood fingerboard with pearl lightning bolt inlay, fixed bridge, 4 per side tuners, gold hardware, P-style/J-style active pickups, volume/treble/bass/balance controls. Available in Black, Grayburst, Metallic Red and Pearl White finishes. Disc. 1994.

		$315	$270	$225	$180	$160	$150	$135

Last Mfr.'s Sug. Retail was $450.

YB410 — offset double cutaway alder body, bolt-on maple neck, 24 fret rosewood fingerboard with pearl dot inlay, fixed bridge, 4 on one side tuners, chrome hardware, P-style pickup, volume/tone controls. Available in Black, Transparent Blue and Transparent Sunburst finishes. New 1994.

Mfr.'s Sug. Retail	$300	$240	$180	$150	$120	$110	$100	$90

YB530 — offset double cutaway alder body, bolt-on maple neck, fretless rosewood fingerboard, fixed bridge, 4 on one side tuners, black hardware, P-style/J-style pickups, volume/tone controls, 3 position switch. Available in Black and Red finishes. New 1994.

Mfr.'s Sug. Retail	$350	$280	$210	$175	$140	$125	$115	$105

YB5639 — similar to YB530, except has 5 strings, 24 fret fingerboard with pearl dot inlay, 4/1 per side tuners, gold hardware, 2 volume/1 tone controls, active electronics. Available in Black, Gold Marble, Grey/Whiteburst, Metallic Red and White finishes. New 1994.

Mfr.'s Sug. Retail	$500	$400	$300	$250	$200	$180	$165	$150

YBT6629 — offset double cutaway walnut body, thru body maple/walnut neck, 24 fret ebony fingerboard with pearl dot inlay, fixed bridge, 4/2 per side tuners, gold hardware, 2 J-style pickups, 2 volume/2 tone controls, active electronics. Available in Natural, Transparent Black and Transparent Red finishes. New 1994.

Mfr.'s Sug. Retail	$1,000	$800	$600	$500	$400	$360	$330	$300

SAND

Instruments currently built in Laguna Beach, California.

Luthier Kirk Sand began playing guitar at six years old and played professionally and taught until the age of nineteen when he moved from his hometown of Springfield, Illinois to Southern California to study classical guitar.

His love of the instrument led him to co-establish the Guitar Shoppe in 1972 with Jim Matthews in Laguna Beach, California, which produces some of the finest custom instruments built today as well as being one of the premier repair facilities on the West Coast. The head of the repair section is Mark Angus (see ANGUS GUITARS) who works full-time as well as building his custom acoustics throughout the year.

By 1979, Kirk's twenty years of dedicated experience with guitars, guitar repair and restoration inspired him to begin building guitars of his own design. Sand guitars feature Sitka or Engleman Spruce tops, Brazilian or Indian rosewood backs and sides, ebony fingerboards, and custom designed active

Sand Guitar
courtesy Kirk Sand

electronics. For further information, contact Sand Guitars through the Index of Current Manufacturers located in the back of this book.

SANOX

Instruments produced in Japan from the late 1970s through the mid 1980s.

Intermediate to good quality guitars featuring some original designs and some designs based on American classics.

(Source: Tony Bacon and Paul Day, The Guru's Guitar Guide)

SANTA CRUZ

Instruments built in and around Santa Cruz, California since 1976. Distribution is handled by the Santa Cruz Guitar Company (SCGC) located in Santa Cruz, California.

The Santa Cruz Guitar Company was formed by Richard Hoover in 1976. Hoover, a former apprentice of luthier John David Morse, has expanded the company production of hand crafted acoustic guitars by working with a group of established luthiers. Orders are placed on standardized models, or custom variations as commissioned.

ACOUSTIC

Grading	100%	98% MINT	95% EXC+	90% EXC	80% VG+	70% VG	60% G

All models have round soundholes with wood inlay rosettes. Body trim consists of ivoroid binding with wood purfling, unless otherwise listed. All models are available in Natural finish, unless otherwise indicated. For current option pricing, availability, or further information, please contact Richard Hoover at Santa Cruz Guitars via the Index of Current Manufacturers located in the rear of this book.

ARCHTOP — single round cutaway hollow style, bound carved spruce top, raised bound ebony pickguard, bound f holes, multi wood purfling, maple back/sides/neck, 21 fret bound ebony fingerboard with abalone fan inlay, adjustable ebony bridge/fingers tailpiece, ebony veneered bound peghead with abalone logo inlay, 3 per side tuners, gold hardware. Curr. mfr.

This instrument comes in three different body dimensions (measured across the lower bout), listed below.

16 Inch Body — available in Natural finish.

	100%	98%	95%	90%	80%	70%	60%
Mfr.'s Sug. Retail	$8,000	$6,000	$4,000	$3,400	$3,200	$2,880	$2,640	$2,400

17 Inch Body — available in Sunburst finish.

Mfr.'s Sug. Retail	$8,500	$6,800	$5,100	$4,250	$3,400	$3,060	$2,805	$2,550

18 Inch Body — Available in Natural finish.

Mfr.'s Sug. Retail	$9,500	$7,600	$5,700	$4,750	$3,800	$3,420	$3,135	$2,850

MODEL D — dreadnought style, spruce top, koa back/sides, mahogany neck, 14/20 fret bound ebony fingerboard, ebony bridge with black pearl dot pins, ebony veneer on bound peghead with pearl logo inlay, 3 per side gold tuners. Curr. mfr.

Mfr.'s Sug. Retail	$2,150	$1,612	$1,075	$985	$790	$710	$650	$590

This model is also available with rosewood back/sides.

12 Fret D Model — folk style, spruce top, herringbone purfling/rosette, black pickguard, mahogany back/sides, 12/20 fret ebony fingerboard with pearl diamond inlay, ebony bridge with pearl dot pins, ebony veneer on slotted peghead with pearl logo inlay, 3 per side gold tuners. Curr. mfr.

Mfr.'s Sug. Retail	$2,800	$2,100	$1,400	$1,305	$985	$880	$810	$745

MODEL F — jumbo style, spruce top, maple back/sides, maple neck, 14/21 fret bound ebony fingerboard with abalone fan inlay, ebony bridge with black pearl dot pins, ebony veneer on bound peghead with pearl logo inlay, 3 per side gold tuners. Curr. mfr.

Mfr.'s Sug. Retail	$2,550	$1,912	$1,275	$1,200	$960	$860	$790	$720

MODEL FS — single round cutaway jumbo style, cedar top, mahogany neck, 21 fret ebony fingerboard, ebony bridge with black pearl dot pins, 3 per side chrome Schaller tuners with ebony buttons. Curr. mfr.

Mfr.'s Sug. Retail	$3,650	$2,737	$1,825	$1,725	$1,380	$1,240	$1,140	$1,035

MODEL H — folk style, koa top, round soundhole, abalone bound body/rosette, koa back/sides, mahogany neck, 14/20 fret bound ebony fingerboard, ebony bridge with black pearl pins, koa veneer on bound peghead, 3 per side gold tuners with ebony buttons. Curr. mfr.

Mfr.'s Sug. Retail	$2,400	$1,800	$1,200	$1,125	$900	$810	$740	$675

Model H A/E — folk style, spruce top, mahogany back/sides/neck, 21 fret ebony fingerboard with pearl/gold ring inlay, ebony bridge with black pearl dot pins, 3 per side gold Schaller tuners with ebony buttons, bridge pickup with micro drive preamp. Curr. mfr.

Mfr.'s Sug. Retail	$3,450	$2,587	$1,725	$1,335	$1,025	$885	$765	$680

Grading	100%	98% MINT	95% EXC+	90% EXC	80% VG+	70% VG	60% G

MODEL OM (Orchestra Model) — concert grand style, spruce top, tortoise pickguard, herringbone rosette, Brazilian rosewood back/sides, mahogany neck, 14/20 fret bound ebony fingerboard with pearl logo inlay at 12th fret, ebony bridge with black pearl dot pins, rosewood peghead veneer, 3 per side gold tuners. Curr. mfr.

Mfr.'s Sug. Retail	$2,650	$1,987	$1,325	$1,265	$1,010	$910	$835	$760

> This model may also have Indian rosewood back/sides.

TONY RICE MODEL — dreadnought style, spruce top, tortoise pickguard, herringbone bound body/rosette, rosewood back/sides, mahogany neck, 14/20 fret bound ebony fingerboard with pearl logo inlay at 12th fret, Tony Rice signature at 14th fret, ebony bridge with black pearl dot pins, ebony peghead veneer, 3 per side gold tuners. Curr. mfr.

Mfr.'s Sug. Retail	$2,875	$2,156	$1,437	$1,375	$1,100	$990	$905	$825

> This model was co-designed by Tony Rice.

VINTAGE ARTIST — dreadnought style, spruce top, tortoise pickguard, herringbone body trim, mahogany back/sides/neck, 14/21 fret bound ebony fingerboard with pearl dot inlay, ebony bridge with black pearl dot pins, Brazilian rosewood veneer on bound peghead with pearl logo inlay, 3 per side chrome tuners. Curr. mfr.

Mfr.'s Sug. Retail	$2,650	$1,987	$1,325	$1,265	$1,010	$910	$835	$760

SANTA ROSA

Instruments built in Asia. Distributed by A R Musical Enterprises of Fishers, Indiana.

Santa Rosa acoustic guitars are geared more towards the entry level or student guitarist.

SANTUCCI

Instruments produced in Rome, Italy and distributed in the U.S. market by the Santucci Corporation of New York City, New York.

The 10 string Santucci TrebleBass ($1,980) was developed by Sergio Santucci, and combines the 6 strings of a guitar with the 4 strings of a bass all on one neck. The active circuitry of the individual guitar/bass pickups are wired to separate outputs (thus processing the two outputs to their respective amplification needs), and can be switched on and off independently. The two octave fretboard and custom made Gotoh tremolo/bass tailpiece give any guitarist ample room for exploration across the sonic range. For further information, contact Santucci via the Index of Current Manufacturers listed in the back of the book.

ELECTRIC

TREBLEBASS — offset double cutaway alder body, thru body 5 piece maple neck, 24 fret ebony fingerboard with pearl dot inlay, custom-made Gotoh bridge consisting of: fixed bridge, bass; standard vibrato, guitar; 4/6 per side tuners, chrome Gotoh hardware, split-bass/single coil/humbucker-guitar EMG pickups, 2 concentric volume/tone controls, 2 mini switches. Available in White, Black, Red, Green, Yellow, and blue finishes with silk screened logo. Mfg. 1990 to current.

Mfr.'s Sug. Retail	$1,980

SARRICOLA

Instruments currently built in Lake Thunderbird, Illinois.

Luthier Bill Sarricola, an ex-Hamer employee, currently offers four different custom built guitar models. Sarricola models feature three different equipment packages on each guitar, as well as other custom options. For further information, contact luthier Bill Sarricola through the Index of Current Manufacturers located in the back of this book.

SATELLITE

Instruments produced in Japan during the late 1970s. Production moved to Korea through the early to late 1980s.

The Satellite trademark is the brandname of a United Kingdom importer. These entry level to intermediate quality solid body and semi-hollowbody guitars featured both original and designs based on popular American classics.

(Source: Tony Bacon and Paul Day, The Guru's Guitar Guide)

SAXON

Instruments built in Japan during the mid 1970s.

The Saxon trademark is a brandname utilized by a United Kingdom importer. These medium quality solid body guitars featured Gibson-based designs.

(Source: Tony Bacon and Paul Day, The Guru's Guitar Guide)

"This poses an interesting question: is the Historic Collection the best ever range of post-Norlin Gibsons, or an extinct dinosaur? Only time will tell."

—Adrian Ingram and Dil Shaw

TCG, Jan/Feb 1993

SCHACK

Instruments produced in Hammerbach, Germany. Distribution in the U.S. market is handled by F.G. Reitz & Co., Inc. of Midland, Michigan.

Schack offers handcrafted basses in a 4-, 5-, or 6-string configuration and exotic wood tops. For further information, contact F.G. Reitz & Co., Inc. through the Index of Current Manufacturers located in the rear of this book.

ELECTRIC

SG 665 BASIC — offset double cutaway asymmetrical figured maple body, maple neck, 24 fret ebony fingerboard, fixed bridge, 3 per side Sperzel tuners, Schack ETS 2D bridge, chrome hardware, 2 humbucker Seymour Duncan pickups, volume/tone control, 3 position switch. Available in Transparent Stain finish. Current mfg.

    Mfr.'s Sug. Retail $1,800 $1,350 $900
       Add $230 for tremolo system.

SG 665 CUSTOM — similar to Basic, except has Flamed Maple body and gold hardware. Current mfg.
    Mfr.'s Sug. Retail $2,030 $1,522 $1,015
       Add $220 for tremolo system.

SG 665 CLASSIC — similar to Custom, except model is even more upscale. Current mfg.
    Mfr.'s Sug. Retail $2,650 $1,987 $1,325
       Add $330 for tremolo system.

ELECTRIC BASS

Unique Series

The Unique Series features the basic Unique body design that is offered in both bolt-on and neck thru models.
Fretless neck with fret inlay stripes add $140.
Two piece bookmatched top add $336.
Contact company for exotic wood availability, or bookmatched Top <u>and</u> Back.

UNIQUE IV BOLT-ON BASIC — offset double cutaway asymmetrical bubinga body, bolt-on maple neck, 24 fret ebony fingerboard, fixed Schack ETS-3D bridge, 2 per side tuners, black hardware, 2 Basstec JB-4 single coil pickups, 2 volume controls, and 3 knob treble/mid/bass EQ control with active electronics. Available in Natural finish. Curr. mfg.

    Mfr.'s Sug. Retail $2,800 $2,100 $1,400
       Unique IV Bolt-on Custom model lists for $3,460, and features gold hardware and exotic woods.

Unique V Bolt-On Basic — similar to the Unique IV, except has five strings.
    Mfr.'s Sug. Retail $2,990 $2,242 $1,495
       Unique V Bolt-on Custom model lists for $3,676, and features exotic woods.

Unique VI Bolt-On Basic — similar to the Unique IV, except has six strings.
    Mfr.'s Sug. Retail $3,475 $2,606 $1,737
       Unique VI Bolt-on Custom model lists for $4,130, and features exotic woods.

UNIQUE IV NECK THRU BASIC — offset double cutaway asymmetrical maple body, goncalo alves top, thru body 9 piece maple/bubinga neck, 24 fret ebony fingerboard, fixed bridge, 2 per side tuners, black hardware, 2 Basstec single coil pickups, 2 volume controls, and a 3 knob treble/mid/bass EQ controls with active electronics. Available in Natural finish. Curr. mfg.

    Mfr.'s Sug. Retail $3,590 $2,692 $1,795
       Unique IV Neck Thru Custom model lists for $4,270, the Unique IV Neck Thru Artwood model lists for $4,540, and Unique IV Neck Thru Rootwood model lists for $5,490.

UNIQUE V NECK THRU BASIC — similar to the Unique IV Neck Thru, except has a 36" scale and 5 strings.
    Mfr.'s Sug. Retail $3,930 $2,947 $1,965
       Unique V Neck Thru Custom model lists for $4,610, Unique V Neck Thru Artwood model lists for $4,870, and Unique V Neck Thru Rootwood model lists for $5,690.

UNIQUE VI NECK THRU BASIC — similar to the Unique IV Neck thru, except has a 36" scale and 6 strings.
    Mfr.'s Sug. Retail $4,270 $3,202 $2,135
       Unique VI Neck Thru Custom model lists for $4,676, Unique VI Neck Thru Artwood model lists for $5,080, and Unique VI Neck Thru Rootwood model lists for $5,900.

THEO SCHARPACH

Instruments built in the Netherlands from 1979 to current.

Luthier Theo Scharpach was born in Vienna, Austria, and was originally trained in the restoration of high quality antique furniture. Scharpach currently resides in Bergeyk, the Netherlands. Scharpach has been plying his lutherie skills for over seventeen years, and his current models range from classical designed nylon string guitars to more experimental seven- and eight-stringed models.

Scharpach Blue Vienna
courtesy Scott Chinery

All commissioned guitars are tailored to the individual player. Scharpach maintains a number of core designs such as the SKD, and SKW which feature conventional soundholes and an open-strung headstock. The Arch model is a semi-acoustic designed for nylon strings, and has an onboard piezo system and microphone (as well as a High Tech class I preamp and an outboard Applied Acoustics blend box). The Dolphin model features a four octave fretboard, while the Classical Guitar has two soundholes for very good sound projection. Scharpach can be contacted at his address found in the Index of Current Manufacturers in the back of this book.

SCHECTER

Originally high quality replacement parts, and then completed guitars produced in Van Nuys, California since 1976.

Schecter Guitar Research started as a maker of high quality replacement parts and build-your-own instrument kits, which eventually led to their own line of finished instruments. The Schecter company, named after David Schecter, began as a repair/modification shop that also did some customizing. Schecter is recognized as one of the first to market tapped pickup assemblies (coil tapping can offer a wider range of sound from an existing pickup configuration). Other designers associated with Schecter were Dan Armstrong and Tom Anderson. By the mid 1980s, Schecter was offering designs based on early Fender-style guitars in models such as the Mercury, Saturn, Hendrix, and Dream Machine. Later in the 1980s Schecter also had the U.S. built Californian series as well as the Japan-made Schecter East models. Currently, Schecter Guitar Research is offering several American built models.

(Source: Tom Wheeler, American Guitars)

ELECTRIC

Grading	100%	98% MINT	95% EXC+	90% EXC	80% VG+	70% VG	60% G

CET — offset double cutaway ash body, figured maple top, bolt-on birdseye maple neck, 22 fret rosewood fingerboard with pearl dot inlay, double locking Schaller vibrato, 6 on one side tuners, chrome hardware, 2 single coil/1 humbucker pickups, volume/tone control, 5 position switch. Available in Black Cherry, Brown Sunburst, Honeyburst, Transparent Aqua, Transparent Purple Transparent Turquoise, Vintage Cherry Sunburst, Oil/Wax finishes. Curr. mfr.

Mfr.'s Sug. Retail	$2,295	$1,836	$1,377	$1,150	$920	$830	$760	$690

This model has flame koa or lacewood top, maple fingerboard with black dot inlay, black or gold hardware optionally available.

In 1994, Black Cherry, Transparent Aqua and Transparent Purple finish were introduced, Brown Sunburst and Honeyburst finishes were discontinued.

CET-H — similar to CET, except has semi hollow mahogany body with routed sound chambers, fixed strings thru brass bridge. Available in Black Cherry, Transparent Aqua, Transparent Purple, Transparent Turquoise and Vintage Cherry Sunburst finishes. New 1994.

Mfr.'s Sug. Retail	$2,495	$1,996	$1,497	$1,250	$1,000	$900	$825	$750

This model has maple fingerboard with black dot inlay, black or gold hardware, 3 single coil or 2 humbucker pickups configuration optionally available.

CUSTOM — offset double cutaway figured maple body, bolt-on birdseye maple neck, 22 fret rosewood fingerboard with clay dot inlay, double locking Schaller vibrato, 6 on one side tuners, gold hardware, 2 single coil/1 humbucker pickups, volume/tone control, 5 position switch. Available in Black Aqua, Black Cherry, Black Purple, Black Turquoise, Brown Sunburst, Honeyburst, Transparent Turquoise and Vintage Cherry Sunburst finishes. Curr. mfr.

Mfr.'s Sug. Retail	$2,995	$2,246	$1,497	$1,475	$1,180	$1,060	$975	$885

In 1994, Black Aqua and Black Purple finishes were introduced, Black Turquoise, Brown Sunburst and Honeyburst finishes were discontinued.

ET-H — offset double cutaway mahogany body with routed sound chambers, spruce top, bolt-on birdseye maple neck, 22 fret maple fingerboard with black dot inlay, fixed strings thru brass bridge, 6 on one side tuners, black hardware, 32 single coil/1 humbucker pickups, volume/tone with coil tap control, 5 position switch. Available in Black Cherry, Transparent Aqua, Transparent Purple, Transparent Turquoise and Vintage Cherry Sunburst finishes. New 1994.

Mfr.'s Sug. Retail	$2,195	$1,756	$1,317	$1,100	$880	$790	$725	$660

PT (formerly PT Traditional) — single cutaway bound alder body, bolt-on birdseye maple neck, 22 fret maple fingerboard with black dot inlay, fixed strings thru brass bridge, 6 on one side tuners, black hardware, 2 humbucker pickups, volume with coil tap/tone with coil tap control, 3 position switch. Available in Black finish. Curr. mfr.

Mfr.'s Sug. Retail	$1,595	$1,276	$957	$900	$720	$650	$595	$540

This model has rosewood fingerboard with pearl dot inlay, chrome or gold hardware optionally available.

PT/2S — similar to PT, except has white pickguard, 2 single coil pickups. Available in Black and Red finishes. New 1994.

Mfr.'s Sug. Retail	$1,595	$1,196	$797	$795	$635	$575	$525	$475

This model has rosewood fingerboard with pearl dot inlay, chrome or gold hardware optionally available.

PT Custom — single cutaway mahogany body, carved bound figured maple top, bolt-on birdseye maple neck, 22 fret rosewood fingerboard with pearl dot inlay, tunomatic bridge/stop tailpiece, 6 on one side tuners, gold hardware, volume with coil tap/tone with coil tap control, 3 position switch. Available in Orange Violin, Transparent Black and Vintage Cherry Sunburst finishes. Curr. mfr.

Mfr.'s Sug. Retail	$2,495	$1,871	$1,247	$1,200	$960	$860	$790	$720

This model has maple fingerboard with black dot inlay, black or chrome hardware optionally available.

In 1994, Transparent Black finish was introduced.

Grading	100%	98% MINT	95% EXC+	90% EXC	80% VG+	70% VG	60% G

STANDARD — offset double cutaway ash body, black pickguard, bolt-on birdseye maple neck, 22 fret maple fingerboard with black dot inlay, standard brass vibrato, 6 on one side tuners, chrome hardware, 3 single coil pickups, volume/tone with coil tap control, 5 position switch. Available in Natural Oil/Wax and Vintage Oil/Wax finishes. New 1994.

Mfr.'s Sug. Retail	$1,295	$971	$647	$645	$515	$465	$425	$385

This model has rosewood fingerboard with pearl dot inlay, 2 single coil/1 humbucker pickups configuration optionally available.

Standard T — similar to Standard, except has double locking Schaller vibrato. New 1994.

Mfr.'s Sug. Retail	$1,445	$1,083	$722	$720	$580	$520	$475	$435

This model has ash body with routed sound chambers optionally available.

TRADITIONAL — offset double cutaway alder body, white pickguard, bolt-on birdseye maple neck, 22 fret rosewood fingerboard with pearl dot inlay, standard brass vibrato, 6 on one side tuners, gold hardware, 3 single coil pickups, volume/tone control, 5 position switch. Available in Cherry Sunburst, Metallic Gold, Brownburst, Vintage Black and Vintage White finishes. Curr. mfr.

Mfr.'s Sug. Retail	$1,595	$1,276	$957	$900	$720	$650	$595	$540

This model has maple fingerboard with black dot inlay, black or chrome hardware optionally available.

Traditional/2SH — similar to Traditional, except has 2 single coil/1 humbucker pickups, double locking Schaller vibrato. New 1994.

Mfr.'s Sug. Retail	$1,745	$1,396	$1,047	$875	$700	$630	$575	$525

ELECTRIC BASS

BASS/4 — offset double cutaway ash body, bolt-on birdseye maple neck, 21 fret rosewood fingerboard with pearl dot inlay, fixed bridge, 4 on one side tuners, black hardware, P-style/J-style pickups, 2 volume/1 tone controls. Available in Black, Honeyburst, Transparent Blue, Transparent Green, Transparent Purple and White finishes. Curr. mfr.

Mfr.'s Sug. Retail	$1,895	$1,516	$1,137	$975	$780	$700	$645	$580

This model has maple fingerboard with black dot inlay, chrome or gold hardware, P-style or P-style/J-style pickup configuration optionally available.

In 1994, Transparent Blue finish was introduced, Black and White finishes were discontinued.

Bass/4 CET — similar to Bass/4, except has bound figured maple top. Available in Black Cherry, Transparent Aqua, Transparent Purple, Transparent Turquoise and Vintage Cherry Sunburst finishes. Curr. mfr.

Mfr.'s Sug. Retail	$2,395	$1,916	$1,437	$1,225	$980	$875	$805	$735

This model has maple fingerboard with black dot inlay, chrome or gold hardware, P-style or P-style/J-style pickup configuration optionally available.

BASS/5 — offset double cutaway asymmetrical ash body, bolt-on birdseye maple neck, 21 fret rosewood fingerboard with pearl dot inlay, fixed bridge, 5 on one side tuners, black hardware, 2 J-style pickups, 2 volume/1 tone controls. Available in Black, Honeyburst, Transparent Blue, Transparent Green, Transparent Purple and White finishes. Curr. mfr.

Mfr.'s Sug. Retail	$2,095	$1,676	$1,257	$1,075	$860	$775	$710	$645

This model has maple fingerboard with black dot inlay, chrome or gold hardware optionally available.

In 1994, Transparent Blue finish was introduced, Black and White finish were discontinued.

Bass/5 CET — similar to Bass/5, except has bound figured maple top. Available in Black Cherry, Transparent Aqua, Transparent Purple, Transparent Turquoise and Vintage Cherry Sunburst finishes. Curr. mfr.

Mfr.'s Sug. Retail	$2,595	$2,076	$1,557	$1,325	$1,060	$955	$875	$795

This model has maple fingerboard with black dot inlay, chrome or gold hardware optionally available.

TIM SCHEERHORN

Instruments built in Kentwood, Michigan since 1989. Instruments are available through Scheerhorn or Elderly Instruments of Lansing, Michigan.

Luthier Tim Scheerhorn has backround training as a tool and die maker, a tool engineer, and is a specialist in process automation for manufacturing. In the past, his hobbies generally involved rebuilding something - either boats or classic cars. But in 1986, Scheerhorn picked up a resonator guitar and later found himself immersed in the world of custom guitar building.

Although Scheerhorn did have prior experience setting up banjos and resonator guitars for other players, he had never built a musical instrument from scratch. He did possess a new OMI Dobro, and a Regal from the 1930s. In February of 1989, Scheerhorn began building guitars based on the Regal model and his own innovations. In the summer of 1989 the guitar was tested by Mike Auldridge (Seldom Scene) at the Winterhawk festival in New York. Encouraged by Auldridge's enthusiasm, Scheerhorn returned to his workshop and continued building.

Scheerhorn limits production to one or two instruments a month. All guitars are handbuilt by Scheerhorn.

ACOUSTIC

Both Scheernhorn models share the same revised resonator design. The resonators are built of bright chrome plated brass, Spun Quarterman cone, and a spider bridge of aluminum. The bridge insert is made of hard maple with ebony tops. Both models also feature chrome Schaller M-6 tuning machines.

"The Kalamazoo plant had been built in continuous operation since 1917, and built when the Gibson Company was only 15 years old."

—Tom Van Hoose, Ph.D

TCG, July/Aug 1990

The **Curly Maple** model ($@,250) has a bookmatched solid curly Maple top, with matching sides and back. The three piece neck consists of Curly Maple and Walnut, and has a 19 fret ebony fingerboard. The body and neck are bound in either an ivoroid or dark tortoise (natural blond finish), and finished in hand-rubbed lacquer. The **Mahogany/Spruce** model ($2,250) has a Sitka Spruce top, mahogany back and sides, and a two piece mahogany neck.

Scheerhorn also builds a Weissenborn Style Reissue dubbed the "**Scheerhorn Hawaiian**" ($2,500). The body is constructed out of solid Figured Koa (top, back, and sides), and the peghead has a Curly Maple overlay. The bridge is cocobolo with a bone saddle, and the cocobolo fingerboard has Curly Maple binding and abalone inlays. This model also features Kluson style tuners, a built in McIntyre pickup, and a hand-rubbed lacquer finish.

SHOENBERG

Instruments built in Nazareth, Pennsylvania since 1985. Distributed by the Music Emporium of Lexington, Massachusetts.

Eric Schoenberg is regarded as one of the great ragtime and fingerstyle guitarists of the last twenty years. Operating out of the Music Emporium in Massachusetts, Schoenberg has released a number of high quality acoustic guitars that are built in conjunction with the C.F. Martin company of Nazareth, Pennsylvania, and indiviually finished by either Schoenberg or luthier Dana Bourgeois.

In the late 1980s, Schoenberg debuted the Soloist model. This guitar was the result of combined efforts from guitarist Schoenberg, luthier Dana Bourgeois, and the C.F. Martin company. The Soloist was a modern version of Martin's OM-style acoustics, and featured top grade woods overseen by Bourgeois. The Martin facilities assembled the body, then finishing touches again were controlled by Schoenberg and Bourgeois. Luthier Bourgeois was involved in the project from 1986 to mid 1990; T.J. Thompson was the next luthier to work with Schoenberg. The instrument featured a European spruce top, Brazilian back and sides, a one piece mahogany neck, 20 fret ebony fingerboard with diamond shaped pearl inlays, and Kluson-styled Grover tuning machines. Retail list price back in the late 1980s was $2,850 (which seems more than reasonable now!)

SCHON

Instruments built in Concord, California during the late 1980s.

Schon guitars are so named for their namesake, Neal Schon (of 'Journey' fame). Rather than just sign off on a production guitar, Schon actually put up his own money and design contributions to get the Schon guitar into production. Production was on the West Coast, so a safe bet is that the majority of instruments are out west as well.

Last address given for Schon Guitars was 1070 San Miguel Road, F-15, Concord, California (94518).

ELECTRIC

Grading	100%	98% MINT	95% EXC+	90% EXC	80% VG+	70% VG	60% G

NS-STD — single cutaway alder 'wings' for body, solid maple neck-through body design, 24 fret bound ebony fingerboard, 25 1/2" scale length, six on a side Schaller tuners, chrome hardware, two custom Schon humbuckers, tune-o-matic style bridge with individual stop "finger" tailpiece, 1 volume and 1 tone knob, five way selector switch. Lacquer finish. Mfg. 1987 to 1990.

$899	$825	$650	$575	$510	$N/A	$N/A

Mfr. Last Suggested Retail was $1,199.

NS-STD W/TREMOLO — same as the NS-STD, except has a Kahler tremolo instead of the stylish stop tailpiece.

$925	$850	$715	$635	$550	$N/A	$N/A

Mfr. Last Suggested Retail was $1,399.

NS-SC — same as the NS-STD, except has 2 single coils and 1 humbucker, as well as a Kahler tremolo.

$899	$825	$650	$575	$510	$N/A	$N/A

Mfr. Last Suggested Retail was $1,499.

SHELDON SCHWARTZ

Instruments currently built in Toronto.

Luthier Sheldon Schwartz currently offers high quality handcrafted acoustic guitars that are immaculately constructed. Schwartz began working on guitars at fifteen, and has had lutherie associations with such builders as Greg Laskin and Linda Manzer. In 1992, Schwartz began building full time, and attended vintage guitar shows to display his work.

Schwartz prefers working with the top quality, master grade woods that generally don't show up in the large production factories, and matches back, sides, tops, and necks for both appearance and tonal qualities. The **Six String Guitar** ($2,100) is constructed of a Sitka Spruce or Western Red Cedar top, Indian Rosewood, Honduran Mahogany, or Curly Maple back and sides, Rosewood binding, Ebony fingerboard and bridge, Mahogany neck, and inlaid Mother-of-Pearl position markers. Depending on the commission, Schwartz also works in other woods such as Koa, Bearclaw Maple, and Brazilian Rosewood. For further information, please contact luthier Sheldon Schwartz through the Index of Current Manufacturers located in the rear of this book.

S.D. CURLEE USA

Instruments built in Matteson, Illinois from 1975 to 1982.

In the early 1970s, Randy Curlee was the owner of a Chicago based music store. Curlee recognized a need for an inexpensive, hand built quality guitar; and in the late 1970s the instruments ranged in price from $350 (guitar models) to $399 (basses). Curlee thought that the "S.D." moniker was better than using his first name. Curlee was also the first to plan on overseas "reproductions", and devised a plan to circumvent that from happening (See S.D. CURLEE INTERNATONAL).

Typical of the times when everybody thought that brass parts helped with sustaining properties, S.D. Curlee instruments featured a squared brass nut, brass bridge, brass neck plate and electronics cover. Necks consisted of hard rock maple, and bodies consisted of exotic woods like butcher block Maple, Brazilian or Honduran mahogany, Black walnut, Purpleheart, Koa, and (later models) poplar. Hardware included Schaller tuners, DiMarzio pickups, and BadAss bridges. Headstocks were 3+3 (2+2 on basses), and featured a master volume knob and a tone knob per pickup, as well as a pickup selector toggle. The neck sat halfway into the body in a channel, and had four bolts in a large rear plate (sort of a bolt-on/set-neck hybrid). After the company closed in 1982, Curlee was involved in Yamaha's guitar production. Curlee also marketed the Zoom sound processors before leaving the music industry.

It is estimated that 15,000 instruments were built during the seven years of production. The majority were basses, and about 3,000 were guitars. Instruments with three digit serial numbers up to around 1000 are the first production models, and serial numbers under 4000 are from the mid to late 1970s. After number 4000, the numbering scheme changed. Individual models are hard to determine, as there were some variations during production. At least 8 different models were named, although the first three (Standards I, II, III) are the original models that the following five were variants of. Finally, as the company was closing down in 1982, Curlee built some Destroyer, Flying V, and other original shapes.

(Source: Michael Wright, Guitar Stories Volume One, pg. 249-254)

S.D. CURLEE INTERNATIONAL

See HONDO.

Instruments built in Japan from the late 1970s to the mid 1980s, as well as in Korea during the same time period.

In the mid 1970s, Randy Curlee proposed a deal with Jerry Freed of Hondo Guitars to build licensed designs of his guitars. Curlee planned to beat other unlicensed "copies" to the market, and make money on the reproductions as well. Guitars had similar designs as the S.D. Curlee USA models, except had S.D. Curlee Design Series across the peghead, and "Aspen" model designation as well.

Curlee also licensed the design to the Matsumoku company in Japan, who produced similar looking models under the S.D. Curlee International logo. The Japanese-produced models were marketed and sold mainly in the Oriental market, while the Hondo versions were distributed in the U.S. as well as the U.K. Some models were distributed by J.C. Penney and Global dealers, and some of the Global dealers even rebranded them under the Global trademark.

(Source: Michael Wright, Guitar Stories Volume One, pg. 250)

SEAGULL GUITARS

Instruments built in La Patrie, Quebec, Canada since 1980. Seagull Acoustic Guitars are distributed by La Si Do, Inc., of St. Laurent, Canada.

In 1968 Robert Godin set up a custom guitar shop in Montreal called Harmonilab. Harmonilab quickly became known for its excellent work and musicians were coming from as far away as Quebec City to have their guitars adjusted.

Although Harmonilab's business was flourishing, Robert was full of ideas for the design and construction of acoustic guitars. So in 1972 the **Norman Guitar Company** was born. From the beginning the Norman guitars showed signs of the innovations that Godin would eventually bring to the guitar market. By 1978 Norman guitars had become quite successful in Canada and France.

In 1980 Godin introduced the Seagull guitar. With many innovations like a bolt-on neck (for consistent neck pitch), pointed headstock (straight string pull) and a handmade solid top, the Seagull was designed for an ease of play for the entry level to intermediate guitar player. Most striking was the satin lacquer finish. Godin borrowed the finishing idea that was used on fine violins, and applied it to the acoustic guitar. When the final version of the Seagull guitar went into production, Godin went about the business of finding a sales force to help introduce the Seagull into the U.S. market. Several independent U.S. sales agents jumped at the chance to get involved with this new guitar, and armed with samples, off they went into the market. A couple of months passed, and not one guitar was sold. Rather than retreat back to Harmonilab, Godin decided that he would have to get out there himself and explain the Seagull guitar concept. So he bought himself an old Ford Econoline van and stuffed it full of about 85 guitars, and started driving through New England visiting guitar shops and introducing the Seagull guitar. Acceptance of this new guitar spread, and by 1985 La Si Do was incorporated and the factory in La Patrie expanded to meet the growing demand.

For full company history, see GODIN.

Grading	100%	98% MINT	95% EXC+	90% EXC	80% VG+	70% VG	60% G

ACOUSTIC

S 6 —dreadnought style bound body, solid cedar top, black pickguard, round soundhole, multistripe rosette, wild cherry back/sides, mahogany neck, 14/21 fret rosewood fingerboard with pearl dot inlay, rosewood bridge with white black dot pins, blackface peghead with screened logo, 3 per side chrome tuners. Available in Natural finish. Mfd. 1993 to date.

Mfr.'s Sug. Retail	$395	$296	$197	$195	$155	$140	$125	$115

This model has single round cutaway, left handed version or folk style body (S 6 Folk) optionally available.

S 12 — similar to S 6, except has 12 strings, 6 per side tuners.

Mfr.'s Sug. Retail	$450	$360	$270	$225	$180	$160	$150	$135

S 6 DELUXE — dreadnought style bound body, solid spruce top, black pickguard, round soundhole, multistripe rosette, wild cherry back/sides, mahogany neck, 14/21 fret rosewood fingerboard with pearl dot inlay, rosewood bridge with white black dot pins, blackface peghead with screened logo, 3 per side chrome tuners. Available in Honeyburst and Natural finishes. Curr mfr.

Mfr.'s Sug. Retail	$435	$326	$217	$215	$175	$155	$140	$130

This model has single round cutaway or left hand version optionally available.

S 12 Deluxe — similar to S 6 Deluxe, except has 12 strings, 6 per side tuners.

Mfr.'s Sug. Retail	$495	$371	$247	$245	$195	$175	$160	$150

S 6 MAHOGANY— dreadnought style bound body, solid cedar top, black pickguard, round soundhole, multistripe rosette, mahogany back/sides/neck, 14/21 fret rosewood fingerboard with pearl dot inlay, rosewood bridge with white black dot pins, blackface peghead with screened logo, 3 per side chrome tuners. Available in Natural finish. Curr mfr.

Mfr.'s Sug. Retail	$450	$360	$270	$225	$180	$160	$150	$135

This model has left handed version optionally available.

Performance Series

S 6 FLAME MAPLE — round cutaway dreadnought style bound body, solid spruce top, roundsoundhole, herringbone rosette, maple back/sides, mahogany neck, 21 fret ebony fingerboard with offset dot inlay, ebony bridge with white black dot pins, bound flame maple veneered peghead with screened logo, 3 per side gold tuners. Available in Blackburst and Natural finishes. Curr mfr.

Mfr.'s Sug. Retail	$820	$656	$492	$425	$340	$310	$280	$255

S 6 BLACKBURST — similar to S 6 Flame Maple, with a see-through "blackburst" finish. Current model.

Mfr.'s Sug. Retail	$893	$669	$446	$425	$340	$310	$280	$255

SM 6 — round cutaway dreadnought style bound body, solid spruce top, black pickguard, round soundhole, multistripe rosette, mahogany back/sides/neck, 14/21 fret rosewood fingerboard with pearl dot inlay, rosewood bridge with white black dot pins, blackface peghead with screened logo, 3 per side chrome tuners. Available in Natural finish. Curr mfr.

Mfr.'s Sug. Retail	$530	$424	$318	$265	$210	$190	$175	$160

SM 12 — similar to SM 6, 12 strings, 6 per side tuners.

Mfr.'s Sug. Retail	$620	$496	$372	$310	$250	$225	$205	$190

SEBRING

Instruments currently built in Korea. Distributed by V. J. Rendano Wholesale Company of Youngstown, Ohio.

Sebring instruments are designed towards the entry level and beginning guitar student. For further information, contact V. J. Rendano Wholesale Company through the Index of Current Manufacturers located in the rear of this book.

SEDONA

Instruments currently built in Asia. Distributed by V M I Industries of Brea, California.

Sedona offers a range of instruments that appeal to the beginning guitarist and entry level player. For further information, contact V M I Industries through the Index of Current Manufacturers located in the back of this book.

SEIWA

Instruments built in Japan during the mid 1980s.

These medium quality solid body guitars featured Fender-based designs, often with two or three single coil pickups.

(Source: Tony Bacon and Paul Day, The Guru's Guitar Guide)

"Yeah, I have over 400 guitars Every model that's made. I keep it so I can go and refer back to it and say this one was better than that one, here's what you should do, and here's what I like better or I don't like it as well."

—*L. Acunto on Les Paul TCG, July/Aug 1990*

SEKOVA

Instruments produced in Japan.

Sekova brand instruments were distributed in the U.S. market by the U.S. Musical Merchandise Corporation of New York, New York.

(Source: Michael Wright, Guitar Stories Volume One, pg. 76)

HENRI SELMER & CO.

Instruments built in Paris, France between 1931 to 1952.

Between 1931 and 1932, Mario Maccaferri designed and built a series of instruments for the French Selmer company. They were originally referred to as the "modele Concert", and featured a "D" shaped soundhole. Although they were used by such notables as Django Reinhardt, a dispute between the company and Maccaferri led to a short production run. In the two years (1931-1932) that Maccaferri was with Selmer, he estimated that perhaps 200 guitars were built. After Macaferri left the business arrangement, the Selmer company continued to produce acoustic guitar models that featured an oval soundhole and a longer scale. All in all, an estimated 950 guitars were built.

(Source: Paul Hostetter, Guitares Maurice Dupont)

SELMER LONDON

See also HOFNER.

Instruments built in West Germany from the late 1950s to early 1970s.

Selmer London was the distribution branch of the Selmer company in the United Kingdom. Selmer London distributed the French-built Selmers, as well as imported the Hofner-built semi-hollowbody models. While a number retained the Hofner trademark, some Hofners were rebranded 'Selmer'. Hofner also produced a number of UK-only export models which were distributed by Selmer London; such as the President and Golden Hofner (top of the hollowbody electric range).

Selmer semi-hollowbody models to watch for include the Triumph (single cutaway and a single pickup), Diplomat (single cutaway but two pickups), the Emperor and the Astra (two cutaways and two pickups). In the early 1970s, Selmer also marketed a solid body guitar called the Studio.

(Source: Tony Bacon and Paul Day, The Guru's Guitar Guide)

SERIES 10

Instruments produced in Korea, and distributed by St. Louis Music of St. Louis, Missouri.

Series 10 instruments are designed for the entry level to intermediate guitar player, and feature designs based on classic American favorites.

SEXAUER

Instruments built in Sausalito, California since the 1970s.

Luthier Bruce Sexauer has been handcrafting quality archtop and flat-top acoustic guitars for the past 29 years. For further information regarding pricing, specifications, and availability please contact luthier Sexauer through the Index of Current Manufacturers located in the back of this book.

SHADOW

Instruments built in West Germany from 1988 through 1994. Distribution was through Shadow Electronics of America, Inc. of Stuart, Florida.

There is a limited number of high quality guitars still in stock at Shadow Electronics of America in Stuart, Florida. Shadow continues to produce their high quality pickups and transducers, as well as their SH-075 Quick Mount MIDI guitar system. Shadow pickups can be ordered as aftermarket replacements, and also can be found in other guitar manufacturers' products. The SH-075 Quick Mount MIDI system combines a hex pickup and the output of a guitar's magnetic pickups to generate a MIDI signal. The SH-075 also has an onboard alphanumeric keypad for sending program changes, assigning MIDI channels, tuning, and other functions. The splitter box at the other end of the MIDI cable decodes the signal into MIDI information and an analog sound from the pickups. For further information, contact Shadow Electronics via the Index of Current Manufacturers located in the back of this book.

ELECTRIC

G Series

All G Series models are available in Blue Stain, Cognac Stain and Red Stain finishes unless otherwise noted.

Grading	100%	98% MINT	95% EXC+	90% EXC	80% VG+	70% VG	60% G

G 202 — offset double cutaway ash body, bolt-on maple neck, 24 fret rosewood fingerboard with pearl dot inlay, double locking vibrato, 6 on one side tuners, chrome hardware, 2 stacked coil/1 active humbucker Shadow pickups, volume/tone control, coil split switch in volume control, on/off switch in tone control, 5 position switch. Available in the three listed finishes, as well as a Black Stain finish. Discontinued 1994.

Mfr.'s Sug. Retail	$1,625	$1,300	$975	$815	$650	$580	$535	$485

> This model is also available with black or gold hardware.

G 213 — offset double cutaway Brazilian Cedro body, flame maple top/bolt-on neck, 24 fret rosewood fingerboard with pearl dot inlay, double locking vibrato, 6 on one side tuners, gold hardware, 2 stacked coil/1 active humbucker pickups, volume/tone control, coil split switch in volume control, on/off switch in tone control, 5 position switch. Discontinued 1994.

Mfr.'s Sug. Retail	$1,995	$1,496	$997	$995	$795	$720	$660	$600

G 214 — similar to G 213, except has quilted maple top and birdseye maple neck.

Mfr.'s Sug. Retail	$2,200	$1,760	$1,320	$1,100	$880	$790	$725	$660

G 233 — similar to G 213, except has standard bridge, piezo bridge pickup, volume control and 3 band EQ.

Mfr.'s Sug. Retail	$1,575	$1,181	$787	$785	$630	$565	$515	$470

> This model is also available with quilted maple top and birdseye maple neck (G 234).
> This model is also available with birdseye maple top/neck (G 235).

G 243 — offset double cutaway Brazilian Cedro body, flame maple top/bolt on neck, 24 fret rosewood fingerboard with pearl dot inlay, standard bridge, 6 on one side tuners, gold hardware, active humbucker/Piezo bridge pickups, 2 volume controls, 3 band EQ. Curr. mfr.

Mfr.'s Sug. Retail	$1,770	$1,327	$885	$880	$705	$635	$580	$530

> This model is also available with a quilted maple top and birdseye maple neck (G 244).
> This model is also available with birdseye maple top/neck (G 245).

S Series

All S Series models are available in Black, Blue Stain, Blue Thunder, Cognac Stain, Gold, Red Stain, Red Thunder, Tobacco Stain, Violet Stain, White and White Thunder finishes.

> All S Series models are available with black, chrome or gold hardware.

S 100 — offset double cutaway basswood body, bolt-on maple neck, 22 fret rosewood fingerboard with pearl dot inlay, double locking vibrato, 6 on one side tuners, 2 single coil/1 humbucker Shadow pickups, volume/tone control, 5 position switch. Curr. mfr.

Mfr.'s Sug. Retail	$995	$796	$597	$500	$400	$360	$330	$300

S 110 — similar to S 100, except has active humbucker pickup, on/off switch, tone control, active electronics.

Mfr.'s Sug. Retail	$1,225	$980	$735	$615	$490	$440	$405	$370

S 120 — similar to S 100, except has 2 active humbucker pickups, 2 volume controls and 3 position switch.

Mfr.'s Sug. Retail	$1,315	$1,052	$789	$660	$530	$475	$435	$395

> This model is also available with an alder body (S 121).

S 130 — similar to S 100, except has standard bridge, piezo bridge pickup and 3 band EQ.

Mfr.'s Sug. Retail	$1,125	$900	$675	$565	$455	$405	$370	$335

> This model is also available with an alder body (S 131).

S 140 — similar to S 100, except has standard bridge, active humbucker/piezo bridge pickups, 2 volume controls, 3 band EQ and active electronics.

Mfr.'s Sug. Retail	$1,315	$1,052	$789	$660	$530	$475	$435	$395

> This model is also available with an alder body (S 141).

SHP 1 — solid body guitar with the appearance of no pickups. Piezo bridge tranducer only, 2 volume controls, 2 tone controls. Mfg. 1990 to 1994.

	$925	$790	$660	$530	$475	$435	$395

SHAFTESBURY

See also NED CALLAN.

Instrument manufactured in Italy and Japan from the late 1960s to the early 1980s; also one model of English-built instruments during the overall time period.

The Shaftesbury trademark is the brandname of a UK importer. Shaftesbury instruments were generally medium to good quality versions of American designs. The Shaftesbury line featured both solid and semi-hollowbody guitars and basses. To hazard a guess, I would assume that the Italian production was featured early on in the late 1960s; as costs rose the importer chose to bring in Japanese-built guitars sometime around the mid-to-late 1970s. As luthier Peter Cook was busy during the 1970s mass-producing decent quality guitars under the Ned Callan, Simms-Watts, and CMI brandnames the 1970s would be a good "guess-timate" for the introduction of Ned Callan/Shaftesbury model instruments.

(Source: Tony Bacon and Paul Day, The Guru's Guitar Guide)

SHANE

Instruments currently built in Fairfax, Virginia.

Shane has been offering quality custom built guitars for a number of years. Both the S100 SC and the S350 Targa offer traditional style bodies, while the SJ Series features a more modern style. For further information, contact Shane Guitars through the Index of Current Manufacturers located in the back of this book.

SHELTONE

Instruments produced in Japan during the 1960s.

The Sheltone trademark is a brandname used by a UK importer. Sheltone instruments are entry level solid body or semi-hollow body guitars.

(Source: Tony Bacon and Paul Day, The Guru's Guitar Guide)

SHENANDOAH

Instruments assembled from imported components in Nazareth, Pennsylvania. Distribution by the C. F. Martin Guitar Company of Nazarath, Pennsylvania.

Shenandoah production began in 1983. Shenandoah guitars can be viewed as an "entry-level" step into the Martin product line. However, Shenandoah guitars may not be as ornate, and may feature different construction methods than the Martin models.

ACOUSTIC

Grading		100%	98% MINT	95% EXC+	90% EXC	80% VG+	70% VG	60% G

Some models have a factory installed thinline bridge pickup. Instruments were produced/assembled between 1983 to 1991.

C-20 — classic style, solid spruce top, round soundhole, wooden bound body, wooden inlay rosette, rosewood back/sides, nato neck, 12/19 fret ebonized rosewood fingerboard, ebonized rosewood tied bridge, rosewood peghead veneer, 3 per side gold tuners with pearl buttons. Available in Natural and Yellow Stained Top finishes.

		$640	$600	$535	$460	$400	$370	$320

Last Mfr.'s Sug. Retail was $1,280.

This model had no factory installed pickup.

D-1832 — dreadnought style, solid spruce top, round soundhole, tortoise pickguard, 3 stripe bound body/rosette, mahogany back/sides, nato neck, 14/20 fret rosewood fingerboard with pearl dot inlay, rosewood bridge with black pins, rosewood peghead veneer, 3 per side chrome tuners. Available in Natural finish.

		$550	$500	$450	$375	$325	$250	$210

Last Mfr.'s Sug. Retail was $1,075.

D-1932 — similar to D-1832, except has quilted mahogany veneer back/sides.

		$725	$670	$620	$540	$470	$425	$385

Add $20 for twelve string version (D12-1932).

Last Mfr.'s Sug. Retail was $1,320.

D-2832 — dreadnought style, solid spruce top, round soundhole, tortoise pickguard, 3 stripe bound body/rosette, rosewood back/sides, nato neck, 14/20 fret ebonized rosewood fingerboard with pearl dot inlay, ebonized rosewood bridge with white black dot pins, rosewood peghead veneer, 3 per side chrome tuners. Available in Natural finish.

		$650	$600	$550	$500	$400	$350	$300

Add $75 for 12 string version of this model (D12-2832).

Last Mfr.'s Sug. Retail was $1,125.

HD-2832 — similar to D-2832, except has herringbone purfling.

		$750	$650	$600	$550	$450	$400	$350

D-3532 — similar to D-2832, except has bound fingerboard.

		$650	$600	$550	$500	$450	$400	$350

Last Mfr.'s Sug. Retail was $1,175.

D-4132 — similar to D-2832, except has abalone bound body/rosette, bound fingerboard with abalone hexagon inlay, white abalone dot bridge pins, bound peghead, gold tuners.

		$900	$865	$780	$690	$630	$575	$525

Last Mfr.'s Sug. Retail was $1,750.

D-6032 — similar to D-2832, tortoise binding, except has birdseye maple back/sides.

		$660	$595	$525	$450	$400	$365	$300

Last Mfr.'s Sug. Retail was $1,320.

"I only wanted two things involved: I wanted the pickup to stand still and the string to move, and I didn't want anything else to happen. I wanted it to sustain as long as it could."

—L. Acunto on Les Paul

TCG, July/Aug 1990

D-6732 — dreadnought style body, solid spruce top, round soundhole, tortoise pickguard, tortoise binding, 3 stripe rosette, quilted ash back/sides, nato neck, 14/20 fret bound ebonized rosewood neck with pearl dot inlay, pearl vine/diamond inlay at 12th fret, ebonized rosewood bridge with white black dot pins, bound peghead with quilted ash veneer, 3 per side gold tuners with ebony buttons. Available in Natural finish.

$750	$680	$625	$575	$535	$480	$425

Last Mfr.'s Sug. Retail was $1,490.

SE-2832 — single round cutaway folk style, solid spruce top, round soundhole, 3 stripe bound body/rosette, rosewood back/sides, nato neck, 14/21 fret bound ebonized rosewood fingerboard with pearl diamond inlay, ebonized rosewood bridge with white black dot pins, rosewood veneer peghead, 3 per side chrome tuners, active EQ with volume/treble/mid/bass slider control. Available in Natural and Sunburst Top finishes.

$750	$680	$600	$550	$500	$460	$400

Last Mfr.'s Sug. Retail was $1,470.

SE-6032 — similar to SE-2832, except has tortoise binding, birdseye maple back/sides/peghead veneer, pearl tuner buttons. Available in Burgundy Burst, Dark Sunburst and Natural finishes.

$770	$720	$660	$610	$560	$520	$460

Last Mfr.'s Sug. Retail was $1,540.

000-2832 — folk style, solid spruce top, round soundhole, tortoise shell pickguard, 3 stripe bound body/rosette, rosewood back/sides, nato neck, 14/20 fret ebonized rosewood fingerboard with pearl dot inlay, ebonized rosewood bridge with white black dot pins, rosewood peghead veneer with abalone torch inlay, 3 per side chrome tuners. Available in Natural finish.

$640	$600	$550	$500	$400	$350	$300

Last Mfr.'s Sug. Retail was $1,210

SHERGOLD

Instruments built in England from 1968 on. Company is currently concentrating on custom orders.

Luthier Jack Golder was one of the mainstays of the Burns London company during the early 1960s, and stayed with the company when it was purchased in 1965 by the American Baldwin Organ company. Baldwin also acquired Gretsch in 1967. Baldwin was assembling imported Burns parts in Booneville, Arkansas; and in 1970 moved the New York Gretsch operation to this facility as it phased out Burns guitar production.

Norman Holder, the ex-Burns mill foreman, rejoined Jack Golder during production of Hayman guitars (and once again affiliated with Jim Burns, who handled some of the Hayman designs). When Dallas-Arbiter, the distributor of Hayman guitars, went under in 1975 both Golder and Holder decided to continue working together on their own line of guitars. Some of the Hayman refinements carried over into the Shergold line (like the Hayman 4040 bass transforming into the Shergold Marathon bass), but the original design concept can be attributed to this team.

The Shergold company has also supplied a number of UK builders with necks and bodies under contract. These companies include BM, Jim Burn's Burns UK, Hayman (under Dallas-Arbiter), Peter Cook's Ned Callan, Pangborn, and Rosetti's "Triumph" model. Author Tony Bacon, in "The Ultimate Guitar Book", notes that Shergold was the last company to make guitars (and parts) in quantity in the United Kingdom.

Possibly one of the easier trademarks to figure out model designations as the pickguard carries both the "Shergold" and model name on it! Shergold models generally feature a double cutaway solid body, and two humbucking pickups. Models include the Activator, Cavalier, Marathon (bass), Masquerador, Meteor, Modulator, and custom built doublenecks.

(Source: Paul Day, The Burns Book)

SHERWOOD

See chapter on House Brands.

This trademark has been identified as a "House Brand" of Montgomery Wards.

(Source: Willie G. Moseley, Stellas & Stratocasters)

SIERRA (U.S.: EXCALIBER SERIES)

Instruments built in San Francisco, California in 1981.

Sierra Guitars was a well-conceived but short-lived company that handcrafted the "Excaliber" line of guitars and basses. Founded in 1981 by Michael Tobias and Ron Armstrong, the San Francisco-based company lasted only one year and produced 50 instruments.

(Model specifications and company history source: Hal Hammer)

Sierra 6.2
courtesy Hal Hammer

ELECTRIC

All Excaliber instruments feature a three piece laminated neck-through design, stainless steel truss rod, chrome plated brass hardware, and select hardwoods. There was a $100 charge for left handed instruments, and an additional $100 charge for vibrato equipment.

The **Model 6.1** ($1,299) had an offset double cutaway body, 1 humbucking pickup located near the bridge, a stop tailpiece, 3+3 headstock, 24 3/4" scale neck, 1 volume control and 1 tone control. The **Model 6.1 A** ($1,429) was similar to the 6.1, except had active electronics and mini toggle switch. The **Model 6.2** ($1,449) featured a similar offset double cutaway body, 2 humbucking pickups, stop tailpiece, 3+3 headstock, 24 3/4" scale neck, 2 volume controls, 1 selector toggle switch, and 1 tone control; while the **Model 6.2 A** ($1,582) had active electronics and mini toggle switch.

ELECTRIC BASS

There was no charge for the fretless neck option on Sierra basses. The **Model 4.1** ($1,429) had an offset double cutaway body with elongated horn on the bass bout, 1 pickup, 2+2 headstock, 2 octave fretted neck, 1 volume control and 1 tone control. The **Model 4.1 A** ($1,559) was similar to the 4.1, except had active electronics and mini toggle switch. The **Model 4.2** ($1,579) shared similar body designs, but had 2 pickups, a 2+2 headstock, 2 octave fretted neck, 2 volume controls and 1 tone control. Again, the **Model 4.2 A** ($1,712) was similar to the 4.2, except had active electronics and mini toggle switch.

SIERRA (UK COMPANY)

Instruments built in England during the early to mid 1960s.

The Jetstar model was a medium quality solid body guitar that featured a design based on Fender; the Jetstar even featured three single coil pickups.

(Source: Tony Bacon and Paul Day, The Guru's Guitar Guide)

SIERRA DESIGNS

Instruments were built in Portland, Oregon during the early 1980s.

Sierra Designs was founded in 1983 by Gene Fields. Fields, who worked at Fender from 1961 to 1983, eventually joined the Fender R & D section in 1966. Fields was the designer of the Starcaster, Fender's bolt neck answer to the ES-335 in the mid 1970s. The **Blue Book of Guitars** will continue to research Sierra Designs guitars, and updated information will be in future editions.

(Source: Teisco Del Rey, Guitar Player magazine, March 1991)

SIGMA

Instruments initially assembled in Asia, and final finishing and inspection performed in Nazareth, Pennsylvania. Distributed by the C. F. Martin Guitar Company of Nazareth, Pennsylvania.

In 1970, the Martin Guitar Company expanded its product line by introducing the Sigma line. The instruments begin their assembly in Japan, and then are shipped in to Pennsylvania where the Martin company can oversee the final finishing and setup. Sigma guitars are great introductory models to the classic Martin design.

(Source: Michael Wright, Guitar Stories Volume One)

ACOUSTIC

Grading	100%	98% EXC+	95% EXC	90% VG+	80% VG	70% VG	60% G
		MINT	EXC+	EXC	VG+	VG	G

"2" Series

CS-2 — classic style, spruce top, round soundhole, bound body, wooden inlay rosette, mahogany back/sides/neck, 20/19 fret ebonized fingerboard/tied bridge, 3 per side chrome tuners. Available in Natural finish. Disc. 1994.

$145	$130	$115	$100	$90	$80	$70

Last Mfr.'s Sug. Retail was $295.

DM-2 — dreadnought style, spruce top, round soundhole, tortoise shell pickguard, 3 stripe bound body/rosette, mahogany back/sides/neck, 14/20 fret rosewood fingerboard with pearl dot inlay, rosewood bridge with black white dot pins, 3 per side chrome tuners. Available in Natural finish. Disc. 1994.

$180	$160	$140	$120	$110	$100	$90

Add $45 for 12 string version (DM12-2).

Last Mfr.'s Sug. Retail was $375.

DM-2E/WH — similar to DM-2, except has ebonized fingerboard/bridge, acoustic pickup, 3 band EQ with volume control. Available in White finish. Disc. 1994.

$315	$280	$260	$240	$205	$175	$160

Add $25 for single round cutaway, white black dot bridge pins. Available in Black finish (DM-2CE/B).

Last Mfr.'s Sug. Retail was $630.

DR-2 — similar to DM-2, except has rosewood back/sides, ebonized fingerboard/bridge. Disc. 1994.

$250	$220	$190	$170	$160	$150	$130

Last Mfr.'s Sug. Retail was $510.

Grading		100%	98% MINT	95% EXC+	90% EXC	80% VG+	70% VG	60% G

GCS-2 — similar to DM-2, except has grand concert style body. Disc. 1994.

				$210	$190	$175	$150	$115	$100	$85

Last Mfr.'s Sug. Retail was $420.

Marquis Series

This series was introduced in 1987.

CS-1 — classic style, spruce top, round soundhole, bound body, wooden inlay rosette, mahogany back/sides/neck, 20/19 fret ebonized fingerboard/tied bridge, 3 per side chrome tuners. Available in Antique Stain finish. Curr. mfr.

Mfr.'s Sug. Retail	$210	$157	$105	$75	$65	$55	$50	$45

DM-1 — dreadnought style, spruce top, round soundhole, black pickguard, bound body, 3 stripe rosette, mahogany back/sides/neck, 14/20 fret ebonized fingerboard with pearl dot inlay, ebonized bridge with black pins, 3 per side chrome tuners. Available in Natural finish. Curr. mfr.

Mfr.'s Sug. Retail	$260	$195	$130	$100	$90	$75	$65	$50

Add $25 for 12 string version (DM12-1).

FDM-1 — similar to DM-1, except has folk style body. New 1994.

Mfr.'s Sug. Retail	$255	$191	$127	$100	$85	$70	$60	$45

GCS-1 — similar to DM-1, except has grand concert style body. Curr. mfr.

Mfr.'s Sug. Retail	$260	$195	$130	$100	$90	$75	$65	$50

CS-4 — classic style, spruce top, round soundhole, bound body, wooden inlay rosette, mahogany back/sides/neck, 12/19 fret rosewood fingerboard, rosewood tied bridge, rosewood peghead veneer, 3 per side chrome tuners with pearl buttons. Available in Antique finish. Curr. mfr.

Mfr.'s Sug. Retail	$340	$255	$170	$140	$110	$100	$85	$60

DM-4 — dreadnought style, spruce top, round soundhole, black pickguard, 3 stripe bound body/rosette, mahogany back/sides/neck, 14/20 fret ebonized fingerboard with pearl dot inlay, pearl horizontal teardrop inlay at 12th fret, ebonized bridge with black white dot pins, rosewood peghead veneer, 3 per side chrome tuners. Available in Black and Natural finishes. Curr. mfr.

Mfr.'s Sug. Retail	$430	$322	$215	$170	$155	$145	$115	$100

Add $30 for Black finish.

Add $40 for 12 string version (DM12-4).

Add $40 for left handed version (DM-4L).

Subtract $20 for stained mahogany top (DM-4M).

Add $45 for herringbone bound body/rosette (DM-4H).

Add $45 for Antique and Tobacco Sunburst finishes (DM-4Y and DM-4S).

In 1994, Antique finish (DM-4Y) was discontinued.

DM-4C — similar to DM-4, except has single round cutaway. New 1994.

Mfr.'s Sug. Retail	$505	$378	$252	$200	$180	$160	$140	$120

Add $45 for Black finish.

DM-4CV — similar to DM-4, except has venetian cutaway. Available in Violin finish.

		$390	$200	$185	$165	$145	$120	$100

Last Mfr.'s Sug. Retail was $560.

DM-4C/3B — similar to DM-4, except has single round cutaway, acoustic pickup, 3 band EQ with volume control. Available in Natural finish. Disc. 1994.

		$375	$350	$300	$285	$255	$235	$215

Last Mfr.'s Sug. Retail was $715.

DM12-4 — similar to DM-4, except has 12 strings, 6 per side tuners. New 1994.

Mfr.'s Sug. Retail	$470	$352	$235	$185	$160	$140	$120	$105

DR-4H — similar to DM-4, except has tortoise pickguard, herringbone bound body/rosette, rosewood back/sides. Available in Natural finish.

Mfr.'s Sug. Retail	$510	$382	$255	$200	$180	$160	$145	$125

DT-4N — similar to DM-4, except has chestnut back/sides/peghead veneer. Available in Violin finish.

Mfr.'s Sug. Retail	$495	$371	$247	$200	$185	$165	$140	$115

Add $35 for Violin finish (DT-4).

Add $75 for 12 string version (DT12-4).

DV-4 — similar to DM-4, except has ovankol back/sides. Available in Antique finish. Disc. 1994.

		$240	$215	$195	$180	$160	$145	$125

Last Mfr.'s Sug. Retail was $595.

GCS-4 — grand concert style, spruce top, round soundhole, black pickguard, 5 stripe bound body/rosette, mahogany back/sides/neck, 14/20 fret ebonized fingerboard with pearl dot inlay, horizontal teardrop inlay at 12th fret, ebonized bridge with black white dot pins, rosewood peghead veneer, 3 per side chrome tuners. Available in Natural finish. Curr. mfr.

Mfr.'s Sug. Retail	$395	$296	$197	$160	$140	$120	$100	$80

Grading	100%	98% MINT	95% EXC+	90% EXC	80% VG+	70% VG	60% G

GCS -4C — similar to GCS-4, except has single round cutaway. Disc. 1994.

	$250	$220	$200	$180	$165	$140	$110

Last Mfr.'s Sug. Retail was $550.

GCS-4C/3B — similar to GCS-4, except has single round cutaway, acoustic pickup, 3 band EQ with volume control. Disc. 1994.

	$365	$325	$300	$285	$255	$235	$215

Last Mfr.'s Sug. Retail was $715.

Studio Series (formerly the Generation III Series)

CS-1 ST — classic style, solid spruce top, round soundhole, bound body, wood inlay rosette, mahogany back/sides/neck, 14/19 fret ebonized fingerboard, ebonized tied bridge, 3 per side chrome tuners with nylon buttons. Available in Natural finish. New 1994.

Mfr.'s Sug. Retail	$335	$251	$167	$135	$105	$95	$85	$70

CR-8 — classic style, solid spruce top, round soundhole, bound body, wooden inlay rosette, rosewood back/sides, mahogany neck, 12/19 fret ebonized fingerboard/tied bridge, 3 per side gold tuners with pearl buttons. Available in Natural finish. Curr. mfr.

Mfr.'s Sug. Retail	$570	$427	$285	$215	$195	$165	$145	$125

DM-1 ST — dreadnought style, solid spruce top, round soundhole, tortoise pickguard, 3 stripe bound body/rosette, mahogany back/sides/neck, 14/20 fret ebonized fingerboard with pearl dot inlay, ebonized bridge with black white dot pins, abalone logo peghead inlay, 3 per side chrome tuners. Available in Natural finish. New 1994.

Mfr.'s Sug. Retail	$345	$258	$172	$145	$115	$95	$85	$75

DR-1 ST — similar to DM-1 ST, except has rosewood back/sides. New 1994.

Mfr.'s Sug. Retail	$375	$281	$187	$140	$115	$100	$85	$75

DM12-1 ST — similar to DM-1 ST, except has 12 strings, 6 per side tuners. New 1994.

Mfr.'s Sug. Retail	$410	$307	$205	$185	$165	$145	$135	$125

DM-18 — dreadnought style, solid spruce top, round soundhole, tortoise pickguard, 3 stripe bound body/rosette, mahogany back/sides/neck, 14/20 fret ebonized fingerboard with pearl dot inlay, ebonized bridge with black white dot pins, abalone logo peghead inlay, 3 per side chrome tuners. Available in Natural finish. Curr. mfr.

Mfr.'s Sug. Retail	$525	$393	$262	$225	$200	$175	$150	$135

DR-28 — dreadnought style, solid spruce top, round soundhole, tortoise shell pickguard, 3 stripe bound body/rosette, rosewood back/sides, mahogany neck, 14/20 fret ebonized fingerboard with pearl dot inlay, ebonized bridge with white abalone dot pins, rosewood veneered peghead with abalone logo inlay, 3 per side chrome tuners. Available in Natural finish. Curr. mfr.

Mfr.'s Sug. Retail	$620	$465	$310	$275	$250	$225	$200	$165

DR-28H — similar to DR-28, except has herringbone bound body, pearl diamond fingerboard inlay.

Mfr.'s Sug. Retail	$670	$502	$335	$300	$275	$240	$215	$180

Add $35 for 12 string version (DR12-28H). Mfd. 1993 to date.

DR-35 — dreadnought style, solid spruce top, round soundhole, tortoise shell pickguard, 5 stripe bound body/rosette, rosewood back/sides, mahogany neck, 14/20 fret bound ebonized fingerboard with pearl dot inlay, ebonized bridge with white abalone dot pins, bound rosewood veneered peghead with abalone logo inlay, 3 per side chrome tuners. Available in Natural finish. Curr. mfr.

Mfr.'s Sug. Retail	$655	$491	$327	$300	$275	$240	$215	$200

DR-41 — dreadnought style, solid spruce top, round soundhole, tortoise shell pickguard, abalone bound body/rosette, rosewood back/sides, mahogany neck, 14/20 fret bound ebonized fingerboard with abalone hexagon inlay, ebonized bridge with white abalone dot pins, bound rosewood veneered peghead with abalone logo inlay, 3 per side chrome tuners. Available in Natural finish. Curr. mfr.

Mfr.'s Sug. Retail	$725	$543	$362	$310	$285	$250	$225	$210

DR-45 — dreadnought style, solid spruce top, round soundhole, tortoise shell pickguard, abalone bound body/rosette, rosewood back/sides, mahogany neck, 14/20 fret abalone bound rosewood fingerboard with abalone hexagon inlay, rosewood bridge with white abalone dot pins, abalone bound rosewood veneered peghead with abalone logo inlay, 3 per side gold tuners. Available in Natural finish. New 1994.

Mfr.'s Sug. Retail	$1,745	$1,308	$872	$760	$700	$650	$600	$575

FD-16M — folk style, spruce top, round soundhole, black pickguard, bound body, 3 stripe rosette, mahogany back/sides/neck, 14/20 fret ebonized fingerboard with pearl dot inlay, ebonized bridge with black pins, 3 per side chrome tuners. Available in Natural finish. New 1994.

Mfr.'s Sug. Retail	$460	$345	$230	$180	$160	$135	$115	$100

000-18M — auditorium style, solid spruce top, round soundhole, tortoise pickguard, 3 stripe bound body, 5 stripe rosette, mahogany back/sides/neck, 14/20 fret ebonized fingerboard with pearl dot inlay, ebonized bridge with black white dot pins, rosewood peghead veneer with abalone logo inlay, 3 per side chrome tuners. Available in Antique finish. Mfd. 1993 to date.

Mfr.'s Sug. Retail	$525	$393	$262	$215	$185	$155	$135	$115

000-18MC/3B — similar to 000-18M, except has venetian cutaway, acoustic pickup, 3 band EQ with volume control. Disc. 1994.

	$660	$350	$320	$300	$280	$240	$200

Last Mfr.'s Sug. Retail was $940.

"The Jazzmaster boasted many refinements in the electrical pickup/harness assembly. While not a stereo guitar that would have competed more directly with Gibson and Gretsch, the system did offer a dazzling array of tonal possibilities through its unique dual control system."

—Randy Applegate & Carl Cook
TCG, May/June 1993

ACOUSTIC BASS

STB-M/E — jumbo style, spruce top, round soundhole, tortoise pickguard, 5 stripe bound body/rosette, maple back/sides/neck, 15/21 fret ebonized fingerboard with pearl dot inlay, ebonized strings thru bridge with pearl dot inlay, maple peghead veneer, 2 per side chrome tuners, acoustic pickup, 3 band EQ with volume control. Available in Natural finish. Mfd. 1993 to date.

Mfr.'s Sug. Retail	$1,145	$858	$572	$510	$475	$415	$400	$365

STB-R/E — similar to STB-M, except has black pickguard, rosewood back/sides.

Mfr.'s Sug. Retail	$1,160	$870	$580	$565	$455	$405	$370	$335

STB-M — similar to STB-M/E, except has no acoustic pickup, 3 band EQ with volume control. New 1994.

Mfr.'s Sug. Retail	$785	$588	$392	$345	$315	$285	$260	$235

Add $15 for black pickguard, rosewood back/sides.

ACOUSTIC ELECTRIC

SE Series

SE-1 — single round cutaway folk style, spruce top, round soundhole, 3 stripe bound body/rosette, mahogany back/sides/neck, 22 fret bound ebonized fingerboard with pearl dot inlay, ebonized bridge with white black dot pins, rosewood peghead veneer with abalone logo inlay, 3 per side chrome tuners, acoustic pickup, volume/2 band EQ control. Available in Black and Natural finishes. New 1994.

Mfr.'s Sug. Retail	$565	$423	$282	$245	$225	$205	$185	$170

SE-18/2BC — single round cutaway folk style, spruce top, round soundhole, 3 stripe bound body/rosette, mahogany back/sides/neck, 22 fret bound ebonized fingerboard with pearl dot inlay, ebonized bridge with white black dot pins, rosewood peghead veneer with abalone logo inlay, 3 per side chrome tuners, acoustic pickup, 2 band EQ with chorus effect, volume control. Available in Black, Natural, Red and Tobacco Sunburst finishes. Mfd. 1993 to 1994.

		$635	$320	$300	$260	$225	$200	$175

Last Mfr.'s Sug. Retail was $905.

SE-18/3B — similar to SE-18/2BC, except has 3 band EQ with volume control. Available in Natural and Tobacco Sunburst finishes. Mfd. 1993 to 1994.

		$600	$300	$275	$250	$225	$200	$175

Last Mfr.'s Sug. Retail was $860.

ELECTRIC

While the focus of the Sigma line has been primarily acoustic guitars (Sigma is a division of the C.F. Martin Guitar Company), there were a handful of solid body guitars and basses distributed during the early 1970s. Two models (SBG2-6, SBE2-9) resemble Gibson SGs (the SBE has a semi-Bigsby vibrato). Sigma's SBF2-6 has a telecaster body mated to a 3+3 headstock, and the bass SBB2-8 sports a Fenderish Precision body (in the earlier Telecaster style) with a 2+2 headstock! They're out there, they're real (real '70s copies, that is), and if you see one - don't say we didn't warn you.

(Sigma catalog reprint courtesy Michael Wright, Guitar Stories Volume One)

SIGNATURE

Instruments produced in Canada from the mid 1980s to current.

The Signature line focuses on high quality 'superstrat' solid body designs.

(Source: Tony Bacon and Paul Day, The Guru's Guitar Guide)

SIGNET

Instruments produced in Japan.

The Signet trademark is a brandname of U.S. importers Ampeg/Selmer.

(Source: Michael Wright, Guitar Stories Volume One, pg. 76)

SILVER CADET

Instruments produced in Korea. Distributed in the U.S. market by Ibanez (Hoshino USA) of Bensalem, Pennsylvania.

The Silver Cadet guitar line provides an entry level step into the wonderful world of electric guitars (buy a guitar, plug it into a loud amp, and **then** tell your parents! They'll either cut your allowance or cut off your electricity). The current quality of these instruments, like other contemporary entry level guitars, is a lot better today than it was twenty or thirty years ago for a beginning student.

Grading		100% MINT	98% EXC+	95% EXC	90% VG+	80% VG+	70% VG	60% G

1963 Silvertone Jupitor
courtesy Rick Wilkowitz

Silvertone Deluxe
courtesy Daniel Gelabert

ELECTRIC

ZR140 — offset double cutaway hardwood body, black pickguard, bolt-on maple neck, 21 fret rosewood fingerboard with pearl dot inlay, standard vibrato, 6 on one side tuners, chrome hardware, 2 single coil/1 humbucker pickups, volume/tone control, 5 position switch. Available in Black, Red and White finishes. New 1994.

Mfr.'s Sug. Retail	$250	$200	$150	$125	$100	$90	$80	$75

ZR350 — similar to ZR140, except has double locking vibrato, humbucker/single coil/humbucker pickups. Available in Black, Red and White finishes. New 1994.

Mfr.'s Sug. Retail	$430	$344	$258	$215	$175	$155	$140	$130

ELECTRIC BASS

ZTB100 — offset double cutaway hardwood body, black pickguard, bolt-on maple neck, 22 fret rosewood fingerboard with pearl dot inlay, fixed bridge, 4 on one side tuners, chrome hardware, P-style pickup, volume/tone control. Available in Black and Red finishes. New 1994.

Mfr.'s Sug. Retail	$300	$240	$180	$150	$120	$110	$100	$90

SILVERTONE

See chapter on House Brands.

This trademark has been identified as a "House Brand" owned and used by Sears and Roebuck. There was no company or factory; Sears owned the name and applied it to various products from such manufacturers as HARMONY, VALCO, DANELECTRO, and KAY. Sears and Roebuck acquired Harmony in 1916 to control its respectable ukulele production. Harmony generally sold around 40 percent of its guitar production to Sears. The following is a word of caution: Just because it says **Silvertone** do not automatically assume it is a Danelectro! In fact, study the guitar to determine possible origin (Harmony, Valco and Kay were originally built in Illinois, Danelectro in New Jersey; so all were U.S. However, some models were built in Japan as well!). Best of all, play it! If it looks good, and sounds okay - it was meant to be played. As most Silvertones were sold either through the catalog or in a store, they will generally be entry level quality instruments.

Certain Silvertone models have garnered some notoriety, such as the Danelectro-produced combination of guitar and amp-in-case. Sears also marketed the Teisco company's TRG-1 (or TRE-100) electric guitar with amp built in! This guitar has a six-on-a-side 'Silvertone' headstock, and a single cutaway "pregnant Telecaster" body design (the small built-in speaker is in the "tummy"). Harmony produced a number of electric hollowbody guitars for the Silvertone label.

Silvertone pricing depends primarily on Harmony versus Danelectro company of origin. Currently, the market is favoring the Danelectro Silvertones, although certain Harmony hollow body electrics do possess eye-catching appeal. Prices may range from $199 up to $600.

GENE SIMMON'S PUNISHER BASS

Instruments built in California, although no information has been revealed as to where, or by whom. Distributed by direct sales (1.609.PUNISHER).

As the rock group KISS began making a comeback stand, a series of ads for the Punisher bass appeared in guitar magazines in 1996. One model, available in natural, tobacco sunburst or black finish, is available and is identical to the same bass Gene Simmons has used for the past two or three tours. The **Punisher** ($1,500) model features a dual cutaway body with equal horns, EMG P/J pickups, Schaller bridge and hardware, and a hardshell case. No options, no left handed models, period - just like Gene's.

SIMMS-WATTS

See also NED CALLAN.

Instruments produced in England during the mid 1970s.

The Simms-Watts trademark is the brandname used on England's own Ned Callan guitars. In fact, without the difference of the headstock label, the instruments are the same as, and produced by, Ned Callan (Peter Cook).

(Source: Tony Bacon and Paul Day, The Guru's Guitar Book)

SIMON & PATRICK

Instruments built in La Patrie, Quebec, Canada since 1985. Simon & Patrick Acoustic Guitars are distributed by La Si Do, Inc., of St. Laurent, Canada.

Robert Godin set up a custom guitar shop in Montreal called Harmonilab in 1968. Harmonilab quickly became known for its excellent work and musicians were coming from as far away as Quebec City to have their guitars adjusted.

Although Harmonilab's business was flourishing, Robert was full of ideas for the design and construction of acoustic guitars. So in 1972 the **Norman Guitar Company** was born. From the beginning the Norman guitars showed signs of the innovations that Godin would eventually bring to the guitar market.

By 1978 Norman guitars had become quite successful in Canada and France. In 1980 Godin introduced the Seagull guitar. With many innovations like a bolt-on neck, pointed headstock and a handmade solid top, the Seagull was designed for an ease of play for the entry level to intermediate guitar player. Godin borrowed the finishing idea that was used on fine violins (a satin-finish lacquer), and applied it to the acoustic guitar.

Acceptance of this new guitar spread, and by 1985 La Si Do was incorporated and the factory in La Patrie expanded to meet the growing demand. In 1985 Godin introduced the Simon & Patrick line (named after his two sons) for people interested in a more traditional instrument. Simon & Patrick guitars still maintained a number of Seagull innovations.

For full company history, see GODIN.

ACOUSTIC GUITAR

S & P 6 — solid cedar top, wild cherry back and sides, rosewood fingerboard and bridge, 3+3 headstock, lacquer finish. Current production.

Mfr.'s Sug. Retail	$395	$335	$276	$260	$220	$190	$160	$140

Guitar is available with a solid spruce top.

Guitar is available in a left handed version.

Guitar may be optionally equipped with EPM electronics.

S & P 12 — similar to S & P 6, except as a 12 string model with 6 on a side tuners, Current production.

Mfr.'s Sug. Retail	$462	$406	$355	$350	$310	$285	$245	$200

S & P CUTAWAY — similar to S & P 6, except model is a steel-string cutaway. Current production.

Mfr.'s Sug. Retail	$545	$506	$490	$450	$410	$370	$330	$290

Guitar is only available in a right handed configuration.

S & P 6 MAHOGANY — similar to the S & P 6, only has mahogany back and sides instead of wild-cherry, and has a satin lacqer finish. Current production.

Mfr.'s Sug. Retail	$450	$396	$346	$345	$300	$270	$230	$175

Guitar is available with a solid spruce top.

Guitar is available in a left handed version.

Guitar may be optionally equipped with EPM electronics.

Simon & Patrick Pro Series

S & P 6 PRO MAHOGANY — similar to the S & P 6, except has a solid spruce top, mahogany back and sides, mahogany neck, and high gloss lacquer finish. Current production.

Mfr.'s Sug. Retail	$760	$706	$684	$625	$580	$500	$450	$390

Guitar is available in a left handed version.

Guitar may be optionally equipped with L.R. Baggs electronics.

S & P 6 PRO FLAME MAPLE — similar to the S & P Pro Mahogany, except has flame maple sides and solid back. Current production.

Mfr.'s Sug. Retail	$850	$790	$765	$715	$670	$590	$540	$480

Guitar is available in a left handed version.

Guitar may be optionally equipped with L.R. Baggs electronics.

S & P 6 PRO FLAME MAPLE CUTAWAY — similar to S & P 6 Pro Flame Maple, but body is in the cutaway configuration. Current production.

Mfr.'s Sug. Retail	$995	$925	$895	$855	$810	$730	$680	$620

S & P 6 PRO ROSEWOOD — similar to the S & P Pro Mahogany, except has Indian rosewood bak and sides. Current production.

Mfr.'s Sug. Retail	$1,005	$934	$904	$865	$820	$740	$690	$630

Guitar is available in a left handed version.

Guitar may be optionally equipped with L.R. Baggs electronics.

S & P 6 PRO ROSEWOOD CUTAWAY — similar to S & P 6 Pro Rosewood, but body is in the cutaway configuration. Current model.

Mfr.'s Sug. Retail	$1,160	$1,078	$1,044	$895	$800	$750	$710	$640

S & P 6 PRO QUILTED MAPLE — similar to the S & P Pro Mahogany, except the back and sides are solid quilted maple. Current production.

Mfr.'s Sug. Retail	$1,290	$1,135	$993	$910	$825	$765	$720	$645

Guitar is available in a left handed version.

Guitar may be optionally equipped with L.R. Baggs electronics.

S

SIMPSON

Instruments produced in New Zealand during the 1960s.

Luthier Ray Simpson built his first electric guitar in 1941. Production ran during the 1960s. A representational model called the Pan-O-Sonic combines both strat-designated overtones with original bridge and wiring designs (the three single coil pickups each have their own on/off switch. If wired differently from a standard 3 or 5 way selector, this switching could offer some pickup combinations not offered traditionally!). Anyone with further information on Simpson guitars is invited to write to the **Blue Book of Guitars.**

(Source: Tony Bacon, The Ultimate Guitar Book)

SIMPSON-JAMES

Instruments built in Westfield, Massachusetts since 1993.

Simpson-James basses are handbuilt in Westfield, Massachusetts by luthiers Christopher Mowatt and Robert Clarke. The company was established in 1993 with the vision of providing custom electric basses to local professional musicians. The basses produced have been unique in that no two instruments were alike, each being a prototype in design and function. Simpson-James currently offers four different neck-thru **SJ-4** 4-string models (list prices range from $1,100 to $1,600), and two **SJ-5** 5-string models (list $1,800). The **Performer Series**, introduced in 1996, is a rebirth of the Great American Workhorse of basses. Offering the same quality in a bolt-neck design, Performer series 4- and 5-strings range from $1,200 to $1,550.

According to product director Christopher Mowatt, Simpson-James is currently hand-building between 2 to 5 instruments per month in their efforts to maintain strict quality control.

DANIEL SLAMAN

Instruments built in Den Haag, Netherlands since 1978. Distributed through Slaman's workshop; or by Casa Benelly in Den Haag and La Guitarra Buena in Amsterdam.

Luthier Daniel Slaman began building classical guitars in 1978. Slaman participated in a guitar making Masterclass hosted by Jose L. Romanillos in 1988, and professes a strong design influence by Romanillos. The majority of Slaman's instruments were built after 1992, and his current project is his 115th. Slaman currently produces between ten and fifteen handcrafted instruments a year, although archtop production is more time consuming and tends to slow overall production down.

Luthier Slaman uses European Spruce for his classical guitar tops, and either Brazilian or Indian Rosewood, Cocobolo or Maple for the back and sides. When building "flamenco instruments", Slaman will offer soundboards of either European Spruce or Western red Cedar, and bodies of Spanish Cypress or Rosewood. Prices on classical models start at $3,000; and flamenco models begin at $2,500.

Slaman also produces an acoustic Archtop guitar model named the **North Sea**. This model features a carved Sitka Spruce top, a two piece Flamed Maple back with matching sides and neck, Ebony tailpiece and pickguard, and an Ebony fingerboard with Mother of Pearl and Mexican Green Abalone inlays. Slaman also uses Schaller gold tuning machines, hand-applied nitro cellulose finish, and Brazilian Rosewood bridge and headplate. The 'North Sea' is available with an optional Benedetto S-6 suspended pickup. Prices on the acoustic Archtop guitars start at $4,500.

SLINGERLAND

Instruments built in Chicago, Illinois during the mid 1930s through the (estimated) mid 1940s.

Slingerland is perhaps better known for the drums the company produced. The Slingerland Banjo and Drum Company was established in 1916 in Chicago. In terms of construction, a banjo and drum do have several similarites (the soundhead stretched over a circular frame and held by a retaining ring). The company introduced the Marvel line of carved top guitars in 1936. A catalog of the time shows that Slingerland guitars were also sold under various brandnames such as Songster, College Pal, and May-Bell, as well as the Slingerland logo.

(Source: Tom Wheeler, American Guitars)

SMD

Instruments built in New York. Distributed by the vintage shop Toys From the Attic in Shelter Lane, New York.

Luthier Chris Stambaugh began building high quality string instruments for his friends and himself out of necessity: they needed the quality but couldn't afford the retail prices. Stambaugh, born and raised in North Berwick, Maine, started building guitars during his tenure at a furniture building company. In 1995, his band won the Maine Musician's Award for Originality.

Now 21 years old, Stambaugh is currently attending the Wentworth Institute of Technology and is majoring in Industrial Design. He was chosen for the Arioch Scholar program, and is one of three students attending on the program's full scholarship. His stated goal is to craft the highest quality instruments for a fair market price, using enviromentally friendly techniques and form and function designs drawn from his educational backround.

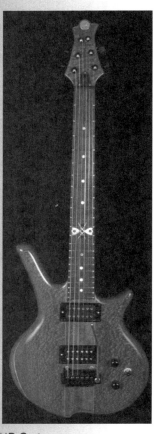

SMD Custom
courtesy Toys From the Attic

ELECTRIC

The **SMD Custom** six string features a neck-through body design, and oil finish, and a specific peghead and body pattern. Everything else about the guitar is left to the customer's choice: tonewoods, pickups, electronics, hardware, neck inlays, and wiring style is based on the preference of the player commissioning the guitar, and is covered in the base price of $1,200. Further options of a gloss finish (add $150) or a tremolo bridge (add $150) are priced extra.

ELECTRIC BASS

Stambaugh's **SMD Custom Bass** is available in four, five, or six string configurations. Similar to the SMD Custom guitar, luthier Stambaugh only specifies an oil finish, peghead and body pattern (the look of the instrument). All other options are left to the customer's choice: tonewoods, pickups, electronics, hardware, and wiring style are based on the preference of the player. While there is no option for a bass tremolo, the gloss finish option is an extra $150. Retail prices start at $1,300 (four string), $1,450 (five string), up to $1,600 (for the six string model). Luthier Stambaugh is also building custom designed banjos (including a Banjo Bass). For further information, contact Stambaugh or the staff at Toys In The Attic via the Index of Current Manufacturers located in the back of this book.

KEN SMITH BASSES

Instruments built in Perkasie, Pennsylvania and Japan. Distributed by Ken Smith Basses, Ltd. of Perkasie, Pennsylvania.

Luthier Ken Smith's original career was a professional studio musician. Inspired by his need for a better quality bass guitar, he built one! His efforts introduced the concept of a high quality custom bass designed to meet the needs of a professional player.

Smith spend a number of years in the early 1970s researching luthier information and building designs. By 1978 he opened his business, and in 1980 the first Smith basses were introduced.

ELECTRIC BASS

Grading		100%	98% MINT	95% EXC+	90% EXC	80% VG+	70% VG	60% G

Add $100 for fretless fingerboard models.
Add $200 for left handed versions.

C.R. CUSTOM IV — double cutaway maple body, figured maple wings, bolt-on 3 piece maple neck, 24 fret pau ferro fingerboard, fixed brass bridge, blackface peghead with pearl logo inlay, 2 per side tuners, chrome hardware, 2 humbucker pickups, volume/treble/bass/mix controls, active electronics. Available in Natural finish. Mfd. 1993 to date.

Mfr.'s Sug. Retail	$2,300	$1,840	$1,380	$1,150	$920	$830	$760	$690

This model has swamp ash wings optionally available.

C.R. Custom V — similar to C.R. Custom IV, except has 5 strings, 3/2 per side tuners.

Mfr.'s Sug. Retail	$2,400	$1,920	$1,440	$1,200	$960	$860	$790	$720

C.R. Custom VI — similar to C.R. Custom IV, except has 6 strings, 3 per side tuners.

Mfr.'s Sug. Retail	$2,500	$2,000	$1,500	$1,250	$1,000	$900	$825	$750

Burner Series

ARTIST — double cutaway mahogany body with exotic wood top/back, bolt-on maple/walnut 5 piece neck, 24 fret rosewood fingerboard with pearl dot inlay, fixed bridge, 2 per side tuners, black hardware, 2 humbucker pickups, volume/treble/bass and mix controls, active electronics. Available in Antique Natural finish. Curr. mfr.

Mfr.'s Sug. Retail	$2,050	$1,537	$1,025	$1,000	$800	$720	$660	$600

Artist V — similar to Artist, except has 5 strings, 3/2 per side tuners.

Mfr.'s Sug. Retail	$2,150	$1,612	$1,075	$1,050	$840	$755	$690	$630

Artist VI — similar to Artist, except has 6 strings, 3 per side tuners.

Mfr.'s Sug. Retail	$2,350	$1,762	$1,175	$1,150	$920	$830	$760	$690

CUSTOM — double cutaway figured maple body, bolt-on maple/walnut 5 piece neck, 24 fret rosewood fingerboard with pearl dot inlay, fixed bridge, 2 per side tuners, black hardware, 2 J-style pickups, volume/treble/bass and mix controls, active electronics. Available in Transparent Antique Natural, Transparent Candy Red and Transparent Cobalt Blue finishes. Curr. mfr.

Mfr.'s Sug. Retail	$1,700	$1,275	$850	$800	$640	$575	$530	$480

Custom V — similar to Custom, except has 5 strings, 3/2 per side tuners.

Mfr.'s Sug. Retail	$1,800	$1,350	$900	$850	$680	$610	$560	$510

Custom VI — similar to Custom, except has 6 strings, 3 per side tuners.

Mfr.'s Sug. Retail	$2,000	$1,500	$1,000	$950	$760	$685	$625	$570

DELUXE — double cutaway swamp ash body, bolt-on maple neck, 24 fret pau ferro fingerboard with pearl dot inlay, fixed brass bridge, 2 per side tuners, black hardware, 2 J-style pickups, 2 volume/1 treble/1 bass controls, active electronics. Available in Antique Natural, Transparent Candy Apple Red, Transparent Cobalt Blue finishes. Curr. mfr.

Mfr.'s Sug. Retail	$1,600	$1,280	$960	$800	$640	$575	$530	$480

Grading	100%	98% MINT	95% EXC+	90% EXC	80% VG+	70% VG	60% G

Deluxe V — similar to Deluxe, except has 5 strings, 3/2 per side tuners.
| Mfr.'s Sug. Retail | $1,700 | $1,360 | $1,020 | $850 | $680 | $610 | $560 | $510 |

Deluxe VI — similar to Deluxe, except has 6 strings, 3 per side tuners.
| Mfr.'s Sug. Retail | $1,900 | $1,520 | $1,140 | $950 | $760 | $685 | $625 | $570 |

STANDARD — double cutaway alder body, bolt-on maple neck, 24 fret pau ferro fingerboard with pearl dot inlay, fixed brass bridge, 2 per side tuners, black hardware, 2 J-style pickups, 2 volume/1 treble/1 bass controls, active electronics. Available in Electric Blue, Ivory White, Onyx Black and Scarlet Red finishes. Curr. mfr.
| Mfr.'s Sug. Retail | $1,400 | $1,120 | $840 | $700 | $560 | $505 | $460 | $420 |

Standard V — similar to Standard, except has 5 strings, 3/2 per side tuners.
| Mfr.'s Sug. Retail | $1,500 | $1,200 | $900 | $750 | $600 | $540 | $495 | $450 |

Standard VI — similar to Standard, except has 6 strings, 3 per side tuners.
| Mfr.'s Sug. Retail | $1,700 | $1,360 | $1,020 | $850 | $680 | $610 | $560 | $510 |

"G" Series

This series has graphite rods adjacent to the truss rod for added strength and durability.

B.M.T. ELITE IV — offset double cutaway mahogany body with walnut/maple veneer, figured maple top/back, thru body 7 piece bubinga/maple/ovankol neck, 24 fret pau ferro fingerboard with pearl dot inlay, fixed brass bridge, blackface peghead with pearl logo inlay, 2 per side tuners, gold hardware, 2 humbucker pickups, volume/treble/mid/bass/mix controls, active electronics. Available in Natural finish. Mfd. 1993 to date.
| Mfr.'s Sug. Retail | $4,300 | $3,440 | $2,580 | $2,150 | $1,720 | $1,550 | $1,420 | $1,290 |

This model has bubinga, koa, lacewood, pau ferro top/walnut back, ovankol, walnut and zebrawood bodies, ebony fingerboard, black and chrome hardware optionally available.

B.M.T. Elite V — similar to B.M.T. Elite IV, except has 5 strings, 3/2 per side tuners.
| Mfr.'s Sug. Retail | $4,400 | $3,520 | $2,640 | $2,200 | $1,760 | $1,585 | $1,450 | $1,320 |

B.M.T. Elite VI — similar to B.M.T. Elite IV, except has 6 strings, 3 per side tuners.
| Mfr.'s Sug. Retail | $4,500 | $3,600 | $2,700 | $2,250 | $1,800 | $1,620 | $1,485 | $1,350 |

B.T. CUSTOM IV — double cutaway mahogany body, figured maple top/back, thru body 5 piece maple/mahogany neck, 24 fret ebony fingerboard with pearl dot inlay, fixed brass bridge, blackface peghead with pearl logo inlay, 2 per side tuners, black hardware, 2 humbucker Smith pickups, volume/concentric treble-bass/mix controls, active electronics. Available in Charcoal Gray, Electric Blue, Natural and Scarlet Red finishes. Curr. mfr.
| Mfr.'s Sug. Retail | $3,600 | $2,700 | $1,800 | $1,715 | $1,320 | $1,190 | $1,090 | $990 |

This model has bubinga, koa, lacewood, pau ferro, ovankol and zebrawood bodies with Natural finish, pau ferro fingerboard, chrome and gold hardware optionally available.

B.T. Custom V — similar to B.T. Custom IV, except has 5 strings, 3/2 per side tuners.
| Mfr.'s Sug. Retail | $3,800 | $2,850 | $1,900 | $1,850 | $1,480 | $1,330 | $1,220 | $1,110 |

B.T. Custom VI — similar to B.T. Custom IV, except has 6 strings, 3 per side tuners.
| Mfr.'s Sug. Retail | $4,000 | $3,200 | $2,400 | $2,000 | $1,600 | $1,440 | $1,320 | $1,200 |

C.R. CUSTOM IV — double cutaway mahogany body, figured maple top/back, thru body 3 piece maple neck, 24 fret pau ferro fingerboard with pearl dot inlay, fixed brass bridge, 2 per side tuners, chrome hardware, 2 humbucker pickups, volume/treble/bass/mix controls, active electronics. Available in Natural finish. New 1993.
| Mfr.'s Sug. Retail | $2,700 | $2,160 | $1,620 | $1,350 | $1,080 | $970 | $890 | $810 |

This group of instruments was formerly the Chuck Rainey Series.

This model has koa, oak and walnut bodies, black and gold hardware optionally available.

C.R. Custom V — similar to C.R. Custom IV, except has 5 strings, 3/2 per side tuners. Mfd. 1992 to date.
| Mfr.'s Sug. Retail | $2,800 | $2,100 | $1,400 | $1,350 | $1,080 | $970 | $890 | $810 |

C.R. Custom VI — similar to C.R. Custom IV, except has 6 strings, 3 per side tuners. Mfd. 1992 to date.
| Mfr.'s Sug. Retail | $2,800 | $2,240 | $1,680 | $1,400 | $1,120 | $1,010 | $925 | $840 |

SMALLMAN GUITARS

Instruments built in New South Wales, Australia from the early 1980s on.

Luthier Greg Smallman continues to push the mechanical limits on the classical guitar form. Though the instruments look conventional, Smallman utilizes a lattice-like internal strutting composed of wood and carbon fiber under a thin top to increase the volume of the guitar. Smallman favors cedar (as opposed to the traditional spruce) for his guitar tops.

(Source: Tony Bacon, The Ultimate Guitar Book)

SOLA-SOUND

Instruments produced in Japan during the early 1970s.

The Sola-Sound trademark was a brandname used by a UK importer. These medium quality solid body guitars featured designs based on classic American favorites.

(Source: Tony Bacon and Paul Day, The Guru's Guitar Book)

SONNET

Instruments produced in Japan.

Sonnet guitars were distributed in the U.S. by the Daimaru New York Corporation of New York, New York.

(Source: Michael Wright, Guitar Stories Volume One)

SORRENTINO

Instruments built in New York, New York circa 1930s.

Current estimation by leading researchers/experts agree that guitars with a "Sorrentino" logo on the headstock were built by Epaminondas Stathopoulos' Epiphone company. Sorrentinos share construction designs and serialization similar to same-period Epiphones, and headstock designs similar to the Epiphone-built **Howard** brandname models. However, the crucial bit of information to be identified is the "who and where" of the trademark's namesake. One Sorrentino (model Premier, serial # 8153) photographed at the 19th Annual Dallas vintage guitar show had a label inside the body which read: "Sorrentino Mfg. Co., USA". Readers with any information are invited to write to the **Blue Book of Guitars**.

(Source: Paul Bechtoldt, Vintage Guitar Magazine, February 1996)

Sorrentino guitar courtesy Tam Milano

SPECTOR

Instruments built in New York from 1976 through 1985. In 1985, production moved to Neptune, New Jersey after Kramer (BKL) bought the company. Some late 1980s models were produced in Japan as higher end models were still built in the U.S. Distribution of Spector basses was handled by Kramer (BKL) of Neptune, New Jersey.

The Spector trademark was owned by Kramer after the purchase in 1985. With the recent re-introduction of the Kramer Musical Instruments company in 1995, the door is open for the return of Spector instruments. Of course, instruments built by Stuart Spector (see SSD) have been available since 1992.

Two members of the Brooklyn Woodworkers Co-operative, Stuart Spector and Alan Charney, established Spector Guitars in 1976. The initial SB-1 bass and G-1 guitar both featured neck-through body design. The new company attracted talent right away, as they hired Vinnie Fodera (then a fledgling bass maker) and Ned Steinberger (a later member of the co-operative) who offered a new bass design that was built as the NS-1 with one pickup. Another model with two pickups was offered as the NS-2, and proved popular indeed. In 1978 Spector expanded to a larger workshop and had 5 employees.

Spector introduced the EMG-equipped bolt-on neck models NS-1B and NS-2J in 1982, and another Steinberger designed bass, the NSX. The original Kramer company (BKL) purchased the Spector company and trademark in 1985, and moved production to their facility in New Jersey. Stuart Spector continued on in a consulting position with Kramer as they continued to produce and distribute Spector basses throughout the late 1980s. Certain model Spectors were produced in Japan. Stuart Spector left his advisory position at Kramer/Spector after three years in 1989, and formed Stuart Spector Designs, Ltd. in 1992. Kramer (BKL) went into bankruptcy in 1989, and was revived as the Kramer Musical instruments company in the early 1990s. Kramer still holds the rights to the Spector trademark and Spector model designs.

(Company information courtesy Stuart Spector, July 1996)

SPECIAL

Instruments built in Yugoslavia during the mid 1960s.

These entry level solid body guitars were built by the Muzicka Naklada company, which was based in Yugoslavia. The model "64" sports a vaguely Fender-ish body design and three single coils, as well as 5 knobs and 3 switches (!).

(Source: Tony Bacon, The Ultimate Guitar Book)

SQUIER

See FENDER.

Instruments produced in Japan in the early 1980s, and later production moved to Korea in 1987 to the Young Chang Akki factory. Squier instruments are distributed by the Fender Musical Instrument company of Scottsdale, Arizona.

In 1982, the Fender division of CBS established **Fender Japan** in conjunction with Kanda Shokai and Yamano music. Production of the Squier instruments, originally intended for European distribution, began in 1983 at the Fugi Gen Gakki facilities in Matsumoto, Japan. The Squier trademark was based on the V.C. Squire string-making company that produced strings for Fender in the 1950s, and was later acquired by Fender (under CBS) in 1965.

What was intended as a "European Commodity" soon became a way for Fender to provide entry level instruments for students and beginning players. The Squier II series was introduced circa 1986.

ELECTRIC

Squier instruments are directly based on Fender original designs, and either carry a large "Squier by Fender" or "Fender - Squier Series" on the headstock. Squier series include the **Bullet** series, the regular **Squier** models, and **Squier II**. Models generally served as an entry-level step in the Fender line of products, and are good instruments for the beginning guitar student.

Squier guitars have a new retail price ranging from $199 to $289; a good clean used Squier will generally bring at least one half to two-thirds of that because of the ties to Fender.

S S D

Instruments built in Woodstock, New York since 1992. Distributed by Armadillo Enterprises of Clearwater, Florida.

Stuart Spector co-founded Spector Guitars in 1976. Spector became well known for the sleek, neck-through body design that proved popular with bass players. In 1985, production moved to Neptune, New Jersey after Kramer (BKL) bought the company. Stuart Spector maintained a consulting position for three years from 1986 to 1989, and oversaw the continuing production by Kramer.

In 1989, Spector left Kramer and founded Stuart Spector Designs, Ltd. He introduced the SD bass in 1992, and along with Joe Veillette began handcrafting instruments, using custom made hardware and the finest hardwoods. Instruments produced of any design are limited to 100 pieces per year. Veillette left SSD in the spring of 1996 to work on his own designs as well as do outside consulting for other firms.

ELECTRIC BASS

Grading	100%	98% MINT	95% EXC+	90% EXC	80% VG+	70% VG	60% G

NS Series

The body of this series was designed by Ned Steinberger.

NS-4 — offset double cutaway figured maple body, thru body 3 piece maple neck, 24 fret pau ferro fingerboard with pearl scooped oval inlay, fixed brass bridge, blackface peghead with pearl logo inlay, 2 per side tuners, gold hardware, P-style/J-style EMG pickups, volume/treble/bass/mix controls, active electronics. Available in Natural finish. Curr. mfr.

Mfr.'s Sug. Retail	$3,500	$2,800	$2,100	$1,750	$1,400	$1,260	$1,150 $1,050

This model has 2 humbucker EMG pickups optionally available.

NS-5 — similar to NS-4, except has 5 strings, 3/2 per side tuners, 2 humbucker EMG pickups.

Mfr.'s Sug. Retail	$3,600	$2,880	$2,160	$1,800	$1,440	$1,295	$1,185 $1,075

NS-6 — similar to NS-4, except has 6 strings, 3 per side tuners, 2 humbucker EMG pickups.

Mfr.'s Sug. Retail	$3,800	$3,040	$2,280	$1,900	$1,520	$1,365	$1,255 $1,140

SD Series

The body of this series was designed by Stuart Spector.

SD-4 — offset double cutaway figured maple body, thru body 3 piece maple neck, 24 fret pau ferro fingerboard with pearl scooped oval inlay, fixed brass bridge, blackface peghead with pearl logo inlay, 2 per side tuners, gold hardware, P-style/J-style EMG pickups, volume/treble/bass/mix controls, active electronics. Available in Natural finish. Curr. mfr.

Mfr.'s Sug. Retail	$3,500	$2,800	$2,100	$1,750	$1,400	$1,260	$1,150 $1,050

This model has 2 humbucker EMG pickups optionally available.

SD-5 — similar to SD-4, except has 5 strings, 3/2 per side tuners, 2 humbucker EMG pickups.

Mfr.'s Sug. Retail	$3,600	$2,880	$2,160	$1,800	$1,440	$1,295	$1,185 $1,075

SD-6 — similar to SD-4, except has 6 strings, 3 per side tuners, 2 humbucker EMG pickups.

Mfr.'s Sug. Retail	$3,800	$3,040	$2,280	$1,900	$1,520	$1,365	$1,255 $1,140

S.S. STEWART

Instruments produced in Philadelphia, Pennsylvania, during the late 1800s.

Instruments also produced as STEWART & BAUER.

S.S. Stewart was a major banjo producer of the late 1800s, and was one of the first to apply mass production techniques to instrument building with good consequences. Stewart became partners with well-known guitar builder George Bauer, and issued guitars under the Stewart & Bauer trademark from Philadelphia. After the company was dissolved, Stewart's family put out guitars under the 'S.S. Stewart's Sons' trademark. The Stewart name also appears on a series of entry level to medium grade guitars built by Harmony and others for Weymann, and the similarities end with the name, not the quality.

(Source: Tom Wheeler, American Guitars)

ST. GEORGE

Instruments produced in Japan during the mid to late 1960s.

The St. George trademark was a brandname used by U.S. importer Buegeleisen & Jacobson of New York, New York. It has also been reported that instruments bearing the St. George label were imported by the WMI Corporation of Los Angles, California. These entry level solid body guitars featured some original body designs; however, production quality from the Japanese manufacturer is still low quality.

(Source: Michael Wright, Guitar Stories Volume One, pg. 76)

ST. MORITZ

Instruments produced in Japan.

While the St. Moritz trademark was a brandname used on Japanese-built guitars, the U.S. distributor has not yet been identified. Further updates will be included in future editions of the **Blue Book of Guitars**.

(Source: Michael Wright, Guitar Stories Volume One, pg. 47)

STACCATO

Instruments built in England during the mid to late 1980s.

These high quality guitars featured neck/body chassis of magnesium alloy, which was then seated into a wood or fiberglass "solid" body. While the luthier/designer is still unknown to us, any reader with information is invited to write to the **Blue Book of Guitars** for future updates.

STAGG

Instruments built in Japan during the mid 1970s.

The Stagg trademark is a brandname of a UK importer. Stagg instruments were entry level to low quality solid body guitars that featured designs based on popular American classics.

(Source: Tony Bacon and Paul Day, The Guru's Guitar Guide)

WM. C. STAHL

See LARSON BROTHERS (1900-1944).

William C. Stahl was a prominent music publisher and teacher of guitar, mandolin, and banjo in Milwaukee from the turn of the century to the early 1940s. He sold instruments to his students but also advertised heavily in the trade papers. The Larson brothers of Maurer & Co. in Chicago supplied most of his guitar and mandolin family instruments, the remainder being made by Washburn, Regal, or others.

The Larson-made Stahl guitars followed the designs of the Maurer and Prairie State brands also built by the Larsons. The difference in the Stahl labeled guitars is that maple is used for bracing rather than spruce. Some of the top-of-the-line Stahl guitars have the Prairie State system of steel rods which strengthen the body and add sustain as well as help to produce a somewhat different sound from other Larson brands. The Larson-made Stahl instruments have a Stahl logo burned or stamped on the inside center strip. I believe Stahl's paper label was also used on some Larsons, as well as the ones made by other builders. Stahl offered guitars and mandolins ranging in quality from student grade to the highest degree of presentation grade instruments.

For more information regarding other Larson-made brands, see MAURER, PRAIRIE STATE, EUPHONON, W.J. DYER, and THE LARSON BROTHERS.

For more detailed information regarding all the Larson brands and a Stahl catalog reprint, see The Larsons' Creations, Guitars and Mandolins, *by Robert Carl Hartman, Centerstream Publishing, P.O. Box 5450, Fullerton, CA 92635, phone/fax (714) 779-9390.*

15" Euphonon with a Stahl label
courtesy Robert Carl Hartman

STANDEL

Instruments produced in Newark, New Jersey during the late 1960s. Distributed by Standel of Temple City, California.

The Standel company was founded by Bob Crooks (an electronics engineer) in the early 1960s, and rose to some prominence in the mid 1960s for their solid-state amplifiers. In 1966 or 1967, Crooks had luthier Stan Koontz design a number of acoustic and electric guitars and basses for the Standel company. The instruments were built in Harptone's New Jersey facilities, and have the 'Standel' logo on the peghead. According to Koontz, only a few hundred of Standel instruments were produced.

In the early 1960s, Bob Crooks asked Semie Moseley (Mosrite) to design a Fender-style solid body guitar for Standel. Moseley quick answer was to flip over a Fender and trace the body outline. Moseley only built about 20 guitars for Crooks, but that original design became the foundation for the Mosrite **Ventures** model.

S

STAR

See GUYATONE.

Instruments produced in Japan during the early to mid 1960s.

While the Star trademark has been reported as a brandname used by an English importer, the trademark also appeared in the U.S. market distributed by Hoshino Gakki Ten (later Hoshino USA, distributor of Ibanez). No matter how you slice the bread, the loaf comes from the same oven. While the quality of these entry level solid body guitars was okay at best, they at least sported original designs. It is believed that Guyatone (Tokyo Sound Company) built the Star instruments.

Classic American guitar designs may have been an influence on the early Japanese models, but the "influence" was <u>incorporated</u> into original designs. The era of copying designs and details began in the early 1970s, but was not the basis for Japanese guitar production. As the entry level models began to get better in quality and meticulous attention to detail, then the American market began to take notice.

STARFIELD

Instruments produced in Japan and America. Distributed by Starfield America, located in North Hollywood, California.

These higher end guitars were a side project of the Hoshino company, although no brochures directly linked Starfield to Hoshino/Ibanez. Starfield is no longer offered in the U.S. market, but Hoshino continues to offer these quality instruments to other markets around the world.

ELECTRIC

Grading		100%	98% MINT	95% EXC+	90% EXC	80% VG+	70% VG	60% G

Altair Series

AMERICAN CLASSIC — offset double cutaway alder body, white pickguard, bolt on maple neck, 22 fret maple fingerboard with offset black dot inlay, standard Wilkinson vibrato, 3 per side locking Magnum tuners, chrome hardware, 3 stacked coil Seymour Duncan pickups, volume/tone control, 5 position switch. Available in Pearl White, Pewter, Popsicle, Sail Blue and Tangerine finishes. Disc. 1994.

			$700	$600	$500	$400	$360	$330	$300

Last Mfr.'s Sug. Retail was $1,000.

Ebony fingerboard with offset pearl dot inlay was optionally available.

American Custom — similar to American Classic, except has mahogany body, flame maple top, no pickguard, gold hardware, 2 humbucker Seymour Duncan pickups. Available in Tobacco Sunburst, Transparent Cherry, Transparent Green and Transparent Grey finishes. Disc. 1994.

			$910	$780	$650	$520	$470	$430	$390

Last Mfr.'s Sug. Retail was $1,300.

American Trad — similar to American Classic, except has mahogany body, black pickguard, fixed bridge, 2 humbucker Seymour Duncan pickups. Available in Transparent Cream, Transparent Green, Transparent Grey, Transparent Mustard and Transparent Red finishes. Disc. 1994.

			$700	$600	$500	$400	$360	$330	$300

Last Mfr.'s Sug. Retail was $1,000.

SJ CLASSIC — offset double cutaway alder body, white pickguard, bolt on maple neck, 22 fret rosewood fingerboard with offset pearl dot inlay, standard vibrato, 3 per side tuners, chrome hardware, 3 single coil pickups, volume/tone control, 5 position switch. Available in Black, Blue Mist, Cream, Destroyer Grey, Mint Green and Peach finishes. Disc. 1994.

			$280	$240	$200	$160	$145	$130	$120

Last Mfr.'s Sug. Retail was $400.

SJ Custom — similar to SJ Classic, except has arched swamp ash body, no pickguard, locking Magnum tuners. Available in Transparent Blue, Transparent Cherry, Transparent Cream, Transparent Green and Transparent Grey finishes. Disc. 1994.

			$420	$360	$300	$240	$215	$195	$180

Last Mfr.'s Sug. Retail was $600.

Grading	100%	98% MINT	95% EXC+	90% EXC	80% VG+	70% VG	60% G

SJ Trad — similar to SJ Classic, except has mahogany body, black pickguard, locking Magnum tuners, 2 single coil/1 humbucker pickups. Available in Transparent Cream, Transparent Green, Transparent Grey, Transparent Mustard and Transparent Red finishes. Disc. 1994.

| | $420 | $360 | $300 | $240 | $215 | $195 | $180 |

Last Mfr.'s Sug. Retail was $600.

Cabriolet Series

AMERICAN SPECIAL — single sharp cutaway asymmetrical mahogany body, carved flame maple top, bolt-on maple neck, 22 fret maple fingerboard with offset black dot inlay, fixed Wilkinson bridge, 3 per side tuners, chrome hardware, 2 humbucker Seymour Duncan pickups, volume/tone control, 5 position switch. Available in Tobacco Sunburst, Transparent Cherry, Transparent Green and Transparent Grey finishes. Disc. 1994.

| | $875 | $750 | $625 | $500 | $450 | $415 | $375 |

Last Mfr.'s Sug. Retail was $1,250.

Ebony fingerboard with offset pearl dot inlay was optionally available.

American Standard — similar to American Special, except has alder body, standard Wilkinson vibrato, locking Magnum tuners, 3 stacked coil Seymour Duncan pickups. Available in Pearl White, Pewter, Popsicle, Sail Blue and Tangerine finishes. Disc. 1994.

| | $665 | $570 | $475 | $380 | $345 | $315 | $285 |

Last Mfr.'s Sug. Retail was $950.

SJ LIMITED — single sharp cutaway asymmetrical semi hollow style, bound birdseye maple top, flower petal soundhole, mahogany back, bolt-on maple neck, 22 fret rosewood fingerboard with offset pearl dot inlay, fixed bridge, 3 per side tuners, chrome hardware, 2 humbucker pickups, volume/tone control, 5 position switch. Available in Tobacco Sunburst, Transparent Cherry, Transparent Green and Transparent Grey finishes. Disc. 1994.

| | $455 | $390 | $325 | $260 | $235 | $215 | $195 |

Last Mfr.'s Sug. Retail was $650.

STARFORCE

Instruments produced in Korea since 1988. Initially exported by Tropical Music of Miami, Florida prior to their purchase of the Dean company.

These medium quality solid body guitars feature designs based on the original Stratocaster, as well as the 'superstrat'. With the introduction of models such as the 8007 with its more original body design, and several bass guitar models, Starforce seeks to expand its market niche.

(Source: Tony Bacon, The Ultimate Guitar Book)

STARWAY

Instruments manufactured in Japan during the mid 1960s.

The Starway trademark was a brandname used by a UK importer. Starway guitars tend to be entry level solid bodies that sport original designs.

(Source: Tony Bacon and Paul Day, The Guru's Guitar Guide)

STATUS

Also STATUS GRAPHITE.

Formerly STRATA.

Instruments built in Essex, England from 1983 to current.

Designer/luthier Rob Green has been building stringed instruments that feature carbon graphite neck-through body designs since the early 1980s. According to author Tony Bacon, Status was the first British guitars that featured carbon graphite parts. These high quality solid body instruments have no headstock (save for 1990's Matrix model) and either two humbuckers or three single coil pickups. The Series II model features wood "wings" on either side of the neck as it passes through the body; while the model 2000 is all graphite in its composition, the model 4000 is a resin-composite body.

ELECTRIC BASS

Empathy Series

H-EM 4 — offset double cutaway laminate body, thru body graphite composite neck, 24 fret phenolic fingerboard, fixed bridge, 2 per side tuners, black hardware, 2 Status pickups, volume/treble/mid/bass/mix controls, mini switch, active electronics. Available in Natural finish. Available with Amazaque, Burl Madrone, Figured Maple, Rosewood and Walnut body woods. Current mfg.
This is a Custom Order instrument and prices will vary depending on specifications.
This model also available with fretless fingerboard.

H-EM 5 — similar to H-EM 4, except has 5 strings, 3/2 per side tuners.
This is a Custom Order instrument and prices will vary depending on specifications.

Grading	100%	98% MINT	95% EXC+	90% EXC	80% VG+	70% VG	60% G

H-EM 6 — similar to H-EM 4, except has 6 strings, 3 per side tuners.
This is a Custom Order instrument and prices will vary depending on specifications.

HL-EM 4 — offset double cutaway laminate body, thru body graphite composite headless neck, 24 fret phenolic fingerboard, tunomatic bridge/tunable tailpiece, 2 per side tuners, black hardware, 2 Status pickups, volume/treble/mid/bass/mix controls, mini switch, active electronics. Available in Natural finish. Available with Amazaque, Burl Madrone, Figured Maple, Rosewood and Walnut body woods. Current mfg.
This is a Custom Order Instrument and prices will vary depending on specifications.
This model also available with fretless fingerboard.

HL-EM 5 — similar to HL-EM 4, except has 5 strings.
This is a Custom Order instrument and prices will vary depending on specifications.

Energy Series

EN-4 — offset double cutaway ash body, bolt-on maple neck, 24 fret rosewood fingerboard, fixed bridge, 2 per side tuners, black hardware, 2 Status pickups, volume/tone/mix controls. Available in Amber, Black, Green, Natural and Red finishes. Current mfg.

Mfr.'s Sug. Retail	$1,395	$1,116	$837	$700	$560	$505	$460	$420

This model also available with walnut body.
This model also available with fretless fingerboard.

EN-5 — similar to EN-4, except has 5 strings, 3/2 per side tuners.

Mfr.'s Sug. Retail	$1,595	$1,196	$797	$795	$635	$575	$525	$475

Series I

S1B-4 — offset double cutaway laminate body, bolt-on maple neck, 24 fret rosewood fingerboard, fixed bridge, 2 per side tuners, black hardware, 2 Status pickups, volume/treble/bass/mix controls, mini switch. Available in Natural finish. Available with Amazaque, Burl Madrone, Maple, Rosewood and Walnut body woods. Current mfg.

Mfr.'s Sug. Retail	$2,195	$1,756	$1,317	$1,100	$880	$790	$725	$660

This model also available with fretless fingerboard.

S1B-5 — similar to S1B-4, except has 5 strings, 3/2 per side tuners.

Mfr.'s Sug. Retail	$2,395	$1,796	$1,197	$1,195	$955	$855	$785	$715

S1B-6 — similar to S1B-4, except has 6 strings, 3 per side tuners.

Mfr.'s Sug. Retail	$2,695	$2,156	$1,617	$1,350	$1,080	$970	$890	$810

S1T-4 — offset double cutaway laminate body, thru body maple neck, 24 fret rosewood fingerboard, fixed bridge, 2 per side tuners, black hardware, 2 Status pickups, volume/treble/mix controls, mini switch. Available in Natural finish. Available with Amazaque, Burl Madrone, Maple, Rosewood and Walnut body woods. Current mfg.

Mfr.'s Sug. Retail	$2,395	$1,796	$1,197	$1,195	$955	$855	$785	$715

This model also available with fretless fingerboard.

S1T-5 — similar to S1T-4, except has 5 strings, 3/2 per side tuners.

Mfr.'s Sug. Retail	$2,595	$1,946	$1,297	$1,295	$1,035	$930	$855	$780

S1T-6 — similar to S1T-4, except has 6 strings, 3 per side tuners.

Mfr.'s Sug. Retail	$2,895	$2,316	$1,737	$1,450	$1,160	$1,040	$955	$870

Series II

H-2-4 — offset double cutaway laminate body, thru body graphite composite neck, 24 fret phenolic fingerboard, fixed bridge, 2 per side tuners, black hardware, 2 Status pickups, volume/treble/mid/bass/mix controls, mini switch, active electronics. Available in Natural finish. Available with Amazaque, Burl Madrone, Maple, Rosewood and Walnut body woods. Current mfg.

Mfr.'s Sug. Retail	$3,495	$2,796	$2,097	$1,750	$1,400	$1,260	$1,150	$1,050

This model also available with fretless fingerboard.

H-2-5 — similar to H-2-4, except has 5 strings, 3/2 per side tuners.

Mfr.'s Sug. Retail	$3,695	$2,771	$1,847	$1,845	$1,475	$1,325	$1,215	$1,100

H-2-6 — similar to H-2-4, except has 6 strings, 3 per side tuners.

Mfr.'s Sug. Retail	$3,895	$3,116	$2,337	$1,950	$1,555	$1,395	$1,280	$1,165

HL-2-4 — offset double cutaway laminate body, thru body graphite composite headless neck, 24 fret phenolic fingerboard, tunomatic bridge/tunable tailpiece, 2 per side tuners, black hardware, 2 Status pickups, volume/treble/mid/bass/mix controls, mini switch, active electronics. Available in Natural finish. Available with Amazaque, Burl Madrone, Maple, Rosewood and Walnut body woods. Current mfg.

Mfr.'s Sug. Retail	$3,595	$2,696	$1,797	$1,795	$1,435	$1,290	$1,185	$1,075

This model also available with fretless fingerboard.

HL-2-5 — similar to HL-2-4, except has 5 strings.

Mfr.'s Sug. Retail	$3,795	$2,846	$1,897	$1,895	$1,515	$1,365	$1,250	$1,135

STEINBERGER

Instruments currently produced in Huntington Beach, California. Steinberger is a division of the Gibson Guitar Corporation, and is distributed by Gibson out of Nashville, Tennesee.

Instruments originally manufactured in New York, then New Jersey. Steinberger was purchased by the Gibson Guitar Corporation in 1990, after a preliminary agreement back in 1986.

Ned Steinberger, like Leo Fender and Nathan Daniels, was an instrument designer who didn't play any instruments. Steinberger revolutionized the bass guitar from the design point-of-view, and popularized the use of carbon graphite in musical instruments.

Ned Steinberger moved to New York in the 1970s after graduating from art school, and started working as a cabinet maker and furniture designer. He soon moved into a space at the Brooklyn Woodworkers Co-operative and met a guitar builder named Stuart Spector. In 1977 Steinberger began suggesting ideas that later became the NS-1 bass ("NS" for Steinberger's initals, and "1" for the number of pickups). The NS-2, with two pickups, was introduced later. Steinberger's involvement with the NS design led him to originally consider mounting the tuning machines on the body instead of at the peghead. He produced his first "headless" bass in early 1978, built entirely out of wood. Displeased with the end result due to the conventional "dead spots" on the neck (sympathetic vibrations in the long neck cancel out some fundamentals, also called the "wolf" tone in acoustic guitars), Steinberger took the instrument and covered it in fiberglass. His previous usage of the stiff reinforcing fibers in furniture making and boat building did not prepare him for the improved tone and sustain the covered bass then generated.

In 1978, Steinberger continued to experiment with graphite. Actually, the material is a molded epoxy resin that is strengthened by carbon and glass fibers. This formed material, also popular in boat hulls, is said to have twice the density and ten times the 'stiffness' of wood - and to be stronger **and** lighter than steel! Others who have utilized this material are Geoff Gould of Modulus Graphite, Status (UK), Ovation, and Moses Instruments. Steinberger publicly displayed the instrument at a 1979 U.S. Trade Show, hoping to sell the design to a guitar company. When no offers materialized, he formed the Steinberger Sound Corporation in 1980 with partners Bob Young (a plastics engineer) and Hap Kuffner and Stan Jay of Mandolin Brothers.

In 1981, the Steinberger bass was debuted at both the MusicMesse in Frankfurt and the NAMM show in Chicago. One of the hot design trends of the 1980s was the headless, reverse tuning instrument - although many were built of wood. Rather than fight "copycat" lawsuits, Steinberger found it easier to license the body and tuning design to other companies. In 1986 the Gibson Guitar corporation agreed to buy Steinberger Sound, and by 1990 had taken full control of the company. Gibson ran Steinberger Sound as a separate entity for a number of years; and Steinberger himself stayed on as a consultant who later developed the Transtrem and DB system detuner bridge.

"These instruments are the foundation of our culture."
—L. Acunto on Scott Chinery
TCG, Sept/Oct 1992

Grading	100%	98% MINT	95% EXC+	90% EXC	80% VG+	70% VG	60% G

ELECTRIC

K Series

This series was co-designed by Steve Klein.

GK 4S — radical ergonomic style basswood body, black pickguard, bolt-on Steinberger Blend neck, 24 fret phenolic fingerboard with white dot inlay, Steinberger vibrato, black hardware, 2 single coil/1 humbucker EMG pickups, volume/tone control, 5 position switch. Available in Black and White finishes. Mfd. 1990 to 1994.

$1,260	$1,080	$900	$720	$650	$595	$540

Last Mfr.'s Sug. Retail was $1,800.

GK 4S-A — similar to GK 4S, except has active electronics. Mfd. 1990 to 1994.

$1,435	$1,230	$1,025	$820	$745	$675	$615

Last Mfr.'s Sug. Retail was $2,050.

This model had Klein's autograph on body.

GK 4T — similar to GK 4S, except has TransTrem vibrato. Mfd. 1990 to 1994.

$1,575	$1,345	$1,125	$900	$810	$740	$675

Last Mfr.'s Sug. Retail was $2,250.

L Series

GL 2S — one piece body/neck construction, rectangular body, 24 fret phenolic fingerboard with white dot inlay, Steinberger vibrato, black hardware, 2 humbucker EMG pickups, volume/tone control, 3 position switch. Available in Black finish. Mfd. 1989 to date.

Mfr.'s Sug. Retail	$2,150	$1,720	$1,290	$1,075	$860	$775	$710	$645

Add $200 for White finish.
Add $300 for left handed version.
Add $500 for 12 string version, no vibrato available.

GL 2T — similar to GL 2S, except has TransTrem vibrato.

Mfr.'s Sug. Retail	$2,600	$2,080	$1,560	$1,300	$1,040	$935	$860	$780

Grading	100%	98% MINT	95% EXC+	90% EXC	80% VG+	70% VG	60% G

GL 4S — one piece body/neck construction, rectangular body, 24 fret phenolic fingerboard with white dot inlay, Steinberger vibrato, black hardware, 2 single coil/1 humbucker EMG pickups, volume/tone control, 5 position switch. Available in Black finish. Mfd. 1989 to date.

	100%	98%	95%	90%	80%	70%	60%
Mfr.'s Sug. Retail	$2,350	$1,880	$1,410	$1,175	$940	$845	$775	$705

GL 4T — similar to GL 4S, except has TransTrem vibrato.

Mfr.'s Sug. Retail	$2,800	$2,240	$1,680	$1,400	$1,120	$1,010	$925	$840

GL 4TA ELITE — similar to GL 4S, except has TransTrem vibrato, coil split switches, active electronics, gold engraving, signed certificate.

Mfr.'s Sug. Retail	$3,050	$2,440	$1,830	$1,525	$1,220	$1,095	$1,000	$910

GL 7TA ELITE — one piece body/neck construction, rectangular body, 24 fret phenolic fingerboard with white dot inlay, TransTrem vibrato, black hardware, humbucker/single coil/humbucker EMG pickups, volume/tone control, 5 position/coil split switches, active electronics, gold engraving, signed certificate. Available in Black finish. Mfd. 1989 to date.

Mfr.'s Sug. Retail	$3,200	$2,560	$1,920	$1,600	$1,280	$1,150	$1,055	$960

M Series

GM 2S — double cutaway maple body, bolt-on Steinberger Blend neck, 24 fret phenolic fingerboard with white dot inlay, Steinberger vibrato, black hardware, 2 humbucker EMG pickups, volume/tone control, 3 position switch. Available in Black, Candy Apple Red, Electric Blue and White finishes. Curr. mfr.

Mfr.'s Sug. Retail	$1,800	$1,440	$1,080	$900	$720	$650	$595	$540

Add $500 for 12 string version, no vibrato.

GM 2T — similar to GM 2S, except has TransTrem vibrato.

Mfr.'s Sug. Retail	$2,250	$1,800	$1,350	$1,125	$900	$810	$740	$675

GM 4S — double cutaway maple body, bolt-on Steinberger Blend neck, 24 fret phenolic fingerboard with white dot inlay, Steinberger vibrato, black hardware, 2 single coil/1 humbucker EMG pickups, volume/tone control, 5 position switch. Available in Black, Candy Apple Red, Electric Blue and White finishes. Mfd. 1988 to date.

Mfr.'s Sug. Retail	$1,900	$1,520	$1,140	$950	$760	$685	$625	$570

GM 4TA — similar to GM 4S, except has TransTrem vibrato, active electronics.

Mfr.'s Sug. Retail	$2,450	$1,960	$1,470	$1,225	$980	$875	$805	$735

GM 7TA — double cutaway maple body, bolt-on Steinberger Blend neck, 24 fret phenolic fingerboard with white dot inlay, Steinberger vibrato, black hardware, humbucker/single coil/humbucker EMG pickups, volume/tone control, 5 position/coil split switches, active electronics. Available in Black, Candy Apple Red, Electric Blue and White finishes. Curr. mfr.

Mfr.'s Sug. Retail	$2,600	$2,080	$1,560	$1,300	$1,040	$935	$860	$780

R Series

GR 4 — offset double cutaway maple body, bolt-on Steinberger Blend neck, 24 fret phenolic fingerboard with white dot inlay, R Trem vibrato, black hardware, 2 single coil rails/1 humbucker Seymour Duncan pickups, volume/tone control, 5 position switch. Available in Black, Candy Apple Red, Electric Blue and White finishes. Curr. mfr.

Mfr.'s Sug. Retail	$1,390	$1,112	$834	$695	$555	$495	$455	$415

S Series

S STANDARD — offset double cutaway poplar body with bottom bout cutaway, bolt-on Steinberger Blend neck, 24 fret phenolic fingerboard with white dot inlay, standard vibrato, reverse peghead, 6 on one side gearless tuners, humbucker/single coil/humbucker exposed pickups, volume/tone control, 5 position/coil split switches. Available in Black and White finishes. Curr. mfr.

Mfr.'s Sug. Retail	$2,250	$1,800	$1,350	$1,125	$900	$810	$740	$675

S Pro — similar to S Standard, except has mahogany body, bound maple top, TransTrem vibrato, active electronics. Available in Black, Cherry Sunburst, Fireburst and White finishes. Curr. mfr.

Mfr.'s Sug. Retail	$2,600	$2,080	$1,560	$1,300	$1,040	$935	$860	$780

GS 7ZA — offset double cutaway hardwood body, bolt-on Steinberger Blend neck, 24 fret phenolic fingerboard with white dot inlay, standard vibrato, reverse headstock, Knife Edge Knut, 6 on one side gearless tuners, black hardware, humbucker/single coil/humbucker pickups, volume/tone control, 5-way pickup selector/coil split switches, active electronics. Available in Black, Candy Apple Red, Electric Blue, Purple and White finishes. Disc. 1992.

			$1,715	$1,470	$1,225	$980	$875	$805	$735

Last Mfr.'s Sug. Retail was $2,450.

GS 7TA — similar to GS 7ZA, except has TransTrem vibrato.

			$1,960	$1,680	$1,400	$1,120	$1,010	$925	$840

Last Mfr.'s Sug. Retail was $2,800.

Grading	100%	98% MINT	95% EXC+	90% EXC	80% VG+	70% VG	60% G

ELECTRIC BASS

L Series

XL 2 — one piece molded body/neck construct, rectangle body, 24 fret phenolic fingerboard with white dot inlay, Steinberger bridge, black hardware, 2 humbucker EMG pickups, 2 volume/1 tone controls. Available in Black finish. Mfd. 1979 to date.

Mfr.'s Sug. Retail	$2,100	$1,680	$1,260	$1,050	$840	$755	$690	$630

Add $200 for White finish.
Add $300 for left handed version.
Add $100 for fretless fingerboard.

XL 2DB — similar to XL 2, except has Steinberger DB bridge.

Mfr.'s Sug. Retail	$2,400	$1,920	$1,440	$1,200	$960	$860	$790	$720

XL 2-5 — similar to XL 2, except has 5 strings.

Mfr.'s Sug. Retail	$2,400	$1,920	$1,440	$1,200	$960	$860	$790	$720

XL 2DBA ELITE — similar to XL 2, except has Steinberger DB bridge, active electronics, gold engraving, signed certificate.

Mfr.'s Sug. Retail	$2,900	$2,320	$1,740	$1,450	$1,160	$1,040	$955	$870

XL 2-5A ELITE — similar to XL 2, except has 5 strings, active electronics, gold engraving, signed certificate.

Mfr.'s Sug. Retail	$2,900	$2,320	$1,740	$1,450	$1,160	$1,040	$955	$870

XL 2TA ELITE — similar to XL 2, except has TransTrem vibrato, active electronics, gold engraving, signed certificate.

Mfr.'s Sug. Retail	$3,000	$2,400	$1,800	$1,500	$1,200	$1,080	$990	$900

M Series

XM 2 — double cutaway maple body, bolt-on Steinberger Blend neck, 24 fret phenolic fingerboard with white dot inlay, Steinberger bridge, black hardware, 2 humbucker EMG pickups, 2 volume/1 tone control. Available in Black, Candy Apple Red, Electric Blue and White finishes. Curr. mfr.

Mfr.'s Sug. Retail	$1,600	$1,280	$960	$800	$640	$575	$530	$480

Add $250 for active electronics.
Add $100 for fretless fingerboard.

XM 2DB — similar to XM 2, except has Steinberger DB bridge.

Mfr.'s Sug. Retail	$1,700	$1,360	$1,020	$850	$680	$610	$560	$510

XM 2-5 — similar to XM 2, except has 5 strings.

Mfr.'s Sug. Retail	$1,800	$1,440	$1,080	$900	$720	$650	$595	$540

XM 2T — similar to XM 2, except has TransTrem vibrato.

Mfr.'s Sug. Retail	$2,200	$1,760	$1,320	$1,100	$880	$790	$725	$660

Q Series

XQ 2 — offset double cutaway maple body, bolt-on Steinberger Blend neck, 24 fret phenolic fingerboard with white dot inlay, Steinberger bridge, black hardware, 2 humbucker EMG pickups, 2 volume/1 tone controls. Available in Black, Candy Apple Red, Electric Blue and White finishes. Curr. mfr.

Mfr.'s Sug. Retail	$1,700	$1,360	$1,020	$850	$680	$610	$560	$510

Add $100 for fretless fingerboard.

XQ 2DB — similar to XQ 2, except has Steinberger DB bridge.

Mfr.'s Sug. Retail	$1,800	$1,440	$1,080	$900	$720	$650	$595	$540

XQ 2-5 — similar to XQ 2, except has 5 strings.

Mfr.'s Sug. Retail	$2,050	$1,640	$1,230	$1,025	$820	$745	$675	$615

XQ 2T — similar to XQ 2, except has TransTrem vibrato.

Mfr.'s Sug. Retail	$2,300	$1,840	$1,380	$1,150	$920	$830	$760	$690

Double Neck

GM 4S/GM 4-12 — refer to model GM 4S, in 6 and 12 string versions, in this section for details.

Mfr.'s Sug. Retail	$4,100	$3,280	$2,460	$2,050	$1,640	$1,475	$1,350	$1,230

GM 4T/GM4-12 — refer to model GM 4T, in 6 and 12 string versions, in this section for details.

Mfr.'s Sug. Retail	$4,600	$3,680	$2,760	$2,300	$1,840	$1,655	$1,520	$1,380

GM 4S/XM 2 — refer to models GM 4S and XM 2, in 6 string guitar and 4 string bass models, in this section for details.

Mfr.'s Sug. Retail	$4,000	$3,200	$2,400	$2,000	$1,600	$1,440	$1,320	$1,200

GM 4T/XM 2 — refer to models GM 4T and XM 2, in 6 string guitar and 4 string bass models, in this section for details.

Mfr.'s Sug. Retail	$4,500	$3,600	$2,700	$2,250	$1,800	$1,620	$1,485	$1,350

Grading		100%	98% MINT	95% EXC+	90% EXC	80% VG+	70% VG	60% G

STELLA

See OSCAR SCHMIDT.

STEPHEN'S

Instruments built in Seattle, Washington. Distributed by Stephen's Stringed Instruments, located in Seattle, Washington.

Luthier/designer Stephen Davies created the "Extended Cutaway" (EC) that appears on his own instruments as well as licensed to certain Washburn models. Davies updated the 1950's four bolt rectangular neckplate with a curved 'half moon' five bolt that helps lock the neck into the neck pocket. This innovative design eliminates the squared block of wood normally found at the end of a neck pocket, allowing proper thumb/hand placement as notes are fretted higher up on the neck and also avoid the old style side-to-side neck motion.

ELECTRIC

In 1996, the electric guitar models were offered at three different price levels. The **Basic** level offers a straight ahead model with solid hardware and Seymour Duncan pickups. At the next level, the **Standard** offers vintage and custom colors, and hand rubbed finishes in the choice of nitrocellulose lacquers or polyurethane for durability. At the **Prime** level, the instruments are offered with exotic wood necks and bodies. Furthermore, each of the three levels can be upgraded from stock quality parts to an enhanced or custom option depending on the customer's order.

S Series

Some following models may be configured above the Basic level. Contact the company for further information.

S-2114 (SATIN MODEL S) — offset double cutaway alder body, bolt-on maple neck, 22 fret maple or rosewood fingerboard with dot inlay, through-body or stop tailpiece, 6 on a side tuners, nickel hardware, either 3 single coil or 2 humbucker Seymour Duncan pickups, 1 volume and 1 tone control, 3 or 5 position switch. Available in oil or satin finish. Mfg. 1995 to current.

Mfr.'s Sug. Retail (Basic) $1,345
Mfr.'s Sug. Retail (Standard) $1,645
Mfr.'s Sug. Retail (Prime) $1,925

S-2122 (CLASSIC DREAM) — offset double cutaway alder body, bolt-on maple neck, 22 fret maple or rosewood fingerboard with dot inlay, vintage-style tremolo, 6 on a side tuners, nickel hardware, 3 single coil Seymour Duncan pickups, 1 volume and 1 tone control, 5 position switch. Available in a cream finish. Mfg. 1995 to current.

Mfr.'s Sug. Retail (Basic) $1,345
Mfr.'s Sug. Retail (Standard) $1,645
Mfr.'s Sug. Retail (Prime) $1,925

S-2166 (BLACK AND WHITE) — offset double cutaway alder body, bolt-on maple neck, 22 fret maple fingerboard with dot inlay, Schaller locking tremolo, 6 on a side tuners, black hardware, 3 single coil Seymour Duncan pickups, 1 volume and 1 tone control, 5 position switch. Available in black finish. Mfg. 1995 to current.

Mfr.'s Sug. Retail (Basic) $1,345
Mfr.'s Sug. Retail (Standard) $1,645
Mfr.'s Sug. Retail (Prime) $1,925

S-22EC — offset double cutaway alder body, bolt-on maple neck, 22 fret ebony fingerboard with pearl dot inlay, double locking vibrato, 6 on one side tuners, black hardware, 2 single coil/1 humbucker Seymour Duncan pickups, volume/tone control, 5 position switch. Available in Raw finish. Mfg. 1992 to 1993.

Mfr.'s Sug. Retail $1,575 $1,260 $945 $850 $725
Add $20 for maple fingerboard.
Add $170 for figured maple top.
Subtract $20 for rosewood fingerboard.
Black, Cherry Sunburst, Natural and Tobacco Sunburst finishes are available at $70 - $100 additional cost.

T Series

Some following models may be configured above the Basic level. Contact the company for further information.

T-3111 (RAW MODEL T) — single cutaway ash or alder body, bolt-on maple neck, 22 fret maple or rosewood fingerboard with dot inlay, vinage-style bridge, 6 on a side tuners, nickel hardware, 2 single coil Seymour Duncan pickups, 1 volume and 1 tone control, 3 position switch. Available in tung oil or satin lacquer finish. Mfg. 1995 to current.

Mfr.'s Sug. Retail (Basic) $1,345
Mfr.'s Sug. Retail (Standard) $1,645
Mfr.'s Sug. Retail (Prime) $1,925

T-3315 (BLUES MACHINE) — single cutaway ash body with three internal sound chambers, bolt-on maple neck, 22 fret maple or rosewood fingerboard with dot inlay, vintage-style bridge, 6 on a side tuners, nickel hardware, 2 single coil Seymour Duncan pickups, 1 volume and 1 tone control, 3 position switch, optional eight-note f-hole. Mfg. 1995 to current.

Mfr.'s Sug. Retail (Basic) $1,345
Mfr.'s Sug. Retail (Standard) $1,645
Mfr.'s Sug. Retail (Prime) $1,925

T-9111 (HONEY BURST) — Single cutaway flamed maple top over alder body, bolt-on maple neck, 22 fret maple or rosewood fingerboard with dot inlay, vintage-style bridge, 6 on a side tuners, gold hardware, 2 single coil Seymour Duncan pickups, 1 volume and 1 tone control, 3 position switch. Mfg. 1995 to current.

Mfr.'s Sug. Retail (Basic) $1,345
Mfr.'s Sug. Retail (Standard) $1,645
Mfr.'s Sug. Retail (Prime) $1,925

T-22EC — single cutaway ash body, black pickguard, bolt-on maple neck, 22 fret rosewood fingerboard with pearl dot inlay, strings thru body bridge, 6 on one side tuners, chrome hardware, 2 single coil Seymour Duncan pickups, volume/tone control, 3 position switch. Available in Black and Natural finishes. Mfg. 1992 to 1993.

Mfr.'s Sug. Retail	$1,595	$1,276	$957	$925	$825

Add $20 for maple fingerboard.
Add $30 for ebony fingerboard.
Add $200 for figured maple top.
Add $30 for Butterscotch, Cherry Sunburst and Tobacco Sunburst finishes.

STERLING

Instruments currently built in Los Angeles, California.

Luthier Boris Gurfinkel has been offering custom built guitars for a number of years. For further information, contact luthier Boris Gurfinkel through the Index of Current Manufacturers located in the rear of this book.

STEVENS

Instruments currently built in Alpine, Texas.

Stevens Electrical Instruments currently offers three different high quality electric guitars. Models feature mahogany or korina bodies, carved maple tops, graphite reinforced necks, Tom Holmes or Stevens' humbucking pickups. The Korina Series model is a reproduction of the classic 1958/1959 Gibson era Flying V or Explorer. For further information, contact Stevens Electrical Instruments through the Index of Current Manufacturers located in the rear of this book.

STICK

Instruments currently produced in Woodland Hills, California.

Although not a guitar or a bass, the Stick instrument is a member of the guitar family. Designer/innovator Emmett Chapman designed the 10-string or 12-string (Grand Stick) "Touch" instrument to complement his two-handed guitar style. For further information, contact Stick Enterprises through the Index of Current Manufacturers located in the rear of this book.

GILBERT L. STILES

Instruments built in Independence, West Virginia and Hialeah, Florida between 1960 and early 1990s.

Luthier/designer Gilbert L. Stiles (1914-1994) had a backround of working with wood, be it millwork, logging or housebuilding. In 1960, he set his mind to building a solid body guitar, and continued building instruments for over the next thirty years. Stiles built solid body electrics, arch tops, flattop guitars, mandolins, and other stringed instruments. It has been estimated that Stiles had produced over 1,000 solid body electric guitars during his career. His arch top and mandolins are still held in high esteem, as well as his banjos.

Stiles guitars generally have "Stiles" or "G L Stiles" on the headstock, or "Lee Stiles" engraved on a plate at the neck/body joint of a bolt-on designed solid body. Dating a Stiles instrument is difficult, given that only the electric solids were given serial numbers consecutively, and would only indicate which **number** guitar it was, not when built.

(Source: Michael Wright, Guitar Stories Volume One, pgs. 19-23)

STOLL

Instruments built in Taunusstein, Germany. Distributed in the U.S. by Salwender International of Trabuco Canyon, California. Distribution in Germany by S K C Graphite of Aschaffenburg, Germany.

Stoll offers high quality steel string acoustic guitar and acoustic bass models. Some guitar models feature the McLoud acoustic pickup system. For further information, contact Salwender International through the Index of Current Manufacturers located in the rear of this book.

STONEHENGE II

Instruments built in Castelfidardo, Italy during the mid 1980s.

Luthier Alfredo Bugari designed his tubular metal-bodied guitar in a semi-solid, semi-hollowbody closed "V" design. This guitar was featured in author/researcher Tony Bacon's 1993 book, The Ultimate Guitar Book.

STRADIVARI

Instruments built in Italy during the late 1600s.

While this reknowned builder is revered for his violins, luthier Antonio Stradivari (1644-1737) did build a few guitars; a handful survive today. The overall design and appearance is reminenscent of the elegant yet simple violins that command such interest today.

(Source: Tony Bacon, The Ultimate Guitar Book)

STRAD-O-LIN

Instruments produced in New York during the 1950s and 1960s. Later models manufactured in Japan.

Strad-O-Lin was a brandname of the Peter Sorkin Music Company. A number of solid body guitars were built at the Multivox company of New York, and distribution of those and the later Japanese built models were handled by the Sorkin company of New York City, New York. Other guitars built and distributed (possibly as rebrands) were ROYCE, PREMIER, BELLTONE, and MARVEL.

STRATA

See STATUS GRAPHITE.

Instruments made in England during the 1980s.

STRATOSPHERE

Instruments built in Springfield, Missouri between 1954 and 1958.

Inventor/designer Russ Deaver and his brother Claude formed the Stratosphere company in 1954, and introduced what is estimated to be the first doubleneck guitar that featured both six- and twelve-string necks. By comparison, Gibson did not release their model until 1958, while other designer contemporaries (Mosrite, Bigsby) had built doublenecks with a smaller octave neck.

In 1955, Stratosphere offered three models: a single neck six string (retail $134.50) called the Standard, the single neck twelve string version ($139.50) and the doubleneck 6/12 ($300). It was estimated that less than 200 instruments were built.

(Source: Teisco Del Rey, Guitar Player magazine, January 1993)

STROMBERG

Instruments built in Boston, Massachusetts between 1906 and the mid-1950s.

The Stromberg business was started in Boston, Massachusetts in 1906 by Charles Stromberg (born in Sweden 1866) who immigrated to Boston April 1886. Charles Stromberg was a master luthier. He specialized his craft in banjo, drum, mandolin, and guitars after working for several years at Thompson and Odell (est. 1874), a Boston based firm that manufactured brass instruments, percussion instruments, fretted instruments, music publications, stringed instruments, and accessories. Thompson & Odell sold the manufacturing of the fretted instrument business to the Vega Company in Boston in 1905. Stromberg was one of the country's leading repairers of harps with his masterful ability in carving headstocks, replacing sound boards, and making new machine mechanisms. His reputation among Boston's early engravers, violin, drum, banjo, and piano makers was highly respected. Charles, in addition, repaired violins, cellos, and basses. Repairs were a steady source of income for the Stromberg business. His oldest son, Harry (born in Chelsea, Massachusetts 1890), worked with Charles from 1907 on and his youngest son, Elmer (born in Chelsea in 1895), apprenticed at the shop with older brother Harry from July 1910 until March 1917, when Elmer left the business to serve in World War I. He returned to the business in March 1919 after serving his country for two years in France during World War I.

At that time, the shop was located at 40 Sudbury Street and later moved to 19 Washington Street in early 1920s. Shop locations were in an area based in the heart of Boston's famous Scollay Square with burlesque and theater establishments. The Strombergs produced drums, mandolins, guitars, and banjos during the early 1920s from the 19 Washington Street location.

Throughout the 1920s (the Jazz Age of banjo music), the Strombergs produced custom tenor banjos. They competed with other banjo manufacturers, and were part of the eastern corridor in banjo manufacturing. The Stromberg reputation was very strong in Boston and the New England area. Banjoists who often desired a custom made instrument chose the Stromberg banjo as it was highly decorative and the sound would carry for the player in large dance halls. In October of 1926, Elmer

Stromberg applied for a patent for a series of tubes around the tone chamber of the banjo just under the head. This created a new sustaining sound and more volume and was called the "Cupperphone". The Stromberg Cupperphone banjo consisted of 41 hollow, perforated metal tubes $^{13}/_{16}$ inches high and $^{13}/_{16}$ inches in diameter fitted to the wooden rim to produce a louder and clearer tone. This was an option for the banjos, and this Cupperphone feature made the Stromberg banjo one of the loudest and heaviest built in the country. The two models offered at this time were the **Deluxe**, and **Marimba** models. The patent was granted in June of 1928.

Harry Stromberg left the business in 1927. By the late 1920s, banjo players were beginning to switch from banjo to guitar to create deeper sounding rhythm sections in orchestras. As the style of music changed, the guitar needed to be heard better. While musicians' needs focused towards the guitar, the banjo's popularity declined and Elmer began producing archtop guitars for Boston musicians.

In June of 1927, the shop relocated to 40 Hanover Street where they began producing archtop guitars. By the early 1930s, banjo players began ordering guitars. As early as 1927, Elmer began taking guitar orders, and offered several types based on a 16 inch body, called the **G** series. The models **G1**, **G2**, and **Deluxe** models were offered featuring a small headstock, with laminated body and segmented f-holes.

During the American Depression of the 1930s, Elmer wanted as many musicians as possible to enjoy his instruments and kept the cost of the instrument affordable. After the Depression, the guitars began to change in looks and construction. By the mid 1930s (1935-37), musicians requested fancier models with larger bodies that could produce more volume. The Stromberg guitar went through at least two major headstock dimension sizes and designs and body specifications between 1936 and 1940. Elmer's response to players' needs (and the competition) was to widen the body on the **G** series guitars to $17^3/_8$ inches, and add two more models: the 19 inch **Master 400** model was introduced around 1937/38, and the **Master 300** was introduced in the same time period. The larger body dimensions of the Master 300 and 400 made them the largest guitars offered from any maker.

Elmer's top-of-the-line model was the Master 400. This guitar would set the Stromberg guitar apart from other rhythm acoustic archtop guitars, especially during the swing era: Elmer added decorative pearl inlay to the headstock, additional binding, and a fine graduated top carving that would carry its sound volume across the brass sections of a large orchestra. By 1940, a new, longer headstock style and the single diagonal brace was added to Master series guitars, switching from a traditional parallel bracing to a single brace for yet more carrying power. The graduation of the tops also changed during this period. By 1940 to '41, a single tension rod adjustment was added to the Master series (and was later added to the Deluxe and G series). By 1941, the G1 and G3 series body dimensions increased to $17^3/_8$ inches, and featured a new tailpiece design that was "Y" shaped in design. The f-holes became non-segmented and followed the graceful design of the Deluxe model.

Elmer Stromberg built all of the guitars and the majority of banjos. His name never appeared on an instrument, with the exception of a Deluxe Cutaway (serial number 634, a short scale made for guitarist Hank Garland). Every label read **Charles A. Stromberg and Son** with a lifetime guarantee to the original purchaser. Elmer is described by many players who knew him as a gentle man with a heart of gold. He wanted to please his family of guitarists with the best instrument he could make.

> *(Stromberg history and model specifications courtesy Jim Speros. Speros is currently compiling a Stromberg text, portions of which were supplied to this edition of the* Blue Book of Guitars. *Interested parties can contact Speros through Stromberg Research, P.O. Box 51, Lincoln, Massachusetts 01773.)*

The apparent rarity of the individual guitars (it is estimated that only 640 guitars were produced), like D'Angelicos, combined with condition and demand, makes it difficult to set a selling price in the vintage market. The **Blue Book of Guitars** recommends at least two or three professional appraisals or estimates before buying/selling/trading any Stromberg guitar (or any other Stromberg instrument, especially the banjos).

STROMBERG GUITAR IDENTIFICATION

Early **G** series (G1, G2, G3, Deluxe) from 1927-1930 has a 16 inch body and a label reading "40 Hanover Street, Tel Bowdoin 1228R-1728-M" (Stromberg's current business card). Narrow banjo-style headstock, Stromberg logo, Victorian-style, hand-painted with floral accents. Fingerboard (G1, G2, G3) mother-of-pearl inlays, diamond shape, oval at 14th fret. The Deluxe model featured solid pearl blocks position markers on an ebony fingerboard. The headstock was Victorian-style, engraved, hand-painted. Pressed back Indian Rosewood or maple, carved spruce top, segmented f-holes. Trapeze-style tailpiece brass with chrome plating on models G1, G2, and G3 (gold plated on the Deluxe model). All shared rosewood bridge with adjustments for bridge height, top location thumb adjustments. Bracing: two parallel braces, 3 ladder type braces.

Mid- to late 1930s (1935-37), the **G-100**, **G1**, **G3**, **Deluxe**, **Ultra Deluxe**, $17^3/_8$ inch body. Blond finish guitars began appearing during the late 1930s. Construction featured a pressed back, carved spruce top, Grover tailpiece (chrome plated). Blue shipping labels inside guitar body read "Charles A. Stromberg & Son" in the late 1930s was typewritten or handwritten. The headstock shape changed to a larger bout and from the early 1930s had a laminated, embossed, plastic engraved Stromberg logo characterizing the new style. Bracing: dual parallel bracing top. The Master 400 had a "stubby" style headstock, parallel braced top, inlaid mother-of-pearl or Victorian laminated style.

1940s Style Guitars

Master 400: body size 19 inches wide x $21^3/_4$ inch length. Top: carved and graduated spruce $^7/_8$ inch thickness. F-holes bound white/black, neck was a 5-piece rock maple with Ivoroid binding (black and white) on fingerboard. The bridge was adjustable compensating rosewood and pickguard was imitation tortoise shell that was inlaid with white and black Ivoroid borders. Available in natural or sunburst finishes. Ebony fingerboard, position markers were three segmented pearl blocks. Bracing: single diagonal brace from upper bout to lower bout (began about 1940). Tailpiece: 5 Cutout "Y" shaped with Stromberg engraving (gold plated).

"GM: How did you end up with the Clapton guitar? TR: Eric gave it to George Harrison. Harrison gave it to Jackie Lomax. Jackie sold it to me...He probably thinks he can still get it back for $500."

—*Greg Martin on Todd Rundgren*

TCG, Sept/Oct 1992

Master 300: body size 19 inches wide x 21¾ inch length. Top: carved and graduated spruce ⅞ inch thickness. F-holes bound white. Neck: rock maple with ebony fingerboard, position markers solid pearl block. Ivoroid binding on fingerboard (black and white). Bridge: adjustable compensating rosewood. The pickguard was imitation tortoise shell inlaid with white and black Ivoroid borders. Available in natural or sunburst finishes. Bracing: single diagonal brace from upper bout to lower bout (began about 1940). Tailpiece: 5 Cutout "Y" shaped with Stromberg engraving (gold plated).

Deluxe: body size 17⅜ inches wide x 20¾ inch length. Top: graduated and carved spruce ⅞ inch thickness. F-holes Ivoroid bound (white/black). Bridge: adjustable compensating rosewood. The pickguard was imitation tortoise shell inlaid with white and black Ivoroid borders. Available in natural or sunburst finishes. The ebony fingerboard had position markers solid pearl blocks. Bracing: single diagonal brace from upper bout to lower bout (1940-41). Tailpiece: 5 Cutout "Y" shaped (gold plated).

G-3: body size 17⅜ inches wide x 20¾ inch length. Top: graduated and carved spruce ⅞ inch thickness. F-holes not bound. Bridge: adjustable compensating rosewood. The pickguard was imitation tortoise shell inlaid with white and black Ivoroid borders. Available in natural or sunburst finishes. The rosewood fingerboard had position markers of two segmented pearl blocks. Bracing: single diagonal brace from upper bout to lower bout (mid- to late 1940s). Tailpiece: 3 Cutout "Y" shaped (gold plated).

G-1: body size 17⅜ inches wide 20¾ inch length. Top: graduated and carved spruce ⅞ inch thickness. F-hole not bound. Bridge: adjustable compensating rosewood. The pickguard was imitation tortoise shell inlaid with white and black Ivoroid borders. Available in natural or sunburst finishes. The rosewood fingerboard had position markers of diamond shaped pearl with four indented circle cutouts in inner corners. Bracing: single diagonal brace from upper bout to lower bout (mid to late '40s). Tailpiece: 3 Cutout "Y" shaped (chrome plated).

CUTAWAYS

Introduced in 1949.

Master 400: body size 18⅜ inches wide x 21¾ inch length. Top: carved and graduated spruce ⅞ inch thickness. F-holes bound white/black. Neck: 5 piece rock maple. Ivoroid binding on fingerboard (black and white). Bridge: adjustable compensating rosewood. The pickguard was imitation tortoise shell inlaid with white and black Ivoroid borders. Available in natural or sunburst finishes. Ebony fingerboard had position markers of three segmented pearl blocks or solid pearl blocks. Bracing: single diagonal brace from upper bout to lower bout. Tailpiece: 5 Cutout "Y" shaped with the new Stromberg Logo engraved and gold plated.

Deluxe Cutaway: body size 17⅜ inches wide x 20¾ inch length. Top: graduated and carved spruce ⅞ inch thickness. F-holes Ivoroid bound white/black. Bridge: adjustable compensating rosewood. The pickguard was imitation tortoise shell inlaid with white and black Ivoroid borders. Available in natural or sunburst finishes. Position markers were solid pearl blocks. Bracing: single diagonal brace from upper bout to lower bout. Tailpiece: 5 Cutout "Y" shaped with Stromberg engraving (gold plated).

G-5 Cutaway (introduced 1950): body size 17⅜ inches wide x 20¾ inch length. Top: graduated and carved spruce ⅞ thickness. F-holes Ivoroid bound white. Bridge: adjustable compensating rosewood. Pickguard was imitation tortoise shell inlaid with white and black Ivoroid borders. Available in natural or sunburst finishes. Ebony fingerboard had position markers of solid pearl blocks. Bracing: single diagonal brace from upper bout to lower bout. Tailpiece: 3 Cutout "Y" shaped with Stromberg engraving (gold plated).

G-3 Cutaway: body size 17⅜ inches wide x 20¾ inch length. Top: graduated and carved spruce ⅞ thickness. F-hole unbound. Bridge: adjustable compensating rosewood. The pickguard was imitation tortoise shell inlaid with white and black Ivoroid borders. Available in natural or sunburst finishes. Rosewood fingerboard had position markers of split pearl blocks. Bracing: single diagonal brace from upper bout to lower bout. Tailpiece: 3 Cutout "Y" shaped (gold plated).

STUART HANDCRAFTED GUITARS

Instruments currently built in Cincinnati, Ohio.

Company offers a number of custom built guitars. For further information, contact Stuart Handcrafted Guitars through the Index of Current Manufacturers located in the rear of this book.

STUDIO KING

See chapter on House Brands.

While this trademark has been identified as a "House Brand", the distributor is currently unknown at this time. As information is uncovered, future listings in the **Blue Book of Guitars** will be updated.

(Source: Willie G. Moseley, Stellas & Stratocasters)

STUMP PREACHER GUITARS

Instruments currently produced in Woodinville, Washington.

John Devitry and staff at Stump Preacher Guitars offer an innovative full scale "travel guitar" that is only 27" long!. The **Stump Preacher** (suggested list $980) model is constructed of carbon graphite, and features a neck core of polyurethane (which can be adjusted for density, therefore producing different tones) under the graphite layer. The guitar is equipped with an EMG dual mode pickup, wood fingerboard, Schaller tuners, and a headless neck/reverse tuning system that is highly innovative! For further information, please contact Stump Preacher guitars through the Index of Current Manufacturers located in the back of this book.

SUKOP

Instruments currently built in Clifton, New Jersey.

Luthier Stephen Sukop offers a high quality, custom, handmade bass guitar. Each Sukop bass is available in a 4-, 5-, or 6-string configuration (fretted or unfretted), features a seven-piece laminated neck, Bartolini pickups, Gotoh tuners, and a Kahler bridge. For further information, contact luthier Stephen Sukop through the Index of Current Manufacturers located in the back of this book.

SUMBRO

Instruments built in Japan during the mid to late 1970s.

The Sumbro trademark is a brandname of UK importer Summerfield Brothers. These entry level to medium quality solid body guitars feature some original designs, as well as designs based on classic American favorites.

(Source: Tony Bacon and Paul Day, The Guru's Guitar Guide)

SUNN

Instruments produced in India from 1989 to 1991. Distributed by the Fender Musical Instruments Corporation (FMIC) of Scottsdale, Arizona.

The Sunn trademark, similar to the same used on the line of P.A. and amplifier equipment, was applied to a line of entry level strat replicas built in India. Oddly enough, the strat-styled guitar carries a "Mustang" designation in the headstock.

(Source: Tony Bacon, The Ultimate Guitar Book)

SUPER TWENTY

Instruments manufactured in Japan during the mid 1960s.

The Super Twenty trademark is a brandname used by an UK importer. This entry level solid body guitar featured an original design and three single coil pickups.

Supro Dual Tone
courtesy Michelle Oleck

SUPERIOR

See chapter on House Brands.

While this trademark has been identified as a "House Brand", the distributor is currently unknown. As information is uncovered, future editions of the **Blue Book of Guitars** will be updated.

(Source: Willie G. Moseley, Stellas & Stratocasters)

SUPERTONE

See chapter on House Brands.

This trademark has been identified as a "House Brand" of Sears, Roebuck and Company. This trademark was used prior to the usage of the "Silvertone" trademark, and was originally applied to radio sets in catalogs.

(Source: Michael Wright, Guitar Stories Volume One)

SUPRO

See VALCO.

See also the chapter on House Brands.

These Valco-built models were constructed of molded fiberglass bodies and bolt-on wood/metal necks. While Supro pickups may sound somewhat funky to the modern ear, there is no denying the '50s cool appeal. Play 'em or display 'em. Either way, you can't go wrong.

Supros are generally priced between $250 and $650, depending on color and amount of knobs. Decide how you will use them, and pay accordingly.

SURFRITE

Instruments built in Bakersfield, California in 1967.

The "Surfrite" prototypes were created by Al Hartel for Mosrite in early 1967, and were built outside the plant. There are five identified prototypes: 2 basses, 2 guitars, and 1 twelve string. The rounded body design also features 2 outside arms that run parallel to the neck and join back behind/part of the headstock. Too labor intensive for production? Well, if they're called prototypes, there's a real good chance that they didn't go into full production.

(Source: Teisco Del Rey, Guitar Player magazine, December 1991)

SURINE

Instruments currently built in Denver, Colorado.

Luthier Scott M. Surine offers several high quality, custom bass guitars. Each Surine bass is available in a 4-, 5-, or 6-string configuration, and features a three-piece laminated neck-thru design, Bartolini pickups, Gotoh tuners, and a Wilkinson bridge. For further information, contact luthier Scott M. Surine through the Index of Current Manufacturers located in the back of this book.

SUZUKI

Instruments built in Korea. Distributed in the U.S. market by Suzuki Guitars of San Diego, California.

Suzuki, while noted for their quality pianos, also offers a range of acoustic and electric guitars designed for the beginning student to intermediate player. For further information, contact Suzuki Guitars through the Index of Current Manufacturers located in the back of this book.

SYLVAN

Instruments built in England during the late 1980s.

The Duke model was a high quality solid body guitar that had a through-body neck as part of its original design.

(Source: Tony Bacon and Paul Day, The Guru's Guitar Guide)

SYNSONICS

Instruments built in Korea since 1989. Distributed in the U.S. market by the Synsonics company of Ridgeland, South Carolina.

These entry level solid body guitars feature a built in amplifier and three inch speaker that can be defeated by an on/off switch. The overall design is Les Paul-derived with a thinner width body and a bolt-on neck, with the speaker mounted in the body area behind the stop tailpiece.

Synsonics also builds a mini solid body guitar dubbed the Junior Pro.

T

20TH CENTURY

Instruments were produced by REGAL (original company of Wulschner & Son) in the late 1890s through the mid 1900s.

Indianapolis retailer/wholesaler Emil Wulschner introduced the Regal line in the 1880s, and in 1896 opened a factory to build guitars and mandolins under the following three trademarks: REGAL, 20th CENTURY, and UNIVERSITY. In the early 1900s the 20th Century trademark was a "sub-brand" distributed by the Fred Gretsch Manufacturing Company. By 1920 the Fred Gretsch Mfg. Co. had settled into its new ten story building in Brooklyn, New York, and was offering music dealers a very large line of instruments that included banjos, mandolins, guitars, violins, drums, and other band instruments. Gretsch used both the 20th Century and Rex trademarks prior to introduction of the GRETSCH trademark in 1933.

21ST CENTURY GUITARS

Instruments built in Neodesha, Kansas during the late 1960s. Distributed by Holman-Woodell, Inc. of Neodesha, Kansas.

The Holman-Woodell company built guitars during the late 1960s in Neodesha, Kansas (around 60 miles due south from Topeka). While they were producing guitars for Wurlitzer, they also built their own Holman brand as well as instruments trademarked Alray. The Holman-Woodell company is also famous for building the La Baye "2 x 4" guitars.

The La Baye "2 X 4" guitar model was introduced at the 1967 Chicago NAMM show by inventor Dan Helland. Unfortunately, the radical "bodyless" design proved too far thinking for the guitar market, and the La Baye trademark officially ended that year. However, the Holman-Woodell company built a number of "2 x 4" guitars out of spare parts, and marketed them first under the Holman trademark. When new owners took over the production facilities, other instruments were released under the "21st Century" trademark. It has been estimated that perhaps up to 100 faux "2 x 4"s were built, but reception of the later instruments was equal to the indifference generated by the first attempt.

(Source: Michael Wright, Guitar Stories Volume One, pg. 164)

TACOMA GUITAR COMPANY

Instruments produced in Tacoma, Washington since 1995. Distributed by Young Chang Akki of Korea.

Young Chang Akki is one of the largest piano and guitar builders worldwide. In addition to their guitar plant in Korea (which has been producing Squier guitars since 1987), they recently opened a huge piano production facility in China.

Several years ago, Young Chang opened a sawmill in Tacoma, Washington to supply wood for its piano factories. As the market for high quality acoustic guitars expanded, the company wisely opened a guitar production facility near the sawmill to take advantage of the available quality wood. Tacoma guitars are U.S. built, and feature models from top designers with numerous years of experience.

The Tacoma Guitar company is currently concentrating on a model line and models to offer. For further information, contact the Tacoma Guitar Company via the Index of Current Manufacturers located in the rear of this book.

TAKAMINE

Instruments are manufactured in Japan, and distributed by the Kaman Music Corporation of Bloomfield, Connecticut.

The Takamine brand was originally set up to be Martin's Sigma series with the help of Coast distributors. However, when the Kaman Music Corporation (Ovation) bought Coast, Martin had to contract Sigma production elsewhere. Ovation encouraged Takamine to enter the market under their own trademark, and have since distributed the guitars in the U.S. market.

(Source: Michael Wright, Guitar Stories Volume One)

Takamine EA-360 acoustic "V" courtesy Thoroughbred Music

ACOUSTIC

Grading			100%	98% MINT	95% EXC+	90% EXC	80% VG+	70% VG	60% G

10-G — dreadnought style, cedar top, round soundhole, bound body, multi stripe purfling/rosette, mahogany back/sides/neck, 14/20 fret rosewood fingerboard, rosewood bridge with white black dot pins, 3 per side gold tuners. Available in Natural finish. New 1994.

Mfr.'s Sug. Retail	$450		$360	$270	$225	$180	$160	$150	$135

Grading	100% MINT	98% EXC+	95% EXC	90% VG+	80% VG	70% VG	60% G

10-EG — similar to 10-G, except has crystal bridge pickups, 4 band EQ. Available in Natural finish. New 1994.

Mfr.'s Sug. Retail	$650	$520	$390	$325	$260	$235	$215	$195

10C-EG — similar to 10-G, except has single round cutaway, crystal bridge pickups, 4 band EQ. Available in Natural finish. New 1994.

Mfr.'s Sug. Retail	$700	$560	$420	$350	$280	$250	$230	$210

15-EG — dreadnought style, cedar top, round soundhole, bound body, 3 stripe purfling, wood marquetry rosette, rosewood back/sides, mahogany neck, 14/20 fret rosewood fingerboard, rosewood bridge with white black dot pins, 3 per side gold tuners, crystal bridge pickups, 4 band EQ. Available in Natural finish. New 1994.

Mfr.'s Sug. Retail	$700	$560	$420	$350	$280	$250	$230	$210

15C-EG — similar to 15-EG, except has single round cutaway. Available in Natural finish. New 1994.

Mfr.'s Sug. Retail	$750	$600	$450	$375	$300	$270	$245	$225

124-G — classic style, spruce top, round soundhole, bound body, wood marquetry rosette, nato back/sides, mahogany neck, 12/19 fret rosewood fingerboard, tied rosewood bridge, 3 per side chrome tuners with plastic buttons. Available in Natural finish. New 1994.

Mfr.'s Sug. Retail	$340	$272	$204	$170	$135	$125	$115	$105

Add $40 for solid spruce top (124S-G).

124-EG — similar to 124-G, except has crystal bridge pickups, 4 band EQ. Available in Natural finish. New 1994.

Mfr.'s Sug. Retail	$480	$384	$288	$240	$190	$170	$155	$145

124C-EG — similar to 124-G, except has single round cutaway, crystal bridge pickups, 4 band EQ. Available in Natural finish. New 1994.

Mfr.'s Sug. Retail	$530	$424	$318	$265	$210	$190	$175	$160

126-G — classic style, spruce top, round soundhole, bound body, wood marquetry rosette, rosewood back/sides, mahogany neck, 12/19 fret rosewood fingerboard, tied rosewood bridge, 3 per side gold tuners with plastic buttons. Available in Natural finish. New 1994.

Mfr.'s Sug. Retail	$450	$360	$270	$225	$180	$160	$150	$135

300 Series

307-F — folk style, spruce top, round soundhole, black pickguard, bound body, 3 stripe rosette, mahogany back/sides/neck, 14/20 fret rosewood fingerboard with white dot inlay, rosewood bridge with white pins, 3 per side chrome tuners. Available in Natural finish. Curr. mfr.

Mfr.'s Sug. Retail	$590	$472	$354	$295	$235	$210	$195	$180

330-G — dreadnought style, spruce top, round soundhole, black pickguard, 3 stripe bound body and rosette, mahogany back/sides/neck, 14/20 fret rosewood fingerboard with white dot inlay, rosewood bridge with white pins, 3 per side chrome tuners. Available in Natural finish. Curr. mfr.

Mfr.'s Sug. Retail	$350	$280	$210	$175	$140	$125	$115	$105

In 1993, Red Stain finish was introduced and discontinued.

330C-EG — similar to 330-G, except has single round cutaway, crystal bridge pickups, 4 band EQ. Available in Natural finish. New 1994.

Mfr.'s Sug. Retail	$550	$440	$330	$275	$220	$200	$180	$165

332-G — dreadnought style, solid spruce top, round soundhole, black pickguard, 3 stripe bound body and rosette, mahogany back/sides/neck, 14/20 fret rosewood fingerboard with white dot inlay, rosewood bridge with white pins, 3 per side chrome tuners. Available in Natural finish. Curr. mfr.

Mfr.'s Sug. Retail	$500	$375	$250	$200	$160	$145	$130	$120

332C-EG — similar to 332-G, except has single round cutaway, crystal bridge pickups, 4 band EQ. Available in Natural finish. New 1994.

Mfr.'s Sug. Retail	$600	$480	$360	$300	$240	$215	$195	$180

334-G — dreadnought style, spruce top, round soundhole, black pickguard, wood bound body and rosette, rosewood back/sides, mahogany neck, 14/20 fret bound rosewood fingerboard with pearl dot inlay, rosewood bridge with white black dot pins, 3 per side gold tuners. Available in Natural finish. Disc. 1994.

		$350	$300	$250	$200	$180	$165	$150

Last Mfr.'s Sug. Retail was $500.

In 1993, Black finish was introduced.

334C-EG — similar to 334-G, except has single round cutaway, crystal bridge pickups, 4 band EQ. Available in Natural finish. New 1994.

Mfr.'s Sug. Retail	$700	$560	$420	$350	$280	$250	$230	$210

334RC/334BC-EG — similar to 334-G, except has single round cutaway, crystal bridge pickups, 4 band EQ. Available in Black Stain and Red stain finishes. New 1994.

Mfr.'s Sug. Retail	$750	$600	$450	$375	$300	$270	$245	$225

335-G — dreadnought style, spruce top, round soundhole, black pickguard, 3 stripe bound body and rosette, mahogany back/sides/neck, 14/20 fret rosewood fingerboard with white dot inlay, rosewood bridge with white pins, 6 per side chrome tuners. Available in Natural finish. Curr. mfr.

Mfr.'s Sug. Retail	$500	$400	$300	$250	$200	$180	$165	$150

Grading	100%	98% MINT	95% EXC+	90% EXC	80% VG+	70% VG	60% G

340-F — dreadnought style, spruce top, round soundhole, black pickguard, 3 stripe bound body and rosette, mahogany back/sides/neck, 14/20 fret rosewood fingerboard with pearl dot inlay, rosewood bridge with black white dot pins, 3 per side chrome tuners. Available in Natural finish. Curr. mfr.

Mfr.'s Sug. Retail	$650	$520	$390	$325	$260	$235	$215	$195

340S-F — similar to 340-F, except has solid spruce top.

Mfr.'s Sug. Retail	$780	$624	$468	$390	$315	$280	$260	$235

340-EF — similar to 340-F, except has crystal bridge pickups, 3 band EQ.

Mfr.'s Sug. Retail	$850	$680	$510	$425	$340	$305	$280	$255

340S-EF — similar to 340-F, except has solid spruce top, crystal bridge pickups, 3 band EQ.

Mfr.'s Sug. Retail	$1,080	$864	$648	$540	$430	$390	$355	$325

341-F — dreadnought style, spruce top, round soundhole, black pickguard, 5 stripe bound body and rosette, campnosparma back/sides, mahogany neck, 14/20 fret bound rosewood fingerboard with pearl dot inlay, rosewood bridge with white black dot pins, bound peghead, 3 per side chrome tuners. Available in Black finish. Curr. mfr.

Mfr.'s Sug. Retail	$780	$624	$468	$390	$315	$280	$260	$235

341-EF — similar to 341-F, except has crystal bridge pickups, 3 band EQ.

Mfr.'s Sug. Retail	$980	$735	$490	$485	$390	$355	$325	$295

341C-EF — similar to 341-F, except has single round cutaway, crystal bridge pickups, 3 band EQ.

Mfr.'s Sug. Retail	$1,070	$856	$642	$535	$430	$390	$355	$325

349-F — dreadnought style, mahogany top, round soundhole, black pickguard, 3 stripe bound body/rosette, mahogany back/sides/neck, 14/20 fret rosewood fingerboard with pearl dot inlay, rosewood bridge with black white dot pins, 3 per side chrome tuners. Available in Natural finish. Curr. mfr.

Mfr.'s Sug. Retail	$660	$528	$396	$330	$265	$240	$220	$200

349-EF — similar to 349-F, except has crystal bridge pickup, 3 band EQ.

Mfr.'s Sug. Retail	$860	$688	$516	$430	$345	$310	$285	$260

381C-EF — rounded cutaway 12 string dreadnought style, spruce top, round soundhole, black pickguard, 5 stripe bound body/rosette, campnosparma back/sides, mahogany neck, 14/20 fret rosewood fingerboard with pearl diamond/dot inlay, rosewood bridge with white black dot pins, 6 per side chrome tuners, crystal bridge pickups, 3 band EQ. Available in Black finish. Curr. mfr.

Mfr.'s Sug. Retail	$1,190	$952	$714	$595	$475	$430	$390	$360

385-F — dreadnought style, spruce top, round soundhole, black pickguard, 5 stripe bound body/rosette, mahogany back/sides/neck, 14/20 fret rosewood fingerboard with pearl dot inlay, rosewood bridge with black white dot pins, 6 per side chrome tuners. Available in Natural finish. Curr. mfr.

Mfr.'s Sug. Retail	$750	$600	$450	$375	$300	$270	$245	$225

385-EF — similar to 385-F, except has crystal bridge pickup, 3 band EQ.

Mfr.'s Sug. Retail	$950	$760	$570	$475	$380	$345	$315	$285

360 Series

360S-F — dreadnought style, solid spruce top, round soundhole, black pickguard, 5 stripe bound body/rosette, rosewood back/sides, 14/20 fret bound rosewood fingerboard with pearl dot inlay, rosewood bridge with white black dot pins, 3 per side chrome tuners. Available in Natural finish. Curr. mfr.

Mfr.'s Sug. Retail	$940	$752	$564	$470	$375	$340	$310	$280

Add $130 for left handed version of this model (360SLH-F).

360C-EF — similar to 360S-F, except has single round cutaway, crystal bridge pickups, 3 band EQ.

Mfr.'s Sug. Retail	$1,120	$896	$672	$560	$450	$405	$370	$335

360S-FP — similar to 360S-F, except has crystal bridge pickups, parametric EQ.

Mfr.'s Sug. Retail	$1,240	$992	$744	$620	$495	$445	$410	$370

Add $90 for round cutaway (360SC-FP).

361EC-EF — single round cutaway dreadnought style, spruce top, round soundhole, black pickguard, 5 stripe bound body, abalone rosette, campnosparma back/sides, mahogany neck, 14/20 fret bound rosewood fingerboard with pearl dot inlay, rosewood bridge with white black dot pins, 3 per side chrome tuners, crystal bridge pickups, 3 band EQ. Available in Ebony Stain finish. Curr. mfr.

Mfr.'s Sug. Retail	$1,050	$840	$630	$525	$420	$380	$345	$315

361SECA-FP — similar to 361EC-EF, except has solid spruce top, abalone logo peghead inlay, parametric EQ.

Mfr.'s Sug. Retail	$1,400	$1,120	$840	$700	$560	$505	$460	$420

400S-F — dreadnought style, solid spruce top, round soundhole, black pickguard, 5 stripe bound body and rosette, rosewood back/sides, mahogany neck, 14/20 fret bound rosewood fingerboard with pearl dot inlay, rosewood bridge with white black dot pins, 6 per side gold tuners. Available in Natural finish. Curr. mfr.

Mfr.'s Sug. Retail	$1,030	$772	$515	$510	$410	$370	$340	$310

"A million great licks may be remembered, but a handful of bad ones are never forgotten."

—Capt. L. Weiss Tulayt,

Sept. 1996

Grading	100%	98% MINT	95% EXC+	90% EXC	80% VG+	70% VG	60% G

Takamine acoustic
courtesy Robin Creasman

400S-FP — similar to 400S-F, except has crystal bridge pickup, parametric EQ.

Mfr.'s Sug. Retail	$1,330	$997	$665	$660	$530	$475	$435	$395

Classic Series

128-C — classic style, spruce top, round soundhole, 5 stripe bound body, wooden rosette, rosewood back/sides, mahogany neck, 12/19 fret rosewood fingerboard, rosewood bridge, 3 per side gold tuners with nylon buttons. Available in Natural finish. Curr. mfr.

Mfr.'s Sug. Retail	$550	$440	$330	$275	$220	$200	$180	$165

128-EC — similar to 128-C, except has mahogany back/sides, crystal bridge pickups, 3 band EQ.

Mfr.'s Sug. Retail	$750	$600	$450	$375	$300	$270	$245	$225

132S-C — classic style, solid cedar top, round soundhole, 5 stripe bound body, wooden rosette, rosewood back/sides, mahogany neck, 12/19 fret rosewood fingerboard, rosewood bridge, 3 per side gold tuners with nylon buttons. Available in Natural finish. Curr. mfr.

Mfr.'s Sug. Retail	$750	$600	$450	$375	$300	$270	$245	$225

132C-EC — similar to 132S-C, except has single round cutaway, spruce top, crystal bridge pickups, 3 band EQ.

Mfr.'s Sug. Retail	$900	$720	$540	$450	$360	$325	$300	$275

132SC-CP — similar to 132S-C, except single round cutaway, crystal bridge pickup, parametric EQ.

Mfr.'s Sug. Retail	$1,150	$920	$690	$575	$460	$415	$380	$345

Hirade Series

This series was designed by Mass Hirade, Takamine founder.

H-5 — classic style, solid cedar top, round soundhole, 5 stripe wood bound body, wooden rosette, rosewood back/sides, mahogany neck, 12/19 fret ebony fingerboard, ebony bridge, 3 per side gold tuners with pearl buttons. Available in Natural finish. Curr. mfr.

Mfr.'s Sug. Retail	$1,500	$1,125	$750	$650	$520	$470	$430	$390

H-8 — similar to H-5, except has solid spruce top.

Mfr.'s Sug. Retail	$2,000	$1,500	$1,000	$900	$720	$650	$595	$540

H-15 — classic style, solid spruce top, round soundhole, wood bound body, wooden rosette, rosewood back/sides, mahogany neck, 12/19 fret ebony fingerboard, ebony bridge with rosette matching inlay, 3 per side gold tuners with pearl buttons. Available in Natural finish. Curr. mfr.

Mfr.'s Sug. Retail	$3,680	$2,760	$1,840	$1,755	$1,350	$1,215	$1,115	$1,015

HP-7 — classic style, solid cedar top, round soundhole, 5 stripe wood bound body, wooden rosette, rosewood back/sides, mahogany neck, 12/19 fret ebony fingerboard, ebony bridge, 3 per side gold tuners with pearl buttons, crystal bridge pickups, parametric EQ. Available in Natural finish. Curr. mfr.

Mfr.'s Sug. Retail	$2,150	$1,612	$1,075	$975	$780	$700	$645	$580

HP-7C — similar to HP-7, except has single round cutaway. New 1994.

Mfr.'s Sug. Retail	$2,150	$1,720	$1,290	$1,075	$860	$775	$710	$645

HP-90 — rounded cutaway classic style, solid spruce top, oval soundhole, wood bound body, wooden rosette, rosewood back/sides, mahogany neck, 20 fret extended ebony fingerboard, ebony bridge, 3 per side gold tuners with pearl buttons, crystal bridge pickups, parametric EQ. Available in Natural finish. Curr. mfr.

Mfr.'s Sug. Retail	$2,600	$1,950	$1,300	$1,215	$920	$830	$760	$690

Natural Series

10-N — dreadnought style, solid cedar top, round soundhole, 3 stripe bound body, 5 stripe rosette, mahogany back/sides/neck, 14/20 fret rosewood fingerboard, rosewood strings thru bridge, 3 per side gold tuners with amber buttons. Available in Natural finish. Curr. mfr.

Mfr.'s Sug. Retail	$820	$656	$492	$410	$325	$295	$270	$245

10-EN — similar to 10-N, except has crystal bridge pickup, 3 band EQ.

Mfr.'s Sug. Retail	$1,000	$800	$600	$500	$400	$360	$330	$300

Add $90 for single round cutaway (10C-EN).

15-N — dreadnought style, solid cedar top, round soundhole, 3 stripe bound body, 5 stripe rosette, rosewood back/sides, mahogany neck, 14/20 rosewood fingerboard, rosewood strings thru bridge, 3 per side gold tuners with amber buttons. Available in Natural finish. Curr. mfr.

Mfr.'s Sug. Retail	$930	$744	$558	$465	$370	$335	$305	$280

15C-NP — similar to 15-N, except has single round cutaway, crystal bridge pickups, parametric EQ.

Mfr.'s Sug. Retail	$1,330	$997	$665	$660	$530	$475	$435	$395

Grading	100%	98% MINT	95% EXC+	90% EXC	80% VG+	70% VG	60% G

18C-NP — single round cutaway dreadnought style, solid spruce top, round soundhole, abalone bound body/rosette, rosewood back/sides, mahogany neck, 14/20 ebony fingerboard, ebony strings thru bridge, abalone logo peghead inlay, 3 per side gold tuners with amber buttons, crystal bridge pickup, parametric EQ. Available in Natural finish. Curr. mfr.

Mfr.'s Sug. Retail	$1,690	$1,352	$1,014	$845	$675	$605	$555	$505

20-N — jumbo style, solid cedar top, round soundhole, 3 stripe bound body, 5 stripe rosette, mahogany back/sides/neck, 14/20 fret rosewood fingerboard, rosewood strings thru bridge, 3 per side gold tuners with amber buttons. Available in Natural finish. Curr. mfr.

Mfr.'s Sug. Retail	$940	$752	$564	$470	$375	$340	$310	$280

20-EN — similar to 20-N, except has crystal bridge pickup, 3 band EQ.

Mfr.'s Sug. Retail	$1,100	$880	$660	$550	$440	$395	$365	$330

25C-NP — single round cutaway jumbo style, solid cedar top, round soundhole, 3 stripe bound body, 5 stripe rosette, mahogany back/sides/neck, 14/20 fret rosewood fingerboard, rosewood strings thru bridge, 3 per side gold tuners, crystal bridge pickups, parametric EQ. Available in Natural finish. New 1994.

Mfr.'s Sug. Retail	$1,380	$1,104	$828	$690	$550	$495	$455	$415

40-N — dreadnought style, solid red cedar top, round soundhole, 3 stripe bound body, 5 stripe rosette, mahogany back/sides/neck, 14/20 fret rosewood fingerboard, rosewood strings thru bridge, 3 per side gold tuners. Available in Natural finish. New 1994.

Mfr.'s Sug. Retail	$820	$656	$492	$410	$325	$295	$270	$245

40C-EN — similar to 40-N, except has single round cutaway, crystal bridge pickups, 3 band EQ. New 1994.

Mfr.'s Sug. Retail	$1,070	$856	$642	$535	$430	$390	$355	$325

45C-NP — single round cutaway dreadnought style, red cedar top, round soundhole, 3 stripe bound body, 5 stripe rosette, rosewood back/sides, mahogany neck, 14/20 fret rosewood fingerboard, rosewood strings thru bridge, 3 per side gold tuners, crystal bridge pickups, parametric EQ. Available in Natural finish. New 1994.

Mfr.'s Sug. Retail	$1,340	$1,072	$804	$670	$535	$480	$440	$400

48C-NP — single round cutaway dreadnought style, solid spruce top, round soundhole, 3 stripe bound body, 5 stripe rosette, rosewood back/sides, mahogany neck, 14/20 fret rosewood fingerboard, rosewood strings thru bridge, 3 per side gold tuners, crystal bridge pickups, parametric EQ. Available in Natural finish. New 1994.

Mfr.'s Sug. Retail	$1,700	$1,360	$1,020	$850	$680	$610	$560	$510

65C-NP — rounded cutaway artist style, solid cedar top, round soundhole, 3 stripe bound body, wooden rosette, rosewood back/sides, mahogany neck, 20 fret ebony fingerboard, classic style ebony bridge, classic style peghead, 3 per side gold tuners with amber buttons, crystal bridge pickups, parametric EQ. Available in Natural finish. Curr. mfr.

Mfr.'s Sug. Retail	$1,290	$1,032	$774	$645	$515	$465	$425	$385

Santa Fe Series

40-SF — folk style, solid cedar top, round soundhole, 3 stripe bound body/rosette, mahogany back/sides/neck, 20 fret ebony fingerboard, turquoise eagle inlay at 12th fret, ebony strings thru bridge, rosewood veneered peghead, 3 per side gold tuners with amber buttons. Available in Natural finish. Mfd. 1993 to date.

Mfr.'s Sug. Retail	$850	$680	$510	$425	$340	$305	$280	$255

40C-ESF — similar to 40-SF, except has single round cutaway, crystal bridge pickup, 4 band EQ.

Mfr.'s Sug. Retail	$1,200	$960	$720	$600	$480	$430	$395	$360

45C-PSF — single round cutaway folk style, solid cedar top, round soundhole, 3 stripe bound body/rosette, rosewood back/sides, mahogany neck, 20 fret ebony fingerboard with turquoise dot inlay, turquoise eagle inlay at 12th fret, ebony strings thru bridge, rosewood veneered peghead, 3 per side gold tuners with amber buttons, crystal bridge pickup, parametric EQ. Available in Natural finish. Mfd. 1993 to date.

Mfr.'s Sug. Retail	$1,500	$1,200	$900	$750	$600	$540	$495	$450

48C-PSF — single round cutaway folk style, solid spruce top, round soundhole, multi-bound body, wood inlay rosette, rosewood back/sides, mahogany neck, 21 fret ebony fingerboard with abalone eagle inlay, strings thru ebony bridge, rosewood peghead veneer with abalone dot/logo inlay, 3 per side gold tuners with amber buttons, piezo bridge pickups, parametric EQ, active electronics. Available in Natural finish. New 1993.

Mfr.'s Sug. Retail	$1,800	$1,440	$1,080	$900	$720	$650	$595	$540

93-ESF — single round cutaway folk style, solid cedar top, round soundhole, multi bound, wood inlay rosette, silky oak back/sides, mahogany neck, 21 fret ebony fingerboard with turquoise eagle inlay, ebony bridge with white black dot pins, silky oak peghead veneer with turquoise dot/abalone logo inlay, 3 per side gold tuners with amber buttons, piezo bridge pickups, parametric EQ, active electronics. Available in Natural finish. Mfd. 1993 only.

			$1,050	$900	$750	$600	$540	$495	$450

Last Mfr.'s Sug. Retail was $1,500.

Grading	100%	98% MINT	95% EXC+	90% EXC	80% VG+	70% VG	60% G

94-PSF — single round cutaway folk style, solid cedar top, round soundhole, multi bound, wood inlay rosette, koa back/sides, mahogany neck, 20 fret rosewood fingerboard with abalone eagle inlay, rosewood strings thru bridge, koa peghead veneer with abalone logo inlay, 3 per side gold tuners with brown pearl buttons, piezo bridge pickups, parametric EQ. Available in Natural finish. Mfd. 1994 only.

	100%	98%	95%	90%	80%	70%	60%
	$1,295	$1,110	$925	$740	$670	$610	$555

Last Mfr.'s Sug. Retail was $1,850.

Specials Series

26-ST — folk style, solid spruce top, round soundhole, abalone bound body and rosette, campnosparma back/sides, mahogany neck, 14/20 fret bound rosewood fingerboard with pearl diamond inlay, rosewood bridge with white black dot pins, bound peghead with abalone logo inlay, 3 per side gold tuners, crystal bridge pickups, parametric EQ. Available in White finish. Curr. mfr.

	100%	98%	95%	90%	80%	70%	60%
Mfr.'s Sug. Retail	$1,580	$1,264	$948	$790	$630	$570	$520	$475

212-ST — similar to 26-ST, except has 12 strings, 6 per side tuners.

	100%	98%	95%	90%	80%	70%	60%
Mfr.'s Sug. Retail	$1,680	$1,344	$1,008	$840	$675	$605	$555	$505

291M-EF — folk style, figured maple top, round soundhole, bound body, abalone purfling/rosette, figured maple back/sides/neck, 14/20 fret bound rosewood fingerboard with pearl diamond inlay, rosewood bridge with white black dot pins, bound peghead with abalone logo inlay, 3 per side gold tuners, crystal bridge pickups, parametric EQ. Available in Brown Sunburst and Ebony Stain finishes. New 1994.

	100%	98%	95%	90%	80%	70%	60%
Mfr.'s Sug. Retail	$1,000	$800	$600	$500	$400	$360	$330	$300

325SRC-EF — single round cutaway dreadnought style, solid spruce top, round soundhole, black pickguard, 5 stripe bound body/rosette, bubinga back/sides, mahogany neck, 14/20 fret bound rosewood fingerboard with pearl dot inlay, rosewood bridge with white black dot pins, 3 per side chrome tuners, crystal bridge pickups, 3 band EQ. Available in Clear Red finish. Curr. mfr.

	100%	98%	95%	90%	80%	70%	60%
Mfr.'s Sug. Retail	$1,150	$920	$690	$575	$460	$415	$380	$345

325SRCA-FP — similar to 325SRC-EF, except has abalone rosette, parametric EQ.

	100%	98%	95%	90%	80%	70%	60%
Mfr.'s Sug. Retail	$1,400	$1,120	$840	$700	$560	$505	$460	$420

350M-F — dreadnought style, spruce top, round soundhole, black pickguard, 5 stripe bound body/rosette, maple back/sides/neck, 14/20 fret rosewood fingerboard with pearl dot inlay, rosewood bridge with white black dot pins, 3 per side chrome tuners. Available in Natural finish. Curr. mfr.

	100%	98%	95%	90%	80%	70%	60%
Mfr.'s Sug. Retail	$780	$624	$468	$390	$315	$280	$260	$235

350MC-EF — similar to 350M-F, except has rounded cutaway, crystal bridge pickups, 3 band EQ.

	100%	98%	95%	90%	80%	70%	60%
Mfr.'s Sug. Retail	$1,100	$880	$660	$550	$440	$395	$365	$330

592ME-FP — dreadnought style, arched flame maple top, round soundhole, 5 stripe bound body and rosette, flame maple back/sides/neck, 14/20 bound rosewood fingerboard with pearl dot inlay, rosewood bridge with white black pins, bound peghead with pearl logo inlay, 3 per side chrome tuners, crystal bridge pickups, parametric EQ. Available in Ebony Stain finish. Curr. mfr.

	100%	98%	95%	90%	80%	70%	60%
Mfr.'s Sug. Retail	$1,480	$1,184	$888	$740	$595	$530	$485	$445

TAKEHARU

Instruments produced in Japan during the early 1980s.

These good quality solid body and semi-hollowbody guitars featured original designs. Anyone with further information is invited to write to the **Blue Book of Guitars** for updates in future editions.

(Source: Tony Bacon and Paul Day, The Guru's Guitar Book)

S. TALKOVICH

Instruments built in Woodstock, Georgia.

Luthier S. Talkovich is currently building guitars in the mold of the classic American designs, but with contemporary parts, hardware, and design features that are the 1990s - not the 1950s. Talkovich features one piece Southern Swamp Ash bodies, Rockwood necks, Lindy Fralin or Rio Grande pickups, Sperzel tuners, and Wilkinson hardware. Rockwood, a process used by Greg Curbow (Curbow String Instruments), is a hardwood composite that is bound by a thermo-setting phenolic resin. This process also eliminates any problems inherent in regular wood necks such as weather flucuations, humidity, and warping. Talkovich modernized the bolt-on neck process by designing a shifted four bolt pattern, as well as a sculpted neck/heel joint.

ELECTRIC

Talkovich currently offers two models of his guitars. The **TSS 3** features a one piece Swamp ash body, black Rockwood neck with either a black or Ash Rockwood 21 fret fingerboard, dot inlays, Sperzel tuners, three Lindy Fralin or Rio Grande single coils, Wilkinson bridge, full shielded control cavity, and Graph-tech nut. Finishes include Natural, or a $75 option of a Black top, Tinted, or 'Burst. Retail lists at $1,775, and includes a deluxe padded gig bag.

The **TSFT 3** is similar to the TSS 3, except that it features a "Fancy Top" of bookmatched American Hard Rock Maple or American Black Walnut. Retail with the deluxe padded gig bag is $1,975.

Confucius asks, "Is a refin. in a factory rare color worth more than one with a standard refinish?"

TAMA

Instruments produced in Japan from 1975 through 1979 by Ibanez. Distributed in the U.S. by the Chesbro Music Company of Idaho Falls, Idaho.

The Tama trademark is better known on the quality drum sets produced by Hoshino. Neverless, the Tama trademark was used on 2 series of acoustic guitars offered during the mid to late 1970s. The first series introduced was entry level to good quality D-45 shaped acoustics that featured a laminated top. However, the quality level jumped on the second series. The second series featured a solid top, mahogany neck, and East Indian and Brazilian rosewoods, as well as a light oil finish.

One way to determine a solid top acoustic from a ply or laminated top is to check the cross section of the wood on the edge of the soundhole. If the wood seems continuous, it's probably a solid top. If you can see layers, or if the inside of the edge is painted (check the wood inside the top - if it is different in appearance from the outside it's probably laminated), then the top is plywood. No, it's not the sheets that you build houses with! A ply wood top is several layers of wood glued and pressed together. However, a solid top guitar will resonate better (because it's one piece of wood) and the tone will get better as the wood ages.

(Tama Guitars overview courtesy Michael R. Stanger, Stringed Instrument Division of Missoula, Montana)

TANARA

Instruments built in Korea. Distributed by the Chesbro Music Company of Idaho Falls, Idaho.

Tanara offers a range of acoustic and electric guitars designed towards the entry level to beginner guitarist. For further information, please contact the Chesboro Music Company through the Index of Current Manufacturers located in the rear of this book.

TAYLOR

Instruments built in El Cajon, California. Previous production was based in Lemon Grove, California from 1974 through 1987. Distributed by Taylor Guitars of El Cajon, California.

Founding partners Bob Taylor, Steve Schemmer, and Kurt Listug were all working at the American Dream guitar repair shop in Lemon Grove, California, in the early 1970s. In 1974, the trio bought the shop and converted it into a guitar building factory. The company went through early "growing pains" throughout the late 1970s, but slowly and surely the guitars began catching on. In 1983, Listug and Taylor bought out Schemmer's share of the company, and re-incorporated. Fueled by sales of models such as the **Grand Concert** in 1984, the company expanded into new facilities in Santee, California (near El Cajon) three years later. Taylor and Listug continue to experiment with guitar construction and models, and recently debuted the **Baby Taylor** model ($398) which is a 3/4 size guitar with a solid top and laminated back and sides.

Tama 3557-12
courtesy Dan Holden

Each Taylor model number also describes the particular guitar in relationship to the overall product line. The first of three numbers denotes the series (Taylor series comprise a specific combination of woods, bindings, inlays, etc). The second number indicates whether it is a six string ("1"), or a 12 string ("5"). The exception to this rule is the 400 series, which include models 420 and 422. Finally, the third number indicates the body size: Dreadnought ("0"), Grand Concert ("2"), and Jumbo ("5"). The Grand Auditorium size models carry a prefix of "GA". Any upper case letters that follow the three digit designation may indicate a cutaway ("C") or a left handed model ("L").

ACOUSTIC

Grading		100%	98% MINT	95% EXC+	90% EXC	80% VG+	70% VG	60% G

400 Series

The 400 series are mahogany and maple guitars with a satin finish, scalloped bracing on the 6-string models, and an optional Acoustic Matrix pickup system.

410 — dreadnought style, solid spruce top, round soundhole, tortoise shell pickguard, 3 stripe bound body/rosette, solid mahogany back/sides/neck, 14/20 fret rosewood fingerboard with pearl dot inlay, rosewood strings thru bridge, rosewood veneer on peghead, 3 per side chrome Grover tuners. Available in Natural finish. Curr. mfr.

Mfr.'s Sug. Retail	$1,098	$878	$658	$550	$440	$395	$365	$330

In 1994, pearl peghead logo inlay was introduced.

410-E — similar to 410, except has acoustic pickup system, slide control preamp. Curr. mfr.

Mfr.'s Sug. Retail	$1,400	$1,050	$700	$650	$520	$470	$430	$390

412 — similar to 410, except has grand concert style body.

Mfr.'s Sug. Retail	$1,098	$878	$658	$550	$440	$395	$365	$330

420 — similar to 410, except has maple back and sides.

Mfr.'s Sug. Retail	$1,298	$1,038	$778	$650	$520	$470	$430	$390

422 — similar to 412, except has maple back and sides.

Mfr.'s Sug. Retail	$1,298	$1,038	$778	$650	$520	$470	$430	$390

Taylor acoustic
courtesy Dave Rodgers

Grading	100%	98% MINT	95% EXC+	90% EXC	80% VG+	70% VG	60% G

450 — similar to 410, except has 12-string configuration.
Mfr.'s Sug. Retail $1,398 $1,048 $699 $650 $520 $470 $435 $400

500 Series

The 500 series are mahogany guitars with abalone soundhole rosettes and pearl fretboard diamond inlays.

510 — dreadnought style, solid spruce top, round soundhole, tortoise shell pickguard, 3 stripe bound body/rosette, solid mahogany back/sides/neck, 14/20 fret ebony fingerboard with pearl dot inlay, ebony bridge with black pins, rosewood veneer on peghead, 3 per side gold tuners. Available in Natural finish. Curr. mfr.
Mfr.'s Sug. Retail $1,598 $1,278 $958 $800 $640 $575 $530 $480

In 1994, pearl peghead logo inlay, abalone rosette, abalone slotted diamond fingerboard inlay, black abalone dot bridge pins replaced original items.

512 — similar to 510, except has grand concert style body.
Mfr.'s Sug. Retail $1,698 $1,358 $1,018 $850 $680 $610 $560 $510

514-C — similar to 510, except has solid cedar top, and a single cutaway.
Mfr.'s Sug. Retail $2,298 $1,723 $1,149 $1,050 $820 $770 $630 $590

555 — similar to 510, except has 12 strings, jumbo style body, solid Sitka spruce top, 6 per side gold tuners.
Mfr.'s Sug. Retail $1,998 $1,598 $1,198 $1,000 $800 $720 $660 $600

600 Series

The 600 series features maple construction, a gloss finish, Amber-stained back and sides, scalloped bracing on the 6-strings, an abalone soundhole rosette, and pear "Leaf Pattern" inlays.

610 — dreadnought style, solid spruce top, round soundhole, tortoise shell pickguard, 3 stripe bound body/rosette, solid maple back/sides, mahogany neck, 14/20 fret bound rosewood fingerboard with pearl dot inlay, rosewood bridge with black pins, rosewood veneer on peghead, 3 per side gold tuners. Available in Amber Stain finish. Curr. mfr.
Mfr.'s Sug. Retail $1,998 $1,498 $999 $950 $760 $685 $625 $570

In 1994, the abalone rosette, bound ebony fingerboard with pearl leaf inlay, ebony bridge with black abalone dot bridge pins, ebony peghead veneer with pearl logo inlay replaced original items.

612 — grand concert style, solid spruce top, round soundhole, tortoise shell pickguard, 3 stripe bound body/rosette, solid maple back/sides, mahogany neck, 14/20 fret bound rosewood fingerboard with pearl dot inlay, rosewood bridge with black pins, rosewood veneer on peghead, 3 per side gold tuners. Available in Natural finish. Disc. 1992.
 $845 $815 $780 $735 $665 $605 $550
Last Mfr.'s Sug. Retail was $1,840.

612-C — similar to 612, except has single sharp cutaway. Mfd. 1993 to date.
Mfr.'s Sug. Retail $2,298 $1,723 $1,149 $1,040 $880 $790 $725 $660

In 1994, single round cutaway, abalone rosette, bound ebony fingerboard with pearl leaf inlay, ebony bridge with black abalone dot bridge pins, ebony peghead veneer with pearl logo inlay replaced original items.

614-C — similar to 612-C, except has Grand Auditorium style, and a single cutaway
Mfr.'s Sug. Retail $2,398 $1,798 $1,199 $1,100 $1,080 $970 $830 $790

615 — jumbo style, solid spruce top, round soundhole, tortoise pickguard, 3 stripe bound body/rosette, solid maple back/sides, mahogany neck, 14/20 fret bound rosewood fingerboard with pearl dot inlay, rosewood bridge with black pins, rosewood veneer on peghead, 3 per side gold tuners. Available in Natural finish. Curr. mfr.
Mfr.'s Sug. Retail $2,198 $1,648 $1,099 $1,050 $840 $755 $690 $630

In 1994, abalone rosette, bound ebony fingerboard with pearl leaf inlay, ebony bridge with black abalone dot bridge pins, ebony peghead veneer with pearl logo inlay replaced original items.

655 — similar to 615, except has 12-string configuration.
Mfr.'s Sug. Retail $2,398 $1,798 $1,199 $1,150 $1,040 $970 $630 $570

700 Series

The 700 series features rosewood construction, gloss finish, abalone soundhole rosette and neck dot inlays.

710 — dreadnought style, solid spruce top, round soundhole, tortoise shell pickguard, 3 stripe bound body/rosette, rosewood back/sides, mahogany neck, 14/20 fret ebony fingerboard with pearl dot inlay, ebony bridge with black pins, rosewood veneer on peghead, 3 per side gold tuners. Available in Natural finish. Curr. mfr.
Mfr.'s Sug. Retail $1,798 $1,438 $1,078 $900 $720 $650 $595 $540

In 1994, abalone rosette, abalone dot fingerboard inlay, black abalone dot bridge pins, pearl logo peghead inlay replaced original items.

712 — grand concert style, solid spruce top, round soundhole, tortoise shell pickguard, 3 stripe bound body and rosette, rosewood back/sides, mahogany neck, 14/20 fret ebony fingerboard with pearl dot inlay, ebony bridge with black pins, rosewood veneer on peghead, 3 per side gold tuners. Available in Natural finish. Curr. mfr.
Mfr.'s Sug. Retail $1,898 $1,423 $949 $830 $760 $685 $625 $570

In 1994, abalone rosette, abalone dot fingerboard inlay, black abalone dot bridge pins, pearl logo peghead inlay replaced original items.

Grading	100%	98% MINT	95% EXC+	90% EXC	80% VG+	70% VG	60% G

714 — similar to 712, except has Grand Auditorium design.
  Mfr.'s Sug. Retail $1,998 $1,498 $999 $950 $840 $770 $630 $570

750 — similar to 710, except has 12-string configuration.
  Mfr.'s Sug. Retail $1,998 $1,598 $1,198 $1,050 $940 $870 $730 $670

800 Series

The 800 series are deluxe rosewood guitars, with gloss finish, scalloped bracing on 6-strings, abalone soundhole rosette, and pearl "Progressive Diamond" fretboard inlay.

810 — dreadnought style, solid spruce top, round soundhole, tortoise shell pickguard, 3 stripe bound body, abalone rosette, rosewood back/sides, mahogany neck, 14/20 fret bound rosewood fingerboard with pearl snowflake inlay, rosewood bridge with black abalone dot pins, rosewood veneer on bound peghead with pearl logo inlay, 3 per side gold tuners. Available in Natural finish. Curr. mfr.
  Mfr.'s Sug. Retail $1,198 $1,114 $1,078 $990 $750 $675 $615 $560

  In 1994, pearl progressive diamond fingerboard inlay replaced original item.

812 — grand concert style, solid spruce top, round soundhole, tortoise shell pickguard, 3 stripe bound body, abalone rosette, rosewood back/sides, mahogany neck, 14/20 fret bound rosewood fingerboard with pearl snowflake inlay, rosewood bridge with black abalone dot pins, rosewood veneer on bound peghead with pearl logo inlay, 3 per side gold tuners. Available in Natural finish. Disc. 1992.
                          $1,370 $1,150 $980 $785 $705 $645 $585

                          Last Mfr.'s Sug. Retail was $1,960.

812-C — similar to 812, except has single sharp cutaway. Mfd. 1993 to date.
  Mfr.'s Sug. Retail $2,298 $1,723 $1,149 $1,050 $920 $830 $760 $690

  In 1994, single round cutaway, pearl progressive diamond fingerboard inlay replaced original items.

814-C — similar to 812, except has Grand Auditorium design and single cutaway.
  Mfr.'s Sug. Retail $2,398 $1,798 $1,199 $1,150 $1,040 $970 $630 $570

815-C — single sharp cutaway jumbo style, solid spruce top, round soundhole, tortoise pickguard, 3 stripe bound body, abalone rosette, rosewood back/sides, mahogany neck, 14/20 fret bound rosewood fingerboard with pearl snowflake inlay, rosewood bridge with black abalone dot pins, rosewood veneer on bound peghead with pearl logo inlay, 3 per side gold tuners. Mfd. 1993 to date.
  Mfr.'s Sug. Retail $2,398 $1,798 $1,199 $1,150 $960 $860 $790 $720

  In 1994, pearl progressive diamond fingerboard inlay replaced original item.

855 — jumbo style, solid spruce top, round soundhole, tortoise shell pickguard, 3 stripe bound body, abalone rosette, rosewood back/sides, mahogany neck, 14/20 fret bound rosewood fingerboard with pearl snowflake inlay, rosewood bridge with black abalone dot pins, rosewood veneer on bound peghead with pearl logo inlay, 6 per side gold tuners. Available in Natural finish. Curr. mfr.
  Mfr.'s Sug. Retail $2,398 $1,798 $1,199 $1,120 $960 $860 $790 $720

  In 1994, pearl progressive diamond fingerboard inlay replaced original item.

900 Series

The 900 series are deluxe rosewood guitars with gloss finishes, scalloped bracing on the 6-strings, Engelmann spruce tops, rosewood binding, abalone top binding, soundhole rosette, and "Cindy" fretboard inlays.

910 — dreadnought style, solid spruce top, round soundhole, tortoise shell pickguard, wood bound body, abalone rosette, maple back/sides/neck, 14/20 fret ebony fingerboard with abalone stylized inlay, ebony bridge with black abalone dot pins, rosewood peghead veneer with abalone stylized T/logo inlay, 3 per side gold tuners. Available in Natural finish. Curr. mfr.
  Mfr.'s Sug. Retail $3,298 $2,638 $1,978 $1,900 $1,480 $1,330 $1,220 $1,110

  In 1993, rosewood back/sides, mahogany neck were optionally available.

  In 1994, abalone purfling, abalone flower fingerboard inlay replaced original items, abalone stylized T peghead inlay was discontinued.

912 — grand concert style, solid spruce top, round soundhole, tortoise shell pickguard, wood bound body, abalone rosette, maple back/sides/neck, 14/20 fret ebony fingerboard with abalone stylized inlay, ebony bridge with black abalone dot pins, rosewood veneer with abalone stylized T/logo inlay on peghead, 3 per side gold tuners. Available in Natural finish. Disc. 1992.
                          $1,890 $1,500 $1,320 $1,085 $975 $895 $815

                          Last Mfr.'s Sug. Retail was $2,715.

912-C — similar to 912, except has single sharp cutaway. Mfd. 1993 to date.
  Mfr.'s Sug. Retail $3,598 $2,878 $2,158 $2,000 $1,600 $1,440 $1,320 $1,200

  In 1994, abalone purfling, abalone flower fingerboard inlay replaced original items, abalone stylized T peghead inlay was discontinued.

914-C — similar to 912, except has Grand Auditorium design and a single cutaway.
  Mfr.'s Sug. Retail $3,698 $2,958 $2,218 $2,000 $1,600 $1,440 $1,320 $1,200

Grading	100%	98% MINT	95% EXC+	90% EXC	80% VG+	70% VG	60% G

Ross Teigen Flying Pig
courtesy Stringman Guitars

915 — jumbo style, solid spruce top, round soundhole, tortoise pickguard, wood bound body, abalone rosette, maple back/sides/neck, 14/20 fret ebony fingerboard with abalone stylized inlay, ebony bridge with black abalone dot pins, rosewood veneer with abalone stylized T/logo inlay on peghead, 3 per side gold tuners. Available in Natural finish. Disc. 1992.

	$1,600	$1,490	$1,210	$1,025	$930	$870	$825

Last Mfr.'s Sug. Retail was $2,815.

955 — jumbo style, solid spruce top, round soundhole, tortoise shell pickguard, wood bound body, abalone rosette, maple back/sides/neck, 14/20 fret ebony fingerboard with abalone stylized inlay, ebony bridge with black abalone dot pins, rosewood veneer with abalone stylized T/logo inlay on peghead, 6 per side gold tuners. Available in Natural finish. Current mfr.

Mfr.'s Sug. Retail	$3,698	$2,773	$1,849	$1,750	$1,400	$1,240	$1,120	$1,000

Koa Series

K-20 — dreadnought style, koa top/back/sides/neck, round soundhole, tortoise pickguard, 3 stripe bound body, abalone rosette, 14/20 fret rosewood fingerboard with pearl diamond inlay, rosewood bridge with black abalone dot pins, ebony veneer with abalone logo inlay on peghead, 3 per side gold tuners. Available in Natural finish. Disc. 1992.

	$1,250	$1,130	$1,060	$845	$760	$690	$630

Last Mfr.'s Sug. Retail was $2,115.

This model had solid spruce top optionally available.

K-22 — grand concert style, koa top/back/sides/neck, round soundhole, tortoise pickguard, 3 stripe bound body, abalone rosette, 14/20 fret rosewood fingerboard with pearl diamond inlay, rosewood bridge with black abalone dot pins, ebony veneer with abalone logo inlay on peghead, 3 per side gold tuners. Available in Natural finish. Disc. 1992.

	$1,250	$1,115	$1,095	$875	$785	$720	$655

Last Mfr.'s Sug. Retail was $2,190.

Signature Series

DCSM — dreadnought style, spruce top, round soundhole, tortoise pickguard, 5 stripe bound body/rosette, rosewood back/sides, mahogany neck, 14/20 fret ebony bound fingerboard with pearl diamond inlay, ebony bridge with black abalone dot pins, rosewood veneered bound peghead with pearl logo inlay, 3 per side gold tuners. Available in Natural finish. Curr. mfr.

Mfr.'s Sug. Retail	$2,198	$1,758	$1,318	$1,150	$920	$830	$760	$690

This model was co-designed by Dan Crary.

LKSM — 12 string jumbo style, spruce top, round soundhole, wood bound body and wooden rosette, mahogany back/sides/neck, 14/20 fret ebony fingerboard, pearl Leo Kottke inlay at 12th fret, ebony bridge with black pins, rosewood peghead veneer with pearl logo inlay, 6 per side gold tuners. Available in Natural finish. Curr. mfr.

Mfr.'s Sug. Retail	$2,598	$1,948	$1,299	$1,250	$1,080	$970	$890	$810

In 1994, 12th fret fingerboard inlay was discontinued.

This model was co-designed by Leo Kottke.

Presentation Series

Taylor's Presentation Series guitars feature Brazilian rosewood presentation-grade guitars. These four models have scalloped bracing, an Engelmann spruce top, rosewood binding, an abalone top binding, soundhole rosette, "Byzantine" fretboard inlays, and peghead and bridge inlays. The dreadnought **PS-10** lists for $7,798, the **Grand Concert PS-12** is $7,898, the **Grand Auditorium PS-14** is $ 7,998, and the **Jumbo PS-15** is also $7,998.

ACOUSTIC BASS

Bob Taylor and Steve Klein collaborated on an acoustic bass design in a 34" scale with a Fishman pickup system. The tapered body features imbuia back and sides and is either available in the Spruce topped AB-1 ($2,750) or the imbuia top AB-2 ($2,750).

Teisco Del Rey
courtesy Kevin Macy

ROSS TEIGEN

Instruments currently built in Naples, Florida.

Luthier Ross Teigen builds lightweight, distinctly designed custom guitars and basses. Teigen has been building guitars and basses since 1979, and attended the Technical College in Red Wing, Minnesota for stringed instrument construction and repair. Teigen worked in Minneapolis, Naples (Florida), and Miami before establishing Teigen Guitars in 1986 on the edge of the Florida Everglades, where he lives with his wife and three children. For further information on models, prices, and custom options, please contact luthier Teigen via the Index of Current Manufacturers located in the back of this book.

TEISCO

See TEISCO DEL REY.

Instruments produced in Japan.

One of the original Teisco importers was George Rose of Los Angeles, California. Some instruments may bear the shortened "Teisco" logo, many others were shipped in unlabeled. Please: no jokes about Teisco "no-casters".

(Source: Michael Wright, Guitar Stories Volume One, pg. 76)

TEISCO DEL REY

Instruments produced in Japan from 1956 to 1973.

In 1946, Mr. Atswo Kaneko and Mr. Doryu Matsuda founded the Aoi Onpa Kenkyujo company, makers of the guitars bearing the Teisco and other trademarks (the company name roughly translates to the **Hollyhock Soundwave or Electricity Laboratories**). The Teisco name was chosen by Mr. Kaneko, and was used primarily in domestic markets. Early models include lap steel and electric-Spanish guitars. By the 1950s, the company was producing slab-bodied designs with bolt-on necks. In 1956, the company name was changed to the Nippon Onpa Kogyo Co., Ltd. - but the guitars still stayed Teisco!

As the demand for guitars in the U.S. market began to expand, Mr. Jack Westheimer of WMI Corporation of Evanston, Illinois started to import Japanese guitars in the late 1950s, perhaps circa 1958. WMI began importing the Teisco-built Kingston guitars in 1961, and also used the Teisco Del Rey trademark extensively beginning in 1964. Other Teisco-built guitars had different trademarks (a "rebranding" technique), and generally indicates the U.S. importer/distributor. The Japanese company again changed names, this time to the Teisco Co. Ltd. The Teisco line included all manners of solid body and semi-hollowbody guitars, and their niche in the American guitar market (as entry level or beginner's guitars) assured steady sales.

In 1967, the Kawai Corporation purchased the Teisco company. Not one to ruin a good thing, Kawai continued distributing the Teisco line to the U.S. (although they did change some designs through the years) until 1973. Due to the recent popularity in the Teisco name, Kawai actually produced some limited edition Teisco Spectrum Five models lately in Japan, although they were not made available to the U.S. market.

(Source: Michael Wright, Vintage Guitar Magazine, from the three part series Teisco Guitars: Rock and Roll Dreams)

One dating method for identifying Teisco guitars (serial numbers are non-existent, and some electronic parts may not conform to the U.S. EIA code) is the change in pickguards that occurred in 1965. Pre-1965 pickguards are plastic construction, while 1965 and post-1965 pickguards are stripped metal.

Pricing on Teisco Del Rey models and other Teiscos is tres bizarre these days. Most models that hang on walls are tagged at $99 (and sometimes lower), but clean cool shaped models sometimes command the $200 to $300 range. However, due to the association of the Spectrum Five model with Eddie Van Halen (he posed with a model on some music magazine, if the rumor is true), some Spectrum Fives are now priced (used) at $1,500!

Teisco Del Rey May Queen
courtesy Rick King

TELE-STAR

Instruments produced in Japan.

The Tele-Star trademark was distributed in the U.S. by the Tele-Star Musical Instrument Corporation of New York, New York.

(Source: Michael Wright, Guitar Stories Volume One, pg. 76)

TEMPEST

Instruments produced in Japan during the early 1980s.

These entry level to medium quality solid and semi-hollow body guitars featured both original designs and designs based on popular American classics.

(Source: Tony Bacon and Paul Day, The Guru's Guitar Guide)

TEUFFEL

Instruments currently built in Germany. Distributed in the U.S. by Salwender International of Trabuco Canyon, California. Distribution in Germany by S K C Graphite of Aschaffenburg, Germany.

Teuffel produces a number of high quality, custom built guitars. For further information, please contact Salwender International through the Index of Current Manufacturers located in the rear of this book.

TEXARKANA

See SEBRING.

Distributed by the V. J. Rendano Co., Ltd.

Texarkana offers a number of instruments designed for the entry level or beginning guitar student. For further information, contact the V. J. Rendano Co., Ltd. via the Index of Current Manufacturers located in the back of this book.

THOMAS

Instruments produced in Italy from the late 1960s through the early 1970s.

Teisco Del Rey Ev-2T "Vox"
courtesy Stringman Guitars

Thomas semi-hollowbodies are medium quality guitars that feature original designs.

(Source: Tony Bacon and Paul Day, The Guru's Guitar Guide)

HARVEY THOMAS

Also appear as THOMAS CUSTOM GUITARS, or simply THOMAS.

Instruments were built in Kent, Washington during the early 1960s.

Flamboyant luthier Harvey Thomas built quality semi-hollowbody guitars whose designs bent the "laws of tradition" that conservative semi-hollowbody guitars normally adhere to. Thomas is also well known for his explorations into the solid body design world as well. Models include the Mandarin, the Mod, Riot King, or the Maltese Surfer.

Most Thomas guitars feature six on a side headstocks, a slim neck design, and 21 fret fingerboard that is clear of the body, and glitter or mirror pickguards. The Maltese Surfer looks like a Maltese Cross with a neck attached to one of the four sides. You'll know 'em when you see 'em, but you won't believe what you're looking at!

(Source: Tony Bacon, The Ultimate Guitar Book)

TILTON

Instruments manufactured in Boston, Massachusetts from 1865 to the early 1900s.

The Oliver Ditson Company, Inc. was formed in 1835 by music publisher Oliver Ditson (1811-1888). Ditson was a primary force in music merchandising, distribution, and retail sales on the East Coast. He also helped establish two musical instrument manufacturers: The John Church Company of Cincinnati, Ohio, and Lyon & Healy (Washburn) in Chicago, Illinois.

In 1865 Ditson established a manufacturing branch of his company under the supervision of John Haynes, called the John C. Haynes Company. This branch built guitars for a number of trademarks, such as Bay State, Tilton, and Haynes Excelsior.

(Source: Tom Wheeler, American Guitars)

TIMTONE

Instruments currently built in Grand Forks, British Columbia (Canada).

Luthier Tim Diebert has been custom building high quality guitars for a number of years. Electric stringed instruments are built in batches of two to four, to ensure that the client's specifications are met. Diebert handcrafts all the wood parts, uses high quality hardware and tuners, and provides a wide variety of magnetic pickups (as well as an optional piezo bridge system) to deliver the tone that is commissioned. For further information, please contact luthier Tim Diebert through the Index of Current Manufacturers located in the back of this book.

TOBIAS

Instruments currently produced in Korea and Nashville, Tennessee. Tobias Guitars has been a division of the Gibson Guitar Corporation since January 1990, and operations were moved to Nashville in 1992. Tobias Guitars are distributed by Gibson Guitar Corporation.

Prior to purchase by Gibson, Tobias Guitars were based in Hollywood, California from 1981 to December 1989.

The following Tobias Guitars history is reprinted courtesy of luthier Michael Tobias.

"Tobias Guitars was started in Orlando, Florida in April 1977. The first serial number I used was 0178 - January 1978. After 578, I went back to 179. My first shop name was the Guitar Shop. I sold that business in 1980 and moved to San Francisco to be partners in a short lived manufacturing business called **Sierra Guitars.** We made about 50 instruments. I left San Francisco in May of 1981 and started a repair shop in Costa Mesa, California.

I stayed in Costa Mesa for sveral months and then moved to Hollywood. The first California serial number was 240, and it was a solid mahogany 6 string guitar. The first South California number was 250. It was a mahogany LP junior style neck thru, one of four made.

Tobias Guitars continued to repair instruments and build custom basses for the next several years with the help of Bob Lee and Kevin Almieda (Kevin went on to work for Music Man). We moved into 1623 Cahuenga Boulevard in Hollywood and after a year quit the repair business. We added Bob McDonald, lost Kevin to Music Man, and then got Makoto Onishi. The business grew by leaps and bounds. In June of 1988, we had so many back orders that we did not accept any new orders until the January NAMM show in 1990.

After several attempts to move the business to larger, better equipped facilities, I sold Tobias Guitars to Gibson on 1/1/90. The first Tobias Gibson serial number was 1094. At that point, Gibson was instrumental in moving us to a bigger shop in Burbank and setting us up with a great spray booth and dust collection system. We finally met So Cal safety codes. Basses built during the 1990-1992 era were built initially by the same crew that had helped establish Tobias Basses as one of the most sought after basses on the planet. We added several people during 1990, and ended up with a great 10 man shop.

Business was still very good. We were not able to make anywhere near enough basses to fill the orders. Instead of trying to jack up production, we tried to get outside vendors to build for us. We had 110

Timtone Custom
courtesy Tim Diebert

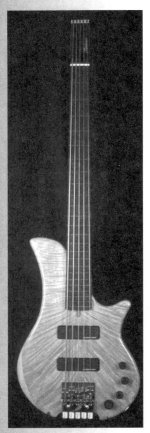

Timtone Custom bass
courtesy Tim Diebert

"Model T" basses made for us by a very fine builder in New England, and then we got the Terada factory in Nagoya, Japan to make the "Standard" bass for us. This was and is a great bass, but the $/yen ratio killed the project. There were about 400 Standards.

Late in 1992, it was decided that in best corporate interests Tobias Guitars would move to Nashville. After much deliberation, no one from the original Tobias Guitars crew went to Nashville. The final LA Tobias/Gibson serial number is 2044. Despite Gibson's ownership of Tobias, all of the basses made up to 2044 were built by my regular crew. We also built about 60 basses that were not numbered or finished by us. Those would be the first production from Tobias/Nashville.

I left the company in December of 1992, and was a consultant for Gibson as they set up operations in Nashville. They had some trouble at first, but have since done a fairly good job making Tobias basses.

By contractual agreement, after my consulting agreement with Gibson was up, I had a one year non competition term. That ended in December of 1993. During that time I moved to The Catskills in upstate New York and set up a small custom shop. I started designing new instruments and building prototypes in preparation for my new venture."

(Biography courtesy Michael Tobias, February 22, 1996)

ELECTRIC BASS

Grading	100%	98% MINT	95% EXC+	90% EXC	80% VG+	70% VG	60% G

Basic Series

B4 — offset double cutaway asymmetrical alder body, thru body maple/bubinga neck, 24 fret rosewood fingerboard, fixed bridge, 2 per side tuners, chrome hardware, 2 Bartolini pickups, 2 volume/treble/midrange/bass controls, bypass switch, active electronics. Available in Amber, Blue, Green, Orange, Purple and Red finishes. Curr. mfr.

Mfr.'s Sug. Retail	$3,100	$2,325	$1,550	$1,450	$1,160	$1,040	$955	$870

This model has bubinga, figured maple, koa, lacewood, walnut or zebra body, maple/purpleheart neck, black hardware optionally available.

Finishes on this model are transparent.

B5 — similar to B4, except has 5 strings.

Mfr.'s Sug. Retail	$3,300	$2,475	$1,650	$1,570	$1,255	$1,125	$1,035	$940

B6 — similar to B4, except has 6 strings and pau ferro fingerboard.

Mfr.'s Sug. Retail	$3,500	$2,625	$1,750	$1,675	$1,340	$1,200	$1,100	$1,000

Classic Series

C4 — offset double cutaway asymmetrical laminated body, thru body walnut/wenge neck, 24 fret pau ferro fingerboard, fixed bridge, 2 per side tuners, chrome hardware, 2 Bartolini pickups, 2 volume/treble/midrange/bass controls, bypass switch, active electronics. Available in Natural finish. Curr. mfr.

Mfr.'s Sug. Retail	$3,400	$2,550	$1,700	$1,625	$1,300	$1,170	$1,070	$975

This model may have black hardware.

Neck may have walnut/purpleheart or walnut/bubinga laminate, maple may replace walnut in some configurations.

This model also available in birdseye maple/walnut, bubinga/wenge/alder, flame maple/wenge/walnut, goncalo alves/walnut, lacewood/wenge/alder, purpleheart/walnut, walnut/wenge/alder, walnut/wenge/walnut, zebra/walnut or zebra/wenge/alder laminate body.

C5 — similar to C4, except has 5 strings.

Mfr.'s Sug. Retail	$3,700	$2,775	$1,850	$1,785	$1,385	$1,245	$1,145	$1,040

C6 — similar to C4, except has 6 strings.

Mfr.'s Sug. Retail	$3,800	$2,850	$1,900	$1,850	$1,480	$1,330	$1,220	$1,110

Killer "B" Series

KB4 — offset double cutaway asymmetrical ash body, bolt-on maple/purpleheart 5 piece neck, 24 fret pau ferro fingerboard, fixed bridge, 2 per side tuners, black hardware, 2 Bartolini pickups, 2 volume/treble/midrange/bass controls, bypass switch, active electronics. Available in Oil finish. Curr. mfr.

Mfr.'s Sug. Retail	$2,500	$1,875	$1,250	$1,200	$960	$860	$790	$720

Add $200 for Candy Colors finish.

Add $60 for fretless fingerboard.

Add $175 for left handed version.

Add $125 for Clear or Solid Colors finishes.

This model also available with alder, maple or lacewood body.

KB5 — similar to KB4, except has 5 strings.

Mfr.'s Sug. Retail	$2,600	$1,950	$1,300	$1,250	$1,000	$900	$825	$750

"August 9, 1995 will live on as the day we lost two major icons of rock and roll. In San Francisco, word came early in the morning of the death of Greatful Dead guitarist Jerry Garcia."

—*James Acunto*

TCG, Sept. 1995

Grading	100%	98% MINT	95% EXC+	90% EXC	80% VG+	70% VG	60% G

KB6 — similar to KB4, except has 6 strings.

Mfr.'s Sug. Retail	$2,700	$2,025	$1,350	$1,300	$1,040	$935	$860	$780

Pro-Standard Series

PS4 — offset double cutaway asymmetrical figured maple body, thru body maple/bubinga 5 piece neck, 24 fret rosewood fingerboard, fixed bridge, 2 per side tuners, black hardware, 2 Bartolini pickups, volume/mix and 3 band EQ controls, active electronics. Available in Black, Natural, Transparent Candy Amber, Transparent Candy Blue, Transparent Candy Red and White finishes. New 1994.

Mfr.'s Sug. Retail	$2,000	$1,600	$1,200	$1,000	$800	$720	$660	$600

This model has bubinga or zebra body with Natural finish optionally available.

PS5 — similar to PS4, except has 5 strings, 3/2 per side tuners.

Mfr.'s Sug. Retail	$2,100	$1,680	$1,260	$1,050	$840	$755	$690	$630

PS6 — similar to PS4, except has 6 strings, 3 per side tuners.

Mfr.'s Sug. Retail	$2,300	$1,840	$1,380	$1,150	$920	$830	$760	$690

Signature Series

S4 — offset double cutaway asymmetrical laminate body, thru body laminate neck, 24 fret pau ferro fingerboard, fixed bridge, 2 per side tuners, chrome hardware, 2 Bartolini pickups, 2 volume/treble/midrange/bass controls, bypass switch, active electronics. Available in Natural finish. Curr. mfr.

Mfr.'s Sug. Retail	$4,900	$3,675	$2,450	$2,140	$1,680	$1,470	$1,325	$1,140

This model may have black hardware.

Neck may have walnut/wenge, walnut/purpleheart or walnut/bubinga laminate. Maple may replace walnut in these laminates.

This model also available in bubinga/wenge/bubinga, figured maple/mahogany/figured maple, goncalo alves/walnut/goncalo alves, koa/wenge/koa, lacewood/wenge/lacewood, pau ferro/mahogany/pau ferro, zebra/walnut/zebra or zebra/wenge/zebra laminate body.

S5 — similar to S4, except has 5 strings.

Mfr.'s Sug. Retail	$5,200	$3,900	$2,600	$2,270	$1,780	$1,565	$1,405	$1,210

S6 — similar to S4, except has 6 strings.

Mfr.'s Sug. Retail	$5,400	$4,050	$2,700	$2,390	$1,870	$1,645	$1,475	$1,275

Standard Series

ST4 — offset double cutaway asymmetrical ash body, thru body maple/bubinga 5 piece neck, 24 fret rosewood fingerboard, fixed bridge, 2 per side tuners, black hardware, 2 Bartolini pickups, volume/mix and 3 band EQ controls, active electronics. Available in Black, Natural, Transparent Candy Amber, Transparent Candy Blue, Transparent Candy Red and White finishes. Curr. mfr.

Mfr.'s Sug. Retail	$1,850	$1,480	$1,110	$950	$760	$685	$625	$570

This model available in fretless fingerboard at no additional cost.

ST5 — similar to ST4, except has 5 strings.

Mfr.'s Sug. Retail	$1,950	$1,560	$1,170	$1,000	$800	$720	$660	$600

ST6 — similar to ST4, except has 6 strings.

Mfr.'s Sug. Retail	$2,300	$1,840	$1,380	$1,150	$920	$830	$760	$690

Toby Deluxe Series

TD4 — offset double cutaway asymmetrical maple body, bolt-on maple neck, 24 fret rosewood fingerboard, fixed bridge, 2 per side tuners, chrome hardware, 2 J-style humbucker pickups, volume/mix/3 band EQ controls, active electronics. Available in Black, Natural, Transparent Candy Amber, Transparent Candy Blue, Transparent Candy Red and White finishes. New 1994.

Mfr.'s Sug. Retail	$900	$720	$540	$450	$360	$325	$300	$275

TD5 — similar to TD4, except has 5 strings, 3/2 per side tuners.

Mfr.'s Sug. Retail	$1,000	$800	$600	$500	$400	$360	$330	$300

Toby Pro Series

TP4 — offset double cutaway asymmetrical maple body, thru body maple/wenge 5 piece neck, 24 fret rosewood fingerboard, fixed bridge, 2 per side tuners, chrome hardware, 2 humbucker pickups, volume/mix/3 band EQ controls, active electronics. Available in Black, Natural, Transparent Candy Amber, Transparent Candy Blue, Transparent Candy Red and White finishes. New 1994.

Mfr.'s Sug. Retail	$1,200	$960	$720	$600	$480	$430	$395	$360

TP5 — similar to TP4, except has 5 strings, 3/2 per side tuners.

Mfr.'s Sug. Retail	$1,300	$1,040	$780	$650	$520	$470	$430	$390

TP6 — similar to TP4, except has 6 strings, 3 per side tuners.

Mfr.'s Sug. Retail	$1,400	$1,120	$840	$700	$560	$505	$460	$420

TOKAI

Instruments produced in Japan from the early 1960s to date.

Tokai instruments were very good Fender and Gibson-based replicas produced during the mid to late 1970s. After 1978 the company built instruments based on these classic American designs; then further branched out into some original designs and 'superstrat' models.

TOMKINS

Instruments built in Harbord, Australia.

These high quality solid body guitars are custom built by luthier Allan Tomkins, and feature designs based on popular Fender classics. Tomkins' guitars are crafted from exotic Australian hardwoods and softwoods such as Tasmanian King Billy Pine, Black Heart Sassafras, Queensland Silky Oak, Crab Apple Birch, or Coachwood. Instruments feature Gotoh tuners and bridges, 21 fret necks, Seymour Duncan or Bill Lawrence pickups, and a nitro-cellulose lacquer finish. For prices or custom options, contact Tomkins Custom Guitars and Basses through the Index of Current Manufacturers located in the back of this book.

TOMMYHAWK

Instruments built in Dover, New Jersey. Distributed by Tom Barth's Music Box of Dover, New Jersey.

Designer Tom Barth offers a 24 inch travel-style guitar that is a one-piece carved mahogany body (back, sides, neck, and bracing). The solid spruce top, bridge, and top bracing are then glued on, forming a solid, projecting little guitar. Retail list price is $325. For further information, please contact Tom Barth through the Index of Current Manufacturers located in the rear of this book.

TONEMASTER

See chapter on House Brands.

This trademark has been indentified as a "House Brand" ascribed to several distributors such as Harris-Teller of Illinois, Schmidt of Minnesota, and Squire of Michigan. While one recognized source has claimed that instruments under this trademark were built by HARMONY, author/researcher Willie G. Moseley has also seen this brand on a VALCO-made lap steel.

(Source: Willie G. Moseley, Stellas & Stratocasters)

TOP TWENTY

Instruments produced in Japan between 1965 to 1976.

The Top Twenty trademark is a brandname used by a UK importer. These entry level quality instruments featured a solid body construction and some original designs.

(Source: Tony Bacon and Paul Day, The Guru's Guitar Guide)

TORRES

Instruments built in Spain.

Noted luthier Antonio de Torres (1817-1892) has been the guitar builder identified as developing the guitar to its current "classical" configuration. In the early 1800s, the European guitar shifted from five "courses" (which could be a single or pair of strings (the low 'E' string was the additional string). Torres developed a larger bodied guitar design, and fan-bracing to support the thinner top. The new design offered a larger tonal range (especially in the bass realm), and was widely adopted both in Spain and throughout Europe.

Torres had two workshops during his career. He produced guitars both in Seville (1852-1869), and his place of birth, Almeria (1875-1892). It has been estimated that Torres built about 320 guitars during his two workshop period. Only 66 instruments have been identified as his work.

(Source: Tony Bacon, The Ultimate Guitar Book)

TOTEM

Instruments currently built in Three Rivers, California.

Totem offers several high quality guitars with bolt-neck designs, ash bodies and maple or myrtle tops, and quality hardware. For further information, please contact Totem via the Index of Current Manufacturers located in the rear of this book.

TOYOTA

Instruments produced in Japan.

Toyota guitars were distributed in the U.S. by the Hershman company of New York, New York.

(Source: Michael Wright, Guitar Stories Volume One, pg. 76)

Tokai Love Rock
19th Annual Dallas Show

Tommyhawk guitar
courtesy Tom Barth

TRANSPERFORMANCE

Tuning mechanisms built in Fort Collins, Colorado.

Rather than the listing of a guitar builder, Transperformance is a Colorado-based company that builds the **L-CAT Automatic Tuning System**. This system is installed in a current model guitar, and features a computer-controlled bridge and tuning mechanism that can physically change tunings on the instrument. The mechanism comes with 120 factory-programmed alternative tunings, and has memory storage for 240 customer installed others as well. At the flip of a button you can move from the conventional guitar tuning, to a "drop-D" to an open G - automatically! The system lists for $2,599 (and up).

JEFF TRAUGOTT

Instruments built in Santa Cruz, California since 1991.

Luthier Jeff Traugott, a former apprentice of John David Morse, spent four-and-a-half years working at the Santa Cruz Guitar Company before striking out on his own. Traugott has been offering quality repair work as well as his own quality handcrafted acoustics for a number of years. While certain features on Traugott's creations look modern, the overall impression is a solid, crafted instrument. Traugott offers four basic models, and all feature a narrow waist design that he features. For further information on model specifications and pricing, please call luthier Jeff Traugott through the Index of Current Manufacturers located in the back of this book.

TRAVELER

Instruments currently built in Redlands, California. Distributed by OMG Music.

Designer J. Corey Oliver offers a full scale travel-style guitar that is only 28 inches in overall length, and two inches thick. Constructed of either maple or mahogany, the **Traveler** (basic list $349) has a single coil pickup (an optional Fishman transducer is also offered), and a storable lower arm for playing in the sitting position. For further information, please call OMG Music through the Index of Current Manufacturers located in the back of this book.

TRAVIS BEAN

Instruments built in Sun Valley, California from 1974 to 1979.

The following Travis Bean history is reprinted here courtesy of Bill Kaman, who has been a Travis Bean fan from the beginning. Additional information supplied by Richard Oblinger ("Obe"), a Travis Bean employee; and Travis Bean, the man behind it all.

T6061

A Short History on the Travis Bean Guitars

Travis Bean: It's the name of a California motorcycle enthusiast who decided in the early '70s that aluminum would be a step forward in guitar design. He thought that it would be a much more stable material for the necks. Using a neck-through-to-the-bridge design also improved the sound and sustain of the guitars. While Travis played some guitar, he was a drummer and kept a drumkit set up at the factory to back up players when they were there to check out equipment.

The company was founded in 1974 and lasted five years, closing in August of 1979. They produced about 3,650 guitars and basses which were as viable an instrument today in the '90s as they were when they were built. Initial production began in 1974 and continued until December 1977 when the factory was closed for "reorganization". In June 1978 it reopened and continued until August 1979 when the plug was pulled by the investors who had "reorganized" the company. Sashi Pattell, an Indian guy, was the major investor and "drove" the company for the last 12 months. During the first 6 months of 1978, limited "unofficial" production continued with a partial production crew who often took guitars in lieu of wages.

In 1977 the guitars were sold through Rothschild Distribution but that ended with the reorganization. When the company closed in 1979 everything was sold off at auction. Mighty Mite bought about 200 bodies and most of the guitar parts but never really did anything with them. There were about 30 TB500 necks left over and it's not known who bought these. Mighty Mite itself was closed and auctioned off a few years later.

The first guitar Travis ever built was a 'Melody Maker' body shape with Gibson humbucking pickups. The aluminum neck had a welded-on peghead and bolted to the body. The neck attachment plate was inlayed in the body and extended back to under the bridge. After experimenting with this guitar a while the idea of a neck-through-to-the-bridge design began to take shape. A second prototype was built which was much closer to the production design in neck and body configuration. This guitar has a serial number of "1", and used Fender humbucking pickups. After these two guitars, limited production began.

These first "limited production" guitars were TB1000 Artists and were produced in 1974. The serial numbers started with #11 and went to #20.

These guitars were handmade by Travis and Mark McElwee, Travis' partner in the compnay , and are quite similar in construction to the second pre-production prototype. The bodies were Koa, Teak, Padauk, Zebra wood, and Alder (Guitar #11 and #18 are known to be Padauk). The necks on these were quite different from the later production models produced on a lathe. These were hand carved from a solid block of Reynolds T6061 aluminum and are solid under the fingerboard and solid through the body. The

Travis Bean Wedge guitar
courtesy William Kaman II

necks have a wide and flat profile which is noticeably thinner than the later production which are much fuller and more rounded. The pickups on these first guitars are humbuckers using Fender bobbins and Alnico magnets; and have 'Travis Bean' engraved on the chrome pickup covers. The guitars are quite thin, about the same thickness as the 1979 final production Artists. Another interesting aspect of these guitars is the peghead. The angle is flatter than later production (about 6 degrees versus a production angle of 12 degrees). There is also about an extra inch between the nut and the beginning of the 'T' cutout. In this extra space there is bolted an aluminum block with 6 holes acting as a string tree to hold the tension over the nut. Later production guitars with the steeper angle didn't need this tie down.

In all, there are quite a few differences between these first 10 prototypes and the production models ranging from the body thickness and top contour, peghead dimensions and angle, neck profile and shape of the body insert piece, to the pickup engraving. These guitars are a bit crude compared to the later production; but after all, they are the first ones made.

Production of the 1000 series continued throughout 1974 with the 1000 Standard being introduced approximately 6 months after the startup. This guitar had all the same dimensions as the 1000 Artist, only differing in that the body was not carved and it had dot fingerboard inlays rather than the large pearl blocks of the Artist. It was a solid 1 3/4" all over. The run of serial numbers on Standards and Artists began with #21 and continued until #1000. At that point the lines were split and each continued with #1001, #1002, etc. While it is unclear if the production records of these first 1000 guitars still exist, it is estimated that there were approximately 1/3 Artists and 2/3's Standards. All the bodies were Koa and most were finished natural; however, the factory did offer black, white, and red. Both straight color and pearl color were offered. There were also several dark blue pearl guitars made (there were two silver guitars made: one for Joe Perry [of Aerosmith] a Standard #1738; and a Wedge Guitar [# 53] for Al Austin). The Koa bodies continued until late 1978 when the painted models began to use magnolia and poplar. The natural finishes continued to use mostly Koa although a natural magnolia is known to exist. All these guitars used black 'speed' knobs which Travis bought directly from Gibson until for some reason Gibson shut them off. After that, clear 'speed' knobs were used. In late 1978 and 1979 black metal knobs were used. Internally, these were referred to as "Sansui" knobs because they looked like they were off a home stereo set! The machine heads were Schaller and Grover and alternated without any pattern throughout the years of production. Towards the end of the company, Gotoh machine heads were used, particularly on the 500 model. The last Artist produced was serial number 1425 and the last Standard produced was serial number 1782. In all, there were about 755 Artists and 1,442 Standards produced.

The TB2000 Bass was introduced in late 1974. The first prototype had serial number "0" and is of similar construction to the first 10 guitars. However, it is much more like a production guitar in that it doesn't have that "handmade" look of the first 10 guitars. This bass is pictured in the first catalogue on the TB2000 models. This bass also had an aluminum nut (the only one made this way). All other production Travis Beans were made with brass nuts. The neck was hand carved by Travis and has a thick squarish feel. It was solid as was the section in the body. The body had a 1/4" edge radius and was Koa. Production started with serial number 11 and the bodies were more rounded and contoured. They were all Koa and made in natural and the same colors as the guitars. A fretless version was also available, as was a short scale model bass. In all about 12 short scale basses were made, two of which were for Bill Wyman in October 1978 (serial number 892 and 893). The last bass made was serial number 1033. In all there were 1,023 basses made.

The 500 model was meant to be a less expensive single coil version of the 1000 model. The first guitars were produced in late 1977, just before the reorganization shutdown. The first 9 guitars were quite different from the balance of production. These had standard 1 3/4" thickness bodies but the aluminum body extension was set in from the top rather than sliding into the middle of the body and being exposed at the back. These guitars had uncoated necks, and the bodies were much more square than later production. Most of these first 500s went to performers like Jerry Garcia and Rory Gallager (who had 3 pickup guitars). Mark McElwee kept one made with a Koa body. In June of 1978 when production resumed with guitar #20 the bodies were more slimmer and had a slanted offcenter shape. The pickguards also were more stylized, and the majority of the necks were coated with the black Imron paint that was used to give the guitar necks a "warmer" feel. There were several made with three pickups (serial numbers 11, 12, 270). Up until around serial number 290, the pickups had black plastic covers with the polepiece exposed. After #290, the covers were solid black plastic with a molded-in stylized 'Travis Bean' logo. The majority of the 500s had magnolia bodies although there were some made from poplar. Most were painted black, white, or red although there were some naturals made. The last 500 was serial number 362 so there were a total of 351 TB500 guitars produced. There were plans for a 500 model Bass but it was never completed.

The Wedges are perhaps the most unique guitars and basses produced by Travis Bean. They were the "Stage" guitars, and the Travis Bean version of a 'Flying V'. They were introduced in 1976 and built for two years. In total, 45 TB3000 Wedge guitars and 36 TB4000 Wedge basses were produced. All the basses were produced in the 1 3/4" thickness. Most of the guitars were 1 3/4" thick, with the exception of the last few (for example, Wedge guitar #49 is 1 3/4", but the next to the last one produced [# 55] was 1 3/8" thick. Also, # 49 has a one piece fingerboard and # 55 is 2 piece). The majority of the Wedges were produced in pearl colors: white, black, and red. An interesting point is that the bodies were the same overall size for both guitars and bass.

There were two doublenecks built. Both were double six strings and used Artist necks. One was a red Wedge and the other a natural Artist. There were also six 5 string guitars made that were Standards and are serial numbers 1732 to 1737. These went to Keith Richards, Travis Bean, Richard Oblinger, Mark McElwee, and Bill Lominic (the head machinist at the company). All these were coated necks and were 1 3/8" thick. Left handed guitars and basses were also available and 'lefty' 1000 Artists and Standards, as well as 2000 basses are known to exist. There were no 'lefty' Wedges or 500s built. There were requests over the years for special custom bodies on guitars, but these requests were turned down. Travis felt that building the custom "one-offs" would dilute the impact of the market place of the standard production. There exist today several instruments with custom bodies (for example: a MAP guitar and a Flying V) but these were retrofitted to existing guitars and not done at the Bean factory.

T

Throughout the production there were several significant changes that took place. The first change was that the horns of the guitars and basses were widened. This was around mid 1977. This was a suggestion from Rothchild Distributing and it was felt that this would improve playability and sales. An estimate is that this took place on Artists around #1100, Standards #1250, and Basses #440. The second change is that the bodies were made thinner by 3/8". This is estimated to have taken place around #1200 on Artists, #1400 on Standards, and #580 on Basses and was probably phased in around the first part of 1978. The third change was that the fingerboards went to a two piece construction. This took place just about the same time as the thinner bodies. Initially, the fingerboard was rosewood (although some early guitars had ebony; they also experimented with phenolic) and was a standard thickness. The center portion of the neck under the fingerboard was machined away to make it lighter. There was a rib left down the middle to support the fingerboard. On the later version the fingerboard was again rosewood, but half the thickness it had been previously. A thin piece of aluminum was added under the fingerboard to bring the fingerboard assembly back to standard thickness. On these guitars the center rib was not left in the middle of the neck since the aluminum underlay would fully support the wood. Also in 1978, a slight radius was introduced to the fingerboard. Up until this they had all been flat like a classical guitar (except for the prototype bass [#0] which has a 7 degree radius). The fourth change that took place around mid 1977 was the coating of the necks. One of the constant complaints about Travis Beans was that the necks felt "cold" and some found them objectional (it's a good thing that these complainers didn't play saxophones!). In response to this the company introduced the option of a black Imron coated neck. Imron is a heavy duty automobile enamel. It was felt that this heavy finish would make the necks feel slightly warmer, and since it was a spray-on finish it would be more like a standard guitar neck. This was an option on any guitar or bass (and as mentioned, pretty much a standard on the 500 series).

There was another small change in the machining of the aluminum piece in the body of the guitars. Approximately the first 300 TB1000 guitars made had the aluminum section in the body cavity machined from the side to take out the weight. The middle of the aluminum was cut completely away so there was a back section, visible at the back of the guitar; and a top section, which the pickups sat on. The rear most portion of the extension under the bridge was left solid. This was then glued into the body after it was finished. From around serial number 300, on the body section of the aluminum was machined from the top which created a "U" shaped channel under the guitar top and pickups. The rear end portion under the bridge was again solid. The improvement in this design was that it created a much more rigid structure in the body of the guitar, plus it allowed the body to be screwed to the neck extension by two wood screws through the walls of the "U" channel under the front pickup. Those two screws plus the three that fasten the bridge to the aluminum through the wood body are all that hold it together. This design made it much easier to remove the neck should it need work or work on the body. The pickups sat directly on either side of the "U" channel and were held in place by allen screws mounted from the rear.

The serial number of the guitar is stamped onto the face of the peghead just above the nut. It was also stamped into the aluminum under the neck pickup. On some it was also written on the bottom of the "U" channel. It was written on the body in two places: the interior of the control cavity, and in the space between the pickups on the inside. On the painted bodies the number in the control cavity was often painted over, and therefore not visible. It is interesting to note that bass #477 has body #478 so either bass #478 has #477 body or the #477 body had a problem and they just used the next body on the assembly line. This does prove that necks and bodies are interchangeable.

The following chart is a rough accounting of the production by year and serial number:

	1974 to Jan. 1976	Jan. 1976 to Dec. 1977	Jan. 1978 to June 1979	Total
TB500	-	-	11-362	351
TB1000A	11-400	400-1000,1000-1162	1163-1425	755
TB1000S	-	1056	1157-1782	1422
TB2000	11-200	201-763	764-1033	1023
TB3000	-	11-50	51-56	45
TB4000	-	11-47	-	36
	600	**1444**	**1611**	**3652**

Where is Travis Bean today? By the time the company was sold at auction, Travis had had his fill of production headaches, Music Industry bullshit, and demanding visits from the Taxmen. He took some time off. Being a tinkerer at heart, and someone who is happier using his hands and building things, he eventually began work building sets for the movie studios (which he continues to do today). His personal interest in music has stayed strong, and he has kept playing - focusing mostly on his drumming. Being true to his machinist/designer/tinker side, he has also developed a new style of rack setup for drums that allows for fast set-up and tear-down. So the answer is, Travis is alive and well and still playing in California.

(Source: C. William Kaman, II, President (Kaman Music Corporation), May 6, 1994)

Travis Bean guitars are offered in the range between $1,000 and $1,250; the rarer Wedge models command a higher price (a total of 45 Wedge guitars and 36 Wedge basses were produced between 1976 and 1978).

TREKER

Instruments currently built in Draper, Utah.

Treker offers a range of quality guitar and bass models that feature the exclusive "Floating Neck" technology. Handcrafted bodies are joined to a neck that has an internal tension bar which offers structural support and allows the fretboard to vibrate free of the traditional static load of the neck/truss rod/fingerboard design. For further information regarding individual models and specifications, or on the 'Floating Neck' concept, please call Treker via the Index of Current Manufacturers located in the back of this book.

"The permanent collection of the [Rock & Roll] museum currently numbers more than 100,000 objects representing artists from the 1920s to the present including Elmore James, Big Joe Turner, Jimi Hendrix, Pete Townshend, Buddy Holly and more."
—TCG, Sept. 1995

TRIGGS GUITARS

Instruments currently built in Nashville, Tennessee.

Luthier James W. Triggs has been building high quality guitars for a number of years, and is currently offering several archtop, flattop, and semi-hollowbody guitar models. Triggs incorporate features of older pre-WWII archtop guitars into his designs, and has a number of inlay and fancy hardware options to further beautify his already elaborate guitars. Triggs, formerly from Kansas, moved to Nashville and served a term of apprenticeship with several other guitar manufacturers before deciding to start his own business specializing in old-world craftsmanship techniques. For further information on individual models, specifications, custom options, and pricing please call luthier Jim Triggs through the Index of Current Manufacturers located in the back of this book.

TRUETONE

See chapter on House Brands.

This trademark has been identified as a "House Brand" of Western Auto. Built by Kay in the 1960s, the six-on-a-side headstock shape shared with this trademark has been dubbed "duck's bill" or "platypus" in reference to the rather bulbous nature of the design.

(Source: Willie G. Moseley, Stellas & Stratocasters)

TUNE GUITAR TECHNOLOGY

These innovatively designed instruments are manufactured in Japan, and distributed by Tune Guitars of North America located in Santa Barbara, California.

Grading	100%	98% MINT	95% EXC+	90% EXC	80% VG+	70% VG	60% G

Tune Guitar Technology offers many different series of high quality, neck-through basses and guitars. Tune Basses all possess innovative, original designs and quality hardware and electronics. For further information, please contact Tune Guitars of North America through the Index of Current Manufacturers located in the back of this book.

Triggs New Yorker
courtesy Scott Chinery

ELECTRIC BASS

CUSTOM 2 — offset double cutaway ash body, bolt-on 3 piece maple neck, 25 fret rosewood fingerboard with white dot inlay, strings thru Gotoh bridge, 2 per side Gotoh tuners, chrome/black hardware, 2 humbucker Tune pickups, volume/treble/bass/mix controls, active electronics. Available in Natural finish. Curr. mfr.

Mfr.'s Sug. Retail	$1,700	$1,360	$1,020	$850	$680	$610	$560	$510

Bass Maniac Custom Series

TBC-4 AS — offset double cutaway ash body, bolt-on 3 piece maple neck, 25 fret rosewood fingerboard with white dot inlay, fixed Gotoh bridge, 2 per side Gotoh tuners, gold hardware, P-style/J-style humbucker Tune pickups, volume/treble/bass/mix controls, active electronics. Available in Natural finish. Curr. mfr.

Mfr.'s Sug. Retail	$1,600	$1,280	$960	$800	$640	$575	$530	$480

TBC-4 — similar to TBC-4 AS, except has mahogany body, bubinga top. Curr. mfr.

Mfr.'s Sug. Retail	$1,750	$1,400	$1,050	$875	$700	$630	$575	$525

This model has koa, lacewood, padauk, walnut or zebrawood tops optionally available.

TBC-5 AS — similar to TBC-4 AS, except has 5 strings, fixed Tune bridge, 3/2 per side tuners. Curr. mfr.

Mfr.'s Sug. Retail	$1,800	$1,440	$1,080	$900	$720	$650	$595	$540

TBC-5 — similar to TBC-4 AS, except has 5 strings, mahogany body, bubinga top, fixed Tune bridge, 3/2 per side tuners. Curr. mfr.

Mfr.'s Sug. Retail	$2,000	$1,600	$1,200	$1,000	$800	$720	$660	$600

This model has koa, lacewood, padauk, walnut or zebrawood tops optionally available.

Kingbass Series

TWB-4 — offset double cutaway mahogany body with pointed bottom bout, koa top, bolt-on 3 piece maple neck, 24 fret ebony fingerboard with white dot inlay, fixed Gotoh bridge, body matching peghead with raised logo, 2 per side Gotoh tuners, gold hardware, 2 humbucker Tune pickups, volume/treble/bass/mix/filter controls, active electronics. Available in Natural finish. Curr. mfr.

Mfr.'s Sug. Retail	$2,250	$1,800	$1,350	$1,125	$900	$810	$740	$675

Add $100 for figured maple top.

This model has padauk or walnut tops optionally available.

TWB-5 — similar to TWB-4, except has 5 strings, 3/2 per side tuners. Curr. mfr.

Mfr.'s Sug. Retail	$2,450	$1,960	$1,470	$1,225	$980	$875	$805	$735

Tune Zi3-4PD bass
courtesy Tune Guitars of North America

Grading	100%	98% MINT	95% EXC+	90% EXC	80% VG+	70% VG	60% G

TWB-6 — similar to TWB-4, except has 6 strings, 3 per side tuners. Curr. mfr.

Mfr.'s Sug. Retail	$2,650	$2,120	$1,590	$1,325	$1,060	$955	$875	$795

Woodbass Series

WB-4 — offset double cutaway ash body with pointed bottom bout/hollow chamber, walnut top, wedge soundhole, bolt-on 3 piece maple neck, 2.25 octave fretless ebony fingerboard with offset white dot inlay, fixed bridge, body matching peghead with raised logo, 2 per side tuners, black hardware, 4 piezo bridge pickups, volume/treble/mid/bass controls, active electronics. Available in Natural finish. Curr. mfr.

Mfr.'s Sug. Retail	$3,200	$2,560	$1,920	$1,600	$1,280	$1,150	$1,055	$960

This model has ash or flame maple tops optionally available.

WB-5 — similar to WB-4, except has 5 strings, 3/2 per side tuners. Curr. mfr.

Mfr.'s Sug. Retail	$3,500	$2,800	$2,100	$1,750	$1,400	$1,260	$1,150	$1,050

WB-6 — similar to WB-4, except has 6 strings, 3 per side tuners. Curr. mfr.

Mfr.'s Sug. Retail	$4,000	$3,200	$2,400	$2,000	$1,600	$1,440	$1,320	$1,200

Zi-II Custom Deluxe Series

Zi-II 4C — offset double cutaway mahogany body with pointed bottom bout, koa top, thru body 3 piece maple neck, 24 fret ebony fingerboard with white dot inlay, fixed Tune bridge, body matching veneered peghead, 2 per side Gotoh tuners, gold hardware, 2 humbucker Tune pickups, volume/treble/bass/mix/filter controls, active electronics. Available in Natural finish. Curr. mfr.

Mfr.'s Sug. Retail	$2,850	$2,280	$1,710	$1,425	$1,140	$1,025	$940	$855

This model has padauk or walnut tops optionally available.

Zi-II 5C — similar to Zi-II 4C, except has 5 strings, 3/2 per side tuners. Curr. mfr.

Mfr.'s Sug. Retail	$3,100	$2,480	$1,860	$1,550	$1,240	$1,115	$1,025	$930

Zi-II 6C — similar to Zi-II 4C, except has 6 strings, 3 per side tuners. Curr. mfr.

Mfr.'s Sug. Retail	$3,350	$2,680	$2,010	$1,675	$1,340	$1,200	$1,100	$1,000

Rick Turner guitar
courtesy Rick Turner

RICK TURNER

Instruments currently built in Topanga, California. Distributed by Rick Turner Guitars of Topanga, California.

Luthier Rick Turner was one of the original three partners that formed Alembic in 1970. In 1978 he left Alembic to form Turner Guitars, and opened a workshop in 1979 in Novato, California. Although artists such as Lindsey Buckingham favored Turner's guitars, the company was closed in 1981. Turner's records show that approximately 130 instruments were built during that time period (1979-1981).

As well as building instruments, Rick Turner has written countless columns on guitar building, repairs, and products profiles in guitar magazines. Turner reopened his guitar shop in 1989, and now offers a range of instruments.

The older models from the 1979 to 1981 period show up occasionally in the vintage market, and the last asking price recorded was $2,000 for a "Lindsey Buckingham" style guitar. A twelve string guitar (the only one out of the original 130) recently had an asking price of $3,500 in Hollywood, California. Current handcrafted models have a new retail price ranging between $1,650 (model 1-A, Jr.) up to $2,585 (model 3-C).

ELECTRIC

MODEL 1-A — single cutaway arched top mahogany top and back, bound in black, five piece laminated neck with multi layer veneer overlays on peghead, 24 fret black bound rosewood fingerboard (15 frets clear of the body), 24 3/4" scale, nickel plated hardware, single Turner Humbucking pickup, Schaller tuners and roller bridge, Turner "stop" tailpiece, one volume and one tone knob. Available in a deep Red stain on the mahogany body and high gloss urethane finish. Current production.

Mfr.'s Sug. Retail   **$2,225**

Add $250 for matching bird's eye maple peghead, fingerboard, pickup ring, tailpiece, and nickel pickup cover.
Add $100 for custom colors such as Gold, Silver, Translucent Blue, Translucent Green, or others.
Add $200 for optional Mike Christian Piezo bridge and Turner blending electronics.

Model 1-B — similar to the Model 1-A, except has an active buffer and line driver preamp.

Mfr.'s Sug. Retail   **$2,375**

Model 1-C — similar to the Model 1-A, except has a quasi-parametric EQ. This model is the duplicate to the original Model 1 (1979-1981).

Mfr.'s Sug. Retail   **$2,475**

MODEL 2 — similar to the Model 1-A, except that an added Turner humbucking pickup is added to the bridge position. Current production.

Mfr.'s Sug. Retail   **$2,325**

MODEL 3-A — similar to the Model 1-A, except has an extended 27 fret ebony fingerboard (17 frets clear of the body), 24 3/4" scale. Current production.

Mfr.'s Sug. Retail $2,335

Add $250 for matching bird's eye maple peghead, fingerboard, pickup ring, tailpiece, and nickel pickup cover.

Add $100 for custom colors such as Gold, Silver, Translucent Blue, Translucent Green, or others.

Add $200 for optional Mike Christian Piezo bridge and Turner blending electronics.

Model 3-B — similar to the Model 3-A, except has an active buffer and line driver preamp.

Mfr.'s Sug. Retail $2,485

Model 3-C — similar to the Model 3-A, except has a quasi-parametric EQ.

Mfr.'s Sug. Retail $2,585

Junior Series

The Junior series was offered beginning in 1995. All models have an alder body, one piece maple neck, and no bindings or wood laminates. By saving on labor and some wood costs, the retail price of the Junior series is about $500 **less** than the Models 1,2, or 3; however, the same hardware and electronic options are offered on the Juniors as is on the regular models.

The **Model 1-A, Jr.** features similar design to the Model 1-A, single pickup, painted alder body, rosewood fingerboard, and passive electronics at a list price of $1,650. The **Model 1-B, Jr.** is the same except has an active buffer and line driver preamp built in ($1,800), and the **Model 1-C, Jr.** features a quasi-parametric EQ ($1,950). All are available in Red, Maroon, Cobalt Blue, or Forest Green. Add $77.25 for a three color sunburst.

Model T series

Another new series designed with the blues or bottleneck player in mind, the Model T features a modern recreation of the early 1930s George Beauchamp/Paul Barth "double horseshoe" magnetic pickup affixed to a Honduran mahogany or American Swamp Ash body that has a colorful front and back laminate of Formica Color-Core. The hard rock maple neck features an adjustable truss rod and double graphite reinforcing, and is designed for heavier strings. Though the design screams retro, the hardware is quite modern: Options include the Wilkinson GTB 100 combination bridge; or Schaller roller bridge combined with either a Turner Bar tailpiece, Bigsby vibrato, or the Hipshot Trilogy (multiple tunings) tailpiece. Retail prices run from the basic model ($1,250) up to the optional bridges ($1,450).

ELECTRIC/ACOUSTIC

Renaissance Series

The Renaissance series is completed in a semi-hollowbody fashion: the solid Cedar top is glued to a neck extension that runs the length of the rosewood of mahogany body. This design also features the Turner "Reference Piezo" 18 volt system .

RENAISSANCE STEEL STRING (RSS-1) — cedar top, mahogany laminate back and sides, bound in black, mahogany neck with adjustable truss rod, 24 fret rosewood fingerboard (joins body at 14th fret), 25 21/32" scale, Paua shell dot inlays and side dots, Turner "Reference Piezo" system, 18 volt Highlander Audio buffer electronics, one volume knob. Natural finish. Current production.

Mfr.'s Sug. Retail $1,700

RSS-2 — similar to the RSS-1, except features a Rosewood laminate back and sides, ebony fingerboard, Tortoise celluloid binding with half-herringbone purfling around top, multiple veneer overlays on peghead.

Mfr.'s Sug. Retail $1,900

RENAISSANCE NYLON STRING (RNS-1) — similar to the RSS-1, except rosewood neck width at nut is 2" or 1 7/8", and Paua shell side dots only. Current production.

Mfr.'s Sug. Retail $1,650

RNS-2 — similar to the RNS-1, except features a Rosewood laminate back and sides, ebony fingerboard, Tortoise celluloid binding with half-herringbone purfling around top, multiple veneer overlays on peghead.

Mfr.'s Sug. Retail $1,850

ELECTRIC BASS

Electroline Series

Electroline basses feature exotic wood, bolt-on necks, reinforcing graphite bars, and Turner-designed pickups and electronics.

ELECTROLINE 1 — swamp Ash or Honduran mahogany body, bolt-on bird's eye maple neck, fretless Ebony or Pakka wood fingerboard, 34" scale, Wilkinson bridge with Turner Reference Piezo pickups, Schaller or Hipshot Ultra-lite tuning machines, on-board Highlander Audio electronics, multiple veneer overlays on peghead. Available in Vintage Clear, Translucent Maroon, Indigo, or Forest Green. Current production.

Mfr.'s Sug. Retail $1,700

Add $77.25 for three color sunburst.

ELECTROLINE 2 — similar to the Electroline 1, except features a 21 fret fretted neck, Turner "Diamond T" magnetic pickup system, and blending electronics. Current production.

Mfr.'s Sug. Retail $1,900

TURTLETONE

Instruments currently built in Tempe, Arizona.

Luthier/designer Walter G. Gura produces a number of solid body instruments that feature interesting and innovative designs. Though Turtletone is a relatively small company, they are utilizing a number of high tech devices like CAD/CAM (Computer Aided Design/Computer Aided Manufacturing) instruments. The guitars feature maple bodies and necks, ebony fingerboard, DiMarzio pickups, and Kahler and Grover hardware. List price for the standard instrument is $1,600, and many special orders/options are available per customer order. The CAD/CAM devices can also assist in customer-specified unusual body designs, as the design can be plotted prior to building. For further information, please contact Turtletone Guitars through the Index of Current Manufacturers located in the back of this book.

TUXEDO

Instruments were made in England, West Germany, and Japan during the early to mid 1960s.

Some guitars may also carry the trademark of DALLAS.

The TUXEDO and DALLAS trademarks are the brandnames used by a UK importer/distributor. Early solid body guitars were supplied by either FENTON-WEILL or VOX in Britain, with entry level German and Japanese original design guitars imported in.

(Source: Tony Bacon and Paul Day, The Guru's Guitar Guide)

T V JONES

Instruments currently built in Whittier, California.

Luthier Tom Jones has been building quality guitars for a number of years. Jones is on the verge of introducing a new line of guitars in addition to his current production (watch for further updates in the fourth edition of the **Blue Book of Guitars**). For further information, please contact luthier Tom Jones via the Index of Current Manufacturers located in the rear of this book.

JAMES TYLER

Instruments currently built in Van Nuys, California.

Luthier James Tyler and his staff are currently building and offering a fairly wide range of custom solid body guitars and basses. Models are constructed of quality tonewoods, solid hardware and "Tyler spec'd" Lindy Fralin or Seymour Duncan pickups. For further information, please contact James Tyler Guitars through the Index of Current Manufacturers located in the back of this book.

U

UNICORD

See **UNIVOX**.

Instruments produced in Japan.

The Merson Musical Supply Company of Westbury, New York was the primary importer of Univox guitars. Merson evolved into Unicord, and also became a distributor for Westbury brand guitars.

(Source: Michael Wright, Guitar Stories Volume One, pg. 76)

UNITED

Instruments made in Elizabeth, New Jersey during the 1940s.

United guitars was owned by Frank Forcillo, ex-D'angelico worker and long time friend. D'Angelico put his name on a series of plywood body guitars that were built at either United or Code (also from New Jersey). The plywood instruments featured solid wood necks fashioned by D'Angelico, but the construction was handled out in the United plant. D'Angelico used to stock the new guitars in his showroom/workshop in New York City.

D'Angelicos by United were not numbered or recorded. The body design is perhaps more reminiscent of a Gibson ES-175, and used to carry the designation "G 7".

(Source: Paul William Schmidt, Acquired of the Angels)

UNIVERSITY

Instruments were produced by REGAL (original company of Wulschner & Son) in the late 1890s.

Indianapolis retailer/wholesaler Emil Wulschner introduced the Regal line in the 1880s, and in 1896 opened a factory to build guitars and mandolins under the following three trademarks: REGAL, 20th CENTURY, and UNIVERSITY. After Wulschner's death in 1900, the factory became part of a larger corporation.

(Source: John Teagle, Washburn: Over One Hundred Years of Fine Stringed Instruments)

UNIVOX

Instruments built in Japan.

Univox guitars were imported into the U.S. by the Merson Musical Supply Company of Westbury, New York. Merson Musical Supply later evolved into the Unicord company.

(Source: Michael Wright, Guitar Stories Volume One, pg. 76)

'71 Univox Carved Eagle
courtesy James Mayfield

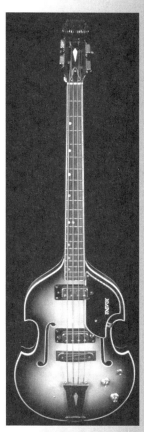

Univox Bass
courtesy Thoroughbred Music

U

V

VALCO

See NATIONAL.

Louis Dopyera bought out the National company; and as he owned more than 50% of the stock in Dobro, "merged" the two companies back together (as National Dobro). In 1936, the decision was made to move the company to Chicago, Illinois. Chicago was a veritable hotbed of mass produced musical instruments during the early to pre-World War II 1900s. Manufacturers like Washburn and Regal had facilities, and major wholesalers and retailers like the Tonk Bros. and Lyon & Healy were based there. Victor Smith, Al Frost, and Louis Dopyera moved their operation to Chicago, and in 1943 formally announced the change to VALCO (The initials of their three first names: V-A-L company). Valco worked on war materials during World War II, and returned to instrument production afterwards. Valco produced the National/Supro/Airline fiberglass body guitars in the 1950s and 1960s, as well as wood-bodied models. In the late 1960s, Valco was absorbed by the Kay company (See KAY). In 1969 or 1970, Kay/Valco Guitars, Inc. went out of business.

(Source: Tom Wheeler, American Guitars)

VALLEY ARTS

Instruments produced in City of Industry, California since 1993. Previous production was based in North Hollywood, California from 1979 to 1993. Distributed by the Samick Music Corporation of City of Industry, California.

Valley Arts originally began as a North Hollywood teaching studio in 1963. The facilities relocated to Studio City, California and through the years became known as a respected retail store that specialized in professional quality music gear. Production moved back to North Hollywood and into larger facilities in 1989, and luthier/co-owner Michael McGuire oversaw a staff of 15 employees.

In 1992, the Samick corporation became involved in a joint venture with Valley Arts, and by June of 1993 had acquired full ownership of the company. Samick operates Valley Arts as the custom shop "wing" for the company, as well as utilizing Valley Arts designs for their production guitars built overseas.

ELECTRIC

Grading	100%	98% MINT	95% EXC+	90% EXC	80% VG+	70% VG	60% G

CUSTOM PRO — offset double cutaway ash body, white pickguard, bolt-on birdseye maple neck, 24 fret rosewood fingerboard with pearl dot inlay, double locking vibrato, 6 on one side tuners, gold hardware, 2 single coil/1 humbucker EMG pickups, volume/tone control, 5 position switch. Available in Burnt Amber, Fireburst, Sunset Gold, Transparent Blue, Transparent, Cream, Transparent Green and Transparent Red finishes. Curr. mfr.

Mfr.'s Sug. Retail	$1,995	$1,496	$997	$995	$795	$720	$660	$600

Add $300 for quilted maple body with ebony fingerboard.

This model has black pickguards optionally available, depending on body finish color.

STANDARD PRO — offset double cutaway maple body, black pickguard, bolt-on maple neck, 24 fret rosewood fingerboard with pearl dot inlay, double locking vibrato, 6 on one side tuners, chrome hardware, 2 single coil/1 humbucker EMG pickups, volume/tone control, 5 position switch. Available in Black, Candy Red, Metallic Teal and White finishes. Disc. 1993.

	$1,395	$1,195	$995	$795	$720	$660	$600

Last Mfr.'s Sug. Retail was $1,995.

This model had black hardware optionally available.

STEVE LUKATHER SIGNATURE — offset double cutaway ash body, black pickguard, bolt-on birdseye maple neck, 24 fret rosewood fingerboard with pearl dot inlay, double locking vibrato, 6 on one side tuners, gold hardware, 2 single coil/1 humbucker EMG pickups, volume/tone control, 5 position switch. Available in Fireburst finish. Disc. 1993.

	$1,450	$1,240	$1,035	$830	$745	$680	$620

Last Mfr.'s Sug. Retail was $2,075.

This model was co-designed by Steve Lukather and had his signature on the back of the headstock.

This model had an ebony fingerboard optionally available.

Grading	100%	98% MINT	95% EXC+	90% EXC	80% VG+	70% VG	60% G

ELECTRIC BASS

CUSTOM PRO BASS — offset double cutaway carved herringbone bound figured maple body, bolt-on birdseye maple neck, 21 fret rosewood fingerboard with pearl dot inlay, fixed bridge, herringbone bound peghead, 4 on one side tuners, black hardware, P-style/J-style EMG pickups, 2 volume/1 tone controls. Available in Burnt Amber, Fireburst, Sunset Gold, Trans Blue, Trans Cream, Trans Green and Trans Red finishes. Curr. mfr.

Mfr.'s Sug. Retail	$2,675	$2,006	$1,337	$1,335	$1,065	$960	$880	$805

This model has ebony fingerboard, gold hardware, Bartolini pickups, 2 P-style or 2 J-style pickup configurations, active electronics optionally available.

VANTAGE

Instruments currently produced in Korea. Original production was based in Japan from 1977 to 1990. Distributed by Music Industries Corporation of Floral Park, New York, since 1987.

This trademark was established in Matsumoto, Japan, around 1977. Instruments have been manufactured in Korea since 1990. Vantage offers a wide range of guitars designed for the beginning student to the intermediate player.

ACOUSTIC

Classic Series

VSC-10 — classic style, spruce top, round soundhole, bound body, wooden inlay rosette, nato back/sides/neck, 12/19 fret rosewood fingerboard/tied bridge, rosewood peghead veneer, 3 per side chrome tuners with plastic buttons. Available in Light Pumpkin finish. Curr. mfr.

Mfr.'s Sug. Retail	$200	$160	$120	$100	$80	$70	$65	$60

VSC-20 — classic style, cedar top, round soundhole, bound body, wooden inlay rosette, ovankol back/sides, nato neck, 12/19 fret rosewood fingerboard/tied bridge, ovankol peghead veneer, 3 per side gold tuners with plastic buttons. Available in Natural finish. Curr. mfr.

Mfr.'s Sug. Retail	$240	$192	$144	$120	$95	$85	$80	$75

VSC-20CE — similar to VSC-20, except has single round cutaway, piezo bridge pickup, 3 band EQ with volume slide control.

Mfr.'s Sug. Retail	$390	$312	$234	$195	$155	$140	$125	$115

VSC-30 — similar to VSC-20, except has rosewood back/sides. Available in Light Pumpkin finish.

Mfr.'s Sug. Retail	$320	$256	$192	$160	$130	$115	$105	$95

Dreadnought Series

VS-5 — dreadnought style, spruce top, round soundhole, black pickguard, bound body, 3 stripe rosette, nato back/sides/neck, 14/20 fret nato fingerboard with white dot inlay, ebonized maple bridge with white black dot pins, 3 per side chrome tuners. Available in Natural finish. Curr. mfr.

Mfr.'s Sug. Retail	$200	$160	$120	$100	$80	$70	$65	$60

Add $10 for left handed version (VS-5/LH).

VS-10 — similar to VS-5, except has 3 stripe bound body.

Mfr.'s Sug. Retail	$220	$176	$132	$110	$90	$80	$70	$65

VS-12 — similar to VS-10, except has 12 strings, 6 per side tuners.

Mfr.'s Sug. Retail	$290	$232	$174	$145	$115	$105	$95	$85

Add $10 for Black finish (VS-12B).

VS-15 — dreadnought style, spruce top, round soundhole, black pickguard, 3 stripe bound body/rosette, nato back/sides/neck, 14/20 fret rosewood fingerboard with white dot inlay, rosewood bridge with black white dot pins, 3 per side chrome tuners. Available in Natural finish. Curr. mfr.

Mfr.'s Sug. Retail	$250	$200	$150	$125	$100	$90	$80	$75

VS-20 — dreadnought style, nato top, round soundhole, black pickguard, 3 stripe bound body/rosette, nato back/sides/neck, 14/20 fret bound rosewood fingerboard with white dot inlay, rosewood bridge with white black dot pins, bound peghead, 3 per side chrome tuners. Available in Black, Natural and Tobacco Sunburst finishes. Curr. mfr.

Mfr.'s Sug. Retail	$270	$216	$162	$135	$110	$100	$90	$80

VS-25 — dreadnought style, cedar top, round soundhole, black pickguard, herringbone bound body/rosette, ovankol back/sides, mahogany neck, 14/20 fret rosewood fingerboard with white dot inlay, rosewood bridge with white black dot pins, 3 per side tuners. Available in Natural finish. Curr. mfr.

Mfr.'s Sug. Retail	$280	$224	$168	$140	$110	$100	$90	$80

Add $50 for solid cedar top (VS-25S).
Add $60 for left handed version with solid cedar top (VS-25S/LH).

VS-25CE — similar to VS-25, except has single sharp cutaway, solid cedar top, piezo bridge pickup, 3 band EQ with volume slide control.

Mfr.'s Sug. Retail	$480	$384	$288	$240	$190	$170	$155	$145

Grading	100%	98% MINT	95% EXC+	90% EXC	80% VG+	70% VG	60% G

VS-25CE-12 — similar to VS-25CE, except has 12 strings, 6 per side tuners.

Mfr.'s Sug. Retail	$530	$424	$318	$265	$210	$190	$175	$160

VS-30 — dreadnought style, maple top, round soundhole, black pickguard, 3 stripe bound body/rosette, maple back/sides/neck, 14/20 fret bound rosewood fingerboard with white dot inlay, rosewood bridge with white black dot pins, bound peghead, 3 per side chrome tuners. Available in Natural finish. Curr. mfr.

Mfr.'s Sug. Retail	$290	$232	$174	$145	$115	$105	$95	$85

VS-33 — dreadnought style, spruce top, round soundhole, black pickguard, 5 stripe bound body/rosette, oak back/sides, mahogany neck, 14/20 fret bound rosewood fingerboard, rosewood bridge with white black dot pins, bound peghead, 3 per side chrome tuners. Available in Transparent Black, Transparent Blue and Transparent Red finishes. Curr. mfr.

Mfr.'s Sug. Retail	$300	$240	$180	$150	$120	$110	$100	$90

VS-35CE — single sharp cutaway dreadnought style, nato top, oval soundhole, 3 stripe bound body/rosette, nato back/sides/neck, 20 fret bound rosewood fingerboard with white dot inlay, rosewood bridge with white black dot pins, bound peghead, 3 per side chrome tuners, piezo bridge pickup, 3 band EQ with volume slide control. Available in Black and Tobacco Sunburst finishes. Curr. mfr.

Mfr.'s Sug. Retail	$430	$344	$258	$215	$175	$155	$140	$130

Add $10 for left handed version of this model (VS-35CE/LH).

VS-50S — dreadnought style, solid spruce top, round soundhole, black pickguard, herringbone bound body/rosette, nato back/sides/neck, 14/20 fret rosewood fingerboard with white dot inlay, rosewood bridge with white black dot pins, bound peghead, 3 per side gold tuners. Available in Natural finish. Curr. mfr.

Mfr.'s Sug. Retail	$350	$280	$210	$175	$140	$125	$115	$105

Add $10 for left handed version of this model (VS-50S/LH).

ACOUSTIC ELECTRIC

VS-40CE — single sharp cutaway dreadnought style, nato top, oval soundhole, 3 stripe bound body/rosette, nato back/sides/neck, 20 fret bound rosewood fingerboard with white dot inlay, rosewood bridge with white black dot pins, bound peghead, 3 per side chrome tuners, piezo bridge pickup, 3 band EQ with volume slide control. Available in Black and White finishes. Curr. mfr.

Mfr.'s Sug. Retail	$440	$352	$264	$220	$175	$160	$145	$135

VS-40CEM — similar to VS-40CE, except has maple back/sides.

Mfr.'s Sug. Retail	$450	$360	$270	$225	$180	$160	$150	$135

Add $10 for left handed version of this model (VS-40CEM/LH).

Add $10 for 12 string version of this model (VS-40CEM-12).

VST-40SCE — single sharp cutaway dreadnought style, solid spruce top, round soundhole, 3 stripe bound body, herringbone rosette, nato back/sides/neck, 20 fret rosewood fingerboard with white dot inlay, rosewood bridge with white black dot pins, bound peghead, 3 per side gold tuners, piezo bridge pickup, 3 band EQ with volume slide control. Available in Natural finish. Curr. mfr.

Mfr.'s Sug. Retail	$500	$400	$300	$250	$200	$180	$165	$150

ELECTRIC

100 Series

All models in this series have offset double cutaway laminated body, bolt-on maple neck, 24 fret maple fingerboard with offset black dot inlay, standard vibrato, and 6 on one side tuners, unless otherwise listed.

111T — chrome hardware, single coil/humbucker pickup, volume/tone control, 3 position switch. Available in Black, Cherry Sunburst, Red and Tobacco Sunburst finishes. Curr. mfr.

Mfr.'s Sug. Retail	$300	$240	$180	$150	$120	$110	$100	$90

Add $10 for left handed version of this model (111T/LH).

118DT — double locking vibrato, black hardware, 2 single coil/1 humbucker pickups, volume/2 tone controls, 5 position switch. Available in Gold Granite, Marble Stone, Metallic Black and Red Granite finishes. Curr. mfr.

Mfr.'s Sug. Retail	$400	$320	$240	$200	$160	$145	$130	$120

118T — chrome hardware, 2 single coil/1 humbucker pickups, volume/2 tone controls, 5 position switch. Available in Black, Cherry Sunburst and Tobacco Sunburst finishes. Curr. mfr.

Mfr.'s Sug. Retail	$330	$264	$198	$165	$130	$120	$110	$100

200 Series

All models in this series have offset double cutaway alder body, bolt-on maple necks, 24 fret maple fingerboard with offset black dot inlay, standard vibrato, 6 on one side tuners, black hardware, volume/2 tone controls, 5 position switch.

213T — 3 single coil pickups. Available in Tobacco Sunburst and Transparent Blue finishes. Curr. mfr.

Mfr.'s Sug. Retail	$360	$288	$216	$180	$145	$130	$120	$110

"... Buyers should demand a detailed invoice or sales receipt indicating non-original features and modifications as well as the manufacturer, model name and number and serial number."

—Jay Scott

TCG, Mar/Apr 1991

Grading	100%	98% MINT	95% EXC+	90% EXC	80% VG+	70% VG	60% G

218T — 2 single coil/1 humbucker pickups. Available in Transparent Black, Transparent Blue and Transparent Red finishes. Curr. mfr.

Mfr.'s Sug. Retail	$370	$296	$222	$185	$150	$135	$120	$110

300 Series

This series is the same as the 200 Series, except has rosewood fingerboards.

311T — single coil/humbucker pickup. Available in Metallic Black Cherry and Metallic Blue finishes. Curr. mfr.

Mfr.'s Sug. Retail	$380	$304	$228	$190	$150	$135	$120	$110

320T — humbucker/single coil/humbucker pickups. Available in Metallic Black, Metallic Black Cherry and Pearl White finishes. Curr. mfr.

Mfr.'s Sug. Retail	$390	$312	$234	$195	$155	$140	$125	$115

400 Series

This series is the same as the 300 Series, except has double locking vibrato.

418DT — 2 single coil/1 humbucker pickups. Available in Black Fishnet, Black Sandstone, Metallic Black and Red Sandstone finishes. Curr. mfr.

Mfr.'s Sug. Retail	$480	$384	$288	$240	$190	$170	$155	$145

600 Series

635V — double cutaway semi hollow style nato body, bound body/F-holes, raised black pickguard, nato neck, 22 fret rosewood fingerboard with offset pearl dot inlay, tunomatic/stop tailpiece, 3 per side tuners, chrome hardware, 2 humbucker pickups, 2 volume/2 tone controls, 3 position switch. Available in Black, Cherry Sunburst and Walnut finishes. Curr. mfr.

Mfr.'s Sug. Retail	$450	$360	$270	$225	$180	$160	$150	$135

Add $40 for gold hardware with Natural finish.

700 Series

All models in this series have offset double cutaway alder body, bolt-on maple neck, 24 fret rosewood fingerboard with offset pearl dot inlay, double locking vibrato, 6 on one side tuners, black hardware, volume/2 tone controls, 5 position switch, unless otherwise noted.

718DT — 2 single coil/1 humbucker pickups, coil tap. Available in Burgundy, Dark Marble Stone, Transparent Black and Transparent Red finishes. Curr. mfr.

Mfr.'s Sug. Retail	$500	$400	$300	$250	$200	$180	$165	$150

720DT — humbucker/single coil/humbucker pickups, coil tap. Available in Dark Marble Stone, Multi-color and Red Granite finishes. Curr. mfr.

Mfr.'s Sug. Retail	$550	$440	$330	$275	$220	$200	$180	$165

728GDT — figured maple top, bound fingerboard, gold hardware, 2 single coil/1 humbucker pickups, coil tap. Available in Antique Violin finish. Curr. mfr.

Mfr.'s Sug. Retail	$630	$504	$378	$315	$250	$225	$205	$190

800 Series

All models in this series have offset double cutaway alder body, bound figured maple top, bolt-on maple neck, bound rosewood fingerboard with offset pearl dot inlay, double locking vibrato, body matching bound peghead, 6 on one side tuners, volume/2 tone controls, 5 position switch.

818DT — black hardware, 2 single coil/1 humbucker pickups, coil tap. Available in Transparent Black, Transparent Blue and Transparent Red finishes. Curr. mfr.

Mfr.'s Sug. Retail	$500	$400	$300	$250	$200	$180	$165	$150

Add $30 for gold hardware (818GDT).

820GDT — gold hardware, humbucker/single coil/humbucker pickups, coil tap. Available in Transparent Blue and Transparent Burgundy finishes. Curr. mfr.

Mfr.'s Sug. Retail	$550	$440	$330	$275	$220	$200	$180	$165

900 Series

928GDT — offset double cutaway ash body, thru body 7 piece maple rosewood neck, 24 fret rosewood fingerboard with offset pearl dot inlay, double locking vibrato, 6 on one side tuners, gold hardware, 2 single coil/1 humbucker pickups, volume/2 tone controls, 5 position/coil tap switches. Available in Transparent Burgundy finish. Curr. mfr.

Mfr.'s Sug. Retail	$850	$680	$510	$425	$340	$305	$280	$255

ELECTRIC BASS

225B — offset double cutaway alder body, bolt-on maple neck, 20 fret maple fingerboard with offset black dot inlay, fixed bridge, 2 per side tuners, chrome hardware, P-style pickup, volume/tone control. Available in Black, Dark Blue Sunburst and Red finishes. Curr. mfr.

Mfr.'s Sug. Retail	$330	$264	$198	$165	$130	$120	$110	$100

330B — similar to 225B, except has rosewood fingerboard with offset pearl inlay, black hardware, P-style/J-style pickups, 2 volume/1 tone controls. Available in Transparent Black, Transparent Blue and Transparent Red finishes. Curr. mfr.

Mfr.'s Sug. Retail	$400	$320	$240	$200	$160	$145	$130	$120

Also available with fretless fingerboard.

525B — similar to 330B, except has higher quality bridge. Available in Black Fishnet and Red Granite finishes. Curr. mfr.

Mfr.'s Sug. Retail	$420	$336	$252	$210	$170	$150	$135	$125

725B — offset double cutaway asymmetrical alder body, bolt-on maple neck, 24 fret rosewood fingerboard with offset pearl dot inlay, fixed bridge, 2 per side tuners, black hardware, P-style/J-style pickups, 2 volume/2 tone controls. Available in Black, Dark Marble Stone, Metallic Black, Pearl White, Red and Transparent Red finishes. Curr. mfr.

Mfr.'s Sug. Retail	$450	$360	$270	$225	$180	$160	$150	$135

Add $10 for left handed version of this model.

Also available with fretless fingerboard.

750B — similar to 725B, except has 5 strings, 3/2 per side tuners. Available in Blue Marble Stone and Pearl White finishes.

Mfr.'s Sug. Retail	$500	$400	$300	$250	$200	$180	$165	$150

Add $50 for active electronics.

930B — offset double cutaway asymmetrical ash body, thru body 7 piece maple/rosewood neck, 24 fret rosewood fingerboard with offset pearl dot inlay, fixed bridge, 2 per side tuners, gold hardware, P-style/J-style pickups, 2 volume/2 tone controls. Available in Transparent Burgundy and Transparent Purple finishes. Curr. mfr.

Mfr.'s Sug. Retail	$750	$600	$450	$375	$300	$270	$245	$225

VANTEK

Instruments produced in Korea, and distributed by Music Industries Corporation of Floral Park, New York.

These instruments are built with the entry level player or beginning student in mind by Vantage in Korea.

VARSITY

See WEYMANN & SONS.

VEGA

Instruments are currently built in Korea, and distributed by ANTARES.

Historically, Vega guitars were produced in Boston, Massachusetts.

The predessor company to Vega was founded in 1881 by Swedish immigrant Julius Nelson, C. F. Sunderberg, Mr. Swenson, and several other men. Nelson was the foreman of a 20-odd man workforce (which later rose to 130 employees during the 1920s banjo boom). Nelson, and his brother Carl, gradually bought out the other partners, and incorporated in 1903 as Vega (which means 'star'). In 1904, Vega acquired banjo maker A. C. Fairbanks & Company after Fairbanks suffered a fire, and Fairbank's David L. Day became Vega's general manager.

Vega built banjos under the Bacon trademark, named after popular banjo artist Frederick J. Bacon. Bacon set up his own production facility in Connecticut in 1921, and a year later wooed Day away from Vega to become the vice president in the newly reformed **Bacon & Day** company. While this company marketed several models of guitars, they had no facility for building them. It is speculated that the Bacon & Day guitars were built by the Regal company of Chicago, Illinois.

In the mid 1920s Vega began marketing a guitar called the **Vegaphone**. By the early 1930s, Vega started concentrating more on guitar production, and less on banjo making. Vega debuted its Electrovox electric guitar and amplifier in 1936, and a electric volume control footpedal in 1937. Vega is reported to have built over 40,000 guitars during the 1930s.

In the 1940s, Vega continued to introduce models such as the Duo-Tron and the Supertron; and by 1949 had become both a guitar producer and a guitar wholesaler as it bought bodies built by Harmony. In 1970 Vega was acquired by the C. F. Martin company for its banjo operations. Martin soon folded Vega's guitar production, and applied the trademark to a line of imported guitars. Ten years later, Martin sold the Vega trademark rights to a Korean guitar production company.

(Source: Tom Wheeler, American Guitars

VEILLETTE GUITARS

Instruments currently built in Woodstock, New York.

Joe Veillette has worked with both Harvey Citron and Stuart Spector as well as doing custom work under his own brandname. Veillette is currently concentrating on new production, as well as doing some consulting for the guitar industry. For further information on model availablility and prices, please contact designer Joe Veillette via the Index of Current Manufacturers located in the back of this book.

VEILLETTE-CITRON

Instruments built in Brooklyn and Kingston, New York from 1976 to 1983.

The Veillette-Citron company was founded in 1975 by namesakes Joe Veillette and Harvey Citron. Rather than copy the current staus quo, both Veillette and Citron built high quality neck-through guitar and bass models that featured brass hardware and their own pickups. The Veillette-Citron company made their official debut at the 1976 NAMM show, and production followed soon after. Working by themselves, and sometimes joined by a workforce of up to five employees, Veillette-Citron instruments were entirely handcrafted.

After the company closed its doors in 1983, Citron went on to write straightforward, fact-filled columns for **Guitar Player** magazine (also Bass Player and Guitar World) and produced a 90 minute video tape entitled **Basic Guitar Set-Up and Repair** (Homespun Tapes). Citron also licensed the X-92 'Breakaway' to the Guild company in 1985. Citron debuted a new line of guitars and basses in 1994, which featured both bolt-on and neck-through designs and Citron-designed pickups.

Joe Veillette began performing with the musical group the Phantoms during the 1980s, and returned to guitar building in 1991 when he joined into a partnership with Stuart Spector. Veillette reintroduced his Shark Baritone guitar, and later left to start his own shop. In addition to custom built guitars, Veillette has also done some consulting work for other instrument manufacturers.

(Source: Baker Rorick, Vintage Guitar Magazine, September 1996)

VEKTOR ELECTRIC UPRIGHT

Instruments currently built in Viersen, Germany.

In 1969, Sven Henrik Gawron began studying the doublebass at the age of 12. Ten years later he attended the Folkwang-Hochschule Conservatory in Essen, Germany, and participated in several modern jazz foundations. Gawron began seriously studying the repair and restoration of acoustic double basses in 1980, which lead to his opening of "Studio fur Kontrabasse" eight years later as a music shop specializing in doublebasses, pickups, and amplification. Gawron collaborated with M. B. Schulz Design in Dusseldorf in 1992 to develop the prototype of the "Vectorbass", a slim, modern electric upright bass. The **Vektor Electric Upright** is available in 4- or 5-string configurations, maple body, and ebony fingerboard. For further information, please contact designer Gawron via the Index of Current Manufacturers located in the back of this book.

VELENO

Guitars were built in Florida during the early 1970s.

Designer/guitar teacher John Veleno came up with the idea for an aluminum body guitar in 1969, and began producing them in 1970. Veleno guitars have a equal horn dual cutaway profile body, and are constructed of two halves of routed aluminum blanks that are later combined together. The neck is a aluminum/magnesium composite, and the 'V'-shaped peghead was designed by Veleno's wife (the red stone on the headstock is a replica of her birthstone, a ruby).

(Source: Tom Wheeler, American Guitars)

VENTURA

Instruments produced in Japan.

Ventura guitars were distributed in the U.S. market by C. Bruno & Company of New York, New York.

(Source: Michael Wright, Guitar Stories Volume One, pg. 76)

VERSOUL

Instruments built in Helsinki, Finland since 1994.

Versoul Ltd. was founded in 1994 by Kari Neiminen, who has over 20 years backround in guitar making and design. Neiminen combines concern for the acoustic tone of his instruments with his innovative designs to produce a masterful instrument. Both the handcrafted **Zoel** and **Touco** models reflect his commitment to excellence. Neiminen's production is on a limited basis (he estimates about one guitar a week) in his humidity controlled workshop. For further information, please contact luthier Neiminen via the Index of Current Manufacturers located in the back of this book.

"... Mediated deals, deals in which a third party attempts to insert himself into a deal as a middleman to make a profit of commission while not owning or having formally consigned the guitar - which seem on the rise, should be handled with particular care and caution."
—Jay Scott
TCG/Mar/Apr 1991

V

Grading	100%	98% MINT	95% EXC+	90% EXC	80% VG+	70% VG	60% G

VESTAX

Instruments currently built in Japan. Distributed by the Vestax Corporation of Fairfield, California.

Vestax offers a quality archtop guitar that echos the classic designs of the 1940s and 1950s. For further information, please contact Vestax via the Index of Current Manufacturers located in the back of this book.

VESTER

Instruments built in Korea during the early 1990s. Distributed in the U.S. market by Midco International of Effingham, Illinois.

The Vester trademark was established in 1990 by Midco International, and widely distributed these solid body guitars that were designed for the entry level beginner to the intermediate guitarist. Midco discontinued the Vester trademark in 1994 in favor of their popular **Lotus** line of guitars.

ELECTRIC

JAR 1370 — offset double cutaway carved alder body, bolt-on maple neck, 24 fret rosewood fingerboard with pearl sharktooth inlay, double locking vibrato, 6 on one side Gotoh tuners, black hardware, 2 single coil/1 humbucker alnico pickups, volume/tone/preamp controls, 5 position switch. Available in Metallic Ice Blue, Metallic Red and Pearl White finishes. Disc. 1994.

	$420	$360	$300	$240	$215	$195	$180

Last Mfr.'s Sug. Retail was $600.

JAR 1380 — offset double cutaway mahogany body, carved bound figured maple top, bolt-on maple neck, 24 fret rosewood fingerboard with mixed sharktooth/dot inlay, block "Vester" inlay at 24th fret, double locking vibrato, 6 on one side tuners, black hardware, 2 active humbucker pickups, volume/tone control, 3 position switch. Available in Cherry Burst, Transparent Black and Transparent Green finishes. Disc. 1994.

	$490	$420	$350	$280	$250	$230	$210

Last Mfr.'s Sug. Retail was $700.

JAR 1400 — offset double cutaway alder body, bolt-on maple neck, 22 fret rosewood fingerboard with mixed pearl sharktooth/dot inlay, double locking vibrato, 6 on one side Gotoh tuners, black hardware, 2 single coil/1 humbucker pickups, volume/tone control, 5 position and coil tap switches. Available in Fluorescent Yellow, Metallic Dark Blue, Metallic Red and Pearl White finishes. Disc. 1994.

	$420	$360	$300	$240	$215	$195	$180

Last Mfr.'s Sug. Retail was $600.

JAR 1412 — offset double cutaway alder body, bolt-on maple neck, 24 fret rosewood fingerboard with pearl dot inlay, fixed bridge, 12 string headstock, 6 per side Gotoh tuners, black hardware, 2 humbucker pickups, volume/tone control, 3 position switch. Available in Metallic Dark Blue, Metallic Red and Pearl White finishes. Disc. 1994.

	$420	$360	$300	$240	$215	$195	$180

Last Mfr.'s Sug. Retail was $600.

JFA 500 — semi hollow offset double cutaway, alder body, bound spruce top, lightning bolt soundhole, maple neck, 22 fret rosewood fingerboard with pearl dot inlay, tunomatic bridge/stop tailpiece, 6 on one side tuners, chrome hardware, single coil/humbucker pickups, volume/tone control, 3 position switch, coil split in tone control. Available in Red, Tobacco Sunburst and White finishes. Disc. 1994.

	$280	$240	$200	$160	$145	$130	$120

Last Mfr.'s Sug. Retail was $400.

JJM 1010 — offset double cutaway alder body, black pickguard, bolt-on maple neck, 22 fret maple fingerboard with black dot inlay, standard vibrato, 6 on one side tuners, chrome hardware, 2 single coil/1 humbucker pickups, volume/tone control, 5 position switch. Available in Black, Red and White finishes. Disc. 1994.

	$210	$180	$150	$120	$110	$100	$90

Last Mfr.'s Sug. Retail was $300.

JJM 1020 — similar to JJM 1010, except has 24 frets, double locking vibrato, humbucker/single coil/humbucker pickups. Available in Black, Fluorescent Yellow, Red and White finishes. Disc. 1994.

	$350	$300	$250	$200	$180	$165	$150

Last Mfr.'s Sug. Retail was $500.

JJR 550 — offset double cutaway alder body, bolt-on maple neck, 22 fret rosewood fingerboard with pearl dot inlay, double locking vibrato, 6 on one side tuners, chrome hardware, single coil/humbucker pickups, volume control, 3 position switch. Available in Blue Green, Metallic Gold and Rubine Red finishes. Disc. 1994.

	$235	$200	$170	$135	$125	$115	$105

Add $30 for graphic designs.

Last Mfr.'s Sug. Retail was $340.

JJR 1070 — offset double cutaway alder body, bolt-on maple neck, 24 fret rosewood bound fingerboard with pearl inverted V inlay, double locking vibrato, 6 on one side tuners, black hardware, humbucker/single coil/humbucker pickups, 3 mini switches. Available in Pearl White finish. Disc. 1994.

	$320	$275	$230	$185	$165	$150	$140

Add $40 for Graphic Designs finish.

Grading	100%	98% MINT	95% EXC+	90% EXC	80% VG+	70% VG	60% G

Last Mfr.'s Sug. Retail was $460.

JJR 1170 — offset double cutaway alder body, set maple neck, 24 fret rosewood fingerboard with pearl sharktooth inlay, double locking vibrato, 6 on one side tuners, black hardware, 2 single coil/1 humbucker alnico pickups, volume/tone and preamp controls, 3 mini switches, active electronics. Available in Black finish. Disc. 1994.

| | $310 | $265 | $220 | $175 | $160 | $145 | $135 |

Last Mfr.'s Sug. Retail was $440.

JJR 1175 — similar to JJR 1170, except has 2 humbucker pickups, no preamp control or mini switches, 5 position switch. Available in Metallic Charcoal Grey and Pearl White finishes. Disc. 1994.

| | $310 | $265 | $220 | $175 | $160 | $145 | $135 |

Subtract $40 for Crackle Blue/Green/Red/Yellow, Crackle Silver/Blue and Crackle Yellow/Blue finishes.

Last Mfr.'s Sug. Retail was $440.

JJR 1290 — offset double cutaway alder body, bound figured maple top, bolt on maple neck, 24 fret bound rosewood fingerboard with pearl dot inlay, double locking vibrato, 6 on one side Gotoh tuners, black hardware, 2 single coil/1 humbucker pickups, volume/tone control, 5 position switch. Available in Cherry Sunburst, Transparent Blue, Transparent Green and Transparent Red finishes. Disc. 1994.

| | $330 | $280 | $235 | $190 | $170 | $155 | $140 |

Last Mfr.'s Sug. Retail was $470.

Models with the Transparent Red finish have reverse headstocks.

JJR 1462 — doubleneck construction. with one side being similar to JAR 1412 and the other being similar to JJR 1030. Both necks have 22 fret rosewood fingerboards with pearl dot inlay, 3 position neck selector switch included. Available in White finish. Disc. 1994.

| | $840 | $720 | $600 | $480 | $430 | $395 | $360 |

Last Mfr.'s Sug. Retail was $1,200.

OAR 1500 — offset double cutaway asymmetrical mahogany body, carved maple top, set mahogany neck, 24 fret rosewood fingerboard with pearl dot inlay, standard vibrato, 3 per side Gotoh locking tuners, chrome hardware, 2 humbucker pickups, volume tone control, 3 position and coil split mini switches. Available in Metallic Red, Pearl Blue and Pearl White finishes. Disc. 1994.

| | $420 | $360 | $300 | $240 | $215 | $195 | $180 |

Last Mfr.'s Sug. Retail was $600.

ELECTRIC BASS

OPR 436 — offset double cutaway asymmetrical maple body, bolt-on maple neck, 24 fret rosewood fingerboard with pearl dot inlay, fixed bridge, 2 per side tuners, chrome hardware, P-style/J-style pickups, 2 volume/1 tone controls. Available in Black and Metallic Red finishes. Disc. 1994.

| | $265 | $225 | $190 | $150 | $135 | $120 | $110 |

Last Mfr.'s Sug. Retail was $380.

OPR 935 — similar to OPR 436, except has alder body and black hardware. Available in Black, Blue and Metallic Red finishes. Disc. 1994.

| | $280 | $240 | $200 | $160 | $145 | $130 | $120 |

Last Mfr.'s Sug. Retail was $400.

OPR 935EQ — similar to OPR 935, except has volume/treble/bass and mix controls and active electronics. Available in Black and Metallic Red finishes.

| | $295 | $250 | $210 | $170 | $150 | $135 | $125 |

Last Mfr.'s Sug. Retail was $420.

OPR 1135 — offset double cutaway asymmetrical alder body, bolt-on maple neck, 24 fret rosewood fingerboard with pearl dot inlay, fixed bridge, 2 per side tuners, black hardware, 2 humbucker pickups, 2 volume/1 tone controls. Available in Black and White finishes. Disc. 1994.

| | $315 | $270 | $225 | $180 | $160 | $150 | $135 |

Last Mfr.'s Sug. Retail was $450.

OPR 1135EQ — similar to OPR 1135, except has volume/treble/bass and mix controls and active electronics.

| | $350 | $300 | $250 | $200 | $180 | $165 | $150 |

Last Mfr.'s Sug. Retail was $500.

OPR 1235 — similar to OPR 1135, except has 5 strings, 3/2 per side tuners, P-style/J-style pickups, 1 volume/2 tone controls, 3 position mini switch. Available in Black and Metallic Red finishes. Disc. 1994.

| | $350 | $300 | $250 | $200 | $180 | $165 | $150 |

Last Mfr.'s Sug. Retail was $500.

OPR 1335EQ — similar to OPR 1235, except has 2 humbucker pickups, volume/ treble/bass and mix controls and active electronics. Available in Black and Pearl White finishes.

| | $385 | $330 | $275 | $220 | $200 | $180 | $165 |

Last Mfr.'s Sug. Retail was $550.

OPR 1435EQ — offset double cutaway carved alder body, bolt-on 5 piece maple/mahogany neck, 24 fret rosewood fingerboard with pearl dot inlay, fixed bridge, 2 per side tuners, black hardware, P-style/J-style pickups, volume/treble/bass/mix controls, active electronics. Available in Fluorescent Blue, Metallic Charcoal Grey and Pearl White finishes. Disc. 1994.

| | $370 | $320 | $265 | $210 | $190 | $175 | $160 |

Last Mfr.'s Sug. Retail was $530.

VICTOR

See chapter on House Brands.

This trademark has been identified as a "House Brand" of the RCA Victor Record Stores.

(Source: Willie G. Moseley, Stellas & Stratocasters)

VIGIER

Instruments produced in Evry, France since 1980.

Luthier Patrice Vigier has been offering high quality solid body instruments since the early 1980s, and features advanced original designs. For example, the Nautilus bass that debuted in 1983 had an onboard circuitry design that allowed instant access to 19 pre-programmed control settings that were stored by the player.

ELECTRIC

ARPEGE III — offset double cutaway asymmetrical flame maple body, thru body maple neck, 22 fret Phenowood fingerboard, double locking vibrato, 3 per side tuners, black hardware, 2 humbucker pickups, volume/tone/mix controls, 3 position and memory switches, coil split in volume control. Available in Antique Violin, Ash, Aquatic Blue, Burgundy, Emerald Green, French Kiss, Honey, Night Blue and Red finishes. Curr. mfr.

Mfr.'s Sug. Retail	$3,770	$2,827	$1,885	$1,880	$1,500	$1,350	$1,235	$1,125

All finishes are transparent.

EXCALIBUR — offset double cutaway ash body, mirrored pickguard, bolt-on maple neck, 24 fret maple fingerboard with black dot inlay, double locking vibrato, 6 on one side Gotoh tuners, chrome hardware, 3 single coil Seymour Duncan pickups, volume/tone control, 5 position switch. Available in Black, Honey, Natural Malt, Ocean Blue and Wine Fire finishes. Curr. mfr.

Mfr.'s Sug. Retail	$1,730	$1,384	$1,038	$865	$690	$625	$570	$520

Add $40 for 2 single coil/1 humbucker pickup configuration.

Add $65 for humbucker/single coil/humbucker pickup configuration.

Excalibur Custom — similar to Excalibur, except has bound flame maple top, body color matching head stock.

Mfr.'s Sug. Retail	$2,045	$1,636	$1,227	$1,025	$820	$745	$675	$615

Add $40 for 2 single coil/1 humbucker pickup configuration.

Add $65 for humbucker/single coil/humbucker pickup configuration.

PASSION III — offset double cutaway asymmetrical alder body, half thru body carbon fiber weave neck, 24 fret Phenowood fingerboard, double locking vibrato, pearl logo inlay on peghead, 3 per side tuners with quick winders, chrome hardware, 2 single coil/1 humbucker Seymour Duncan pickups, push/pull volume control with active electronics switch, 6 position rotary tone control with parametric EQ, 3 position switch. Available in Antique Violin, Black, Burnt Metal, Devil Burnt Metal, Ferrari Red, Flip Flop Blue, Fuschia, Lemon, Natural, Night Blue, Pearl White, Peppermint, Silver Black, Sunburst Grey and Transparent Red finishes. Curr. mfr.

Mfr.'s Sug. Retail	$3,150	$2,520	$1,890	$1,575	$1,260	$1,130	$1,040	$945

ELECTRIC BASS

ARPEGE III — offset double cutaway asymmetrical flame maple body, thru body maple neck, 21 fret Phenowood fingerboard, fixed bridge, 2 per side tuners, black hardware, 2 single coil pickups, volume/tone/mix/bypass controls, memory switch. Available in Antique Violin, Ash, Aquatic Blue, Burgundy, Devil Burnt, Emerald Green, French Kiss, Honey, Night Blue and Red finishes. Curr. mfr.

Mfr.'s Sug. Retail	$3,685	$2,763	$1,842	$1,840	$1,470	$1,325	$1,215	$1,100

All finishes are transparent.

Add $295 for 5-string version of this model.

Add $690 for 6-string version of this model.

PASSION III — double offset cutaway asymmetrical alder body, half thru carbon fiber weave neck, 21 fret Phenowood fingerboard, fixed bridge, 2 per side tuners, black hardware, 2 single coil pickups, volume/tone/mix controls, parametric EQ/active electronic switches. Available in Antique Violin, Black, Devil Burnt Metal, Ferrari Red, Flip Flop Blue, Fuschia, Lemon, Natural, Night Blue, Pearl White, Peppermint, Silver Black, Sunburst Grey and Transparent Red finishes. Curr. mfr.

Mfr.'s Sug. Retail	$2,960	$2,220	$1,480	$1,475	$1,180	$1,060	$975	$885

Passion III Custom — similar to Passion III, except has flame maple body, chrome hardware. Available in Antique Violin, Aquatic Blue, Ash, Burgundy, Devil Burnt, Emerald Green, French Kiss, Honey, Night Blue and Red finishes.

Mfr.'s Sug. Retail	$3,240	$2,592	$1,944	$1,625	$1,300	$1,170	$1,070	$975

Add $285 for 5-string version of this model.

Add $580 for 6-string version of this model.

VIRTUOSO

Instruments built in England from 1986 to date.

Custom builder Jerry Flint produces a number of high quality solid body instruments based on classic Fender designs.

(Source: Tony Bacon and Paul Day, The Guru's Guitar Guide)

VISION

Instruments produced in Japan during the late 1980s.

These medium to good quality solid body guitars featured a design based on the classic Stratocaster.

(Source: Tony Bacon and Paul Day, The Guru's Guitar Guide)

VIVI-TONE

Instruments built in Kalamazoo, Michigan during the early 1930s.

After pioneering such high quality instruments for Gibson in the 1920s (such as the F-5 Mandolin), Designer/engineer/builder Lloyd Loar founded the Vivi-Tone company to continue exploring designs too radical for Gibson. It is rumored that Loar designed a form of stand-up bass that was amplified while at Gibson, but this prototype was never developed. Loar, along with partners Lewis A. Williams and Walter Moon started Vivi-Tone in 1933. Loar continued building his pioneering designs, such as an acoustic guitar with sound holes in the rear, but failed to find commercial success. However, it is because of his early successes at Gibson that researchers approach the Vivi-tone designs with some wonderment instead of discounting the radical ideas altogether.

(Source: Tom Wheeler, American Guitars)

VOX

Instruments originally built in England from 1960 to 1966; production then moved to Italy for the late 1960s up to the early 1970s. After Italian production ceased, some solid body models were built in Japan during the 1980s.

The Vox company, perhaps better known for its amplifier design, also built fashionable and functional guitars and basses during the 1960s. While the early guitar models produced tended to be entry level instruments based on popular Fender designs, later models expressed an originality that fit in well with the 1960s British "Pop" music explosion.

Thomas Walter Jennings was born in London, England on February 28, 1917. During World War II he saw action with the English Royal Engineers, and received a medical discharge in 1941. By 1944 Jennings had a part-time business dealing in secondhand accordians and other musical instruments, and by 1946 had set up shop. Along with fellow musical acquaintance Derek Underdown, Jennings produced the Univox organ in 1951 and formed the Jennings Organ Company not long after. Based on the success of his organs for several years, Jennings teamed up with engineer Dick Denney to build amplifiers under the Vox trademark. In mid 1958, Jennings reincorporated the company as Jennings Musical Instruments (JMI). When rock 'n roll hit Britain, Vox amps were there.

The first Vox guitars were introduced in 1961. Early models like the Stroller or Clubman were entry level instruments based on Fender designs. Quality improved a great deal when Vox brought in necks built by EKO in Recanati, Italy. Tom Jennings then assembled a three engineer design team of Bob Pearson (quality and materials control), Mike Bennett (prototypes), and Ken Wilson (styling design) to develop a more original-looking instrument. The resulting 5-sided Phantom in late 1962 featured a Strat-ish three single coil pickup selection and a Bigsby-derived tremolo. Further Phantom models were developed in 1963, as well as the Mark VI series ("teardrop" body shapes). When production moved to Italy in 1964, Vox guitars were built by EKO. Vox also offered a 12 string Mandoguitar, and a Bouzouki. A number of hollowbody models such as the Lynx, Bobcat, and Cougar were made by Crucianelli in Italy during the mid 1960s.

In order to generate funds for the company, Jennings sold a substantial amount of shares to the Royston group in 1964, and later that same year the entire shareholding was acquired. JMI is officially renamed Vox Sound Ltd. Thomas Organs was already supplying JMI for organs in the British market, and was looking for a reciprocal agreement to import Vox amps to the U.S. market. However, Joe Benaron (president of Thomas Organs) was really into transistors, and began "supplementing" the British tube models with solid-state amps developed at Thomas laboratories at La Sepulveda, California. To clearly illustrate this sorry state of affairs, compare a U.S. "Super Beatle" amp against a British AC-100. The Vox line begins the slump that befell other corporate-run music instrument producers during the late 1960s and 1970s. Soon Japanese-built models appear on the market with Vox on their headstock, including a Les Paul copy issued in 1970. Later, the Vox name appeared on a series of original design solid body guitars (24 series, 25 series, White Shadows) during the early to mid 1980s.

Identification of Vox instruments is fairly easy, as the model names generally appear on the pickguards. However, there are models and configurations that do need to be doublechecked! Collectible Vox guitars seem to be the models built between 1962 and 1969, and solid body models are favored over the hollowbody ones.

(Instruments identified in part through Vox catalog reprint courtesy Kevin Macy, Weaseltone Reprints)

ACOUSTIC

In the late 1960s, Thomas Organ distributed a number of Vox acoustic guitars. Steel-string models such as the **Country Western**, **Folk XII**, and **Fold Twelve Electro** had a simple horizontal "Vox" logo on the peghead. The **Rio Grande**,

late 1960s Vox
courtesy Mike Coulson

Shenandoah (12 string), and **Silver Sage** (12 string) had more ornate inlay decorations around the logo, and the horizontal Vox lettering was thicker.

ELECTRIC

In general, the Vox solid body guitars that feature Fender-ish designs (like the Clubman or Stroller) in 80% -90% condition are priced between $200 and $300. "Plain" hollowbody model (like the Bobcat) may run $250-$350; the more elaborate models like the late 1960s guitars with all the "bells and whistles" (built in "E" tuner and effects) may be priced between $300 to $550 (although some really clean models may be as high as $900).

ACE — offset double cutaway body, bolt-on neck, 6 on a side headstock, 2 single coil pickups, chrome hardware, volume/2 tone controls, 3-way selector switch. Available in White, Red, and Sunburst. Mfg. 1960 to 1966.

Super Ace — similar to the Ace, except has three single coil pickups. Pickup selector switch mounted on lower treble bout. Mfg. 1960 to 1966.

APACHE — asymetrical rounded body, six on a side tuners, 3 single coils pickups, chrome hardware, vibrato bridge, volume/2 tone knobs, pickup selector switch. Mfg. 1960 to 1966.

APOLLO — single Florentine cutaway hollow body, six on a side headstock, 1 single coil pickup with black cover, raised white pickguard, 2 f-holes, chrome hardware, trapeze bridge, volume/tone controls. Features an "E tuner" on/off switch, a Treble/Bass boost on/off switch and control, and Distortion on/off switch and control all mounted on a metal plate on lower body bout. Available in Sunburst or Cherry finishes. Mfg. 1966 to 1969.

BOBCAT — dual cutaway hollow body, 3+3 headstock, 3 single coil pickups, raised white pickguard, 2 f-holes, chrome hardware, roller bridge/tremolo system, 2 volume/2 tone controls, pickup selector switch. Mfg. 1966 to 1969.

BOSSMAN — single cutaway hollow body, rounded treble bout, six on a side headstock, 1 single coil pickup with black cover, raised white pickguard, 2 f-holes, chrome hardware, trapeze bridge, volume/tone controls. Features an "E tuner" on/off switch, a Treble/Bass boost on/off switch and control, and Distortion on/off switch and control all mounted on a metal plate on lower body bout. Available in Sunburst or Cherry finishes. Mfg. 1966 to 1969.

BULLDOG — offset double cutaway body with beveled ridge along top edge, 3+3 headstock, 3 single coils, chrome hardware, vibrato bridge, volume/2 tone controls, pickup selector switch on lower treble bout. Mfg. 1969 to 1970.

The Bulldog model is a relatively rare solid body electric. 80% - 90% models generally run around $400.

CHEETAH — dual cutaway hollow body, six on a side headstock, 2 single coil pickups with chrome covers, raised black pickguard, 2 f-holes, chrome hardware, roller bridge/tremolo system, volume/2 tone controls, pickup selector switch, "E tuner" on/off switch mounted on lower treble bout. "On-board" effects mounted on a metal plate features a Treble/Bass boost on/off switch and control, Distortion on/off switch and control, "Percussion" (a repeating echo-like function) on/off switch and control. Available in Sunburst or Cherry finishes. Mfg. 1964 to 1969.

CLUBMAN — offset double cutaway body, bolt-on neck, 19 fret neck with white dot position markers, six on a side tuners, chrome hardware, bridge/fixed tailpiece, 2 single coil pickups, 2 volume/1 tone knobs, white pickguard. Available in White or Red. Mfg. 1960 to 1966.

CONSORT (First Series) — similar to the Super Ace, except has smaller rounded off horns, a Bigsby-styled tremolo system, Sycamore neck and rosewood fingerboard. Available in Red or Sunburst. Mfg. 1961 to 1963.

CONSORT (Second Series) — similar to the Consort (First Series), except has a different "Vox" vibrato. Mfg. 1963 to 1965.

DELTA — similar to the Phantom model, except has knobs everywhere! Controls mounted on a black pickguard: built-in "E" tuner, distortion booster, treble/bass boost, and repeat "Percussion". 2 single coil pickups, roller bridge/"Bigsby"-style tremolo. Available in a White finish. Mfg. 1968 to 1969.

GRAND PRIX — single Florentine cutaway hollow body, six on a side headstock, 2 Ferro-Sonic single coil pickups with chrome covers, 21 fret neck with white block inlays, raised black pickguard, 2 f-holes, chrome hardware, roller bridge/tremolo system, extra palm vibrato, volume/2 tone controls, pickup selector switch, "E tuner" on/off switch mounted on a small plate. "On-board" effects mounted on a metal plate features a Treble/Bass boost on/off switch and control, Distortion on/off switch and control, "Wah Wah" control, and "Percussion" (a repeating echo-like function) on/off switch and control. Available in Sunburst or Cherry finishes. Mfg. 1967 to 1969.

HARLEM — offset double cutaway body, six on a side headstock, 2 single coils, chrome hardware, white pickguard, volume/2 tone controls, pickup selector switch located on upper bass bout. Mfg. 1965 to 1968.

The fingerboard on the Harlem model is scalloped on the treble side, and straight on the bass side.

Retail Price of the Vox Harlem in 1965 was $189.

INVADER — offset Mosrite-styled double cutaway solid body, six on a side tuners, 22 fret neck with white block inlays, ornate inlaid headstock design, 2 single coil pickups, chrome hardware, Bigsby-styled tremolo with extra palm bar, 1 volume/2 tone knobs, pickup selector switch, built-in "E" tuner. "On-board" effects mounted on the black pickguard includes a Treble/Bass boost on/off switch and control, Distortion on/off switch and control, "Wah Wah" control, and "Percussion" (a repeating echo-like function) on/off switch and control. Available in Sunburst finish. Mfg. 1968 to 1969.

LYNX — dual cutaway hollow body, 3+3 headstock, 3 single coil pickups, raised white pickguard, 2 f-holes, chrome hardware, roller bridge/tremolo system, 2 volume/2 tone controls, pickup selector switch. Mfg. 1964 to 1969.

Super Lynx Deluxe — similar to the Lynx, except has two single coil pickups and black control knobs. Mfg. 1964 to 1967.

MANDOGUITAR — Rounded single cutaway body, 6+6 headstock, octave-sized neck. 2 single coils, chrome hardware, white pickguard, volume/tone controls, pickup selector switch. Mfg. 1963 to 1966.

Mark Series

80% to 90% instruments are generally priced between $600 and $900.

MARK VI ACOUSTIC — teardrop shaped semi-hollow body, six on a side tuners, chrome hardware, roller bridge/tremolo system, f-hole, 3 single coils, raised black pickguard, volume/2 tone controls and pickup selector all mounted on metal control plate on lower rear bout. Mfg. 1964 to 1968.

Mark VI Special — similar to the Mark VI Acoustic, except has solid body, 6 pushbuttons mounted on pickguard, controls mounted to the body, and extra control knob near the pickup selector. Mfg. 1964 to 1968.

Mark IX (9 String Guitar) — similar to the Mark VI Special, except has a 3+6 headstock design, 9 strings (3 single bass, 3 pairs treble), white pickguard, volume/2 tone controls, pickup selector switch. Mfg. 1964 to 1968.

Mark XII — similar to the Mark IX, except has 6+6 headstock and 12 strings. Mfg. 1964 to 1968.

Phantom (First Series)

The first Phantom series guitars are the first original design from the Vox company. Some of the other early model solid body guitars introduced prior to 1962 were generally entry level models based on Fender designs.

80% to 90% instruments are generally priced between $400 and $600.

PHANTOM I — original series solid body electric. Mfg. 1962 to 1963.

Phantom II — similar to the Phantom I, features some variations on the first model. Mfg. 1962 to 1963.

Phantom (Second Series)

80% to 90% instruments are generally priced between $600 and $900.

PHANTOM VI — 5 sided body, six on a side "spearpoint" headstock, chrome hardware, roller bridge/tremolo system, 3 single coil pickups, white pickguard, volume/2 tone controls, pickup selector knob. Mfg. 1963 to 1968.

Phantom XII — similar to the Phantom VI, except has 12 strings. Mfg. 1963 to 1968.

Phantom XII Stereo — similar to the Phantom XII, except has a stop tailpiece, three split 3+3 single coil pickups, 3 volume/3 tone knobs for bass side pickups mounted on upper forward side of the body, 3 volume/3 tone knobs for treble side pickups mounted on lower rear side of the body, three on/off stereo pickup function selectors, one 5-way pickup selector switch. Mfg. 1963 to 1968.

Phantom Guitar Organ — similar to the Phantom VI, except has extra tone generating circuitry housed in body, 2 single coil pickups, Organ on/off switch, 3-way pickup selector knob, guitar tone knob, guitar volume knob, organ volume knob, 6 pushbuttons, octave knob, organ tone knob, flute voice knob, 3 sustain/percussion controls. Mfg. 1965 to 1967.

Guitar Organs in 80% to 90% range are generally priced between $900 and $1800.

SHADOW — offset double cutaway body, six on a side headstock, 3 single coil pickups, chrome hardware, white pickguard, tremolo, squarish tremolo cover has Vox logo on it, volume/2 tone controls, pickup selector knob on lower treble bout. Mfg. 1960 to 1966.

SOUNDCASTER — similar to the Super Ace, except has a mute switch (for introducing "novel banjo effects") built near bridge, and contoured body. Available in Red, White, Blue, and Black finishes. Mfg. 1962 to 1966.

SPITFIRE VI — offset double cutaway body, six on a side tuners, chrome hardware, white pickguard, tremolo bridge, 3 single coils, volume/2 tone controls, pickup selector switch located on lower treble bout. Mfg. 1965 to 1968.

Spitfire XII — similar to the Spitfire VI, except has twelve strings. Mfg. 1965 to 1968.

Hurricane — similar to the Spitfire VI, except only has 2 single coil pickups (no mid body pickup). Mfg. 1965 to 1968.
Retail Price of the Vox Hurricane in 1965 was $169.

STARSTREAM — teardrop hollow body, six on a side headstock, 2 Ferro-Sonic single coil pickups with chrome covers, 21 fret neck with white block inlays, ornate headstock inlays around logo, raised black pickguard, 1 f-hole, chrome hardware, roller bridge/tremolo system, extra palm vibrato, volume/2 tone controls, pickup selector switch, "E tuner" on/off switch mounted on a small metal plate. "On-board" effects mounted on a metal plate features a Treble/Bass boost on/off switch and control, Distortion on/off switch and control, "Wah Wah" control, and "Percussion" (a repeating echo-like function) on/off switch and control. Available in Sunburst, Cherry, or Sandburst finishes. Mfg. 1967 to 1969.

Starstream XII — similar to the Starstream, except has a 6+6 headstock and 12 string configuration.

STROLLER — similar to the Clubman model, except only has one single coil pickup. Available in Red or White finishes. Mfg. 1960 to 1966.

TEMPEST XII — offset double cutaway body, 6+6 headstock (12 string), 3 single coil pickups, chrome hardware, white pickguard, volume/2 tone controls, pickup selector switch located in lower treble bout. Mfg. 1964 to 1966.
Some models may be equipped with a tremolo system.

THUNDERJET — double offset cutaway solid body, 22 fret neck with dot inlay, six on a side tuners, 1 black single coil pickup, chrome hardware, roller bridge/'Bigsby'-styled tremolo system, 1 volume/2 tone knobs, built-in "E" tuner, Treble/Bass boost on/off switch and control, and Distortion on/off switch and control. Controls all mounted on a white pickguard. Available in Sunburst, White, or Cherry finishes. Mfg. 1968 to 1969.

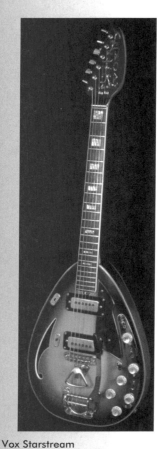

Vox Starstream
courtesy James Sabino

TORNADO — single cutaway semi-hollow body design, 2 f-holes, raised white pickguard, roller bridge/trapeze tailpiece, 3+3 asymetrical headstock, 1 pickup (neck position), 1 volume knob and 1 tone knob. Mfg. 1965 to 1967.

TYPHOON — similar to the Tornado model, except has a 3+3 headstock, 2 single coil pickups, and the pickup selector switch is located on the upper bass bout. Mfg. 1965 to 1968.

ULTRASONIC — dual cutaway hollow body, six on a side headstock, 2 single coil pickups with chrome covers, 21 fret neck with white block inlays, raised black pickguard, 2 f-holes, chrome hardware, roller bridge/tremolo system, extra palm vibrato, volume/2 tone controls, pickup selector switch, "E tuner" on/off switch mounted on lower treble bout. "On-board" effects mounted on a metal plate features a Treble/Bass boost on/off switch and control, Distortion on/off switch and control, "Wah Wah" control, and "Percussion" (a repeating echo-like function) on/off switch and control. Available in Sunburst or Cherry finishes. Mfg. 1967 to 1969.

VIPER — dual cutaway hollow body, six on a side headstock, 2 Ferro-Sonic single coil pickups with chrome covers, 21 fret neck with white block inlays, raised black pickguard, 2 f-holes, chrome hardware, trapeze Vox tailpiece, volume/2 tone controls, pickup selector switch, "E tuner" on/off switch mounted on lower treble bout. "On-board" effects mounted on a metal plate features a Treble/Bass boost on/off switch and control, Distortion on/off switch and control, "Wah Wah" control, and "Percussion" (a repeating echo-like function) on/off switch and control. Available in Sunburst or Cherry finishes. Mfg. 1967 to 1969.

ELECTRIC BASS

APOLLO IV — dual cutaway hollow body, four on a side headstock, 1 single coil pickup, raised white pickguard, 2 f-holes, chrome hardware, roller bridge/trapeze tailpiece, volume/tone controls. "On-board" effects mounted on a metal plate features a "G tuner" on/off switch, Treble/Bass boost on/off switch and control, and Distortion on/off switch and control. Mfg. 1964 to 1967.

ASTRO IV — violin-shaped semi-hollow body, four on a side tuners, 21 fret neck with white dot inlays, 2 single coil pickups, raised black pickguard, trapeze bridge, 1 volume/2 tone knobs, built-in "G" tuner mounted on a small metal plate, pickup selector switch. "On-board" effects mounted on a metal plate features a Treble/Bass boost on/off switch and control, and Distortion on/off switch and control. Mfg. 1967 to 1969.

BASSMASTER — offset double cutaway body, four on a side tuners, 2 single coil pickups, white pickguard, chrome hardware, volume/tone controls. Mfg. 1960 to 1964.

CONSTELLATION IV — teardrop shaped semi-hollow body, four on a side tuners, chrome hardware, fixed bridge, f-hole, 2 chrome covered single coils, raised black pickguard, volume/2 tone controls and pickup selector. "On-board" effects mounted on a metal plate features a "G tuner" on/off switch, Treble/Bass boost on/off switch and control, and Distortion on/off switch and control. Mfg. 1966 to 1968.

MARK IV — teardrop solid body, four on a side tuners, 2 single coil pickups, fixed bridge, volume/tone controls, pickup selector switch. Mfg. 1964 to 1968.

PHANTOM IV — 5 sided body, four on a side tuners, fixed bridge, chrome hardware, white pickguard, 2 single coil pickups, volume/tone controls, pickup selector switch. Mfg. 1963 to 1968.

STINGER IV — teardrop shaped semi-hollow body, four on a side tuners, chrome hardware, fixed bridge, f-hole, 2 chrome covered single coils, raised black pickguard, volume/2 tone controls and pickup selector. Mfg. 1964 to 1968.

WYMAN BASS — teardrop shaped semi-hollow body, solitary slash f-hole, 2 pickups, 1 volume knob and 1 tone knob, four on a side "spear" headstock. Mfg. 1966 to 1967.

This model was endorsed by Bill Wyman (Rolling Stones).

A protective snap-on pad was attached to the back of the Wyman bass.

VULCAN

Instruments produced in Korea during the mid 1980s.

Vulcan trademark instruments featured designs based on Fender and Gibson classics. However, these solid body guitars were low to entry level quality, and may appeal to the novice player only.

(Source: Tony Bacon and Paul Day, The Guru's Guitar Guide)

V

W & S

See WEYMANN & SONS.

WABASH

See chapter on House Brands.

This trademark has been identified as a "House Brand" of Wexler.

(Source: Willie G. Moseley, Stellas & Stratocasters)

WAL

Instruments built by Electric Wood in High Wycombe (Bucks), England since 1978.

In the mid 1970s, Pete Stevens joined London-based repairman Ian Waller to design the Wal Custom bass guitar. In 1978 the two incorporated into the company called Electric Wood, and produced numerous custom basses. Ian Waller later passed away; however, Stevens continues production to date. Wal custom basses are available directly from Electric Wood or through a few selected dealers.

Walker 'The Empress'
courtesy Scott Chinery

WALKER

Instruments built in North Stonington, Connecticut since 1984.

Luthier Kim Walker was involved in the musical instrument making business since 1973, and began building F-5 style mandolins in 1982. Walker worked for a number of years at George Gruhn's repair and restoration workshop, and served as both a prototype builder and R&D/Custom shop supervisor at Guild in the late 1980s.

Walker currently offers three different archtop models, and his combination of premier woods and over twenty years experience make for a truly solid, high quality guitar. For further information on model specifications, pricing, and availability please contact luthier Walker via the Index of Current Manufacturers located in the back of this book.

WANDRE

See also DAVOLI.

Instruments produced in Italy during the early to mid 1960s.

Wandre guitars help define where art design and guitar production crosses. These solid body (and some hollow body) guitars featured aluminum necks (called "Duraluminum") with wood fingerboards, and plastic coverings on the body. The futuristic body designs of the Rock Oval, Spazial, and Framez may have some visual appeal, but the level of playing quality isn't as high as the coolness factor may indicate. There's always some interest in the vintage market for these instruments, but the nature of the interest stems primarily from disbelief at the design!

(Source: Tony Bacon and Paul Day, The Guru's Guitar Guide)

WARR

Instruments currently built in Long Beach, California.

Luthier/designer Mark D.Warr is offering a multi-stringed single neck instrument that features a conventional body, but can be played in a variety of styles. For further information on model specification and pricing, please contact Mark Warr via the Index of Current Manufacturers located in the rear of this book.

WARRIOR

Instruments built in Rossville, Georgia since 1995.

Luthier Bruce Bennett and partners are currently offering three high quality custom built bass models that feature neck-through designs, exotic woods, and an innovative "through body stringing" that corrects the floppy feeling of the low B-string. Retail prices range from $2,700 up to $3,400, and a variety of options are offered. Warrior has also introduced the **Crusader** bass, a bolt-neck model that incorporated many of the designs that the regular models possess. For further information, please contact Warrior Basses via the Index of Current Manufacturers located in the back of this book.

WARWICK

Instruments produced in Markneukirchen, Germany since 1982 by Warwick Gmbh & Co. Musicequipment KG. Distributed exclusively in the U.S. by Dana B. Goods, located in Santa Barbara, California.

Walker Archtop
courtesy Kim Walker

Grading	100% MINT	98% EXC+	95% EXC	90% VG+	80% VG	70% G	60%

Hans Peter Wilfer, son of Framus' Frederick Wilfer, established the Warwick trademark in 1982. The Warwick company has since produced high quality bass guitars.

ACOUSTIC BASS

ALIEN — single sharp cutaway concert style, spruce top, asymmetrical soundhole located in upper bout, rosewood thumb rest, wood bound body, ovankol soundhole cap, ovankol back/sides, 2 piece mahogany neck with wenge center strip, 24 fret wenge fingerboard, wenge/metal bridge, ebony peghead veneer with pearl W inlay, 2 per side chrome tuners, piezo pickup, 4 band EQ, active electronics. Available in Natural finish. Curr. mfr.

Mfr.'s Sug. Retail	$3,300	$2,475	$1,650	$1,565	$1,200	$1,080	$990	$900

ELECTRIC BASS

All models in this group of instruments have tunomatic bridge/stop tailpiece, ebony peghead veneer with pearl W inlay, slanted tuners, unless otherwise listed. All models have fretless fingerboards optionally available, unless otherwise listed.

BUZZARD — offset double cutaway zebrano body, wenge/zebrano neck, 24 fret wenge fingerboard, pearl model name peghead inlay, 4 on one side tuners, gold hardware, 2 P-style MEC pickups, volume/treble/mid/bass/mix controls, active electronics. Available in Natural finish. Curr. mfr.

Mfr.'s Sug. Retail	$3,900	$3,120	$2,340	$1,950	$1,560	$1,400	$1,285	$1,170

This model was designed by John Entwistle.

This model not available with fretless fingerboard.

CORVETTE PRO LINE — offset double cutaway contoured ash body, 3 piece wenge neck, 24 fret wenge fingerboard, 2 per side tuners, gold hardware, 2 J-style active MEC pickups, 2 volume/1 tone controls. Available in Blue Ocean, Burgundy Red, Honey Violin and Nirvana Black finishes. New 1994.

Mfr.'s Sug. Retail	$1,700	$1,360	$1,020	$850	$680	$610	$560	$510

All finishes on this instrument are Oil finishes.

Corvette Pro Line 5 — similar to Corvette Pro Line, except has 5 strings, 3/2 per side tuners. New 1994.

Mfr.'s Sug. Retail	$2,100	$1,680	$1,260	$1,050	$840	$755	$690	$630

Corvette Pro Line 6 — similar to Corvette Pro Line, except has 6 strings, 3 per side tuners. New 1994.

Mfr.'s Sug. Retail	$2,400	$1,920	$1,440	$1,200	$960	$860	$790	$720

Corvette Limited — similar to Corvette Pro Line, except features a semi-hollowbody design and f-holes. Production was limited to 100 instruments.

There has not been sufficient trading of this model to quote prices.

Warwick Dolphin Pro
courtesy Mike Braswell

DOLPHIN PRO I — offset double cutaway asymmetrical boire body, half thru body 7 piece wenge/zebrano neck, 24 fret wenge fingerboard with pearl dolphin inlay, 2 per side tuners, chrome hardware, J-style/humbucker MEC pickups, concentric volume-balance/concentric treble-bass control, active electronics, push/pull electronics switch in volume control, push/pull coil split switch in tone control. Available in Natural finish. Curr. mfr.

Mfr.'s Sug. Retail	$3,600	$2,700	$1,800	$1,700	$1,360	$1,225	$1,120	$1,025

Dolphin Pro I-5 — similar to Dolphin Pro I, except has 5 strings, 3/2 per side tuners. Curr. mfr.

Mfr.'s Sug. Retail	$4,300	$3,225	$2,150	$2,040	$1,620	$1,400	$1,285	$1,170

DOLPHIN PRO II — offset double cutaway asymmetrical ash body, bolt-on 3 piece maple neck, 24 fret wenge fingerboard, 2 per side tuners, chrome hardware, 2 J-style MEC pickups, volume/concentric treble-bass/balance controls, active electronics, push/pull electronics switch in volume control. Available in Black, Black Stain, Blue, Blue Stain, Red Stain and Wine Red finishes. Disc. 1994.

	$1,435	$1,230	$1,025	$820	$745	$675	$615

Last Mfr.'s Sug. Retail was $2,050.

This model had Bartolini or EMG pickups optionally available.

FORTRESS — offset double cutaway maple body, bolt-on 3 piece wenge neck, 24 fret wenge fingerboard, 2 per side tuners, chrome hardware, P-style/J-style MEC pickups, volume/treble/bass/balance control. Available in Black Stain, Blue Stain, Red Stain and White finishes. Curr. mfr.

Mfr.'s Sug. Retail	$1,200	$960	$720	$600	$480	$430	$395	$360

Fortress-A — similar to Fortress, except has 2 humbucker Seymour Duncan pickups, 2 volume/1 treble/1 bass controls, active electronics. New 1994.

Mfr.'s Sug. Retail	$1,400	$1,120	$840	$700	$560	$505	$460	$420

Fortress-5A — similar to Fortress, except has 5 strings, 3/2 per side tuners, 2 humbucker Seymour Duncan pickups, 2 volume/1 treble/1 bass controls, active electronics. New 1994.

Mfr.'s Sug. Retail	$1,600	$1,280	$960	$800	$640	$575	$530	$480

STREAMER — offset double cutaway contoured ash body, bolt-on cherry neck, 24 fret maple fingerboard with pearl dot inlay, 2 per side tuners, chrome hardware, P-style/J-style active MEC pickups, 2 volume/2 tone controls. Available in Natural finish. Curr. mfr.

Mfr.'s Sug. Retail	$2,100	$1,680	$1,260	$1,050	$840	$755	$690	$630

In 1994, cherry body, 5 piece maple/bubinga neck, wenge fingerboard replaced original items.

Streamer 5 — similar to Streamer, except has 5 strings, 3/2 per side tuners, 2 J-style active MEC pickups. Curr. mfr.

Mfr.'s Sug. Retail	$2,500	$2,000	$1,500	$1,300	$1,040	$935	$860	$780

Grading	100%	98% MINT	95% EXC+	90% EXC	80% VG+	70% VG	60% G

Streamer 6 — similar to Streamer, except has 6 strings, 7 piece neck, 3 per side tuners, 2 humbucker active MEC pickups. New 1994.

| Mfr.'s Sug. Retail | $2,800 | $2,240 | $1,680 | $1,400 | $1,120 | $1,010 | $925 | $840 |

STREAMER STAGE I — offset double cutaway contoured flame maple body, thru body 5 piece maple/wenge neck, 24 fret wenge fingerboard with pearl dot inlay, 2 per side tuners, gold hardware, P-style/J-style MEC pickups, volume/treble/bass/balance control, active electronics, push/pull electronics switch in volume control. Available in Natural finish. Curr. mfr.

| Mfr.'s Sug. Retail | $2,800 | $2,100 | $1,400 | $1,325 | $1,060 | $955 | $875 | $795 |

Streamer Stage I-5 — similar to Streamer Stage I, except has 5 strings, 7 piece maple/wenge neck, 3/2 per side tuners, 2 humbucker Bartolini pickups. Curr. mfr.

| Mfr.'s Sug. Retail | $3,800 | $2,850 | $1,900 | $1,850 | $1,480 | $1,330 | $1,220 | $1,110 |

In 1994, 7 piece maple/bubinga neck replaced original item.

Streamer Stage I-6 — similar to Streamer Stage I, except has 6 strings, 7 piece maple/wenge neck, 3 per side tuners, 2 humbucker Bartolini pickups.

| Mfr.'s Sug. Retail | $4,300 | $3,440 | $2,580 | $2,235 | $1,840 | $1,655 | $1,520 | $1,380 |

In 1994, 7 piece maple/bubinga neck replaced original item.

STREAMER STAGE II — offset double cutaway contoured afzelia body, half thru 7 piece wenge/afzelia neck, 24 fret ebony fingerboard with pearl/abalone Tao inlay, abalone W peghead inlay, 2 per side tuners, gold hardware, 2 J-style MEC pickups, volume/concentric treble-bass/mid/balance control, active electronics, push/pull electronics switch in volume control. Available in Natural finish. Curr. mfr.

| Mfr.'s Sug. Retail | $3,400 | $2,550 | $1,700 | $1,615 | $1,240 | $1,115 | $1,025 | $930 |

This model has Bartolini or EMG pickups optionally available.

In 1994, wenge fingerboard replaced original item.

Streamer Stage II-5 — similar to Streamer Stage II, except has 5 strings, 3/2 per side tuners. Curr. mfr.

| Mfr.'s Sug. Retail | $3,900 | $2,925 | $1,950 | $1,810 | $1,435 | $1,225 | $1,120 | $1,025 |

STREAMER STAGE III — offset double cutaway asymmetrical boire body, half thru body 7 piece wenge/zebrano neck, 24 fret ebony fingerboard with pearl oval inlay, 2 per side tuners, chrome hardware, 1 single coil/1 humbucker pickups, concentric volume-balance/concentric treble-bass control, active electronics. Available in Natural finish. Disc. 1990.

| | | $2,520 | $2,160 | $1,800 | $1,440 | $1,295 | $1,185 | $1,075 |

Last Mfr.'s Sug. Retail was $3,600.

THUMB BASS — offset double cutaway asymmetrical contoured bubinga body, half thru body 7 piece wenge/bubinga neck, 24 fret wenge fingerboard, 2 per side tuners, black hardware, 2 J-style MEC pickups, volume/concentric treble-bass/concentric mid-balance control, active electronics. Available in Natural finish. Curr. mfr.

| Mfr.'s Sug. Retail | $3,000 | $2,250 | $1,500 | $1,450 | $1,160 | $1,040 | $955 | $870 |

Thumb Bass 5 — similar to Thumb Bass, except has 5 strings, 3/2 per side tuners.

| Mfr.'s Sug. Retail | $3,500 | $2,625 | $1,750 | $1,650 | $1,320 | $1,190 | $1,090 | $990 |

Thumb Bass 6 — similar to Thumb Bass, except has 6 strings, 3 per side tuners, 2 humbucker Bartolini pickups.

| Mfr.'s Sug. Retail | $4,500 | $3,375 | $2,250 | $2,125 | $1,685 | $1,460 | $1,335 | $1,215 |

THUMB BOLT ON — offset double cutaway asymmetrical contoured walnut body, bolt-on 3 piece wenge neck, 24 fret wenge fingerboard, 2 per side tuners, black hardware, 2 J-style MEC pickups, volume/concentric treble-bass/concentric mid-balance controls, active electronics. Available in Natural finish. New 1994.

| Mfr.'s Sug. Retail | $2,300 | $1,840 | $1,380 | $1,150 | $920 | $830 | $760 | $690 |

Thumb Bolt On 5 — similar to Thumb Bolt On, except has 5 strings, 4 piece wenge neck, 3/2 per side tuners. New 1994.

| Mfr.'s Sug. Retail | $2,700 | $2,160 | $1,620 | $1,350 | $1,080 | $970 | $890 | $810 |

Thumb Bolt On 6 — similar to Thumb Bolt On, except has 6 strings, 5 piece wenge neck, 3 per side tuners, 2 humbucker MEC pickups. New 1994.

| Mfr.'s Sug. Retail | $3,000 | $2,400 | $1,800 | $1,500 | $1,200 | $1,080 | $990 | $900 |

WASHBURN

Instruments currently produced both in Chicago, Illinois and Korea. Distributed by Washburn International, located in Vernon Hills, Illinois.

Historically, Washburn instruments were produced in Chicago, Illinois area from numerous sources from the late 1800s to 1940s.

The Washburn trademark was originated by the Lyon & Healy company of Chicago, Illinois. George Washburn Lyon and Patrick Joseph Healy were chosen by Oliver Ditson, who had formed the Oliver Ditson Company, Inc. in 1835 as a musical publisher. Ditson was a primary force in music merchandising, distribution, and retail sales on the East Coast. In 1864 the Lyon & Healy music store opened for business. The late 1800s found the company ever expanding from retail, to producer, and finally distributor. The Washburn trademark was formally filed for in 1887, and the name applied to quality stringed instruments produced by a manufacturing department of Lyon & Healy.

Lyon & Healy were part of the Chicago musical instrument production conglomerate that produced musical instruments throughout the early and mid 1900s. As in business, if there is demand, a successful business will supply. Due to their early pioneering of mass production, the Washburn facility averaged up to one hundred instruments a day! Lyon & Healy/Washburn were eventually overtaken by the Tonk Bros. company, and the Washburn trademark was eventually discarded.

When the trademark was revived in 1964, the inital production of acoustic guitars came from Japan. Washburn electric guitars were re-introduced to the American market in 1979, and featured U.S. designs on Japanese-built instruments. Production of the entry level models was switched to Korea during the mid to late 1980s. As the company gained a larger foothold in the guitar market, American production was reintroduced in the late 1980s as well. Grover Jackson (ex-Jackson/Chavel) was instrumental in introducing new designs for Washburn for the Chicago series in 1993.

(Early company history courtesy of John Teagle in his book Washburn: Over One Hundred Years of Fine Stringed Instruments. The actual history is a lot more involved and convoluted than the above outline suggests, and Teagle's book does a fine job of unravelling the narrative)

Grading	100%	98% MINT	95% EXC+	90% EXC	80% VG+	70% VG	60% G

ACOUSTIC

Classic Guitar Series

C20 — classic style, spruce top, round soundhole, 3 stripe bound body, wooden inlay rosette, mahogany back/sides/neck, 12/19 fret rosewood fingerboard, tied rosewood bridge, 3 per side nylon head chrome tuners. Available in Natural finish. New 1994.

Mfr.'s Sug. Retail	$180	$144	$108	$90	$70	$65	$60	$50

C40 — classic style, spruce top, round soundhole, 3 stripe bound body, wooden inlay rosette, mahogany back/sides/neck, 12/19 fret rosewood fingerboard, tied rosewood bridge, 3 per side nylon head chrome tuners. Available in Natural finish. Curr. mfr.

Mfr.'s Sug. Retail	$250	$200	$150	$130	$100	$90	$80	$75

C60 ZARAZOGA — classic style, spruce top, round soundhole, 3 stripe bound body, wooden inlay rosette, rosewood back/sides, mahogany neck, 12/19 fret rosewood fingerboard, tied rosewood bridge, rosewood peghead veneer, 3 per side nylon head gold tuners. Available in Natural finish. Disc. 1994.

	$260	$220	$185	$150	$135	$120	$110

Last Mfr.'s Sug. Retail was $370.

C64CE — single round cutaway classic style, spruce top, round soundhole, bound body, wood marquetry rosette, ovankol back/sides, mahogany neck, 19 fret rosewood fingerboard, tied rosewood bridge, 3 per side gold tuners with nylon buttons, acoustic bridge pickup, volume/tone control. Available in Natural finish. New 1994.

Mfr.'s Sug. Retail	$500	$400	$300	$250	$200	$180	$165	$150

C80S — classic style, solid spruce top, round soundhole, 3 stripe bound body, wooden inlay rosette, rosewood back/sides, mahogany neck, 12/19 fret rosewood fingerboard, tied rosewood bridge, rosewood peghead veneer, 3 per side nylon head gold tuners. Available in Natural finish. Curr. mfr.

Mfr.'s Sug. Retail	$480	$360	$240	$230	$185	$165	$150	$140

C84CE — single round cutaway classic style, solid spruce top, round soundhole, 3 stripe bound body, wood marquetry rosette, rosewood back/sides, mahogany neck, 12/19 fret rosewood fingerboard, tied rosewood bridge, rosewood peghead veneer, 3 per side nylon head gold tuners, acoustic bridge pickup, 4 band EQ. Available in Natural finish. Curr. mfr.

Mfr.'s Sug. Retail	$650	$520	$390	$355	$290	$260	$240	$220

In 1994, solid cedar top replaced original item.

C94SCE — single round cutaway classic style, solid cedar top, round soundhole, 3 stripe bound body, wooden inlay rosette, jacaranda back/sides, mahogany neck, 19 fret rosewood fingerboard, tied rosewood bridge, rosewood peghead veneer, 3 per side nylon head gold tuners, acoustic bridge pickup, volume/tone control, 3 band EQ. Available in Natural finish. New 1994.

Mfr.'s Sug. Retail	$900	$720	$540	$450	$360	$325	$300	$275

C100SW VALENCIA — classic style, solid cedar top, round soundhole, 3 stripe bound body, wood marquetry rosette, rosewood back/sides, mahogany neck, 12/19 fret ebony fingerboard, jacaranda bridge with bone saddle, rosewood peghead veneer, 3 per side pearl head gold tuners. Available in Natural finish. Disc. 1991.

	$1,050	$900	$750	$600	$540	$495	$450

Last Mfr.'s Sug. Retail was $1,500.

"Band like The Who and Zeppelin to me were just hype from day one and you know they are going to hype us until we're dead."

—Lawrence Acunto on

Steve Miller

TCG, Mar/Apr 1993

Grading	100%	98% MINT	95% EXC+	90% EXC	80% VG+	70% VG	60% G

C200SW SEVILLA — similar to C100SW, except has ebony reinforcement in the neck. Disc. 1991.

	$1,330	$1,140	$950	$760	$685	$625	$570

Last Mfr.'s Sug. Retail was $1,900.

Steel String Guitar Series

D8 — dreadnought style, spruce top, round soundhole, black pickguard, bound body, 3 stripe purfling/rosette, mahogany back/sides/neck, 14/20 fret rosewood fingerboard with pearl dot inlay, rosewood bridge with black white dot pins, rosewood peghead veneer with screened logo, 3 per side chrome tuners. Available in Natural finish. New 1994.

Mfr.'s Sug. Retail	$200	$160	$120	$100	$80	$70	$65	$60

D8M — similar to D8, except has mahogany top. New 1994.

Mfr.'s Sug. Retail	$190	$152	$114	$95	$75	$70	$65	$55

D10 — dreadnought style, spruce top, round soundhole, black pickguard, 3 stripe bound body and rosette, mahogany back/sides/neck, 14/20 fret rosewood fingerboard with pearl dot inlay, rosewood bridge with pearl dot black pins, 3 per side chrome Grover tuners. Available in Natural finish. Curr. mfr.

Mfr.'s Sug. Retail	$280	$210	$140	$130	$100	$90	$80	$75

D10CE — similar to D10, except has single round cutaway, acoustic bridge pickup, volume/tone control, 3 band EQ. Available in Black finish. Mfd. 1993 to date.

Mfr.'s Sug. Retail	$450	$337	$225	$220	$175	$160	$145	$135

D12 — dreadnought style, spruce top, round soundhole, black pickguard, 3 stripe bound body and rosette, mahogany back/sides/neck, 14/20 fret rosewood fingerboard with pearl dot inlay, rosewood bridge with pearl dot black pins, 3 per side chrome diecast tuners. Available in Black, Brown, Natural and White finishes. Disc. 1994.

	$245	$210	$175	$140	$125	$115	$105

Last Mfr.'s Sug. Retail was $350.

D12LH — similar to D12, except is left handed version. Available in Natural finish. Curr. mfr.

Mfr.'s Sug. Retail	$380	$304	$228	$190	$150	$135	$120	$110

D12S — similar to D12, except has solid spruce top. Available in Black and Natural finishes. New 1994.

Mfr.'s Sug. Retail	$400	$320	$240	$200	$160	$145	$130	$120

D12CE — similar to D12, except has single round cutaway, pearl W inlay at 12th fret, acoustic bridge pickup, volume/tone control, 3 band EQ. Available in Black, Natural, Tobacco Sunburst, White and Woodstone Brown finishes. Mfd. 1993 to date.

Mfr.'s Sug. Retail	$600	$450	$300	$295	$250	$225	$205	$190

In 1994, solid spruce top replaced original item (D12SCE), Tobacco Sunburst, White and Woodstone Brown finishes were discontinued.

D1212 — dreadnought style, spruce top, round soundhole, black pickguard, 3 stripe bound body and rosette, mahogany back/sides/neck, 14/20 fret rosewood fingerboard with pearl dot inlay, rosewood bridge with pearl dot black pins, 6 per side chrome diecast tuners. Available in Black, Brown, Natural, Tobacco Sunburst and White finishes. Curr. mfr.

Mfr.'s Sug. Retail	$400	$300	$200	$195	$155	$140	$125	$115

In 1994, Tobacco Sunburst finish was discontinued.

D1212CE — similar to D1212, except has single round cutaway, acoustic bridge pickup, volume/tone control, 3 band EQ. Available in Natural and Tobacco Sunburst finishes. Disc. 1994.

	$475	$405	$340	$270	$245	$225	$205

Last Mfr.'s Sug. Retail was $680.

D1212E — similar to D1212, except has acoustic bridge pickup, volume/tone control, 3 band EQ. Available in Natural finish. New 1994.

Mfr.'s Sug. Retail	$530	$424	$318	$265	$210	$190	$175	$160

D13 — dreadnought style, spruce top, round soundhole, black pickguard, 3 stripe bound body and rosette, ovankol back/sides, mahogany neck, 14/20 fret rosewood fingerboard with pearl dot inlay, rosewood bridge with white black dot pins, 3 per side chrome diecast tuners. Available in Natural finish. Disc. 1994.

	$275	$235	$195	$155	$140	$125	$115

Last Mfr.'s Sug. Retail was $390.

D13S — similar to D13, except has solid spruce top. New 1994.

Mfr.'s Sug. Retail	$450	$360	$270	$225	$180	$160	$150	$135

D1312 — similar to D13, except has 12 strings, 6 per side tuners. Disc. 1994.

	$315	$270	$225	$180	$160	$150	$135

Last Mfr.'s Sug. Retail was $450.

D1312S — similar to D13, except has 12 strings, solid spruce top, 6 per side tuners. New 1994.

Mfr.'s Sug. Retail	$500	$400	$300	$250	$200	$180	$165	$150

D14 — dreadnought style, spruce top, round soundhole, tortoise pickguard, 3 stripe bound body and rosette, rosewood back/sides, mahogany neck, 14/20 fret rosewood fingerboard with pearl dot inlay, rosewood bridge with pearl dot white pins, 3 per side chrome diecast tuners. Available in Natural and Tobacco finishes. Disc. 1992.

	$245	$210	$175	$140	$125	$115	$105

Last Mfr.'s Sug. Retail was $350.

Grading	100%	98% MINT	95% EXC+	90% EXC	80% VG+	70% VG	60% G

W

D17SCE— single round cutaway dreadnought style, solid spruce top, round soundhole, black pickguard, 3 stripe bound body/rosette, mahogany back/sides/neck, 20 fret bound rosewood fingerboard with pearl diamond inlay, stylized W inlay at 12th fret, rosewood bridge with black white dot pins, pearl diamond inlay on bridge wings, bound peghead, 3 per side gold tuners with pearl buttons, acoustic bridge pickup, volume/tone control, 3 band EQ, 1/4/XLR output jack. Available in Black and Natural finishes. Curr. mfr.

Mfr.'s Sug. Retail	$800	$600	$400	$395	$315	$280	$260	$235

Add $50 for 12 string version of this model (D17SCE12). Available in Natural finish only.

D17CE — similar to D17SCE, except has flamed sycamore top/back/sides. Available in Brown and Wine Red finishes. Curr. mfr.

Mfr.'s Sug. Retail	$830	$664	$498	$415	$330	$300	$275	$250

D17CE12 — similar to D17SCE, except has 12 strings, flamed sycamore top/back/sides, 6 per side tuners. Disc. 1994.

	$620	$530	$440	$355	$320	$295	$270

Last Mfr.'s Sug. Retail was $880.

D20S — dreadnought style, solid spruce top, round soundhole, tortoise shell pickguard, 3 stripe bound body and rosette, flame maple back/sides, mahogany neck, 14/20 fret rosewood fingerboard with pearl diamond/12th fret W inlay, rosewood bridge with pearl dot white pins, rosewood veneer on peghead, 3 per side chrome diecast tuners. Available in Natural finish. Disc. 1994.

	$370	$320	$265	$210	$190	$175	$160

Last Mfr.'s Sug. Retail was $530.

D21S — dreadnought style, solid spruce top, round soundhole, tortoise shell pickguard, 3 stripe bound body/rosette, rosewood back/sides, mahogany neck, 14/20 fret rosewood fingerboard with pearl diamond/12th fret W inlay, rosewood bridge with pearl dot white pins, rosewood peghead veneer, 3 per side gold diecast tuners. Available in Natural and Tobacco Sunburst finishes. Curr. mfr.

Mfr.'s Sug. Retail	$560	$448	$336	$280	$225	$205	$190	$170

In 1994, Tobacco Sunburst finish was discontinued.

D21SE — similar to D21S, except has acoustic bridge pickup, volume/tone control, 3 band EQ. Available in Natural finish. Disc. 1992.

	$400	$340	$285	$230	$205	$190	$170

Last Mfr.'s Sug. Retail was $570.

D21SLH — similar to D21S, except is left handed. Available in Natural finish. Disc. 1992.

	$350	$300	$250	$200	$180	$165	$150

Last Mfr.'s Sug. Retail was $510.

D24S12 — jumbo style, solid spruce top, round soundhole, tortoise pickguard, bound body, 3 stripe purfling/rosette, mahogany back/sides/neck, 14/20 fret rosewood fingerboard with pearl dot inlay, rosewood bridge with white black dot pins, 6 per side chrome Grover tuners. Available in Natural finish. New 1994.

Mfr.'s Sug. Retail	$550	$440	$330	$275	$220	$200	$180	$165

D25S — jumbo style, solid spruce top, round soundhole, tortoise pickguard, bound body 3 stripe purfling/rosette, ovankol back/sides, 5 piece mahogany/rosewood neck, 14/20 fret rosewood fingerboard with pearl diamond/12th fret W inlay, rosewood bridge with pearl dot white pins, 3 per side gold diecast tuners. Available in Natural and Tobacco Sunburst finishes. Mfd. 1993 to date.

Mfr.'s Sug. Retail	$500	$400	$300	$260	$220	$200	$180	$165

In 1994, bound fingerboard/peghead, Tobacco Sunburst finish were introduced, solid cedar top replaced original item, 12th fret inlay was discontinued.

D25S12 — similar to D25S, except has 12 strings. Disc. 1994.

	$350	$300	$250	$200	$180	$165	$150

Last Mfr.'s Sug. Retail was $500.

D28S — dreadnought style, solid spruce top, round soundhole, black pickguard, 3 stripe bound body and rosette, 3 piece rosewood back/sides, mahogany neck, 14/20 fret bound rosewood fingerboard with snowflake inlay, rosewood bridge with pearl dot white pins, bound peghead, 3 per side gold diecast tuners. Available in Natural finish. Curr. mfr.

Mfr.'s Sug. Retail	$600	$480	$360	$300	$240	$215	$195	$180

D28SLH — similar to D28S, except is left handed. Disc. 1992.

	$405	$350	$290	$230	$205	$190	$175

Last Mfr.'s Sug. Retail was $580.

D28S12 — similar to D28S, except has 12 strings, 6 per side tuners. Disc. 1994.

	$455	$390	$325	$260	$235	$215	$195

Last Mfr.'s Sug. Retail was $650.

D2812LH— similar to D28S, except is left handed version, has 12 strings, 6 per side tuners. Disc. 1992.

	$435	$370	$310	$250	$225	$205	$190

Last Mfr.'s Sug. Retail was $620.

D29S — dreadnought style, solid cedar top, round soundhole, tortoise shell pickguard, 3 stripe bound body and rosette, rosewood back/sides, 5 piece mahogany/rosewood neck, 14/20 fret rosewood fingerboard with diamond/12th fret W inlay, rosewood bridge with pearl dot white pins, 3 per side gold diecast tuners. Available in Natural finish. Disc. 1994.

	$385	$330	$275	$220	$200	$180	$165

Last Mfr.'s Sug. Retail was $550.

Grading	100%	98% MINT	95% EXC+	90% EXC	80% VG+	70% VG	60% G

D30S — jumbo style, solid cedar top, round soundhole, tortoise pickguard, bound body, 3 stripe purfling, 5 stripe rosette, birdseye maple back/sides, mahogany neck, 14/20 fret rosewood fingerboard with pearl dot inlay, rosewood bridge with pearl dot white pins and bone saddle, birdseye maple peghead veneer, 3 per side chrome diecast tuners. Available in Natural finish. Disc. 1994.

	$525	$450	$375	$300	$270	$245	$225

Last Mfr.'s Sug. Retail was $750.

D32S — similar to D30S, except has Makassar back/sides, bound fingerboard/peghead, Makassar veneer on peghead. Disc. 1994.

	$560	$480	$400	$320	$290	$265	$240

Last Mfr.'s Sug. Retail was $800.

D32S12 — similar to D32S, except has 12 strings. Disc. 1992.

	$545	$470	$390	$315	$280	$260	$235

Last Mfr.'s Sug. Retail was $780.

D61SW PRAIRIE SONG — dreadnought style, solid spruce top, round soundhole, rosewood pickguard, 3 stripe bound body, 5 stripe rosette, rosewood back/sides, mahogany neck, 14/20 fret rosewood fingerboard with pearl dot inlay, rosewood bridge with pearl dot black pins, rosewood veneer on peghead, 3 per side chrome diecast tuners. Available in Natural finish. Disc. 1994.

	$840	$720	$600	$480	$430	$395	$360

Last Mfr.'s Sug. Retail was $1,200.

In 1993, ovankol back/sides replaced original item.

D61SCE — single round cutaway dreadnought style, solid spruce top, round soundhole, wood bound body, 3 stripe wood purfling, 5 stripe rosette, ovankol back/sides, mahogany neck, 14/20 fret rosewood fingerboard with pearl dot inlay, rosewood bridge with pearl dot black pins, rosewood peghead veneer, 3 per side chrome diecast tuners. Available in Natural finish. Mfd. 1993 to date.

Mfr.'s Sug. Retail	$1,500	$1,200	$900	$750	$600	$540	$495	$450

D61SW12 — similar to D61SW, except has 12 strings. Disc. 1992.

	$660	$565	$470	$375	$340	$310	$280

Last Mfr.'s Sug. Retail was $940.

D68SW HARVEST — dreadnought style, solid spruce top, round soundhole, rosewood pickguard, maple/rosewood binding and rosette, rosewood back/sides, 5 piece mahogany/rosewood neck, 14/20 fret rosewood fingerboard with pearl dot inlay, ebony bridge with pearl dot black pins, rosewood veneered maple bound peghead with abalone Washburn inlay, 3 per side pearloid head chrome diecast tuners. Available in Natural finish. Disc. 1994.

	$1,050	$900	$750	$600	$540	$495	$450

Last Mfr.'s Sug. Retail was $1,500.

D68SCE — single round cutaway dreadnought style, solid spruce top, round soundhole, wood bound body, 5 stripe wood purfling/rosette, rosewood back/sides, 5 piece mahogany/rosewood neck, 14/20 fret rosewood fingerboard with pearl dot inlay, rosewood bridge with black pearl dot pins, wood bound rosewood veneered peghead with abalone Washburn inlay, 3 per side pearloid head chrome diecast tuners, acoustic bridge pickup, 4 band EQ. Available in Natural finish. Mfd. 1993 to date.

Mfr.'s Sug. Retail	$1,800	$1,350	$900	$875	$700	$630	$575	$525

D70SW HARVEST DELUXE — dreadnought style, solid spruce top, round soundhole, rosewood pickguard, maple/rosewood bound body, abalone inlay rosette, 3 piece rosewood back/sides, 5 piece mahogany/rosewood neck, 14/20 fret ebony fingerboard with abalone eye inlay, ebony bridge with abalone box inlay and Washburn inlay, 3 per side pearloid head chrome diecast tuners. Available in Natural finish. Mfd. 1990 to 1994.

	$1,400	$1,200	$1,000	$800	$720	$660	$600

Last Mfr.'s Sug. Retail was $2,000.

D90SW GOLDEN HARVEST — similar to D70SW, except has abalone bound body, tree of life abalone inlay on fingerboard, unbound peghead and pearloid head gold diecast tuners. Disc. 1994.

	$2,800	$2,400	$2,000	$1,600	$1,440	$1,320	$1,200

Last Mfr.'s Sug. Retail was $4,000.

J21CE — single round cutaway jumbo style, spruce top, oval soundhole, bound body, 3 stripe purfling, 5 stripe rosette, mahogany back/sides/neck, 21 fret bound rosewood fingerboard, pearl diamond inlay at 12th fret, rosewood bridge with white black dot pins, bound rosewood veneered peghead with screened logo, 3 per side chrome tuners, acoustic bridge pickup, 4 band EQ. Available in Black, Natural and Tobacco Sunburst finishes. New 1994.

Mfr.'s Sug. Retail	$650	$520	$390	$325	$260	$235	$215	$195

R301 — concert style, solid spruce top, round soundhole, bound body, 3 stripe purfling/rosette, mahogany back/sides/neck, 12/18 fret rosewood fingerboard with pearl dot inlay, rosewood bridge with black white dot pins, rosewood veneered slotted peghead, 3 per side diecast chrome tuners. Available in Natural finish. New 1994.

Mfr.'s Sug. Retail	$600	$480	$360	$300	$240	$215	$195	$180

This instrument is a reissue of an 1896 model.

R306 — concert style, solid cedar top, round soundhole, bound body, 3 stripe purfling/rosette, rosewood back/sides, mahogany neck, 12/18 fret rosewood fingerboard with pearl multi symbol inlay, rosewood bridge with carved fans/pearl dot inlay, white abalone dot bridge pins, rosewood veneered slotted peghead with pearl fan/diamond inlay, 3 per side diecast chrome tuners with pearl buttons. Available in Natural finish. Mfd. 1993 to date.

Mfr.'s Sug. Retail	$800	$640	$480	$400	$320	$290	$265	$240

This instrument is a reissue of an 1896 model.

W

"I just said to Capital, 'Here's a record guys, I am going to go out and do 190 dates, I'll see you later.'... When I got back home there was a check in my mail box for $300,000. I thought, 'Hey, singles are kinda cool.'"

—Lawrence Acunto on Steve Miller
TCG, Mar/Apr 1993

Grading	100%	98% MINT	95% EXC+	90% EXC	80% VG+	70% VG	60% G

WD20S — dreadnought style, solid spruce top, round soundhole, black pickguard, bound body, 3 stripe rosette, mahogany back/sides/neck, 14/20 fret rosewood fingerboard with pearl dot inlay, rosewood bridge with black white dot pins, rosewood peghead veneer with screened logo, 3 per side chrome tuners. Available in Natural finish. Mfd. 1993 to date.

Mfr.'s Sug. Retail	$430	$344	$258	$215	$175	$155	$140	$130

WD20SCE — similar to WD20S, except has single round cutaway, acoustic bridge pickup, volume/tone control, 3 band EQ. New 1994.

Mfr.'s Sug. Retail	$700	$560	$420	$350	$280	$250	$230	$210

WD40S — dreadnought style, solid cedar top, round soundhole, black pickguard, bound body, 3 stripe rosette, rosewood back/sides, mahogany neck, 14/20 fret rosewood fingerboard with pearl dot inlay, rosewood bridge with black white dot pins, rosewood peghead veneer with screened logo, 3 per side chrome tuners. Available in Natural finish. Mfd. 1993 to date.

Mfr.'s Sug. Retail	$530	$424	$318	$265	$210	$190	$175	$160

Stephen's Extended Cutaway Series

This series has a patented neck to body joint that allows full access to all 24 frets and is called the patented Stephen's Extended Cutaway, designed by Stephen Davies.

DC60 LEXINGTON — single round cutaway dreadnought style, solid spruce top, oval soundhole, bound body, 3 stripe purfling/rosette, ovankol back/sides, mahogany neck, 24 fret bound rosewood fingerboard with pearl dot inlay, rosewood bridge with black dot pins, 3 per side pearloid chrome diecast tuners. Available in Natural finish. Disc. 1992.

			$580	$500	$415	$330	$300	$275	$250

Last Mfr.'s Sug. Retail was $830.

DC60E — similar to DC60, except has acoustic bridge pickup, 4 band EQ. Disc. 1994.

			$980	$840	$700	$560	$505	$460	$420

Last Mfr.'s Sug. Retail was $1,400.

DC80 CHARLESTON — single round cutaway dreadnought style, solid cedar top, oval soundhole, bound body, 3 stripe purfling/rosette, rosewood back/sides, mahogany neck, 24 fret bound rosewood fingerboard with diamond inlay, rosewood bridge with pearl dot white pins, rosewood veneer on bound peghead, 3 per side pearloid head gold diecast tuners. Available in Natural finish. Disc. 1992.

			$630	$540	$450	$360	$325	$300	$275

Last Mfr.'s Sug. Retail was $900.

DC80E — similar to DC80, except has acoustic bridge pickup, 4 band EQ. Disc. 1994.

			$1,050	$900	$750	$600	$540	$495	$450

Last Mfr.'s Sug. Retail was $1,500.

J20S — jumbo style, solid cedar top, oval soundhole, bound body, 5 stripe rosette, walnut back/sides, mahogany neck, 21 fret rosewood fingerboard with pearl snowflake inlay at 12th fret, rosewood bridge with pearl dot white pins and bone saddle, walnut veneer on peghead, 3 per side chrome diecast tuners. Available in Natural finish. Disc. 1994.

			$630	$540	$450	$360	$325	$300	$275

Last Mfr.'s Sug. Retail was $900.

J50S — jumbo style, solid spruce top, oval soundhole, bound body, 5 stripe rosette, birds eye maple back/sides, mahogany neck, 21 fret bound rosewood fingerboard with pearl snowflake inlay at the 12th fret, rosewood bridge with pearl dot white pins and bone saddle, birds eye maple veneer on bound peghead, 3 per side pearl button gold diecast tuners. Available in Natural finish. Disc. 1994.

			$805	$690	$575	$460	$415	$380	$345

Last Mfr.'s Sug. Retail was $1,150.

ACOUSTIC BASS

AB20 — single sharp cutaway dreadnought style, spruce top, diagonal sound channels, bound body, mahogany back/sides, maple neck, 23 fret rosewood fingerboard with pearl dot inlay, rosewood bridge with brass insert, 2 per side tuners, chrome hardware, EQUIS II bass preamp system. Available in Black, Natural and Tobacco Sunburst finishes. Curr. mfr.

Mfr.'s Sug. Retail	$900	$720	$540	$450	$360	$325	$300	$275

This model is also available with hardwood top/back/sides and fretless fingerboard.

AB25 — similar to AB20, except has 5 strings. Available in Black and Tobacco Sunburst finishes.

Mfr.'s Sug. Retail	$1,000	$800	$600	$500	$400	$360	$330	$300

AB40 — single round cutaway jumbo style, arched spruce top, diagonal sound channels, bound body, quilted ash back/sides, multi layer maple neck, 24 fret bound ebony fingerboard with pearl dot inlay, ebonized rosewood bridge with brass insert, bound peghead with pearl Washburn logo and stylized inlay, 2 per side tuners, gold hardware, active electronics, 1 volume/2 tone controls, EQUIS II bass preamp system. Available in Natural and Tobacco Sunburst finishes. Curr. mfr.

Mfr.'s Sug. Retail	$2,250	$1,800	$1,350	$1,125	$900	$810	$740	$675

Subtract $150 for fretless fingerboard (AB40FL).

AB42 — similar to AB40, except has humbucker pickup. Available in Tobacco Sunburst finish. Curr. mfr.

Mfr.'s Sug. Retail	$2,500	$2,000	$1,500	$1,250	$1,000	$900	$825	$750

Grading		100%	98% MINT	95% EXC+	90% EXC	80% VG+	70% VG	60% G

AB45 — similar to AB40, except has 5 strings, 3/2 per side tuners. Available in Tobacco Sunburst finish. Disc. 1991.

		$1,610	$1,380	$1,150	$920	$830	$760	$690

Last Mfr.'s Sug. Retail was $2,300.

ACOUSTIC ELECTRIC

Festival Series

EA10 — single sharp cutaway folk style, spruce top, oval soundhole, bound body, 3 stripe purfling/rosette, mahogany back/sides/neck, 21 fret bound rosewood fingerboard with pearl dot inlay, rosewood bridge with white black dot pins, bound peghead with screened logo, 3 per side chrome Grover tuners, acoustic bridge pickup, 4 band EQ. Available in Black and Natural finishes. New 1994.

Mfr.'s Sug. Retail	$650	$520	$390	$325	$260	$235	$215	$195

EA20 NEWPORT — single sharp cutaway parlor style, mahogany top, oval soundhole, bound body, 3 stripe rosette, mahogany back/sides/neck, 21 fret rosewood fingerboard with pearl dot inlay, rosewood bridge with pearl dot white pins, 3 per side chrome diecast tuners, acoustic bridge pickup, volume/tone control, 3 band EQ. Available in Black, Natural, White and Tobacco Sunburst finishes. Mfd. 1979 to date.

Mfr.'s Sug. Retail	$800	$640	$480	$410	$340	$305	$280	$255

The White finish model has pearl dot black bridge pins.

In 1994, Natural finish was introduced.

EA2012 — similar to EA20, except has 12 strings, 6 per side tuners. Available in Black and Natural finishes. Disc. 1994.

		$630	$540	$450	$360	$325	$300	$275

Last Mfr.'s Sug. Retail was $900.

EA22 — single sharp cutaway folk style, spruce top, oval soundhole, bound body, 5 stripe purfling, 9 stripe rosette, mahogany back/sides/neck, 21 fret bound rosewood fingerboard with pearl wings inlay, rosewood bridge with white black dot pins, bound blackface peghead with screened signature/logo, 3 per side chrome Grover tuners, acoustic bridge pickup, volume/tone control, 3 band EQ. Available in Black finish. New 1994.

Mfr.'s Sug. Retail	$1,000	$800	$600	$500	$400	$360	$330	$300

This model is a Nuno Bettencourt Limited Edition instrument. A numbered commemorative metal plate is found inside the body.

EA30 MONTEREY — single sharp cutaway dreadnought style, spruce top, oval soundhole, bound body, 3 stripe purfling, 5 stripe rosette, flame maple back/sides, mahogany neck, 21 fret rosewood fingerboard, rosewood bridge with white pearl dot pins, 3 per side chrome diecast tuners, acoustic bridge pickup, volume/tone control, 3 band EQ. Available in Natural, Transparent Red, Transparent Blue and Transparent Black finishes. Disc. 1992.

		$510	$440	$365	$290	$260	$240	$220

Add $100 for left handed version of this model (EA30LH).

Add $40 for 12 string version of this model (EA3012). Available in Natural finish.

Last Mfr.'s Sug. Retail was $730.

EA36 MARQUEE (formerly EA46) — single cutaway dreadnought style, figured maple top, 3 stripe bound body, diagonal sound channels, figured maple back/sides, mahogany neck, 23 fret rosewood bound fingerboard with pearl diamond inlay, rosewood bridge with pearl dot black pins, flame maple veneer on bound peghead, 3 per side pearl button gold diecast tuners, acoustic bridge pickup, volume/tone control, 3 band EQ. Available in Natural and Tobacco Sunburst finishes. Curr. mfr.

Mfr.'s Sug. Retail	$1,000	$800	$600	$500	$400	$360	$330	$300

EA3612 — similar to EA36, except has 12 strings, 6 per side tuners. Disc. 1994.

		$735	$630	$525	$420	$380	$345	$315

Last Mfr.'s Sug. Retail was $1,050.

EA40 WOODSTOCK — single sharp cutaway dreadnought style, arched spruce top, oval soundhole, bound body, abalone purfling/rosette, mahogany back/sides/neck, 21 fret bound rosewood fingerboard, rosewood bridge with pearl dot black pins, 3 per side chrome diecast tuners, EQUIS II preamp system. Available in Black and White finishes. Disc. 1992.

		$770	$660	$550	$440	$395	$365	$330

Add $40 for string version of this model (EA4012). Disc. 1992

Last Mfr.'s Sug. Retail was $1,100.

This model had birdseye maple back/sides with Natural finish optionally available.

EA44 — single sharp cutaway dreadnought style, solid cedar top, oval soundhole, bound body, 3 stripe purfling/rosette, rosewood back/sides, mahogany neck, 20 fret bound rosewood fingerboard with pearl diamond inlay, rosewood bridge with white black pins, bound peghead with rosewood veneer, 3 per side chrome tuners with pearl buttons, acoustic bridge pickup, volume/tone control, 3 band EQ. Available in Black, Natural and Tobacco Sunburst finishes. Disc. 1994.

		$770	$660	$550	$440	$395	$365	$330

Last Mfr.'s Sug. Retail was $1,100.

Grading	100%	98% MINT	95% EXC+	90% EXC	80% VG+	70% VG	60% G

EA45 — single sharp cutaway dreadnought style, solid cedar top, oval soundhole, bound body, 3 stripe purfling/rosette, rosewood back/sides, mahogany neck, 20 fret bound rosewood fingerboard with pearl diamond inlay, rosewood bridge with white black pins, bound peghead with rosewood veneer, 3 per side chrome tuners with pearl buttons, acoustic bridge pickup, volume/tone control, 3 band EQ. Available in Natural and Tobacco Sunburst finishes. Curr. mfr.

Mfr.'s Sug. Retail	$1,150	$920	$690	$575	$460	$415	$380	$345

EC41 TANGLEWOOD — classical style, spruce top, oval soundhole, 5 stripe bound body/rosette, ovankol back/sides, mahogany neck, 21 fret bound rosewood fingerboard with pearl dot inlay, rosewood bridge, ovankol veneer on bound peghead, 3 per side pearl button gold tuners, EQUIS II preamp system. Available in Natural finish. Disc 1992.

	$490	$420	$350	$280	$250	$230	$210

Last Mfr.'s Sug. Retail was $700.

Solid Body Series

SBC20 — single round cutaway classic style, spruce top, round soundhole, bound body, wooden inlay rosette, routed out mahogany body, mahogany neck, 22 fret rosewood fingerboard with pearl dot inlay, rosewood bridge, 3 per side chrome diecast tuners, Sensor pickups, volume/tone control. Available in Natural finish. Disc. 1992.

	$385	$330	$275	$220	$200	$180	$165

Last Mfr.'s Sug. Retail was $550.

SBC70 — single cutaway classic style routed out mahogany body, multi bound spruce top, mahogany neck, 22 fret bound rosewood fingerboard, tied rosewood bridge, rosewood veneered slotted peghead, 3 per side chrome tuners with pearloid buttons, acoustic bridge pickup, volume/tone controls. Available in Natural finish. New 1994.

Mfr.'s Sug. Retail	$700	$560	$420	$350	$280	$250	$230	$210

SBF24 — single round cutaway dreadnought style, spruce top, round soundhole, bound body, wooden inlay rosette, routed out mahogany body, mahogany neck, 22 fret rosewood fingerboard with pearl dot inlay, rosewood bridge with white pearl dot pins, 3 per side chrome diecast tuners, Sensor pickups, volume/tone control, active electronics. Available in Natural, Pearl White and Black finishes. Disc. 1992.

	$400	$340	$285	$230	$205	$190	$170

Last Mfr.'s Sug. Retail was $570.

SBF80 — single cutaway dreadnought style routed out mahogany body, multi bound figured maple top, mahogany neck, 22 fret bound rosewood fingerboard with pearl slotted diamond inlay, rosewood bridge with white abalone dot pins, bound figured maple peghead with screened logo, 3 per side chrome Grover tuners with pearloid buttons, acoustic bridge pickup, volume/treble/bass controls, active electronics. Available in Cherry Sunburst finish. Mfd. 1993 to date.

Mfr.'s Sug. Retail	$750	$600	$450	$375	$300	$270	$245	$225

ELECTRIC

FALCON — double cutaway mahogany body, bound carved maple top, thru body mahogany neck, 22 fret bound rosewood fingerboard with brass circle inlay, strings thru bridge, bound blackface peghead with screened logo, 3 per side tuners, chrome hardware, 2 humbucker Washburn pickups, 2 volume/2 tone controls, 3 position switch. Available in Sunburst finish. Mfd. 1980 to 1986.

	$250	$175	$150	$125	$100	$90	$80

Falcon Standard — similar to Falcon, except has coil tap switch in tone controls.

	$300	$210	$180	$150	$120	$110	$100

Falcon Deluxe — similar to Falcon, except has abalone fingerboard inlay, coil tap switch in tone controls.

	$350	$245	$210	$175	$140	$125	$115

Classic Series

HB30 — double cutaway semi hollow style, arched flamed sycamore top, raised black pickguard, bound body/f-holes, flamed sycamore back/sides, maple neck, 20 fret bound rosewood fingerboard with pearl dot inlay, tunomatic bridge/stop tailpiece, bound blackface peghead with pearl diamond/W/logo inlay, 3 per side Grover tuners, chrome hardware, 2 humbucker Washburn pickups, 2 volume/2 tone controls, 3 position switch. Available in Cherry and Tobacco Sunburst finishes. New 1994.

Mfr.'s Sug. Retail	$620	$496	$372	$310	$250	$225	$205	$190

HB35S — double cutaway semi hollow style, arched flamed sycamore top, raised black pickguard, bound body/f-holes, flamed sycamore back/sides, maple neck, 20 fret bound rosewood fingerboard with pearl split rectangle inlay, tunomatic bridge/stop tailpiece, bound blackface peghead with pearl diamond/W/logo inlay, 3 per side Grover tuners, gold hardware, 2 humbucker Washburn pickups, 2 volume/2 tone controls, 3 position switch. Available in Natural, Tobacco Sunburst and Wine Red finishes. Curr. mfr.

Mfr.'s Sug. Retail	$780	$624	$468	$400	$320	$290	$265	$240

"It's true, but my first love is guitar. I played the rhythm guitar parts in Foreigner on what I called my "wooden" Tele. It's a 1962 that has had the finish removed."

—Lawrence Acunto on Ian McDonald TCG, Mar/Apr 1993

Grading	100%	98% MINT	95% EXC+	90% EXC	80% VG+	70% VG	60% G

J-6S — single cutaway hollow style, arched spruce top, raised black pickguard, bound body/f-holes, maple back/sides, 5 piece maple/rosewood neck, 20 fret bound rosewood fingerboard with split rectangle abalone inlay, adjustable ebony bridge/trapeze tailpiece, bound blackface peghead with abalone diamond/W/logo inlay, 3 per side Grover tuners, gold hardware, 2 humbucker pickups, 2 volume/2 tone controls, 3 position switch. Available in Natural and Tobacco Sunburst finishes. Curr. mfr.

Mfr.'s Sug. Retail	$800	$640	$480	$430	$360	$325	$300	$275

In 1994, flamed sycamore back/sides replaced original item.

J-10 — single cutaway hollow style, arched solid spruce top, bound body and f-holes, raised bound tortoise pickguard, flame maple back/sides, multi layer maple neck, 20 fret bound ebony fingerboard with pearl/abalone split rectangle inlay, ebony bridge, trapeze tailpiece, bound peghead with abalone Washburn logo and stylized inlay, 3 per side pearl button tuners, gold hardware, 2 humbucker pickups, 2 volume/tone controls, 3 position switch. Available in Natural and Tobacco Sunburst finishes. Disc. 1992.

		$1,260	$1,080	$900	$720	$650	$595	$540

Last Mfr.'s Sug. Retail was $1,800.

WP50 — single cutaway style, carved bound flame maple top, mahogany body/neck, raised white pickguard, 22 fret bound rosewood fingerboard with pearl trapezoid inlay, tunomatic bridge/stop tailpiece, 3 per side pearl button tuners, chrome hardware, 2 humbucker Washburn pickups, 2 volume/tone controls, 3 position switch. Available in Cherry Sunburst and Tobacco Sunburst finishes. Disc. 1992.

		$420	$360	$300	$240	$215	$195	$180

Last Mfr.'s Sug. Retail was $600.

WP80 — similar to WP50, except has carved maple top, black raised pickguard, ebonized fingerboard and gold hardware. Available in Black and White finishes. Disc. 1992.

		$475	$405	$340	$270	$245	$225	$205

Last Mfr.'s Sug. Retail was $680.

WT522 — single cutaway alder body, figured ash top, white pickguard, controls mounted on a metal plate, bolt-on maple neck, 21 fret maple fingerboard with black dot inlay, strings thru Wilkinson bridge, 6 on one side Grover tuners, chrome hardware, 2 single coil Washburn pickups, volume/tone control. Available in Black, Blonde and Tobacco Sunburst finishes. New 1994.

Mfr.'s Sug. Retail	$500	$400	$300	$250	$200	$180	$165	$150

KC Series

KC20 — offset double cutaway hardwood body, arched top and back, scalloped cutaways, bolt-on maple neck, 22 fret rosewood fingerboard with pearl dot inlay, standard vibrato, 6 on one side tuners, chrome hardware, 2 single coil/1 humbucker Washburn pickups, volume/tone control, 5 position switch. Available in Black and White finishes. Disc. 1992.

		$245	$210	$175	$140	$125	$115	$105

Add $50 for left handed version of this model (KC20LH).

Last Mfr.'s Sug. Retail was $350.

KC40 — offset double cutaway alder body, arched top and back, bolt-on maple neck, 22 fret rosewood fingerboard with pearl dot inlay, double locking vibrato, 6 on one side tuners, chrome hardware, 2 single coil/1 humbucker Washburn pickups, volume/tone control, 5 position switch. Available in Black and White finishes. Disc. 1992.

		$330	$280	$235	$190	$170	$155	$140

Add $70 for left handed version of this model (KC40LH).

Last Mfr.'s Sug. Retail was $470.

KC42 — similar to KC40, except has reverse peghead. Available in Black, Woodstone Fluorescent Red and Woodstone Fluorescent Yellow finishes. Disc. 1992.

		$350	$300	$250	$200	$180	$165	$150

Last Mfr.'s Sug. Retail was $500.

KC44 — similar to KC40, except has humbucker/single coil/humbucker Washburn pickups. Available in Black Rain and White Rain finishes.

		$350	$300	$250	$200	$180	$165	$150

Last Mfr.'s Sug. Retail was $500.

KC70 — similar to KC40, except has black hardware, 3 individual pickup selector and coil tap switches. Available in Black, Metallic Black Cherry, White Rain, Woodstone Brown, Woodstone Red and Woodstone Silver finishes.

		$455	$390	$325	$260	$235	$215	$195

Add $100 for left handed version of this model (KC70LH).

Last Mfr.'s Sug. Retail was $650.

Grading	100%	98% MINT	95% EXC+	90% EXC	80% VG+	70% VG	60% G

KC90 — offset double cutaway alder body, arched top and back, scalloped cutaways, bolt-on maple neck, 24 fret rosewood fingerboard with pearl dot inlay, double locking vibrato, 6 on one side tuners, black hardware, 2 Seymour Duncan single coil/1 humbucker pickups, 5 position and coil tap switches. Available in Black, Blond, Metallic Red, Natural Gold, Transparent Red and White. Disc. 1992.

	$680	$580	$485	$390	$355	$325	$295

Last Mfr.'s Sug. Retail was $970.

Mercury Series

MG30 — offset double cutaway hardwood body, bolt-on maple neck, 24 fret rosewood fingerboard with offset pearl dot inlay, double locking vibrato, 6 on one side tuners, chrome hardware, 2 single coil/1 humbucker Washburn pickups, volume/tone control, 5 position switch with coil tap. Available in Metallic Red, Pacific Blue Rain and Tobacco Sunburst finishes. Disc. 1994.

	$335	$290	$240	$190	$170	$155	$145

Last Mfr.'s Sug. Retail was $480.

MG34 — similar to MG30, except has maple fingerboard with black offset dot inlay, humbucker/single coil/humbucker pickups. Available in Black, Metallic Dark Blue and Purple Rain finishes. Disc. 1994.

	$350	$300	$250	$200	$180	$165	$150

Last Mfr.'s Sug. Retail was $500.

MG40 — offset double cutaway alder body, white pickguard, bolt-on maple neck, 24 fret rosewood fingerboard with offset pearl dot inlay, double locking vibrato, 6 on one side tuners, black hardware, volume/tone control, 5 position switch with coil tap. Available in Black, Ice Pearl, Metallic Red and Pearl Blue finishes. Disc. 1994.

	$400	$340	$285	$230	$205	$190	$170

Last Mfr.'s Sug. Retail was $570.

MG42 — similar to MG40, except has 2 humbucker pickups. Available in Metallic Purple and Midnight Blue Metallic finishes. Disc. 1994.

	$400	$340	$285	$230	$205	$190	$170

Last Mfr.'s Sug. Retail was $570.

MG43 — similar to MG40, except has maple fingerboard with offset black dot inlay, 3 single coil pickups. Available in Black and Metallic Red finishes. Disc. 1994.

	$385	$330	$275	$220	$200	$180	$165

Last Mfr.'s Sug. Retail was $550.

MG44 — similar to MG40, except has maple fingerboard with offset black dot inlay, humbucker/single coil/humbucker pickups. Available in Black, Black Cherry Metallic, Metallic Red and Midnight Blue Metallic finishes. Disc. 1994.

	$410	$355	$295	$235	$210	$195	$180

Last Mfr.'s Sug. Retail was $590.

MG52 — offset double cutaway hardwood body, white pickguard, bolt-on maple neck, 24 fret rosewood fingerboard with offset pearl dot inlay, tunomatic bridge/stop tailpiece, 6 on one side tuners, chrome hardware, 2 humbucker Washburn pickups, volume/tone control, 5 way switch with coil tap. Available in Metallic Dark Blue and Tobacco Sunburst finishes. Disc. 1994.

	$300	$260	$215	$175	$155	$140	$130

Last Mfr.'s Sug. Retail was $430.

MG70 — offset double cutaway alder body, flamed maple top, transparent pickguard, bolt-on maple neck, 24 fret rosewood fingerboard with offset pearl dot inlay, double locking vibrato, 6 on one side tuners, gold hardware, volume/tone control, 5 position switch with coil tap. Available in Transparent Blue and Vintage Sunburst finishes. Disc. 1994.

	$490	$420	$350	$280	$250	$230	$210

Last Mfr.'s Sug. Retail was $700.

MG72 — similar to MG70, except has 2 humbucker pickups. Available in Transparent Purple and Vintage Sunburst finishes. Disc. 1994.

	$490	$420	$350	$280	$250	$230	$210

Last Mfr.'s Sug. Retail was $700.

MG74 — similar to MG70, except has maple fingerboard with offset black dot inlay, humbucker/single coil/humbucker pickups. Available in Transparent Purple and Vintage Sunburst finishes. Disc. 1994.

	$500	$430	$360	$290	$260	$240	$220

Last Mfr.'s Sug. Retail was $720.

MG300 — offset double cutaway hardwood body, bolt-on maple neck, 24 fret rosewood fingerboard with offset pearl dot inlay, double locking Floyd Rose vibrato, 6 on one side tuners, chrome hardware, 2 single coil/1 humbucker exposed Washburn pickups, volume/tone control, 5 position switch. Available in Ice Pearl, Metallic Red and Pacific Blue Rain finishes. New 1994.

Mfr.'s Sug. Retail	$500	$400	$300	$250	$200	$180	$165	$150

MG340 — offset double cutaway hardwood body, bolt-on maple neck, 24 fret maple fingerboard with offset black dot inlay, double locking Floyd Rose vibrato, 6 on one side tuners, chrome hardware, humbucker/single coil/humbucker exposed Washburn pickups, volume/tone control, 5 position switch. Available in Black, Pearl Blue and Purple Rain finishes. New 1994.

Mfr.'s Sug. Retail	$500	$400	$300	$250	$200	$180	$165	$150

Grading	100% MINT	98% EXC+	95% EXC	90% VG+	80% VG	70% VG	60% G

MG401 — offset double cutaway alder body, figured ash top, bolt-on maple neck, 24 fret rosewood fingerboard with offset pearl dot inlay, standard Schaller vibrato, 6 on one side tuners, chrome hardware, 2 single coil/1 humbucker exposed Washburn pickups, volume/tone with coil tap control, 5 position switch. Available in Antique Natural, Blonde, Natural and Transparent Burgundy finishes. New 1994.

Mfr.'s Sug. Retail	$600	$480	$360	$300	$240	$215	$195	$180

MG522 — offset double cutaway alder body, figured ash top, bolt-on maple neck, 24 fret rosewood fingerboard with offset pearl dot inlay, tunomatic bridge/stop tailpiece, 6 on one side tuners, chrome hardware, 2 humbucker exposed Washburn pickups, volume/tone with coil tap control, 3 position switch. Available in Tobacco Sunburst and Transparent Black finishes. New 1994.

Mfr.'s Sug. Retail	$530	$424	$318	$265	$210	$190	$175	$160

MG700 — offset double cutaway alder body, figured sycamore top, bolt-on maple neck, 24 fret rosewood fingerboard with offset pearl dot inlay, double locking Floyd Rose vibrato, 6 on one side Grover tuners, gold hardware, 2 single coil/1 humbucker exposed Washburn pickups, volume/tone control, 5 position switch. Available in Antique Natural and Vintage Sunburst finishes. New 1994.

Mfr.'s Sug. Retail	$700	$560	$420	$350	$280	$250	$230	$210

MG701 — offset double cutaway alder body, figured sycamore top, bolt-on maple neck, 24 fret rosewood fingerboard with offset pearl dot inlay, standard Wilkinson vibrato, 6 on one side locking Schaller tuners, chrome hardware, 2 single coil/1 humbucker exposed Washburn pickups, volume/tone control, 5 position switch. Available in Antique Natural, Transparent Blue and Vintage Sunburst finishes. New 1994.

Mfr.'s Sug. Retail	$730	$584	$438	$365	$290	$260	$240	$220

MG821 — offset double cutaway alder body, bound figured sycamore top, bolt-on maple neck, 24 fret rosewood fingerboard with offset pearl dot inlay, standard Wilkinson vibrato, 6 on one side locking Schaller tuners, chrome hardware, 2 humbucker exposed Washburn pickups, volume/tone with coil tap control, 5 position switch. Available in Tobacco Sunburst and Transparent Burgundy finishes. New 1994.

Mfr.'s Sug. Retail	$780	$624	$468	$390	$315	$280	$260	$235

Signature Series

EC26 ATLANTIS — offset double cutaway basswood body, bolt-on maple neck, 26 fret rosewood fingerboard with pearl dot inlay, locking vibrato, 6 on one side locking tuners, chrome hardware, single coil/humbucker Seymour Duncan pickup, volume/tone control, 5 position switch. Available in Black, Red and White finishes. Disc. 1991.

	$770	$660	$550	$440	$395	$365	$330

Last Mfr.'s Sug. Retail was $1,100.

This model featured the patented Stephen's Extended Cutaway.

N2 — offset double cutaway alder body, bolt-on maple neck, 22 fret rosewood fingerboard with pearl dot inlay, double locking vibrato, reverse headstock, 6 on one side tuners, chrome hardware, 2 humbucker Washburn pickups, volume control, 3 position switch. Available in Natural and Padauk finishes. Curr. mfr.

Mfr.'s Sug. Retail	$800	$600	$400	$350	$280	$250	$230	$210

This model was co-designed with Nuno Bettencourt.

SB80 — double cutaway mahogany body, arched bound flame maple top, raised white pickguard, mahogany neck, 22 fret bound rosewood fingerboard with pearl wings inlay, tunomatic bridge/stop tailpiece, 3 per side tuners, chrome hardware, 2 humbucker Washburn pickups, 2 volume/2 tone controls, 3 position switch. Available in Natural and Vintage Sunburst finishes. Curr. mfr.

Mfr.'s Sug. Retail	$750	$600	$450	$375	$320	$290	$265	$240

SS40 — offset double cutaway poplar body, bolt-on maple neck, 22 fret maple fingerboard with abalone inlay, double locking Floyd Rose vibrato, 6 on one side Grover tuners, gold hardware, 2 angled humbucker exposed Washburn pickups, volume control, 5 position switch. Available in Black finish. Mfd. 1992 to date.

Mfr.'s Sug. Retail	$800	$640	$480	$400	$320	$290	$265	$240

This model was co-designed with Steve Stevens.

In 1994, black dot fingerboard inlay replaced original item.

USA Factory Series

All the instruments in this series are hand built in Chicago. They all feature Seymour Duncan and Bill Lawrence pickups.

Laredo Series

LT82 — single cutaway alder body, white pickguard, controls mounted on a metal plate, bolt-on maple neck, 22 fret maple fingerboard with black dot inlay, strings thru Wilkinson bridge, 6 on one side Gotoh tuners, chrome hardware, 2 single coil pickups, volume/tone control, 3 position switch. Available in Black, Natural, Transparent Blue, Transparent Red, Tobacco Sunburst and Vintage Sunburst finishes. Mfd. 1992 to date.

Mfr.'s Sug. Retail	$800	$640	$480	$400	$320	$290	$265	$240

This model has rosewood fingerboard with pearl dot inlay optionally available.

In 1994, Natural, Transparent Blue, Transparent Red and Vintage Sunburst finishes were introduced, ash body, pearloid pickguard, abalone dot fingerboard inlay replaced original items, Tobacco Sunburst finish was discontinued.

"To single out Europeans and the Japanese as culprits in the escalation in prices of classic American guitars is shortsighted, unfair, and wrong; a global economy means all commodities, including vintage American guitars, are subject to purchase by anyone in the world who can afford them."
—Jay Scott
TCG, July/Aug 1990

Grading	100%	98% MINT	95% EXC+	90% EXC	80% VG+	70% VG	60% G

LT92 — similar to LT82, except has ash body, pearloid pickguard. Available in Natural and Tobacco Sunburst finishes.

		$700	$600	$500	$400	$360	$330	$300

Last Mfr.'s Sug. Retail was $1,000.

This model has rosewood fingerboard with pearl dot inlay optionally available.

Mercury (USA) Series

MG90 — offset double cutaway mahogany body, bolt-on maple neck, 24 fret rosewood fingerboard with offset pearl dot inlay, standard Wilkinson vibrato, 6 on one side locking Gotoh tuners, chrome hardware, 2 single coil/1 humbucker exposed pickups, volume/tone control, 5 position switch. Available in Natural finish. New 1994.

Mfr.'s Sug. Retail	$900	$720	$540	$450	$360	$325	$300	$275

MG94 — offset double cutaway alder body, bolt-on maple neck, 24 fret maple fingerboard with offset black dot inlay, double locking vibrato, 6 on one side tuners, chrome hardware, humbucker/single coil/humbucker pickups, volume/tone control, 5 position switch. Available in Green Iridescent, Iridescent, Midnight Blue Metallic and 3 Tone Sunburst finishes. Disc. 1994.

	$700	$600	$500	$400	$360	$330	$300

Last Mfr.'s Sug. Retail was $1,000.

This model has rosewood fingerboard with pearl dot inlay optionally available.

MG100 — offset double cutaway ash body, bolt-on maple neck, 24 fret rosewood fingerboard with offset pearl dot inlay, standard Wilkinson vibrato, 6 on one side locking Gotoh tuners, chrome hardware, 2 single coil/1 humbucker exposed pickups, volume/tone control, 5 position switch. Available in Antique Natural, Transparent Blue, Transparent Red and Vintage Sunburst finishes. New 1994.

Mfr.'s Sug. Retail	$1,100	$880	$660	$550	$440	$395	$365	$330

MG102 — offset double cutaway ash body, bolt-on maple neck, 24 fret rosewood fingerboard with offset pearl dot inlay, standard Wilkinson vibrato, 6 on one side locking Gotoh tuners, chrome hardware, 2 humbucker exposed pickups, volume/tone control, 5 position switch. Available in Antique Natural, Transparent Blue and Transparent Red finishes. New 1994.

Mfr.'s Sug. Retail	$1,100	$880	$660	$550	$440	$395	$365	$330

MG104 — offset double cutaway alder body, quilted maple top, bolt-on maple neck, 24 fret maple fingerboard with offset black dot inlay, double locking vibrato, 6 on one side tuners, chrome hardware, humbucker/single coil/humbucker pickups, volume/tone control, 5 position switch. Available in Transparent Red and Vintage Sunburst finishes. Disc. 1994.

	$770	$660	$550	$440	$395	$365	$330

Last Mfr.'s Sug. Retail was $1,100.

MG112 — offset double cutaway alder body, bound quilted maple top, bolt-on maple neck, 24 fret rosewood fingerboard with offset pearl dot inlay, tunomatic bridge/stop tailpiece, 6 on one side Gotoh tuners, chrome hardware, 2 humbucker exposed pickups, volume/tone control, 5 position switch. Available in Black, Transparent Blue, Transparent Purple, Transparent Red and Vintage Sunburst finishes. Mfd. 1992 to date.

Mfr.'s Sug. Retail	$1,200	$900	$600	$500	$400	$360	$330	$300

In 1994, ash body, double locking Floyd Rose vibrato replaced original items, quilted maple top, Transparent Red finish were discontinued.

MG120 — offset double cutaway mahogany body, quilted maple top, bolt-on maple neck, 24 fret rosewood fingerboard with offset pearl dot inlay, standard Wilkinson vibrato, 6 on one side locking Gotoh tuners, chrome hardware, 2 single coil/1 humbucker exposed pickups, volume/tone control, 5 position switch. Available in Transparent Blue, Transparent Red and Vintage Sunburst finishes. New 1994.

Mfr.'s Sug. Retail	$1,300	$1,040	$780	$650	$520	$470	$430	$390

MG122 — offset double cutaway mahogany body, quilted maple top, bolt-on maple neck, 24 fret rosewood fingerboard with offset pearl dot inlay, standard Wilkinson vibrato, 6 on one side locking Gotoh tuners, chrome hardware, 2 humbucker exposed pickups, volume/tone control, 5 position switch. Available in Transparent Purple, Transparent Red and Vintage Sunburst finishes. New 1994.

Mfr.'s Sug. Retail	$1,300	$1,040	$780	$650	$520	$470	$430	$390

MG142 — offset double cutaway mahogany body, quilted maple top, bolt-on maple neck, 24 fret ebony fingerboard with offset pearl dot inlay, tunomatic bridge/stop tailpiece, graphite nut, 6 on one side tuners, chrome hardware, 2 humbucker pickups, volume/tone control, 5 position switch. Available in Transparent Red and Vintage Sunburst finishes. Disc. 1994.

	$1,190	$1,020	$850	$680	$610	$560	$510

Last Mfr.'s Sug. Retail was $1,700.

MG154 — similar to MG142, except has double locking vibrato, humbucker/single coil/humbucker pickups. Disc. 1994.

	$1,260	$1,080	$900	$720	$650	$595	$540

Last Mfr.'s Sug. Retail was $1,800.

Nuno Bettencourt Series

This series was co-designed with Nuno Bettencourt and features the patented Extended Stephen's Cutaway.

Grading	100% MINT	98% EXC+	95% EXC	90% VG+	80% VG	70% VG	60% G

N4EA — offset double cutaway alder body, bolt-on maple neck, 22 fret ebony fingerboard with pearl dot inlay, double locking vibrato, reverse peghead, 6 on one side tuners, chrome hardware, 2 humbucker pickups, volume control, 3 position switch. Available in Natural finish. Mfd.1992 to date.

Mfr.'s Sug. Retail	$1,500	$1,200	$900	$750	$600	$540	$495	$450

N4EP — similar to N4EA, except has padauk body. Mfd. 1992 to date.

Mfr.'s Sug. Retail	$1,600	$1,280	$960	$800	$640	$575	$530	$480

N4ESA — similar to N4EA, except has swamp ash body. New 1994.

Mfr.'s Sug. Retail	$1,600	$1,280	$960	$800	$640	$575	$530	$480

Silverado Series

This series incorporates the patented Stephen's Extended Cutaway; and has rosewood or maple fingerboards.

LS93 — offset double cutaway ash body, pearloid pickguard, bolt-on maple neck, 22 fret fingerboard with pearl dot inlay, standard Wilkinson vibrato, 6 on one side locking Gotoh tuners, chrome hardware, 3 single coil pickups, 1 volume/2 tone controls, 5 position switch. Available in Black, Natural, Transparent Blue, Transparent Red and Vintage Sunburst finishes. New 1994.

Mfr.'s Sug. Retail	$1,000	$800	$600	$500	$400	$360	$330	$300

LT93 — offset double cutaway alder body, pearloid pickguard, bolt-on maple neck, 22 fret fingerboard with black dot inlay, standard vibrato, 6 on one side locking tuners, chrome hardware, 3 single coil pickups, volume/2 tone controls, 5 position switch. Available in Black and Tobacco Sunburst finishes. Mfd. 1992 to 1994.

	$910	$780	$650	$520	$470	$430	$390

Last Mfr.'s Sug. Retail was $1,300.

LT103 — similar to LT93, except has flame maple or swamp ash body. Available in Natural and Tobacco Sunburst finishes. Disc. 1994.

	$1,120	$960	$800	$640	$575	$530	$480

Last Mfr.'s Sug. Retail was $1,600.

Steve Stevens Signature Series

This series was co-designed with Steve Stevens.

SS80 — offset double cutaway poplar body, bolt-on maple neck, 22 fret maple fingerboard with abalone dot inlay, double locking vibrato, 6 on one side tuners, gold hardware, 2 humbucker pickups, volume control, 3 position switch. Available in Black finish. Mfd. 1992 to date.

Mfr.'s Sug. Retail	$1,500	$1,200	$900	$750	$600	$540	$495	$450

SS100 — similar to SS80, except has black dot inlay, black hardware. Available in Vintage Frankenstein Graphic finishes. Mfd. 1992 to 1994.

	$1,260	$1,080	$900	$720	$650	$595	$540

Last Mfr.'s Sug. Retail was $1,800.

Wings Series

SB50 — double cutaway mahogany body, black pickguard, mahogany neck, 22 fret rosewood fingerboard with pearl dot inlay, tunomatic bridge/stop tailpiece, 3 per side vintage Keystone tuners, chrome hardware, 2 single coil "soapbar" pickups, volume/2 tone controls, 3 position switch. Available in Ivory, Tobacco Sunburst and Wine Red finishes. Mfd. 1992 to 1994.

	$630	$540	$450	$360	$325	$300	$275

Last Mfr.'s Sug. Retail was $900.

SB100 — similar to SB50, except has bound arched figured maple top, no pickguard, bound fingerboard with pearl stylized V inlay, 2 humbucker pickups. Available in Cherry Sunburst and Vintage Sunburst finishes. Mfd. 1992 to 1994.

	$1,750	$1,500	$1,250	$1,000	$900	$825	$750

Last Mfr.'s Sug. Retail was $2,500.

ELECTRIC BASS

Axxess Series

XS2 — offset double cutaway hardwood body, maple neck, 24 fret rosewood fingerboard with pearl dot inlay, fixed bridge, 4 on one side tuners, chrome hardware, P-style Washburn pickup, push/pull volume/tone control. Available in Black, Red and White finishes. Disc. 1992.

	$280	$240	$200	$160	$145	$130	$120

Last Mfr.'s Sug. Retail was $400.

XS4 — offset double cutaway alder body, maple neck, 24 fret rosewood fingerboard with pearl dot inlay, fixed bridge, 4 on one side tuners, chrome hardware, P-style/J-style Washburn pickups, volume/treble/bass controls, active electronics. Available in Black and Red finishes. Disc. 1992.

	$335	$290	$240	$190	$170	$155	$145

Last Mfr.'s Sug. Retail was $480.

W

Grading	100%	98% MINT	95% EXC+	90% EXC	80% VG+	70% VG	60% G

XS5 — similar to XS4, except has 5 strings, 4/1 tuners and 2 J-style Washburn pickups. Available in Black, Red and White finishes.

| | $405 | $350 | $290 | $230 | $205 | $190 | $175 |
Last Mfr.'s Sug. Retail was $580.

XS6 — similar to XS4, except has 6 strings. Available in Metallic Cherry Black and Pearl White finishes.

| | $420 | $360 | $300 | $240 | $215 | $195 | $180 |
Last Mfr.'s Sug. Retail was $600.

XS8 — similar to XS4, except black hardware, 2 single coil Status pickups and active 2 band EQ fader control. Available in Charcoal Rain, Black and White finishes.

| | $560 | $480 | $400 | $320 | $290 | $265 | $240 |
Last Mfr.'s Sug. Retail was $800.

Bantam Series

XB200 — offset double cutaway asymmetrical hardwood body, bolt-on maple neck, 24 fret rosewood fingerboard with offset pearl dot inlay, fixed bridge, 2 per side tuners, chrome hardware, P-style/J-style Washburn pickups, 2 volume/1 tone controls, 3 position switch. Available in Black, Metallic Red and Pearl Blue finishes. New 1994.
Mfr.'s Sug. Retail $480 $384 $288 $240 $190 $170 $155 $145

XB400 — offset double cutaway asymmetrical alder body, figured ash top, bolt-on maple neck, 24 fret rosewood fingerboard with offset pearl dot inlay, fixed bridge, 2 per side tuners, chrome hardware, 2 humbucker Washburn pickups, 2 volume/1 tone controls, 3 position switch, active electronics. Available in Tobacco Sunburst, Transparent Burgundy and Transparent Blue finishes. New 1994.
Mfr.'s Sug. Retail $580 $464 $348 $290 $230 $205 $190 $175

XB500 — similar to XB400, except has 5 strings, 3/2 per side tuners, 2 P-style Washburn pickups. Available in Black and Natural finishes. New 1994.
Mfr.'s Sug. Retail $650 $520 $390 $325 $260 $235 $215 $195

XB600 — similar to XB400, except has 6 strings, 3 per side tuners, 2 P-style Washburn pickups. Available in Black and Natural finishes. New 1994.
Mfr.'s Sug. Retail $800 $640 $480 $400 $320 $290 $265 $240

XB800 — offset double cutaway asymmetrical alder body, figured sycamore top, bolt-on maple neck, 24 fret rosewood fingerboard with offset pearl dot inlay, fixed bridge, 2 per side tuners, gold hardware, 2 humbucker Status pickups, volume/treble/bass/pan controls, active electronics. Available in Antique Natural, Transparent Burgundy, Transparent Blue and Vintage Sunburst finishes. New 1994.
Mfr.'s Sug. Retail $800 $640 $480 $400 $320 $290 $265 $240

Classic Series

B200 — single cutaway alder body, bound carved maple top, 3 piece maple neck, 22 fret bound rosewood fingerboard with pearl dot inlay, fixed bridge, 2 per side tuners, chrome hardware, 2 Washburn pickups, 2 volume/2 tone controls. Available in Metallic Dark Blue finish. Disc. 1994.
| | $525 | $450 | $375 | $300 | $270 | $245 | $225 |
Last Mfr.'s Sug. Retail was $750.

Mercury Series

MB2 — offset double cutaway hardwood body, bolt-on maple neck, 24 fret rosewood fingerboard with offset pearl dot inlay, fixed bridge, 4 on one side tuners, chrome hardware, P-style pickup, volume/tone control. Available in Black, Pacific Blue Rain and White finishes. Disc. 1994.
| | $330 | $280 | $235 | $190 | $170 | $155 | $140 |
Last Mfr.'s Sug. Retail was $470.

MB4 — offset double cutaway alder body, bolt-on maple neck, 24 fret rosewood fingerboard with offset pearl dot inlay, fixed bridge, 4 on one side tuners, chrome hardware, P-style/J-style Washburn pickups, volume/treble/bass controls, 3 position switch, active electronics. Available in Black, Black Cherry Metallic, Ice Pearl, Midnight Blue Metallic and Natural finishes. Disc. 1994.
| | $385 | $330 | $275 | $220 | $200 | $180 | $165 |
Last Mfr.'s Sug. Retail was $550.

This model was also available in maple fingerboard with black dot inlay.

MB5 — similar to MB4, except has 5 strings, 4/1 per side tuners, 2 J-style pickups. Available in Black, Ice Pearl and Natural finishes. Disc. 1994.
| | $470 | $400 | $335 | $265 | $240 | $220 | $200 |
Last Mfr.'s Sug. Retail was $670.

MB6 — similar to MB4, except has 6 strings, 4/2 per side tuners, 2 J-style pickups. Available in Natural finish. Disc. 1994.
| | $525 | $450 | $375 | $300 | $270 | $245 | $225 |
Last Mfr.'s Sug. Retail was $750.

"In the past decade the vintage American guitar has taken its rightful place in the international market of collectible Americana."

—Jay Scott

TCG, July/Aug 1990

Grading	100%	98% MINT	95% EXC+	90% EXC	80% VG+	70% VG	60% G

MB8 — offset double cutaway alder body, flame maple top, bolt-on maple neck, 24 fret rosewood fingerboard with offset pearl dot inlay, fixed bridge, 4 on one side tuners, gold hardware, 2 humbucker active Status pickups, volume/treble/bass/mix controls, active electronics. Available in Tobacco Sunburst, Transparent Blue and Transparent Purple finishes. Disc. 1994.

	$560	$480	$400	$320	$290	$265	$240

Last Mfr.'s Sug. Retail was $800.

This model was also available in maple fingerboard with black dot inlay.

Status Series 1000

S60 — offset double cutaway one piece maple body/neck construction, walnut top/back laminates, 24 fret carbonite fingerboard, no headstock, tunable bridge, brass hardware, 2 single coil Status pickups, volume/tone control, active electronics with fader control. Available in Black and White finishes. Disc. 1992.

	$700	$600	$500	$400	$360	$330	$300

Last Mfr.'s Sug. Retail was $1,000.

S70 — similar to S60. Available in Natural, Transparent Blue and Transparent Red finishes. Disc. 1994.

	$840	$720	$600	$480	$430	$395	$360

Last Mfr.'s Sug. Retail was $1,200.

This model was also available with fretless fingerboard (S70FL).

USA Factory Series

XB1000 — offset double cutaway asymmetrical ash body, bolt-on maple neck, 24 fret rosewood fingerboard with pearl dot inlay, fixed Wilkinson bridge, blackface peghead with screened logo, 2 per side Gotoh tuners, chrome hardware, humbucker Bartolini pickup, volume/mid/concentric treble/bass controls. Available in Black, Transparent Blue and Transparent Red finishes. New 1994.

Mfr.'s Sug. Retail	$1,500	$1,200	$900	$750	$600	$540	$495	$450

WATKINS

Instruments built in England from 1960 to 1982. Trademark was changed to W E M (Watkins Electric Music) in the mid 1960s, and then to WILSON in the late 1960s.

The Watkins trademark appears on entry level to medium quality solid body and semi-hollowbody models that primarily appealed to novice players. Models include such designation as the **Rapier, Circuit 4, Mercury, Ranger**, and **Sapphire**. While production was maintained until 1982, the trademark name changed, or should we say evolved twice during this company's history.

(Source: Tony Bacon and Paul Day, The Guru's Guitar Guide)

ABRAHAM WECHTER

Instruments built in Paw Paw, Michigan. Distributed by Wechter Guitars of Paw Paw, Michigan.

Luthier Abraham Wechter began his guitar building career in the early 1970s by making dulcimers and repairing guitars in Seattle, Washington. Shortly thereafter he started looking for a mentor to apprentice with. In December of 1974, he moved to Detroit to begin an apprenticeship with Richard Schneider. He was captivated by Schneider's art, along with the scientific work Schneider was doing with Dr. Kasha.

Wechter worked with Schneider developing prototypes for what later became the "Mark" project at Gibson Guitars. Schneider was working regularly for Gibson developing prototypes, and as a result Wechter started working for Gibson as a model (prototype) builder. Schneider and Wechter moved to Kalamazoo in December 1976. After a few years, Wechter was given the opportunity to work as an independent consultant to Gibson. He continued on until June of 1984, performing prototype work on many of the guitars Gibson produced during that time period.

While at Gibson, Wechter continued his apprenticeship with Schneider, building handmade, world-class guitars. He actually rented space from Schneider during this time and started building his own models. In 1984, when Gibson moved to Nashville, Wechter decided to remain in Michigan. Wechter moved to Paw Paw, Michigan, a rural town about 20 miles west of Kalamazoo, where he set up shop and started designing and building his own guitars.

Wechter built handmade classical, jazz-nylon, bass, and steel-string acoustic guitars. He did a tremendous amount of research into how and why guitars perform. As a result, he became sought after by many high profile people in the industry. Between 1985 and 1995, Wechter designed and hand built guitars for artists like John McLaughlin, Steve Howe, Al DiMeola, Giovanni, John Denver, Earl Klugh, and Jonas Hellborg. During this time period he developed a reputation as one of the world's finest craftsman and guitar designers.

In November of 1994, Wechter built a prototype of an innovative new design, and realized that it would have applications far beyond the high price range he was working in. This was the birth of the Pathmaker guitar. The Pathmaker model is a revolutionary acoustic guitar. The double cutaway construction (patent pending) provides a full 19 frets clear of the body in a design that is both inherently stable and visually striking.

Wechter is currently laying the groundwork for mass production and distribution of the Pathmaker - the first production models being available by January, 1997. A limited number of handmade premier

Walthari Mittenwald
courtesy Billy Thurman

W

models are being built, along with a small number of classical and jazz-nylon guitars. For more information on availability and pricing, contact Wechter Guitars via the Index of Current Manufacturers located in the back of this book.

(Biography courtesy Abraham Wechter and Michael Davidson, August 2, 1996)

ACOUSTIC

Pathmaker Series

In November of 1994, Wechter built a prototype of an innovative new design that led to the introduction of the **Pathmaker**. The unique double cutaway body design features a neck with 19 frets clear of the body. Standard features include a solid Sitka Spruce top, rosewood or figured Maple back and sides, mahogany neck, 22 fret Rosewood fingerboard with dot inlay, rosette of Abalone inlay, and a Rosewood peghead veneer. Finished in Satin or gloss, the suggested retail price with hardshell case is $1,549.

The Pathmaker is also offered in two Electric/Acoustic models. The Pathmaker with a Fishman Axis system retails at $1,699, and can be upgraded to the Axis+ (add $30) or Axis-M (add $50). The Pathmaker "Recessed Tailblock" has a Fishman Matrix transducer mounted on the tailblock of the instrument, as well as an on-board AGP-2 Preamp and active Bass, Treble, and Volume controls. The suggested retail price is $1,899.

H. WEISSENBORN

Instruments built in California during the 1920s and early 1930s.

H. Weissenborn instruments were favorites of slide guitar players in Hawaii and the West Coast in the early 1900s. All four models featured koa construction, and different binding packages per model. Further model specifications and information updates will be contained in future editions of the **Blue Book of Guitars.**

WELSON

Instruments produced in Italy from the early 1970s to the early 1980s.

The Welson company produced medium quality guitars based on Gibson designs, as well as their own original designs and semi-hollowbody models. Welson also built guitars for the Vox company, and for Wurlitzer (U.S.).

(Source: Tony Bacon and Paul Day, The Guru's Guitar Guide)

W E M

See WATKINS.

Instruments built in England.

W E M (Watkins Electric Music) was the first of two name changes for the Watkins company (1960-1982).

WESTBURY

See UNICORD.

Instruments produced in Japan.

The Merson Musical Supply Company of Westbury, New York was the primary importer of Univox guitars. Merson evolved into Unicord, and also became a distributor for Westbury brand guitars.

(Source: Michael Wright, Guitar Stories Volume One, pg. 76)

WESTONE

Instruments produced in Japan from 1981 to 1987. Subsequent instruments were built in Korea. Distributed in the U.S. by St. Louis Music of St. Louis, Missouri.

The Matsumoku company of Japan had been manufacturing guitars for other trademarks (such as Aria, Epiphone, and Vantage) since the 1960s. In 1981, Matsumoku decided to market their own original designs under their own trademark in addition to their current production for others. Matsumoku guitars are generally well-built, solid playing guitars. In 1984, St. Louis Music announced that it would be merging Westones with their Electra brand (which was introduced back in the late 1970s). Through the mid 1980s, models were sold under the Electra/Westone imprint, then Westone only as the Electra aspect was discontinued. In 1987 Matsumoku stopped producing instruments, so guitar production switched to Korea.

Most guitars were designed as part of a certain series. The overall body design would then feature different pickup combinations, or the addition of a tremolo; popular series includes the Pantera (1986-1987), Thunder (1981-1987), Spectrum (1984-1987), and the Clipper Six (1986-1988) which was designed by Mark Ray of the United Kingdom.

Weissenborn Model 1
courtesy Gary Sullivan

Wilkins Studio "T"
courtesy Pat Wilkins

WEYMANN & SON

Instruments built in Philadelphia, Pennsylvania from 1864 to the early part of the 1900s. Some models under the Weymann & Son trademark were built by Regal (Chicago, Illinois), and Vega (Boston, Massachusetts).

H.A. Weymann & Son, Incorporated was established in 1864 in Philadelphia. Later, it incorporated as the Weymann Company in 1904, and distributed numerous guitar models that ranged from entry level student up to fine quality. Other trademarks may include **Weymann, Keystone State, W & S,** and **Varsity.** Some of the guitars were actually produced by Vega or Regal, and share similarities to the company of origin's production instruments.

MARK WHITEBROOK

Instruments built in California during the 1970s.

Mark Whitebrook was an apprentice to luthier Roy Noble for a number of years. Whitebrook built high quality acoustic guitars, and was luthier to James Taylor for a number of years. Further information will be updated in future editions of the **Blue Book of Guitars**.

WILKES

Instruments built in England from the mid 1970s to date.

These high quality solid body guitars feature both original and designs based on popular American classics. Models include the Answer, Extrovert, Poet, Skitzo, and the Slut (?!). We know what you're thinking, and you're right: Send photos for future updates of the **Blue Book of Guitars**.

(Source: Tony Bacon and Paul Day, The Guru's Guitar Book)

PAT WILKINS

Instruments currently built in Portsmouth, Virginia. Distributed by OFB Guitars of Portsmouth, Virginia.

Luthier Pat Wilkins has been acknowledged as a premier finisher of quality instruments for over ten years. Wilkins joined former Schecter Research President Bill Ricketts and ex-Zion Guitars luthier Kenny Marshall in custom building limited production guitars and basses. Models feature bolt-on neck, tilt-back headstocks, locking machine heads, numerous different pickup combinations, and spectacular finishes. For further information, please contact OFB Guitars via the Index of Current Manufacturers located in the back of this book.

WILSON

See WATKINS.

Instruments built in England.

The Wilson logo is the final one used by the Watkins company (1960-1982). Models include the three pickup **Sapphire III** solid body, and some electric hollowbody designs.

(Source: Tony Bacon, The Ultimate Guitar Book)

WINSTON

Instruments produced in Japan.

The Winston trademark was a brandname used by U.S. importers Buegeleisen & Jacobson of New York, New York.

WITTMAN

Instruments built in Williamsport, Pennsylvania during the 1990s.

Wittman basses featured exotic woods and a sleek body profile, and different stringing configurations. For further information regarding model specifications and pricing, contact Wittman Guitars through the Index of Current Manufacturers located in the rear of this book.

WOLLERMAN GUITARS

Instruments currently built in Sheffield, Illinois. Wollerman Guitars also builds instruments for SUPERVOLT, STONE AXE, BIGGUN, BRICK, and JUNK trademarks. Wollerman Guitars also markets LEDSLED amplification and V-Max pickups.

Luthier/designer Mark Wollerman has been building handcrafted instruments since 1983. Wollerman, a guitarist himself, built his "new" guitar years ago when his finances were low. The **Devastator**, Wollerman's first handcrafted guitar, was used constantly as he participated with bands. Outside of a few model revisions, the same guitar is still currently produced. Wollerman founded his company in the early 1980s on the premise of building affordable guitars for musicians.

Wilkins Custom
courtesy Pat Wilkins

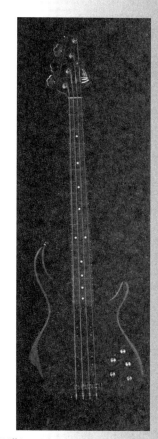

Wilkins 4 String Bass
courtesy Pat Wilkins

W

Wollerman offers over 170 guitar body designs, each which are available in eight different lines and five different sizes. Wollerman also offers electric mandolins and electric violins. Wollerman instruments are currently available both in the U.S., and in 21 countries worldwide. A large 112 page catalog of options and body styles is available for a nominal fee. For further information, please contact Wollerman guitars via the Index of Current Manufacturers located in the back of this book.

ELECTRIC

All Standard Wollerman guitars feature a 25 1/2" scale, 21 fret rosewood fingerboard, graphite nut, Pro sealed tuning pegs, heavy duty hardtail bridge, chrome hardware, one standard humbucking pickup, and one volume control. Wollerman models have individual unique features that differentiate from model to model. Options can be added or subtracted to come up with custom versions of each model.

According to Mark Wollerman, some of the more popular body styles are the **Raider**, **Swept-Wing**, **Pro-57**, **J.P. 63**, **Blaster**, **Twister**, **Torqmaster**, and the **Junkmaster**.

Wollerman Series

The **Pearl Deluxe** features the full Power Tone bodies with highly figured tops available in White, Black, Gold, Red, Blue, or Green pearloid. Sides are finished in Black or White Naugahyde, and backs in a Gloss White. The **Super Pearl Deluxe** is an extra cost option of pearloid backs instead of Gloss White. There are many custom paint and solid body options, and the retail price lists at $429 and up.

Biggun Series

The **Biggun** series is a special variation of the **Wollerman**, **Supervolt**, **Brick**, and **Rawhide** lines. Models feature a 10% oversized body, 27" scale length, and 1 3/4" neck width (at nut). A true Baritone neck (28 1/2") is also available. Retail prices list at $449 and up.

Supervolt Series

Supervolt models feature bodies similar to the full Power Tone bodies, except have Gloss White textured Fiberglass tops and backs and choice of pickguards/sidetrim in Black, Red, White, Blue, Yellow, and Green. Other options include color co-ordinated pickup covers, and swirl pickguards. Retail prices begin at $319 and up.

Brick Series

Similar to the Supervolt, except feature tops, backs, and sides that resemble brick walls! Models feature gray "cement lines" and Red, White, Black, or Brown bricks. Retail list begins at $359 and up.

Stone Axe Series

Stone Axe models feature the Full Power Tone bodies and pickguards, but the bodies have a finish like they were carved out of stone. Colors include Turquoise Dust, Red Quartz, Gray Stone, Sandstone, Pueblo Stone, Black Stone, Soap Stone, and Ironstone. Retail prices list at $339 and up.

Rawhide Series

Rawhide series guitars have the Wollerman Full Power Tone bodies with tops and backs constructed of "Leatherwood", and pickguards covered in black or white Naugahyde. Retail list begins at $299 and up.

Junk Series

The **Junk** guitar and bass series is the "enviromentally conscious" line from Wollerman. These instruments feature a neck-through body design based on laminating the extra wood left over from other projects. These laminated bodies feature a natural look, durable all wood construction, and decent tone. A number of other guitar companies began building multi-laminated wood body guitars as far back as the 1970s, all with high end prices. However, this series is moderately priced, and begins at $259 and up.

Special Guitar Operations

The Special Guitar Operations is the high end custom shop maintained by Wollerman. **S.G.O. guitars** and **basses** (list $499 and up) feature the best parts, pickups, and woods available - as well as the flexibility for custom designs. Most bass guitar orders are processed through the S.G.O., and **Wollerman basses** (list $299 and up) feature a 34" scale, rosewood fingerboard, chrome hardware, a JB pickup, and one volume control. Most of the guitar designs are available in bass format. Wollerman also produces 4-string **Tenor** guitars (list $239 and up), **Mini** guitars (similar to the full scale models, yet begin at $229 and up), **electric Mandolins** ($199 and up), and **left handed guitars** (most models, and parts are available too - list $219 and up).

RANDY WOOD

Instruments built in Savannah, Georgia, since 1978.

Luthier Randy Wood was one of three partners who formed GTR, Inc. in Nashville in 1970. Wood left GTR to form the Old Time Picking Parlor in 1972, a combination custom instrument shop and nightclub that featured Bluegrass music. In 1978, he sold the Parlor and moved to Savannah, Georgia to concentrate on instruments building. Since then, he has produced over 1,500 stringed instruments from guitars to mandolins, dobros, violins, and banjos.

WOODY'S CUSTOM GUITARS

Instruments produced in New York City since mid 1970s.

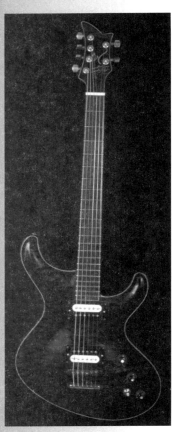

Woody's Custom
courtesy Woody Phiffer

Luthier/designer Woody Phiffer has been building and producing innovative high quality guitars for several years. His current model features a carved top <u>and</u> back, carved pickup covers, exotic woods, and quality hardware and pickups. Phiffer's list price is around $3,900, although prices do change in reponse to custom options. For further information, please contact luthier Phiffer through the Index of Current Manufacturers located in the back of this book.

WORLD TEISCO

See TEISCO DEL REY.

W R C GUITARS

Instruments produced in Calimesa, California since 1990. Distributed by WRC Music International, Inc. of Hemet, California.

After designing guitar models that updated and surpassed their original inspirations, luthier/designer Wayne R. Charvel left his namesake company. Charvel did design one model for Gibson (US-1) that quite frankly looks like a Charvel Model 6 with "Gibson" on the pointy headstock. In 1989, Charvel's new company produced guitars briefly under the 'Ritz' trademark. In 1990, the logo was changed to W.R.C. The Neptune Series, which uses seashells as part of the top inlay, was designed in conjunction with current staff member Eric J. Galletta.

ELECTRIC

Grading	100%	98% MINT	95% EXC+	90% EXC	80% VG+	70% VG	60% G

Woody's Custom
courtesy Woody Phiffer

Classic Series

WRC CLASSIC — offset double cutaway alder body, bolt-on maple neck, 24 fret rosewood fingerboard with pearl dot inlay, strings thru Wilkinson bridge, 3 per side Grover tuners, chrome hardware, 2 single coil/1 humbucker exposed Ken Armstrong pickups, volume/tone controls, 3 mini switches. Available in Black, Blond, Candy Apple Red, Electric Blue, Seafoam Green, Pearl White, Transparent Blue, Transparent Green, Transparent Tangerine, and White finishes. New 1994.

Mfr.'s Sug. Retail	$900	$720	$540	$450	$360	$325	$300	$275

This model has the following features optionally available: standard Wilkinson vibrato, double locking Floyd Rose vibrato, single cutaway body with 2 single coil pickups, volume/tone control, 3 position switch.

Exotic Series

WRC EXOTIC — offset double cutaway alder body, figured wood top, bolt-on maple neck, 24 fret rosewood fingerboard with pearl dot inlay, strings thru Wilkinson bridge, 3 per side Grover tuners, black hardware, 2 single coil/1 humbucker exposed pickups, volume/tone controls, 3 mini switches. Available in Cherry Burst, Honey Burst, Natural, Tobacco Burst, Transparent Candy Blue, Transparent Candy Green, Transparent Candy Purple, Transparent Candy Red and Transparent Candy Tangerine finishes. New 1994.

Mfr.'s Sug. Retail	$1,600	$1,280	$960	$800	$640	$575	$530	$480

This model has the following features optionally available: ebony or maple fingerboards, standard Wilkinson vibrato with locking Gotoh tuners, double locking Floyd Rose vibrato, chrome or gold hardware, single cutaway body with 2 single coil pickups, volume/tone control, 3 position switch.

Neptune Series

This series, designed by Wayne R. Charvel and Eric J. Galletta, uses Pacific seashells for finish.

CUSTOM — offset double cutaway basswood body, bolt-on figured maple neck, 22 fret ebony fingerboard, strings thru Wilkinson bridge, 3 per side Gotoh tuners, gold hardware, 2 humbucker Seymour Duncan pickups, volume/tone controls, 3 position switch. Available in Black Snake, Neptune Avalon, Neptune Gold, Neptune Violet Oyster, Paua, Tiger Cowrie and White Nautilus shell finishes. Current production.

Mfr.'s Sug. Retail	$3,000	$2,400	$1,800	$1,500	$1,200	$1,080	$990	$900

This model has the following features optionally available: 24 fret fingerboard, rosewood or maple fingerboard, abalone or pearl fingerboard inlay, black, cloud, dolphin or dot fingerboard inlay design, standard Wilkinson vibrato or double locking Floyd Rose vibrato, multi variations of pickup and control configurations.

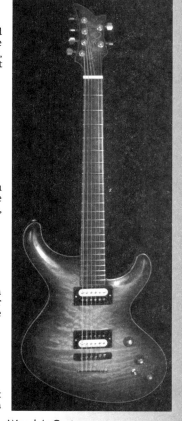

DELUXE — offset double cutaway basswood body, bolt-on figured maple neck, 24 fret rosewood fingerboard with abalone dot inlay, tunomatic bridge/stop tailpiece, 3 per side tuners, black hardware, exposed humbucker Seymour Duncan pickup, volume control. Available in Black Snake, Neptune Avalon, Neptune Violet Oyster and Tiger Cowrie shell finishes. Current production.

Mfr.'s Sug. Retail	$2,400	$1,920	$1,440	$1,200	$960	$860	$790	$720

This model has the following features optionally available: ebony or maple fingerboard, pearl dot fingerboard inlay, standard Wilkinson vibrato with locking Grover tuners or double locking Floyd Rose vibrato, chrome or gold hardware, multi variations of pickup and control configurations.

STANDARD — offset double cutaway alder body, bolt-on maple neck, 24 fret rosewood fingerboard with pearl dot inlay, double locking Floyd Rose vibrato, 3 per side Grover tuners, chrome hardware, 2 humbucker Seymour Duncan pickups, volume/tone control, 3 position switch. Available in Neptune Avalon shell finish. Current production.

Mfr.'s Sug. Retail	$2,000	$1,600	$1,200	$1,000	$800	$720	$660	$600

This model has standard Wilkinson vibrato with locking Grover tuners optionally available.

Woody's Custom
courtesy Woody Phiffer

WRIGHT GUITAR TECHNOLOGY

Instruments currently built in Eugene, Oregon.

Luthier Wright was briefly involved with Stephen Mosher's Moses Graphite necks, and then turned to producing a quality travel guitar. The **Soloette** model has even traveled on the NASA's space shuttle recently! For further information on this innovative design, please contact Wright Guitar Technology via the Index of Current Manufacturers located in the back of this book.

WURLITZER

Instruments built in America during the 1960s. Wurlitzer then began importing models from Italy during the 1970s.

During the 1960s, Wurlitzer distributed guitars built in the Holman-Woodell facility in Neodesha, Kansas (makers of other trademarks such as Holman, Alray, 21st Century, and La Baye). Instruments were medium quality solid or semi-hollowbody guitars. As U.S. production prices rose, Wurlitzer began importing semi-hollowbody guitars built by the Welson company in Italy in the early 1970s.

XOTIC GUITARS

Instruments built in Van Nuys, California. Distribution is directly handled by the company as they offer numerous options per instrument.

Luthier Taku Sakashta and staff build high quality acoustic Archtop and steel string guitars, as well as solid body basses. All are offered with custom options per model.

ACOUSTIC

Archtop Series

The following archtop models are available with numerous custom body wood choices, hardware wood choices, and finishes. For further information, contact luthier Sakashta through the Index of Current Manufacturers located in the rear of this book.

AVALON — 17" single cutaway body features AAA quarter-sawn Sitka spruce top, parallel bracing, AA Eastern rock maple sides and matching back, one piece Honduran mahogany neck and East Indian rosewood fingerboard with pearl inlays, either ebony or rosewood tailpiece, rosewood bridge, pickguard, peghead overlay. Current production.

    Mfr.'s Sug. Retail   **$6,550**
> Add $290 for Kent Armstrong floating pickup.
>
> Add $300 for installed Tom Holmes custom body mounted pickup.

KARIZMA — 17" single cutaway body features AAA quarter-sawn Engleman spruce top, x-bracing, AA Eastern rock maple sides and matching back, one piece Honduran mahogany neck and East Indian rosewood fingerboard with pearl inlays, either ebony or rosewood tailpiece, rosewood bridge, pickguard, peghead overlay. Current production.

    Mfr.'s Sug. Retail   **$6,550**
> Add $290 for Kent Armstrong floating pickup.
>
> Add $300 for installed Tom Holmes custom body mounted pickup.

Steel String Acoustic Guitars

The following steel string models are available with numerous custom wood options for tops, backs and sides. Prices range from $100 for German Spruce top to $1,000 for Brazilian rosewood back and sides, with the majority of choices ranging between $150 and $250 for quilted maple backs up to cocobolo backs and sides. Contact luthier Sakashta for further information and availability.

AUDITORIUM — Sitka or Engleman spruce or Western red cedar top, East Indian rosewood back and matching sides, bound Honduras mahogany one piece neck with Gaboon ebony fingerboard and peghead, diamond or dot position markers, Brazilian rosewood bridge, Abalone soundhole ring decoration, three on a side Schaller tuning machines, Nitro cellulose natural lacquer finish. Current production.

    Mfr.'s Sug. Retail   **$2,850**
> Price includes deluxe hard shell case.

S O — similar to Auditorium model, except modified. Current production.

    Mfr.'s Sug. Retail   **$2,950**

DREADNOUGHT — Sitka or Engleman spruce or Western red cedar top, East Indian rosewood back and matching sides, bound Honduras mahogany one piece neck with Gaboon ebony fingerboard and peghead, diamond or dot position markers, Brazilian rosewood bridge, Abalone soundhole ring decoration, three on a side Schaller tuning machines, Nitro cellulose natural lacquer finish. Current production.

    Mfr.'s Sug. Retail   **$2,900**
> Price includes deluxe hard shell case.

S D — similar to Dreadnought model, except modified. Current production.

    Mfr.'s Sug. Retail   **$3,000**

JUMBO — Sitka or Engleman spruce or Western red cedar top, East Indian rosewood back and matching sides, bound Honduras mahogany one piece neck with Gaboon ebony fingerboard and peghead, diamond or dot position markers, Brazilian rosewood bridge, Abalone soundhole ring decoration, three on a side Schaller tuning machines, Nitro cellulose natural lacquer finish. Current production.

    Mfr.'s Sug. Retail   **$3,100**
> Price includes deluxe hard shell case.

S J — similar to Jumbo model, except modified. Current production.

    Mfr.'s Sug. Retail   **$3,200**

ELECTRIC

Jam Master Series

The Jam Master model is a double cutaway archtop semi hollowbody electric guitar, and features some wood and finish options for the three models:

> Add $180 for maple neck on models two or three.

Xotic Archtop
courtesy Taku Sakashta

Add $80 for solid brass tailpiece (replaces stock Gotoh or Schaller).
Add $120 for gold hardware.
Add $200 for two tone sunburst.
Add $250 for three tone sunburst.

JAM MASTER MODEL ONE — book matched Calelo walnut top, back and matching sides, bound American black walnut neck with Gaboon ebony fingerboard and pearl inlays, Gaboon ebony or cocobolo pickguard, Gotoh or Schaller tuning machines, original design aluminum or Gotoh or Schaller tailpiece, Tom Holmes H-450 humbucker (neck position), Tom Holmes H-453 humbucker (Bridge position), 2 volume knobs, 2 tone knobs with series/parallel switching, 1 toggle switch. Available in high gloss nitrocellulose Natural or Transparent Black finish. Current production.

Mfr.'s Sug. Retail $5,800

Jam Master Model Two — book matched bigleaf maple top, back and matching sides, bound Honduran mahogany neck with Brazilian rosewood fingerboard and pearl inlays, Gaboon ebony or cocobolo pickguard, Gotoh or Schaller tuning machines, original design aluminum or Gotoh or Schaller tailpiece, Tom Holmes H-450 humbucker (neck position), Tom Holmes H-453 humbucker (Bridge position), 2 volume knobs, 2 tone knobs with series/parallel switching, 1 toggle switch. Available in high gloss nitrocellulose Blonde, Cherry Red, or Transparent Black finish. Current production.

Mfr.'s Sug. Retail $5,800

Jam Master Model Three — book matched Sitka spruce top, bigleaf maple back and matching sides, bound eastern rock maple neck with Gaboon ebony fingerboard and pearl inlays, Gaboon ebony or cocobolo pickguard, Gotoh or Schaller tuning machines, original design aluminum or Gotoh or Schaller tailpiece, Tom Holmes H-450 humbucker (neck position), Tom Holmes H-453 humbucker (Bridge position), 2 volume knobs, 2 tone knobs with series/parallel switching, 1 toggle switch. Available in high gloss nitrocellulose Blonde, Cherry Red, or Transparent Black finish. Current production.

Mfr.'s Sug. Retail $5,800

ELECTRIC BASS

The following models are available with fretless necks at no extra charge. Each bass is outfitted with Xotic's Super 125 Pre-amp, an active tone system that offers Series/Parallel switching and pre-set gain controls.

TB STANDARD — offset double cutaway ash body, with bolt-on one piece maple neck and birdseye maple fingerboard, abalone dot position markers, two on a side Hipshot Ultra lite tuning machines, Kahler bridge, two Kent Armstrong pickups, master volume control, blend control, master tone control, and three band EQ controls. Finished in Transparent black, Transparent Red, and Transparent Purple finishes. Current production.

Mfr.'s Sug. Retail $2,480

TB STANDARD 5-STRING — same as the Standard 4-string, except has 3/2 on a side tuners and five string configuration.

Mfr.'s Sug. Retail $2,680

TB STANDARD 6-STRING — same as the Standard 4-string, except has 3/3 on a side tuners and six string configuration.

Mfr.'s Sug. Retail $2,880

TB CUSTOM — offset double cutaway ash body with laminated top and back of either Padauk, Quilted Maple, Figured Maple, Zebra Wood or Wenge; three piece maple set neck, ebony fingerboard, aluminum rings design position markers, two on a side Hipshot Ultra lite tuning machines, Kahler bridge, two Kent Armstrong pickups, master volume control, blend control, master tone control, and three band EQ controls. Finished in Clear Semigloss. Current production.

Mfr.'s Sug. Retail $2,950

TB CUSTOM 5-STRING — same as the Custom 4-string, except has 3/2 on a side tuners and five string configuration.

Mfr.'s Sug. Retail $3,100

TB CUSTOM 6-STRING — same as the Custom 4-string, except has 3/3 on a side tuners and six string configuration.

Mfr.'s Sug. Retail $3,300

TB-2 PREMIER — offset double cutaway ash body with laminated top and back of either Spalted Maple, Ziricote, Oriental Ebony, or Madrone Burl; three piece maple and veneer set neck, ebony fingerboard, aluminum rings design position markers, two on a side Hipshot Ultra lite tuning machines, Kahler bridge, two Kent Armstrong pickups, master volume control, blend control, master tone control, and three band EQ controls. Finished in Clear Semigloss. Current production.

Mfr.'s Sug. Retail $3,500

TB PREMIER 5-STRING — same as the Premier 4-string, except has 3/2 on a side tuners and five string configuration.

Mfr.'s Sug. Retail $3,700

TB PREMIER 6-STRING — same as the Premier 4-string, except has 3/3 on a side tuners and six string configuration.

YAMAHA

Y

"By the way, did I mention the phone call I got the other day from a guy who bought a 1957 PAF gold top for $300 at a garage sale..."
—TCG, Sept. 1995

Instruments currently produced in Taiwan. Previous production was centered in Japan, as the company headquarters is located in Hamamatsu, Japan. Distribution in the U.S. market by the Yamaha Corporation of America, located in Buena Park, California.

Yamaha has a tradition of building musical instruments for over 100 years. The first Yamaha solid body electric guitars were introduced to the American market in 1966. While the first series relied on designs based on classic American favorites, the second series developed more original designs. In the mid 1970s, Yamaha was recognized as the first Oriental brand to emerge as a prominent force equal to the big-name US builders.

Production shifted to Taiwan in the early 1980s as Yamaha built its own facility to maintain quality. The company is also active in producing band instruments, stringed instruments, amplifiers, and P.A. equipment.

ACOUSTIC

Grading	100%	98% MINT	95% EXC+	90% EXC	80% VG+	70% VG	60% G

Classic Series

CG40A — classic style, spruce top, round soundhole, bound body, wooden inlay rosette, jelutong back/sides, nato neck, 12/19 fret sonokeling fingerboard/bridge, 3 per side chrome tuners. Available in Natural finish. Curr. mfr.

Mfr.'s Sug. Retail	$170	$127	$85	$75	$60	$55	$50	$45

CG100A — classic style, spruce top, round soundhole, bound body, wooden inlay rosette, nato back/sides/neck, 12/19 fret bubinga fingerboard, nato bridge, 3 per side chrome tuners. Available in Natural finish. Curr. mfr.

Mfr.'s Sug. Retail	$270	$202	$135	$120	$95	$85	$80	$75

CS100A — similar to CG100A, except has 7/8 size body. New 1994.

Mfr.'s Sug. Retail	$310	$232	$155	$135	$110	$100	$90	$80

CG110A — classic style, spruce top, round soundhole, bound body, wooden inlay rosette, nato back/sides/neck, 12/19 fret bubinga fingerboard, nato bridge, 3 per side chrome tuners. Available in Natural finish. Curr. mfr.

Mfr.'s Sug. Retail	$280	$224	$168	$140	$110	$100	$90	$80

CG110SA — similar to CG110A, except has solid spruce top. New 1994.

Mfr.'s Sug. Retail	$400	$320	$240	$200	$160	$145	$130	$120

CG120A — similar to CG110A, except has different rosette, rosewood fingerboard and bridge.

Mfr.'s Sug. Retail	$350	$262	$175	$155	$125	$110	$100	$90

CG130A — similar to CG110A, except has rosewood back/sides/bridge, gold hardware.

Mfr.'s Sug. Retail	$390	$292	$195	$170	$135	$125	$115	$105

CG150SA — classic style, solid spruce top, round soundhole, bound body, wooden inlay rosette, ovankol back/sides, nato neck, 12/19 fret rosewood fingerboard, rosewood bridge, rosewood veneer on peghead, 3 per side gold tuners. Available in Natural finish. Curr. mfr.

Mfr.'s Sug. Retail	$460	$345	$230	$195	$155	$140	$125	$115

This model has solid cedar top (CG150CA) optionally available.

CG170SA — classic style, solid spruce top, round soundhole, wooden inlay bound body and rosette, rosewood back/sides, nato neck, 12/19 fret rosewood fingerboard, rosewood bridge, rosewood veneer on peghead, 3 per side gold tuners. Available in Natural finish. Curr. mfr.

Mfr.'s Sug. Retail	$600	$450	$300	$260	$210	$190	$170	$160

This model has solid cedar top (CG170CA) optionally available.

CG180SA — similar to 170SA, except has different binding/rosette, ebony fingerboard.

Mfr.'s Sug. Retail	$710	$532	$355	$315	$250	$225	$205	$190

FG Series

FG300A — dreadnought style, spruce top, round soundhole, bound body, 3 stripe rosette, black pickguard, jelutong back/sides, nato neck, 14/20 fret sonokeling fingerboard with pearl dot inlay, sonokeling bridge with white pins, 3 per side chrome tuners with plastic buttons. Available in Natural finish. Curr. mfr.

Mfr.'s Sug. Retail	$230	$172	$115	$100	$80	$70	$65	$60

Grading	100%	98% MINT	95% EXC+	90% EXC	80% VG+	70% VG	60% G

FG400A — dreadnought style, spruce top, round soundhole, bound body, 3 stripe rosette, black pickguard, nato back/sides/neck, 14/20 fret bubinga fingerboard with pearl dot inlay, nato bridge with white pins, 3 per side chrome tuners with plastic buttons. Available in Natural finish. Disc. 1994.

			$180	$155	$130	$100	$90	$80	$75

Last Mfr.'s Sug. Retail was $260.

FG401 — similar to FG400A, except has jumbo style body. Available in Natural finish. New 1994.

Mfr.'s Sug. Retail	$300	$240	$180	$150	$120	$110	$100	$90

FG410A — dreadnought style, spruce top, round soundhole, bound body, 5 stripe rosette, black pickguard, nato back/sides/neck, 14/20 fret bubinga fingerboard with pearl dot inlay, nato bridge with white pearl dot pins, 3 per side chrome tuners with plastic buttons. Available in Natural finish. Disc. 1994.

	$230	$195	$165	$130	$120	$110	$100

Last Mfr.'s Sug. Retail was $330.

FG410-12A — similar to FG410A, except has 12 strings, 6 per side tuners. Disc. 1994.

	$250	$215	$180	$145	$130	$120	$110

Last Mfr.'s Sug. Retail was $360.

FG410EA — similar to FG410A, except has piezo pickups and volume/2 tone controls. Disc. 1994

	$365	$310	$260	$210	$190	$170	$160

Last Mfr.'s Sug. Retail was $520.

FG411 — dreadnought style, spruce top, round soundhole, black pickguard, bound body, 5 stripe rosette, nato back/sides/neck, 14/20 fret rosewood fingerboard with pearl dot inlay, nato bridge with white black dot pins, 3 per side diecast chrome tuners. Available in Natural and Violin Sunburst finishes. New 1994.

Mfr.'s Sug. Retail	$370	$296	$222	$185	$150	$135	$120	$110

Add $50 for left handed configuration (FG411L).

This model has agathis back/sides/neck with Black finish optionally available.

FG411C — similar to FG411, except has single round cutaway. Available in Natural finish. New 1994.

Mfr.'s Sug. Retail	$600	$480	$360	$300	$240	$215	$195	$180

This model has agathis back/sides optionally available.

FG411-12 — similar to FG411, except has 12 strings, bubinga fingerboard, 6 per side tuners.

Mfr.'s Sug. Retail	$450	$360	$270	$225	$180	$160	$150	$135

FG411C-12 — similar to FG411, except has 12 strings, single round cutaway, 6 per side tuners, piezo bridge pickup, volume/treble/bass controls.

Mfr.'s Sug. Retail	$750	$600	$450	$375	$300	$270	$245	$225

This model has agathis back/sides with Black finish optionally available.

FG411S — dreadnought style, solid spruce top, round soundhole, black pickguard, bound body, 5 stripe rosette, nato back/sides/neck, 14/20 fret rosewood fingerboard with pearl dot inlay, nato bridge with white black dot pins, 3 per side diecast tuners. Available in Violin Sunburst finish. New 1994.

Mfr.'s Sug. Retail	$410	$328	$246	$205	$165	$145	$135	$125

Add $50 for left handed configuration (FG411SL).

FG411SC — similar to FG411S, except has single round cutaway, solid spruce top, piezo bridge pickup, volume/treble/bass controls. Available in Natural and Violin Sunburst finishes. New 1994.

Mfr.'s Sug. Retail	$660	$528	$396	$330	$265	$240	$220	$200

FG411S-12 — similar to FG411S, except has 12 strings, 6 per side tuners.

Mfr.'s Sug. Retail	$490	$392	$294	$245	$195	$175	$160	$150

FG420A — dreadnought style, spruce top, round soundhole, black pickguard, 3 stripe bound body, abalone rosette, nato back/sides/neck, 14/20 fret bound bubinga fingerboard with pearl dot inlay, rosewood bridge with white pearl dot pins, 3 per side chrome tuners. Available in Natural finish. Disc. 1994.

	$265	$225	$190	$150	$135	$120	$110

Last Mfr.'s Sug. Retail was $380.

This model was also available in a left handed version (FG420-LA).

FG420-12A — similar to FG420A, except has 12 strings, 6 per side tuners. Disc. 1994

	$295	$250	$210	$170	$150	$135	$125

Last Mfr.'s Sug. Retail was $420.

FG420E-12A — similar to FG420A, except has 12 strings, piezo electric pickups and volume/treble/bass controls.

Mfr.'s Sug. Retail	$530	$424	$318	$265	$210	$190	$175	$160

FG421 — dreadnought style, spruce top, black pickguard, round soundhole, 5 stripe bound body/rosette, nato back/sides/neck, 14/20 fret bound rosewood fingerboard with pearl dot inlay, rosewood bridge with white black dot pins, 3 per side diecast chrome tuners. Available in Natural finish. New 1994.

Mfr.'s Sug. Retail	$430	$344	$258	$215	$175	$155	$140	$130

Grading	100%	98% MINT	95% EXC+	90% EXC	80% VG+	70% VG	60% G

FG430A — dreadnought style, spruce top, round soundhole, black pickguard, 3 stripe bound body, abalone rosette, nato back/sides/neck, 14/20 fret bound rosewood fingerboard with pearl dot inlay, rosewood bridge with white pearl dot pins, bound peghead, 3 per side chrome tuners. Available in Natural finish. Disc. 1994.

| | $300 | $260 | $215 | $175 | $155 | $140 | $130 |

Last Mfr.'s Sug. Retail was $430.

FG435A — dreadnought style, spruce top, round soundhole, black pickguard, agathis back/sides, nato neck, 14/20 bound bubinga fingerboard with pearl snowflake inlay, rosewood bridge with white pearl dot pins, bound peghead, 3 per side chrome tuners. Available in Black, Marine Blue, Oriental Blue, Tinted and Tobacco Brown Sunburst finishes. Disc. 1994.

| | $295 | $250 | $210 | $170 | $150 | $135 | $125 |

Last Mfr.'s Sug. Retail was $420.

FG441 — dreadnought style, spruce top, round soundhole, black pickguard, 3 stripe bound body, abalone rosette, ovankol back/sides, nato neck, 14/20 fret bound rosewood fingerboard with pearl dot inlay, rosewood bridge with black white dot pins, bound blackface peghead with pearl leaf/logo inlay, 3 per side chrome tuners. Available in Natural and Tobacco Brown Sunburst finishes. New 1994.

| Mfr.'s Sug. Retail | $460 | $368 | $276 | $230 | $185 | $165 | $150 | $140 |

Add $70 for left handed configuration (FG441L).

This model has agathis back/sides with Black finish optionally available.

FG441C — similar to FG441, except has single round cutaway, piezo bridge pickup, volume/treble/bass controls. Available in Natural and Tobacco Brown Sunburst finishes. New 1994.

| Mfr.'s Sug. Retail | $750 | $600 | $450 | $375 | $300 | $270 | $245 | $225 |

This model has agathis back/sides with Black and Marine Blue finish optionally available.

FG441S — similar to FG441, except has solid spruce top. Available in Natural finish. New 1994.

| Mfr.'s Sug. Retail | $510 | $382 | $255 | $250 | $200 | $180 | $165 | $150 |

FG441S-12 — similar to FG441, except has 12 strings, solid spruce top, 6 per side tuners. Available in Natural finish. New 1994.

| Mfr.'s Sug. Retail | $580 | $464 | $348 | $290 | $230 | $205 | $190 | $175 |

FG450SA — dreadnought style, solid spruce top, round soundhole, black pickguard, bound body, abalone rosette, ovankol back/sides, nato neck, 14/20 fret bound rosewood fingerboard with pearl snowflake inlay, rosewood bridge with black pearl dot pins, bound peghead with rosewood veneer, 3 per side chrome tuners. Available in Natural finish. Disc 1994.

| Mfr.'s Sug. Retail | $500 | $400 | $300 | $250 | $200 | $180 | $165 | $150 |

This model had left handed configuration (FG450S-LA) optionally available.

FG460SA — similar to 450SA, except has rosewood back/sides, gold hardware. Disc 1994.

| | $410 | $355 | $295 | $235 | $210 | $195 | $180 |

Last Mfr.'s Sug. Retail was $590.

FG460S-12A — similar to FG450SA, except has 12 strings, rosewood back/sides, 6 per side tuners, gold hardware. Disc 1994.

| | $435 | $370 | $310 | $250 | $225 | $205 | $190 |

Last Mfr.'s Sug. Retail was $620.

FG461S — dreadnought style, solid spruce top, round soundhole, black pickguard, bound body, abalone purfling/rosette, rosewood back/sides, nato neck, 14/20 fret bound rosewood fingerboard with pearl cross inlay, rosewood bridge with black pearl dot inlay, bound blackface peghead with pearl leaf/logo inlay, 3 per side diecast gold tuners. Available in Natural finish. New 1994.

| Mfr.'s Sug. Retail | $650 | $520 | $390 | $325 | $260 | $235 | $215 | $195 |

FG470SA — dreadnought style, solid spruce top, round soundhole, black pickguard, bound body, abalone rosette, rosewood back/sides, nato neck, 14/20 fret bound rosewood fingerboard with pearl snowflake inlay, rosewood bridge with black pearl dot pins, bound peghead with rosewood veneer, 3 per side gold tuners. Available in Natural finish. Disc 1994.

| | $460 | $395 | $330 | $265 | $240 | $220 | $200 |

Last Mfr.'s Sug. Retail was $660.

FJ645A — jumbo style, spruce top, round soundhole, black pickguard, bound body, abalone rosette, agathis back/sides, nato neck, 14/20 fret bound rosewood fingerboard with pearl pyramid inlay, nato bridge with white pearl dot pins, bound peghead, 3 per side chrome tuners. Available in Black Burst finish. Disc. 1994.

| | $385 | $330 | $275 | $220 | $200 | $180 | $165 |

Last Mfr.'s Sug. Retail was $550.

FJ651 — jumbo style, spruce top, round soundhole, black pickguard, 5 stripe bound body/rosette, agathis back/sides, mahogany neck, 14/20 fret bound rosewood fingerboard with pearl pentagon inlay, rosewood bridge with white black dot inlay, bound blackface peghead with pearl leaves/logo inlay, 3 per side diecast gold tuners. Available in Violin Sunburst finish. New 1994.

| Mfr.'s Sug. Retail | $560 | $448 | $336 | $280 | $225 | $205 | $190 | $170 |

ding	100%	98% MINT	95% EXC+	90% EXC	80% VG+	70% VG	60% G

FS310A— parlor style, spruce top, round soundhole, black pickguard, bound body, 5 stripe rosette, nato back/sides/neck, 14/20 fret bubinga fingerboard with pearl dot inlay, nato bridge with white pins, 3 per side chrome tuners. Available in Natural finish. Curr. mfr.

	$230	$195	$165	$130	$120	$110	$100

Last Mfr.'s Sug. Retail was $330.

Handcrafted Series

GC30 — classic style, solid white spruce top, round soundhole, bound body, wooden inlay rosette, rosewood back/sides, mahogany neck, 12/19 fret ebony fingerboard, jacaranda bridge, rosewood peghead veneer, 3 per side gold tuners. Available in Natural finish. Curr. mfr.

Mfr.'s Sug. Retail	$1,300	$975	$650	$625	$500	$450	$415	$375

This model has solid cedar top (GC30C) optionally available.

GC40 — classic style, solid white spruce top, round soundhole, bound body, wooden inlay rosette, jacaranda back/sides, mahogany neck, 12/19 fret ebony fingerboard, jacaranda bridge, jacaranda peghead veneer, 3 per side gold tuners. Available in Natural finish. Curr. mfr.

Mfr.'s Sug. Retail	$2,000	$1,500	$1,000	$950	$760	$685	$625	$570

This model has solid cedar top (GC40C) optionally available.

GC50 — classic style, solid spruce top, round soundhole, bound body, wooden inlay rosette, jacaranda back/sides, mahogany neck, 12/19 fret ebony fingerboard, jacaranda bridge, jacaranda peghead veneer with stylized Y groove, 3 per side gold tuners. Available in Lacquer finish. Curr. mfr.

Mfr.'s Sug. Retail	$3,100	$2,480	$1,860	$1,550	$1,240	$1,115	$1,025	$930

This model has solid cedar top (GC50C) optionally available.

GC60 — classic style, solid spruce top, round soundhole, bound body, wooden inlay rosette, jacaranda back/sides, mahogany neck, 12/19 fret ebony fingerboard, jacaranda bridge, jacaranda peghead veneer with stylized Y groove, 3 per side gold tuners. Available in Lacquer finish. Disc. 1994.

	$2,940	$2,520	$2,100	$1,680	$1,510	$1,385	$1,260

Last Mfr.'s Sug. Retail was $4,200.

This model had solid cedar top (GC60C) optionally available.

GC70 — classic style, solid spruce top, round soundhole, bound body, wooden inlay rosette, jacaranda back/sides, mahogany neck, 12/19 fret ebony fingerboard, jacaranda bridge, jacaranda peghead veneer with stylized Y groove, 3 per side gold tuners. Available in Shellac finish. Disc. 1994.

	$3,710	$3,180	$2,650	$2,120	$1,910	$1,750	$1,590

Last Mfr.'s Sug. Retail was $5,300.

This model had solid cedar top (GC70C) optionally available.

This model was available with no peghead groove (GC71).

GD10 — classic style, solid spruce top, round soundhole, wooden inlay rosette, rosewood back/sides, mahogany neck, 12/19 fret ebony fingerboard, rosewood bridge, rosewood peghead veneer, 3 per side gold tuners. Available in Natural finish. Curr. mfr.

Mfr.'s Sug. Retail	$760	$570	$380	$350	$280	$250	$230	$210

This model has solid cedar top (GD10C) optionally available.

GD20 — classic style, solid spruce top, round soundhole, wooden inlay rosette, rosewood back/sides, mahogany neck, 12/19 fret ebony fingerboard, rosewood bridge, rosewood peghead veneer, 3 per side gold tuners. Available in Natural finish. Curr. mfr.

Mfr.'s Sug. Retail	$950	$712	$475	$450	$360	$325	$300	$275

This model has solid cedar top (GD20C) optionally available.

LA8 — dreadnought style, solid spruce top, round soundhole, 3 stripe bound body, abalone rosette, rosewood back/sides, mahogany neck, 14/20 fret bound ebony fingerboard with pearl snowflake/cross inlay, ebony bridge with white black dot pins, bound rosewood veneered peghead with pearl logo inlay, 3 per side gold tuners. Available in Natural finish. New 1994.

Mfr.'s Sug. Retail	$900	$720	$540	$450	$360	$325	$300	$275

LA18 — mid-size dreadnought style, solid spruce top, round soundhole, bound body, abalone rosette, mahogany back/sides, mahogany neck, 14/20 fret bound ebony fingerboard with pearl dot inlay, ebony bridge with white pearl dot pins, bound peghead with rosewood veneer and pearl/abalone double L inlay, 3 per side gold tuners. Available in Natural finish. Curr. mfr.

Mfr.'s Sug. Retail	$1,130	$847	$565	$525	$420	$380	$345	$315

LA28 — similar to LA18, except has rosewood back/sides and pearl diamond inlay. Curr. mfr.

Mfr.'s Sug. Retail	$1,600	$1,200	$800	$700	$560	$505	$460	$420

LD10 — dreadnought style, solid white spruce top, round soundhole, black pickguard, abalone bound body and rosette, rosewood back/sides, mahogany neck, 14/20 fret bound rosewood fingerboard with pearl dot inlay, rosewood bridge with black pearl dot pins, bound peghead with rosewood veneer, 3 per side gold tuners. Available in Natural finish. Curr. mfr.

Mfr.'s Sug. Retail	$760	$570	$380	$350	$280	$250	$230	$210

Grading	100%	98% MINT	95% EXC+	90% EXC	80% VG+	70% VG	60% G

LD10E — similar to LD10, except has piezo electric pickups and pop up volume/2 tone and mix controls. Curr. mfr.
Mfr.'s Sug. Retail $950 $712 $475 $425 $340 $305 $280 $255

LL15 — dreadnought style, solid spruce top, round soundhole, black pickguard, 5 stripe bound body and rosette, mahogany back/sides/neck, 14/20 fret ebony fingerboard with pearl dot inlay, ebony bridge with black pearl dot pins, rosewood veneer on peghead, 3 per side gold tuners. Available in Natural finish. Curr. mfr.
Mfr.'s Sug. Retail $1,130 $847 $565 $525 $420 $380 $345 $315

LL35 — dreadnought style, solid white spruce top, round soundhole, black pickguard, 3 stripe bound body, abalone rosette, jacaranda back/sides, mahogany neck, 14/20 fret bound ebony fingerboard with pearl snowflake inlay, ebony bridge with black pearl dot pins, bound peghead with rosewood veneer and pearl/abalone double L inlay, 3 per side gold tuners. Available in Natural finish. Curr. mfr.
Mfr.'s Sug. Retail $1,900 $1,425 $950 $875 $700 $630 $575 $525

LW15 — dreadnought style, solid spruce top, round soundhole, black pickguard, 5 stripe bound body/rosette, mahogany back/sides/neck, 14/20 fret bound rosewood fingerboard with pearl flower inlay, rosewood bridge with black white dot pins, bound rosewood veneered peghead with pearl logo inlay, 3 per side chrome tuners. Available in Natural finish. New 1994.
Mfr.'s Sug. Retail $700 $560 $420 $350 $280 $250 $230 $210

LW25 — dreadnought style, solid spruce top, round soundhole, black pickguard, 5 stripe bound body/rosette, rosewood back/sides, mahogany neck, 14/20 fret bound ebony fingerboard with pearl flower inlay, ebony bridge with black white dot pins, bound rosewood veneered peghead with pearl logo inlay, 3 per side gold tuners. Available in Natural finish. New 1994.
Mfr.'s Sug. Retail $800 $640 $480 $400 $320 $290 $265 $240

ACOUSTIC ELECTRIC

APX Series

APX4 — single round cutaway dreadnought style, spruce top, oval soundhole, 5 stripe bound body and rosette, agathis back/sides, nato neck, 22 fret rosewood fingerboard with pearl dot inlay, rosewood bridge with white black dot pins, blackface peghead with screened flowers/logo, 3 per side chrome tuners, bridge piezo pickup, volume/treble/bass controls. Available in Black, Natural and Violin Sunburst finishes. Curr. mfr.
Mfr.'s Sug. Retail $510 $382 $255 $250 $200 $180 $165 $150

APX4-12 — similar to APX4, except has 12 strings, 6 per side tuners. New 1994.
Mfr.'s Sug. Retail $600 $480 $360 $300 $240 $215 $195 $180

APX6 — single round cutaway dreadnought style, spruce top, oval soundhole, 5 stripe bound body, wooden inlay rosette cap, agathis back/sides, nato neck, 24 fret extended rosewood fingerboard with pearl dot inlay, rosewood bridge with white pearl dot pins, 3 per sides chrome tuners, bridge/body piezo pickups, pop up volume/treble/bass/mix controls. Available in Black, Cherry Sunburst and Cream White finishes. Disc. 1994.
$510 $440 $365 $290 $260 $240 $220
Last Mfr.'s Sug. Retail was $730.

APX6C — similar to APX6, except has volume/tone controls, 3 band EQ. New 1994.
Mfr.'s Sug. Retail $750 $600 $450 $375 $300 $270 $245 $225
This model has left handed configuration (APX6CL) optionally available.

APX6N — classic style, spruce top, oval soundhole, 5 stripe bound body, wooden inlay rosette, ovankol back/sides, nato neck, 14/22 fret rosewood fingerboard, rosewood bridge, 3 per side gold tuners, bridge/body piezo pickups, volume/treble/bass/mix controls. Available in Natural finish. Disc. 1994.
$510 $440 $365 $290 $260 $240 $220
Last Mfr.'s Sug. Retail was $730.

APX7 — single round cutaway dreadnought style, spruce top, oval soundhole, 5 stripe bound body, wooden inlay rosette cap, agathis back/sides, mahogany neck, 24 fret extended bound rosewood fingerboard with pearl dot inlay, rosewood bridge with white pearl dot pins, bound peghead, 3 per side gold tuners, 2 bridge/body piezo pickups, volume/treble/bass/mix controls. Available in Black, Blue Burst and Light Brown Sunburst finishes. Curr. mfr.
Mfr.'s Sug. Retail $850 $680 $510 $425 $340 $305 $280 $255
This model has ovankol back/sides (APX7CT) optionally available.

APX7CN — single round cutaway classic style, spruce top, oval soundhole, 5 stripe bound body, rosette decal, ovankol back/sides, nato neck, 24 fret extended rosewood fingerboard, rosewood tied bridge, rosewood veneered peghead, 3 per side gold tuners with pearloid buttons, piezo bridge pickup, volume/tone controls, 3 band EQ. Available in Natural finish. New 1994.
Mfr.'s Sug. Retail $900 $720 $540 $450 $360 $325 $300 $275

APX8 — similar to APX7, except has bridge piezo pickup, mode switch. Available in Gray Burst and Light Brown Sunburst finishes.
Mfr.'s Sug. Retail $950 $760 $570 $475 $380 $345 $315 $285

Grading	100%	98% MINT	95% EXC+	90% EXC	80% VG+	70% VG	60% G

APX8C — single round cutaway folk style, spruce top, oval soundhole, 5 stripe bound body, wooden abalone inlay rosette cap, agathis back/sides, mahogany neck, 24 fret bound extended fingerboard with pearl dot inlay, rosewood bridge with white black dot pins, bound blackface peghead with screened leaves/logo, 3 per side gold tuners, piezo bridge pickups, volume/tone/mix controls, 3 band EQ. Available in Blackburst, Brownburst and Translucent Blueburst finishes. New 1994.

Mfr.'s Sug. Retail	$1,100	$880	$660	$550	$440	$395	$365	$330

APX8C-12 — similar to APX8C, except has 12 strings, 6 per side tuners. New 1994.

Mfr.'s Sug. Retail	$1,190	$952	$714	$595	$475	$430	$390	$360

APX8D — similar to APX8C, except has solid spruce top. New 1994.

Mfr.'s Sug. Retail	$1,200	$960	$720	$600	$480	$430	$395	$360

APX9-12 — single round cutaway dreadnought style, spruce top, oval soundhole, 5 stripe bound body, wooden inlay rosette cap, agathis back/sides, mahogany neck, 24 fret extended bound rosewood fingerboard with pearl dot inlay, rosewood bridge with white pearl dot pins, bound peghead, 6 per side chrome tuners, 2 bridge/body piezo pickups, volume/treble/bass/mix controls, mode switch. Available in Black, Blue Burst and Light Brown Sunburst finishes. Disc. 1994.

			$805	$690	$575	$460	$415	$380	$345

Last Mfr.'s Sug. Retail was $1,150.

APX10C — single round cutaway dreadnought style, spruce top, oval soundhole, 5 stripe bound body, abalone rosette cap, sycamore back/sides, mahogany neck, 24 fret extended bound ebony fingerboard with pearl diamond inlay, ebony bridge with white pearl dot pins, bound peghead, 3 per side gold tuners, bridge/body piezo pickups, volume/treble/bass/mix controls, mode switch. Available in Antique Stain Sunburst, Black Burst and Burgundy Red finishes. Mfd. 1993 to date.

Mfr.'s Sug. Retail	$1,330	$1,064	$798	$700	$560	$505	$460	$420

This model has left handed configuration (APX10CL) optionally available.

In 1994, Antique Brown Sunburst finish was introduced, Burgundy Red finish was discontinued.

APX10CT — similar to APX10C, except has rosewood back/sides. Available in Natural finish. New 1994.

Mfr.'s Sug. Retail	$1,500	$1,200	$900	$750	$600	$540	$495	$450

APX10CN — single round cutaway classic style, spruce top, oval soundhole, 5 stripe bound body, wooden inlay rosette, rosewood back/sides, mahogany neck, 24 fret ebony fingerboard, rosewood bridge, rosewood veneer on peghead, 3 per side gold tuners, bridge/body piezo pickups, volume/treble/bass/mix controls, mode switch. Available in Natural finish. Curr. mfr.

Mfr.'s Sug. Retail	$1,200	$960	$720	$600	$480	$430	$395	$360

APX20C — single round cutaway dreadnought style, spruce top, oval soundhole, abalone bound body, abalone rosette cap, sycamore back/sides, mahogany neck, 24 fret extended bound ebony fingerboard with abalone/pearl pentagon inlay, ebony bridge with white pearl dot pins, bound peghead, 3 per side gold tuners, bridge/body piezo pickups, volume/treble/bass/mix controls, mode switch. Available in Cream White and Light Brown Sunburst finishes. Curr. mfr.

Mfr.'s Sug. Retail	$1,600	$1,280	$960	$800	$640	$575	$530	$480

In 1994, volume/tone/mix controls, 3 band EQ replaced original item.

APX20D — single round cutaway dreadnought style, spruce top, oval soundhole, abalone bound body, abalone rosette cap, sycamore back/sides, mahogany neck, 24 fret extended bound ebony fingerboard with abalone/pearl pentagon inlay, ebony bridge with white pearl dot pins, bound peghead, 3 per side gold tuners, bridge/body piezo pickups, volume/tone/mix controls, 3 band EQ. Available in Cream White and Antique Stain Sunburst finishes. New 1994.

Mfr.'s Sug. Retail	$2,000	$1,600	$1,200	$1,000	$800	$720	$660	$600

APX SPECIAL I — single round cutaway dreadnought style, tiger stripe sycamore top, oval soundhole, 5 stripe bound body and rosette, agathis back/sides, nato neck, 22 fret rosewood fingerboard with pearl dot inlay, rosewood bridge with white pearl dot pins, bridge piezo pickup, volume/treble/bass controls. Available in Orange Stain and Red Blonde finishes. Curr. mfr.

Mfr.'s Sug. Retail	$610	$457	$305	$300	$240	$215	$195	$180

APX SPECIAL II — similar to APX Special I, except has birdseye maple top. Available in Faded Burst and Purple Burst finishes.

Mfr.'s Sug. Retail	$610	$457	$305	$300	$240	$215	$195	$180

ELECTRIC

Image Series

AE1200S — single round cutaway hollow body, laminated spruce top, bound body and f-holes, raised bound tortoise pickguard, beech/birch back/sides, mahogany neck, 20 fret bound ebony fingerboard with abalone split block inlay, metal/grenadilla bridge with trapeze tailpiece, bound peghead, 3 per side tuners, gold hardware, 2 humbucker pickups, 2 volume/tone controls, 3 position switch, coil split in tone controls. Available in Antique Stain and Natural finishes. Curr. mfr.

Mfr.'s Sug. Retail	$1,800	$1,350	$900	$800	$640	$575	$530	$480

Grading	100%	98% MINT	95% EXC+	90% EXC	80% VG+	70% VG	60% G

AES1500 — single round cutaway hollow body, curly maple top, bound body and f-holes, raised black pickguard, maple back/sides, 3 piece maple neck, 22 fret bound rosewood fingerboard with pearl dot inlay, bridge/stop tailpiece, abalone Yamaha symbol and scroll inlay on peghead, 3 per side tuners, gold hardware, 2 DiMarzio humbucker pickups, 2 volume/tone controls, 3 position switch, coil split in tone controls. Available in Orange Stain and Pearl Snow White finishes. Curr. mfr.

Mfr.'s Sug. Retail	$1,900	$1,425	$950	$850	$680	$610	$560	$510

AES1500B — similar to AES1500, except has Bigsby vibrato. Available in Antique Sunburst, Black, Natural and Orange Stain finishes. New 1994.

Mfr.'s Sug. Retail	$2,000	$1,600	$1,200	$1,000	$800	$720	$660	$600

AEX1500 — single round cutaway hollow style, arched sycamore top, raised black pickguard, bound body and f-holes, figured maple back/sides/neck, 20 fret bound ebony fingerboard with pearl dot inlay, adjustable ebony bridge/trapeze tailpiece, bound blackface peghead with pearl scroll/logo inlay, 3 per side tuners, gold hardware, humbucker/piezo bridge pickups, humbucker volume/tone controls, piezo volume/tone/3 band EQ controls. Available in Antique Stain, Faded Burst and Natural finishes. New 1994.

Mfr.'s Sug. Retail	$1,800	$1,440	$1,080	$900	$720	$650	$595	$540

SA1100 — double cutaway semi hollow body, laminated maple top/back/sides, bound body, raised black pickguard, mahogany neck, 22 fret bound rosewood fingerboard with pearl dot inlay, bridge/stop tailpiece, 3 per side tuners, chrome hardware, 2 humbucker pickups, 2 volume/tone controls, 3 position switch, coil split in tone controls. Available in Black, Brown Sunburst, Natural and Orange Sunburst finishes. Disc. 1994.

			$735	$630	$525	$420	$380	$345	$315

Last Mfr.'s Sug. Retail was $1,050.

SA2200 — similar to SA1100, except has flame maple top, ebony fingerboard with abalone split block inlay, bound peghead with abalone Yamaha logo and stylized inlay and gold hardware. Available in Brown Sunburst and Violin Sunburst finishes. Curr. mfr.

Mfr.'s Sug. Retail	$1,700	$1,275	$850	$750	$600	$540	$495	$450

Pacifica Series

112 — offset double cutaway alder body, white pickguard, bolt-on maple neck, 22 fret bubinga fingerboard with pearl dot inlay, standard vibrato, 6 on one side tuners, chrome hardware, 2 single coil/1 humbucker pickups, volume/tone controls, 5 position switch. Available in Antique Sunburst, Black and Yellow Natural finishes. New 1994.

Mfr.'s Sug. Retail	$320	$256	$192	$160	$130	$115	$105	$95

This model has basswood body optionally available.

120SD — single cutaway alder body, bolt-on maple neck, 22 fret bubinga fingerboard with pearl dot inlay, strings thru fixed bridge, 6 on one side tuners, chrome hardware, 2 humbucker pickups, volume/tone controls, 3 position switch. Available in Antique Sunburst, Black and Yellow Natural finishes. New 1994.

Mfr.'s Sug. Retail	$300	$240	$180	$150	$120	$110	$100	$90

This model has basswood body optionally available.

604 — offset double cutaway alder body, pearloid pickguard, bolt-on maple neck, 22 fret rosewood fingerboard with pearl dot inlay, standard vibrato, 6 on one side tuners, chrome hardware, 2 single coil/1 humbucker pickups, volume/tone control, 5 position switch. Available in Antique Sunburst, Black, Cherry Sunburst and Sea Foam Green finishes. New 1994.

Mfr.'s Sug. Retail	$750	$600	$450	$375	$300	$270	$245	$225

812S — single cutaway alder body, black pickguard, bolt-on maple neck, 24 fret rosewood fingerboard with pearl dot inlay, double locking vibrato, 6 on one side tuners, black hardware, 2 stacked coil/1 humbucker pickups, volume/tone control, 5 position switch with coil split. Available in Black, Dark Red Metallic and Lightning Blue finishes. Disc. 1994.

			$510	$440	$365	$290	$260	$240	$220

Last Mfr.'s Sug. Retail was $730.

821 — offset double cutaway alder body, black pickguard, bolt-on maple neck, 24 fret rosewood fingerboard with pearl dot inlay, double locking vibrato, 6 on one side tuners, black hardware, humbucker/stacked coil/humbucker pickups, volume/tone control, 5 position switch with coil split. Available in Black, Dark Red Metallic and Lightning Blue finishes. Disc. 1994.

			$510	$440	$365	$290	$260	$240	$220

Last Mfr.'s Sug. Retail was $730.

This model was also available with reverse peghead (821-R).

904 — offset double cutaway alder body, ash top, white pickguard, bolt-on maple Warmoth neck, 22 fret rosewood fingerboard with pearl dot inlay, 6 on one side tuners, nickel hardware, 2 single coil/1 humbucker pickups, volume/tone controls, 5 position switch. Available in Faded Blue, Faded Burst, Old Violin Sunburst and Translucent Black finishes. New 1994.

Mfr.'s Sug. Retail	$1,250	$1,000	$750	$625	$500	$450	$415	$375

912J — offset double cutaway swamp ash body, white pickguard, bolt-on maple neck, 22 fret fingerboard with pearl dot inlay, double locking vibrato, 6 on one side tuners, chrome hardware, 2 stacked coil/1 humbucker DiMarzio pickups, volume/tone control, 5 position switch. Available in Black, Crimson Red, Faded Burst and Translucent Blue finishes. Curr. mfr.

Mfr.'s Sug. Retail	$1,250	$937	$625	$530	$425	$385	$350	$320

"I had to be better than the guys in the music stores. My first guitar was not even playable which is why I developed such a strong left hand."
—D. Mangold on Nancy Wilson
TCG, Feb. 1996

Grading	100%	98% MINT	95% EXC+	90% EXC	80% VG+	70% VG	60% G

1212 — offset double cutaway basswood body, black pickguard, bolt-on maple neck, 24 fret rosewood fingerboard with pearl slash inlay, double locking vibrato, 6 on one side tuners, black hardware, 2 stacked coil/1 humbucker DiMarzio pickups, volume/tone control, 5 position switch with coil split. Available in Black, Dark Blue Metallic and Dark Red Metallic finishes. Disc. 1994.

	$740	$635	$530	$425	$385	$350	$320

Last Mfr.'s Sug. Retail was $1,060.

1221 — similar to 1212, except has humbucker/stacked coil/humbucker DiMarzio pickups. Available in Black and Dark Blue Metallic Flake finishes. Disc. 1994.

	$740	$635	$530	$425	$385	$350	$320

Last Mfr.'s Sug. Retail was $1,060.

1221M — similar to 1221, except has maple fingerboard with black slash inlay. Disc. 1994.

	$740	$635	$530	$425	$385	$350	$320

Last Mfr.'s Sug. Retail was $1,060.

1221MS — similar to 1221M, except has single cutaway body. Available in Black and Yellow Pearl finishes. Disc. 1994.

	$740	$635	$530	$425	$385	$350	$320

Last Mfr.'s Sug. Retail was $1,060.

1230 — similar to 1221, except has 3 humbucker DiMarzio pickups. Available in Black, Dark Red Metallic and Lightning Blue finishes. Disc. 1994.

	$740	$635	$530	$425	$385	$350	$320

Last Mfr.'s Sug. Retail was $1,060.

1230S — similar to 1230, except has single cutaway body. Available in Black and Dark Blue Metallic finishes. Disc. 1994.

	$740	$635	$530	$425	$385	$350	$320

Last Mfr.'s Sug. Retail was $1,060.

1412 — offset double cutaway mahogany body with 2 tone chambers, arched flame maple top, 7 piece maple/mahogany thru body neck, 24 fret bound ebony fingerboard with abalone/pearl block inlay, double locking vibrato, 6 on one side tuners, chrome hardware, 2 stacked coil/1 humbucker DiMarzio pickups, volume/tone control, 5 position switch with coil split. Available in Blonde, Cherry, Faded Burst, and Rose Burst finishes. Disc. 1994.

	$1,540	$1,320	$1,100	$880	$790	$725	$660

Last Mfr.'s Sug. Retail was $2,200.

In 1992 , Translucent Black finish was introduced.

RGZ Series

RGZ112P — offset double cutaway alder body, black pickguard, bolt-on maple neck, 22 fret bubinga fingerboard with pearl dot inlay, standard vibrato, 6 on one side tuners, chrome hardware, 2 single coil/1 humbucker pickups, volume/tone control, 5 position switch. Available in Black, Lightning Blue and Vivid Red finishes. Disc. 1994.

	$210	$180	$150	$120	$110	$100	$90

Last Mfr.'s Sug. Retail was $300.

RGX120D — offset double cutaway alder body, bolt-on maple neck, 22 fret bubinga fingerboard with pearl dot inlay, standard vibrato, 6 on one side tuners, chrome hardware, 2 humbucker pickups, volume/tone controls, 3 position switch. Available in Black, Vintage Red and White finishes. New 1994.

Mfr.'s Sug. Retail	$330	$264	$198	$165	$130	$120	$110	$100

This model has basswood body optionally available.

RGX121D (formerly RGZ121P) — similar to RGX120D, except has humbucker/single coil/humbucker pickups, 5 position switch. Available in Black, Blue Metallic, Vintage Red and Yellow Natural finishes. Curr. mfr.

Mfr.'s Sug. Retail	$360	$270	$180	$165	$130	$120	$110	$100

RGZ321P — similar to RGZ120D, except has double locking vibrato, humbucker/single coil/humbucker pickups, 5 position switch. Available in Black, Lightning Blue and 3D Blue. Disc. 1994.

	$320	$275	$230	$185	$165	$150	$140

Last Mfr.'s Sug. Retail was $460.

RGX421DM — offset double cutaway alder body, bolt-on maple neck, 24 fret rosewood fingerboard with pearl dot inlay, double locking vibrato, 6 on one side tuners, chrome hardware, volume/tone controls, 5 position switch. Available in Aqua, Black Pearl, Natural and Red Metallic finishes. New 1994.

Mfr.'s Sug. Retail	$570	$456	$342	$285	$230	$205	$190	$170

This model has maple fingerboard (RGZ421DM) optionally available.

RGZ612P — offset double cutaway alder body, black pickguard, bolt-on maple neck, 24 fret rosewood fingerboard with pearl dot inlay, double locking vibrato, 6 on one side tuners, black hardware, 2 single coil/1 humbucker pickups, volume/tone control, 5 position switch with coil split. Available in Black, Dark Red Metallic and Lightning Blue finishes. Disc. 1994.

	$500	$430	$360	$290	$260	$240	$220

Last Mfr.'s Sug. Retail was $720.

RGZ612PL — similar to RGZ612P, except is left handed. Disc. 1994.

	$580	$500	$415	$330	$300	$275	$250

Last Mfr.'s Sug. Retail was $830.

Grading	100%	98% MINT	95% EXC+	90% EXC	80% VG+	70% VG	60% G

RGX621D (formerly RGZ621P) — offset double cutaway alder body, bolt-on maple neck, 24 fret rosewood fingerboard with pearl offset dot inlay, double locking vibrato, 6 on one side tuners, black hardware, humbucker/single coil/humbucker pickups, volume/tone controls, 5 position switch. Available in Antique Sunburst, Black, Blue Metallic and Red Metallic finishes. Curr. mfr.

Mfr.'s Sug. Retail	$800	$600	$400	$360	$290	$260	$240	$220

RGX820R — offset double cutaway basswood body, bolt-on maple neck, 22 fret rosewood fingerboard with green dot inlay, double locking vibrato, reverse peghead, 6 on one side tuners, black hardware, 2 humbucker pickups, volume control, 3 position switch. Available in Black, Green Plaid and Red Metallic finishes. Mfd. 1993 to date.

Mfr.'s Sug. Retail	$1,050	$840	$630	$525	$420	$380	$345	$315

RGX821 — offset double cutaway alder body, bolt-on maple neck, 24 fret rosewood fingerboard with abalone oval inlay, double locking vibrato, 6 on one side tuners, gold hardware, humbucker/single coil/humbucker pickups, volume/tone controls, 5 position switch. Available in Antique Sunburst, Blackburst, Faded Blue and Violetburst finishes. New 1994.

Mfr.'s Sug. Retail	$1,000	$800	$600	$500	$400	$360	$330	$300

This model has a scalloped fingerboard from the 20th to the 24th fret.

Weddington Series

SPECIAL — single cutaway mahogany body, set in mahogany neck, 22 fret rosewood fingerboard with pearl dot inlay, adjustable bar bridge/tailpiece, 3 per side tuners, chrome hardware, 2 humbucker DiMarzio pickups, 2 volume/tone controls, 5 position switch with coil split. Available in Black, Cherry and Cream White finishes. Disc. 1994

			$700	$600	$500	$400	$360	$330	$300

Last Mfr.'s Sug. Retail was $1,000.

CLASSIC — similar to Standard, except has arched bound maple top, bound fingerboard with pearl split block inlay, pearl Yamaha symbol and stylized oval inlay on peghead and tunomatic bridge/stop tailpiece. Available in Cherry Sunburst, Metallic Black, Metallic Red top/Natural sides finishes. Curr. mfr.

Mfr.'s Sug. Retail	$1,600	$1,200	$800	$700	$560	$505	$460	$420

CUSTOM — similar to Classic, except has figured maple top, mahogany/maple neck, ebony fingerboard with pearl/abalone inlay, ebony veneer on peghead with pearl Yamaha symbol and stylized scroll inlay. Available in Cherry, Faded Burst and Roseburst finishes. Curr. mfr.

Mfr.'s Sug. Retail	$2,200	$1,650	$1,100	$990	$780	$650	$595	$540

ELECTRIC BASS

Attitude Series

CUSTOM — offset double cutaway alder body, white pickguard, bolt-on maple neck, 21 fret maple fingerboard with offset black slot inlay, solid brass fixed bridge with 4 built-in piezo electric pickups, 4 on one side tuners, chrome hardware, woofer/P-style/piezo DiMarzio pickups, volume/tone control, mini toggle pickup select switch, stereo outputs. Available in Crimson Red, Dark Blue Metallic and Light Violet Metallic finishes. Curr. mfr.

Mfr.'s Sug. Retail	$1,500	$1,200	$900	$750	$600	$540	$495	$450

DELUXE — offset double cutaway alder body, white pickguard, bolt-on maple neck, 21 fret rosewood fingerboard with pearl dot inlay, fixed bridge, 4 on one side tuners, chrome hardware, Yamaha "Six Pack" pickup, volume/tone control, 5 position switch. Available in Metallic Black, Metallic Red, Pacific Blue and White finishes. Disc. 1994.

			$630	$540	$450	$360	$325	$300	$275

Last Mfr.'s Sug. Retail was $900.

LIMITED — offset double cutaway alder body, white pickguard, bolt-on maple neck, 21 fret maple fingerboard with offset black slot inlay, solid brass fixed bridge, 4 on one side tuners, "Hipshot" XTender, chrome hardware, woofer/P-style DiMarzio pickups, 2 volume/1 tone controls, mini toggle pickup select/woofer cut switches, stereo outputs. Available in Lightning Red and Thunder Blue finishes. Disc. 1992.

			$1,260	$1,080	$900	$720	$650	$595	$540

The Limited was co-designed by Billy Sheehan.

Last Mfr.'s Sug. Retail was $1,800.

Limited II — similar to Limited, except has pearloid pickguard, scalloped fingerboard from 17th thru 21st fret, black hardware. Available in Black and Sea Foam Green finishes. New 1994.

Mfr.'s Sug. Retail	$1,800	$1,440	$1,080	$900	$720	$650	$595	$540

The Limited II was co-designed by Billy Sheehan.

SPECIAL — offset double cutaway alder body, white pickguard, bolt-on maple neck, 21 fret maple fingerboard with offset black slot inlay, fixed bridge, 4 on one side tuners, chrome hardware, woofer/P-style DiMarzio pickups, 2 volume/1 tone controls. Available in Black, Lightning Red, Sea Foam Green and Thunder Blue finishes. New 1994.

Mfr.'s Sug. Retail	$700	$560	$420	$350	$280	$250	$230	$210

STANDARD — offset double cutaway alder body, white pickguard, bolt-on maple neck, 21 fret rosewood fingerboard with pearl dot inlay, fixed bridge, 4 on one side tuners, chrome hardware, P-style/J-style pickups, volume/tone control, 3 position switch. Available in Black Pearl, Crimson Red, Dark Blue Metallic and White finishes. Curr. mfr.

Mfr.'s Sug. Retail	$800	$600	$400	$365	$290	$260	$240	$220

Grading		100%	98% MINT	95% EXC+	90% EXC	80% VG+	70% VG	60% G

Standard 5 — similar to Standard, except has 5 strings, 4/1 per side tuners. Disc. 1994.

		$650	$555	$465	$370	$335	$305	$280

Last Mfr.'s Sug. Retail was $930.

BB Series

BB200 — offset double cutaway alder body, bolt-on maple neck, 21 fret rosewood fingerboard with pearl dot tuners, fixed bridge, 4 on one side tuners, chrome hardware, P-style pickup, volume/tone control. Available in Black, Vivid Red and White finishes. Disc. 1994.

		$260	$220	$185	$150	$135	$120	$110

Last Mfr.'s Sug. Retail was $370.

This model had fretless fingerboard (BB200F) optionally available.

BB300 — similar to BB200, except the bridge is of higher quality. Disc. 1994.

		$300	$260	$215	$175	$155	$140	$130

Last Mfr.'s Sug. Retail was $430.

This model had left handed version (BB300L) optionally available.

BB350 — offset double cutaway alder body, bolt-on maple neck, 21 fret rosewood fingerboard with pearl dot inlay, fixed bridge, 4 on one side tuners, chrome hardware, 2 J-style pickups, 2 volume/1 tone controls. Available in Black, Blue Metallic, Natural and Vintage Red finishes. New 1994.

Mfr.'s Sug. Retail	$500	$400	$300	$250	$200	$180	$165	$150

BB350F/L — similar to BB350, except has fretless fingerboard or left handed configuration.

Mfr.'s Sug. Retail	$1,070	$856	$642	$535	$430	$390	$355	$325

BB1500A — offset double cutaway alder body, black lam pickguard, bolt-on maple neck, 21 fret rosewood fingerboard with pearl dot inlay, brass fixed bridge, 4 on one side tuners, gold hardware, 2 stacked humbucker pickups, volume/treble/mid/bass/mix controls, active electronics. Available in Black pearl, Natural and Wine Red finishes. New 1994.

Mfr.'s Sug. Retail	$1,000	$800	$600	$500	$400	$360	$330	$300

This model has fretless fingerboard (BB1500AF) optionally available.

BB5000A — offset double cutaway alder body, mahogany/maple thru body neck, 24 fret ebony fingerboard with pearl oval inlay, 5 string fixed bridge, 4/1 per side tuners, brass hardware, P-style/J-style pickups, volume/tone/mix controls, active electronics. Available in Cream White, Gunmetal Blue and Purple Pearl finishes. Disc. 1994.

		$1,190	$1,020	$850	$680	$610	$560	$510

Last Mfr.'s Sug. Retail was $1,700.

NATHAN EAST SIGNATURE — offset double cutaway alder body, figured maple top, bolt-on maple neck, 24 fret ebony fingerboard with pearl block inlay, brass fixed bridge, figured maple veneered peghead with screened artist's signature/logo, 3/2 per side tuners, gold hardware, 2 humbucker pickups, volume/treble/mid/bass/mix controls, active electronics. Available in Amberburst and Translucent Blue finishes. New 1994.

Mfr.'s Sug. Retail	$2,600	$2,080	$1,560	$1,300	$1,040	$935	$860	$780

This model was co-designed by Nathan East.

RBX Series

RBX250 — offset double cutaway alder body, bolt-on maple neck, 22 fret rosewood fingerboard with pearl dot inlay, fixed bridge, 4 on one side tuners, chrome hardware, P-style pickup, volume/tone controls. Available in Black, Crimson Red, Lightning Blue and Pearl Snow White finishes. Curr. mfr.

Mfr.'s Sug. Retail	$330	$247	$165	$150	$120	$110	$100	$90

This model has basswood body, fretless fingerboard (BB250F) optionally available.

In 1994, Blue Indo and Natural finishes were introduced; Crimson Red and Lightning Blue finishes were discontinued.

RBX350 — offset double cutaway alder body, bolt-on maple neck, 22 fret rosewood fingerboard with pearl dot inlay, fixed bridge, 4 on one side tuners, chrome hardware, P-style/J-style pickups, volume/tone/mix controls. Available in Black, Crimson Red, Lightning Blue and Pearl Snow White finishes. Curr. mfr.

Mfr.'s Sug. Retail	$400	$320	$240	$200	$160	$145	$130	$120

In 1994, Aqua, Blue Indo and Brown Stain were introduced; Crimson Red and Lightning Blue finishes were discontinued.

RBX350L — similar to RBX350, except has left handed configuration.

Mfr.'s Sug. Retail	$520	$390	$260	$235	$190	$170	$155	$140

RBX650 — similar to RBX350, except has black hardware. Available in Black Pearl, Dark Blue Metallic and Red Metallic finishes. Mfd. 1992 to date.

Mfr.'s Sug. Retail	$700	$525	$350	$335	$265	$240	$220	$200

In 1994, Faded Blue and Natural finishes were introduced; Dark Blue Metallic was discontinued.

Grading	100%	98% MINT	95% EXC+	90% EXC	80% VG+	70% VG	60% G

RBX1000 — offset double cutaway sculpted ash body, bolt-on maple neck, 24 fret rosewood fingerboard with pearl dot inlay, fixed brass bridge, 4 on one side tuners, chrome hardware, P-style/J-style pickups, volume/treble/bass/mix controls, active electronics. Available in Natural, Translucent Black and Translucent Violet finishes. Curr. mfr.

Mfr.'s Sug. Retail	$1,100	$825	$550	$510	$410	$370	$340	$310

In 1994, Blue Stain and Brown Stain finishes were introduced; Translucent Violet finish was discontinued.

TRB Series

TRB4 — offset double cutaway carved ash body, bolt-on maple neck, 24 fret rosewood fingerboard with pearl dot inlay, brass fixed bridge, 2 per side brass tuners, gold hardware, 2 stacked humbucker pickups, volume/treble/mid/bass/mix controls, active electronics. Available in Blue Stain, Brown Stain, Cherry Sunburst and Natural finishes. New 1994.

Mfr.'s Sug. Retail	$1,500	$1,200	$900	$750	$600	$540	$495	$450

TRB4P — offset double cutaway figured maple/rosewood/maple body, maple/mahogany thru body neck, 24 fret ebony fingerboard with pearl dot inlay, solid brass bridge, 2 per side brass tuners, P-style/J-style/piezo bridge pickups, volume/treble/bass/2 mix controls, piezo pickup switch. Available in Red Blonde, Translucent Blue and Translucent Red Sunburst finishes. Disc. 1994.

		$1,400	$1,200	$1,000	$800	$720	$660	$600

Last Mfr.'s Sug. Retail was $2,000.

TRB5 — offset double cutaway carved ash body, bolt-on maple neck, 24 fret rosewood fingerboard with pearl dot inlay, brass fixed bridge, 3/2 per side brass tuners, gold hardware, 2 stacked humbucker pickups, volume/treble/mid/bass/mix controls, active electronics. Available in Amber Stain, Blue Stain, Charcoal Gray and Cherry Sunburst finishes. New 1994.

Mfr.'s Sug. Retail	$1,600	$1,280	$960	$800	$640	$575	$530	$480

TRB5P — offset double cutaway figured maple/rosewood/maple body, maple/mahogany thru body neck, 24 fret ebony fingerboard with pearl dot inlay, solid brass bridge, 3/2 per side brass tuners, P-style/J-style/piezo bridge pickups, volume/treble/bass/2 mix controls, piezo pickup switch. Available in Red Blonde, Translucent Blue and Translucent Red Sunburst finishes. Curr. mfr.

Mfr.'s Sug. Retail	$2,500	$1,875	$1,250	$1,150	$920	$830	$760	$690

TRB6 — offset double cutaway carved ash body, bolt-on maple neck, 24 fret rosewood fingerboard with pearl dot inlay, brass fixed bridge, 3 per side brass tuners, gold hardware, 2 stacked humbucker pickups, volume/treble/mid/bass/mix controls, active electronics. Available in Amber Stain and Charcoal Gray finishes. New 1994.

Mfr.'s Sug. Retail	$1,800	$1,440	$1,080	$900	$720	$650	$595	$540

TRB6P — offset double cutaway figured maple/rosewood/maple body, maple/mahogany thru body neck, 24 fret ebony fingerboard with pearl dot inlay, solid brass bridge, 3 per side brass tuners, 2 J-style/piezo bridge pickups, volume/treble/bass/2 mix controls, piezo pickup switch. Available in Red Blonde, Translucent Blue and Translucent Red Sunburst finishes. Curr. mfr.

Mfr.'s Sug. Retail	$2,700	$2,025	$1,350	$1,300	$1,040	$935	$860	$780

TRB PATITUCCI SIGNATURE — offset double cutaway alder body, carved figured maple top, bolt-on maple neck, 24 fret ebony fingerboard with pearl 3/4 oval inlay, brass fixed bridge, figured maple veneered peghead with screened artist's signature/logo, 3 per side brass tuners, gold hardware, 2 stacked humbucker pickups, volume/treble/mid/bass/mix controls, active electronics. Available in Amber Stain and Charcoal Gray finishes. New 1994.

Mfr.'s Sug. Retail	$2,600	$2,080	$1,560	$1,300	$1,040	$935	$860	$780

This model was co-designed by John Patitucci.

YAMAKI

See DAION.

Instruments produced in Japan during the late 1970s through the 1980s.

YAMATO

Instruments produced in Japan during the late 1970s to the early 1980s.

Yamato guitars are medium quality instruments that feature both original and designs based on classic American favorites.

(Source: Tony Bacon and Paul Day, The Guru's Guitar Guide)

ERIC YUNKER

Instruments built in San Francisco during the early 1980s.

Luthier Eric Yunker (1953-1985) was described as "a man of many skills - poet, printer, inventor, graphic artist, musician, guitar sculptor." Yunker would combine the sculpting aspect of a guitar body and make it playable as well. One of the Yunker guitars is on display in the ZZ Top area at the Rock and Roll Hall of Fame and Museum in Cleveland, Ohio.

(Source: Jas Obrecht, Guitar Player magazine, March 1986)

YURIY

Instruments currently built in Buffalo Grove, Illinois.

Yuriy's **Angel** model ($3,500) features a hand-carved curly maple top, one-piece mahogany back, three-piece mahogany neck, and rosewood fingerboard. Yuriy offers a number of options on their model, such as inlays, exotic woods, pickups, hardware, and bindings. For further information, contact Yuriy Guitars through the Index of Current Manufacturers located in the rear of this book.

Z

ZEIDLER

Instruments currently built in Philadelphia, Pennsylvania.

Luthier John R. Zeidler has been building quality custom instruments for over eighteen years. Zeidler's backround encompasses woodworking, metalsmithing, tool making and music. Zeidler is currently producing high quality archtop and flattop guitars, as well as mandolins. For further information on models, availability, and pricing, please call luthier Zeidler via the Index of Current Manufacturers located in the back of this book.

ZEMAITIS

Instruments handbuilt in England since 1957.

Tony Zemaitis was born Antanus (Anthony) Casimere (Charles) Zemaitis in 1935. While his grandparents were Lithuanian, both Tony and his parents were born in the UK. At age 16 he left college to be an apprentice at cabinet making. As part of a hobby, he refashioned an old damaged guitar found in the family attic. In 1955, the first turning point to luthiery: Zemaitis built his first "half decent" guitar, a classical, nylon string with peghead. In the mid to late 1950s, Zemaitis served for two years in Britian's National Service.

Upon his return to civilian life, Zemaitis continued his guitar building hobby, only now a number of the guitars began turning up onto the folk scene. By 1960 he was selling guitars for the price of the materials, and a number of the originals that Zemaitis calls "Oldies" still exist. Early users include Spencer Davis, Long John Baldry, and Jimi Hendrix.

In 1965, Zemaitis' "hobby" had acquired enough interest that he was able to become self employed. By the late 1960s, the orders were coming in from a number of top players such as Ron Wood, Eric Clapton, and George Harrison. The house and shop all moved lock, stock, and barrel to Kent in 1972. A "Student" model was introduced in 1980, but proved to be too popular and time consuming to produce the number of orders, so it was discontinued.

In the late 1980s, Zemaitis was surprised to see that his guitars were even more valuable in the secondhand market than originally priced. As his relative output is limited, an alarming trend of forgeries have been turning up in England, Japan, and the U.S. 1995 was the 40th Anniversary of the first classical guitar built in 1955, and Zemaitis also hit sixty "still fit, healthy and going strong". Guitar production is limited to 10 guitars a year, and what started as a pleasant hobby has still remained pleasurable through the years.

(Source: Tony Zemaitis, March 1996)

Courtesy Keith Smart and Keith Rogers, "The Z Gazette" Volume I Issue I

(magazine of the Zemaitis Guitar Owners Club [UK])

Methodology of serial numbers and dating on guitars is going to remain a bit of a mystery in this edition, as to the number of forgeries that keep turning up (and we're not going to add tips to the "help-yourself merchants" As Tony likes to call them). Tony Zemaitis has granted NO ONE permission to build reproductions and no licensing deals have been made to any company. The **Blue Book of Guitars** strongly recommends two or three written estimates of any ZEMAITIS instrument from accredited sources.

However, we can supply an overview of model histories and designations. During the late 1950s, a few basic acoustic models were built to learn about sizes, shapes, wood response, and sound holes. From 1960 to 1964, guitar building was still a hobby, so there was no particular standard; also, the paper labels inside are hand labeled.

In 1965, Zemaitis "turned pro" and introduced the "Standard", "Superior", and "Custom" models of acoustic guitars. These terms are relative, not definitive as there is some overlapping from piece to piece. While some soundholes are round, there are a number of acoustic guitars built with the "heart shaped" sound hole.

The electric solidbody guitar was discussed and inspired by Eric Clapton on a visit to Zemaitis' workshop in 1969. The handful of early models had aluminum plates on the faces, and later were followed by solid silver, then finally returned to aluminum as the British tax people proved difficult. Zemaitis' good friend and engraver Danny O'Brien handles the ornate engraving on the M/F (Metal Front) models. The first "test" guitar was sold off cheaply at the time, but the second was purchased by Tony McPhee (Groundhogs); the third guitar built was purchased by Ron Wood. The M/F guitar model has since moved worldwide. There is a variation model called the "Disc Front" which has a round faced metal plate around the pickups as opposed to the entire front. An ultimate version called the Pearl Front is just that: a pearl topped solid body guitar - and the written description hardly does justice to the actual piece.

The "Student" model was introduced in 1980. Designed as a basic guitar that could be later upgraded, the model proved so popular that it was quickly discontinued for fear that the production would overtake other work altogether! In the late 1980s, clients began asking for either more decorations or copies of older models. At this point Zemaitis upgraded his system to the "Custom", "Deluxe", and "Custom Deluxe" which are still in use to date. Again, these three models are relative, not definitive as some crossing back and forth does go on.

Zeidler Jazz Deluxe Special
courtesy Scott Chinery

Zemaitis Custom Disc
 courtesy Keith Smart

ZENTA

Instruments originally produced in Japan in the late 1960s to the late 1970s. During the 1970s, production moved to Korea.

These entry level solid body and semi-hollowbody guitars featured both original design and designs based on classic American favorites.

(Source: Tony Bacon and Paul Day, The Guru's Guitar Guide)

Zemaitis Superior M/F
courtesy Keith Smart

ZENTECH

Instruments currently built in Girdwood, Arkansas.

Zentech offers several quality custom built electric guitar models.

ZETA

Instruments currently built in Oakland, California. Distributed by Zeta Music Systems, Inc. of Oakland, California.

Zeta currently offers the **Crossover** bass, which allows bassists the flexibilty of either upright or electric playing. Zeta also offers quality acoustic/electric violins, and a MIDI violin synthesizer.

ELECTRIC

MIRROR 6 MIDI GUITAR — radical double cutaway asymmetrical ash body, bolt-on maple neck, 24 fret ebony fingerboard with offset white block inlay, strings thru body bridge, reverse headstock, 6 on one side Gotoh tuners, black hardware, single coil/humbucker/hex EMG pickups, volume/tone/blend/midi controls, 3 position pickup, synth and hex switches. Available in Black, Metallic Grey, Pearl White, Red and Sea Foam Green finishes. Mfd. 1989 to 1994.

$2,095	$1,795	$1,495	$1,195	$1,075	$985	$895

Last Mfr.'s Sug. Retail was $2,995.

Add $800 for double locking vibrato.

ZIM GAR

Instruments produced in Japan.

Zim Gar instruments were distributed by U.S. importer Gar Zim Musical Instrument Corporation of Brooklyn, New York.

(Source: Michael Wright, Guitar Stories Volume One, pg. 76)

KEVIN ZIMMERLY

Instruments produced in Bay Shore, New York since 1993.

Luthier Kevin Zimmerly has been building high quality custom basses for the last three years. Zimmerly draws on his backround of over 22 years in the music industry for design ideas and innovations. For further information regarding models and pricing, please contact luthier Zimmerly via the Index of Current Manufacturers located in the back of this book.

ZIMNICKI

Instruments currently built in Allen Park, Michigan.

Luthier Gary Zimnicki has been developing his woodworking skills since the late 1970s, and is currently focusing on building quality archtop and flattop guitars. Zimnicki uses aged tonewoods, wood bindings, Ebony fingerboards, Schaller gold tuners, and nitrocellulose lacquer finishes on his creations, and works with the customer on other design specifications. For further information, please contact luthier Zimnicki through the Index of Current Manufacturers located in the back of this book.

ZION

Instruments built in Greensboro, North Carolina since 1980. Distributed by Zion Guitar Technology of Greensboro, North Carolina.

Luthier Ken Hoover founded Zion Guitar Technology in 1980, after ten years of repair and custom building experience. Zion guitars have been famous for their high quality and amazing custom finishes. Hoover developed the Radicaster model in 1987 (see listing for **Classic Maple** below), and the Zion guitar staff maintains an output of 40 to 50 guitars a month.

ELECTRIC

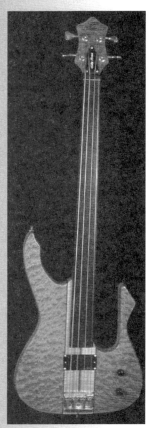

Zimmerly 4 String "Silly Bass"
courtesy Kevin Zimmerly

Grading		100%	98% MINT	95% EXC+	90% EXC	80% VG+	70% VG	60% G

BURNING DESIRE — offset double cutaway basswood body, bolt-on maple neck, 22 fret ebony fingerboard with pearl dot inlay, standard Kahler vibrato, graphite nut, 6 on one side locking Sperzel tuners, chrome hardware, 2 stacked coil/1 humbucker Joe Barden pickups, volume/tone control, 3 mini switches. Available in Black with Neon Flames finish. Current production.

Mfr.'s Sug. Retail	$2,995	$2,246	$1,497	$1,495	$1,195	$1,075	$985	$895

Limited number produced yearly.

Grading	100%	98% MINT	95% EXC+	90% EXC	80% VG+	70% VG	60% G

CLASSIC MAPLE — offset double cutaway basswood body, arched bound figured maple top, bolt-on maple neck, 22 fret ebony fingerboard with pearl dot inlay, locking vibrato, 6 on one side locking tuners, 2 single coil/1 humbucker Zion pickups, volume/tone control, 5 position switch. Available in Amber Top, Black, Transparent Blue Burst, Tobacco Burst and Vintage Burst finishes. Current production.

Mfr.'s Sug. Retail	$1,995	$1,496	$997	$995	$795	$720	$660	$600

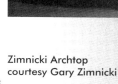

Zimnicki Archtop
courtesy Gary Zimnicki

This model is available with EMG, PJ Marx or Seymour Duncan pickups.

This model available with standard vibrato (RT Classic).

This model also available with maple fingerboard.

GRAPHIC SERIES — similar to Classic Maple, except has basswood body. Available in Frosted Marble, Guilded Frost, Marble Rock and Techno Frost finishes. Current production.

Mfr.'s Sug. Retail	$1,895	$1,516	$1,137	$950	$760	$685	$625	$570

PICKASSO — similar to Burning Desire, except has black hardware and Zion pickups. Available in Black, Blue/Purple/Pink and Pink/Orange/Yellow finishes. Current production.

Mfr.'s Sug. Retail	$2,495	$1,996	$1,497	$1,250	$1,000	$900	$825	$750

T MODEL — offset double cutaway basswood body, pearloid pickguard, bolt-on maple neck, 22 fret ebony fingerboard with pearl dot inlay, standard Gotoh vibrato, graphite nut, 6 on one side locking Sperzel tuners, 3 stacked coil Zion pickups, volume/tone control, 5 position switch. Available in Black, Cream and Tobacco Burst finishes. Mfd. 1991 to date.

Mfr.'s Sug. Retail	$1,495	$1,196	$897	$750	$600	$540	$495	$450

This model also available with maple fingerboard.

T Model Maple Top — similar to T Model, except has figured maple top and Zion vibrato. Available in Blue Burst, Tobacco Burst and Vintage Burst finishes. Curr. mfr.

Mfr.'s Sug. Retail	$1,895	$1,516	$1,137	$950	$760	$685	$625	$570

This model is available in left-handed version (Maple Top Left T).

ELECTRIC BASS

RAD BASS — offset double cutaway basswood body, bolt-on maple neck, 20 fret ebony fingerboard, fixed bridge, 4 per side Gotoh tuners, black hardware, P-style/J-style EMG pickups, 2 volume/1 tone controls. Available in Amber Top, Classic Black, Frosted Marble Blue, Frosted Marble Purple, Frosted Marble Red, Purple Burst, Techno-Frost, Tobacco Burst, Transparent Blue Burst, Vintage Burst finishes. Current production.

Mfr.'s Sug. Retail	$1,995	$1,496	$997	$995	$795	$720	$660	$600

ZOID

Instruments built in Tampa, Florida during the 1990s.

Zoid light Guitars feature high density transparent bodies and internal lighting systems in three body shapes (and thirty-two colors). Retail prices begin at $1,400 to $1,800.

ZOLLA

Instruments built in San Diego, California during the 1990s.

Zolla Guitars built high quality custom guitars and basses (4-, 5-, and 6-string configurations) as well as the Doc George Oates "Gun Guitar", which (as the name describes) is a 6-string rifle-shaped instrument!

ZON

Instruments originally built in Buffalo, New York from 1982 to 1986. Production and company location shifted in 1986 to Redwood City, California, where instruments continue to be built.

Luthier/musician Joseph M. Zon originally began building instruments in upstate New York back in 1982. Four years later Zon Guitars moved into larger facilities across country in California to meet the greater demand for his high quality basses.

ELECTRIC BASS

Michael Manring Hyperbass Series

VERSION I — offset deep cutaway teardrop poplar body, quilted maple top, composite neck, fretless phenolic fingerboard, fixed Schaller bridge, blackface peghead with screened model name/logo, 2 per side Zon/Gotoh tuners, black hardware, humbucker Bartolini pickup, volume/treble/bass controls, active electronics. Available in Natural top/Black back finishes. Current production.

Mfr.'s Sug. Retail	$3,295	$2,636	$1,977	$1,650	$1,320

This instrument has a 3 octave fingerboard and was co-designed by Michael Manring.

Version II — similar to Version I, except has detunable Zon/ATB bridge, detunable Zon/Gotoh/Hipshot tuners.

Mfr.'s Sug. Retail	$4,995	$3,746	$2,497	$2,495	$1,995

"They are good guitars - they're made well. They have great necks, and are very easy to play. People never got used to their futuristic design."

—Fred Popovich

TCG, Mar/Apr 1991

Grading		100%	98% MINT	95% EXC+	90% EXC	80% VG+	70% VG	60% G

Version III — similar to Version I, except has detunable Zon/ATB bridge, detunable Zon/Gotoh/Hipshot tuners, and piezo body pickup.

Mfr.'s Sug. Retail $7,995 $5,996 $3,997 $3,995 $3,195

Legacy Series

ELITE — offset double cutaway teardrop poplar body, California walnut top, composite neck, 24 fret phenolic fingerboard with pearl dot inlay, fixed Zon bridge, blackface peghead with screened model name/logo, 2 per side Schaller tuners, chrome hardware, 2 humbucker Bartolini pickups, 2 volume/2 tone controls, active electronics. Available in Black, Emerald Green, Heather, Ice Blue, Lazer Blue, Midnight Blue, Mint Green, Mist Green, Natural, Pearl Blue, Porsche Red, Powder Blue and Yellow finishes. Current production.

Mfr.'s Sug. Retail $2,775 $2,220 $1,665 $1,390 $1,110

This model has the following tops optionally available: birdseye maple, curly maple, goncalo alves, koa, quilted maple, zebrawood.

Elite V — similar to Elite, except has 5 strings, 3/2 per side tuners. Introduced in 1986.

Mfr.'s Sug. Retail $3,275 $2,620 $1,965 $1,640 $1,310

Elite VI — similar to Elite, except has 6 strings, 3 per side tuners. Introduced in 1988.

Mfr.'s Sug. Retail $3,575 $2,681 $1,787 $1,785 $1,430

ELITE SPECIAL — offset double cutaway teardrop poplar body, bubinga top, composite neck, 24 fret phenolic fingerboard with pearl dot inlay, fixed Zon bridge, blackface peghead with screened model name/logo, 2 per side Schaller tuners, chrome hardware, 2 multi coil Bartolini pickups, 2 volume/2 tone controls, coil select switch, active electronics. Available in Natural top/Black back finishes. Current production.

Mfr.'s Sug. Retail $2,995 $2,246 $1,497 $1,495 $1,195

Elite V Special — similar to Elite Special, except has 5 strings, 3/2 tuners per side.

Mfr.'s Sug. Retail $3,495 $2,796 $2,097 $1,750 $1,400

Elite VI Special — similar to Elite Special, except has 6 strings, 3 tuners per side.

Mfr.'s Sug. Retail $3,795 $2,846 $1,897 $1,895 $1,515

STANDARD — offset double cutaway teardrop ash body, bolt-on composite neck, 24 fret phenolic fingerboard, fixed Wilkinson bridge, blackface peghead with screened model name/logo, 2 per side Zon/Gotoh tuners, chrome hardware, 2 humbucker Bartolini pickups, 2 volume/2 tone controls, active electronics. Available in Natural finish. Current production.

Mfr.'s Sug. Retail $2,195 $1,756 $1,317 $1,100 $880

This model has figured maple body optionally available.

Standard V — similar to Standard, except has 5 strings, 3/2 per side tuners.

Mfr.'s Sug. Retail $2,495 $1,996 $1,497 $1,250 $1,000

Standard VI — similar to Standard, except has 6 strings, 3 per side tuners.

Mfr.'s Sug. Retail $2,695 $2,156 $1,617 $1,350 $1,080

Sonus Series

SONUS — offset double cutaway ash body, bolt-on composite neck, 24 fret phenolic fingerboard, fixed Wilkinson bridge, blackface peghead with screened model name/logo, 2 per side Zon/Gotoh tuners, chrome hardware, 2 P-style bartolini pickups, 2 concentric volume/treble/bass controls, active electronics. Available in Natural finish. Current production.

Mfr.'s Sug. Retail $1,875 $1,500 $1,125 $940 $750

Sonus V — similar to Sonus, except has 5 strings, 3/2 per side tuners.

Mfr.'s Sug. Retail $2,175 $1,740 $1,305 $1,090 $870

Sonus VI — similar to Sonus, except has 6 strings, 3 per side tuners.

Mfr.'s Sug. Retail $2,475 $1,856 $1,237 $1,235 $985

SONUS SPECIAL — offset double cutaway ash body, bubinga top, bolt-on composite neck, 24 fret phenolic fingerboard, fixed Wilkinson bridge, blackface peghead with screened model name/logo, 2 per side Zon/Gotoh tuners, chrome hardware, 2 P-style Bartolini pickups, 2 concentric volume/treble/bass controls, active electronics. Available in Natural finish. Current production.

Mfr.'s Sug. Retail $2,150 $1,720 $1,290 $1,075 $860

Sonus V Special — similar to Sonus Special, except has 5 strings, 3/2 per side tuners.

Mfr.'s Sug. Retail $2,450 $1,960 $1,470 $1,225 $980

Sonus VI Special — similar to Sonus Special, except has 6 strings, 3 per side tuners.

Mfr.'s Sug. Retail $2,750 $2,200 $1,650 $1,375 $1,100

ZORKO

Instruments built in Chicago, Illinois during the early to mid 1960s.

The Zorko trademark is the brandname of the Dopyera Brothers (See DOBRO and VALCO), and was used to market an electric pickup-equipped upright "mini-bass". In 1962, Everett Hull from Ampeg acquired the rights to the design. Hull improved the design, and Jess Oliver devised a new ' diaphram-style' pickup. The Ampeg company then marketed the model as the "Baby Bass".

(Source: Tony Bacon and Barry Moorhouse, The Bass Book, pg. 35)

Some models in between 70% to 90% have been seen priced between $650 and $1,200. Pricing depends on condition of the body; also, compare pickups between the Zorko and an Ampeg. There may be retro fit kits from Azola, Clevinger, or some of the pickup companies (piezo bridge kits) that may fit a Zorko "mini-bass".

Z

Z

Serialization

POTENTIOMETER CODING: "SOURCE DATE" CODE

An Important Instrument Dating Breakthrough
developed by Hans Moust (author, "The Guild Guitar Book")

Stamped on every potentiometer (volume and tone "pots") is a six or seven digit "source code" that tells who made the pot, as well as the week and the year. The "source dating" code is a piece of standardization that is administered by the Electronics Industries Association (EIA), formed in 1924. The EIA assigns each manufacturer a three digit code (there are some with one, two or four digits). Moust's research has indicated no source date codes on any guitar pots before the late 1940s, and no single digit year code after 1959 (6 digit source code).

It's fairly easy to crack the source code. The first three digits indicate the company that built the potentiometer. Some times these digits may be separated by a space, a hyphen, or a period. The most common company codes found are:

137	CTS	304	Stackpole
140	Clarostat	134	Centralab
106	Allen Bradley	381	Bourns Networks

If the code is only six digits long, then the fourth digit is the year code (between 1947 and 1959). If the code is seven digits long, then the fourth and fifth digits indicate the year. The final two digits in either of the codes indicate the week of the year the potentiometer was built. Any final two digits with a code number over 52 possibly indicates a part number instead of a week of the year code.

When dating an instrument by the 'pot code', keep two things in mind: The potentiometers must be original to the piece (new solder, or a date code that is off by ten or more years is a good giveaway to spot replacement pots); and that the pot code only indicates when the potentiometer was built! If the pot is an original, it indicates a date that the guitar could not have been built before - so it's always a good idea to have extra reference material around.

Moust's research has indicated that virtually all Fenders from 1966 to 1969 have pots dated from 1966. Moust has speculated that when CBS bought Fender, they found a good deal on pots and bought a three year supply. Guild apparently had the same good fortune in 1979, for when Moust visited the factory they still had a good supply of '79 pots - which explains why every Guild since then has had similar dated pots!

Finally, a word of caution: not all potentiometer manufacturers subscribed to the EIA source code date, and early Japanese components did not use the international coding like the American and European builders. If the code does not fit the above criteria, don't "force it" and skew your dating results.

(Source: George Gruhn and Walter Carter, Guitar Player magazine, October 1990)

ALEMBIC SERIAL NUMBERS

Alembic began building custom basses and installing custom electronics in 1969 as the company was just forming. Since 1971 the serial numbers can be found stamped on the back of the headstock. Every instrument the company has produced also has a corresponding instrument file which contains the original work order (specifications), returned warranty, and any other relevant paperwork. In general, the first two numbers in the serial number are the year built; certain models may also have a letter code that designates the model. The final digits indicate the individual instrument and its place in the overall Alembic production.

TOM ANDERSON GUITARWORKS SERIALIZATION

Tom Anderson spent a number of years building necks and guitar bodies before producing completed guitars. Outside of custom built specialties, 1987 was the first year that the volume began to resemble production numbers.

Although every guitar built is tracked in the company files, many are remembered by staff luthiers who had a hand in producing them. Engraved on the neck plate of each guitar is the date it was completed along with "MADE IN CALIFORNIA".

An example of this would be: 12-21-92P, or 5-27-93A, or 9-15-95N. An A, N, or P lets you know if the instrument was completed in the A.M.(A), P.M.(P) or, if production is moving well, at approximately Noon(N).

BENEDETTO SERIAL NUMBERS

As of August 1996, Robert Benedetto had completed a total of almost 650 instruments. Nearly 400 have been of the archtop series, with the remainder comprising of violins, violas, mandolins, and some electric solidbody guitars and basses.

Archtop guitars are numbered in their own series, comprising of a four or five digit number. The Last two digits in the number indicate the year the guitar was made; the Preceding digits indicate the instrument's number.

Example: Guitar # 29193 would be the 291st archtop, made in 1993.

Violins and violas have a separate numbering system apart from the archtops, as do the electric solidbody guitars and basses. Mandolins built were not numbered.

Further information and a full serial number list can be found in Robert Benedetto's own book, "Making an Archtop Guitar" (Center stream Publishing, 1994).

D'ANGELICO SERIAL NUMBERS

Master Luthier John D'Angelico (1905-1964) opened his own shop at age 27, and every guitar was hand built - many to the specifications or nuances of the customer commisioning the instrument. In the course of his brief lifetime, he created 1,164 numbered guitars, as well as unnumbered violins, mandolins, novelty instruments, and the necks for the plywood semi-hollowbody electrics. The nature of this list is to help identify the numbered guitars as to the date produced.

D'Angelico kept a pair of ledger books and some loose sheets of paper as a log of the guitars created, models, date of completion (or possibly the date of shipping), the person or business to whom the guitar was sold, and the date. The following list is a rough approximation of the ledgers and records.

First "Loose Sheets"

1002 through 1073	1932 to 1934

Ledger Book One

1169 through 1456	1936 to 1939
1457 through 1831	1940 to 1949
1832 through 1849	1950

Ledger Book Two

1850 through 2098	1950 to 1959
2099 through 2122	1960
2123	1961

Second "Loose Sheets"

2124 through 2164	Dates not recorded

Again, I must stress that the above system is a guide only. In 1991, author Paul William Schmidt published a book entitled "Acquired of the Angels: The lives and works of master guitar makers John D'Angelico and James L. D'Aquisto" (The Scarecrow Press, Inc.; Metuchen, N.J. & London). In appendix 1 the entire ledger information is reprinted save information on persons or business to whom the guitar was sold. I fully recommend this book to anyone seeking information on luthiers John D'Angelico and James L. D'Aquisto.

D'AQUISTO SERIAL NUMBERS

Master Luthier James L. D'Aquisto (1935-1995) met John D'Angelico around 1953. At the early age of 17 D'Aquisto became D'Angelico's apprentice, and by 1959 was handling the decorative procedures and other lutherie jobs.

D'Aquisto, like his mentor before him, kept ledger books as a log of the guitars created, models, date of completion (or possibly the date of shipping), the person or business to whom the guitar was sold, and the date. The following list is a rough approximation of the ledger. As the original pages contain some idiosyncrasies, the following list will by nature be inaccurate as well - and should only be used as a guide for dating individual instruments. The nature of this list is only to help identify the numbered guitars as to the date produced.

The D'Aquisto Ledger

1001 through 1035	1965 to 1969
1036 through 1084	1970 to 1974
1085 through 1133	1975 to 1979
1134 through 1175	1980 to 1984
1176 through 1228	1985 to 1990

Beginning in 1988, serial number was 1203.

Other guitars that D'Aquisto built had their own serial numbers. For example, solid body and semi-hollow body guitars from 1976 to 1987 had an "E" before the three digit number. D'Aquisto also built some classical models, some flat-top acoustics, and some hollow body electric models (hollowbody guitars run from #1 to #30, 1976 to 1980; and #101 to #118, 1982 to 1988).

In 1991, author Paul William Schmidt published a book entitled "Acquired of the Angels: The lives and works of master guitar makers John D'Angelico and James L. D'Aquisto" (The Scarecrow Press, Inc.; Metuchen, N.J. & London). In appendix 2 the entire ledger information is reprinted up to the year 1988 except for information on persons or business to whom the guitar was sold. I fully recommend this book to anyone seeking information on luthiers John D'Angelico and James L. D'Aquisto.

DANELECTRO SERIALIZATION

Danelectro serial numbers are usually located in the neck pocket, although they do also turn up in other hidden areas of the body. Most Danelectros carry a four digit code. The code pattern is "XXYZ": XX is the week of the year (01-52), Y is still a mystery (Batch code or

Designator?), and Z is the last digit of the production years. As the Z number is duplicated every 10 years, model designation and features should also be used in determining the date. Some guitars built during the first nine weeks of each year (01 through 09, XX code) may not have the 0 as the first number. There are two variations on this code. In late 1967, the Coral and Dane series were offered, and were numbered with a "ZXX" code. The other original models still maintain their four digit code. However, the Convertible model (an original series) is cosmetically changed in 1968 to a Dane-style headstock, and changes to the new three digit code.

(Serialization courtesy of Paul Bechtoldt and Doug Tulloch, "Guitars from Neptune". This book is the definitive listing for models, specifications, and company information - plus it carries many examples of the company's advertising as a reference tool)

DEAN SERIALIZATION

Serialization for the "Made in the U.S.A." instruments is fairly straightforward to decipher. The serial numbers were stamped into the back of the headstock, and the first two digits of the serial number are the year of manufacture. The following five digits represent the instrument number. Examples of this would be:

79 00619	manufactured in 1979
81 39102	manufactured in 1981

The imported Deans do not carry the stamped and year-coded serial numbers, and would have to be dated through configuration, headstock design, and other design factors.

EPIPHONE SERIAL NUMBERS

In 1917, Epaminondas "Epi" Stathopoulos began using the **House of Stathopoulo** brand on the family's luthiery business. By 1923 the business was incorporated, and a year later the new trademark was unvieled on a line of banjos. Stathopoulos combined his nickname Epi with the Greek word for sound, phone. When the company was recapitalized in 1928, it became the Epiphone Banjo Company.

Guitars were introduced in 1930, and were built in New York City, New York through 1953. Company manufacturing was moved to Philadelphia due to union harrassment in New York, and Epiphone continued on through 1957. Serial numbers on original Epiphones can be found on the label.

Number	Year	Number	Year
1000 - 3000 [electrics only]	1937-1938	51000 - 52000	1944
4000 - 5000 [electrics only]	1939-1941	52000 - 54000	1945
5000 [acoustics]	1932	54000 - 55000	1946
6000	1933	56000	1947
7000	1934	57000	1948
8000 - 9000	1935	58000	1949
10000	1930-1932, 1936	59000	1950
11000	1937	60000 - 63000	1951
12000	1938	64000	1952
13000	1939-1940	64000 - 66000	1953
14000 - 15000	1941-1942	68000	1954
16000 - 18000	1943	69000	1955-1957
19000	1944 In 1944, a change was made in the numbering sequence.	75000 - 85000	1948-1949

In May of 1957, Epiphone was purchased by CMI and became a division of Gibson. Parts and materials were shipped to the new home in Kalamazoo, Michigan. Ex-Epiphone workers in New Berlin, New York "celebrated" by hosting a bonfire behind the plant with available lumber (finished and unfinished!).

Gibson built Epiphone guitars in Kalamazoo from 1958 to 1969. Hollow body guitars had the serial number on the label inside, and prefixed with a "A-" plus four digits for the first three years. Electric solid body guitars had the serial number inked on the back of the headstock, and the first number indicates the year: "8" (1958), "9" (1959), and "0" (1960).

In 1960, the numbering scheme changed as all models had the serial number pressed into the back on the headstock. There were numerous examples of duplication of serial numbers, so when dating a Epiphone from this time period consideration of parts/configuration and other details is equally important.

Number	Year	Number	Year
100 - 41199	1961	118300 - 120999	1963 or 1967*
41200 - 61180	1962	121000 - 139999	1963
61450 - 64222	1963	140000 - 140100	1963 or 1967*
64240 - 70501	1964	140101 - 144304	1963
71180 - 95846	1962* *(Numerical sequence may not coincide to year sequence)	144305 - 144380	1963 or 1964
95849 - 99999	1963*	144381 - 145000	1963
000001 - 099999	1967*	147001 - 149891	1963 or 1964
100000 - 106099	1963 or 1967*	149892 - 152989	1963
106100 - 108999	1963	152990 - 174222	1964
109000 - 109999	1963 or 1967*	174223 - 179098	1964 or 1965
110000 - 111549	1963	179099 - 199999	1964
111550 - 115799	1963 or 1967*	200000 - 250199	1964
115800 - 118299	1963	250540 - 290998	1965
		300000 - 305999	1965

Number	Year	Number	Year
306000 - 306099	1965 or 1967*	503405 - 520955	1965 or 1968*
307000 - 307984	1965	520956 - 530056	1968
309653 - 310999	1965 or 1967*	530061 - 530850	1966 or 1968 or 1969*
311000 - 320149	1965	530851 - 530993	1968 or 1969
320150 - 320699	1967*	530994 - 539999	1969
320700 - 325999	1967*	540000 - 540795	1966 or 1969*
325000 - 326999	1965 or 1966	540796 - 545009	1969
327000 - 329999	1965	555000 - 556909	1966*
330000 - 330999	1965 or 1967 or 1968*	558012 - 567400	1969
331000 - 346119	1965	570099 - 570755	1966*
346120 - 347099	1965 or 1966	580000 - 580999	1969
348000 - 349100	1966	600000 - 600999	1966 to 1969*
349101 - 368639	1965	601000 - 606090	1969
368640 - 369890	1966	700000 - 700799	1966 or 1967*
370000 - 370999	1967	750000 - 750999	1968 or 1969
380000 - 380999	1966 to 1968*	800000 - 800999	1966 to 1969*
381000 - 385309	1966	801000 - 812838	1966 or 1969*
390000 - 390998	1967	812900 - 819999	1969
400001 - 400999	1965 to 1968*	820000 - 820087	1966 or 1969*
401000 - 408699	1966	820088 - 823830	1966*
408800 - 409250	1966 or 1967	824000 - 824999	1969
420000 - 438922	1966	828002 - 847488	1966 or 1969*
500000 - 500999	1965 to 1966, or 1968 to 1969*	847499 - 858999	1966 or 1969*
		859001 - 895038	1967*
501009 - 501600	1965	895039 - 896999	1968*
501601 - 501702	1968	897000 - 898999	1967 or 1969*
501703 - 502706	1965 or 1968*	899000 - 972864	1968*
503010 - 503109	1968		

In 1970, production of Epiphone instruments moved to Japan. Japanese Epiphones were manufactured between 1970 to 1983. According to author/researcher Walter Carter, the serial numbers on these are unreliable as a usable tool for dating models. Comparison to catalogs is one of the few means available. Earlier Kalamazoo labels were generally orange with black printing and said "Made in Kalamazoo", while the Japanese instruments featured blue labels which read "Made in Japan". While not a solid rule of thumb, research of the model should be more thorough than just glancing at the label.

During the early 1980s, the Japanese production costs became pricey due to the changing ratio of the dollar/yen. Production moved to Korea, and again the serial numbers are not an exact science as a dating mechanism. In 1993, a structure was developed where the number (or pair of numbers) following the initial letter indicates the year of production (i.e. "3" indicates 1993, or a "93" would indicate the same).

Some top of the line Epiphones were produced in the U.S. at either Gibson's Nashville or Montana facilities in the 1990s. These instruments are the only ones that correspond to the standard post-1977 Gibson serialization. Like Gibson numbers, there are 8 digits in the complete number, and follows the code of YDDDYNNN. The YY (first and fifth) indicate the year built. DDD indicates the day of the year (so DDD can't be above 365), and the NNN indicates the instrument's production ranking for that day (NNN = 021 = 21st guitar built). The Nashville facility begins each day at number 501, and the Montana workshop begins at number 101. **However**, in 1994, the Nashville-produced Epiphones were configured as YYNNNNNN: YY = 94 (the year) and NNNNNN is the ranking for the entire year.

Information for this chart of Epiphone serial numbers can be found in Walter Carter's book Epiphone: The Complete History *(Hal Leonard, 1995). Not only a fascinating story and chronology of the original Epiphone company and its continuation, but Carter also provides an overview of product catalogs as well as serial numbers. Walter Carter serves as the Gibson Historian as well as being a noted songwriter and author. He also wrote* The Martin Book, *and co-authored several with expert George Gruhn including* Gruhn's Guide to Vintage Guitars, Acoustic Guitars and Other Fretted Instruments, *and* Electric Guitars and Basses: A Photographic History *(all available through GPI/Miller-Freeman books).*

FENDER SERIALIZATION

Serial numbers, in general, are found on the bridgeplate, the neckplate, the backplate or the peghead. From 1950-1954, serial numbers are found on the bridgeplate or vibrato backplate. From 1954-1976, the serial numbers are found on the neckplate, both top or bottom of the plate. From 1976 to date, the serial number appears with the peghead decal. Vintage Reissues have their serial numbers on the neckplate and have been in use since 1982.

When trying to determine the manufacturing date of an instrument by serialization, it is best to keep in mind that there are no clear cut boundaries between where the numbers began and when they ended. There are constant overlapping of serial numbers between years and models. The following are approximate numbers and dates.

Year	Number	Year	Number
1950	0001-0750	1957	14900-025200
1951	0200-1900	1958	022700-38200
1952	0400-4900	1959	31400-60600
1953	2020-5030	1960	44200-58600
1954	2780-7340	1961	55500-81700
1955	6600-12800	1962	71600-99800
1956	7800-16000	1963	81600-99200

In 1962, as the serialization count neared 100000, for one reason or another, the transition did not occur. Instead, an L preceded a 5 digit sequence. It ran this way from 1962 to 1965.

1962	L00400-L13200
1963	L00200-L40300
1964	L20600-L76200
1965	L34980-L69900

In 1965, when CBS bought Fender Musical Instruments, Inc., the serialization has come to be known as the F Series, due to an "F" being stamped onto the neckplate. This series of numbers went from 1965 to 1973. The approximate numbers and years are as follows:

1965	100001-147400		1970	278910-305415
1966	112170-600200		1971	272500-380020
1967	162165-602550		1972	301395-412360
1968	211480-627740		1973	359415-418360
1969	238945-290835			

In late 1976, Fender decided to move to a new numbering scheme for their serialization. The numbers appeared on the pegheads and for the remainder of 1976 they had a prefix of 76 or S6 preceding a 5 digit sequence. In 1977, the serialization went to a letter for the decade, S for the '70's, E for the '80's, N for the '90's, followed by a single digit for the year and then 5 to 6 digits. Examples of this would be:

S8 - 1978	E5 - 1985
E0 - 1980	N1 - 1991

The idea was fine, the actuality was a different matter. As instrument production did not meet the levels that the decals had been produced for, there are several overlapping years, sometimes several prefixes found within a single year's production. Dating an instrument by serialization alone can get you within an approximate range of years, but should not be used as a definitive means of actual production. Fender also had a letter designation of "C" for the "Collector's Series" that were made in the early 1980's.

Identifying Features on Fender Musical Instruments

Fingerboard Construction

From 1950 to 1959, all necks were made out of a solid piece of maple with the frets being driven right into the neck, this is the standard design for maple necks. From 1959 to 1962, the maple neck was planed flat and a rosewood fingerboard with frets and inlay was glued to the top of the neck. This is known as the "slab top" fingerboard. From 1962 to 1983, the maple necks were rounded to the neck's radius and a thinner piece of rosewood being glued to the neck area. This design is called the "veneer" fingerboard. From 1983 to date, Fender returned to the "slab top" fingerboard design of the 1959 to 1962 era.

Neckplate Identification

From 1950 to 1971, the neck was attached to the body by means of a 4 screw neckplate. From 1971 to 1981, the neckplate was changed to 3 screws, with a micro neck adjustment device being added. In 1981, a transition from the 3 screw design back to the 4 screw design began to occur. By 1983, the 4 screw neckplate was back in standard production, with the micro neck adjuster remaining.

FRAMUS SERIAL NUMBERS

Framus serial numbers were generally placed on the back of the peghead or on a label inside the body. The main body of the serial number is followed by an additional pair of digits and a letter. This additional pair of numbers indicate the production year.

For example:

51334 63L =	1963
65939 70L =	1970

(Serial number information courtesy Tony Bacon and Barry Moorehouse, The Bass Book, GPI Books, 1995)

G & L SERIAL NUMBERS

According to G & L expert Paul Bechtoldt, all G & L serial numbers are seven digits long, with the first digit being a letter prefix indicating a guitar ("G") system or bass ("B") system. The Broadcaster was the only model to have its own prefix digits ("BC") and numbering system. All production serial numbers started at #500, as prior numbers were reserved for special instruments or presentations. Most G & L instruments have both body and neck dating, leading to some confusion as to the actual building date. However, the final authority exists in the G & L log book - manually looking up the serial number of the instrument.

First Recorded Serial Number For Each Year

YEAR	GUITAR	BASS	YEAR	GUITAR	BASS
1980	G000530	B000518	1987	G020241	B018063
1981	G003122	B001917	1988	G023725	B019627
1982	G009886	B008525	1989	G024983	B020106
1983	G011654	B010382	1990	G026344	B021788
1984	G013273	B014266	1991	G027163	B023013
1985	G014690	B016108	1992	G029962	B024288
1986	G017325	B017691			

(Information courtesy Paul Bechtoldt, G & L: Leo's Legacy, Woof Associates, 1994. This book is a must-have for anyone interested in G & L instruments, as the book documents models, variances, and the company history.)

GIBSON SERIALIZATION

Identifying Gibson instruments by serial number is tricky at best and downright impossible in some cases. The best methods of identifying them is by using a combination of the serial number, the factory order number and any features that are particular to a specific time that changes may have occurred in instrument design, i.e. logo design change, headstock volutes, etc. There have been 6 different serial number styles used to date on Gibson instruments. The first started in 1902 and ran until 1947. The serial numbers started with number 100 and go to 99999. All numbers are approximates. In most cases, only the upper end instruments were assigned identification numbers.

YEAR	LAST #	YEAR	LAST #
1903	1150	1925	82700
1904	1850	1926	83600
1905	2550	1927	85400
1906	3350	1928	87300
1907	4250	1929	89750
1908	5450	1930	90200
1909	6950	1931	90450
1910	8750	1932	90700
1911	10850	1933	91400
1912	13350	1934	92300
1913	16100	1935	92800
1914	20150	1936	94100
1915	25150	1937	95200
1916	32000	1938	95750
1917	39500	1939	96050
1918	47900	1940	96600
1919	53800	1941	97400
1920	62200	1942	97700
1921	69300	1943	97850
1922	71400	1944	98250
1923	74900	1945	98650
1924	80300	1946	99300
		1947	99999

White oval labels were used on instruments from 1902 - 1954, at which time the oval label was changed to an orange color. On instruments with round soundholes, this label is visible directly below it. On F hole instruments, it is visible through the upper f hole. The second type of serial numbers used started with an "A" prefix and ran from 1947 - 1961. The first number is A 100.

YEAR	LAST #	YEAR	LAST #
1947	A 1305	1955	A 21910
1948	A 2665	1956	A 24755
1949	A 4410	1957	A 26820
1950	A 6595	1958	A 28880
1951	A 9420	1959	A 32285
1952	A 12460	1960	A 35645
1953	A 17435	1961	A 36150
1954	A 18665		

When production of solid body guitars began, an entirely new serial number system was developed. Though not used on the earliest instruments produced, those done in 1952, a few of these instruments have 3 digits stamped on the headstock top. Some time in 1953, instruments were ink stamped on the headstock back with 5 or 6 digit numbers, the first indicating the year, the following numbers are production numbers. The production numbers run in a consecutive order and, aside from a few oddities in the change over (1961-1962) years, it is fairly accurate to use them when identifying solid body instruments produced between 1953 and 1961.

     Examples of this system: 4 2205 = 1954
                                 614562 = 1956

In 1961 Gibson started a new serial number system that covered all instrument lines. It consisted of numbers that are impressed into the wood. It is also generally known to be the most frustrating and hard to understand system that Gibson has employed. The numbers are between the years 1961-1969. There are several instances where batches of numbers are switched in order, duplicated, not just once, but up to four times, and seem to be randomly assigned, throughout the decade. In general though, the numbers are approximately as follows:

YEAR	APPROXIMATE SERIAL RANGE	YEAR	APPROXIMATE SERIAL RANGE
1961	100-42440	1967	055000-063999
1962	42441-61180	1967	064000-066010
1963	61450-64220	1967	067000-070910
1964	64240-70500	1967	090000-099999
1962	71180-96600	1963, 1967	100000-106099
1963	96601-99999	1963	106100-108900
1967	000001-008010	1963, 1967	109000-109999
1967	010000-042900	1963	110000-111549
1967	044000-044100	1963, 1967	111550-115799
1967	050000-054400	1963	115800-118299

YEAR	APPROXIMATE SERIAL RANGE	YEAR	APPROXIMATE SERIAL RANGE
1963, 1967	118300-120999	1965, 1966, 1968, 1969	500000-500999
1963	121000-139999	**1965**	**501010-501600**
1963, 1967	140000-140100	1968	501601-501702
1963	140101-144304	1965, 1968	501703-502706
1964	144305-144380	1968	503010-503110
1963	144381-145000	1965, 1968	503405-520955
1963	147009-149864	1968	520956-530056
1964	149865-149891	1966, 1968, 1969	530061-530850
1963	149892-152989	1968, 1969	530851-530993
1964	152990-174222	1969	530994-539999
1964, 1965	174223-176643	1966, 1969	540000-540795
1964	176644-199999	1969	540796-545009
1964	200000-250335	1966	550000-556910
1965	250336-291000	1969	558012-567400
1965	301755-302100	1966	570099-570755
1965	302754-305983	1969	580000-580999
1965, 1967	306000-306100	1966, 1967, 1968, 1969	600000-600999
1965, 1967	307000-307985	1969	601000-601090
1965, 1967	309848-310999	1969	605901-606090
1965	311000-320149	1966, 1967	700000-700799
1967	320150-320699	1968, 1969	750000-750999
1965	320700-321100	1966, 1967, 1968, 1969	800000-800999
1965	322000-326600	1966, 1969	801000-812838
1965	328000-328500	1969	812900-814999
1965	328700-329179	1969	817000-819999
1965, 1967	329180-330199	1966, 1969	820000-820087
1965, 1967, 1968	330200-332240	1966	820088-823830
1965	332241-347090	1969	824000-824999
1965	348000-348092	1966, 1969	828002-847488
1966	348093-349100	1966	847499-858999
1965	349121-368638	1967	859001-880089
1966	368640-369890	1967	893401-895038
1967	370000-370999	1968	895039-896999
1966	380000-385309	1967	897000-898999
1967	390000-390998	1968	899000-899999
1965, 1966, 1967, 1968	400001-400999	1968	900000-902250
1966	401000-407985	1968	903000-920899
1966	408000-408690	1968	940000-941009
1966	408800-409250	1968	942001-943000
1966	420000-426090	1968	945000-945450
1966	427000-429180	1968	947415-956000
1966	430005-438530	1968	959000-960909
1966	438800-438925	1968	970000-972864

From 1970-1975 the method of serializing instruments at Gibson became even more randomized. All numbers were impressed into the wood and a six digit number assigned, though no particular order was given and some instruments had a letter prefix. The orange labels inside hollow bodied instruments was discontinued in 1970 and were replaced by white and orange rectangle labels on the acoustics, small black, purple and white rectangle labels were placed on electric models. Also in 1970 the words "MADE IN USA" were impressed into the back of instrument headstocks, though a few instruments from the 1950s also had "MADE IN USA" impressed into their headstocks.

Year(s)	Approximate Series Manufacture
1970, 1971, and 1972	100000s, 600000s, 700000s, 900000s
1973	000001s, 100000s, 200000s, 800000s and a few "A" + 6 digit numbers
1974 and 1975	100000s, 200000s, 300000s, 400000s, 500000s, 600000s, 800000s and a few "A-B-C-D-E-F" + 6 digit numbers

During the period from 1975-1977 Gibson used a transfer that had eight digit numbers, the first two indicate the year, 99=1975, 00=1976 and 06=1977, the following six digits are in the 100000 to 200000 range. "MADE IN USA" were also included on the transfer and some models had "LIMITED EDITION" also applied. A few bolt on neck instruments had a date ink stamped on the heel area.

In 1977, Gibson began using the serialization method that is in practice today. It utilizes an impressed eight digit numbering scheme that covers both serializing and dating functions. The pattern is as follows: YDDDYPPP - YY is the production year, DDD is the day of the year, PPP is the plant designation and instrument rank. The numbers 001-499 show Kalamazoo production, 500-999 show Nashville production. The Kalamazoo numbers were discontinued in 1984. When acoustic production began at the plant built in Bozeman, Montana, in 1989, the series' numbers were reorganized. Bozeman instruments began using 001-299 designations and, in 1990, Nashville instruments began using 300-999 designations. It should also be noted that the Nashville plant has not reached the 900s since 1977, so these numbers have been reserved for prototypes. Examples:

70108276 means the instrument was produced on Jan.10,1978, in Kalamazoo and was the 276th instrument stamped that day.

82765501 means the instrument was produced on Oct. 3,1985, in Nashville and was the 1st instrument stamped that day.

In addition to the above serial number information, Gibson also used Factory Order Numbers (FON) to track batches of instruments being produced at the time. This system is also useful in helping to date and authenticate instruments. There are three separate groupings of numbers that have been identified and are used for their accuracy. The numbers are usually stamped or written on the instrument's back and seen through the lower F hole or round soundhole, or maybe impressed on the back of the headstock.

1908-1923 approximate #'s

YEAR	FON	YEAR	FON
1908	259	1916	2667, 3508
1909	309	1917	3246, 11010
1910	545, 927	1918	9839, 11159
1911	1260, 1295	1919	11146, 11212
1912	1408, 1593	1920	11329, 11367
1913	1811, 1902	1921	11375, 11527
1914	1936, 2152	1922	11565, 11729
1915	2209, 3207	1923	11973

FONs for the years 1935-1941 usually consisted of the batch number, a letter for the year and the instrument number. Examples are as follows: 722 A 23, 465 D 58, 863 E 02.

Code Letter and Year

A	1935
B	1936
C	1937
D	1938
E	1939
F	1940
G	1941

Code Letter and Year

Z	1952
Y	1953
X	1954
W	1955
V	1956
U	1957
T	1958
S	1959
R	1960
Q	1961

After 1961 the use of FONs was discontinued at Gibson.

From 1952-1961, the FON scheme followed the pattern of a letter, the batch number and an instrument number and looked like these examples: Y 2230 21, V 4867 8, R 6785 15.

There are still some variances that Gibson uses on some instruments produced today, but for the most part the above can be used for identifying instruments. For the most accurate identification you would need to contact the Gibson Guitar Corporation itself.

Identifying Features on Gibson Musical Instruments

The most constant and easily found feature that goes across all models of Gibson production is the logo, or lack of one, found on the peghead. The very earliest instruments made are generally found with a star inside a crescent design, or a blank peghead. This lasted till approximately 1902. From 1902 to the late 1920s, "The Gibson", inlaid in pearl and placed at a slant, is found on the peghead. In the late 1920s, this style of logo was changed to having "The Gibson" read straight across the peghead as opposed to being slanted. Flat top acoustics production began at approximately this time and these instruments generally do not have "The" on the inlay, it just has "Gibson" in script writing. By 1933, this was the established peghead logo for Gibson. Just before WWII, Gibson began making the lettering on the logo thicker and this became standard on most prewar instruments. Right after WWII, the styling of the logo remained but it became slanted once again. In 1947, the logo that is still in use today made its debut. This logo has a block styling with the "G" having a tail, the "i" dot is touching the "G", the "b" and "o" are open and the "n" is connected at the bottom. The logo is still slanted. By 1951, the dot on the "i" is no longer connected to the "G". In 1967, the logo styling became even more squared (pantographed) with the "b" and "o" becoming closed and the "i" dot being removed. In 1970, Gibson replaced the black tinted piece of wood that had been used on peghead face with a black fiber that the logo and other peghead inlay were placed into. With the change in peghead facing came a slightly smaller logo lettering. In 1972, the "i" dot reappeared on the peghead logo. In 1981, the "n" is connected at the top to the "o". There are a few models through the years that do not follow this timeline, ie: reissues and limited editions, but most of the production instruments can be found with the above feature changes.

Another dating feature of Gibsons are the use of a headstock volute found on instruments between 1970 and 1973. Also in 1965, Gibson switched from the 17 degrees to 14 degrees on the tilt of the peghead. Before 1950, peghead thickness varied, getting narrower towards the top of the peghead. After 1950, pegheads all became one uniform thickness, from bottom to top.

GRETSCH SERIALIZATION

Before World War II, serial numbers were penciled onto the inside backs of Gretsch's higher end instruments. By 1949, small labels bearing "Fred Gretsch Mfg. Co.", serial and model number replaced the penciled numbers inside the instruments. This label was replaced by a different style label, an orange and grey one, sometime in 1957. A few variations of this scheme occurred throughout the company's history, the most common being the use of impressed numbers in the headstock of instruments, beginning about 1949. Serial numbers were also stamped into the headstock nameplate of a few models. The numbers remain consecutive throughout and the following chart gives approximations of the years they occurred.

APPROXIMATE SERIALIZATION RANGE	YEARS	APPROXIMATE SERIALIZATION RANGE	YEARS
001 - 1000	1939-1945	21001 - 26000	1957
1001 - 2000	1946-1949	26001 - 30000	1958
2001 - 3000	1950	30001 - 34000	1959
3001 - 5000	1951	34001 - 39000	1960
5001 - 6000	1952	39001 - 45000	1961
6001 - 8000	1953	45001 - 52000	1962
8001 - 12000	1954	52001 - 63000	1963
12001 - 16000	1955	63001 - 78000	1964
16001 - 21000	1956	78001 - 85000	1965

In the latter part of 1965, Gretsch decided to begin using a date coded system of serialization. It consists of the first digit, sometimes two, identifying the month, the second or third identifying the year and the following digit (or digits) are the number of the instrument produced that month. Some examples of this system would be:

997 - September, 1969, 7th instrument produced. 11255 - November, 1972, 55th instrument produced. On solid body instruments, impressed headstock numbers were used, with "Made in USA" being added in 1967. Hollow body instruments still made use of a label placed on the inside back of the instrument. About 1973, the label style changed once again, becoming a black and white rectangle with "Gretsch Guitars" and the date coded serialization on it. A hyphen was also added between the month and the year to help avoid confusion; 12-4387 - December, 1974, 387th instrument produced. 3-745 - March, 1977, 45th instrument produced.

IBANEZ SERIAL NUMBERS

Author/researcher Michael Wright successfully discussed the Ibanez/Hoshino history in his book, "Guitar Stories Volume One" (Vintage Guitar Books, 1995). In the course of his text, he provided some key developements in the Ibanez history that helps date the various series offered. As serial numbers and potentiometer codes on Japanese guitars aren't much help in the way of clues, here is Wright's overview:

1959-1967: Elger Acoustics are built in Ardmore, Pennsylvania; and are distributed by Medley Music, Grossman Music (Cleveland), Targ and Dinner (Chicago), and the Roger Balmer Company on the west coast. Elger imported from Japan the Tama acoustics, Ibanez acoustics, and some Elger electrics.

1962-1965: Introduction of entry level bolt-neck solid body electrics, and some set-neck archtop electrics by 1965.

1971-1977: The copy era begins for Ibanez ("Faithful Reproductions") as solid body electrics based on Gibson, Fender, and Rickenbacker models (both bolt-ons and set-necks) arrive. These are followed by copies of Martin, Guild, Gibson, and Fender acoustics.

1973: Ibanez's Artist series acoustics and electrics are debuted. In 1974, the Artist-style neck joint; later in 1976 an Artist 'Les Paul' arrives. This sets the stage for the LP variant double cutaway Artist model in 1978.

1975: Ibanez began to use a meaningful numbering system as part of their warranty program. In general, the letter stands for the month (January = A, February = B, etc) and the following two digits are the year. The rest of the four or five digits are still a mystery.

1977: Ibanez's first original design, the Iceman, arrives with a rather forward-shaped lower bout and "goosebeak" headstock. A bass with the neck-through design (similar to a Rickenbacker 4001) is available, and a full series of neck-through designs are available in the Musician models. The George Benson (GB-10) model and more original design series like the Performer and Professional also appear.

1979-1987: Ibanez switches to the bolt-neck Strat design and other variants in the Roadster series, followed by the Blazer in 1980, and the Roadstar II models by 1982. The Pro Line of solid bodies appears in 1985. The early 1980s are the time for "pointy body designs" such as the Destroyer II (Explorer-based model), Rocket Roll II (Flying V), and the original XV500. In 1984, the Lonestar acoustics are introduced, and Ibanez responds to the MIDI challenge of Roland by unveiling the IMG 2010 MIDI guitar system.

1987: Ibanez hits the Hard Rock/Heavy Metal route full bore with popular artist endorsements and the Power, Radius, and Saber series. These models have more in common with the 'superstrat' design than traditional feel. The early to mid 1980s is when Ibanez really begins making inroads to the American guitar consumer.

1988: The Ibanez American Master series, a product of the new American Custom Shop, is introduced. Steve Vai's JEM appears on the U.S. market.

1989-1990: Ibanez covers the entry level approach with the EX series, built in Korea. In 1990, The Steve Vai JEM 7-string "Universe" model (it's like six plus one more!) proceeds to pop young guitarists' corks nationwide.

This overview, while brief, will hopefully identify years, trends, and series. For further information and deeper clarification, read Michael Wright's Guitar Stories Volume One.

MARTIN GUITAR SERIAL NUMBERS

YEAR	LAST #	YEAR	LAST #
1898	8348	1918	13450
1899	8716	1919	14512
1900	9128	1920	15848
1901	9310	1921	16758
1902	9528	1922	17839
1903	9810	1923	19891
1904	9988	1924	22008
1905	10120	1925	24116
1906	10329	1926	28689
1907	10727	1927	34435
1908	10883	1928	37568
1909	11018	1929	40843
1910	11203	1930	45317
1911	11413	1931	49589
1912	11565	1932	52590
1913	11821	1933	55084
1914	12047	1934	58679
1915	12209	1935	61947
1916	12390	1936	65176
1917	12988	1937	68865

YEAR	LAST #	YEAR	LAST #
1938	71866	1966	217215
1939	74061	1967	230095
1940	76734	1968	241925
1941	80013	1969	256003
1942	83107	1970	271633
1943	86724	1971	294270
1944	90149	1972	313302
1945	93623	1973	333873
1946	98158	1974	353387
1947	103468	1975	371828
1948	108269	1976	388800
1949	112961	1977	399625
1950	117961	1978	407800
1951	122799	1979	419900
1952	128436	1980	430300
1953	134501	1981	436474
1954	141345	1982	439627
1955	147328	1983	446101
1956	152775	1984	453300
1957	159061	1985	460575
1958	165576	1986	468175
1959	171047	1987	476216
1960	175689	1988	483952
1961	181297	1989	493279
1962	187384	1990	503309
1963	193327	1991	512487
1964	199626	1992	522655
1965	207030	1993	535223
		1994	551696

Identifying Features on Martin Musical Instruments

When trying to determine the year of an instrument's construction some quick notes about features can be helpful. The few notes contained here are for readily identifying the instrument upon sight and are by no means meant to be used for truly accurate dating of an instrument. All items discussed are for flat top steel string guitars. The earliest dreadnoughts, and indeed just about all instruments produced with a neck that joins the body at the 12th fret, have bodies that are bell shaped on the top, as opposed to the more square shouldered styles of most dreadnoughts. Between 1929 to 1934, Martin began placing 14 fret necks on most of their instruments and this brought about the square shouldered body style. A few models maintained 12 fret necks into the late 1940s and one model had a 12 fret neck until the late 1980s. Turn of the century instruments have square slotted pegheads with an intricate pearl fern inlay that runs vertically up the peghead. This was replaced by a vertical inlay known as the "flowerpot" or the "torch" inlay, in approximately 1905. By approximately 1934, a solid peghead with a vertical pearl "C.F. Martin" inlay had replaced the former peghead design. In 1932, the "C.F. Martin & Co. Est. 1833" scroll logo began appearing on certain models' pegheads. Bridges from the 1900s are rectangular with "pyramid" wings. In approximately 1929, the "belly" bridge replaced the rectangle bridge. This bridge has a straight slot cut across the entire length of the bridge. In 1965, the straight cut saddle slot was changed to a routed slot. It was in approximately 1936, that Martin began using the "tied" bridge on their instruments. Pickguards were not standard features on instruments till approximately 1933. They were tortoise shell pickguards, which lasted until 1966, when they were replaced by black pickguards.

MATSUMOKU SERIAL NUMBERS

(ARIA PRO II, VANTAGE, WASHBURN, WESTONE)

Any Matsumoku-produced instrument will have the first number as the identifier for the year, or possibly a two digit combination. Matsumoku stopped production in Japan in 1987, so an initial digit of "8" cannot be 1988 - the combination of the "8" plus the next digit will give the eighties designation.

The Matsumoku company built guitars for a number of trademarks. Although the Arai Company started their own "ARIA" guitar production in the 1960s, Matsumoku built guitars for them under contract from 1980 to 1987. Matsumoku also built guitars for **Vantage** between 1980 to 1986.

In 1979, the new series of **Washburn** electrics were designed in America, and produced in Japan by Matsumoku. After success with other company's trademarks, Matsumoku marketed their own **Westone** instruments between 1981 to 1987. As Matsumoku stopped production in Japan in 1987, Westone production was moved to Korea.

(Dating information courtesy Tony Bacon and Paul Day, The Guru's Guitar Guide, Bold Strummer Ltd, 1990)

MOONSTONE SERIALIZATION

The most important factor in determining the year of manufacture for Moonstone instruments is that each model had its own set of serial numbers. There is no grouping of models by year of manufacture.

D-81 Eagle	L001-L004	1981
	L005-L011	1982

Eagle (electrics)

	52950-52952	1980
	52953-52954	1981
	52955-52959	1982
	52960	1983

Earthaxe - 26 total instruments made

	0001-0013	1975
	0014-0026	1976

Eclipse Guitars - 81 total instruments made

	79001-79003	1979
	8004-8036	1980
	8037-8040	1981
	1041-1052	1981
	1053-1075	1982
	1076-1081	1983

Eclipse Bass - 124 total instruments made

	3801-3821	1980
	3822-3828	1981
	3029-3062	1981
	3063-3109	1982
	3110-3118	1983
	3119-3123	1984

Exploder Guitar - 65 total instruments made

	7801-7806	1980
	7007-7020	1981
	7021-7052	1982
	7053-7065	1983

Exploder Bass - 35 total instruments made.

	6801-6803	1980
	6004-6013	1981
	6014-6031	1982
	6032-6035	1983

Flying V Guitar - 52 total instruments made

	5801-5812	1980
	5013-5028	1981
	5029-5045	1982
	5046-5048	1983
	5049-5052	1984

Flying V Bass - 6 total instruments made

	9001-9006	1981

M-80 - 64 total instruments made

	4801-4808	1980
	4809-4816	1981
	4017-4031	1981
	4032-4052	1982
	4053-4064	1983

Moondolins

	T001-T002	1981
	T003-T006	1983
	T007	1984

Vulcan Guitar - 162 total instruments made

	5027	1977
	5028-5034	1978
	107835-107838	1978
	17939-179115	1979
	179116-179120	1980
	80121-80129	1980
	80130-80134	1981
	8135-8167	1981
	8168-8185	1982
	8186-8191	1983
	7988-7991	1984

Vulcan Bass - 19 total instruments made

	V001-V002	1982
	V003-V016	1983
	V017-V019	1984

MUSIC MAN SERIAL NUMBERS

The serial numbers found on the original Music Man/Leo Fender's CLF produced instruments ("pre-Ernie Ball") are not encoded in a system that indicates the production date, but such information can be found on the end of the neck. As with the earlier Fenders, the neck would have to be removed from the body to view this information.

The Ernie Ball Music Man serialization utilizes a numbering system that indicates the year through the first two digits (for example: 93537 = 1993).

PEAVEY SERIAL NUMBERS

While more musicians may be aware of Peavey through the numerous high quality amplifiers and P.A. systems they build, the company has been producing solidbody guitars and basses since 1978. Peavey serial numbers exist more for the company's warrantee program than an actual dating system. According to researcher Michael Wright, the earliest serial numbers had six digits; by 1978 the company switched to eight digits. Peavey can supply the shipping date (which is within a few weeks of actual production) for the more inquisitive. Replacement manuals are generally available for Peavey products. For further information, contact Peavey Electronics through the Index of Current Manufacturers located in the back of this book.

(Information courtesy Michael Wright, Guitar Stories Volume One)

STROMBERG SERIALIZATION

This Boston-based instrument shop was founded by Charles Stromberg, a Swedish immigrant, in 1906. Stromberg generally concentrated on banjo and drum building, leaving the guitar lutherie to his son Elmer. Elmer joined the family business in 1910, and began building guitars in the late 1920s.

Total production of guitars reached about 640. The labels on the guitars were business cards, so the instruments can be dated (roughly) by the telephone number on the cards.

Bowdoin 1228R-1728-M	1920-1927
Bowdoin 1242 W	1927-1929
Bowdoin 1878 R	1929-1932
CA 3174	1932-1945 (In the late 1930s, the Blue shipping labels inside the guitar body were either typewritten or handwritten)
CA 7-3174	1949-1955

(Source: Jim Speros, Stromberg research)

YAMAHA SERIAL NUMBERS

As far as we can tell, the serial numbers on Yamaha guitars prior to 1984 follow no identifiable sequence. After 1984, the first letter indicates the year, and the second letter indicates the month. The first seven years are a linear substitution code (1984 = K, 1985 = L, 1986 = M, 1987 = N, 1988 = O, 1989 = P, 1990 = Q), but then the nineteen nineties "wrap" back around (1991 = H, 1992 = I, 1993 = J). Furthermore, the months January (H) through September (P) follow through, but the last three jump to the end of the alphabet (October = X, November = Y, December = Z).

(Information courtesy Michael Wright, Guitar Stories Voluem One)

The Hall of Confusion

With apologies to the 1970 #1 hit song "Ball of Confusion" by the Temptations, We here at the **Blue Book** have opened up this Hall as an addendum to the guitar text. In the course of research, cross-referencing, and too much coffee certain names of companies appear but can't be pinned down. We assume that instruments that appear in advertising and discussed in books were produced; we also assume (at the risk of making an **ass** of **u** and **me**) that somebody owns them, plays them, and has some information that they can share about them!

Research for future editions of the **Blue Book of Guitars** is an on-going process. What we don't know, we ask; we also enjoy "putting the spotlight" on those sources of information that help us gather knowledge. Anyone interested in writing about any of the following companies or trademarks is invited to contact us at the following:

Blue Book of Guitars
8009 34th Avenue South #175
Minneapolis, Minnesota 55425
800.877.4867
(FAX) 612. 853.1486
http//:www.bluebookinc.com
email: guitars@bluebookinc.com

We'll be happy to hear from you. In the meantime, let's take a little stroll down the Hall and maybe a diligent player/reader/luthier can shed some light in the dark corners...

Alex Axe ("El Matador" bass)
Anson Custom Guitars
Artesano
Astro Guitars
Blue Comet
Boehm
Rex Bogue (luthier)
Joseph Bohmann
Borys
Bremer
Brune
Brunet (The "Metalmaster")
Burny (Fernandes line)
Carriveau
Carruthers
C & R Guitars
Centerstage
Columbia
Concorde
Cortez
Damila Guitars
Steve Davis
DD Guitar Design
Deathless Creations
Dega
Del Vecchio
Erickson
E S H (England)
Firstman (Japan)
Fisher Communications (The Fisher "Trout")
Gadden
Goldklang (acoustics)
Oscar Graf
Griffin ("Bat")
Guitarlia
Halle
Hasselberger
Hauke

Herman Hauser (luthier)
Hawk (guitars and basses)
Hendrick (Catalyst model)
Nick Hoffman Guitars (Brian Jones Model)
Stephen Holst (Eugene, Oregon)
Holzappel & Beitel (late 1800s)
Honey (Japan, 1960s)
Hosono (California)
Hummingbird (Japan, 1960s)
Idol
Doug Irwin (luthier)
J E M (Pre-Ibanez)
Joaquim Duarte
   (Spotted by Gary Whitehead of Ottawa, Ontario)
JK Bennett ("Widowmaker")
K-Muse Photon
   Distributed by Phi Tech (late 1980s).
Kamouraska (Etude model)
   Distributed from Canada.
Killer Guitars
Kinscherff (Austin, Texas)
Kraft
Kulick Custom Guitars and Basses
La Jolla Luthiers
La Primera
   Distributed by Pennino of Westminister, California (late 1970s?).
La Garde (Seyne, France)
Landola Luthiers
Lys Acoustics (Canada - late 1970s)
McBride ("Side Arm")
Mains Custom Guitars
Manne
Marsdan Guitar Mfg. (The "Sasquatch")
Mario Mazzella (luthier)
M C I/Intertek
Merrari (935 Shark V, Explorer)

Minister (Japan)
Mitre Guitars
Mory (Japan, 1960s)
Moridaira
Moser (luthier Neal Moser)
Neal Mosher
Mouradian (CS-74 bass)
Naruber (Japan, 1960s)
Neily
Newman Custom Guitars
Oneida
Outbound (the travel guitar)
Pagani (late 1800s)
Panaramic (Europe, 1960s)
Paradis (Switzerland, 1980s)
   Distributed by Sam Ash Music Stores.
Pederson Guitars (Albuquerque, New Mexico)
Pekko Bass (Finland)
Bruce Petros (Holland, Wisconsin)
Phoenix (Phoenix, Arizona)
Pittilla
Pleasant
Jonathan W. Rose (Strasburg, Virginia)
Quantum
R.A. Gresco
Roch
Santa Fe Guitars (Santa Fe, New Mexico)
Sardonyx
Saunders (DC-111 bass, Cougar guitar)
Schroeder
Scorpion Custom Guitars
Shanti (Avery, California)
Silver Mellowtone (Japan, 1960s)

Silver Street (Nightwing Series)
   Company was based in Michigan during the mid to late 1980s, and built other guitars such as the Taxi, Cobra, and Spitfire models.
Skylark
   Distributed by J.C. Penney (early 1980s)
St. Blues (St. Louis, Missouri)
Staccato Guitars
John Starrett
Stelling (Afton, Virginia)
J. R. Stetson & Co.
Stevenson
J. R. Stewart
Strings and Things
   Originally located in Memphis, Tennessee.
Stoneman (Bradford, Pennsylvania)
Stutz
Thompson (Vernon, British Columbia)
Thos Sha Czar Guitars (a bowl-backed bass in the late 1970s)
Tilben Company
Time Guitars (Alan Stack)
Tombo
Tornese
Toucan Guitars
James Trusear Guitar Station
Tung (New York)
Vagabond (Albany, New York)
Vintage Guitar Company ("Groovemaster")
Walthari Mittenwald (acoustics)
Westminster
   Distributed by Pennino of Westminister, California (late 1970s?)
York
Zenbu ("White Tiger")
Zen-On

Trademark Index

ABEL AXE
P.O. Box 895
Evanston WY 82931
307.789.8049
(FAX) 307.789.6929

ACACIA INSTRUMENTS
2091 Pottstown Pike
Pottstown PA 19465
610.469.3820
email: Acacia@Prolog.net
http://www.essentialstrings.com/
acacia.htm

ALEMBIC, INC.
3005 Wiljan Court Building A
Santa Rosa CA 95407-5702
707.523.2611
(Fax) 707.523.2935

ALHAMBRA
Distributed by Quality First Products
137 N. Quail Run
Forest City NC 28043
800.872.5856
704.245.8904
(Fax) 704.245.8965

ALLEN
Allen Guitars & Mandolins
P.O. Box 1883
Colfax CA 95713
916.346.6590
Allen@Netshel.net

ALVAREZ
A Division of St. Louis Music Inc.
1400 Ferguson Avenue
St. Louis MO 63133
800.727.4512
314.727.4512
(FAX) 314.727.8929

ALVAREZ/YAIRI
See Alvarez for distribution information.

AMADA
*Distributed by Geneva International
Corporation.*
29 Hintz Road
Wheeling IL 60090
800.533.2388
847.520.9970
(FAX) 847.520.9593

AMERICAN SHOWSTER
856 Route 9
Bayville NJ 08721
908.269.8900
(FAX) 908.269.9888

AMIGO
Distributed by Midco International
P.O. Box 748
908 W. Fayette Avenue
Effingham IL 62401
800.35.MIDCO
800.356.4326
(FAX) 800.700.7006

**ANDERSEN STRINGED
INSTRUMENTS**
503 N 36th
Seattle WA 98103
206.632.5986
(FAX) 206.632.6675
www.hacyon.com/ralevine/andersen

**TOM ANDERSON
GUITARWORKS**
2697 Lavery Court Unit 27
Newbury Park CA 91320-1505
805.498.1747
(Fax) 805.498.0878

ANGUS GUITARS
P.O. Box 737
Laguna Beach CA 92652
714.497.2110

ANTARES
*Distributed by VMI Industries
Vega Musical Instruments*
P.O. Box 1357
Brea CA 92622
800.237.4864
714.572.1492
(FAX) 714.572.9321

ANTONIO LORCA
*Distributed by David Perry Guitar
Imports*
See Listing under JOSE RAMIREZ

APPLAUSE
*Distributed by the Kaman Music
Corporation*
See Listing Under OVATION

ARBOR
Distributed by Midco International
P.O. Box 748
Effingham IL 62401
800.356.4326
217.342.9211
(FAX) 217.347.0316

ARIA

ARIA PRO II
Aria USA/NHF
9244 Commerce Highway
Pennsauken NJ 08110
800.877.7789
800.524.0441
609.663.8900
(Fax) 609.663.0436

DAN ARMSTRONG
Design Consultant
13385 Astoria Street
Sylmar CA 91342-2436
818.362.6901

ARTISTA
*Distributed by Musicorp/MBT
Hondo Guitar Company*
P.O. Box 30819
Charleston SC 29417
800.845.1922
803.763.9083
(FAX) 803.763.9096

ASI
Audio Sound International, Inc.
3875 Culligan Avenue
Indianapolis IN 46218
317.352.1539

ASTURIAS
Distributed by J.T.G. of NASHVILLE
1024 C 18th Avenue South
Nashville TN 37212
615.329.3036
(FAX) 615.329.4028

ATHELETE
*Athelete Acoustic Basses and
Guitars*
213 Ashland Place #7
New York NY 11217
718.797.2047
(FAX) 718.797.2162

ATLANSIA
P.O. Box 465
Barker TX 77413

AUDIO OPTICS
Audio Optics, Inc.
P.O. Box 691
Santa Barbera CA 93102
800.548.6669
805.563.2202
(FAX) 805.569.4060
email: info@AOLIGHTWAVE.COM
http://www.mallennium.com/AOLIGHTW
AVE.COM

AUERSWALD
Gustav-Schwab-Str. 10
d-78467 Konstanz Germany
49.7531.66157
(FAX) 49.7531.56911

AUGUSTINO LOPRINZI
1929 Drew Street
Clearwater FL 34625
813.447.2276

AXELSON
Axelson Guitar
706 Lake Avenue South
Duluth MN 55802
218.723.8734

AXTECH
See Listing under SAEHAN

AXTRA
Axtra Guitars, Inc.
6611 28th Avenue
Kenosha WI 53141
414.654.7900

AZOLA
Azola Music Products
382 Enterprise St. #108
San Marcos CA 92069
619.591.9162
(FAX) 619.591.9362

JAMES R. BAKER
183 E. 10th Street
Huntington Station NY 11746
516.427.9211

BAKES
Bakes Guitars
54 National Street
Elgin IL 60123
847.931.0707

CARL BARNEY
P.O. Box 128
Southbury CT 06488
203.264.9207

BARTOLINI
Distributed by T.J. Wagner & Son
P.O. Box 59
Fairport NY 14450
716.425.9730
(Fax) 716.425.9466
Bartolini Pickups and Electronics
P.O. Box 934
Livermore CA 94450
510.443.1037

BASS O LIN
55 Railroad Avenue
Haverstraw NY 10923
914.942.5123
609.971.1643

B.C. RICH
B.C. Rich International, Inc.
17205 Eucalyptus, B-5
Hesperia CA 92345
619.956.1599
(FAX) 619.956.1565
B.C. Rich Guitars USA
432 N. Arrowhead Ave.
San Bernadino CA 92401
909.888.6080
(FAX) 909.884.1767

BELLA GUITARS
P.O. Box 1223
Chalmette LA 70044-1223
504.279.0867

BENEDETTO
RR 1 - Box 1347
E. Stroudsburg PA 18301
717.223.0883
(FAX) 717.223.7711
http://benedetto-guitars.com/bg

BENEDICT
P.O. Box 78
Cedar MN 55011
612.434.4236

BENTLY
A Division of St. Louis Music Company
See Listing Under ALVAREZ

BIAXE
Biaxe Retrofits
P.O. Box 15426
Stamford CT 06901-0426
516.487.1902

BLACKHURST
Blackhurst Guitars
631 Lindhurst
Roseville CA 95687
916.773.5295

BLADE GUITARS
Distributed by
Levinson Ltd.
ALLschwilerstr. 35
4055 Basel Switzerland
61.482.1802
41.61.3013370
(Fax) 41.61.3017784

BLAIR
Blair Guitars
P.O. Box 93
Ellington CT 06029-0093
413.737.0705
(FAX) 203.872.9942

BLUE STAR MUSIC
P.O. Box 493
North Front Street
Lovingston VA 22949
804.263.6746

BLUESOUTH
BlueSouth Guitars
P.O. Box 3562
Muscle Shoals AL 35662
205.764.7431

BOGART
Bogart Basses
Distributed by Salwender International
See Listing under TEUFFEL

BOOGIE BODY
Boogie Body/Vintage Voicing
Technologies
P.O. Box 2012
Gig Harbor WA 98335
206.851.6627
http://www.win.com/~grafx/boogie/
boogie.html

BOOM
Boom Basses
24 Parkhurst St.
Chico CA 95628
916.893.4845
(FAX) 916.893.4845

BORN TO ROCK
Born to Rock Design Inc.
470 West End, # 4 G
New York NY 10024
800.496.7625
212.496.5342
(FAX) 212.496.5342

BOSSA BASS COMPANY
Exclusively Distributed by Soniq
Trading, Inc.
11657 Oxnard Street, Suite 211
North Hollywood CA 91606
818.761.9260
(FAX) 818.761.9282

DANA BOURGEOIS GUITARS
235 Goddard Road
Lewiston ME 04240
207.786.9320
(FAX) 207.786.4018
dbguitars@aol.com

BOZO
Bozo Podunavac
2340 Englewood Road
Englewood FL 34233-633
941.474.3288

BREEDLOVE GUITAR CO.
19885 Eighth Street
Tumalo OR 97701
541.385.8339
(Fax) 541.385.8183
lpattis@aol.com

BRIAN MOORE CUSTOM GUITARS
S Patterson Business Park
Rural Delivery 6 Route 22
Brewster NY 10509
800.795.7529
914.279.4142
(FAX) 914.279.5477
http://www.BMCGuitars.com

CLINT BRILEY
Briley Guitars
1926 Albany Drive
Clearwater FL 34623
813.669.0256
randy@flanet.com

BRUBAKER GUITARS
250 Chartley Dr.
Reistertown MD 21136
410.833.8681
(FAX) 410.833.8681

BSX
BSX Bass, Inc.
4101 Brodhead Road
Aliquippa PA 15001
412.378.8697
(FAX) 412.378.4079

BURNS LONDON
Burns London Ltd.
Unit 21, Bookham Industrial Estate
Church Road
Great Bookham, Surrey
London KT 23 3EU
0932.875255
(FAX) 0932.873057

BUSCARINO GUITARS
Buscarino Guitars, Inc.
9075 130th Avenue, Unit B
Largo FL 34643
813.586.4992
(FAX) 813.581.4535

CALVIN CRAMER
Distributed by Musima North America,
Inc.
13540 N. Florida Avenue,
Suite 206 A
Tampa FL
813.961.8357
(FAX) 813.961.8514

M. CAMPELLONE GUITARS
725 Brance Avenue Mill #15
Providence RI 02904
401.351.4229

CARL THOMPSON
171 court Street
Brooklyn NY 11201

CARMINE STREET GUITARS
42 Carmine Street
New York NY 10014
212.239.3866
619.239.3866

CARRIVEAU
4427 N. 7th Avenue
Phoenix AZ 85013

CARRUTHERS
346 Sunset Avnue
Venice CA 90291
310.392.3910
(FAX) 310.392.0389

CARVIN
Factory direct sales only.
12340 World Trade Drive
San Diego CA 92128
800.854.2235
619.487.8700
(FAX) 619.487.8160
www.carvinguitars.com

C B ALYN GUITARWORKS
935 Galloway Street
Pacific Palisades CA 90272
310.454.8196
(FAX) 310.459.7517

CHANDLER INDUSTRIES, INC.
370 Lang Road
Burlingame CA 94010-2003
415.342.1490
(Fax) 415.342.9692

CHARVEL
Distributed by the International Music
Corporation (IMC)
1316 E. Lancaster Avenue
Fort Worth TX 76102
800.433.5627
817.336.5114
(FAX) 817.870.1271

CITRON
Harvey Citron Enterprises
282 Chestnut Hill Road #4
Woodstock NY 12498
914.679.7138
(FAX) 914.679.3221

C.A.L.
Clevinger, Azola, & Lee
See CLEVINGER or AZOLA for product
information

CLEVINGER
Clevinger Bass by Robert Lee
553 Kenmore Avenue
Oakland CA 94610
510.444.2542

CLIFTON
Clifton Basses
34 Shooters Hill Rd.
Blackheath England SE3 7BD
081.858.7795

CLOVER
Zum Wetterschact 9
D-4350 Recklinghausen
Germany
02361.15881
(FAX) 02361.183473
Distributed through the Luthiers
Access Group
P.O. Box 388798
Chicago IL 60638-8798
708.974.4022
(FAX) 708.974.4022

COLLINGS
Collings Guitars, Inc.
11025 Signal Hill Drive
Austin TX 78737-2834
512.288.7776
(Fax) 512.288.6045

BILL COMINS
P.O. Box 611
Willow Grove PA 19090
215.784.0314

CONKLIN
Conklin Guitars
P.O. Box 1394
Springfield MO 65801
417.886.3525
(Fax) 417.886.2934

CORT
Cort Musical Intruments
3451 W. Commercial Avenue
Northbrook IL 60062
708.498.9850
708.498.5370
www.cort.com

COTE
Cote Company
Box 66905
St. Petersburg FL 33736-6905
813.360.2183
OR
P.O. Box 1063
Largo FL 34649
813.360.2183
http://sunray.com/cote

CRAFTER
Exclusively distributed in the U.S. by
HSS
A Division of Hohner, Inc.
10223 Sycamore Drive
Ashland VA 23005
804.550.2700
(FAX) 801.550.2670

CRAFTERS OF TENNESSEE, LLC
14860 Lebanon Road
Old Hickory TN 37138
615.773.7200
(FAX) 615.773.7201

STEVE CRIPE
Steve Cripe Estate
P.O. Box 358
Trilby FL 33593
904.583.4680

ARTHUR CROW
Crow Archtop Guitars
13541 N. 115th
Longmont CO 80501
303.776.2523

CURBOW
Curbow String Instruments, Inc.
24 Allen Lane
Morgantown GA 30560
706.374.2873
(FAX) 706.374.2530

CUSTOM GUITAR WORKS
941 S. Pittsburch
Tulsa OK 74112
918.836.9300

CUSTOM GUITAR COMPANY
1035 Wood Duck Avenue
Santa Clara CA 95050
408.244.6519

D'ANGELICO II
Archtop Enterprises, Inc.
1980 Broadcast Plaza
Merrick NY 11566
516.868.4877
516.223.3421

D'ANGELICO REPLICA
Working Musician
1760 Claridge Street
Arcadia CA 91006
818.255.5554

DAVE MAIZE
999 Holton Road
Talent OR 97540
503.535.9052
(FAX) 503.535.9052
www.wave.net/upg/mgsam

DAVE KING
4737 SE 28th Avenue
Portland OR 97202
503.235.9782

DE CAVA
De Cava Fretted Instruments
P.O. Box 131
Stratford CT 06497
203.377.0096

DE LACUGO
De Lacugo Guitars
6911 Sycamore Rd.
Atascadero CA 93422
805.461.3663

DEAN
Dean USA
7091 N.W. 51st Street
Miami FL 33166
305.594.3909
(FAX) 305.594.0786

DEERING
7936-D Lester Avenue
Lemon Grove CA 92045
619.464.8252

DEMARINO
DeMarino Guitars
303 Merrick Rd.
Copiague NY 11726
516.842.5445
(FAX) 516.842.5004

DILLON
Dillon Guitars
Rd 4 Box 115 A
Bloomsburg PA 17815
717.784.7552

DINGWALL
Dingwall Designer Guitars
P.O. Box 9194
Saskatoon SK Canada S7K 7E8
306.242.6201
(FAX) 306.244.2404

D'LECO
P.O. Box 60432
Oklahoma City OK 73146-0432
405.524.0448
(FAX) 405.524.0448

DOBRO
Distributed by Consolidated Musical Instruments (Gibson)
Original Musical Instrument Co., Inc.
181808 Redondo Circle
Huntington Beach CA 92648
714.848.9823
(FAX) 714.843.5731

DODGE
Dodge Guitar Company
2120 Longview Drive
Tallahassee FL 32303
904.562.3662
904.562.4331

DON GROSH
Don Grosh Cusom Guitars
15748 Live Oak Springs Canyon Rd.
Canyon Country CA 91351
805.252.6716

DUESENBERG
Distributed by Salwender International
See listing under TEUFFEL

GUITARES MAURICE DUPONT
Distributed by Paul Hostetter
2550 Smith Grade
Santa Cruz CA 95060
408.427.2241
(FAX) 408.427.0343
music@cruzio.com

EAGLE
Eagle Country Instruments
Rieslingweg 12C
Murr Germany
49.714.424736
(FAX) 49.714.4209115

EHLERS
Rob Ehlers
408 4th Avenue
Oregon City OR 97045
503.655.7546

ELRICK
Elrick Bass Guitars
932 W. Barry Avenue
Chicago IL 60657
312.327.1016

EMERY
Distributed by Resound Vintage Guitars
7438 Hwy. 53
Britt MN 55710
218.741.9515

ENCORE
Distributed by John Hornby Skewes & Co., Ltd.
Salem House
Parkinson Approach
Garforth Leeds
LS25 2HR England
0113.286.6411
(FAX) 0113.286.8518
Represented in the U.S. by Chandler
370 Lang Road
Burlingame CA 94010
415.342.1490
(FAX) 415.342.9692

EPIPHONE
Distributed by Consolidated Musical Instruments (Gibson)
Epiphone Company
1050 Acorn Drive Suite A
Nashville TN 37210
800.283.7135
615.871.4500
(FAX) 615.872.7768
www.gibson.com

ERLEWINE
Erlewine Guitars
4402 Burnet Rd.
Austin TX 78756-3319
512.302.1225
(FAX) 512.371.1655

ERNIE BALL/MUSIC MAN
151 Suburban Road
P.O. Box 4117
San Luis Obispo CA 93401
800.543.2255
805.544.7726
(Fax) 805.544.7275

ESP
ESP Guitar Company
7561 Sunset Blvd. #202
Hollywood CA 90046
800.423.8388
213.969.0877
(FAX) 213.969.9335
http://www.espguitars.com

GUITARRAS FRANCISCO ESTEVE
Camino al Mar, 15
46120 Alboraya
Valencia Espana
34.618.55974
(FAX) 34.618.56077

EUGEN
Eugen Guitars AS
P.O. B. 1782 Nordnes
5024 Bergen Norway
+47.55.23.28.60
(FAX) +47.55.23.26.25

EVERETT
Everett Guitars
2338 Johnson Ferry Rd.
Atlanta GA 30341
404.451.2485
770.451.2485

F GUITARS
16 McKinstry Street
Hamilton Ontario Canada
L8L 6C1
905.522.2533
905.522.1582
905.528.5667

FACTORY MUSIC OUTLET
1181 Kenmore Avenue
Kenmore NY 14217
716.877.2676

FARNELL
Farnell Custom Guitars
Distributed by Le Pik Guitar Piks
10700 Jersey Blvd. Suite 670
Rancho Cucamonga CA 91730

FENDER
Fender Musical Instruments Corporation
7975 North Hayden Road
Scottsdale AZ 85258
602.596.9690
(Fax) 602.596.1384
http://www.fender.com

FERNANDES
Fernandes Guitars USA, Inc.
16123 Valerio Street
Van Nuys CA 91406
800.318.8599
818.988.6790
(Fax) 818.988.3094

FERRINGTON
Santa Monica, California
(No workshop telephone)

FITZPATRICK JAZZ GUITARS
54 Enfield Avenue
Wickford RI 02852
401.294.4801

FLANDERS CUSTOM GUITARS
Distributed by Fretboard Korner
520 Hawkins Avenue
Lake Ronkonkoma NY 11779-2327
516.588.4167

FLEISHMAN
Fleishman Instruments
4500 Whitney Place
Boulder CO 80303
303.499.1614

FICHTER
Boettgerstr. 9
D-60389 Frankfurt
Germany
049.69.462422
(FAX) 049.69.462422
email: 100424.1526@compuserve.com
http://www.fichterbasses.com

FISHER
Fisher Guitars
P.O. Box 402
410 Main Street
Coalport PA 16627
814.672.8782

FODERA
68 34th Street
Brooklyn NY 11232
718.832.3455
(FAX) 718.832.3458

FOSTER
Foster Guitar Manufacturing
19366 Robinwood Ln.
Covington LA 70433
504.892.9822

FRITZ BROTHERS
c/o Connie Fritz
10655 Salt Air Road
Theodore AL 36582

FROGGY BOTTOM GUITARS
RR 1 Box 1505
Newfane VT 05345
802.348.6665
802.348.6665

FURY
Fury Guitar Mfg., Ltd.
902 Avenue J North
Saskatoon SAK.
Canada S7L 2I2
306.244.4063

FYLDE GUITARS
Unit 35, Progress Industrial Park
Orders Lane Kirkham
Lancashire England PR4 2TZ
01772.671010
(Fax) 01772.671010

G & L MUSICAL PRODUCTS
Distributed by BBE Sound, Inc.
5381 Production Drive
Huntington Beach CA 92649
714.897.6766
(Fax) 714.896.0736

GALLAGHER
J.W. Gallagher & Son
P.O. Box 128
7 Main Street
Wartrace TN 37183
615.389.6455

GEDDAN
114 A Shore Road
Port Washington NY 11050
516.864.1936

GIANNINI
Distributed by Music Industries Corporation
99 Tulip Avenue
Floral Park NY 11001
516.352.4110

GIBSON
Consolidated Musical Instruments
1818 Elm Hill Park
Nashville TN 37210-3781
800.283.7135
615.871.4500
(Fax) 615.889.5509
http://www.gibson.com

GILBERT
1485 LaHonda Road
Woodside CA 94062
415.851.1239
(FAX) 415-851-3284

G L F
Distributed by the GLF Custom Shop
19817 Jackie Ln.
Rogers MN 55374
612.428.8818

GMP GUITARS
G M Precision Products, Inc.
510 E. Arrow Highway
San Dimas CA 91773
909.592.5144
(FAX) 909.599.0798

GODIN
Godin Guitars
Distributed by La Si Do, Inc.
4240 Sere Street
St. Laurent Quebec Canada
H4T 1A6
514.343.5560
(FAX) 514.343.5098
sales@lasido.com
www.lasido.com

GOODALL
Goodall Guitars
P.O. Box 3542
Kailua-Kona HI 96745
808.329.8237
(FAX) 808.325.7842
email: goodall@aloha.net

GOODFELLOW
Goodfellow Basses are built by the Lowden Guitar Company
Distributed in the USA by Quality First Products
137 North Quail Run
Forest City NC 28043
800.872.5856
(FAX) 704.245.8965

GOYA
Distributed by the Martin Guitar Company
See Listing under MARTIN

OSCAR GRAF
P.O. Box 2502
Clarendon Ontario
Canada K0H 1J0
613.279.2610

KEVIN GRAY
Kevin Gray Guitars
P.O. Box 12056
Dallas TX 75225
214.692.1064

GREEN MOUNTAIN GUITARS
P.O. Box 2331
Boulder CO 80306
303.444.9466
Guitars built by the Breedlove Guitar Company
19885 8th St.
Tumalo OR 97701
801.486.0222
(FAX) 541.385.8183

GREMLIN
Distributed by Midco International
See Listing under ARBOR

GRETSCH
Fred Gretsch Enterprises
P.O. Box 2468
Savannah GA 31402
912.748.1101
(Fax) 912.748.1106

D & F PRODUCTS
6735 Hidden Hills Drive
Cincinnati OH 45230
513.232.4972

GRIMES
Grimes Guitars
755-G Kamehameiki
Kula HI 96790
808.878.2076
(FAX) 808.878.2076
grimer@maui.net
www.maui.net/~grimer/

BILL GRUGGETT
Distributed by Stark-Marquadt
Productions & Service
Bakersfield CA
805.831.8613
Distributed by Jacobson's Service
Fine Guitars
Denver CO
303.935.2007

GTX
Distributed by the Kaman Music Corporation
See Listing under OVATION

GUDELSKY
Gudelsky Musical Instruments
2963 Gopher Canyon Road
Vista CA 92084
619.726.0610

GUILD
Distributed by the Fender Musical Instrument Corp.
See Listing under FENDER
60 Industrial Drive
Westerly RI 02891
401.596.0141
(Fax) 401.596.0436

GUITORGAN
Musiconics
2209 N. 42nd
Waco TX 76710

HALLMARK
Exclusively distributed by Front Porch Music
1711 19th Street
Bakersfield CA 93301
800.900.2JAM

HAMATAR
253 Lakeside Beach
Spicewood TX 78669
210.693.5820

HAMBURGUITAR
33467 Fernwood Street
Westland MI 48185
313.722.6931

HAMER GUITARS
Distributed by the Kaman Music Corporation
See Listing Under OVATION
835 West University Drive
Arlington Heights IL 60004
708.255.6112

HANEWINCKEL
Hanewinckel Guitars
17730 S. Alburtis Avenue #11
Artesia CA 90701
310.924.4328

HARDBODY COMPOSITE GUITARS
Bi-Mar International
P.O. Box 463085
Escondido CA 92046
619.749.6583

HARPER'S
Harper's Guitars
P.O. Box 2877
Apple Valley CA 92307, or
22992 Ottawa Road
Apple Valley CA 92308
619.240.1792
(FAX) 619.240.1792

HERITAGE
Heritage Guitar, Inc.
225 Parsons Street
Kalamazoo MI 49007
616.385.5721
(Fax) 616.385.3519

H.G. LEACH GUITARS
P.O. Box 1315
Cedar Ridge CA 95924
916.477.2938

HILL
Hill Guitar Company
3615 Superior Avenue
Bldg. 42, 6th Floor
Cleveland OH 44114
216.361.5050
(FAX) 216.361.5051

DENNIS HILL
Dennis Hill, Luthier
Leitz Music, Inc.
508 Harrison Avenue
Panama City FL 32401
904.769.0111
(FAX) 904.785.1179

H M L
Howard M. Leese Guitars
P.O. Box 580
Milton WA 98354
206.863.8759
(Fax) 206.863.8762

HOFNER
Distributed by the Entertainment Music Marketing Corp.
770-12 Grand Boulevard
Deer Park NY 11729
516.243.0600
(Fax) 516.243.0605

HOHNER
Exclusively distributed in the U.S. by HSS
A Division of Hohner, Inc.
Lakeridge Park
101 Sycamore Drive
Ashland VA 23005-9998
800.446.6010
804.550.2700
(Fax) 804.550.2670
www.hohnerusa.com

HOLLENBECK
160 Half Moon Street
Lincoln IL 62656
217.732.6933

HOLLISTER
Hollister Guitars
P.O. Box 159
S. Harwich MA 02661
508.771.7333

STEPHEN HOLST GUITARS
354 E. 30th Avenue
Eugene OR 97405
541.687.7845
guitar@rio.com
www.rio.com/~guitars/

HONDO
Distributed by Musicorp/MBT
Hondo Guitar Company
P.O. Box 30819
Charleston SC 29417
800.845.1922
803.763.9083
(FAX) 803.763.9096
www.hondo.com

HOSONO
Hosono Guitar Works
820 Thompson Avenue, Unit 13
Glendale CA 91201
818.244.0251

HUMAN BASE
HauptstraBe 27a
65529 Waldems
Germany
061.26.1570
(FAX) 061.26.1819

THOMAS HUMPHREY
37 W. 26th Street
Room 1201
New York NY 10010
212.696.1693

HUSKEY
Huskey Guitar Works
P.O. Box 2250
Hillsboro MO 63050

HYUNDAI
Hyundai Guitars
126 Route 303
West Nyack NY 10994
914.353.3520
(FAX) 914.353.3540

IBANEZ
Hoshino (USA), Inc.
1726 Winchester Road
Bensalem PA 19020-0886
800.669.4226
215.638.8670
(Fax) 215.245.8583
Ibanez Canada
2165-46th Avenue
Lachine Quebec H8T 2P1
Ibanez Australia
88 Bourke Road
Alexandria Sydney NSW 2015
Ibanez New Zealand
5 Amokura Street
Henderson Auckland

ITHACA GUITAR WORKS
215 N. Cayuga
Ithaca NY 14850
607.272.2602
http://www.guitarworks.com

JACKSON
Distributed by the International Music Corporation (IMC)
See Listing Under CHARVEL

JAROS
Jaros Custom Guitars
RD 2 Box 6225
Rochester PA 15074
412.774.5615

JASMINE
Distributed by the Kaman Music Corporation
See Listing Under OVATION

J.B. PLAYER
Distributed by J.B. Player International
PO Box 30819
Charleston SC 29417
800.845.1922
803.763.9083
(Fax) 803.763.9096
www.jbplayer.com

JENNINGS-THOMPSON
Jennings-Thompson Guitars & Basses
632 Ralph Ablanedo #206
Austin TX 78230
512.292.1332
(FAX) 512.280.4715

JERRY JONES GUITARS
P.O. Box 22507
Nashville TN 37203
615.255.0088
(Fax) 615.255.7742

JONATHAN ROSE GUITARS
1208 W. Main Street
Henderson TN 37075
615.822.6818
800.597.1720

JOSE RAMIREZ
Distributed by David Perry Guitar Imports
14519 Woodstar Court
Leesburg VA 22075-6055
800.593.1331
703.771.1331
(FAX) 703.771.8170

J.T.G. OF NASHVILLE
1024 C 18th Avenue South
Nashville TN 37212
615.329.3036
(FAX) 615.329.4028

K & S
K & S Guitars, Inc.
2923 Adeline Street
Berkeley, CA 94703
510.843.2883
510.548.7538
(FAX) 510.644.1958
email:
BMIEX@GLOBEL.CALIFORNIA.COM

STEPHEN KAKOS
6381 Maple Road
Mound MN 55364
612.472.4732
(FAX) 612.472.4732

KAWAI
Kawai America Corporation
2055 E. University Drive
Compton CA 90220
800.421.2177
310.631.1771
(FAX) 310.604.6913

KAY
Distributed by A.R. Musical Enterprises, Inc.
9031 Technology Drive
Fishers IN 46038
800.428.4807
317.577.6999
(Fax) 317.577.7288

KEN BEBENSEE
K B Guitars & Basses
P.O. Box 12115
San Luis Obispo CA 93401
805.541.8842

KENDRICK
Kendricks Amplifiers
P.O. Box 160
Pflugerville TX 78660
512.990.5486

KENNETH LAWRENCE
Kenneth Lawrence Instruments
441 1st Street
Arcata CA 95521
707.822.2543

KICS
Distributed by KICS USA/RAJ Guitar Crafts
10150 Apache
Adelanto CA 92301
800.603.KICS (5427)
619.246.3866
(FAX) 619.246.3494

KIMAXE
Distributed by Kenny & Michael's Company, Inc.
811 E. 14th Place
Los Angeles CA 90021
213.746.2848
(FAX) 213.747.1161

KIMBERLY
Distributed c/o Lindert Guitars
P.O. Box 172
51 Purtteman Gulch Road
Chelan WA 98816
509.682.2360
(FAX) 509.682.1209
Kimex Trading Co., Ltd.
Room 1411, Han Suh River Park
11-11, Yeo Eui Do-Dong
Yeong Deung Po-Ku, Seoul Korea
82.2.786.1014
82.2.783.0408
(FAX) 82.2.786.5578

KINAL
3239 E. 52nd Avenue
Vancouver British Columbia
CANADA V5S 1T9
604.433.6544

KINSCHERFF
632 Ralph Ablanedo #206
Austin TX 78748
512.280.8207
(FAX) 512.280.4715

KLEIN
Klein Acoustic Guitars Division
Klein Electric Guitars Division
2560 Knob Hill Road
Sonoma CA 95476
707.938.4189
(FAX) 707.938.8769
info@klein.micronet.org

KNOWBUDGE PRODUCTIONS
3463 State Street # 305
Santa Barbara CA 93105
805.963.2908

KNUTSON
Knutson Luthiery
P.O. Box 945
Forrestville CA 95436
707.887.2709

KOLL
Koll Guitar Company
2402 SE Belmont Street
Portland OR 97214
503.235.9797
503.231.1912

KRAMER
Kramer Musical Industries (KMI)
3320 Highway 66
Neptune NJ 07753
908.922.8600

KYDD
Kydd Products
P.O. Box 2650
Upper Darby PA 19082
800.622.KYDD

La MANCHA
Distributed by Hep Cat
2605-A Fessey Park Road
Nashville TN 37204
800.775.0650
615.385.3676
http://www.lamancha.com

La PATRIE GUITARS
Distributed By La Si Do, Inc.
4240 Sere'
St. Laurent Quebec
Canada H4T 1A6
514.343.5560
(FAX) 514.343.5098

MARK LACEY
Lacey Guitars
P.O. Box 24646
Nashville TN 37202
615.952.3045
laceygtr@ix.netcom.com

LADO
Lado Musical, Inc.
689 Warden Avenue Unit 6
Scarborough Ontario Canada
M1L 3Z5
416.690.5010
(Fax) 416.690.5022

LADY LUCK
Lady Luck Industries, Inc.
P.O. Box 195
Cary IL 60013
708.639.8907
(Fax) 708.639.7010

LAG
Lag Guitars S.A.
Route de Saint Pons
34600 Bedarieux
France
33.67.95.45.00
(Fax) 33.67.95.06.51

LAGARDE
779 Ave. Marcel Paul
F-83500 La Seyne S/Mer
France

LAKEWOOD
Lakewood Guitars
Distributed by Dana B. Goods
5427 Hollister Avenue
Santa Barbara CA 3111-2345
800.765.8663
805.964.9610
(FAX) 805.964.9749

LAKLAND
2044 N. Dominick
Chicago IL 60614
312.871.9637

LANDOLA
Distributed by Quality First Products
137 N. Quail Run
Forest City NC 28043
800.872.5856
704.245.8904
(Fax) 704.245.8965

LARKIN
Castlegregory
Co. Kerry Ireland
353.66.39330
(FAX) 353.66.39330

LARRIVEE
Larrivee Guitars, Ltd.
1896 Victoria Diversion
Vancouver British Columbia Canada V5N 2K4
604.879.8111
(Fax) 604.879.5440

LEA ELECTRIC GUITARS
23 Division Street
East Islip, New York 11730
516.581.2804

LEDUC
Leduc/Logabass Instruments
10121 Stonehurst Avenue
Sun Valley CA 91352
516.266.1957
(FAX) 516.266.2568

LEWIS
Fine Guitars and Mandolins
20807 E. Spring Ranches Rd.
Grass Valley VA 95949
916.272.4124

LINC LUTHIER
1318 N. Monte Vista Avenue #11
Upland CA 91786
909.931.0642
(FAX) 909.931.1713
Linclnc@aol.com

LINDA MANZER
Box 924, Station P
Toronto Ontario Canada M5S
2Z2
416.927.1539
416.927.8233
email: manzer@interlog.com
http://www.scsi.org/manzer.guitars

LINDERT
Lindert Guitars, Inc.
Box 172
Chelan WA 98816
509.682.2360
(FAX) 509.682.1209

LOGABASS
Distributed by Leduc/Logabass Instruments
See Listing Under LEDUC
S S S Sound Co., Ltd.
P.O. Box No. 1
Kanie Aichi Japan 497
05675.2.3888

LONE STAR
Distributed by M&M Merchandisers, Inc.
1923 Bomar Avenue
Fort Worth TX 76103
800.299.9035
http://www.flash.net/~mandm

LOPER
Joe Loper
Distributed by Guitar Works
Route 1
Box 90 H
Hawthorne FL 32640
352.481.2287

LOTUS
Distributed by Midco International
See Listing under ARBOR

LOWDEN
The Lowden Guitar Company
Distributed by Quality First Products
137 N. Quail Run
Forest City NC 28043
800.872.5856
704.245.8904
(Fax) 704.245.8965

LOWRY GUITARS
2565 Cloverdale Avenue, Unit J
Concord CA 94518
510.827.4803

LTD
Distributed by the ESP Guitar Company
See Listing Under ESP

G.W. Lyon
Distributed by Washburn International
See Listing Under WASHBURN

RIC MCCURDY
19 Hudson Street
New York NY 10013
212.274.8352

MCINTURFF
Terry C. McInturff Guitars
Route 1, Box 311-11
Fuquay Varina NC 27526
919.552.4586
email: terryguitars@wake-tech.campus
.mci.net

MCLAREN
McLaren Products
3519 Mt. Ariane Dr.
San Diego CA 92111
619.569.6524

MCSWAIN
McSwain Guitars
1708 Dilworth Road West
Charlotte NC 28203
704.377.2845

S.B. MACDONALD CUSTOM INSTRUMENTS
22 Fairmont Street
Huntington NY 11743
516.421.9056
Luthier@sprynet.com

MAC YASUDA
Mac Yasuda Guitars
1100 Quail St., Suite 100
Newport Beach CA 92660
714.833.7882
(FAX) 714.833.7774

MANEA
Manea Custom Guitars
414 Gates Road
Goodlettsville TN 37072-2740
615.860.9889
(FAX) 615.860.9889

MANSON
A.B. Manson & Co.
Easterbrook, Hittisliegh
Exeter England EX6 6LR
0647.24139
(FAX) 0647.24140

MANTRA
21055 Milano
Via Aosta, 13
Italy
02.33.10.54.60
(FAX) 02.33.60.72.20

MARCHIONE
Marchione Guitars
20 West 20th St., Suite 806
New York NY 10011
212.675.5215
http://www.marchione.com/

MARLEAUX
Zellweg 20
38678 Clausthal-Zellerfeld
Germany
046.53.23/8.17.47
(FAX) 049.53.23/23.79

MARTIN
The Martin Guitar Company
510 Sycamore Street
Nazareth PA 18064-9233
800.345.3103
610.759.2837
(Fax) 610.759.5757
info@mguitar.com
www.mguitar.com

MASTER
Master Handmade Guitars
7336 Santa Monica Blvd.
Los Angeles CA 90046
213.876.4456

MASTER'S BASS
Master's Bass Company
3001 Fadal Avenue
Waco TX 76708
817.756.3310

MAXTONE
Ta Feng Long Enterprises Co., Ltd.
P.O. Box 536
Tai Chung Taiwan ROC
04.3212115
(FAX) 8864.3212493

M D X
MDX Sound Lab
736 Cromwell
West Point MS 39773
601.494.8777
http://www.mdxguitars.com
email: dann@mdxguitars.com

MEGAS
1070 Van Dyke
San Francisco CA 94124
415.822.3100

MEISEL
Meisel Stringed Instruments
Box 90
Springfield NJ 07081
201.379.5000
(FAX 201.379.5020

MELOBAR
Melobar Guitars, Inc.
Distributed by Smith Family Music Products
9175 Butte Road
Sweet ID 83670
800.942.6509
208.584.3349
(FAX) 208.584.3312
Enhancr@micron.net

MENKEVICH GUITARS
6013 Tulip Street
Philadelphia PA 19135
215.288.8417

MERCHANT
Merchant Vertical Bass Co.
307 Seventh Avenue
New York NY 10001-6007
212.989.2517

MERCURY
Mercury Guitars
P.O. Box 7658
Berkeley CA 94707
510.528.0575
email: mercuryg@aol.com

MESROBIAN
P.O. Box 204
Salem MA 01970-0204
508.740.6986

METROPOLITAN
Distributed by Alamo Music Products
3526 East T.C. Jester Blvd.
Houston TX 77018
713.957.0470
(FAX) 713.957.3316
http://www.io.com/~robintx
email: robintx@io.com

MICHAEL DOLAN
3222 Airway Dr. #4
Santa Rosa CA 95403
707.575.0654

BOB MICK GUITARS
Distributed by Martin Distributing
323 Jasper
Las Cruces NM 88001
505.527.4029
(FAX) 505.525.9407

MIGHTY MITE
Distributed by Westheimer Corporation
3451 West Commercial Avenue
Northbrook IL 60062
708.498.9850

MIKE CHISTIAN
Mike Christian Guitar Technology
P.O. Box 1937
West Babylon NY 11704
516.422.4791
(FAX) 516.422.5030

MIKE LULL
Mike Lull's Guitar Works
13240 NE 20th, Suite #3
Bellevue WA 98005
206.643.8074
(FAX) 206.746.5748
http://www.halcyon.com/guitarwk/

MIRAGE
M J Guitar Engineering
2661 Gravenstein Highway, Suite B
Sebastopol CA 95472
707.829.0745
http://www.spiderweb.com/mjguitar

MITCHELL
Mitchell Guitars
906 17th St.
Wall NJ 07719-3103
908.681.3430

MODULUS GRAPHITE
Modulus Graphite, Inc.
575 Seventh Street
San Francisco CA 94103
415.703.0500
(Fax) 415.703.0979

MONTALVO
Distributed by K & S Guitars
2923 Adeline St.
Berkeley CA 94703
510.843.2883

MONTANA
Distributed by the Kaman Music Corporation
See Listing Under OVATION

MONTELEONE
P.O. Box 52
Islip NY 11751
516.277.3620

MOON (JAPAN)
Distributed through the Luthiers Access Group
P.O. Box 388798
Chicago IL 60638-8798
708.974.4022
(FAX) 708.974.4022
Moon Corporation
3F 2-28-7 Akabane Kita-ku
Tokyo Japan T115
81.3.3598.1661
(FAX) 81.3.3598.1682

MOONSTONE GUITARS
P.O. Box 757
Eureka CA 95502
707.445.9045

MORELLI
Morelli Guitars
P.O. Box 687
Port Chester NY 10573
914.937.3798
(FAX) 914.937.3798

MORRELL
Distributed by the Joe Morrell Music Distributing Co.
2306 West State Street
Bristol TN 37620
800.545.5811

MORSE
3235 Paper Mill Rd.
Soquel CA 95073
408.426.4745

MORTORO
P.O. Box 161225
Miami FL 33116-1225
305.238.7947

MOSER
Neal Moser Guitars
Distributed by GMW Guitar Works
220 N. Glendora Avenue
Glendora CA 91740
818.914.8082

MOSES UPRIGHT BASSES
Moses, Inc.
32591 Fox Hollow Road
Eugene OR 97405
503.484.6068
(FAX) 503.484.6068

MOSRITE
Unified Sound Association, Inc.
P.O. Box 80
Booneville AK 72927
704.733.9225

MOSSMAN
1813 Main Street
Sulphur Springs TX 75482
903.885.4992
(RES) 903.885.9749

MTD
Michael Tobias Design
760 Zena Highwoods Road
Kingston NY 12401
914.246.0670

MUNCY
Muncy Guitar Company
128 Oak Drive
Kingston TN 37763
423.717.0165

NASH
Distributed by Musima North America, Inc.
13540 N. Florida Avenue, Suite 206 A
Tampa FL
813.961.8357
(FAX) 813.961.8514

NASHVILLE GUITAR
Nashville Guitar Company
P.O. Box 160412
Nashville TN 37216
615.262.4891
(FAX) 615.262.4891

NATIONAL RESO-PHONIC
National Reso-Phonic Guitars, Inc.
871 C Via Esteban
San Luis Obispo CA 93401
805.546.8442
(Fax) 805.546.8430

NEO
NEO Products, Inc.
Distributed by Lady Luck Industries, Inc.
P.O. Box 563
4626 Sands Way
Buckingham PA 18912
215.862.5551
(FAX) 215.862.1840

NEUSER
Neuser Co., Ltd.
Distributed by Armadillo Enterprises
923 McMullen Booth Road
Clearwater FL 34619
800.793.5273
813.642.8000
(FAX) 813.797.9448

N.I.C.E.
N.I.C.E. Custom Guitars
Klybeckstrasse 99
CH-4057 Basel Switzerland

NICKERSON
Nickerson Guitars
8 Easthampton Rd.
Northampton MA 01060
413.586.8521

ROY NOBLE
Stringed Instrument Division
123 W. Alder
Missoula MT 59802
406.549.1502
(FAX) 406.549.3380

TONY NOBLES
Distributed by Precision Guitarworks
9705 Burnet Rd. #109
Austin TX 78758

NORMAN
Distributed by La Si Do, Inc.
See Listing Under GODIN
4240 Sere'
St. Laurent Quebec Canada
H4T 1A6

NOVAK
Novak Fanned Fret Guitars
940 A Estabrook
San Leandro CA 94577
510.483.3599

NYC MUSIC PRODUCTS
c/o Matthews & Ryan Musical Products
68 34th Street
Brooklyn NY 11232
718.832.6333
(FAX) 718.832.5270

OFB
OFB Guitars
953 REON Drive #B
Virginia Beach VA 23464-3811
804.523.9278

OLSON
Olson Guitars
11840 Sunset Avenue
Circle Pines MN 55014
612.780.5301
(FAX) 612.780.8513

OPTEK
Optek Music Systems
8109 Ebenezer Church Rd.
Raleigh NC 27612
919.510.8393

OSCAR SCHMIDT
Oscar Schmidt International
Distributed by Washburn International
255 Corporate Woods Parkway
Vernon Hills IL 600061-3109
800.877.6863
847.913.5511
(FAX) 847.913.7772

OTHON
Othon Guitars
8838 Greenback Lane
Ovale CA 95662
916.988.8533
(FAX) 916.988.0170

OUTBOUND
Outbound, the Travel Guitar
1319 Spruce Street, Suite 205
Boulder CO 80302
800.487.1887
303.449.1887
(FAX) 303.447.1905
moorejt@indra.com

OVATION
Distributed by the Kaman Music Corporation
P.O. Box 507
Bloomfield CT 06002-0507
800.647.2244
860.243.7105
(FAX) 860.243.7287
www.kamanmusic.com

OVERWATER
Atlas Works, Nelson Street
Carlisle, Cumbria
United Kingdom
CA2 5ND
01228.590591
(FAX) 01228.590597

PALMER
P.O. Box 520504
Miami FL 33152-0504
813.681.2136

PARKER
Parker Guitars
Distributed by Korg USA
89 Frost Street
Westbury NY 11590
800.645.3188
516.333.9100
(Fax) 516.333.9108

PATRICK EGGLE
Patrick Eggle Guitars
Distributed by Quality First Products
137 North Quail Run
Forest City NC 28043
800.872.5856
704.245.8904
(Fax) 704.245.8965

PATTERSON
Patterson Guitars
1417 Iowa Avenue West
Falcon Heights MN 55108
612.647.5701
(FAX) 612.647.5701

PAUL REED SMITH
Paul Reed Smith Guitars
107 Log Canoe Circle
Stevensville MD 21666
410.643.9970
(FAX) 410.643.9980

PBC
PBC Guitar Technology, Inc.
217 S. Third St.
Route 309
Coopersburg PA 18036-0110
800.722.6163
610.282.0235
(FAX) 610.282.2742

PEAR CUSTOM
Pear Custom Guitars
1024 Serpentine Ln. #118
Pleasanton CA 94566
510.462.2857

PEAVEY
Peavey Electronics Corporation
711 A Street
Meridian MS 39301
601.483.5365
(Fax) 601.486.1278

M V PEDULLA
M V Pedulla Guitars
83 E. Water Street
Rockland MA 02370
617.871.0073
(Fax) 617.878.4028

PEDERSON
Pederson Guitars
1017 Arno St. SE
Albuquerque NM 87102
505.247.8694

PENSA CLASSIC
Distributed by Rudy's Music Shop
169 West 48th St.
New York NY 10036
212.391.1699
(FAX) 212.768.3782

PERFORMANCE
3621 Cahuenga Blvd.
Hollywood CA 90068
213.883.0781
(FAX) 213.883.0997

PETROS
Petros Guitars
345 Country Rd. CE
Holland WI 54130
414.766.1295

PHANTOM GUITAR WORKS
Phantom Guitar Works, Inc.
2000 NE 42nd, Suite 231
Portland OR 97213
503.282.6799
(FAX) 503.282.6799

PHILIP KUBIKI
Philip Kubicki Technology
57 Crooks Avenue
Clifton NJ 07011
800.888.1899
201.772.3333
(FAX) 201.772.5410

PHOENIX
Phoenix Guitar Company
2705 E. Indian School Rd.
Phoenix AZ 85016
602.553.0005

PICATO
Distributed by Saga Musical Instruments
See Listing Under REGAL

PIMENTEL & SONS
3316 LaFayette NE
Albuquerque NM 87107
505.884.1669

RONALD PINKHAM
Distributed by Woodsound Studio
P.O. Box 149
Glen Cove ME 04846
207.596.7407

R & L
Roman & Lipman
World Class Guitars
36 Tamarack Avenue
Danbury CT 06811
203.746.4995

RAINSONG
Rainsong Graphite Guitars
Distributed by Kuau Technology, Ltd.
P.O. Box 578
Puunene HI 96784-0578
800.277.7664
808.242.1190
(Fax) 808.978.4261
http:\\rainsong.com
rsguitar@AOL.com

RAJ GUITAR CRAFTS
Distributed by KICS USA/RAJ Guitar Crafts
See Listing Under KICS

RAMTRAK
24900 Capital
Redford MI 48239
313.538.1200
(FAX) 313.538.1255

RANSOM
15 LaFayette St.
San Francisco CA 94103
415.864.3281

RAREBIRD GUITARS
P.O. Box 211094
Denver CO 80221-9998
303.657.0056
6406 Raleigh Street
Arvada CO 80003-6435

R. C. ALLEN
2801 New Deal Road
Almonte CA 91733
818.442.8806

REGAL
Distributed by Saga Musical Instruments
429 Littlefield Avenue
South San Francisco CA 94080
800.BUY.SAGA
415.588.5558
415.871.7590

RESURRECTION GUITARS
2329 NE Dixie Highway
Jensen Beach FL 34957
407.334.0410
(Fax) 407.334.2507

REYNOLDS
Reynolds Musical Instruments
8905 Sam Carter
Austin TX 78736
512.288.5298

RIBBECKE
Ribbecke Guitars
P.O. Box 1581
Santa Rosa CA 95402
707.433.3778

RICKENBACKER
Rickenbacker International Corporation
3895 S. Main Street
Santa Ana CA 92707-5710
714.545.5574
(Fax) 714.754.0135

ROBERTS
Roberts Roto-Neck
471 West Lambert Rd., Suite 104
Brea CA 92621
714.256.7276
(FAX) 714.256.7288

ROBIN
Robin Guitars
Distributed by Alamo Music Products
3526 East T.C. Jester Blvd.
Houston TX 77018
713.957.0470
(FAX) 713.957.3316
http://www.io.com/~robintx
email: robintx@io.com

ROBINSON
Robinson Custom Guitars
23 Columbus Avenue
Newburyport MA 01950
508.465.3959
(FAX) 508.465.3959

RODRIGUEZ
Distributed by the Fender Musical Instrument Corp.
See Listing Under FENDER

ROLAND
Roland Musical Instruments
7200 Cominon Circle
Los Angeles CA 90040-3696
213.685.5141
(FAX) 213.722.0911
rolandpr@aol.com
www.rolandus.com

ROSCOE
P.O. Box 5404
Greensboro NC 27435
910.274.8810
(FAX) 910.370.1798

JONATHAN W. ROSE
46 Calamus Lane
Strasburg VA 22657
540.465.4964

ROY CUSTOM GUITARS
37 Falcon Street
Chelmsford, Ontario
Canada P0M 1L0
705.855.5347

ROBERT RUCK
37676 Hood Canal Drive NE
Hansville WA 98340
360.297.4024

RUSTLER
Rustler Guitars
314 Third Northwest
Mason City IA 50401
515.424.6331
(FAX) 515.424.0453

R W K
RWK Guitars
P.O. Box 1068
Highland Park IL 60035
800.454.7078

RYBSKI
Distributed through the Luthiers Access Group
P.O. Box 388798
Chicago IL 60638-8798
708.974.4022
(FAX) 708.974.4022

SADOWSKY
Sadowsky Guitars Ltd.
1600 Broadway #1000
New York NY 10019
212.586.3960
(FAX) 212.765.5231
email: sadowsky@bway.net
http://www.sadowsky.com

SAEHAN
Saehan International
Bldg. 1599-11
Sedcho Dong #1503
15th Floor
Seoul Korea
82.252.36455
(FAX) 82.252.36459

SAMICK
Samick Music Corporation
18521 Railroad Street
City of Industry CA 91748
800.592.9393
818.964.4700
(Fax) 818.965.5224

SAND
Kirk Sand Guitars
1027 B.N. Coast Hwy.
Laguna Beach CA 92651
714.497.2110

SANTA CRUZ
Santa Cruz Guitar Company
328 Ingalls Street
Santa Cruz CA 95060
408.425.0999
(Fax) 408.425.3604

SANTA FE GUITARS
Santa Fe Violin Guitar Works
1412 Llano St.
Santa Fe NM 87505
505.988.4240

SANTA ROSA
Distributed by AR Musical Enterprises
See listing under KAY.

SANTUCCI
Santucci Treblebass
69 W. 38th Street
New York NY 10018
212.302.6805
(FAX) 212.581.4617

SARRICOLA
Sarricola Guitars
Available through Sarricola Custom Shop
3 Barbados Ct. N.
Lake Thunderbird IL 61560
815.437.2127

SCHACK
Distributed by F.G. Reitz & Co., Inc.
314 West Wackerly Rd., Suite 200
Midland MI 48640
517.835.4646
(FAX) 517.835.6336

SCHARPACH
Theo Scharpach
Acterste Aa 14
5571 VE Bergeyk
The Netherlands
31.497.541278
(FAX) 31.497.541278

SCHECTER
Schecter Guitar Research
6920 Santa Monica Blvd.
Los Angeles CA 90038
213.851.5230
(FAX) 213.851.9409

SCHEERHORN
Scheerhorn Custom Resonator Guitars
1454 52nd St.
Kentwood MI 49508
616.281.3927

SCHOENBERG
Distributed by the Music Emporium
165 Mass Ave
Lexington MA 02173
617.860.0049

SCHWARTZ GUITARS
26 Rose Valley Cresent
Toronto Ontario
Canada M6N 4W1
416.604.4518

SEAGULL
Seagull Guitars
Distibuted by La Si Do, Inc.
See Listing Under GODIN
4240 Sere'
St. Laurent Quebec Canada
H4T 1A6

SEBRING
Distributed by V.J. Rendano Wholesale Company
7152 Market Street
Youngstown OH 44512
800.321.4048
216.758.0881
(FAX) 216.758.1096

SEDONA
Distributed by V M I Industries
See listing under ANTARES

SERIES 10
A Division of St. Louis Music Company
See Listing Under ALVAREZ

SEXAUER
Sexauer Luthier
265 B Gate 5 Road
Saulsalito CA 94965
800.735.0650
http:\\www.hooked.net~luthier
email: luthier@hooked.net

SHADOW
Shadow Electronics of America
2700 S.E. Market Place
Stuart FL 34994
407.221.8177
(FAX) 407.221.8178
Shadow Western States Technical Center
602.861.3056
(FAX) 602.861.6991

SHANE
3211 Barbara Lane, Unit 2
Fairfax VA 22031
703.641.4951

SHANTI
P.O. Box 341
Avery CA 95224
209.795.5299

SHENANDOAH
Distributed by the Martin Guitar Company
See Listing Under MARTIN

SIGMA
Distributed by the Martin Guitar Company
See Listing Under MARTIN

SILBER
Distributed by K & S Guitars
2923 Adeline Street
Berkeley CA 94703
510.843.2883

SILVER CADET
Distributed by Ibanez USA
See Listing Under IBANEZ

**GENE SIMMONS'
PUNISHER**
P.O. Box 16075
Beverly Hills CA 90209
609.PUNISHER
609.786.4743

SIMON & PATRICK
Distributed by La Si Do, Inc.
See Listing under GODIN

SIMPSON-JAMES
Simpson-James Guitars
17 Spruce Circle
Westfield MA 01085-2610
413.568.6654
http://www.connix.com/~sjguitar

DANIEL SLAMAN
Westeinde 58
2512 H E
Den Haag The Netherlands
070.3894232
(FAX) 011.31.118.479.411

S M D
Distributed by Toys In The Attic
138 Shelter Lane
Levittown NY 11756
914.421.0069
516.579.5733

KEN SMITH
Ken Smith Basses, Ltd.
215 S. Fifth Street
Perkasie PA 18944
215.453.8887
(FAX) 215.453.8084

SPECTOR
*Distributed by Kramer Musical
Industries*
See Listing Under KRAMER

SQUIER
*Distributed by the Fender Musical
Instruments Corporation*
See Listing Under FENDER

SSD
Distributed by Armadillo Enterprises
923 McMullen Booth Road
Clearwater FL 34619
800.793.5273
813.642.8000
(FAX) 813.797.9448
Stuart Spector Design, Ltd.
1450 Route 212
Saugerties NY 12477
914.246.1385
(FAX) 914.246.0833

STATUS GRAPHITE
Coleman's Bridge
Colchester Road
Witham Essex England CM8
3HP
01376.500575
(FAX) 01376.500569

STEINBERGER
Steinberger Sound
A Division of Gibson Guitar Corporation
18108 Redondo Circle
Huntington Beach CA 92648
800.507.8346
714.848.7044
(FAX) 714.843.5731

STELLING
Stelling Banjo Works
7258 Banjo Lane
Afton VA 22920
800.5.STRING
804.295.1917
stelling@esinet.net

STEPHEN'S
Stephen's Stringed Instruments
1733 Westlake Avenue
North Seattle WA 98109
206.286.1443
(Fax) 206.286.1728

STERLING
Distributed by Guitar Heaven
7503 Sunset Blvd.
Los Angeles CA 90046

STEVEN'S
Steven's Electrical Instruments
112 N. Sixth Street
Alpine TX 79830
915.837.5989
(FAX) 915.837.5989

STICK
Stick Enterprises
6011 Woodlake Avenue
Woodland Hills CA 91367
818.884.2001
(FAX) 818.883.0668

STOLL
Distributed by Salwender International
See Listing Under TEUFFEL

STONEMAN
Stoneman Guitars
20 Russell Blvd.
Bradford PA 16701
814.362.8820

STUART
Stuart Handcrafted Guitars
P.O. Box 4101
Cincinnati OH 45204-0101
513.881.0554

**STUMP PREACHER
GUITARS**
Stump Preacher Guitars, Inc.
12064 NE 178th St.
Woodinville WA 98072
800.427.8867
206.402.1935
(FAX) 206.487.8262

SUKOP
Sukop Electric Guitars
57 Crooks Avenue
Clifton NJ 07011
800.888.1899
201.772.3333
(FAX) 201.772.5410

SURINE
Surine Electric Basses
P.O. Box 6440
Denver CO 80206
303.388.3956

SUZUKI
Suzuki Guitars
P.O. Box 261030
San Diego CA 92196
619.566.9710

SYNSONICS
*Distributed by V.J. Rendano Wholesale
Company*
See Listing Under SEBRING

TACOMA GUITAR
Tacoma Guitar Company
4615 E. 192nd St.
Tacoma WA 98446
206.847.6508
(FAX) 206.847.8524
TacomaGtr@aol.com

TAKAMINE
*Distributed by the Kaman Music
Corporation*
See Listing Under OVATION

S. TALKOVICH
P.O. Box 98
Woodstock GA 30188
770.926.8876
email: talkgtr@aol.com

TANARA
*Distributed by the Chesbro Music
Company*
P.O. Box 2009
327 Broadway
Idaho Falls ID 83403-2009
800.243.7276
208.522.8691
(FAX) 208.522.8712

TAYLOR GUITARS
1940 Gillespie Way
El Cajon CA 92020
619.258.1207
(Fax) 619.258.4052

TEIGEN
Teigen Guitars
P.O. Box 990421
Naples FL 33999
941.455.5724

TEUFFEL
Distributed by Salwender International
19455 Dorado Drive
Trabuco Canyon CA 92679.1610
714.589.6024

TEXARKANA
*Distributed by V.J. Rendano Wholesale
Company*
See Listing Under SEBRING

THOMPSON
9905 Coldstream Creek Rd.
Vernon BC Canada V1B 1C8
604.542.9410
(FAX) 604.542.9410

C P THORNTON
Box 3040, R.R. #2
Bryant Pond ME 04219
207.364.7383

TIMTONE
Timtone Custom Guitars
P.O. Box 193
3159 Highway 21 N.
Danville WA 99121-0193
604.442.5651
(FAX) 604.442.5651

TOBIAS
*Distributed by Consolidated Musical
Instruments (Gibson)*
Tobias Guitars
1050 Acorn Drive, Suite C
Nashville TN 37210
800.743.6456
615.872.8420
(FAX) 615.872.8475

TOMKINS
*Tomkins Custom Guitars and
Basses*
17 Eric Street
Harbord
N.S.W. 2096 Australia
+61.2.9905.2442
(FAX) +61.2.9905.5998

TOMMYHAWK
Tom Barth's Music Box
291 West Clinton Street
Dover NJ 07801
800.558.4295
201.366.6611
(FAX) 201.366.5243
email: guitarbase@gbase.com
http://www.gbase.com/tbmusic/

TOTEM
Totem Guitars
40861 Ferndale Dr.
Three Rivers CA 93271
209.561.4009

TRANSPERFORMANCE
2526 Courtland Court
Fort Collins CO 80526-1324
970.482.9132
(FAX) 970.482.9132

JEFF TRAUGOTT
Jeff Traugott Guitars
2553 B Mission Street
Santa Cruz CA 95060
408.426.2313

TRAVELER
Distributed by OMG Music
800.475.5552
The Traveler Guitar
325 Alabama, Suite 9
Redlands CA 92373
909.307.2626
(FAX) 909.307.2628

TREKER
12334 S. Pony Express Road
Draper UT 84020
801.571.2500

TRIGGS
Triggs Guitars
277 Clovernook Drive
Nashville TN 37210
615.391.5844

TUNE
Tune Guitar Technology Co., Ltd.
*Distributed by Tune Guitars of North
America*
P.O. Box 691
Santa Barbara CA 93102
800.548.6669

TUNG
Tung Basses
213 Ashland Place #1
New York NY 11217
718.797.2047
(FAX) 718.797.2162

RICK TURNER
Rick Turner Guitars
P.O. Box 1612
Topanga CA 90290
800.547.8563
310.455.2839
(FAX) 310.455.2839

TURTLETONE
2030 E. Broadway #1018
Tempe AZ 85282
602.894.1079
(FAX) 602.894.1079

T V JONES
P.O. Box 163
Whittier CA 90608
310.693.0068

JAMES TYLER
Tyler Guitars
6166 Sepulveda Blvd.
Van Nuys CA 91411
818.901.0278
(FAX) 818.901.0294

VAGABOND
Vagabond Travel Guitar
P.O. Box 845
Albany NY 12201
518.436.9942
vagguitar@aol.com

VALLEY ARTS
*Distributed by Samick Music
Corporation
See Listing Under SAMICK*

VANTAGE
*Distributed by Music Industries
Corporation*
99 Tulip Avenue
Floral Park NY 11001
800.431.6699
516.352.4110
(Fax) 516.352.0754

VANTEK
*Distributed by Music Industries
Corporation
See Listing Under VANTAGE*

VEILLETTE
Veillette Guitars
2628 Route 212
Woodstock NY 12498
914.679.6154

VEKTOR ELECTRIC UPRIGHT
Vektor-Germany
Markstr. 5
41751 Viersen
Germany
49.21.62.5.33.09

VERSOUL
Kutomotie 13
Fin-00380 Helsinki
Finland
358.0.565.1876
(FAX) 358.0.565.1876

VESTAX
Vestax Corporation
2870 Cordelia Rd., Suite 100
Fairfield CA 94585
707.427.1920
(FAX) 707.427.2023

VIGIER
*Vigier Guitars, Basses, and Strings
(U.S.) Players International*
111 W. Second Street
San Dimas CA 91773
909.592.6682
(FAX) 909.599.0908

WAL
Electric Wood
Sandown Works
Chairborough Rd.
High Wycombe, Bucks
England HP12 3HH
44.1494.442925
(FAX) 44.1494.472468

WALKER
Walker Guitars
314 Pendleton Hill Rd.
North Stonington CT 06359
203.599.8753

WARR
Warr Guitars
6933 Keynote St.
Long Beach CA 90808
310.421.7293
(FAX) 310.421.7293

WARRIOR
100 Direct Connection Drive
Rossville GA 30741
706.891.3009
http://www.warrior.w1.com

WARWICK
*Exclusively Distributed by Dana B.
Goods*
5427 Hollister Avenue
Santa Barbara CA 93111-2345
800.765.8663
805.964.9610
(Fax) 805.964.9749

WASHBURN
Distributed by Washburn International
255 Corporate Woods Parkway
Vernon Hills IL 60061-3109
800.US.SOUND
708.913.5511
(Fax) 708.913.7772
jhawk103@aol.com
www.washburn.com

ABRAHAM WECHTER
Distributed by Wechter Guitars
34654 32nd Street
Paw Paw MI 49079-9516
616.657.3479
email: wechter@guitar.net
email: michaeld@net-link.net
http://www.guitar.net/wechterguitars/

PAT WILKINS
Pat Wilkins Guitars and Basses
5 Fairway Drive
Portsmouth VA 23701
804.465.7535
(FAX) 804.465.7535

WITTMAN
Wittman Custom Basses
691 Woodland Avenue
Williamsport PA 17701
717.327.1527
717.321.0604

WOLLERMAN
Wollerman Guitars
P.O. Box 457
Sheffield IL 61361
815.454.2775
(FAX) 815.454.2700

RANDY WOOD
*Distributed Exclusively by Joe
Pichkur's Guitar Center*
2 Crest Avenue
Elmont NY 11003
516.488.5343

WOODY'S CUSTOM GUITARS
213 Ashland Place #1
New York NY 11217
718.797.2047
(FAX) 718.797.2162

WRC
WRC Music International, Inc.
4191 Park Avenue
Hemet CA 92544
909.929.8734

WRIGHT
Wright Guitar Technology
3724 Gilham Court
Eugene OR 97408
503.343.0872
(FAX) 503.484.3612

XOTIC
Taku Sakashta, Luthier
7625 Hayvenhurst Avenue #19
Van Nuys CA 91406
818.781.7308

YAMAHA
Yamaha Corporation of America
6600 Orangethorpe Avenue
Buena Park CA 90620
800.322.4322
714.522.9011
(Fax) 714.522.9587
www.yamahaguitars.com

YURIY
Yuriy Guitars
P.O. Box 7201
Buffalo Grove IL 60089
708.577.5984
(FAX) 708.459.8023

ZEIDLER
J. R. Zeidler
1441 S. Broad St.
Philadelphia PA 19147
215.271.6858
jrzeidler@aol.com
http://www.cyboard.com/ent/
zeidler.html

ZEMAITIS
A.C. Zemaitis
108 Walderslade Road
Chatham Kent
England ME5 0LL
(MEDWAY) 01634.865086

ZENTECH
P.O. Box 751 GP
Girdwood AK 99587
907.783.2502

ZETA
Zeta Music Systems
2230 Livingston Street
Oakland CA 94606
510.261.1702
(FAX) 510.261.1708

ZIMMERLY
17 Oswego Drive
Bay Shore NY 11706
516.968.5523

ZIMNICKI
Zimnicki Guitars
15106 Garfield
Allen Park MI 48101
313.381.2817
gkbmtzim@aol.com

ZION
Zion Guitar Technology
2606-404 Phoenix Drive
Greensboro NC 27406
910.852.7603
(FAX) 910.852.1889

ZOID
Zoid Light Guitars
736 S. 50th St.
Bldg. H-20
Tampa FL 33619
813.247.5268

ZOLLA
Zolla Guitars
4901 Morena Blvd., Suite 908
San Diego CA 92117
619.270.5530
(FAX) 619.270.0450

ZON
Zon Guitars
2682 Middlefield Road
Redwood City CA 94063
415.366.3516

Amps/Effects/Strings/Pickups

Now that you've bought the guitar of your dreams, what are you going to plug it into?

A Quick Reference of Amplifier Manufacturers

ADA
420 Lesser Street
Oakland CA 94601
800.241.8888
510.532.1152
(FAX) 510.532.1641

AGUILAR
Aguilar Electronics
1600 Broadway #1004T
New York NY 10019
212.757.2823
(FAX) 212.757.2452

AMPEG
St.Louis Music (SLM)
1400 Ferguson Avenue
St. Louis MO 63133
800.727.4512
314.727.4512
(FAX) 314.727.8929

ART
*Applied Research and
Technologies*
215 Tremont Street
Rochester NY 14608-2366
716.436.2720
(FAX) 716.436.3942
artroch@aol.com
www.artroch.com

BEDROCK
Bedrock Amplification, Inc.
1600 Concord Street
Framingham MA 01701-3531
508.877.4055
(FAX) 508.877.4125

BLUESLAND
Tone City Engineering & Mfg.
860 Simcoe Street
St. Paul MN 55117
612.489.1587
(FAX) 612.489.1587
www.ally.ios.com/~toomuc19

BOGNER
Bogner Amplification
5112 Lankershim Blvd.
North Hollywood CA 91601
818.763.4323
(FAX) 818.763.7089

BOYDEN
Boyden Amplifiers
7883 Hestia Place
Pensacola FL 32506
904.455.1604

CARVIN
12340 World Trade Drive
San Diego CA 92128
800.854.2235
619.487.1600
(FAX) 619.487.8160
www.carvinguitars.com

CB LABS, INC.
203.335.1093

CRATE
St.Louis Music (SLM)
1400 Ferguson Avenue
St. Louis MO 63133
800.727.4512
314.727.4512
(FAX) 314.727.8929

DEAN MARKLEY
Dean Markley Amplifiers
P.O. Box 507
Bloomfield CT 06002-0507
800.647.2244
860.243.7941
(FAX) 860.243.7287

DEMETER
Demeter Amplification
2912 Colorado Avenue
Santa Monica CA 90404
310.829.4383
(FAX) 310829.3755

DR. Z
909.763.2402
drz@icgroup.net

EBS
*Available through Armadillo
Enterprises*
923 McMullen Booth Road Ste.
B
Clearwater FL 34619
813.796.8868
(FAX) 813.797.9448
In Sweden:
Framnasbacken 12
Solna S171 42 Sweden
46.873.50010
(FAX) 46.873.50015

EDEN
Eden Electronics, Inc.
P.O. Box 338
310 First St.
Montrose MN 55363
612.675.3650
(FAX) 612.675.3651

EDGERTON
P.O. Box 3656
189 S. Rogers Road
Bldg. 1624
Olathe KS 66062
913.768.9300
(FAX) 913.768.9383

EGNATER
Egnater Amplification
25550 Colleen St.
Oak Park MI 48237-1302
810.399.6208
(FAX) 810.399.5312

EPIPHONE
Available through Gibson USA
1050 Acorn Drive
Suite A
Nashville TN 37210
800.283.7135
615.871.4500
(FAX) 615.872.7768
www.gibson.com

EVANS
Evans Custom Amplifiers
Dept. T2
5900 Barbell Circle
McLeansville NC 27301
800.697.2347

EVIL AMPS
*Available through Junglewood
Music*
708.656.9175

FATBOY
Fatboy Amplifiers
708.509.9404

FENDER
*Fender Musical Instruments
Corp.*
7975 N Hayden Road
Scottsdale AZ 85258
602.596.9690
(FAX) 602.596.1384
www.fender.com

FENTON
Fenton Music Group
P.O. Box 669786
Marietta GA 30066
800.336.8662
404.592.9122

GALLIEN-KRUEGER
Gallien-Krueger, Inc.
2240 Paragon Drive
San Jose CA 95131-1306
408.441.7970
(FAX) 408.441.8085

GORILLA
400 W. Alondra Blvd.
Gardena CA 90248
800.9PI.GNOS
213.770.4444
(FAX) 310.538.9560

GROOVE TUBES
Available through G.T. Electronics
12866 Foothill Blvd.
Sylmar CA 91342
818.361.4500
(FAX) 818.365.9884

HARTKE
Hartke Systems
575 Underhill Blvd.
Syosset NY 11791
800.328.2882
516.364.2244
(FAX) 516.364.3888

HIWATT
16123 Valerio St.
Van Nuys, CA 91406
818.988.6790
(FAX) 818.988.3094

HOFFMAN
Hoffman Amplifiers
4209 S. Tamiami Trail
Sarasota FL 34231
813.923.5900

HOLLAND
Holland Amplifiers
753 Spence Circle
Virginia Beach VA 23462
804.467.0146
(FAX) 804.427.1783

HONDO
Hondo Amplifiers
P.O. Box 30819
Charleston SC 29417
803.763.9083
(FAX) 803.763.9096
www.hondo.com

HOUND DOG
Hound Dog Corporation
P.O. Box 253
Huntingdon Valley PA 19006
215.355.6424
(FAX) 215.355.6424

HUGHES & KETTNER
1848 S. Elmhurst Road
Mt. Prospect IL 60656-5711
800.452.6771
708.439.6771
(FAX) 708.439.6781

JLA
Jarrod Lee
2411 Fifth Ave.
Los Angeles CA 90018
213.733.3796
(FAX) 213.733.3796

KENDRICK
Kendrick Amplifiers
P.O. Box 160
Pflugerville TX 78660
512.990.5486

KICS USA
10150 Apache Road
Adelanto CA 92301-2243
619.246.3866
(FAX) 619.246.3494

KJL
Acoustic Analysis, Inc.
1529 Hanging Moss Ln.
Gretna LA 70056
504.394.6458

KROSSROAD
Krossroad Music Corporation
707 N. Highland
Chanute KS 66720
316.431.6625
(FAX) 316.431.6144

LANEY
1726 Winchester Road
Bensalem PA 19020
800.669.4226
215.638.8670
(FAX) 215.245.8538

LEDSLED
Ledsled Amplification
815.454.2775

LINE 6
11260 Playa Court
Culver City CA 90230
310.390.5956
(FAX) 310.390.1713
(FAX-BACK) 800.511.8604 ext. 2100
email: sales@Line6.com

LOUIS
Louis Electric Amplifier Company
P.O. Box 188
Bergenfield NJ 07621
201.384.6166

MANN
Mann Pro Sound
2660 E. Ganley
Tuscon AZ 85706
520.295.3920
(FAX) 520.295.3924

MARSHALL
89 Frost St.
Westbury NY 11590
800.645.3188
516.333.9100
(FAX) 516.333.9108

MATCHLESS
Matchless LLC
9830 Alburtis Ave.
Santa Fe Springs CA 90670
310.801.4840
(FAX) 310.801.4828

MESA/BOOGIE
1317 Ross Street
Petaluma CA 94954
707.778.6565
email: www.mesaboogie.com

NAYLOR
J.F. Naylor Engineering
23109 Gratiot Ave.
Eastpointe MI 48021
810.778.7180
(FAX) 810.778.4824

ORANGE
Available through Gibson USA
1050 Acorn Drive
Suite A
Nashville TN 37210
800.283.7135
615.871.4500
(FAX) 615.872.7768
www.gibson.com

PARK
89 Frost St.
Westbury NY 11590
800.645.3188
516.333.9100
FAX 516.333.9108

PEAVEY
Peavey Electronics
711 A St.
Meridian MS 39301
601.483.5365
(FAX) 601.486.1278
AOL Keyword: Peavey
CompuServe: Go Peavey
www.peavey.com

PENN
Penn Instrument Co.
P.O. Box 308
Colts Neck NJ 07722
908.946.4568
(FAX) 908.946.2835

PIGNOSE
400 W. Alondra Blvd.
Gardena CA 90248
800.9PI.GNOS
213.770.4444
(FAX) 310.538.9560

RANDALL
255 Corporate Woods Parkway
Vernon Hills IL 60061
800.877.6863
708.913.5511
(FAX) 708.913.7772

REDBEAR
Available through Gibson USA
1050 Acorn Drive
Suite A
Nashville TN 37210
800.283.7135
615.871.4500
(FAX) 615.872.7768
www.gibson.com

RIVERA
*Rivera Research &
Development Corporation*
13310 Ralston Ave.
Sylmar CA 91342
818.833.7066
(FAX) 818.833.9656

RMS
803.763.0220

ROCKTRON
Rocktron Corporation
2870 Technology Drive
Rochester Hills MI 48309
800.432.ROCK
810.853.3055
(FAX) 810.353.5937
email: rocktron@eaglequest.com

RODGERS
Rodgers Amplifiers
5975 Taylor Rd. #10
Naples FL 33942
813.594.5875
941.594.5875

SA FLA
Sa Fla Tweed Replicas
Paul Markwalter
954.524.7169

SHRAPNEL
Shrapnel Amplication Company
707.224.0951

SOLDANO
Soldano Custom Amplificaion
1537 NW Ballard Way
Seattle WA 98107
206.781.4636

SOVTEK
New Sensor Corporation
20 Cooper Square
New York NY 10003
800.633.5477
212.529.0466
(FAX) 212.529.0486

SWR
SWR Engineering, Inc.
12823 Foothill Blvd
Unit B
Sylmar CA 91342
818.898.3355
(FAX) 818.899.3365

THD
THD Electronics, Ltd.
5429 Russell Ave NW
Seattle WA 98107-4015
206.789.5500
FAX 206.784.7888

THUNDERFUNK
Thunderfunk Labs
610 Magazine St.
Nashville TN 37203
708.263.7400
615.742.1818

TONE KING
Tone King Amplifier Co.
703 S. Luzerne Ave.
Baltimore MD 21224
410.327.6530
(FAX) 410.327.6530

TORRES
Torres Inc./Sparpco Inc.
1630 Palm Ave.
San Mateo CA 94402
415.571.6887
(FAX) 415.571.1507

TRACE ELLIOT
Available through Kaman Music, Inc.
P.O. Box 507
Bloomfield CT 06002-0507
800.647.2244
860.243.7941
(FAX) 860.243.7287
www.kamanmusic.com

TRAINWRECK
Trainwreck Circuits
59 Preston Road
Colonia NJ 07067-2420
908.381.5126

TUBEWORKS
8201 E. Pacific Place
Denver CO 80231
800.326.0269
303.750.3801
(FAX) 303.750.2162

VANTAGE
Available through Music Industries
99 Tulip Avenue, Suite 101
Floral Park NY 11001
800.431.6699

VHT
1200 Lawerence Drive #465
Newbury Park CA 91320
805.376.9899
(FAX) 805.376.9999

VICTORIA
Victoria Amp Co.
1504 Newman Court
Naperville IL 60564-4132
708.369.3527

VOX
Available through Korg USA
89 Frost St.
Westbury NY 11590
800.645.3188
516.333.9100
(FAX) 516.333.9108

VVT/SPEEDSTER
Vintage Voicing Technologies
P.O. Box 2012
Gig Harbor WA 98335
206.851.6627

WARWICK
805.964.9610

WASHBURN
255 Corporate Woods Parkway
Vernon Hills IL 60061
800.877.6863
708.913.5511
(FAX) 708.913.7772

WIZARD
Wizard Amplification
123-1450 Johnson Road
White Rock British Columbia
Canada V4B 5E9
604.536.5700
(FAX) 604.536.7336

There are a growing number of companies who are making effects, either in footpedal or rackmount configuration. Effects offer the guitarist/bassist tonal coloration and variety in sounds.

A brief survey of Effects Companies.

ALESIS
3630 Holdrege Avenue
Los Angeles CA 90016
310.841.2272
alecorp@alesis1.usa.com

ART
Applied Research and Technology
215 Tremont Street
Rochester NY 14608
716.436.2720
(FAX) 716.436.3942
artrochaol.com
artroch@cis.compuserve.com
www.artroch.com

BIXONIC 'EXPANDORA'
Distributed by Sound Barrier International
P.O. Box 4732
133 Frazier Avenue
Chattanooga TN 37405-0732
423.75.MUSIC
423.756.8742

BOSS
Distributed by the Roland Corporation
7200 Dominion Circle
Los Angeles CA 90040-3647
213.685.5141
(FAX) 213.722.9233
roland@aol.com
www.rolandus.com

CROWTHER AUDIO
(The Hotcake)
P.O. Box 96104
Balmoral Auckland 1030
New Zealand

DIGITECH
8760 South Sandy Parkway
Sandy UT 84070
801.566.8919
(FAX) 801.566.7005
(Int'l FAX) 603.672.4246
www.digitech.com

DOD
8760 South Sandy Parkway
Sandy UT 84070
801.566.8800
(FAX) 801.566.7005
(Int'l FAX) 603.672.4246
www.dod.com

ELECTRO-HARMONIX
New Sensor
20 Cooper Square
New York NY 10003
212.529.0466

FRANTONE
(The Hepcat)
1763 Columbia Avenue
Lancaster PA 17603
717.397.2470

FULLTONE CUSTOM EFFECTS
3815 Beethoven St.
Los Angeles CA 90066
310.397.3456
email: Robintrowr@AOL.com (Robin Trower)

IBANEZ
Hoshino USA
Dept. GPE43
P.O. Box 886
Bensalem PA 19020
215.638.8670
(FAX) 215.245.8583

JGR ELECTRONICS
(The Retro Rocket)
P.O. Box 39
Oak Ridge NJ 07438
201.838.0072

KLON
(The Centaur)
P.O. Box 1025
Brookline MA 02146
617.738.8409
(FAX) 617.738.8531

LOVETONE
Box 102
Henley-on-Thames
Oxfordshire
RG9 1XX England
UK PHONE: 0.1491.571411
US PHONE: 714.856.9946
email: lovetone@channel.co.uk
http://www.channel.co.uk/lovetone/

REAL MCCOY CUSTOM 3
(Blues Dog) 713.460.2300
(FAX) 713.460.0059

PEAVEY
Peavey Electronics
711 A Street
Meridian MS 39301
601.486.1278
AOL keyword: Peavey
CompuServe: Go Peavey
www.peavey.com

PRESCRIPTION ELECTRONICS
P.O. Box 42233
Portland OR 97242
503.239.9106
(FAX) 503.239.9106

ROCKMAN
Dept. AP
P.O. Box 846
Benicia CA 94510
707.745.2722
dunlop@a.crl.com

ROCKTRON
Rocktron Guitar Technology
2870 Technology Drive
Rochester Hills MI 48309
810.853.3055
rocktron@eaglequest.com
www.rocktron.com

ROLLS
RFX
5143 S. Main Street
Salt Lake City UT 84107-4740
801.263.9053
(FAX) 801.263.9068
david@rolls.com
www.xmission.com/~rollsrfx

SWEET SOUND ELECTRONICS
P.O. Box 514
Trenton MI 48183-0514
313.676.3106
(FAX) 313.676.3106

T C ELECTRONICS
T C Electronics of Denmark
705 Lakefield Road
Westlake Village CA 91361-2611
805.373.1828
(FAX) 805.379.2648
tc@tcelectronic.com
www.tcelectronic.com

TECH 21 NYC
(SANSAMP)
1600 Broadway
New York NY 10019
212.315.1116
(FAX) 212.315.0825

TONEWORKS
Distributed by Korg USA
89 Frost Street
Westbury NY 11590

TUBEWORKS
8201 E. Pacific Place
Denver CO 80231
800.326.0269
303.750.3801
(FAX) 303.750.2162

VISUAL SOUND
11 Bedford Avenue, Suite R-2
Norwalk CT 06850
800.686.3317
203.866.7101
(FAX) 203.852.1123

VOODOO LABS
Digital Music Corp.
5312-J Derry Avenue
Agoura Hills CA 91301
818.991.3881
(FAX) 818.991.4185

WAY HUGE ELECTRONICS
818.981.1908

ZOOM
Distributed by Samson Technologies Corporation
P.O. Box 9031
Syosset NY 11971
516.364.2244

Another aspect of tone generation is Strings. How strings interact with the instrument and the player is another crucial portion of the overall "chain" of the sound produced.

The following is a brief review of String Companies.

ADAMAS
Distributed by Kaman Music (OVATION)
P.O. Box 507
Bloomfield CT 06002-0507
203.243.7941
www.kamanmusic.com

CHARLIE STRINGER (SNARLING DOGS)
Dept. GW
P.O. Box 4241
Warren NJ 07059
908.469.2828
(FAX) 908.469.2882

CONCERTISTE
Picato Musician Strings
Unit 24, Treorchy Ind. Est.
Treorchy Mid Glamorgan
United Kingdom CF42 6EJ
44.144.343.7928
(FAX) 44.144.343.3624

J. D'ADDARIO
J. D'Addario & Co.
595 Smith Street
Farmingdale NY 11735
800.323.2746
516.391.5400
(FAX) 516.391.5410
strings@daddario.com
www.daddario.com

D'AQUISTO
20 E. Industry Court
P.O. Box 569
Deer Park NY 11729
516.586.4426

DEAN MARKLEY
3350 Scott Blvd. #45
Santa Clara CA 95054
408.988.2456
www.deanmarkley.com

DR STRINGS
7 Palisades Avenue
Emerson NJ 07630
201.599.0100
(FAX) 201.599.0404
email: DRStrings@aol.com

ERNIE BALL
P.O. Box 4117
San Luis Obispo CA 93401
805.544.7726

FENDER
Fender Musical Instruments Corp.
7975 N Hayden Road
Scottsdale AZ 85258
602.596.9690
(FAX) 602.596.1385
www.fender.com

GHS
G.H.S. Corporation
P.O. Box 136
2813 Wilber Avenue
Battle Creek MI 49016
800.388.4447
616.968.3351
(FAX) 616.968.6913
rmcfee@tdsnet.com
www.ghsstrings.com

GIBSON
Gibson Strings & Accessories
A Manufacturing Division of Gibson Guitar Corp.
1725 Fleetwood Drive
Elgin IL 60123
800.544.2766
708.741.7315
(FAX) 708.741.4644
www.gibson.com

JOHN PEARSE STRINGS
P.O. Box 295
Center Valley PA 18034
610.691.3302

LABELLA
256 Broadway
Newburg NY 12550
914.562.4400

MARI
14 W. 71st Street
New York NY 10023-4209
212.799.6781
(FAX) 212.721.3932

MARTIN STRINGS
C.F.Martin & Co.
510 Sycamore Street
Nazareth PA 18064
800.633.2060
info@mguitar.com
www.mguitar.com

MAXIMA
57 Crooks Avenue
Clifton NJ 07011
201.722.3333
garpc@ix.netcom.com

SABINE
NitroStasis Strings
13301 Highway 441
Alachua FL 32615-8544
904.418.2000
(FAX) 904.418.2001
sabine@sabineinc.com
www.sabineinc.com

S.I.T. STRINGS
815 S. Broadway
Akron OH 44311
330.434.8010
email: sitstrings@aol.com

THOMASTIK-INFELD
P.O. Box 93
Northport NY 11768
800.644.5268
email: 100420.745@com-puserve.com
http://kfs.oeaw.ac.at/thom/home.html

YAMAHA STRINGS
6600 Orangethorpe Avenue
Buena Park CA 90620
714.522.9011
(FAX) 714.739.2680

The Link between the Strings and the Amp: Pickups!

A Review of Pickup companies

ADDER PLUS
830 Seton Court
Unit 12
Wheeling IL 60090
847.537.0202
(FAX) 847.537.0355

KENT ARMSTRONG
Distributed by WD Music Products, Inc.
4070 Mayflower Road
Fort Myers FL 33916
813.337.7575

AUDIO OPTICS
Audio Optics, Inc.
P.O. Box 691
Santa Barbara CA 93102
800.548.6669
805.563.2202
(FAX) 805.569.4060
info@aollightwave.com
www.mallennium.com/aolightwave

BARCUS BERRY
Distributed by BBE Sound, Inc
5381 Production Drive
Huntington Beach CA 92649
800.233.8346
714.897.6766
(FAX) 714.896.0736

JOE BARDEN
P.O. Box 1254
Vienna VA 22183
703.938.8638

BARTOLINI
Bartolini Pickups and Electronics
2133 Research Drive #16
Livermore CA 94550
510.443.1037
(FAX) 510.449.7692

CHANDLER
Chandler Guitars
370 Lang Road
Burlingame CA 94010-2003
415.342.1490
(FAX) 415.342.9692

DEAN MARKLEY
Dean Markley Strings, Inc.
3350 Scott Blvd. #45
Santa Clara CA 95054
800.800.1008
408.988.2456
(FAX) 408.988.0441

DIMARZIO
Dimarzio, Inc.
1388 Richmond Terrace
Staten Island NY 10310
800.221.6468
718.981.9286
(FAX) 718.720.5296

SEYMOUR DUNCAN
5427 Hollister Avenue
Santa Barbara CA 93111-2345
800.SDU.NCAN
800.964.9610
(FAX) 805.964.9749

EMG
EMG. Inc.
P.O. Box 4394
Santa Rosa CA 95402
707.525.9941
(FAX) 707.575.7046
EMGDoug@aol.com
www.emginc.com

EPM
6-399 S. Edgeware Road
St. Thomas Ontario
Canada N5P 4B8
519.633.5195
(FAX) 519.633.8314
EPM@webgate.net

FISHMAN
Fishman Transducers, Inc.
Fishman Audio Division
340-D Fordham Road
Wilmington MA 01887-2113
508.988.9199
(FAX) 508.988.0770

LINDY FRALIN
Lindy Fralin Pickups
3415 Floyd Ave.
Richmond VA 23221
804.358.2699
(FAX) 804.358.3431

GROOVE TUBES
Distributed by G.T. Electronics
12866 Foothill Blvd.
Sylmar CA 91342
818.361.4500
(FAX) 818.365.9884
gttubes@aol.com

HIGHLANDER
Highlander Musical Audio Products
305 Glenwood Avenue
Ventura CA 93003-4426
805.658.1819
(FAX) 805.658.6828

TOM HOLMES
Tom Holmes
P.O. Box 414
Joelton TN 37080
615.876.3453

LACE SENSORS
Actodyne General Inc.
5561 Engineer Drive
Huntington Beach CA 92649
800.575.LACE
714.898.2776
(FAX) 714.893.1045

LANE POOR
Lane Poor Music Co.
347 Pleasant St.
Fall River MA 02721
508.679.1922

WILLIAM LAWRENCE
Also KEYSTONE PICKUPS
William Lawrence Design Corp.
314 Taylor Street
Bethlehem PA 18015
610.866.5211
(FAX) 610.866.5495

L. R. BAGGS
L.R. Baggs Co.
483 N Frontage Road
Nipomo CA 93444
805.929.3545
(FAX) 805.929.2043
Baggsco@aol.com

PAN
Pan Electric
Dept. BM
207 Rundlview Dr. N.E.
Calgary AB Canada T1Y 1H7
403.285.8893

SHADOW
Shadow Electronics of America
2700 SE Market Place
Stuart FL 34997
407.221.8177
(FAX) 407.221.8178

SUNRISE
Sunrise Pickup Systems
8101 Orion Ave. #19
Van Nuys CA 91406
818.785.3428
(FAX) 818.785.9972
JimSunrise@earthlink.net
www.Sunrisepickups.com

VAN ZANDT
Distributed and Produced by VAN ZANDT Pickups
205 Robinson Rd.
Combine TX 75159
214.476.8844
(FAX) 214.476.8844

ZETA
Zeta Music Systems
2230 Livingston St.
Oakland CA 94606
800.622.6434
510.261.1702
(FAX) 510.261.1708

Index